McGraw-Hill Dictionary of
BIOLOGY

McGraw-Hill Dictionary of
BIOLOGY

Sybil P. Parker
EDITOR IN CHIEF

McGraw-Hill Book Company

New York   St. Louis   San Francisco

Auckland   Bogotá   Guatemala   Hamburg
Johannesburg   Lisbon   London   Madrid   Mexico
Montreal   New Delhi   Panama   Paris   San Juan
São Paulo   Singapore   Sydney   Tokyo   Toronto

On the cover: Electron micrograph of supercooled bacterial cells and bacteriophages observed in the Moran cryoelectron microscope. (Courtesy of Humberto Fernández-Moran)

1 2 3 4 5 6 7 8 9 0   FGFG   8 9 1 0 9 8 7 6 5

ISBN 0-07-045419-1

Library of Congress Cataloging in Publication Data

McGraw-Hill dictionary of biology.

Material previously published in the 1984 3rd ed. of the McGraw-Hill dictionary of scientific and technical terms.
 1. Biology—Dictionaries.   I. Parker, Sybil P.
II. McGraw-Hill Book Company.   III. McGraw-Hill dictionary of scientific and technical terms.
QH302.5.M38   1985   574′.03′21   85-12584
ISBN 0-07-045419-1

Editorial Staff

Consulting and Contributing Editors
from the McGraw-Hill Dictionary of Scientific and Technical Terms

How to Use the Dictionary

ALPHABETIZATION

The terms in the *McGraw-Hill Dictionary of Biology* are alphabetized on a letter-by-letter basis; word spacing, hyphen, comma, solidus, and apostrophe in a term are ignored in the sequencing. For example, an ordering of terms would be:

> **aminoacetic acid**
> **amino acid**
> **α-aminohydrocinnamic acid**
> **2-aminoisovaleric acid**
> **anti-infective vitamin**
> **Antilopinae**

FORMAT

The basic format for a defining entry provides the term in boldface, the field in small capitals, and the single definition in lightface:

> **term** [FIELD] Definition.

A field may be followed by multiple definitions, each introduced by a boldface number:

> **term** [FIELD] **1.** Definition. **2.** Definition. **3.** Definition.

A term may have definitions in two or more fields:

> **term** [ANAT] Definition. [MYCOL] Definition.

A simple cross-reference entry appears as:

> **term** *See* another term.

A cross-reference may also appear in combination with definitions:

> **term** [ANAT] Definition. [MYCOL] *See* another term.

CROSS-REFERENCING

A cross-reference entry directs the user to the defining entry. For example, the user looking up "apical bud" finds:

> **apical bud** *See* terminal bud.

The user then turns to the "T" terms for the definition.

Cross-references are also made from variant spellings, acronyms, abbreviations, and symbols.

> **cAMP** *See* cyclic adenylic acid.
> **carotin** *See* carotene.
> **ID$_{50}$** *See* infective dose 50.

ALSO KNOWN AS . . . , etc.

A definition may conclude with a mention of a synonym of the term, a variant spelling, an abbreviation for the term, or other such information, introduced by "Also known as . . . ," "Also spelled . . . ," "Abbreviated . . . ," "Symbolized . . . ," "Derived from . . . ." When a term has more than one definition, the positioning of any of these phrases conveys the extent of applicability. For example:

term [ANAT] 1. Definition. Also known as synonym.
2. Definition. Symbolized B.

In the above arrangement, "Also known as . . ." applies only to the first definition. "Symbolized . . ." applies only to the second definition.

term [ANAT] 1. Definition. 2. Definition. [BOT] Definition.
Also known as synonym.

In the above arrangement, "Also known as . . ." applies only to the second field.

term [ANAT] Also known as synonym. 1. Definition.
2. Definition. [BOT] Definition.

In the above arrangement, "Also known as . . ." applies to both definitions in the first field.

term Also known as synonym. [ANAT] 1. Definition.
2. Definition. [BOT] Definition.

In the above arrangement, "Also known as . . ." applies to all definitions in both fields.

Field Abbreviations and Scope

ANAT anatomy
BIOCHEM biochemistry
BIOL biology
BIOPHYS biophysics
BOT botany
CELL BIO cell biology
ECOL ecology
EMBRYO embryology
EVOL evolution
GEN genetics
HISTOL histology
INV ZOO invertebrate zoology
MICROBIO microbiology
MOL BIO molecular biology
MYCOL mycology
PALEOBOT paleobotany
PALEON paleontology
PHYSIO physiology
PL PATH plant pathology
SYST systematics
VERT ZOO vertebrate zoology
VIROL virology
ZOO zoology

anatomy—The branch of morphology concerned with the gross and microscopic structure of animals, especially humans.

biochemistry—The study of the chemical substances that occur in living organisms, the processes by which these substances enter into or are formed in the organisms and react with each other and the environment, and the methods by which the substances and processes are identified, characterized, and measured.

biology—The science of living organisms, concerned with the study of embryology, anatomy, physiology, cytology, morphology, taxonomy, genetics, evolution, and ecology.

biophysics—The hybrid science involving the methods and ideas of physics and chemistry to study and explain the structures of living organisms and the mechanics of life processes.

botany—That branch of biological science which embraces the study of plants and plant life, including algae; deals with taxonomy, morphology, physiology, and other aspects.

cell biology—The branch of biological science which deals with the structure, behavior, growth, and reproduction of cells and the function and chemistry of cells and cell components.

ecology—The study of the interrelationships between organisms and their environment.

embryology—The study of the development of the organism from the zygote, or fertilized egg.

evolution—The processes of biological and organic change in organisms by which descendants come to differ from their ancestors, and a history of the sequence of such change.

genetics—The science concerned with biological inheritance, that is, with the causes of the resemblances and differences among related individuals.

histology—The study of the structure and chemical composition of animal tissues as related to their function.

invertebrate zoology—A branch of zoology concerned with the taxonomy, behavior, and morphology of invertebrate animals.

microbiology—The science and study of microorganisms, especially bacteria and rickettsiae, and of antibiotic substances.

molecular biology—That branch of biology which attempts to interpret biological events in terms of the molecules in the cell.

mycology—A branch of biological science concerned with the study of fungi.

paleobotany—The study of fossil plants and vegetation of the geologic past.

paleotology—The study of life in the geologic past as recorded by fossil remains.

physiology—The branch of biological science concerned with the basic activities that occur in cells and tissues of living organisms and involving physical and chemical studies of these organisms.

plant pathology—The branch of botany concerned with diseases of plants.

systematics—The science of animal and plant classification.

vertebrate zoology—A branch of zoology concerned with the taxonomy, behavior, and morphology of vertebrate animals.

virology—The science that deals with the study of viruses.

zoology—The science that deals with the taxonomy, behavior, and morphology of animal life.

McGraw-Hill Dictionary of
BIOLOGY

A

aapamoor [ECOL] A moor with elevated areas or mounds supporting dwarf shrubs and sphagnum, interspersed with low areas containing sedges and sphagnum, thus forming a mosaic.

aardwolf [VERT ZOO] *Proteles cristatus*. A hyenalike African mammal of the family Hyaenidae.

abaca [BOT] *Musa textilis*. A plant of the banana family native to Borneo and the Philippines, valuable for its hard fiber. Also known as Manila hemp.

abactinal [INV ZOO] In radially symmetrical animals, pertaining to the surface opposite the side where the mouth is located.

abalone [INV ZOO] A gastropod mollusk composing the single genus *Haliotis* of the family Haliotidae. Also known as ear shell; ormer; paua.

A band [HISTOL] The region between two adjacent I bands in a sarcomere; characterized by partial overlapping of actin and myosin filaments.

abapertural [INV ZOO] Away from the shell aperture, referring to mollusks.

abapical [BIOL] On the opposite side to, or directed away from, the apex.

abaxial [BIOL] On the opposite side to, or facing away from, the axis of an organ or organism.

abb [VERT ZOO] A coarse wool from the fleece areas of lesser quality.

abdomen [ANAT] 1. The portion of the vertebrate body between the thorax and the pelvis. 2. The cavity of this part of the body. [INV ZOO] The elongate region posterior to the thorax in arthropods.

abdominal regions [ANAT] Nine theoretical areas delineated on the abdomen by two horizontal and two parasagittal lines: above, the right hypochondriac, epigastric, and left hypochondriac; in the middle, the right lateral, umbilical, and left lateral; and below, the right inguinal, hypogastric, and left inguinal.

abducens [ANAT] The sixth cranial nerve in vertebrates; a paired, somatic motor nerve arising from the floor of the fourth ventricle of the brain and supplying the lateral rectus eye muscles.

abduction [PHYSIO] Movement of an extremity or other body part away from the axis of the body.

abductor [PHYSIO] Any muscle that draws a part of the body or an extremity away from the body axis.

aberrant [BIOL] An atypical group, individual, or structure, especially one with an aberrant chromosome number.

Abies [BOT] The firs, a genus of trees in the pine family characterized by erect cones, absence of resin canals in the wood, and flattened needlelike leaves.

abiocoen [ECOL] A nonbiotic habitat.

abiogenesis [BIOL] The obsolete concept that plant and animal life arise from nonliving organic matter. Also known as autogenesis; spontaneous generation.

abiotic [BIOL] Referring to the absence of living organisms.

abiotic environment [ECOL] All physical and nonliving chemical factors, such as soil, water, and atmosphere, which influence living organisms.

abiotic substance [ECOL] Any fundamental chemical element or compound in the environment.

abjection [MYCOL] The discharge or casting off of spores by the spore-bearing structure of a fungus.

abomasum [VERT ZOO] The final chamber of the complex stomach of ruminants; has a glandular wall and corresponds to a true stomach.

aboral [INV ZOO] Opposite to the mouth.

abortive [BIOL] Imperfectly formed or developed.

abortive transduction [MICROBIO] Failure of exogenous fragments that were introduced into a bacterial cell by viruses to become inserted into the bacterial chromosome.

abranchiate [ZOO] Without gills.

abrupt [BOT] Ending suddenly, as though broken off.

abscisic acid [BIOCHEM] $C_{16}H_{20}O_4$ A plant hormone produced by fruits and leaves that promotes abscission and dormancy and retards vegetative growth. Formerly known as abscisin.

abscisin *See* abscisic acid.

abscission [BOT] A physiological process promoted by abscisic acid whereby plants shed a part, such as a leaf, flower, seed, or fruit.

absolute threshold [PHYSIO] The minimum stimulus energy that an organism can detect.

absorption [PHYSIO] Passage of a chemical substance, a pathogen, or radiant energy through a body membrane.

abstriction [MYCOL] In fungi, the cutting off of spores in hyphae by formation of septa followed by abscission of the spores, especially by constriction.

abterminal [BIOL] Referring to movement from the end toward the middle; specifically, describing the mode of electric current flow in a muscle.

Acala [BOT] A type of cotton indigenous to Mexico and cultivated in Texas, Oklahoma, and Arkansas.

acalyculate [BOT] Lacking a calyx.

Acalypteratae [INV ZOO] A large group of small, two-winged flies in the suborder Cyclorrhapha characterized by small or rudimentary calypters. Also spelled Acalyptratae.

Acalyptratae See Acalypteratae.

acantha [BIOL] A sharp spine; a spiny process, as on vertebrae.

Acanthaceae [BOT] A family of dicotyledonous plants in the order Scrophulariales distinguished by their usually herbaceous habit, irregular flowers, axile placentation, and dry, dehiscent fruits.

acanthaceous [BOT] Having sharp points or prickles; prickly.

Acantharia [INV ZOO] A subclass of essentially pelagic protozoans in the class Actinopodea characterized by skeletal rods constructed of strontium sulfate (celestite).

Acanthaster [INV ZOO] A genus of Indo-Pacific starfishes, including the crown-of-thorns, of the family Asteriidae; economically important as a destroyer of oysters in fisheries.

acanthella [INV ZOO] A transitional larva of the phylum Acanthocephala in which rudiments of reproductive organs, lemnisci, a proboscis, and a proboscis receptacle are formed.

acanthocarpous [BOT] Having spiny fruit.

Acanthocephala [INV ZOO] The spiny-headed worms, a phylum of helminths; adults are parasitic in the alimentary canal of vertebrates.

Acanthocheilonema perstans [INV ZOO] A tropical filarial worm, parasitic in man.

acanthocladous [BOT] Having spiny branches.

Acanthodes [PALEON] A genus of Carboniferous and Lower Permian eellike acanthodian fishes of the family Acanthodidae.

Acanthodidae [PALEON] A family of extinct acanthodian fishes in the order Acanthodiformes.

Acanthodiformes [PALEON] An order of extinct fishes in the class Acanthodii having scales of acellular bone and dentine, one dorsal fin, and no teeth.

Acanthodii [PALEON] A class of extinct fusiform fishes, the first jaw-bearing vertebrates in the fossil record.

acanthoid [BIOL] Shaped like a spine.

Acanthometrida [INV ZOO] An order of marine protozoans in the subclass Acantharia with 20 or less skeletal rods.

Acanthophis antarcticus [VERT ZOO] The death adder, a venomous snake found in Australia and New Guinea; venom is neurotoxic.

Acanthophractida [INV ZOO] An order of marine protozoans in the subclass Acantharia; skeleton includes a latticework shell and skeletal rods.

acanthopodous [BOT] Having a spiny or prickly petiole or peduncle.

acanthopore [PALEON] A tubular spine in some fossil bryozoans.

Acanthopteri [VERT ZOO] An equivalent name for the Perciformes.

Acanthopterygii [VERT ZOO] An equivalent name for the Perciformes.

acanthosoma [INV ZOO] The last primitive larval stage, the mysis, in the family Sergestidae.

Acanthosomatidae [INV ZOO] A small family of insects in the order Hemiptera.

acanthosphere [BOT] A specialized ciliated body in *Nitella* cells.

acanthostegous [INV ZOO] Being overlaid with two series of spines, as the ovicell or ooecium of certain bryozoans.

acanthozooid [INV ZOO] A specialized individual in a bryozoan colony that secretes tubules which project as spines above the colony's outer surface.

Acanthuridae [VERT ZOO] The surgeonfishes, a family of perciform fishes in the suborder Acanthuroidei.

Acanthuroidei [VERT ZOO] A suborder of chiefly herbivorous fishes in the order Perciformes.

Acari [INV ZOO] The equivalent name for Acarina.

Acaridiae [INV ZOO] A group of pale, weakly sclerotized mites in the suborder Sarcoptiformes, including serious pests of stored food products and skin parasites of warm-blooded vertebrates.

Acarina [INV ZOO] The ticks and mites, a large order of the class Arachnida, characterized by lack of body demarcation into cephalothorax and abdomen.

acarology [INV ZOO] A branch of zoology dealing with the mites and ticks.

acarophily [ECOL] A symbiotic relationship between plants and mites.

acarpellous [BOT] Lacking carpels.

acarpous [BOT] Not producing fruit.

acaulous [BOT] 1. Lacking a stem. 2. Being apparently stemless but having a short underground stem.

acceleration globulin [BIOCHEM] A globulin that acts to accelerate the conversion of prothrombin to thrombin in blood clotting; found in blood plasma in an inactive form.

acceleration tolerance [PHYSIO] The maximum g forces an individual can withstand without losing control or consciousness.

acceleratory reflex [PHYSIO] Any reflex originating in the labyrinth of the inner ear in response to a change in the rate of movement of the head.

accessorius [ANAT] Any muscle that reinforces the action of another.

accessory bud [BOT] An embryonic shoot occurring above or to the side of an axillary bud. Also known as supernumerary bud.

accessory cell [BOT] A morphologically distinct epidermal cell adjacent to, and apparently functionally associated with, guard cells on the leaves of many plants.

accessory gland [ANAT] A mass of glandular tissue separate from the main body of a gland. [INV ZOO] A gland associated with the male reproductive organs in insects.

accessory movement *See* synkinesia.

accessory nerve [ANAT] The eleventh cranial nerve in tetrapods, a paired visceral motor nerve; the bulbar part innervates the larynx and pharynx, and the spinal part innervates the trapezius and sternocleidomastoid muscles.

accessory sexual characters [ANAT] Those structures and organs (excluding the gonads) composing the genital tract and including accessory glands and external genitalia.

accessory species [ECOL] A species comprising 25–50% of a community.

accidental species [ECOL] A species which constitutes less than one-fourth of the population of a stand.

accidental whorl [ANAT] A type of whorl fingerprint pattern which is a combination of two different types of pattern, with the exception of the plain arch, with two or more deltas; or a pattern which possesses some of the requirements for two or more different types; or a pattern which conforms to none of the definitions; in accidental whorl tracing three types appear: an outer (O), inner (I), or meeting (M).

Accipitridae [VERT ZOO] The diurnal birds of prey, the largest and most diverse family of the order Falconiformes, including hawks, eagles, and kites.

acclimated microorganism [ECOL] Any microorganism that is able to adapt to environmental changes such as a change in temperature, or a change in the quantity of oxygen or other gases.

acclimation *See* acclimatization.

acclimatization [EVOL] Adaptation of a species or population to a changed environment over several generations. Also known as acclimation.

accommodation [ECOL] A population's location within a habitat. [PHYSIO] A process in most vertebrates whereby the focal length of the eye is changed by automatic adjustment of the lens to bring images of objects from various distances into focus on the retina.

accommodation reflex [PHYSIO] Changes occurring in the eyes when vision is focused from a distant to a near object; involves pupil contraction, increased lens convexity, and convergence of the eyes.

accrescent [BOT] Growing continuously with age, especially after flowering.

accretion line [HISTOL] A microscopic line on a tooth, marking the addition of a layer of enamel or dentin.

accumbent [BOT] Describing an organ that leans against another; specifically referring to cotyledons having their edges folded against the hypocotyl.

accumulator plant [BOT] A plant or tree that grows in a metal-bearing soil and accumulates an abnormal content of the metal.

acellular [BIOL] Not composed of cells.

acellular gland [PHYSIO] A gland, such as intestinal glands, the pancreas, and the parotid gland, that secretes a noncellular product.

acellular slime mold [MYCOL] The common name for members of the Myxomycetes.

acentric [BIOL] Not oriented around a middle point. [GEN] A chromosome or chromosome fragment lacking a centromere.

acentrous [VERT ZOO] Lacking vertebral centra and having the notochord persistent throughout life, as in certain primitive fishes.

Acephalina [INV ZOO] A suborder of invertebrate parasites in the protozoan order Eugregarinida characterized by nonseptate trophozoites.

acephalocyst [INV ZOO] An abnormal cyst of the *Echinococcus granulosus* larva, lacking a head and brood capsules, found in human organs.

acephalous [BOT] Having the style originate at the base instead of at the apex of the ovary. [ZOO] Lacking a head.

Acer [BOT] A genus of broad-leaved, deciduous trees of the order Sapindales, commonly known as the maples; the sugar or rock maple (*A. saccharum*) is the most important commercial species.

acerate [BOT] Needle-shaped, specifically referring to leaves.

Acerentomidae [INV ZOO] A family of wingless insects belonging to the order Protura; the body lacks tracheae and spiracles.

acervate [BIOL] Growing in heaps or dense clusters.

acervulus [MYCOL] A cushion- or disk-shaped mass of hyphae, peculiar to the Melanconiales, on which there are dense aggregates of conidiophores.

acetabulum [ANAT] A cup-shaped socket on the hipbone that receives the head of the femur. [INV ZOO] 1. A cavity on an insect body into which a leg inserts for articulation. 2. The sucker of certain invertebrates such as trematodes and tapeworms.

acetaldehydase [BIOCHEM] An enzyme that catalyzes the oxidation of acetaldehyde to acetic acid.

acetic acid bacteria *See* Acetobacter.

acetic fermentation [MICROBIO] Oxidation of alcohol to produce acetic acid by the action of bacteria of the genus *Acetobacter*.

acetic thiokinase [BIOCHEM] An enzyme that catalyzes the formation of acetyl coenzyme A from acetate and adenosinetriphosphate.

acetoacetyl coenzyme A [BIOCHEM] $C_{25}H_{41}O_{18}N_7P_3S$ An intermediate product in the oxidation of fatty acids.

Acetobacter [MICROBIO] A genus of gram-negative, aerobic bacteria of uncertain affiliation comprising ellipsoidal to rod-shaped cells as singles, pairs, or chains; they oxidize ethanol to acetic acid. Also known as acetic acid bacteria; vinegar bacteria.

Acetobacter aceti [MICROBIO] An aerobic, rod-shaped bacterium capable of efficient oxidation of glucose, ethyl alcohol, and acetic acid; found in vinegar, beer, and souring fruits and vegetables.

Acetobacter suboxydans [MICROBIO] A short, nonmotile vinegar bacterium that can oxidize ethanol to acetic acid; useful for industrial production of ascorbic and tartaric acids.

acetolactic acid [BIOCHEM] $C_5H_8O_4$ A monocarboxylic acid formed as an intermediate in the synthesis of the amino acid valine.

Acetomonas [MICROBIO] A genus of aerobic, polarly flagellated vinegar bacteria in the family Pseudomonadaceae; used industrially to produce vinegar, gluconic acid, and L-sorbose.

acetone body See ketone body.

acetone fermentation [MICROBIO] Formation of acetone by the metabolic action of certain anaerobic bacteria on carbohydrates.

acetylase [BIOCHEM] Any enzyme that catalyzes the formation of acetyl esters.

acetylcholine [BIOCHEM] $C_7H_{17}O_3N$ A compound released from certain autonomic nerve endings which acts in the transmission of nerve impulses to excitable membranes.

acetylcholinesterase [BIOCHEM] An enzyme found in excitable membranes that inactivates acetylcholine.

acetyl coenzyme A [BIOCHEM] $C_{23}H_{39}O_{17}N_7P_3S$ A coenzyme, derived principally from the metabolism of glucose and fatty acids, that takes part in many biological acetylation reactions; oxidized in the Krebs cycle.

acetyl phosphate [BIOCHEM] $C_2H_5O_5P$ The anhydride of acetic and phosphoric acids occurring in the metabolism of pyruvic acid by some bacteria; phosphate is used by some microorganisms, in place of ATP, for the phosphorylation of hexose sugars.

Achaenodontidae [PALEON] A family of Eocene dichobunoids, piglike mammals belonging to the suborder Palaeodonta.

acheb [ECOL] Short-lived vegetation regions of the Sahara composed principally of mustards (Cruciferae) and grasses (Gramineae).

achene [BOT] A small, dry, indehiscent fruit formed from a simple ovary bearing a single seed.

achilary [BOT] In flowers, having the lip (labellum) undeveloped or lacking.

Achilles jerk [PHYSIO] A reflex action seen as plantar flection in response to a blow to the Achilles tendon. Also known as Achilles tendon reflex.

Achilles tendon [ANAT] The tendon formed by union of the tendons of the calf muscles, the soleus and gastrocnemius, and inserted into the heel bone.

Achilles tendon reflex See Achilles jerk.

achlamydeous [BOT] Lacking a perianth.

Acholeplasma [MICROBIO] The single genus of the family Acholeplasmataceae, comprising spherical and filamentous cells.

Acholeplasmataceae [MICROBIO] A family of the order Mycoplasmatales; characters same as for the order and class (Mollicutes); do not require sterol for growth.

achordate [VERT ZOO] Lacking a notochord.

achroglobin [BIOCHEM] A colorless respiratory pigment present in some mollusks and urochordates.

Achromatiaceae [MICROBIO] A family of gliding bacteria of uncertain affiliation; cells are spherical to ovoid or cylindrical, movements are slow and jerky, and microcysts are not known.

achromatic interval [PHYSIO] The difference between the achromatic threshold and the smallest light stimulus at which the hue is detectable.

achromatic threshold [PHYSIO] The smallest light stimulus that can be detected by a dark-adapted eye, so called because all colors lose their hue at this illumination.

achromatin [CELL BIO] The portion of the cell nucleus which does not stain easily with basic dyes.

Achromatium [MICROBIO] The type genus of the family Achromatiaceae.

achromatophilia [BIOL] The property of not staining readily.

achromic [BIOL] Colorless; lacking normal pigmentation.

Achromobacter [MICROBIO] A genus of motile and nonmotile, gram-negative, rod-shaped bacteria in the family Achromobacteraceae.

Achromobacteraceae [MICROBIO] Formerly a family of true bacteria, order Eubacteriales, characterized by aerobic metabolism.

Achroonema [MICROBIO] A genus of bacteria in the family Pelonemataceae; cells have smooth, delicate, porous walls.

aciculignosa [ECOL] Narrow sclerophyll or coniferous vegetation that is mostly subalpine, subarctic, or continental.

Acidaminococcus [MICROBIO] A genus of bacteria in the family Veillonellaceae; cells are often oval or kidney-shaped and occur in pairs; amino acids can supply the single energy source.

acid-base balance [PHYSIO] Physiologically maintained equilibrium of acids and bases in the body.

acid cell [HISTOL] A parietal cell of the stomach.

acid-fast bacteria [MICROBIO] Bacteria, especially mycobacteria, that stain with basic dyes and fluorochromes and resist decoloration by acid solutions.

acid-fast stain [MICROBIO] A differential stain used in identifying species of *Mycobacterium* and one species of *Nocardia*.

acidophil [BIOL] 1. Any substance, tissue, or organism having an affinity for acid stains. 2. An organism having a preference for an acid environment. [HISTOL] 1. An alpha cell of the adenohypophysis. 2. See eosinophil.

acidophilic erythroblast See normoblast.

acidotrophic [BIOL] Having an acid nutrient requirement.

acid phosphatase [BIOCHEM] An enzyme in blood which catalyzes the release of phosphate from phosphate esters; optimum activity at pH 5.

acinar [ANAT] Pertaining to an acinus.

acinar cell [ANAT] Any of the cells lining an acinous gland.

Acinetobacter [MICROBIO] A genus of nonmotile, short, plump, almost spherical rods in the family Neisseriaceae; strictly aerobic; resistant to penicillin.

aciniform [ZOO] Shaped like a berry or a bunch of grapes.

acinous [BIOL] Of or pertaining to acini.

acinous gland [ANAT] A multicellular gland with sac-shaped secreting units. Also known as alveolar gland.

acinus [ANAT] The small terminal sac of an acinous gland, lined with secreting cells. [BOT] An individual drupelet of a multiple fruit.

Acipenser [VERT ZOO] A genus of actinopterygian fishes in the sturgeon family, Acipenseridae.

Acipenseridae [VERT ZOO] The sturgeons, a family of actinopterygian fishes in the order Acipenseriformes.

Acipenseriformes [VERT ZOO] An order of the subclass Actinopterygii represented by the sturgeons and paddlefishes.

Acmaeidae [INV ZOO] A family of gastropod mollusks in the order Archaeogastropoda; includes many limpets.

acme [PALEON] The time of largest abundance or variety of a fossil taxon; the taxon may be either general or local.

acmic [ECOL] A phase or period in which an aquatic population undergoes seasonal changes.

Acnidosporidia [INV ZOO] An equivalent name for the Haplosporea.

Acoela [INV ZOO] An order of marine flatworms in the class Turbellaria characterized by the lack of a digestive tract and coelomic cavity.

Acoelea [INV ZOO] An order of gastropod mollusks in the subclass Opistobranchia; includes many sea slugs.

Acoelomata [INV ZOO] A subdivision of the animal kingdom; individuals are characterized by lack of a true body cavity.

acoelous [ZOO] 1. Lacking a true body cavity or coelom. 2. Lacking a true stomach or digestive tract.

acolpate [BOT] Of pollen grains, lacking furrows or grooves.

Aconchulinida [INV ZOO] An order of protozoans in the subclass Filosia comprising a small group of naked amebas having filopodia.

aconitase [BIOCHEM] An enzyme involved in the Krebs citric acid cycle that catalyzes the breakdown of citric acid to *cis*-aconitic and isocitric acids.

aconite [BOT] Any plant of the genus *Aconitum*. Also known as friar's cowl; monkshood; mousebane; wolfsbane.

acorn [BOT] The nut of the oak tree, usually surrounded at the base by a woody involucre.

acorn barnacle [INV ZOO] Any of the sessile barnacles that are enclosed in conical, flat-bottomed shells and attach to ships and near-shore rocks and piles.

acorn disease [PL PATH] A virus disease of citrus plants characterized by malformation of the fruit, which is somewhat acorn-shaped.

acorn worm [INV ZOO] Any member of the class Enteropneusta, free-living animals that usually burrow in sand or mud. Also known as tongue worm.

acotyledon [BOT] A plant without cotyledons.

acouchi [VERT ZOO] A hystricomorph rodent represented by two species in the family Dasyproctidae; believed to be a dwarf variety of the agouti.

acoustic nerve See auditory nerve.

acoustic reflex [PHYSIO] Brief, involuntary closure of the eyes due to stimulation of the acoustic nerve by a sudden sound.

acquired [BIOL] Not present at birth, but developed by an individual in response to the environment and not subject to hereditary transmission.

Acrania [ZOO] A group of lower chordates with no cranium, jaws, vertebrae, or paired appendages; includes the Tunicata and Cephalochordata.

Acrasiales [BIOL] A group of microorganisms that have plant and animal characteristics; included in the phylum Myxomycophyta by botanists and Mycetozoia by zoologists.

Acrasida [MYCOL] An order of Mycetozoia containing cellular slime molds.

Acrasieae [BIOL] An equivalent name for the Acrasiales.

acrasin [BIOCHEM] The chemotactic substance thought to be secreted by, and to effect aggregation of, myxamebas during their fruiting phase.

acraspedote [INV ZOO] Describing tapeworm segments which are not overlapping.

acroblast [CELL BIO] A vesicular structure in the spermatid formed from Golgi material.

acrocarpous [BOT] In some mosses of the subclass Eubrya, having the sporophyte at the end of a stem and therefore exhibiting the erect habit.

acrocentric chromosome [CELL BIO] A chromosome having the centromere close to one end.

Acroceridae [INV ZOO] The humpbacked flies, a family of orthorrhaphous dipteran insects in the series Brachycera.

acrodomatia [ECOL] Specialized structures on certain plants adapted to shelter mites; relationship is presumably symbiotic.

acrodont [ANAT] Having teeth fused to the edge of the supporting bone.

acromere [HISTOL] The distal portion of a rod or cone in the retina.

acromion [ANAT] The flat process on the outer end of the scapular spine that articulates with the clavicle and forms the outer angle of the shoulder.

acron [EVOL] Unsegmented head of the ancestral arthropod. [INV ZOO] 1. The preoral, nonsegmented portion of an arthropod embryo. 2. The prostomial region of the trochophore larva of some mollusks.

acropetal [BOT] From the base toward the apex, as seen in the formation of certain organs or the spread of a pathogen.

Acrosaleniidae [PALEON] A family of Jurassic and Cretaceous echinoderms in the order Salenoida.

acroscopic [BOT] Facing, or on the side toward, the apex.

acrosin [BIOCHEM] A proteolytic enzyme located in the acrosome of a spermatozoon; thought to be involved in penetration of the egg.

acrosome [CELL BIO] The anterior, crescent-shaped body of spermatozoon, formed from Golgi material of the spermatid. Also known as perforatorium.

acrospore [MYCOL] In fungi, a spore formed at the outer tip of a hypha.

acrotarsium [ANAT] Instep of the foot.

Acrothoracica [INV ZOO] A small order of burrowing barnacles in the subclass Cirripedia that inhabit corals and the shells of mollusks and barnacles.

Acrotretacea [PALEON] A family of Cambrian and Ordovician inarticulate brachiopods of the suborder Acrotretidina.

Acrotretida [INV ZOO] An order of brachiopods in the class Inarticulata; representatives are known from Lower Cambrian to the present.

Acrotretidina [INV ZOO] A suborder of inarticulate brachiopods of the order Acrotretida; includes only species with shells composed of calcium phosphate.

Actaeonidae [INV ZOO] A family of gastropod mollusks in the order Tectibranchia.

Actaletidae [INV ZOO] A family of insects belonging to the order Collembola characterized by simple tracheal systems.

ACTH See adrenocorticotropic hormone.

Actidione [MICROBIO] Trade name for the antibiotic cyclohexamide.

actin [BIOCHEM] A muscle protein that is the chief constituent of the Z-band myofilaments of each sarcomere.

actinal [INV ZOO] In radially symmetrical animals, referring to the part from which the tentacles or arms radiate or to the side where the mouth is located.

Actiniaria [INV ZOO] The sea anemones, an order of coelenterates in the subclass Zoantharia.

Actinobacillus [MICROBIO] A species of gram-negative, oval, spherical, or rod-shaped bacteria that are of uncertain affiliation; coccal and bacillary cells are often interspersed, giving a "Morse code" form; species are pathogens of animals, occasionally of humans.

Actinobifida [MICROBIO] A genus of bacteria in the family Micromonosporaceae with a dichotomously branched substrate; an aerial mycelium is formed which produces single spores.

actinocarpous [BOT] Having flowers and fruit radiating from one point.

actinochitin [BIOCHEM] A form of birefringent or anisotropic chitin found in the seta of certain mites.

Actinochitinosi [INV ZOO] A group name for two closely related suborders of mites, the Trombidiformes and the Sarcoptiformes.

actinomere [INV ZOO] One of the segments composing the body of a radially symmetrical animal.

actinomorphic [BIOL] Descriptive of an organism, organ, or part that is radially symmetrical.

Actinomyces [MICROBIO] The type genus of the family Actinomycetaceae; anaerobic to facultatively anaerobic; includes human and animal pathogens.

Actinomyces bovis [MICROBIO] A nonmotile, gram-positive, anaerobic bacterium that causes actinomycosis.

Actinomycetaceae [MICROBIO] A family of bacteria in the order Actinomycetales; gram-positive, diphtheroid cells which form filaments but not mycelia; chemoorganotrophs that ferment carbohydrates.

Actinomycetales [MICROBIO] An order of bacteria; cells form branching filaments which develop into mycelia in some families.

actinomycete [MICROBIO] Any member of the bacterial family Actinomycetaceae.

actinomycin [MICROBIO] The collective name for a large number of red chromoprotein antibiotics elaborated by various strains of *Streptomyces*.

Actinomyxida [INV ZOO] An order of protozoan invertebrate parasites of the class Myxosporidea characterized by trivalved spores with three polar capsules.

actinophage [MICROBIO] A bacteriophage that infects and lyses members of the order Actinomycetales.

Actinophryida [INV ZOO] An order of protozoans in the subclass Heliozoia; individuals lack an organized test, a centroplast, and a capsule.

Actinoplanaceae [MICROBIO] A family of bacteria in the order Actinomycetales with well-developed mycelia and spores formed on sporangia.

Actinoplanes [MICROBIO] A genus of bacteria in the family Actinoplanaceae having aerial mycelia and spherical to subspherical sporangia; spores are spherical and motile by means of a tuft of polar flagella.

Actinopodea [INV ZOO] A class of protozoans belonging to the superclass Sarcodina; most are free-floating, with highly specialized pseudopodia.

Actinopteri [VERT ZOO] An equivalent name for the Actinopterygii.

Actinopterygii [VERT ZOO] The ray-fin fishes, a subclass of the Osteichthyes distinguished by the structure of the paired fins, which are supported by dermal rays.

actinostele [BOT] A protostele characterized by xylem that is either star-shaped in cross section or has ribs radiating from the center.

actinostome [BIOL] 1. The mouth of a radiate animal. 2. The peristome of an echinoderm.

Actinostromariidae [PALEON] A sphaeractinoid family of extinct marine hydrozoans.

actinotrocha [INV ZOO] The free-swimming larva of *Phoronis*, a genus of small, marine, tubicolous worms.

actinula [INV ZOO] A larval stage of some hydrozoans that has tentacles and a mouth; attaches and develops into a hydroid in some species, or metamorphoses into a medusa.

action current [PHYSIO] The electric current accompanying membrane depolarization and repolarization in an excitable cell.

action potential [PHYSIO] A transient change in electric potential at the surface of a nerve or muscle cell occurring at the moment of excitation.

action spectrum [PHYSIO] Graphic representation of the comparative effects of different wavelengths of light on living systems or their components.

actium [ECOL] A rocky seashore community.

activation [MOL BIO] A change that is induced in an amino acid before it is utilized for protein synthesis.

activation [PHYSIO] The designation for all changes in the ovum during fertilization, from sperm contact to the dissolution of nuclear membranes.

activator RNA [GEN] Ribonucleic acid molecules which form a sequence-specific complex with receptor genes linked to producer genes.

active site [MOL BIO] The region of an enzyme molecule at which binding with the substrate occurs. Also known as binding site; catalytic site.

active transport [PHYSIO] The pumping of ions or other substances across a cell membrane against an osmotic gradient, that is, from a lower to a higher concentration.

actomyosin [BIOCHEM] A protein complex consisting of myosin and actin; the major constituent of a contracting muscle fibril.

actophilous [ECOL] Having a seashore growing habit.

acuate [BIOL] 1. Having a sharp point. 2. Needleshaped.

acuity [BIOL] Sharpness of sense perception, as of vision or hearing.

Aculeata [INV ZOO] A group of seven superfamilies that constitute the stinging forms of hymenopteran insects in the suborder Apocrita.

aculeus [INV ZOO] 1. A sharp, hairlike spine, as on the wings of certain lepidopterans. 2. An insect stinger modified from an ovipositor.

Aculognathidae [INV ZOO] The ant-sucking beetles, a family of coleopteran insects in the superfamily Cucujoidea.

acuminate [BOT] Tapered to a slender point, especially referring to leaves.

acute [BIOL] Ending in a sharp point.

acute transfection [GEN] Short-term deoxyribonucleic acid infection of cells.

acutifoliate [BOT] Having sharply pointed leaves.

acutilobate [BOT] Having sharply pointed lobes.

acyclic [BOT] Having flowers arranged in a spiral instead of a whorl.

acyl carnitine See fatty acyl carnitine.

acyl carrier protein [BIOCHEM] A protein in fatty acid synthesis that picks up acetyl and malonyl groups from acetyl coenzyme A and malonyl coenzyme A and links them by condensation to form β-keto acid acyl carrier protein, releasing carbon dioxide and the sulfhydryl form of acyl carrier protein. Abbreviated ACP.

acyl-coenzyme A See fatty acyl-coenzyme A.

adambulacral [INV ZOO] Lying adjacent to the ambulacrum.

adapertural [INV ZOO] Near the aperture, specifically of a conch.

adapical [BOT] Near or toward the apex or tip.

adaptation [GEN] The occurrence of genetic changes in a population or species as the result of natural selection so that it adjusts to new or altered environmental conditions. [PHYSIO] The

occurrence of physiological changes in an individual exposed to changed conditions; for example, tanning of the skin in sunshine, or increased red blood cell counts at high altitudes.

adaptive disease [PHYSIO] The physiologic changes impairing an organism's health as the result of exposure to an unfamiliar environment.

adaptive divergence [EVOL] Divergence of new forms from a common ancestral form due to adaptation to different environmental conditions.

adaptive enzyme [MICROBIO] Any bacterial enzyme formed in response to the presence of a substrate specific for that enzyme.

adaptive radiation [EVOL] Diversification of a dominant evolutionary group into a large number of subsidiary types adapted to more restrictive modes of life (different adaptive zones) within the range of the larger group.

adaxial [BIOL] On the same side as or facing toward the axis of an organ or organism.

adder [VERT ZOO] Any of the venomous viperine snakes included in the family Viperidae.

adduction [PHYSIO] Movement of one part of the body toward another or toward the median axis of the body.

adductor [ANAT] Any muscle that draws a part of the body toward the median axis.

Adeleina [INV ZOO] A suborder of protozoan invertebrate parasites in the order Eucoccida in which the sexual and asexual stages are in different hosts.

adelphous [BOT] Having stamens fused together by their filaments.

adenase [BIOCHEM] An enzyme that catalyzes the hydrolysis of adenine to hypoxanthine and ammonia.

adenine [BIOCHEM] $C_5H_5N_5$ A purine base, 6-aminopurine, occurring in ribonucleic acid and deoxyribonucleic acid and as a component of adenosinetriphosphate.

adeno-associated satellite virus [VIROL] A defective virus that is unable to reproduce without the help of an adenovirus.

adenohypophysis [ANAT] The glandular part of the pituitary gland, composing the anterior and intermediate lobes.

adenoid [ANAT] 1. A mass of lymphoid tissue. 2. Lymphoid tissue of the nasopharynx. Also known as pharyngeal tonsil.

adenomere [EMBRYO] The embryonic structure which will become the functional portion of a gland.

Adenophorea [INV ZOO] A class of unsegmented worms in the phylum Nematoda.

adenophyllous [BOT] Having leaves with glands.

adenosine [BIOCHEM] $C_{10}H_{13}N_5O_4$ A nucleoside composed of adenine and D-ribose.

adenosine 3',5'-cyclic monophosphate See cyclic adenylic acid.

adenosine 3',5'-cyclic phosphate See cyclic adenylic acid.

adenosinediphosphatase [BIOCHEM] An enzyme that catalyzes the hydrolysis of adenosinediphosphate. Abbreviated ADPase.

adenosinediphosphate [BIOCHEM] $C_{10}H_{15}N_5$-$O_{10}P_2$ A coenzyme composed of adenosine and two molecules of phosphoric acid that is important in intermediate cellular metabolism. Abbreviated ADP.

adenosine 3′,5′-monophosphate See cyclic adenylic acid.

adenosinemonophosphate See adenylic acid.

adenosinetriphosphatase [BIOCHEM] An enzyme that catalyzes the hydrolysis of adenosinetriphosphate. Abbreviated ATPase.

adenosinetriphosphate [BIOCHEM] $C_{10}H_{16}N_5$-$O_{12}P_3$ A coenzyme composed of adenosinediphosphate with an additional phosphate group; an important energy compound in metabolism. Abbreviated ATP.

adeno-SV40 hybrid virus [VIROL] A defective virus particle in which part of the genetic material of papovavirus SV40 is encased in an adenovirus protein coat.

adenovirus [VIROL] A group of animal viruses which cause febrile catarrhs and other respiratory diseases.

adenylic acid [BIOCHEM] 1. A generic term for a group of isomeric nucleotides. 2. The phosphoric acid ester of adenosine. Also known as adenosinemonophosphate (AMP).

adeoniform [INV ZOO] 1. A lobate, bilamellar zooarium. 2. Resembling the fossil bryozoan *Adeona*.

Adephaga [INV ZOO] A suborder of insects in the order Coleoptera characterized by fused hind coxae that are immovable.

adequate stimulus [PHYSIO] The energy of any specific mode that is sufficient to elicit a response in an excitable tissue.

adhesion [BOT] Growing together of members of different and distinct whorls.

adhesive cell [INV ZOO] Any of various glandular cells in ctenophores, turbellarians, and hydras used for adhesion to a substrate and for capture of prey. Also known as colloblast; glue cell; lasso cell.

Adimeridae [INV ZOO] An equivalent name for the Colydiidae.

adipocellulose [BIOCHEM] A type of cellulose found in the cell walls of cork tissue.

adipogenesis [PHYSIO] The formation of fat or fatty tissue.

adipose [BIOL] Fatty; of or relating to fat.

adipose fin [VERT ZOO] A modified posterior dorsal fin that is fleshy and lacks rays; found in salmon and typical catfishes.

adipose tissue [HISTOL] A type of connective tissue specialized for lipid storage.

adjustor neuron [ANAT] Any of the interconnecting nerve cells between sensory and motor neurons of the central nervous system.

ad lib [BIOL] Shortened form for ad libitum; without limit or restraint.

adnate [BIOL] United through growth; used especially for unlike parts. [BOT] Pertaining to growth with one side adherent to a stem.

adnexa [BIOL] Subordinate or accessory parts, such as eyelids, Fallopian tubes, and extraembryonic membranes.

adonitol [BIOCHEM] $C_5H_{12}O_5$ A pentitol from the dicotyledenous plant *Adonis vernalis;* large crystals that are optically inactive and melt at 102°C; it does not reduce Fehling's solution, and is freely soluble in water and hot alcohol. Also known as adonite; ribitol.

adont hinge [INV ZOO] A type of ostracod hinge articulation which either lacks teeth and has overlapping valves or has a ridge and groove.

adoral [ZOO] Near the mouth.

ADP See adenosinediphosphate

ADPase See adenosinediphosphatase.

adrenal cortex [ANAT] The cortical moitie of the suprarenal glands which secretes glucocorticoids, mineralocorticoids, androgens, estrogens, and progestagens.

adrenal cortex hormone [BIOCHEM] Any of the steroids produced by the adrenal cortex. Also known as adrenocortical hormone; corticoid.

adrenal gland [ANAT] An endocrine organ located close to the kidneys of vertebrates and consisting of two morphologically distinct components, the cortex and medulla. Also known as suprarenal gland.

adrenaline See epinephrine.

adrenal medulla [ANAT] The hormone-secreting chromaffin cells of the adrenal gland that produce epinephrine and norepinephrine.

adrenergic [PHYSIO] Describing the chemical activity of epinephrine or epinephrine-like substances.

adrenergic blocking agent [BIOCHEM] Any substance that blocks the action of epinephrine or an epinephrine-like substance.

adrenochrome [BIOCHEM] $C_9H_9O_3N$ A brick-red oxidation product of epinephrine which can convert hemoglobin into methemoglobin.

adrenocorticotropic hormone [BIOCHEM] The chemical secretion of the adenohypophysis that stimulates the adrenal cortex. Abbreviated ACTH. Also known as adrenotropic hormone.

adrenotropic [PHYSIO] Of or pertaining to an effect on the adrenal cortex.

adrenotropic hormone See adrenocorticotropic hormone.

adret [ECOL] The sunny (usually south) face of a mountain featuring high timber and snow lines.

adventitia [ANAT] The external, connective-tissue covering of an organ or blood vessel. Also known as tunica adventitia.

adventitious [BIOL] Also known as adventive. 1. Acquired spontaneously or accidentally, not by heredity. 2. Arising, as a tissue or organ, in an unusual or abnormal place.

adventitious bud [BOT] A bud that arises at points on the plant other than at the stem apex or a leaf axil.

adventitious root [BOT] A root that arises from any plant part other than the primary root (radicle) or its branches.

adventitious vein [INV ZOO] The vessel between the intercalary and accessory veins on certain insect wings.

adventive [BIOL] 1. An organism that is introduced accidentally and is imperfectly naturalized; not native. 2. See adventitious.

advolution [BIOL] Development or growth with increasing similarities; growth toward; the opposite of evolution.

aebi [BIOL] A unit for the standardization of a phosphatase.

Aechminidae [PALEON] A family of extinct ostracods in the order Paleocopa in which the hollow central spine is larger than the valve.

aeciospore [MYCOL] A spore produced by an aecium.

aecium [MYCOL] The fruiting body or sporocarp of rust fungi.

aedeagus [INV ZOO] The copulatory organ of a male insect.

Aedes [INV ZOO] A genus of the dipterous subfamily Culicinae in the family Culicidae, with species that are vectors for many diseases of man.

Aedes aegypti [INV ZOO] A cosmopolitan mosquito that transmits the etiological agents of yellow fever, dengue, equine encephalomyelitis, and Bancroft's filariasis.

Aeduellidae [PALEON] A family of Lower Permian palaeoniscoid fishes in the order Palaeonisciformes.

Aegeriidae [INV ZOO] The clearwing moths, a family of lepidopteran insects in the suborder Heteroneura characterized by the lack of wing scales.

Aegialitidae [INV ZOO] An equivalent name for the Salpingidae.

Aegidae [INV ZOO] A family of isopod crustaceans in the suborder Flabellifera whose members are economically important as fish parasites.

aegithognathous [VERT ZOO] Referring to a bird palate in which the vomers are completely fused and truncate in appearance.

Aegothelidae [VERT ZOO] A family of small Australo-Papuan owlet-nightjars in the avian order Caprimulgiformes.

Aegypiinae [VERT ZOO] The Old World vultures, a subfamily of diurnal carrion feeders of the family Accipitridae.

Aegyptianella [MICROBIO] A genus of the family Anaplasmataceae; organisms from inclusions in red blood cells of birds.

Aegyptopithecus [PALEON] A primitive primate that is thought to represent the common ancestor of both the human and ape families.

aelophilous [BOT] Describing a plant whose disseminules are dispersed by wind.

Aelosomatidae [INV ZOO] A family of microscopic fresh-water annelid worms in the class Oligochaeta characterized by a ventrally ciliated prostomium.

Aepophilidae [INV ZOO] A family of bugs in the hemipteran superfamily Saldoidea.

Aepyornis [PALEON] A genus of extinct ratite birds representing the family Aepyornithidae.

Aepyornithidae [PALEON] The single family of the extinct avian order Aepyornithiformes.

Aepyornithiformes [PALEON] The elephant birds, an extinct order of ratite birds in the superorder Neognathae.

aerenchyma [BOT] A specialized tissue in some water plants characterized by thin-walled cells and large intercellular air spaces.

aerial [BIOL] Of, in, or belonging to the air or atmosphere.

aerial mycelium [MYCOL] A mass of hyphae that occurs above the surface of a substrate.

aerial root [BOT] A root exposed to the air, usually anchoring the plant to a tree, and often functioning in photosynthesis.

aerial stem [BOT] A stem with an erect or vertical growth habit above the ground.

aerobe [BIOL] An organism that requires air or free oxygen to maintain its life processes.

aerobic bacteria [MICROBIO] Any bacteria requiring free oxygen for the metabolic breakdown of materials.

aerobic process [BIOL] A process requiring the presence of oxygen.

aerobiology [BIOL] The study of the atmospheric dispersal of airborne fungus spores, pollen grains, and microorganisms; and, more broadly, of airborne propagules of algae and protozoans, minute insects such as aphids, and pollution gases and particles which exert specific biologic effects.

aerobioscope [MICROBIO] An apparatus for collecting and determining the bacterial content of a sample of air.

aerobiosis [BIOL] Life existing in air or oxygen.

Aerococcus [MICROBIO] A genus of bacteria in the family Streptococcaceae; spherical cells have the tendency to form tetrads; they ferment glucose with production of dextrorotatory lactic acid (homofermentative).

aerocyst [BOT] An air vesicle in certain species of algae.

Aeromonas [MICROBIO] A genus of bacteria in the family Vibrionaceae; straight, motile rods with rounded ends; most species are pathogenic to marine and fresh-water animals.

Aerosporin [MICROBIO] Trade name for the antibiotic polymyxin B.

aerotaxis [BIOL] The movement of an organism, especially aerobic and anaerobic bacteria, with reference to the direction of oxygen or air.

aerotropism [BOT] A response in which the growth direction of a plant component changes due to modifications in oxygen tension.

aeschynomenous [BOT] Having sensitive leaves that droop when touched, such as members of the Leguminosae.

Aesculus [BOT] A genus of deciduous trees or shrubs belonging to the order Sapindales. Commonly known as buckeye.

Aeshnidae [INV ZOO] A family of odonatan insects in the suborder Anisoptera distinguished by partially fused eyes.

aesthesia See esthesia.

aesthete [BOT] A plant organ with the capacity to respond to definite physical stimuli.

aestidurilignosa [ECOL] A mixed woodland of evergreen and deciduous hardwoods.

aestilignosa [ECOL] A woodland of tropophytic vegetation in temperate regions.

aestivation [BOT] The arrangement of floral parts in a bud. [PHYSIO] The condition of dormancy or torpidity.

Aetosauria [PALEON] A suborder of Triassic archosaurian quadrupedal reptiles in the order

Thecodontia armored by rings of thick, bony plates.

afferent [PHYSIO] Conducting or conveying inward or toward the center, specifically in reference to nerves and blood vessels.

afferent neuron [ANAT] A nerve cell that conducts impulses toward a nerve center, such as the central nervous system.

affinity labeling [BIOCHEM] A method for introducing a label into the active site of an enzyme by relying on the tight binding between the enzyme and its substrate (or cofactors).

aflatoxin [BIOCHEM] The toxin produced by some strains of the fungus *Aspergillus flavus*, the most potent carcinogen yet discovered.

African violet [BOT] *Saintpaulia ionantha*. A flowering plant typical of the family Gesneriaceae.

afterbirth [EMBRYO] The placenta and fetal membranes expelled from the uterus following birth of offspring in viviparous mammals.

afterimage [PHYSIO] A visual sensation occurring after the stimulus to which it is a response has been removed.

afterpotential [PHYSIO] A small positive or negative wave that follows and is dependent on the main spike potential, seen in the oscillograph tracing of an action potential passing along a nerve.

afterripening [BOT] A period of dormancy after a seed is shed during which the synthetic machinery of the seed is prepared for germination and growth.

aftershaft [VERT ZOO] An accessory, plumelike feather near the upper umbilicus on the feathers of some birds.

agameon [BIOL] An organism which reproduces only by asexual means. Also known as agamospecies.

agamete [BIOL] An asexual reproductive cell that develops into an adult individual.

agamic [BIOL] Referring to a species or generation which does not reproduce sexually.

Agamidae [VERT ZOO] A family of Old World lizards in the suborder Sauria that have acrodont dentition.

agamogony [BIOL] Asexual reproduction, specifically schizogony.

agamospecies *See* agameon.

agamospermy [BOT] Apogamy in which sexual union is incomplete because of abnormal development of the pollen and the embryo sac.

Agaontidae [INV ZOO] A family of small hymenopteran insects in the superfamily Chalcidoidea; commonly called fig insects for their role in cross-pollination of figs.

Agaricales [MYCOL] An order of fungi in the class Basidiomycetes containing all forms of fleshy, gilled mushrooms.

agarophyte [BOT] Any seaweed that yields agar.

Agavaceae [BOT] A family of flowering plants in the order Liliales characterized by parallel, narrow-veined leaves, a more or less corolloid perianth, and an agavaceous habit.

age [BIOL] Period of time from origin or birth to a later time designated or understood; length of existence.

age distribution [ECOL] The distribution of different age groups in a population.

agenesis [BIOL] Absence of a tissue or organ due to lack of development.

aggressive mimicry [ZOO] Mimicry used to attract or deceive a species in order to prey upon it.

aging [BIOL] Growing older.

Aglaspida [PALEON] An order of Cambrian and Ordovician merostome arthropods in the subclass Xiphosurida characterized by a phosphatic exoskeleton and vaguely trilobed body form.

aglomerular [HISTOL] Lacking glomeruli.

Aglossa [VERT ZOO] A suborder of anuran amphibians represented by the single family Pipidea and characterized by the absence of a tongue.

aglycon [BIOCHEM] The nonsugar compound resulting from the hydrolysis of glycosides; an example is $3,5,7,3',4'$-pentahydroxyflavylium, or cyanidin.

aglyphous [VERT ZOO] Having solid teeth.

agmatine [BIOCHEM] $C_5H_{14}N_4$ Needlelike crystals with a melting point of 231°C; soluble in water; a product of the enzymatic decarboxylation of argenine. Also known as 4-(aminobutyl)guanidine.

agnate [BIOL] Related exclusively through male descent.

Agnatha [VERT ZOO] The most primitive class of vertebrates, characterized by the lack of true jaws.

Agonidae [VERT ZOO] The poachers, a small family of marine perciform fishes in the suborder Cottoidei.

agouti [VERT ZOO] A hystricomorph rodent, *Dasyprocta*, in the family Dasyproctidae, represented by 13 species.

agranular leukocyte [HISTOL] A type of white blood cell, including lymphocytes and monocytes, characterized by the absence of cytoplasmic granules and by a relatively large spherical or indented nucleus.

agrestal [ECOL] Growing wild in the fields.

agriculture [BIOL] The production of plants and animals useful to man, involving soil cultivation and the breeding and management of crops and livestock.

Agriochoeridae [PALEON] A family of extinct tylopod ruminants in the superfamily Merycoidodontoidea.

agrioecology [ECOL] The ecology of cultivated plants.

Agrionidae [INV ZOO] A family of odonatan insects in the suborder Zygoptera characterized by black or red markings on the wings.

Agrobacterium [MICROBIO] A genus of bacteria in the family Rhizobiaceae; cells do not fix free nitrogen, and three of the four species are plant pathogens, producing galls and hairy root.

Agrobacterium tumefaciens [MICROBIO] A pathogenic soil bacterium that causes root and stem galls on plants in over 40 families of angiosperms.

Agromyzidae [INV ZOO] A family of myodarian cyclorrhaphous dipteran insects of the subsection Acalypteratae; commonly called leaf-miner flies because the larvae cut channels in leaves.

agrophilous [ECOL] Having a natural habitat in grain fields.

agrostology [BOT] A division of systematic botany concerned with the study of grasses.

ahermatypic [INV ZOO] Non-reef-building, applied to corals.

aiophyllous *See* evergreen.

air cell [ZOO] A cavity or receptacle for air such as an alveolus, an air sac in birds, or a dilation of the trachea in insects.

air layering [BOT] A method of vegetative propagation, usually of a wounded part, in which the branch or shoot is enclosed in a moist medium until roots develop, and then it is severed and cultivated as an independent plant.

air pollution [ECOL] The presence in the outdoor atmosphere of one or more contaminants such as dust, fumes, gas, mist, odor, smoke, or vapor in quantities and of characteristics and duration such as to be injurious to human, plant, or animal life or to property, or to interfere unreasonably with the comfortable enjoyment of life and property.

air sac [INV ZOO] One of large, thin-walled structures associated with the tracheal system of some insects. [VERT ZOO] In birds, any of the small vesicles that are connected with the respiratory system and located in bones and muscles to increase buoyancy.

air spora [BIOL] Airborne fungus spores, pollen grains, and microorganisms.

Aistopoda [PALEON] An order of Upper Carboniferous amphibians in the subclass Lepospondyli characterized by reduced or absent limbs and an elongate, snakelike body.

Aizoaceae [BOT] A family of flowering plants in the order Caryophyllales; members are unarmed leaf-succulents, chiefly of Africa.

akaryote [CELL BIO] A cell that lacks a nucleus.

akinete [BOT] A thick-walled resting cell of unicellular and filamentous green algae.

ala [BIOL] A wing or winglike structure.

alang-alang *See* cogon.

alanine [BIOCHEM] $C_3H_7NO_2$ A white, crystalline, nonessential amino acid of the pyruvic acid family.

alar [BIOL] Winglike or pertaining to a wing.

alarm reaction [BIOL] The sum of all nonspecific phenomena which are elicited by sudden exposure to stimuli, which affect large portions of the body, and to which the organism is quantitatively or qualitatively not adapted.

alarm song [INV ZOO] A stress signal occurring in many families of beetles.

Alaudidae [VERT ZOO] The larks, a family of Oscine birds in the order Passeriformes.

albatross [VERT ZOO] Any of the large, long-winged oceanic birds composing the family Diomedeidae of the order Procellariformes.

albinism [BIOL] The state of having colorless chromatophores, which results in the absence of pigmentation in animals that are normally pigmented.

albomycin [MICROBIO] An antibiotic produced by *Actinomyces subtropicus*; effective against penicillin-resistant pneumococci and staphylococci.

albuginea [HISTOL] A layer of white, fibrous connective tissue investing an organ or other body part.

albumen [CELL BIO] The white of an egg, composed principally of albumin.

albumin [BIOCHEM] Any of a group of plant and animal proteins which are soluble in water, dilute salt solutions, and 50% saturated ammonium sulfate.

albumin-globulin ratio [BIOCHEM] The ratio of the concentrations of albumin to globulin in blood serum.

albuminoid [BIOCHEM] *See* scleroprotein. [BIOL] Having the characteristics of albumin.

albumose [BIOCHEM] A protein derivative formed by the action of a hydrolytic enzyme, such as pepsin.

Alcaligenes [MICROBIO] A genus of gram-negative, aerobic rods and cocci of uncertain affiliation; cells are motile, and species are commonly found in the intestinal tract of vertebrates.

Alcedinidae [VERT ZOO] The kingfishers, a worldwide family of colorful birds in the order Coraciiformes; characterized by large heads, short necks, and heavy, pointed bills.

Alcidae [VERT ZOO] A family of shorebirds, predominantly of northern coasts, in the order Charadriiformes, including auks, puffins, murres, and guillemots.

Alciopidae [INV ZOO] A pelagic family of errantian annelid worms in the class Polychaeta.

alcohol dehydrogenase [BIOCHEM] The enzyme that catalyzes the oxidation of ethanol to acetaldehyde.

alcoholic fermentation [MICROBIO] The process by which certain yeasts decompose sugars in the absence of oxygen to form alcohol and carbon dioxide; method for production of ethanol, wine, and beer.

Alcyonacea [INV ZOO] The soft corals, an order of littoral anthozoans of the subclass Alcyonaria.

Alcyonaria [INV ZOO] A subclass of the Anthozoa; members are colonial coelenterates, most of which are sedentary and littoral.

aldehyde dehydrogenase [BIOCHEM] An enzyme that catalyzes the conversion of an aldehyde to its corresponding acid.

aldehyde lyase [BIOCHEM] Any enzyme that catalyzes the nonhydrolytic cleavage of an aldehyde.

alder [BOT] The common name for several trees of the genus Alnus.

aldolase [BIOCHEM] An enzyme in anaerobic glycolysis that catalyzes the cleavage of fructose 1,6-diphosphate to glyceraldehyde 3-phosphate; used also in the reverse reaction.

aldosterone [BIOCHEM] $C_{21}H_{28}O_5$ A steroid hormone extracted from the adrenal cortex that functions chiefly in regulating sodium and potassium metabolism.

alecithal [CELL BIO] Referring to an egg without yolk, such as the eggs of placental mammals.

Alepocephaloidei [VERT ZOO] The slickheads, a suborder of deap-sea teleostean fishes of the order Salmoniformes.

aletophyte [ECOL] A weedy plant growing on the roadside or in fields where natural vegetation has been disrupted by man.

aleuron [BOT] Protein in the form of grains stored in the embryo, endosperm, or perisperm of many seeds.

aleurospore [MYCOL] A simple terminal or lateral, thick-walled, nondeciduous spore produced by some fungi of the order Moniliales.

alewife [VERT ZOO] *Pomolobus pseudoharengus.* A food fish of the herring family that is very abundant on the Atlantic coast.

Alexinic unit [BIOL] A unit for the standardization of blood serum.

Aleyrodidae [INV ZOO] The whiteflies, a family of homopteran insects included in the series Sternorrhyncha; economically important as plant pests.

alfalfa [BOT] *Medicago sativa.* A herbaceous perennial legume in the order Rosales, characterized by a deep taproot. Also known as lucerne.

algae [BOT] General name for the chlorophyll-bearing organisms in the plant subkingdom Thallobionta.

algae bloom [ECOL] A heavy growth of algae in and on a body of water as a result of high phosphate concentration from farm fertilizers and detergents.

algae wash [ECOL] A shoreline drift consisting almost entirely of filamentous algae.

algal [BOT] Of or pertaining to algae.

algesia [PHYSIO] Sensitivity to pain.

algesimeter [PHYSIO] A device used to determine pain thresholds.

algesireceptor [PHYSIO] A pain-sensitive cutaneous sense organ.

algology [BOT] The study of algae.

allesterase [BIOCHEM] Any one of the lipases or nonspecific esterases.

alimentary [BIOL] Of or relating to food, nutrition, or diet.

alimentary canal [ANAT] The tube through which food passes; in man, includes the mouth, pharynx, esophagus, stomach, and intestine.

alimentation [BIOL] Providing nourishment by feeding.

Alismataceae [BOT] A family of flowering plants belonging to the order Alismatales characterized by schizogenous secretory cells, a horseshoe-shaped embryo, and one or two ovules.

Alismatales [BOT] A small order of flowering plants in the subclass Alismatidae, including aquatic and semiaquatic herbs.

Alismatidae [BOT] A relatively primitive subclass of aquatic or semiaquatic herbaceous flowering plants in the class Liliopsida, generally having apocarpous flowers, and trinucleate pollen and lacking endosperm.

alisphenoid [ANAT] 1. The bone forming the greater wing of the sphenoid in adults. 2. Of or pertaining to the sphenoid wing.

allvincular [INV ZOO] In some bivalves, having the long axis of the short ligament transverse to the hinge line.

alkali chlorosis [PL PATH] Yellowing of plant foliage due to excess amounts of soluble salts in the soil.

alkaline phosphatase [BIOCHEM] A phosphatase active in alkaline media.

alkaline tide [PHYSIO] The temporary decrease in acidity of urine and body fluids after eating, attributed by some to the withdrawal of acid from the body due to gastric digestion.

allantoic acid [BIOCHEM] $C_4H_8N_4O_4$ A crystalline acid obtained by hydrolysis of allantoin; intermediate product in nucleic acid metabolism.

allantoin [BIOCHEM] $C_4H_6N_4O_3$ A crystallizable oxidation product of uric acid found in allantoic and amniotic fluids and in fetal urine.

allantoinase [BIOCHEM] An enzyme, occurring in nonmammalian vertebrates, that catalyzes the hydrolysis of allantoin.

allantois [EMBRYO] A fluid-filled, saclike, extraembryonic membrane lying between the chorion and amnion of reptilian, bird, and mammalian embryos.

allantoxanic acid [BIOCHEM] $C_4H_3N_3O_4$ An acid formed by oxidation of uric acid or allantoin.

allanturic acid [BIOCHEM] $C_3H_4N_2O_3$ An acid formed principally by the oxidation of allantoin.

Alleculidae [INV ZOO] The comb claw beetles, a family of mostly tropical coleopteran insects in the superfamily Tenebrionoidea.

Allee's principle [GEN] The concept of an intermediate optimal population density by which groups of organisms often flourish best if neither too few nor too many individuals are present.

Alleghenian life zone [ECOL] A biome that includes the eastern mixed coniferous and deciduous forests of New England.

allele [GEN] One of a pair of genes, or of multiple forms of a gene, located at the same locus of homologous chromosomes. Also known as allelomorph.

allelic mutant [GEN] A cell or organism with characters different from those of the parent due to alterations of one or more alleles.

allelochemic [PHYSIO] Pertaining to a semiochemical that acts as an interspecific agent of communication.

allelomorph *See* allele.

allelotropism [BIOL] A mutual attraction between two cells or organisms.

Allen-Doisy unit [BIOL] A unit for the standardization of estrogens.

alliance [SYST] A group of related families ranking between an order and a class.

alligator [VERT ZOO] Either of two species of archosaurian reptiles in the genus *Alligator* of the family Alligatoridae.

Alligatorinae [VERT ZOO] A subgroup of the crocodilian family Crocodylidae that includes alligators, caimans, *Melanosuchus*, and *Paleosuchus*.

Allium [BOT] A genus of bulbous herbs in the family Liliaceae including leeks, onions, and chives.

allochoric [BOT] Describing a species that inhabits two or more closely related communities, such as forest and grassland, in the same region.

Alloeocoela [INV ZOO] An order of platyhelminthic worms of the class Turbellaria distinguished by a simple pharynx and a diverticulated intestine.

allogenic [ECOL] Caused by external factors, as in reference to the change in habitat of a natural community resulting from draught.

allograft [BIOL] Graft from a donor transplanted to a genetically dissimilar recipient of the same species.

Allogromiidae [INV ZOO] A little-known family of protozoans in the order Foraminiferida; adults are characterized by a chitinous test.

Allogromiina [INV ZOO] A suborder of marine and fresh-water protozoans in the order Foraminiferida characterized by an organic test of protein and acid mucopolysaccharide.

allometry [BIOL] 1. The quantitative relation between a part and the whole or another part as the organism increases in size. Also known as heterauxesis; heterogony. 2. The quantitative relation between the size of a part and the whole or another part, in a series of related organisms that differ in size.

allomone [PHYSIO] A chemical produced by an organism which induces in a member of another species a behavioral or physiological reaction favorable to the emitter; may be mutualistic or antagonistic.

allomorphosis [EVOL] Allometry in phylogenetic development.

Allomyces [MYCOL] A genus of aquatic phycomycetous fungi in the order Blastocladiales characterized by basal rhizoids, terminal hyphae, and zoospores with a single posterior flagellum.

allopatric [ECOL] Referring to populations or species that occupy naturally exclusive, but usually adjacent, geographical areas.

allopelagic [ECOL] Relating to organisms living at various depths in the sea in response to influences other than temperature.

allophore [HISTOL] A chromatophore which contains a red pigment that is soluble in alcohol; found in the skin of fishes, amphibians, and reptiles.

allopolyploid [GEN] An organism or strain arising from a combination of genetically distinct chromosome sets from two diploid organisms.

all-or-none law [PHYSIO] The principle that transmission of a nerve impulse is either at full strength or not at all.

allosome [GEN] 1. Sex chromosome. 2. Any atypical chromosome.

allosteric effector [BIOCHEM] A small molecule that reacts either with a nonbinding site of an enzyme molecule, or with a protein molecule, and causes a change in the function of the molecule. Also known as allosteric modulator.

allosteric enzyme [BIOCHEM] Any of the regulatory bacterial enzymes, such as those involved in end-product inhibition.

allosteric modulator See allosteric effector.

allosteric transition [BIOCHEM] A reversible exchange of one base pair for another on a protein molecule that alters the properties of the active site and changes the biological activity of the protein.

allostery [BIOCHEM] The property of an enzyme able to shift reversibly between an active and an inactive configuration.

Allotheria [PALEON] A subclass of Mammalia that appeared in the Upper Jurassic and became extinct in the Cenozoic.

Allotriognathi [VERT ZOO] An equivalent name for the Lampridiformes.

allotype [SYST] A paratype of the opposite sex to the holotype.

alloxan [BIOCHEM] $C_4H_2N_2O_4$ Crystalline oxidation product of uric acid; induces diabetes experimentally by selective destruction of pancreatic beta cells. Also known as mesoxalyurea.

allspice [BOT] The dried, unripe berries of a small, tropical evergreen tree, *Pimenta officinalis*, of the myrtle family; yields a pungent, aromatic spice.

alm [ECOL] A meadow in alpine or subalpine mountain regions.

almond [BOT] *Prunus amygdalus*. A small deciduous tree of the order Rosales; it produces a drupaceous edible fruit with an ellipsoidal, slightly compressed nutlike seed.

Almquist unit [BIOL] A unit for the standardization of vitamin K.

Alopiidae [VERT ZOO] A family of pelagic isurid elasmobranchs commonly known as thresher sharks because of their long, whiplike tail.

alpaca [VERT ZOO] *Lama pacos*. An artiodactyl of the camel family (Camelidae); economically important for its long, fine wool.

alpage [ECOL] A summer grazing area composed of natural plant pasturage in upland or mountainous regions.

alpestrine [ECOL] Referring to organisms that live at high elevation but below the timberline. Also known as subalpine.

alpha cell [HISTOL] Any of the acidophilic chromophiles in the anterior lobe of the adenohypophysis.

alpha globulin [BIOCHEM] A heterogeneous fraction of serum globulins containing the proteins of greatest electrophoretic mobility.

alpha helix [MOL BIO] A spatial configuration of the polypeptide chains of proteins in which the chain assumes a helical form, 0.54 nanometer in pitch, 3.6 amino acids per turn, presenting the appearance of a hollow cylinder with radiating side groups.

alpha hemolysis [MICROBIO] Partial hemolysis of red blood cells with green discoloration in a blood agar medium by certain hemolytic streptococci.

alpha rhythm [PHYSIO] An electric current from the occipital region of the brain cortex having a pulse frequency of 8 to 13 per second; associated with a relaxed state in normal human adults.

alpha taxonomy [SYST] The level of taxonomic study concerned with characterizing and naming species.

Alpheidae [INV ZOO] The snapping shrimp, a family of decapod crustaceans included in the section Caridea.

alpine [ECOL] Any plant native to mountain peaks or boreal regions.

alpine tundra [ECOL] Large, flat or gently sloping, treeless tracts of land above the timberline.

alternate [BOT] 1. Of the arrangement of leaves on opposite sides of the stem at different levels. 2. Of the arrangement of the parts of one whorl between members of another whorl.

alternation of generations See metagenesis.

alterne [ECOL] A community exhibiting alternating dominance with other communities in the same area.

altherbosa [ECOL] Communities of tall herbs, usually succeeding where forests have been destroyed.

altitude acclimatization [PHYSIO] A physiological adaptation to reduced atmospheric and oxygen pressure.

altitudinal vegetation zone [ECOL] A geographical band of physiognomically similar vegetation correlated with vertical and horizontal gradients of environmental conditions.

altricial [VERT ZOO] Pertaining to young that are born or hatched immature and helpless, thus requiring extended development and parental care.

alula [ZOO] 1. Digit of a bird wing homologous to the thumb. 2. See calypter.

alvar [ECOL] Dwarfed vegetation characteristic of certain Scandinavian steppelike communities with a limestone base.

alveator [INV ZOO] A type of pedicellaria in echinoderms.

alveolar [BIOL] Of or relating to an alveolus.

alveolar gland See acinous gland.

alveolar oxygen pressure [PHYSIO] The oxygen pressure in the alveoli; the value is about 105 mm Hg.

alveolitoid [INV ZOO] A type of tabulate coral having a vaulted upper wall and a lower wall parallel to the surface of attachment.

alveolus [ANAT] 1. A tiny air sac of the lung. 2. A tooth socket. 3. A sac of a compound gland.

Alydidae [INV ZOO] A family of hemipteran insects in the superfamily Coreoidea.

Alysiella [MICROBIO] A genus of bacteria in the family Simonsiellaceae; cells are arranged in pairs within the filaments.

amanthophilous [BOT] Of plants having a habitat in sandy plains or hills.

Amaranthaceae [BOT] The characteristic family of flowering plants in the order Caryophyllales; they have a syncarpous gynoecium, a monochlamydeous perianth that is more or less scarious, and mostly perfect flowers.

Amaryllidaceae [BOT] The former designation for a family of plants now included in the Liliaceae.

ambergris [PHYSIO] A fatty substance formed in the intestinal tract of the sperm whale; used in the manufacture of perfume.

amber mutation [GEN] Alteration of a codon to UAG, a codon that results in premature polypeptide chain termination in bacteria.

ambidextrous [PHYSIO] Capable of using both hands with equal skill.

ambigenous [BOT] Of a perianth whose outer leaves resemble the calyx while the inner leaves resemble the corolla.

ambiguous codon [GEN] A codon capable of coding for more than one amino acid sequence.

ambitus [BIOL] The periphery or external edge, as of a mollusk shell or leaf.

Amblyopsidae [VERT ZOO] The cave fishes, a family of actinopterygian fishes in the order Percopsiformes.

Amblyopsiformes [VERT ZOO] An equivalent name for the Percopsiformes.

Amblypygi [INV ZOO] An order of chelicerate arthropods in the class Arachnida, commonly known as the tailless whip scorpions.

amboceptor unit [BIOL] A unit for the standardization of blood serum.

ambulacrum [INV ZOO] In echinoderms, any of the radial series of plates along which the tube feet are arranged.

ambulatorial [ZOO] 1. Capable of walking. 2. In reference to a forest animal, having adapted to walking, as opposed to running, crawling, or leaping.

Ambystoma [VERT ZOO] A genus of common salamanders; the type genus of the family Ambystomatidae.

Ambystomatidae [VERT ZOO] A family of urodele amphibians in the suborder Salamandroidea; neoteny occurs frequently in this group.

Ambystomoidea [VERT ZOO] A suborder to which the family Ambystomatidae is sometimes elevated.

ameba [INV ZOO] The common name for a number of species of naked unicellular protozoans of the order Amoebida; an example is a member of the genus Amoeba.

Amebelodontinae [PALEON] A subfamily of extinct elephantoid proboscideans in the family Gomphotheriidae.

amebocyte [INV ZOO] One of the wandering ameboid cells in the tissues and fluids of many invertebrates that function in assimilation and excretion.

ameboid movement [CELL BIO] A type of cellular locomotion involving the formation of pseudopodia.

ameiosis [GEN] Nonreduction of chromosome number due to suppression of one of the miotic divisions, as in parthenogenesis.

Ameiuridae [VERT ZOO] A family of North American catfishes belonging to the suborder Siluroidei.

ameloblast [EMBRYO] One of the columnar cells of the enamel organ that form dental enamel in developing teeth.

amensalism [ECOL] An interaction between species in which one species is harmed and the other is unaffected.

ament [BOT] A catkin.

Amera [INV ZOO] One of the three divisions of the phylum Vermes proposed by O. Bütschli in 1910 and given the rank of a subphylum.

American boreal faunal region [ECOL] A zoogeographic region comprising marine littoral animal communities of the coastal waters off east-central North America.

American-Egyptian cotton [BOT] A type of cotton developed by hybridization of Egyptian and American plants.

American lion See puma.

Amerosporae [MYCOL] A spore group of the Fungi Imperfecti characterized by one-celled or threadlike spores.

ametabolous metamorphosis [INV ZOO] A growth stage of certain insects characterized by an increase in size without distinct external changes.

ametoecious [ECOL] Of a parasite that remains with the same host.

amictic [INV ZOO] 1. In rotifers, producing diploid eggs that are incapable of being fertilized. 2. Pertaining to the egg produced by the amictic female.

amidase [BIOCHEM] Any enzyme that catalyzes the hydrolysis of nonpeptide C≡N linkages.

amidocarbonic acid See carbamic acid.

amidohydrolase [BIOCHEM] An enzyme that catalyzes deamination.

Amiidae [VERT ZOO] A family of actinopterygian fishes in the order Amiiformes represented by a single living species, the bowfin (*Amia calva*).

Amiiformes [VERT ZOO] An order of actinopterygian fishes characterized by an abbreviate heterocercal tail, fusiform body, and median fin rays.

amine oxidase [BIOCHEM] An enzyme that catalyzes the oxidation of tyramine and tryptamine to aldehyde.

aminoacetic acid See glycine.

ACP See acyl carrier protein.

amino acid [BIOCHEM] Any of the organic compounds that contain one or more basic amino groups and one or more acidic carboxyl groups and that are polymerized to form peptides and proteins; only 20 of the more than 80 amino acids found in nature serve as building blocks for proteins; examples are tyrosine and lysine.

***para*-aminobenzoic acid** [BIOCHEM] $C_7H_7O_2N$ A yellow-red, crystalline compound that is part of the folic acid molecule; essential in metabolism of certain bacteria. Abbreviated PABA.

4-(aminobutyl)guanidine See agmatine.

aminoformic acid See carbamic acid.

α-aminohydrocinnamic acid See phenylalanine.

α-aminoisovaleric acid See valine.

2-aminoisovaleric acid See valine.

2-amino-3-methylbutyric acid See valine.

aminopeptidase [BIOCHEM] An enzyme which catalyzes the liberation of an amino acid from the end of a peptide having a free amino group.

α-amino-β-phenylpropionic acid See phenylalanine.

aminopolypeptidase [BIOCHEM] A proteolytic enzyme that cleaves polypeptides containing either a free amino group or a basic nitrogen atom having at least one hydrogen atom.

aminoprotease [BIOCHEM] An enzyme that hydrolyzes a protein and unites with its free amino group.

amino sugar [BIOCHEM] A monosaccharide in which a nonglycosidic hydroxyl group is replaced by an amino or substituted amino group; an example is D-glucosamine.

amino terminal [BIOCHEM] The end part of a polypeptide chain which contains a free α-amino group.

aminotransferase See transaminase.

amitosis [CELL BIO] Cell division by simple fission of the nucleus and cytoplasm without chromosome differentiation.

ammocoete [ZOO] A protracted larval stage of lampreys.

ammocolous [ECOL] Describing plants having a habitat in dry sand.

Ammodiscacea [INV ZOO] A superfamily of foraminiferal protozoans in the suborder Textulariina, characterized by a simple to labyrinthic test wall.

Ammodytoidei [VERT ZOO] The sand lances, a suborder of marine actinopterygian fishes in the order Perciformes, characterized by slender, eel-shaped bodies.

ammonifiers [ECOL] Fungi, or actinomycetous bacteria, that participate in the ammonification part of the nitrogen cycle and release ammonia (NH_3) by decomposition of organic matter.

ammonite [PALEON] A fossil shell of the cephalopod order Ammonoidea.

ammonoid [PALEON] A cephalopod of the order Ammonoidea.

Ammonoidea [PALEON] An order of extinct cephalopod mollusks in the subclass Tetrabranchia; important as index fossils.

Ammotheidae [INV ZOO] A family of marine arthropods in the subphylum Pycnogonida.

amnicolous [ECOL] Describing plants having a habitat on sandy riverbanks.

amnion [EMBRYO] A thin extraembryonic membrane forming a closed sac around the embryo in birds, reptiles, and mammals.

Amniota [VERT ZOO] A collective term for the Reptilia, Aves, and Mammalia, all of which have an amnion during development.

amniotic fluid [PHYSIO] A substance that fills the amnion to protect the embryo from desiccation and shock.

Amoeba [INV ZOO] A genus of naked, rhizopod protozoans in the order Amoebida characterized by a thin pellicle and thick, irregular pseudopodia.

Amoebida [INV ZOO] An order of rhizopod protozoans in the subclass Lobosia characterized by the absence of a protective covering (test).

Amoebobacter [MICROBIO] A genus of bacteria in the family Chromatiaceae; cells are spherical and nonmotile, have gas vacuoles, and contain bacteriochlorophyll *a* on vesicular photosynthetic membranes.

amorphic allele [GEN] An allele that lacks gene activity.

Amorphosporangium [MICROBIO] A genus of bacteria in the family Actinoplanaceae with irregular sporangia and rod-shaped spores; they are motile by means of polar flagella.

AMP *See* adenylic acid.

3',5'-AMP *See* cyclic adenylic acid.

Ampeliscidae [INV ZOO] A family of tube-dwelling amphipod crustaceans in the suborder Gammaridea.

Ampharetidae [INV ZOO] A large, deep-water family of polychaete annelids belonging to the Sedentaria.

Ampharetinae [INV ZOO] A subfamily of annelids belonging to the family Ampharetidae.

amphiarthrosis [ANAT] An articulation of limited movement in which bones are connected by fibrocartilage, such as that between vertebrae or that at the tibiofibular junction.

amphiaster [INV ZOO] Type of spicule found in some sponges.

Amphibia [VERT ZOO] A class of vertebrate animals in the superclass Tetrapoda characterized by a moist, glandular skin, gills at some stage of development, and no amnion during the embryonic stage.

Amphibicorisae [INV ZOO] A subdivision of the insect order Hemiptera containing surface water bugs with exposed antennae.

Amphibioidei [INV ZOO] A family of tapeworms in the order Cyclophyllidea.

amphibiotic [ZOO] Being aquatic during the larval stage and terrestrial in the adult stage.

amphibious [BIOL] Capable of living both on dry or moist land and in water.

amphiblastic cleavage [EMBRYO] The unequal but complete cleavage of telolecithal eggs.

amphiblastula [EMBRYO] A blastula resulting from amphiblastic cleavage. [INV ZOO] The free-swimming flagellated larva of many sponges.

amphibolic [ZOO] Possessing the ability to turn either backward or forward, as the outer toe of certain birds.

amphibolic pathway [BIOCHEM] A microbial biosynthetic and energy-producing pathway, such as the glycolytic pathway.

Amphibolidae [INV ZOO] A family of gastropod mollusks in the order Basommatophora.

amphicarpic [BOT] Having two types of fruit, differing either in form or ripening time.

Amphichelydia [PALEON] A suborder of Triassic to Eocene anapsid reptiles in the order Chelonia; these turtles did not have a retractable neck.

amphichrome [BOT] A plant that produces flowers of different colors on the same stalk.

Amphicoela [VERT ZOO] A small suborder of amphibians in the order Anura characterized by amphicoelous vertebrae.

amphicoelous [VERT ZOO] Describing vertebrae that have biconcave centra.

amphicribral [BOT] Having the phloem surrounded by the xylem, as seen in certain vascular bundles.

amphicryptophyte [BOT] A marsh plant with amphibious vegetative organs.

Amphicyonidae [PALEON] A family of extinct giant predatory carnivores placed in the infraorder Miacoidea by some authorities.

amphicytula [EMBRYO] A zygote that is capable of holoblastic unequal cleavage.

amphid [INV ZOO] Either of a pair of sensory receptors in nematodes, believed to be chemoreceptors and situated laterally on the anterior end of the body.

amphidetic [INV ZOO] Of a bivalve ligament, extending both before and behind the beak.

amphidiploid [GEN] An organism having a diploid set of chromosomes from each parent.

Amphidiscophora [INV ZOO] A subclass of sponges in the class Hexactinellida characterized by an anchoring tuft of spicules and no hexasters.

Amphidiscosa [INV ZOO] An order of hexactinellid sponges in the subclass Amphidiscophora characterized by amphidisc spicules, that is, spicules having a stellate disk at each end.

amphigastrium [BOT] Any of the small appendages located ventrally on the stem of some liverworts.

amphigean [ECOL] An organism that is native to both Old and New Worlds.

Amphilestidae [PALEON] A family of Jurassic triconodont mammals whose subclass is uncertain.

Amphilinidea [INV ZOO] An order of tapeworms in the subclass Cestodaria characterized by a protrusible proboscis, anterior frontal glands, and no holdfast organ; they inhabit the coelom of sturgeon and other fishes.

Amphimerycidae [PALEON] A family of late Eocene to early Oligocene tylopod ruminants in the superfamily Amphimerycoidea.

Amphimerycoidea [PALEON] A superfamily of extinct ruminant artiodactyls in the infraorder Tylopoda.

amphimixis [PHYSIO] The union of egg and sperm in sexual reproduction.

Amphimonadidae [INV ZOO] A family of zoomastigophorean protozoans in the order Kinetoplastida.

Amphineura [INV ZOO] A class of the phylum Mollusca; members are bilaterally symmetrical, elongate marine animals, such as the chitons.

Amphinomidae [INV ZOO] The stinging or fire worms, a family of amphinomorphan polychaetes belonging to the Errantia.

Amphinomorpha [INV ZOO] Group name for three families of errantian polychaetes: Amphenomidae, Euphrosinidae, and Spintheridae.

amphioxus [ZOO] Former designation for the lancelet, *Branchiostoma*.

amphiphloic [BOT] Pertaining to the central vascular cylinder of stems having phloem on both sides of the xylem.

amphiphyte [ECOL] A plant growing on the boundary zone of wet land.

amphiplatyan [ANAT] Describing vertebrae having centra that are flat both anteriorly and posteriorly.

amphiploid [GEN] A polyploid produced when chromosomes of a species hybrid double.

amphipneustic [VERT ZOO] Having both gills and lungs through all life stages, as in some amphibians.

Amphipoda [INV ZOO] An order of crustaceans in the subclass Malacostraca; individuals lack a carapace, bear unstalked eyes, and respire through thoracic branchiae or gills.

amphipodous [INV ZOO] Having both walking and swimming legs.

amphisarca [BOT] An indehiscent fruit characterized by many cells and seeds, pulpy flesh, and a hard rind; melon is an example.

Amphisbaenidae [VERT ZOO] A family of tropical snakelike lizards in the suborder Sauria.

Amphisopidae [INV ZOO] A family of isopod crustaceans in the suborder Phreactoicoidea.

amphispore [MYCOL] A specialized urediospore with a thick, colorful wall; a resting spore.

Amphissitidae [PALEON] A family of extinct ostracods in the suborder Beyrichicopina.

Amphistaenidae [VERT ZOO] The worm lizards, a family of reptiles in the suborder Sauria; structural features are greatly reduced, particularly the limbs.

amphistome [INV ZOO] An adult type of digenetic trematode having a well-developed ventral sucker (acetabulum) on the posterior end.

amphistylic [VERT ZOO] Having the jaw suspended from the brain case and the hyomandibular cartilage, as in some sharks.

amphitene See zygotene.

amphithecium [BOT] The external cell layer during development of the sporangium in mosses.

Amphitheriidae [PALEON] A family of Jurassic therian mammals in the infraclass Pantotheria.

amphitriaene [INV ZOO] A poriferan spicule having three divergent rays at each end.

amphitrichous [BIOL] Having flagella at both ends, as in certain bacteria.

Amphitritinae [INV ZOO] A subfamily of sedentary polychaete worms in the family Terebellidae.

amphitropical distribution [ECOL] Distribution of mostly temperate organisms which are discontinuous between the Northern and Southern hemispheres.

amphitropous [BOT] Having a half-inverted ovule with the funiculus attached near the middle.

Amphiumidae [VERT ZOO] A small family of urodele amphibians in the suborder Salamandroidea composed of three species of large, eellike salamanders with tiny limbs.

amphivasal [BOT] Having the xylem surrounding the phloem, as seen in certain vascular bundles.

Amphizoidae [INV ZOO] The trout stream beetles, a small family of coleopteran insects in the suborder Adephaga.

Amphoriscidae [INV ZOO] A family of calcareous sponges in the order Sycettida.

amphotericin [MICROBIO] An amphoteric antifungal antibiotic produced by *Streptomyces nodosus* and having of two components, A and B.

amphotericin A [MICROBIO] The relatively inactive component of amphotericin.

amphotericin B [MICROBIO] $C_{46}H_{73}O_{20}N$ The active component of amphotericin, suitable for systemic therapy of deep or superficial mycotic infections.

amplexicaul [BOT] Pertaining to a sessile leaf with the base or stipules embracing the stem.

amplexus [BOT] Having the edges of a leaf overlap the edges of a leaf above it in vernation.

amplexus [VERT ZOO] The copulatory embrace of frogs and toads.

ampliate [BIOL] Widened or enlarged.

amplification [GEN] 1. Treatment with an antibiotic or other agent to increase the relative proportion of plasmid to bacterial deoxyribonucleic acid. 2. Bulk replication of a gene library.

Ampulicidae [INV ZOO] A small family of hymenopteran insects in the superfamily Sphecoidea.

ampulla [ANAT] A dilated segment of a gland or tubule. [BOT] A small air bladder in some aquatic plants. [INV ZOO] The sac at the base of a tube foot in certain echinoderms.

ampulla of Lorenzini [VERT ZOO] Any of the cutaneous receptors in the head region of elasmobranchs; thought to have a thermosensory function.

ampulla of Vater [ANAT] Dilation at the junction of the bile and pancreatic ducts and the duodenum in man. Also known as papilla of Vater.

Ampullariella [MICROBIO] A genus of bacteria in the family Actinoplanaceae having cylindrical or bottle-shaped sporangia and rod-shaped spores arranged in parallel chains; motile by means of a polar tuft of flagella.

ampullary organ [PHYSIO] An electroreceptor most sensitive to direct-current and low-frequency electric stimuli; found over the body surface of electric fish and also in certain other fish such as sharks, rays, and catfish.

amygdalin [BIOCHEM] $C_6H_5CH(CN)OC_{12}H_{21}O_{10}A$ glucoside occurring in the kernels of certain plants of the genus *Prunus*.

amylase [BIOCHEM] An enzyme that hydrolyzes reserve carbohydrates, starch in plants and glycogen in animals.

amylolysis [BIOCHEM] The enzyme-catalyzed hydrolysis of starch to soluble products.

amylolytic enzyme [BIOCHEM] A type of enzyme capable of denaturing starch molecules; used in textile manufacture to remove starch added to slash sizing agents.

amylopectin [BIOCHEM] A highly branched, high-molecular-weight carbohydrate polymer composed of about 80% corn starch.

amyloplast [BOT] A colorless cell plastid packed with starch grains and occurring in cells of plant storage tissue.

amylopsin [BIOCHEM] An enzyme in pancreatic juice that acts to hydrolyze starch into maltose.

amylose [BIOCHEM] A linear starch polymer.

Amynodontidae [PALEON] A family of extinct hippopotamuslike perissodactyl mammals in the superfamily Rhinoceratoidea.

Anabaena [BOT] A genus of blue-green algae in the class Cyanophyceaa; members fix atmospheric nitrogen.

Anabantidae [VERT ZOO] A fresh-water family of actinopterygian fishes in the order Perciformes, including climbing perches and gourami.

Anabantoidel [VERT ZOO] A suborder of fresh-water labyrinth fishes in the order Perciformes.

anabiosis [BIOL] State of suspended animation induced by desiccation and reversed by addition of moisture; can be achieved in rotifers.

anabolic [BIOCHEM] Pertaining to anabolism. [EVOL] Pertaining to anaboly.

anabolism [BIOCHEM] A part of metabolism involving the union of smaller molecules into larger molecules; the method of synthesis of tissue structure.

anaboly [EVOL] The addition, through evolutionary differentiation, of a new terminal stage to the morphogenetic pattern.

Anacanthini [VERT ZOO] An equivalent name for the Gadiformes.

Anacardiaceae [BOT] A family of flowering plants, the sumacs, in the order Sapindales; many species are allergenic to man.

anaconda [VERT ZOO] *Eunectes murinus*. The largest living snake, an arboreal-aquatic member of the boa family (Boidae).

Anactinochitinosi [INV ZOO] A group name for three closely related suborders of mites and ticks: Onychopalpida, Mesostigmata, and Ixodides.

Anacystis [BOT] A genus of blue-green algae in the class Cyanophycea.

anadromous [VERT ZOO] Said of a fish, such as the salmon and shad, that ascends fresh-water streams from the sea to spawn.

Anadyomenaceae [BOT] A family of green marine algae in the order Siphonocladales characterized by the expanded blades of the thallus.

anaerobe [BIOL] An organism that does not require air or free oxygen to maintain its life processes.

anaerobic bacteria [MICROBIO] Any bacteria that can survive in the partial or complete absence of air; two types are facultative and obligate.

anaerobic condition [BIOL] The absence of oxygen, preventing normal life for organisms that depend on oxygen.

anaerobic glycolysis [BIOCHEM] A metabolic pathway in plants by which, in the absence of oxygen, hexose is broken down to lactic acid and ethanol with some adenosinetriphosphate synthesis.

anaerobic petri dish [MICROBIO] A glass laboratory dish for plate cultures of anaerobic bacteria; a thioglycollate agar medium and restricted air space give proper conditions.

anaerobiosis [BIOL] A mode of life carried on in the absence of molecular oxygen.

anaerophyte [ECOL] A plant that does not need free oxygen for respiration.

anakinesis [BIOCHEM] A process in living organisms by which energy-rich molecules, such as adenosinetriphosphate, are formed.

anal [ANAT] Relating to or located near the anus.

anal fin [VERT ZOO] An unpaired fin located medially on the posterior ventral part of the fish body.

analgesia [PHYSIO] Insensibility to pain with no loss of consciousness.

anal gland [INV ZOO] A gland in certain mollusks that secretes a purple substance. [VERT ZOO] A gland located near the anus or opening into the rectum in many vertebrates.

analogous [BIOL] Referring to structures that are similar in function and general appearance but not in origin, such as the wing of an insect and the wing of a bird.

anal plate [EMBRYO] 1. An embryonic plate formed of endoderm and ectoderm through which the anus later ruptures. [VERT ZOO] 1. One of the plates on the posterior portion of the plastron in turtles. 2. A large scale anterior to the anus of most snakes.

anal sphincter [ANAT] Either of two muscles, one voluntary and the other involuntary, controlling closing of the anus in vertebrates.

Anamnia [VERT ZOO] Vertebrate animals which lack an amnion in development, including Agnatha, Chondrichthyes, Osteichthyes, and Amphibia.

Anamniota [VERT ZOO] The equivalent name for Anamnia.

anamorphism *See* anamorphosis.

anamorphosis [EVOL] Gradual increase in complexity of form and function during evolution of a group of animals or plants. Also known as anamorphism.

Anancinae [PALEON] A subfamily of extinct proboscidean placental mammals in the family Gomphotheriidae.

anaphase [CELL BIO] 1. The stage in mitosis and in the second meiotic division when the centromere splits and the chromatids separate and move to opposite poles. 2. The stage of the first meiotic division when the two halves of a bivalent chromosome separate and move to opposite poles.

anaphoresis [PHYSIO] Movement of positively charged ions into tissues under the influence of an electric current.

Anaplasma [MICROBIO] A genus of the family Anaplasmataceae; organisms form inclusions in red blood cells of ruminants.

Anaplasmataceae [MICROBIO] A family of the order Rickettsiales; obligate parasites, either in or on red blood cells or in the plasma of various vertebrates.

Anaplotheriidae [PALEON] A family of extinct tylopod ruminants in the superfamily Anaplotherioidea.

Anaplotherioidea [PALEON] A superfamily of extinct ruminant artiodactyls in the infraorder Tylopoda.

anapolysis [INV ZOO] Lifetime retention of ripe proglottids in some tapeworms.

anapophysis [ANAT] An accessory process on the dorsal side of the transverse process of the lumbar vertebrae in man and other mammals.

Anapsida [VERT ZOO] A subclass of reptiles characterized by a roofed temporal region in which there are no temporal openings.

Anasca [PALEON] A suborder of extinct bryozoans in the order Cheilostomata.

Anaspida [PALEON] An order of extinct fresh- or brackish-water vertebrates in the class Agnatha.

Anaspidacea [INV ZOO] An order of the crustacean superorder Syncarida.

Anaspididae [INV ZOO] A family of crustaceans in the order Anaspidacea.

anastral [CELL BIO] Lacking asters.

Anatidae [VERT ZOO] A family of waterfowl, including ducks, geese, mergansers, pochards, and swans, in the order Anseriformes.

anatomy [BIOL] A branch of morphology dealing with the structure of animals and plants.

anatropous [BOT] Having the ovule fully inverted so that the micropyle adjoins the funiculus.

anaxial [BIOL] Lacking an axis, therefore being irregular in form.

Ancalomicrobium [MICROBIO] A genus of prosthecate bacteria; nonmotile, unicellular forms with two to eight prosthecae per cell; reproduction is by budding of cells.

ancestroecium [INV ZOO] The tube that encloses an ancestrula.

ancestrula [INV ZOO] The first polyp of a bryozoan colony.

anchor [INV ZOO] 1. An anchor-shaped spicule in the integument of sea cucumbers. 2. An anchor-shaped ossicle in echinoderms.

anchovy [VERT ZOO] Any member of the Engraulidae, a family of herringlike fishes harvested commercially for human consumption.

ancipital [BOT] Having two edges, specifically referring to flattened stems, as of certain grasses.

ancora [INV ZOO] The initial, anchor-shaped growth stage of graptolithinids.

ancyloid [INV ZOO] A limpet-shaped or patelliform shell with the apex directed anteriorly.

ancylopoda [PALEON] A suborder of extinct herbivorous mammals in the order Perissodactyla.

Ancylostoma [INV ZOO] A genus of roundworms, commonly known as hookworms, in the order Ancylostomidae; parasites of man, dogs, and cats.

Ancylostoma duodenale [INV ZOO] The Old World hookworm, a human intestinal parasite that causes microcytic hypochromic anemia.

Ancylostomidae [INV ZOO] A family of nematodes belonging to the group Strongyloidea.

Andreaeales [BOT] The single order of mosses of the subclass Andreaeobrya.

Andreaeceae [BOT] The single family of the Andreaeales, an order of mosses.

Andreaeobrya [BOT] The granite mosses, a subclass of the class Bryopsida.

Andrenidae [INV ZOO] The mining or burrower bees, a family of hymenopteran insects in the superfamily Apoidea.

androecium [BOT] The aggregate of stamens in a flower.

androgen [BIOCHEM] A class of steroid hormones produced in the testis and adrenal cortex which act to regulate masculine secondary sexual characteristics.

androgenesis [EMBRYO] Development of an embryo from a fertilized irradiated egg, involving only the male nucleus.

androgenetic merogony [EMBRYO] The fertilization of egg fragments that lack a nucleus.

androgenic gland [INV ZOO] Any of the accessory glands associated with the sperm duct in

male crustaceans and required for differentiation of a functional male.

androgen unit [BIOL] A unit for the standardization of male sex hormones.

android pelvis *See* masculine pelvis.

andromerogony [EMBRYO] Development of an egg fragment following cutting, shaking, or centrifugation of a fertilized or unfertilized egg.

androphile [ECOL] An organism, such as a mosquito, showing a preference for humans as opposed to animals.

androphore [BOT] A stalk that supports stamens or antheridia. [INV ZOO] A gonophore in coelenterates in which only male elements develop.

androsin [BIOCHEM] $C_{15}H_{20}O_8$ A glucoside found in the herb *Apocynum androsaemifolium;* yields glucose and acetovanillone on hydrolysis.

androsperm [BIOL] A sperm cell carrying a Y chromosome.

androstane [BIOCHEM] $C_{19}H_{32}$ The parent steroid hydrocarbon for all androgen hormones. Also known as etioallocholane.

androstenedione [BIOCHEM] $C_{19}H_{26}O_2$ Any one of three isomeric androgens produced by the adrenal cortex.

androsterone [BIOCHEM] $C_{19}H_{30}O_2$ An androgenic hormone occurring as a hydroxy ketone in the urine of men and women.

Anelytropsidae [VERT ZOO] A family of lizards represented by a single Mexican species.

anemochory [ECOL] Wind dispersal of plant and animal disseminules.

anemophilous [BOT] Pollinated by wind-carried pollen.

anemotaxis [BIOL] Orientation movement of a free-living organism in response to wind.

anemotropism [BIOL] Orientation response of a sessile organism to air currents and wind.

anenterous [ZOO] Having no intestine, as a tapeworm.

Anepitheliocystidia [INV ZOO] A superorder of digenetic trematodes proposed by G. LaRue.

anesthesia [PHYSIO] 1. Insensibility, general or local, induced by anesthetic agents. 2. Loss of sensation, of neurogenic or psychogenic origin.

anestrus [VERT ZOO] A prolonged period of inactivity between two periods of heat in cyclically breeding female mammals.

aneuploidy [GEN] Deviation from a normal haploid, diploid, or polyploid chromosome complement by the presence in excess of, or in defect of, one or more individual chromosomes.

aneurine *See* thiamine.

angioblast [EMBRYO] A mesenchyme cell derived from extraembryonic endoderm that differentiates into embryonic blood cells and endothelium.

angiogenesis [EMBRYO] The origin and development of blood vessels.

angiosperm [BOT] The common name for members of the plant division Magnoliophyta.

Angiospermae [BOT] An equivalent name for the Magnoliophyta.

angiotensin [BIOCHEM] A decapeptide hormone that influences blood vessel constriction and aldosterone secretion by the adrenal cortex. Also known as hypertensin.

anglerfish [VERT ZOO] Any of several species of the order Lophiiformes characterized by remnants of a dorsal fin seen as a few rays on top of the head that are modified to bear a terminal bulb.

Anguidae [VERT ZOO] A family of limbless, snakelike lizards in the suborder Sauria, commonly known as slowworms or glass snakes.

Anguilliformes [VERT ZOO] A large order of actinopterygian fishes containing the true eels.

Anguilloidei [VERT ZOO] The typical eels, a suborder of actinopterygian fishes in the order Anguilliformes.

angular leaf spot [PL PATH] A bacterial disease of plants characterized by angular spots on leaves and caused by *Pseudomonas lachrymans* in cucumbers and *Xanthomonas malvacearum* in cotton.

Anhimidae [VERT ZOO] The screamers, a family of birds in the order Anseriformes characterized by stout bills, webbed feet, and spurred wings.

Anhingidae [VERT ZOO] The anhingas or snakebirds, a family of swimming birds in the order Pelecaniformes.

anhydrase [BIOCHEM] Any enzyme that catalyzes the removal of water from a substrate.

anhydrobiosis [PHYSIO] A type of cryptobiosis induced by dehydration.

Aniliidae [VERT ZOO] A small family of nonvenomous, burrowing snakes in the order Squamata.

animal [ZOO] Any living organism distinguished from plants by the lack of chlorophyll, the requirement for complex organic nutrients, the lack of a cell wall, limited growth, mobility, and greater irritability.

animal community [ECOL] An aggregation of animal species held together in a continuous or discontinuous geographic area by ties to the same physical environment, mainly vegetation.

animal ecology [ECOL] A study of the relationships of animals to their environment.

Animalia [SYST] The animal kingdom.

animal kingdom [SYST] One of the two generally accepted major divisions of living organisms which live or have lived on earth (the other division being the plant kingdom).

animal locomotion [ZOO] Progressive movement of an animal body from one point to another.

animal pole [CELL BIO] The region of an ovum which contains the least yolk and where the nucleus gives off polar bodies during meiosis.

animal virus [VIROL] A small infectious agent able to propagate only within living animal cells.

Anisakidae [INV ZOO] A family of parasitic roundworms in the superfamily Ascaridoidea.

anise [BOT] The small fruit of the annual herb *Pimpinella anisum* in the family Umbelliferae; fruit is used for food flavoring, and oil is used in medicines, soaps, and cosmetics.

anisocarpous [BOT] Referring to a flower whose number of carpels is different from the number of stamens, petals, and sepals.

anisochela [INV ZOO] A chelate sponge spicule with dissimilar ends.

anisodactylous [VERT ZOO] Having unequal digits, especially referring to birds with three toes forward and one backward.

anisogamete *See* heterogamete.

anisomerous [BOT] Referring to flowers that do not have the same number of parts in each whorl.

anisometric particle [VIROL] Any unsymmetrical, rod-shaped plant virus.

Anisomyaria [INV ZOO] An order of mollusks in the class Bivalvia containing the oysters, scallops, and mussels.

anisophyllous [BOT] Having leaves of two or more shapes and sizes.

Anisoptera [INV ZOO] The true dragonflies, a suborder of insects in the order Odonata.

anisostemonous [BOT] Referring to a flower whose number of stamens is different from the number of carpels, petals, and sepals.

Anisotomidae [INV ZOO] An equivalent name for Leiodidae.

anisotropy [BOT] The property of a plant that assumes a certain position in response to an external stimulus. [ZOO] The property of an egg that has a definite axis or axes.

ankle [ANAT] The joint formed by the articulation of the leg bones with the talus, one of the tarsal bones.

Ankylosauria [PALEON] A suborder of Cretaceous dinosaurs in the reptilian order Ornithischia characterized by short legs and flattened, heavily armored bodies.

anlage [EMBRYO] Any group of embryonic cells when first identifiable as a future organ or body part. Also known as blastema; primordium.

annatto [BOT] *Bixa orellana*. A tree found in tropical America, characterized by cordate leaves and spinose, seed-filled capsules; a yellowish-red dye obtained from the pulp around the seeds is used as a food coloring.

anneal [GEN] To recombine strands of denatured bacterial deoxyribonucleic acid that were separated.

Annedidae [VERT ZOO] A small family of limbless, snakelike, burrowing lizards of the suborder Sauria.

Annelida [INV ZOO] A diverse phylum comprising the multisegmented wormlike animals.

Anniellidae [VERT ZOO] A family of limbless, snakelike lizards in the order Squamata.

Annonaceae [BOT] A large family of woody flowering plants in the order Magnoliales, characterized by hypogynous flowers, exstipulate leaves, a trimerous perianth, and distinct stamens with a short, thick filament.

annual plant [BOT] A plant that completes its growth in one growing season and therefore must be planted annually.

annual ring [BOT] A line appearing on tree cross sections marking the end of a growing season and showing the volume of wood added during the year.

annuation [ECOL] The annual variation in the presence, absence, or abundance of a member of a plant community.

annular budding [BOT] Budding by replacement of a ring of bark on a stock with a ring bearing a bud from a selected species or variety.

annulus [ANAT] Any ringlike anatomical part. [BOT] 1. An elastic ring of cells between the operculum and the mouth of the capsule in mosses. 2. A line of cells, partly or entirely surrounding the sporangium in ferns, which constricts, thus causing rupture of the sporangium to release spores. 3. A whorl resembling a calyx at the base of the strobilus in certain horsetails. [MYCOL] A ring of tissue representing the remnant of the veil around the stipe of some agarics.

Anobiidae [INV ZOO] The deathwatch beetles, a family of coleopteran insects of the superfamily Bostrichoidea.

anole [VERT ZOO] Any arboreal lizard of the genus *Anolis*, characterized by flattened adhesive digits and a prehensile outer toe.

Anomalinacea [INV ZOO] A superfamily of marine and benthic sarcodinian protozoans in the order Foraminiferida.

Anomaluridae [VERT ZOO] The African flying squirrels, a small family in the order Rodentia characterized by the climbing organ, a series of scales at the root of the tail.

anomaly [BIOL] An abnormal deviation from the characteristic form of a group.

Anomocoela [VERT ZOO] A suborder of toadlike amphibians in the order Anura characterized by a lack of free ribs.

anomocoelous [ANAT] Describing a vertebra with a centrum that is concave anteriorly and flat or convex posteriorly.

Anomphalacea [PALEON] A superfamily of extinct gastropod mollusks in the order Aspidobranchia.

Anomura [VERT ZOO] A section of the crustacean order Decapoda that includes lobsterlike and crablike forms.

Anopheles [INV ZOO] A genus of mosquitoes in the family Culicidae; members are vectors of malaria, dengue, and filariasis.

anopheline [INV ZOO] Pertaining to mosquitoes of the genus *Anopheles* or a closely related genus.

Anopla [INV ZOO] A class or subclass of the phylum Rhynchocoela characterized by a simple tubular proboscis and by having the mouth opening posterior to the brain.

Anoplocephalidae [INV ZOO] A family of tapeworms in the order Cyclophyllidea.

Anoplura [INV ZOO] The sucking lice, a small group of mammalian ectoparasites usually considered to constitute an order in the class Insecta.

Anostraca [INV ZOO] An order of shrimplike crustaceans generally referred to as the subclass Branchiopoda.

anoxybiosis [PHYSIO] A type of cryptobiosis induced by lack of oxygen.

Ansbacher unit [BIOL] A unit for the standardization of vitamin K.

Anser [VERT ZOO] A genus of birds in the family Anatidae comprising the typical geese.

Anseranatini [VERT ZOO] A subfamily of aquatic birds in the family Anatidae represented by a single species, the magpie goose.

Anseriformes [VERT ZOO] An order of birds, including ducks, geese, swans, and screamers, characterized by a broad, flat bill and webbed feet.

Anson unit [BIOL] A unit for the standardization of trypsin and proteinases.

ant [INV ZOO] The common name for insects in the hymenopteran family Formicidae; all are social, and colonies exhibit a highly complex organization.

antagonism [BIOL] 1. Mutual opposition as seen between organisms, muscles, physiologic actions, and drugs. 2. Opposing action between drugs and disease or drugs and functions.

antarctic faunal region [ECOL] A zoogeographic region describing both the marine littoral and terrestrial animal communities on and around Antarctica.

anteater [VERT ZOO] Any of several mammals, in five orders, which live on a diet of ants and termites.

antebrachium See forearm.

antecosta [INV ZOO] The internal, anterior ridge of the tergum or sternum of many insects that provides a surface for attachment of the longitudinal muscles.

antelope [VERT ZOO] Any of the hollow-horned, hoofed ruminants assigned to the artiodactyl subfamily Antilopinae; confined to Africa and Asia.

antenna chlorophyll [BIOCHEM] Chlorophyll molecules which collect light quanta.

antennal gland [INV ZOO] An excretory organ in the cephalon of adult crustaceans and best developed in the Malacostraca. Also known as green gland.

Antennata [INV ZOO] An equivalent name for the Mandibulata.

antenodal [INV ZOO] Before or in front of the nodus, a cross vein near the middle of the costal border of the wing of dragonflies.

anter [INV ZOO] Part of a bryozoan operculum which serves to close off a portion of the operculum.

anteriad [ZOO] Toward the anterior portion of the body.

anterior [ZOO] Situated near or toward the front or head of an animal body.

anterior commissure [ANAT] A bundle of nerve fibers that cross the midline of the brain in front of the third ventricle and serve to connect parts of the cerebral hemispheres.

anteromedial [ZOO] Anterior and toward the middle of the body.

antetheca [PALEON] The last or exposed septum at any stage of fusulinid growth.

anthelate [BOT] An open, paniculate cyme.

anther [BOT] The pollen-producing structure of a flower.

antheraxanthin [BIOCHEM] A neutral yellow plant pigment unique to the Euglenophyta.

antheridiophore [BOT] A specialized stemlike structure that supports an antheridium in some mosses and liverworts.

antheridium [BOT] 1. The sex organ that produces male gametes in cryptogams. 2. A minute structure within the pollen grain of seed plants.

antheriferous [BOT] Anther-bearing.

antherozoid [BOT] A motile male gamete produced by plants.

anther smut [MYCOL] *Ustilago violacea.* A smut fungus that attacks certain plants and forms spores in the anthers.

anthesis [BOT] The flowering period in plants.

Anthicidae [INV ZOO] The antlike flower beetles, a family of coleopteran insects in the superfamily Tenebrionoidea.

anthill [INV ZOO] A mound of earth deposited around the entrance to ant and termite nests in the ground.

anthoblast [INV ZOO] A developmental stage of some corals; produced by budding.

anthocarpous [BOT] Describing fruits having accessory parts.

anthocaulis [INV ZOO] The stemlike basal portion of some solitary corals; the oral portion becomes a new zooid.

Anthocerotae [BOT] A small class of the plant division Bryophyta, commonly known as hornworts or horned liverworts.

anthocodium [INV ZOO] The free, oral end of an anthozoan polyp.

Anthocoridae [INV ZOO] The flower bugs, a family of hemipteran insects in the superfamily Cimicimorpha.

anthocyanidin [BIOCHEM] Any of the colored aglycone plant pigments obtained by hydrolysis of anthocyanins.

anthocyanin [BIOCHEM] Any of the intensely colored, sap-soluble glycoside plant pigments responsible for most scarlet, purple, mauve, and blue coloring in higher plants.

Anthocyathea [PALEON] A class of extinct marine organisms in the phylum Archaeocyatha characterized by skeletal tissue in the central cavity.

anthocyathus [INV ZOO] The oral portion of the anthocaulus of some solitary corals that becomes a new zooid.

Anthomedusae [INV ZOO] A suborder of hydrozoan coelenterates in the order Hydroida characterized by athecate polyps.

Anthomyzidae [INV ZOO] A family of cyclorrhaphous myodarian dipteran insects belonging to the subsection Acalypteratae.

anthophagous [ZOO] Feeding on flowers.

anthophore [BOT] A stalklike extension of the receptacle bearing the pistil and corolla in certain plants.

Anthosomidae [INV ZOO] A family of fish ectoparasites in the crustacean suborder Caligoida.

anthostele [INV ZOO] A thick-walled, nonretractile aboral region of certain coelenterates.

Anthozoa [INV ZOO] A class of marine organisms in the phylum Coelenterata including the soft, horny, stony, and black corals, the sea pens, and the sea anemones.

anthozooid [INV ZOO] Any of the individual zooids of a compound anthozoan.

anthracnose [PL PATH] A fungus disease of plants caused by members of the Melanconiales and characterized by dark or black limited stem lesions.

Anthracosauria [PALEON] An order of Carboniferous and Permian labyrinthodont amphibians that includes the ancestors of living reptiles.

Anthracotheriidae [PALEON] A family of middle Eocene and early Pleistocene artiodactyl mammals in the superfamily Anthracotherioidea.

Anthracotherioidea [PALEON] A superfamily of extinct artiodactyl mammals in the suborder Paleodonta.

anthraquinone pigments [BIOCHEM] Coloring materials which occur in plants, fungi, lichens, and insects; consists of about 50 derivatives of the parent compound, anthraquinone.

Anthribidae [INV ZOO] The fungus weevils, a family of coleopteran insects in the superfamily Curculionoidea.

anthropochory [ECOL] Dispersal of plant and animal disseminules by humans.

anthropodesoxycholic acid *See* chenodeoxycholic acid.

anthropogenic [ECOL] Referring to environmental alterations resulting from the presence or activities of humans.

anthropoid [VERT ZOO] Pertaining to or resembling the Anthropoidea.

Anthropoidea [VERT ZOO] A suborder of mammals in the order Primates including New and Old World monkeys.

anthropology [BIOL] The study of the interrelations of biological, cultural, geographical, and historical aspects of humankind.

anthroposphere [ECOL] A term sometimes used to refer to the biosphere of the great geological activities of humankind. Also known as noosphere.

Anthuridea [INV ZOO] A suborder of crustaceans in the order Isopoda characterized by slender, elongate, subcylindrical bodies, and by the fact that the outer branch of the paired tail appendage (uropod) arches over the base of the terminal abdominal segment, the telson.

Antiarchi [PALEON] A division of highly specialized placoderms restricted to fresh-water sediments of the Middle and Upper Devonian.

antibacterial agent [MICROBIO] A synthetic or natural compound which inhibits the growth and division of bacteria.

antibiosis [ECOL] Antagonistic association between two organisms in which one is adversely affected.

antibiotic [MICROBIO] A chemical substance, produced by microorganisms and synthetically, that has the capacity in dilute solutions to inhibit the growth of, and even to destroy, bacteria and other microorganisms.

antibiotic assay [MICROBIO] A method for quantitatively determining the concentration of an antibiotic by its effect in inhibiting the growth of a susceptible microorganism.

antiboreal faunal region [ECOL] A zoogeographic region including marine littoral faunal communities at the southern end of South America.

anticholinesterase [BIOCHEM] Any agent, such as a nerve gas, that inhibits the action of cholinesterase and thereby destroys or interferes with nerve conduction.

anticlinal [BOT] Perpendicular to the surface or periphery of an organ.

anticodon [GEN] A three-nucleotide sequence of transfer RNA that complements the codon in messenger RNA.

anticryptic [ECOL] Pertaining to protective coloration that makes an animal resemble its surroundings so that it is inconspicuous to its prey.

anticusp [INV ZOO] An anterior, downward projection in conodonts.

antidiuretic hormone *See* vasopressin.

antienzyme [BIOCHEM] An agent that selectively inhibits the action of an enzyme.

antifertilizin [BIOCHEM] An immunologically specific substance produced by animal sperm to implement attraction by the egg before fertilization.

antifibrinolysin [BIOCHEM] Any substance that inhibits the proteolytic action of fibrinolysin.

antihemophilic factor [BIOCHEM] A soluble protein clotting factor in mammalian blood. Also known as factor VIII; thromboplastinogen.

anti-infective vitamin *See* vitamin A.

Antilocapridae [VERT ZOO] A family of artiodactyl mammals in the superfamily Bovoidea; the pronghorn is the single living species.

Antilopinae [VERT ZOO] The antelopes, a subfamily of artiodactyl mammals in the family Bovidae.

antimere [INV ZOO] Any one of the equivalent parts into which a radially symmetrical animal may be divided.

antimicrobial agent [MICROBIO] A chemical compound that either destroys or inhibits the growth of microscopic and submicroscopic organisms.

antimycin A [MICROBIO] $C_{28}H_{40}O_9N_2$ An antifungal antibiotic produced by *Streptomyces kitazawaensis;* the principal fraction of antimycin.

antiparallel [GEN] Pertaining to parallel molecules that point in opposite directions, as the strands of deoxyribonucleic acid.

Antipatharia [INV ZOO] The black or horny corals, an order of tropical and subtropical coelenterates in the subclass Zoantharia.

antipetalous [BOT] Having stamens positioned opposite to, rather than alternating with, the petals.

antipodal [BOT] Any of three cells grouped at the base of the embryo sac, that is, at the end farthest from the micropyle, in most angiosperms.

antirachitic vitamin *See* vitamin D.

antirostrum [INV ZOO] The terminal segment of the appendages of ce.tain mites.

antisense [GEN] A strand of deoxyribonucleic acid having a sequence identical to messenger ribonucleic acid.

antisense strand [MOL BIO] The strand of a double-stranded deoxyribonucleic acid molecule from which ribonucleic acid is transcribed.

antitermination factor [BIOCHEM] Protein that interferes with normal termination of ribonucleic acid synthesis.

antithrombin [BIOCHEM] A substance in blood plasma that inactivates thrombin.

antitumor antibiotic [MICROBIO] A substance, such as actinomycin, luteomycin, or mitomycin C, which is produced by microorganisms and is effective against some forms of cancer.

antivernalization [BOT] Delayed flowering in plants due to treatment with heat.

antivitamin [BIOCHEM] Any substance that prevents a vitamin from normal metabolic functioning.

antixerophthalmic vitamin *See* vitamin A.

antler [VERT ZOO] One of a pair of solid bony, usually branched outgrowths on the head of members of the deer family (Cervidae); shed annually.

ant lion [INV ZOO] The common name for insects of the family Myrmeleontidae in the order Neuroptera; larvae are commonly called doodlebugs.

antrorse [BIOL] Turned or directed forward or upward.

antrum [ANAT] A cavity of a hollow organ or a sinus.

Anura [VERT ZOO] An order of the class Amphibia comprising the frogs and toads.

anus [ANAT] The posterior orifice of the alimentary canal.

aorta [ANAT] The main vessel of systemic arterial circulation arising from the heart in vertebrates. [INV ZOO] The large dorsal or anterior vessel in many invertebrates.

aortic arch [ANAT] The portion of the aorta extending from the heart to the third thoracic vertebra; single in warm-blooded vertebrates and paired in fishes, amphibians, and reptiles.

aortic body *See* aortic paraganglion.

aortic paraganglion [ANAT] A structure in vertebrates belonging to the chromaffin system and found on the front of the abdominal aorta near the mesenteric arteries. Also known as aortic body; organs of Zuckerkandl.

aortic valve [ANAT] A heart valve comprising three flaps which guards the passage from the left ventricle to the aorta and prevents the backward flow of blood.

apandrous [BOT] Lacking male organs or having nonfunctional male organs.

Apatemyidae [PALEON] A family of extinct rodentlike insectivorous mammals belonging to the Proteutheria.

apatetic [ECOL] Pertaining to the imitative protective coloration of an animal subject to being preyed upon.

Apathornithidae [PALEON] A family of Cretaceous birds, with two species, belonging to the order Ichthyornithiformes.

ape [VERT ZOO] Any of the tailless primates of the families Hylobatidae and Pongidae in the same superfamily as humans.

apetalous [BOT] Lacking petals.

apex [ANAT] 1. The upper portion of a lung extending into the root. 2. The pointed end of the heart. **3.** The tip of the root of a tooth. [BOT] The pointed tip of a leaf.

apex impulse [PHYSIO] The point of maximum outward movement of the left ventricle of the heart during systole, normally localized in the fifth left intercostal space in the midclavicular line. Also known as left ventricular thrust.

Aphanomyces [MYCOL] A genus of fungi in the phycomycetous order Saprolegniales; species cause root rot in plants.

Aphasmidea [INV ZOO] An equivalent name for the Adenophorea.

Aphelenchoidea [INV ZOO] A superfamily of plant and insect-associated nematodes in the order Tylenchida.

Aphelocheiridae [INV ZOO] A family of hemipteran insects belonging to the superfamily Naucoroidea.

aphid [INV ZOO] The common name applied to the soft-bodied insects of the family Aphididae; they are phytophagous plant pests and vectors for plant viruses and fungal parasites.

Aphididae [INV ZOO] The true aphids, a family of homopteran insects in the superfamily Aphidoidea.

Aphidoidea [INV ZOO] A superfamily of sternorrhynchan insects in the order Homoptera.

Aphis [INV ZOO] A genus of aphid, the type genus of the family Aphididae.

Aphredoderidae [VERT ZOO] A family of actinopterygian fishes in the order Percopsiformes containing one species, the pirate perch.

aphrodisiac [PHYSIO] Any chemical agent or odor that stimulates sexual desires.

Aphroditidae [INV ZOO] A family of scale-bearing polychaete worms belonging to the Errantia.

Aphrosalpingoidea [PALEON] A group of middle Paleozoic invertebrates classified with the calcareous sponges.

Aphyllidae [INV ZOO] An Australian family of hemipteran insects composed of two species; not placed in any higher toxonomic group.

aphyllous [BOT] Lacking foliage leaves.

aphytic zone [ECOL] The part of a lake floor that lacks plants because it is too deep for adequate light penetration.

apical [BOT] Relating to the apex or tip.

apical bud *See* terminal bud.

apical dominance [BOT] Inhibition of lateral bud growth by the apical bud of a shoot, believed to be a response to auxins produced by the apical bud.

apical meristem [BOT] A region of embryonic tissue occurring at the tips of roots and stems.

apical plate [INV ZOO] A group of cells at the anterior end of certain trochophore larvae; believed to have nervous and sensory functions.

apiculate [BOT] Ending abruptly in a short, sharp point.

Apidae [INV ZOO] A family of hymenopteran insects in the superfamily Apoidea including the honeybees, bumblebees, and carpenter bees.

Apioceridae [INV ZOO] A family of orthorrhaphous dipteran insects in the series Brachycera.

apiology [INV ZOO] The scientific study of bees, particularly honeybees.

Apis [INV ZOO] A genus of bees, the type genus of the Apidae.

Apis mellifera [INV ZOO] The western honeybee, an economically important species for its honey.

Apistobranchidae [INV ZOO] A family of spioniform annelid worms belonging to the Sedentaria.

Aplacophora [INV ZOO] A subclass of vermiform mollusks in the class Amphineura characterized by no shell and calcareous integumentary spicules.

aplanogamete [BIOL] A gamete that lacks motility.

aplanospore [MYCOL] A nonmotile, asexual spore, usually a sporangiospore, common in the Phycomycetes.

aplysiatoxin [BIOCHEM] A bislactone toxin produced by the blue-green alga *Lyngbya majuscula*.

Apneumonomorphae [INV ZOO] A suborder of arachnid arthropods in the order Araneida characterized by the lack of book lungs.

apneusis [PHYSIO] In certain lower vertebrates, sustained tonic contraction of the respiratory muscles to allow prolonged inspiration.

apocarpous [BOT] Having carpels separate from each other.

apocrine gland [PHYSIO] A multicellular gland, such as a mammary gland or an axillary sweat gland, that extrudes part of the cytoplasm with the secretory product.

Apocynaceae [BOT] A family of tropical and subtropical flowering trees, shrubs, and vines in the order Gentianales, characterized by a well-developed latex system, granular pollen, a poorly developed corona, and the carpels often united by the style and stigma; well-known members are oleander and periwinkle.

Apoda [VERT ZOO] The caecilians, a small order of wormlike, legless animals in the class Amphibia.

Apodacea [INV ZOO] A subclass of echinoderms in the class Holothuroidea characterized by simple or pinnate tentacles and reduced or absent tube feet.

apodeme [INV ZOO] An internal ridge or process on an arthropod exoskeleton to which organs and muscles attach.

Apodes [VERT ZOO] An equivalent name for the Anguilliformes.

Apodi [VERT ZOO] The swifts, a suborder of birds in the order Apodiformes.

Apodida [INV ZOO] An order of worm-shaped holothurian echinoderms in the subclass Apodacea.

Apodidae [VERT ZOO] The true swifts, a family of apodiform birds belonging to the suborder Apodi.

Apodiformes [VERT ZOO] An order of birds containing the hummingbirds and swifts.

apoenzyme [BIOCHEM] The protein moiety of an enzyme; determines the specificity of the enzyme reaction.

apoferritin [BIOCHEM] A protein found in intestinal mucosa cells that has the ability to combine with ferric ion.

apogamy [BIOL] Asexual, parthenogenetic development of diploid cells, such as the development of a sporophyte from a gametophyte without fertilization.

apogeny [BOT] Loss of the function of reproduction.

apogeotropism [BOT] Negative geotropism; growth up or away from the soil.

Apogonidae [VERT ZOO] The cardinal fishes, a family of tropical marine fishes in the order Perciformes; males incubate eggs in the mouth.

Apoidea [INV ZOO] The bees, a superfamily of hymenopteran insects in the suborder Apocrita.

apolysis [INV ZOO] In most tapeworms, the shedding of ripe proglottids.

apomeiosis [CELL BIO] Meiosis that is either suppressed or imperfect.

apomixis [EMBRYO] Parthenogenetic development of sex cells without fertilization.

apomorph [SYST] Any derived character occurring at a branching point and carried through one descending group in a phyletic lineage.

apomyoglobin [BIOCHEM] Myoglobin that lacks its heme group.

aponeurosis [ANAT] A broad sheet of regularly arranged connective tissue that covers a muscle or serves to connect a flat muscle to a bone.

apophyllous [BOT] Having the parts of the perianth distinct.

apophysis [ANAT] An outgrowth or process on an organ or bone. [MYCOL] A swollen filament in fungi.

apoprotein [BIOCHEM] The protein portion of a conjugated protein exclusive of the prosthetic group.

apopyle [INV ZOO] Any one of the large pores in a sponge by which water leaves a flagellated chamber to enter the exhalant system.

Aporidea [INV ZOO] An order of tapeworms of uncertain composition and affinities; parasites of anseriform birds.

aporogamy [BOT] Entry of the pollen tube into the embryo sac through an opening other than the micropyle.

aposematic [ECOL] Pertaining to colors or structures on an organism that provide a special means of defense against enemies. Also known as sematic.

apospory [MYCOL] Suppression of spore formation with development of the haploid (sexual) generation directly from the diploid (asexual) generation.

apostatic selection [ECOL] Predation on the most abundant forms in a population, leading to balanced distribution of a variety of forms.

Apostomatida [INV ZOO] An order of ciliated protozoans in the subclass Holotrichia; majority are commensals on marine crustaceans.

apotele [ANAT] A scalloped ridge around the edge of an otolith.

apothecium [MYCOL] A spore-bearing structure in some Ascomycetes and lichens in which the fruiting surface or hymenium is exposed during spore maturation.

apozymase [BIOCHEM] The protein component of a zymase.

appendage [BIOL] Any subordinate or nonessential structure associated with a major body part. [ZOO] Any jointed, peripheral extension, especially limbs, of arthropod and vertebrate bodies.

appendicular skeleton [ANAT] The bones of the pectoral and pelvic girdles and the paired appendages in vertebrates.

appendiculate [BIOL] Having or forming appendages.

appendix [ANAT] 1. Any appendage. 2. *See* vermiform appendix.

appestat [PHYSIO] The center for appetite regulation in the hypothalamus.

appetitive behavior [ZOO] Any behavior that increases the probability that an animal will be able to satisfy a need; for example, a hungry animal will move around to find food.

apple [BOT] *Malus domestica.* A deciduous tree in the order Rosales which produces an edible, simple, fleshy, pome-type fruit.

apple of Peru *See* jimsonweed.

applied ecology [ECOL] Activities involved in the management of natural resources.

apposition eye [INV ZOO] A compound eye found in diurnal insects and crustaceans in which each ommatidium focuses on a small part of the whole field of light, producing a mosaic image.

appressed [BIOL] Pressed close to or lying flat against something.

apricot [BOT] *Prunus armeniaca.* A deciduous tree in the order Rosales which produces a simple fleshy stone fruit.

aproctous [ZOO] Lacking an anus.

Apsidospondyli [VERT ZOO] A term used to include, as a subclass, amphibians in which the vertebral centra are formed from cartilaginous arches.

apterium [VERT ZOO] A bare space between feathers on a bird's skin.

apterous [BIOL] Lacking wings, as in certain insects, or winglike expansions, as in certain seeds.

Apterygidae [VERT ZOO] The kiwis, a family of nocturnal ratite birds in the order Apterygiformes.

Apterygiformes [VERT ZOO] An order of ratite birds containing three living species, the kiwis, characterized by small eyes, limited eyesight, and nostrils at the tip of the bill.

Apterygota [INV ZOO] A subclass of the Insecta characterized by being primitively wingless.

Apus [VERT ZOO] A genus of birds comprising the Old World swifts.

apyrase [BIOCHEM] Any enzyme that hydrolyzes adenosinetriphosphate, with liberation of phosphate and energy, and that is believed to be associated with actomyosin activity.

aquatic [BIOL] Living or growing in, on, or near water; having a water habitat.

aqueous desert [ECOL] A marine bottom environment with little or no macroscopic invertebrate shelled life.

aqueous humor [PHYSIO] The transparent fluid filling the anterior chamber of the eye.

aquiculture [BIOL] Cultivation of natural faunal resources of water. Also spelled aquaculture.

Aquifoliaceae [BOT] A family of woody flowering plants in the order Celastrales characterized by pendulous ovules, alternate leaves, imbricate petals, and drupaceous fruit; common members include various species of holly (*Ilex*).

aquiherbosa [ECOL] Herbaceous plant communities in wet areas, such as swamps and ponds.

aquiprata [ECOL] Communities of plants which are found in areas such as wet meadows where groundwater is a factor.

Arabellidae [INV ZOO] A family of polychaete worms belonging to the Errantia.

arabinose [BIOCHEM] $C_5IH_{10}O_5$ A pentose sugar obtained in crystalline form from plant polysaccharides such as gums, hemicelluloses, and some glycosides.

Araceae [BOT] A family of herbaceous flowering plants in the order Arales; plants have stems, roots, and leaves, the inflorescence is a spadix, and the growth habit is terrestrial or sometimes more or less aquatic; well-known members include dumb cane (*Dieffenbachia*), jack-in-the-pulpit (*Arisaema*), and *Philodendron*.

Arachnia [MICROBIO] A genus of bacteria in the family Actinomycetaceae; branched diphtheroid rods and branched filaments from filamentous microcolonies; facultatively anaerobic; the single species is a human pathogen.

Arachnida [INV ZOO] A class of arthropods in the subphylum Chelicerata characterized by four pairs of thoracic appendages.

arachnoid [ANAT] A membrane that covers the brain and spinal cord and lies between the pia mater and dura mater. [BOT] Of cobweblike appearance, caused by fine white hairs. Also known as araneose. [INV ZOO] Any invertebrate related to or resembling the Arachnida.

arachnoidal granulations [ANAT] Projections of the arachnoid layer of the cerebral meninges through the dura mater. Also known as arachnoid villi; Pacchionian bodies.

Arachnoidea [INV ZOO] The name used in some classification schemes to describe a class of primitive arthropods.

arachnoid villi *See* arachnoidal granulations.

arachnology [INV ZOO] The study of arachnids.

Aradidae [INV ZOO] The flat bugs, a family of hemipteran insects in the superfamily Aradoidea.

Aradoidea [INV ZOO] A small superfamily of hemipteran insects belonging to the subdivision Geocorisae.

Araeoscelidia [PALEON] A provisional order of extinct reptiles in the subclass Euryapsida.

Arales [BOT] An order of monocotyledonous plants in the subclass Arecidae.

Araliaceae [BOT] A family of dicotyledonous trees and shrubs in the order Umbellales; there are typically five carpels and the fruit, usually a berry, is fleshy or dry; well-known members are ginseng (*Panax*) and English ivy (*Hedera helix*).

Aramidae [VERT ZOO] The limpkins, a family of birds in the order Gruiformes.

Araneae [INV ZOO] An equivalent name for Araneida.

Araneida [INV ZOO] The spiders, an order of arthropods in the class Arachnida.

araneology [INV ZOO] The study of spiders.

Arbacioida [INV ZOO] An order of echinoderms in the superorder Echinacea.

arboreal [BOT] Relating to or resembling a tree. Also known as arboreous. [ZOO] Living in trees.

arboreous [BOT] 1. Wooded. 2. *See* arboreal.

arborescence [BIOL] The state of being treelike in form and appearance.

arboretum [BOT] An area where trees and shrubs are cultivated for educational and scientific purposes.

arboriculture [BOT] The cultivation of ornamental trees and shrubs.

arborization [BIOL] A treelike arrangement, such as a branched dendrite or axon.

arbor vitae [ANAT] The treelike arrangement of white nerve tissue seen in a median section of the cerebellum.

arborvitae [BOT] Any of the ornamental trees, sometimes called the tree of life, in the genus *Thuja* of the order Pinales.

arbovirus [VIROL] Small, arthropod-borne animal viruses that are unstable at room temperature and inactivated by sodium deoxycholate; cause several types of encephalitis. Also known as arthropod-borne virus.

arcade [INV ZOO] A type of cell associated with the pharyngeal region of nematodes and united with like cells by an arch.

Arcellinida [INV ZOO] An order of rhizopodous protozoans in the subclass Lobosia characterized by lobopodia and a well-defined aperture in the test.

Archaeoceti [PALEON] The zeuglodonts, a suborder of aquatic Eocene mammals in the order Cetacea; the oldest known cetaceans.

Archaeocidaridae [PALEON] A family of Carboniferous echinoderms in the order Cidaroida characterized by a flexible test and more than two columns of interambulacral plates.

Archaeocopida [PALEON] An order of Cambrian crustaceans in the subclass Ostracoda characterized by only slight calcification of the carapace.

Archaeogastropoda [INV ZOO] An order of gastropod mollusks that includes the most primitive snails.

Archaeopteridales [PALEOBOT] An order of Upper Devonian sporebearing plants in the class Polypodiopsida characterized by woody trunks and simple leaves.

Archaeopteris [PALEOBOT] A genus of fossil plants in the order Archaeopteridales; used sometimes as an index fossil of the Upper Devonian.

Archaeopterygiformes [PALEON] The single order of the extinct avian subclass Archaeornithes.

Archaeopteryx [PALEON] The earliest known bird; a genus of fossil birds in the order Archaeopterygiformes characterized by flight feathers like those of modern birds.

Archaeornithes [PALEON] A subclass of Upper Jurassic birds comprising the oldest fossil birds.

archallaxis [BIOL] Deviation from an ancestral pattern early in development, eliminating duplication of the phylogenetic history.

Archangiaceae [MICROBIO] A family of bacteria in the order Myxobacterales; microcysts are rod-shaped, ovoid, or spherical and are not enclosed in sporangia, and fruiting bodies are irregular masses.

Archangium [MICROBIO] The single genus of the family Archangiaceae; sporangia are lacking, and there is no definite slime wall.

Archanthropinae [PALEON] A subfamily of the Hominidae, set up by F. Weidenreich, which is no longer used.

archegoniophore [BOT] The stalk supporting the archegonium in liverworts and ferns.

archegonium [BOT] The multicellular female sex organ in all plants of the Embryobionta except the Pinophyta and Magnoliophyta.

archencephalon [EMBRYO] The primitive embryonic forebrain from which the forebrain and midbrain develop.

archenteron [EMBRYO] The cavity of the gastrula formed by ingrowth of cells in vertebrate embryos. Also known as gastrocoele; primordial gut.

archeocyte [INV ZOO] A type of ovoid amebocyte in sponges, characterized by large nucleolate nuclei and blunt pseudopodia; gives rise to germ cells.

archerfish [VERT ZOO] The common name for any member of the fresh-water family Toxotidae in the order Perciformes; individuals eject a stream of water from the mouth to capture insects.

Archeria [PALEONTOL] Genus of amphibians, order Embolomeri, in early Permian in Texas; fish eaters.

archespore [BOT] A cell from which the spore mother cell develops in either the pollen sac or the ovule of an angiosperm.

archetype [EVOL] A hypothetical ancestral type conceptualized by eliminating all specialized character traits.

Archiacanthocephala [INV ZOO] An order of worms in the phylum Acanthocephala; adults are endoparasites of terrestrial vertebrates.

Archiannelida [INV ZOO] A group name applied to three families of unrelated annelid worms: Nerillidae, Protodrilidae, and Dinophilidae.

Archichlamydeae [BOT] An artificial group of flowering plants, in the Englerian system of classification, consisting of those families of dicotyledons that lack petals or have petals separate from each other.

archicoel [ZOO] The segmentation cavity persisting between the ectoderm and endoderm as a body cavity in certain lower forms.

archigastrula [EMBRYO] A gastrula formed by invagination, as opposed to ingrowth of cells.

Archigregarinida [INV ZOO] An order of telosporean protozoans in the subclass Gregarinia; endoparasites of invertebrates and lower chordates.

archinephridium [INV ZOO] One of a pair of primitive nephridia found in each segment of some annelid larvae.

archinephros [VERT ZOO] The paired excretory organ of primitive vertebrates and the larvae of hagfishes and caecilians.

archipallium [PHYSIO] The olfactory pallium or the olfactory cerebral cortex; phylogenetically, the oldest part of the cerebral cortex.

Archosauria [VERT ZOO] A subclass of reptiles composed of five orders: Thecodontia, Saurischia, Ornithischia, Pterosauria, and Crocodilia.

Archostemata [INV ZOO] A suborder of insects in the order Coleoptera.

arch pattern [ANAT] A fingerprint pattern in which ridges enter on one side of the impression, form a wave or angular upthrust, and flow out the other side.

arcocentrum [ANAT] A centrum formed of modified, fused mesial parts of the neural or hemal arches.

arctic-alpine [ECOL] Of or pertaining to areas above the timberline in mountainous regions.

arctic tree line [ECOL] The northern limit of tree growth; the sinuous boundary between tundra and boreal forest.

Arctiidae [INV ZOO] The tiger moths, a family of lepidopteran insects in the suborder Heteroneura.

Arctocyonidae [PALEON] A family of extinct carnivorelike mammals in the order Condylarthra.

Arctolepiformes [PALEON] A group of the extinct joint-necked fishes belonging to the Arthrodira.

Arcturidae [INV ZOO] A family of isopod crustaceans in the suborder Valvifera characterized by an almost cylindrical body and extremely long antennae.

arcuale [EMBRYO] Any of the four pairs of primitive cartilages from which a vertebra is formed.

arcuate [ANAT] Arched or curved; bow-shaped.

Arcyzonidae [PALEON] A family of Devonian paleocopan ostracods in the superfamily Kirkbyacea characterized by valves with a large central pit.

Ardeidae [VERT ZOO] The herons, a family of wading birds in the order Ciconiiformes.

area amniotica [EMBRYO] The transparent part of the blastodisc in mammals.

area opaca [EMBRYO] The opaque peripheral area of the blastoderm of birds and reptiles, continuous with the yolk.

area pellucida [EMBRYO] The central transparent area of the blastoderm of birds and reptiles, overlying the subgerminal cavity.

area placentalis [EMBRYO] The part of the trophoblast in immediate contact with the uterine mucosa in the embryos of early placental vertebrates.

area vitellina [EMBRYO] The outer nonvascular zone of the area opaca; consists of ectoderm and endoderm.

Arecaceae [BOT] The palms, the single family of the order Arecales.

Arecales [BOT] An order of flowering plants in the subclass Arecidae composed of the palms.

Arecidae [BOT] A subclass of flowering plants in the class Liliopsida characterized by numerous, small flowers subtended by a prominent spathe and often aggregated into a spadix, and broad, petiolate leaves without typical parallel venation.

areg [ECOL] A sand desert.

arena See lek.

Arenicolidae [INV ZOO] The lugworms, a family of mud-swallowing worms belonging to the Sedentaria.

arenicolous [ZOO] Living or burrowing in sand.

areography [ECOL] Descriptive biogeography.

areola [ANAT] 1. The portion of the iris bordering the pupil of the eye. 2. A pigmented ring surrounding a nipple, vesicle, or pustule. 3. A small space, interval, or pore in a tissue.

areola mammae [ANAT] The circular pigmented area surrounding the nipple of the breast. Also known as areola papillaris; mammary areola.

areola papillaris See areola mammae.

areolar tissue [HISTOL] A loose network of fibrous tissue and elastic fiber that connects the skin to the underlying structures.

aretyl formic acid See pyruvic acid.

Argasidae [INV ZOO] The soft ticks, a family of arachnids in the suborder Ixodides; several species are important as ectoparasites and disease vectors for man and domestic animals.

argentaffin cell [HISTOL] Any of the cells of the gastrointestinal tract that are thought to secrete serotonin.

argentaffin fiber See reticular fiber.

Argentinoidei [VERT ZOO] A family of marine deepwater teleostean fishes, including deep-sea smelts, in the order Salmoniformes.

argentophil [BIOL] Of cells, tissues, or other structures, having an affinity for silver.

Argidae [INV ZOO] A small family of hymenopteran insects in the superfamily Tenthredinoidea.

arginase [BIOCHEM] An enzyme that catalyzes the splitting of urea from the amino acid arginine.

arginine [BIOCHEM] $C_6H_{14}N_4O_2$ A colorless, crystalline, water-soluble, essential amino acid of the α-ketoglutaric acid family.

Arguloida [INV ZOO] A group of crustaceans known as the fish lice; taxonomic status is uncertain.

argyrophil lattice fiber See reticular fiber.

Arhynchobdellae [INV ZOO] An order of annelids in the class Hirudinea characterized by the lack of an eversible proboscis; includes most of the important leech parasites of man and warmblooded animals.

Arhynchodina [INV ZOO] A suborder of ciliophoran protozoans in the order Thigmotrichida.

arhythmicity [BIOL] A condition characterized by the absence of an expected behavioral or physiologic rhythm.

arid biogeographic zone [ECOL] Any region of the world that supports relatively little vegetation due to lack of water.

Arid Transition life zone [ECOL] The zone of climate and biotic communities occurring in the chaparrals and steppes from the Rocky Mountain forest margin to California.

arietiform [VERT ZOO] Shaped like a ram's horns; specifically, describing the dark facial marking that extends across the nose of kangaroo rats.

Arlidae [VERT ZOO] A family of tropical salt-water catfishes in the order Siluriformes.

aril [BOT] An outgrowth of the funiculus in certain seeds that either remains as an appendage or envelops the seed.

arilode [BOT] An aril originating from tissues in the micropyle region; a false aril.

Arionidae [INV ZOO] A family of mollusks in the order Stylommatophora, including some of the pulmonate slugs.

arista [INV ZOO] The bristlelike or hairlike structure in many organisms, especially at or near the tip of the antenna of many Diptera.

Aristolochiaceae [BOT] The single family of the plant order Aristolochiales.

Aristolochiales [BOT] An order of dicotyledonous plants in the subclass Magnoliidae; species are herbaceous to woody, often climbing, with perigynous to epigynous, apetalous flowers, uniaperturate or nonaperturate pollen, and seeds with a small embryo and copious endosperm.

aristopedia [INV ZOO] Replacement of the arista by a nearly perfect leg.

Aristotle's lantern [INV ZOO] A five-sided feeding and locomotor apparatus surrounding the esophagus of most sea urchins.

arm [ANAT] The upper or superior limb in humans which comprises the upper arm with one bone and the forearm with two bones.

armadillo [VERT ZOO] Any of 21 species of edentate mammals in the family Dasypodidae.

Armillaria root rot [PL PATH] A fungus disease of forest and orchard trees initiated by invasion of the root system, then of the lower trunk, by *Armillaria mellea*. Also known as bark-splitting disease.

Armilliferidae [INV ZOO] A family of pentastomid arthropods belonging to the suborder Porocephaloidea.

Armour unit [BIOL] A unit for the standardization of adrenal cortical hormones and trypsin.

armyworm [INV ZOO] Any of the larvae of certain species of noctuid moths composing the family Phalaenidae; economically important pests of corn and other grasses.

Arneth's classification See Arneth's index.

Arneth's count See Arneth's index.

Arneth's formula See Arneth's index.

Arneth's index [HISTOL] A system for dividing peripheral blood granulocytes into five classes according to the number of nuclear lobes, the least mature cells being tabulated on the left, giving rise to the terms "shift to left" and "shift to right" as an indication of granulocytic immaturity or hypermaturity respectively. Also known as Arneth's classification; Arneth's count; Arneth's formula.

Arnold sterilizer [MICROBIO] An apparatus that employs steam under pressure at 212°F (100°C) for fractional sterilization of specialized bacteriological culture media.

Arodoidea [INV ZOO] A superfamily of hemipteran insects belonging to the subdivision Geocorisae.

arolium [INV ZOO] A pad projecting between the tarsal claws of some insects and arachnids.

aromatic amino acid [BIOCHEM] An organic acid containing at least one amino group and one or more aromatic groups; for example, phenylalanine, one of the essential amino acids.

arrested evolution [EVOL] Evolution that was extremely slow in comparison with that characteristic of most organic lineages.

arrhenotoky [BIOL] Production of only male offspring by a parthenogenetic female.

Arridae [VERT ZOO] A family of catfishes in the suborder Siluroidei found from Cape Cod to Panama.

arrowroot [BOT] Any of the tropical American plants belonging to the genus *Maranta* in the family Marantaceae.

arrowworm [INV ZOO] Any member of the phylum Chaetognatha; useful indicator organism for identifying displaced masses of water.

Artacaminae [INV ZOO] A subfamily of polychaete annelids in the family Terebellidae of the Sedentaria.

arteriole [ANAT] An artery of small diameter that terminates in capillaries.

arteriovenous anastomosis [ANAT] A blood vessel that connects an arteriole directly to a venule without capillary intervention.

artery [ANAT] A vascular tube that carries blood away from the heart.

arthochromatic erythroblast *See* normoblast.

Arthoniaceae [BOT] A family of lichens in the order Hysteriales.

Arthrobacter [MICROBIO] A genus of gram-positive, aerobic rods in the coryneform group of bacteria; metabolism is respiratory, and cellulose is not attacked.

arthrobranch [INV ZOO] In Malacostraca, the gill attached to the joint between the body and the first leg segment.

arthrodia [ANAT] A diarthrosis permitting only restricted motion between a concave and a convex surface, as in some wrist and ankle articulations. Also known as gliding joint.

Arthrodira [PALEON] The joint-necked fishes, an Upper Silurian and Devonian order of the Placodermi.

Arthrodonteae [BOT] A family of mosses in the subclass Eubrya characterized by thin, membranous peristome teeth composed of cell walls.

Arthromitaceae [MICROBIO] Formerly a family of nonmotile bacteria in the order Caryophanales found in the intestine of millipedes, cockroaches, and toads.

Arthropoda [INV ZOO] The largest phylum in the animal kingdom; adults typically have a segmented body, a sclerotized integument, and many-jointed segmental limbs.

arthropod-borne virus *See* arbovirus.

arthropodin [BIOCHEM] A water-soluble protein which forms part of the endocuticle of insects.

arthrosis [ANAT] An articulation or suture uniting two bones.

arthrospore [BOT] A jointed, vegetative resting spore resulting from filament segmentation in some blue-green algae and hypha segmentation in many Basidiomycetes.

Arthrotardigrada [INV ZOO] A suborder of microscopic invertebrates in the order Heterotardigrada characterized by toelike terminations on the legs.

Arthur unit [BIOL] A unit for the standardization of splenin A.

artichoke [BOT] *Cynara scolymus*. A herbaceous perennial plant belonging to the order Asterales; the flower head is edible.

articulamentum [INV ZOO] The innermost layer of a calcareous plate in a chiton.

articular cartilage [ANAT] Cartilage that covers the articular surfaces of bones.

articular disk [ANAT] A disk of fibrocartilage, dividing the cavity of certain joints.

articular membrane [INV ZOO] A flexible region of the cuticle between sclerotized areas of the exoskeleton of an arthropod; functions as a joint.

Articulata [INV ZOO] 1. A class of the Brachiopoda having hinged valves that usually bear teeth. 2. The only surviving subclass of the echinoderm class Crinoidea.

articulation [ANAT] *See* joint. [BOT] A joint between two parts of a plant that can separate spontaneously. [INV ZOO] A joint between rigid parts of an animal body, as the segments of an appendage in insects. [PHYSIO] The act of enunciating speech.

artifact [HISTOL] A structure in a fixed cell or tissue formed by manipulation or by the reagent.

artificial parthenogenesis [PHYSIO] Activation of an egg by chemical and physical stimuli in the absence of sperm.

Artiodactyla [VERT ZOO] An order of terrestrial, herbivorous mammals characterized by having an even number of toes and by having the main limb axes pass between the third and fourth toes.

arytenoid [ANAT] Relating to either of the paired, pyramid-shaped, pivoting cartilages on the dorsal aspect of the larynx, in man and most other mammals, to which the vocal cords and arytenoid muscles are attached.

Ascaphidae [VERT ZOO] A family of amphicoelous frogs in the order Anura, represented by four living species.

ascarid [INV ZOO] The common name for any roundworm belonging to the superfamily Ascaridoidea.

Ascaridata [INV ZOO] An equivalent name for the Ascaridina.

Ascaridida [INV ZOO] An order of parasitic nematodes in the subclass Phasmidia.

Ascarididae [INV ZOO] A family of parasitic nematodes in the superfamily Ascaridoidea.

Ascaridina [INV ZOO] A suborder of parasitic nematodes in the order Ascaridida.

Ascaridoidea [INV ZOO] A large superfamily of parasitic nematodes of the suborder Ascaridina.

Ascaris [INV ZOO] A genus of roundworms that are intestinal parasites in mammals, including man.

Ascaris lumbricoides [INV ZOO] A large parasitic roundworm in the small intestine of man.

Ascaroidea [INV ZOO] An equivalent name for Ascaridoidea.

ascending aorta [ANAT] The first part of the aorta, extending from its origin in the heart to the aortic arch.

Aschelmintha [INV ZOO] A theoretical grouping erected by B. G. Chitwood as a series that includes the phylum Nematoda.

Aschelminthes [INV ZOO] A heterogeneous phylum of small to microscopic wormlike animals; individuals are pseudocoelomate and mostly unsegmented and are covered with a cuticle.

Ascidiacea [INV ZOO] A large class of the phylum Tunicata; adults are sessile and may be solitary or colonial.

ascidiform [BOT] Pitcher-shaped, as certain leaves.

ascidium [BOT] A pitcher-shaped plant organ or part.

Asclepiadaceae [BOT] A family of tropical and subtropical flowering plants in the order Gentianales characterized by a well-developed latex system; milkweed (*Asclepias*) is a well-known member.

ascocarp [MYCOL] The mature fruiting body bearing asci with ascospores in higher Ascomycetes.

ascogenous [MYCOL] Pertaining to or producing asci.

ascogonium [MYCOL] The specialized female sexual organ in higher Ascomycetes.

Ascolichenes [BOT] A class of the lichens characterized by the production of asci similar to those produced by Ascomycetes.

Ascomycetes [MYCOL] A class of fungi in the subdivision Eumycetes, distinguished by the ascus.

ascon [INV ZOO] A sponge or sponge larva having incurrent canals leading directly to the paragaster.

ascorbic acid [BIOCHEM] $C_6H_8O_6$ A white, crystalline, water-soluble vitamin found in many plant materials, especially citrus fruit. Also known as vitamin C.

ascospore [MYCOL] An asexual spore representing the final product of the sexual process, borne on an ascus in Ascomycetes.

Ascothoracica [INV ZOO] An order of marine crustaceans in the subclass Cirripedia occurring as endo- and ectoparasites of echinoderms and coelenterates.

ascus [MYCOL] An oval or tubular spore sac bearing ascospores in members of the Ascomycetes.

Aselloidea [INV ZOO] A group of free-living, freshwater isopod crustaceans in the suborder Asellota.

Asellota [INV ZOO] A suborder of morphologically and ecologically diverse aquatic crustaceans in the order Isopoda.

asexual [BIOL] 1. Not involving sex. 2. Exhibiting absence of sex or of functional sex organs.

asexual reproduction [BIOL] Formation of new individuals from a single individual without the involvement of gametes.

ash [BOT] 1. A tree of the genus *Fraxinus*, deciduous trees of the olive family (Oleaceae) characterized by opposite, pinnate leaflets. 2. Any

of various Australian trees having wood of great toughness and strength; used for tool handles and in work requiring flexibility.

Asilidae [INV ZOO] The robber flies, a family of predatory, orthorrhaphous, dipteran insects in the series Brachycera.

Asopinae [INV ZOO] A family of hemipteran insects in the superfamily Pentatomoidea including some predators of caterpillars.

asparaginase [BIOCHEM] An enzyme that catalyzes the hydrolysis of asparagine to asparaginic acid and ammonia.

asparagine [BIOCHEM] $C_4H_8N_2O_3$ A white, crystalline amino acid found in many plant seeds.

asparagus [BOT] *Asparagus officinalis*. A dioecious, perennial monocot belonging to the order Liliales; the shoot of the plant is edible.

aspartase [BIOCHEM] A bacterial enzyme that catalyzes the deamination of aspartic acid to fumaric acid and ammonia.

aspartate [BIOCHEM] A compound that is an ester or salt of aspartic acid.

aspartic acid [BIOCHEM] $C_4H_7NO_4$ A nonessential, crystalline dicarboxylic amino acid found in plants and animals, especially in molasses from young sugarcane and sugarbeet.

aspartokinase [BIOCHEM] An enzyme that catalyzes the reaction of aspartic acid with adenosinetriphosphate to give aspartyl phosphate.

aspartoyl [BIOCHEM] —COCH₂CH(NH₂)CO— A bivalent radical derived from aspartic acid.

aspartyl phosphate [BIOCHEM] $H_2O_3POOCH_2$-CHNH₂COOH An intermediate in the biosynthesis of pyrimidines.

aspect [ECOL] Seasonal appearance.

aspection [ECOL] Seasonal change in appearance or constitution of a plant community.

aspen [BOT] Any of several species of poplars (*Populus*) characterized by weak, flattened leaf stalks which cause the leaves to flutter in the slightest breeze.

Aspergillaceae [MYCOL] Former name for the Eurotiaceae.

Aspergillales [MYCOL] Former name for the Eurotiales.

aspergillic acid [BIOCHEM] $C_{12}H_{20}O_2N_2$ A diketopiperazine-like antifungal antibiotic produced by certain strains of *Aspergillus flavus*.

aspergillin [MYCOL] 1. A black pigment found in spores of some molds of the genus *Aspergillus*. 2. A broad-spectrum antibacterial antibiotic produced by the molds *Aspergillus flavus* and *A. fumigatus*.

Aspergillus [MYCOL] A genus of fungi including several species of common molds and some human and plant pathogens.

Aspergillus fumigatus [MYCOL] A pathogenic fungus causing aspergillosis in man and animals; source of the antibiotic fumagillin.

Aspergillus niger [MYCOL] A pathogenic fungus causing black mold in many plants, wet stem rot in sisal, and otomycosis in man; used industrially for fermentative production of enzymes and citric acid.

asperifoliate [BOT] Rough-leaved.

asperulate [BOT] Delicately roughened.

asphradium [INV ZOO] An organ, believed to be a chemoreceptor, in mollusks. Also spelled osphradium.

aspiculate [INV ZOO] Lacking spicules, referring to Porifera.

Aspidiotinae [INV ZOO] A subfamily of homopteran insects in the superfamily Coccoidea.

Aspidiphoridae [INV ZOO] An equivalent name for the Sphindidae.

Aspidobothria [INV ZOO] An equivalent name for the Aspidogastrea.

Aspidobothroidea [INV ZOO] A group of trematodes accorded class rank by W. J. Hargis.

Aspidobranchia [INV ZOO] An equivalent name for the Archaeogastropoda.

Aspidochirotacea [INV ZOO] A subclass of bilaterally symmetrical echinoderms in the class Holothuroidea characterized by tube feet and 10–30 shield-shaped tentacles.

Aspidochirotida [INV ZOO] An order of holothurioid echinoderms in the subclass Aspidochirotacea characterized by respiratory trees and dorsal tube feet converted into tactile warts.

Aspidocotylea [INV ZOO] An equivalent name for the Aspidogastrea.

Aspidodiadematidae [INV ZOO] A small family of deep-sea echinoderms in the order Diadematoida.

Aspidogastrea [INV ZOO] An order of endoparasitic worms in the class Trematoda having strongly developed ventral holdfasts.

Aspidogastridae [INV ZOO] A family of trematode worms in the order Aspidogastrea occurring as endoparasites of mollusks.

Aspidorhynchidae [PALEON] The single family of the Aspidorhynchiformes, an extinct order of holostean fishes.

Aspidorhynchiformes [PALEON] A small, extinct order of specialized holostean fishes.

Aspinothoracida [PALEON] The equivalent name for Brachythoraci.

aspiration [MICROBIO] The use of suction to draw up a sample in a pipette.

asporogenic mutant [MICROBIO] A bacillus that is unable to form spores due to alterations at any of several gene loci.

asporogenous [BOT] Not producing spores, especially of certain yeasts.

Aspredinidae [VERT ZOO] A family of salt-water catfishes in the order Siluriformes found off the coast of South America.

ass [VERT ZOO] Any of several perissodactyl mammals in the family Equidae belonging to the genus *Equus*, especially *E. hemionus* and *E. asinus*.

assemblage [ECOL] A group of organisms sharing a common habitant by chance. [PALEON] A group of fossils occurring together at one stratigraphic level.

assemblage zone [PALEON] A biostratigraphic unit defined and identified by a group of associated fossils rather than by a single index fossil.

assimilation [PHYSIO] Conversion of nutritive materials into protoplasm.

assimilative nitrate reduction [MICROBIO] The reduction of nitrates by some aerobic bacteria for purposes of assimilation.

assimilative sulfate reduction [MICROBIO] The reduction of sulfates by certain obligate anaerobic bacteria for purposes of assimilation.

associated automatic movement *See* synkinesia.

association [ECOL] Major segment of a biome formed by a climax community, such as an oak-hickory forest of the deciduous forest biome.

association area [PHYSIO] An area of the cerebral cortex that is thought to link and coordinate activities of the projection areas.

association center [INV ZOO] In invertebrates, a nervous center coordinating and distributing stimuli from sensory receptors.

association fiber [ANAT] One of the white nerve fibers situated just beneath the cortical substance and connecting the adjacent cerebral gyri.

association neuron [ANAT] A neuron, usually within the central nervous system, between sensory and motor neurons.

assortative mating [GEN] Nonrandom mating with respect to phenotypes.

Astacidae [INV ZOO] A family of fresh-water crayfishes belonging to the section Macrura in the order Decapoda, occurring in the temperate regions of the Northern Hemisphere.

astacin [BIOCHEM] $C_{40}H_{48}O_4$ A red carotenoid ketone pigment found in crustaceans, as in the shell of a boiled lobster.

Astacinae [INV ZOO] A subfamily of crayfishes in the family Astacidae including all North American species west of the Rocky Mountains.

astaxanthin [BIOCHEM] $C_{40}H_{52}O_4$ A violet carotenoid pigment found in combined form in certain crustacean shells and bird feathers.

Asteidae [INV ZOO] A small, obscure family of cyclorrhaphous myodarian dipteran insects in the subsection Acalyptratae.

astelic [BOT] Lacking a stele or having a discontinuous arrangement of vascular bundles.

aster [BOT] Any of the herbaceous ornamental plants of the genus *Aster* belonging to the family Compositae.

Asteraceae [BOT] An equivalent name for the Compositae.

Asterales [BOT] An order of dicotyledonous plants in the subclass Asteridae, including aster, sunflower, zinnia, lettuce, artichoke, and dandelion; ovary is inferior, flowers are borne in involucrate, centripetally flowering heads, and the calyx, when present, is modified into a set of scale-, hair-, or bristlelike structures called the pappus.

Asteridae [BOT] A large subclass of dicotyledonous plants in the class Magnoliopsida; plants are sympetalous, with unitegmic, tenuinucellate ovules and with the stamens usually as many as, or fewer than, the corolla lobes and alternate with them.

Asteriidae [INV ZOO] A large family of echinoderms in the order Forcipulatida, including many predatory sea stars.

Asterinidae [INV ZOO] The starlets, a family of echinoderms in the order Spinulosida.

asternal [ANAT] 1. Not attached to the sternum. 2. Without a sternum.

Asteroidea [INV ZOO] The starfishes, a subclass of echinoderms in the subphylum Asterozoa characterized by five radial arms.

Asteroschematidae [INV ZOO] A family of ophiuroid echinoderms in the order Phrynophiurida with individuals having a small disk and stout arms.

Asterozoa [INV ZOO] A subphylum of echinoderms characterized by a star-shaped body and radially divergent axes of symmetry.

aster wilt [PL PATH] A fungus disease of asters caused by *Fusarium oxysporum* f. *callistephi*.

aster yellows [PL PATH] A widespread virus disease of asters, other ornamental plants, and many vegetables, characterized by yellowing and dwarfing; leafhoppers are vectors.

Asticcacaulis [MICROBIO] A genus of prosthecate bacteria; cells are rod-shaped with an appendage (pseudostalk), and reproduction is by binary fission of cells.

astichous [BOT] Not arranged in rows.

astogeny [INV ZOO] Morphological and size changes associated with zooids of aging colonial animals.

astomatal [BOT] Lacking stomata. Also known as astomous.

Astomatida [INV ZOO] An order of mouthless protozoans in the subclass Holotrichia; all species are invertebrate parasites, typically in oligochaete annelids.

astomatous [INV ZOO] Lacking a mouth, especially a cytostome, as in certain ciliates.

astomocnidae nematocyst [INV ZOO] A stinging cell whose thread has a closed end and either is adhesive or acts as a lasso to entangle prey.

astomous [BOT] 1. Having a capsule that bursts irregularly and is not dehiscent by an operculum. 2. *See* astomatal.

astraeid [INV ZOO] Of a group of corals that are imperforate.

astragalus [ANAT] The bone of the ankle which articulates with the bones of the leg. Also known as talus.

Astrapotheria [PALEON] A relatively small order of large, extinct South American mammals in the infraclass Eutheria.

Astrapotheroidea [PALEON] A suborder of extinct mammals in the order Astrapotheria, ranging from early Eocene to late Miocene.

Astrea [INV ZOO] A genus of mollusks in the class Gastropoda.

astrobiology [BIOL] The study of living organisms on celestial bodies other than the earth.

astrocyte [HISTOL] A star-shaped cell; specifically, a neuroglial cell.

astroglia [HISTOL] Neuroglia composed of astrocytes.

Astropectinidae [INV ZOO] A family of echinoderms in the suborder Paxillosina occurring in all seas from tidal level downward.

astropyle [INV ZOO] A small, rounded projection from the central capsule of some radiolarians.

astrosphere [CELL BIO] The center of the aster exclusive of the rays.

asty [INV ZOO] A bryozoan colony.

asulcal [BIOL] Without a sulcus.

atactostele [BOT] A type of monocotyledonous siphonostele in which the vascular bundles are dispersed irregularly throughout the center of the stem.

atavism [EVOL] Appearance of a distant ancestral form of an organism or one of its parts due to reactivation of ancestral genes.

Ateleopoidei [VERT ZOO] A family of oceanic fishes in the order Cetomimiformes characterized by an elongate body, lack of a dorsal fin, and an anal fin continuous with the caudal fin.

Atelopodidae [VERT ZOO] A family of small, brilliantly colored South and Central American frogs in the suborder Procoela.

Atelostomata [INV ZOO] A superorder of echinoderms in the subclass Euechinoidea characterized by a rigid, exoclyic test and lacking a lantern, or jaw, apparatus.

Athalamida [INV ZOO] An order of naked amebas of the subclass Granuloreticulosia in which pseudopodia are branched and threadlike (reticulopodia).

Athecanephria [INV ZOO] An order of tubedwelling, tentaculate animals in the class Pogonophora characterized by a saclike anterior coelom.

athecate [INV ZOO] Lacking a theca.

Atherinidae [VERT ZOO] The silversides, a family of actinopterygian fishes of the order Atheriniformes.

Atheriniformes [VERT ZOO] An order of actinopterygian fishes in the infraclass Teleostei, including flyingfishes, needlefishes, killifishes, silversides, and allied species.

Athiorhodaceae [MICROBIO] Formerly the nonsulfur photosynthetic bacteria, a family of small, gram-negative, nonsporeforming, motile bacteria in the suborder Rhodobacteriineae.

athrocyte [HISTOL] A cell that engulfs extraneous material and stores it as granules in the cytoplasm.

Athyrididina [PALEON] A suborder of fossil articulate brachiopods in the order Spiriferida characterized by laterally or, more rarely, ventrally directed spires.

Atlantacea [INV ZOO] A superfamily of mollusks in the subclass Prosobranchia.

atlas [ANAT] The first cervical vertebra.

ATP *See* adenosinetriphosphate.

ATPase *See* adenosinetriphosphatase.

Atractidae [INV ZOO] A family of parasitic nematodes in the superfamily Oxyuroidea.

atrial septum [ANAT] The muscular wall between the atria of the heart. Also known as interatrial septum.

Atrichornithidae [VERT ZOO] The scrubbirds, a family of suboscine perching birds in the suborder Menurae.

atrichous [CELL BIO] Lacking flagella.

atriopore [ZOO] The opening of an atrium as seen in lancelets and tunicates.

atrioventricular canal [EMBRYO] The common passage between the atria and ventricles in the heart of the mammalian embryo before division of the organ into right and left sides.

atrioventricular valve [ANAT] A structure located at the orifice between the atrium and ventricle which maintains a unidirectional blood flow through the heart.

atrium [ANAT] 1. The heart chamber that receives blood from the veins. 2. The main part of the tympanic cavity, below the malleus. 3. The external chamber to receive water from the gills in lancelets and tunicates.

Atrypidina [PALEON] A suborder of fossil articulate brachiopods in the order Spiriferida.

attenuation [BOT] Tapering, sometimes to a long point. [MICROBIO] Weakening or reduction of the virulence of a microorganism.

Atyidae [INV ZOO] A family of decapod crustaceans belonging to the section Caridea.

Auchenorrhyncha [INV ZOO] A group of homopteran families and one superfamily, in which the beak arises at the anteroventral extremity of the face and is not sheathed by the propleura.

audition [PHYSIO] Ability to hear.

auditory [PHYSIO] Pertaining to the act or the organs of hearing.

auditory association area [PHYSIO] The cortical association area in the brain just inferior to the auditory projection area, related to it anatomically and functionally by association fibers.

auditory impedance [PHYSIO] The acoustic impedance of the ear.

auditory nerve [ANAT] The eighth cranial nerve in vertebrates; either of a pair of sensory nerves composed of two sets of nerve fibers, the cochlear nerve and the vestibular nerve. Also known as acoustic nerve; vestibulocochlear nerve.

auditory placode [EMBRYO] An ectodermal thickening from which the inner ear develops in vertebrates.

Auerbach's plexus See myenteric plexus.

aufwuch [ECOL] A plant or animal organism which is attached or clings to surfaces of leaves or stems of rooted plants above the bottom stratum.

auk [VERT ZOO] Any of several large, short-necked diving birds (*Alca*) of the family Alcidae found along North Atlantic coasts.

Aulodonta [INV ZOO] An order of echinoderms proposed by R. Jackson in 1921.

aulodont dentition [INV ZOO] In echinoderms, groovedteeth with epiphyses that do not meet, so the foramen magnum of the jaw is open.

Aulolepidae [PALEON] A family of marine fossil teleostean fishes in the order Ctenothrissiformes.

aulophyte [ECOL] A nonparasitic plant that lives in the cavity of another plant for shelter.

Auloporidae [PALEON] A family of Paleozoic corals in the order Tabulata.

aural [BIOL] Pertaining to the ear or the sense of hearing.

Aurelia [INV ZOO] A genus of scyphozoans.

aurelia [INV ZOO] A morphological grouping of paramecia, including the elongate, cigar-shaped

species which appear to be nearly circular in cross section.

aureofacin [MICROBIO] An antifungal antibiotic produced by a strain of *Streptomyces aureofaciens*.

Aureomycin [MICROBIO] The trade name for the antibiotic chlortetracycline.

aureothricin [MICROBIO] $C_9H_{10}O_2N_2S_2$ An antibacterial antibiotic produced by a strain of *Actinomyces*.

aureusidin [BIOCHEM] $C_{15}H_{11}O_5$ A yellow flavonoid pigment found typically in the yellow snapdragon. Also known as 4,6,3′,4′-tetrahydroxyaurone.

auricle [ANAT] 1. An ear-shaped appendage to an atrium of the heart. 2. Any ear-shaped structure. 3. See pinna.

auricularia larva [INV ZOO] A barrel-shaped, food-gathering larval form with a winding ciliated band, common to holothurians and asteroids.

auricularis [ANAT] Any of the three muscles attached to the cartilage of the external ear.

aurophore [INV ZOO] A bell-shaped structure which is part of the float of certain coelenterates.

Australian faunal region [ECOL] A zoogeographic region that includes the terrestrial animal communities of Australia and all surrounding islands except those of Asia.

Australopithecinae [PALEON] The near-humans, a subfamily of the family Hominidae composed of the single genus *Australopithecus*.

Australopithecus [PALEON] A genus of near-humans in the subfamily Australopithecinae representing a side branch of human evolution.

austral region [ECOL] A North American biogeographic region including the region between transitional and tropical zones.

Austroastacidae [INV ZOO] A family of crayfish in the order Decapoda found in temperate regions of the Southern Hemisphere.

Austrodecidae [INV ZOO] A monogeneric family of marine arthropods in the subphylum Pycnogonida.

Austroriparian life zone [ECOL] The zone in which occurs the climate and biotic communities of the southeastern coniferous forests of North America.

autecology [ECOL] The ecological relations between a plant species and its environment.

autoasphyxiation [PHYSIO] Asphyxiation by the products of metabolic activity.

autobasidium [MYCOL] An undivided basidium typically found in higher Basidiomycetes.

autocarp [BOT] 1. A fruit formed as the result of self-fertilization. 2. A fruit consisting of the ripened pericarp without adnate parts.

autocarpy [BOT] Production of fruit by self-fertilization.

autochory [ECOL] Active self-dispersal of individuals or their disseminules.

autochthon [PALEON] A fossil occurring where the organism once lived.

autochthonous microorganism [MICROBIO] An indigenous form of soil microorganisms, responsible for chemical processes that occur in the soil under normal conditions.

autocopulation [INV ZOO] Self-copulation; sometimes occurs in certain hermaphroditic worms.

autodeme [ECOL] A plant population in which most individuals are self-fertilized.

autogamy [BIOL] A process of self-fertilization that results in homozygosis; occurs in some flowering plants, fungi, and protozoans.

autogenesis See abiogenesis.

autograft [BIOL] A tissue transplanted from one part to another part of an individual's body.

autohemolysis [PHYSIO] The spontaneous lysis of blood which occurs during an incubation in a hematological procedure.

autohemorrhage [INV ZOO] Voluntary exudation or ejection of nauseous or poisonous blood by certain insects as a defense against predators.

autoicous [BOT] Having male and female organs on the same plant but on different branches. Also spelled autoecious.

autologous [BIOL] Derived from or produced by the individual in question, such as an autologous protein or an autologous graft.

autolysosome See autophagic vacuole.

autolytic enzyme [BIOCHEM] A bacterial enzyme, located in the cell wall, that causes disintegration of the cell following injury or death.

Autolytinae [INV ZOO] A subfamily of errantian polychaetes in the family Syllidae.

automatism [BIOL] Spontaneous activity of tissues or cells.

autonomic nervous system [ANAT] The visceral or involuntary division of the nervous system in vertebrates, which enervates glands, viscera, and smooth, cardiac, and some striated muscles.

autonomic reflex system [PHYSIO] An involuntary biological control system characterized by the uncontrolled functioning of smooth muscles and glands to maintain an acceptable internal environment.

autophagic vacuole [CELL BIO] A membrane-bound cellular organelle that engulfs pieces of the substance of the cell itself. Also known as autolysosome.

autophagocytosis [CELL BIO] The cellular process of phagocytizing a portion of protoplasm by a vacuole within the cell.

autophagy [CELL BIO] The cellular process of self-digestion.

autopolyploid [GEN] A cell or organism having three or more sets of chromosomes all derived from the same species.

autosexing [BIOL] Displaying differential sex characters at birth, noted particularly in fowl bred for sex-specific colors and patterns.

autoskeleton [INV ZOO] The endoskeleton of a sponge.

autosome [GEN] Any chromosome other than a sex chromosome.

autostylic [VERT ZOO] Having the jaws attached directly to the cranium, as in chimeras, amphibians, and higher vertebrates.

autosyndesis [CELL BIO] The act of pairing of homologous chromosomes from the same parent during meiosis in polyploids.

autotomy [ZOO] The process of self-amputation of appendages in crabs and other crustaceans and tails in some salamanders and lizards under stress.

autotroph [BIOL] An organism capable of synthesizing organic nutrients directly from simple inorganic substances, such as carbon dioxide and inorganic nitrogen.

autozooecium [INV ZOO] The tube enclosing an autozooid.

autozooid [INV ZOO] An unspecialized feeding individual in a bryozoan colony, possessing fully developed organs and exoskeleton.

auxanogram [MICROBIO] A plate culture provided with variable growth conditions to determine the effects of specific environmental factors.

auxanography [MICROBIO] The study of growth-inhibiting or growth-promoting agents by means of auxanograms.

auxesis [PHYSIO] Growth resulting from increase in cell size.

auximone [BIOCHEM] Any of certain growth-promoting substances occurring principally in sphagnum peat decomposed by nitrogen bacteria.

auxin [BIOCHEM] Any organic compound which promotes plant growth along the longitudinal axis when applied to shoots free from indigenous growth-promoting substances.

auxoautotrophic [BIOL] Requiring no exogenous growth factors.

auxocyte [BIOL] A gamete-forming cell, such as an oocyte or spermatocyte, or a sporocyte during its growth period.

auxoheterotrophic [BIOL] Requiring exogenous growth factors.

auxospore [INV ZOO] A reproductive cell in diatoms formed in association with rejuvenescence by the union of two cells that have diminished in size through repeated divisions.

auxotonic [BOT] Induced by growth rather than by exogenous stimuli.

auxotrophic mutant [GEN] An organism that requires a specific growth factor, such as an amino acid, for its growth.

available-chlorine method [MICROBIO] A technique for the standardization of chlorine disinfectants intended for use as germicidal rinses on cleaned surfaces; increments of bacterial inoculum are added to different disinfectant concentrations, and after incubation the results indicate the capacity of the disinfectant to handle an increasing bacterial load before exhaustion of available chlorine, the germicidal principle.

avalanche conduction [PHYSIO] Conduction of a nerve impulse through several neurons which converge, increasing the discharge intensity by summation.

Avena [BOT] A genus of grasses (family Gramineae), including oats, characterized by an inflorescence that is loosely paniculate, two-toothed lemmas, and deeply furrowed grains.

Avena unit [BIOL] A unit for the standardization of auxins.

avenin [BIOCHEM] The glutelin of oats.

Aves [VERT ZOO] A class of animals composed of the birds, which are warm-blooded, egg-laying vertebrates primarily adapted for flying.

avianize [VIROL] To attenuate a virus by repeated culture on chick embryos.

avicolous [ECOL] Living on birds, as of certain insects.

avicularium [INV ZOO] A specialized individual in a bryozoan colony with a beak that keeps other animals from settling on the colony.

aviculture [VERT ZOO] Care and breeding of birds, especially wild birds, in captivity.

avidin [BIOCHEM] A protein constituting 0.2% of the total protein in egg white; molecular weight is 70,000 daltons; combines firmly with biotin but loses this ability when subjected to heat.

avifauna [VERT ZOO] 1. Birds, collectively. 2. Birds characterizing a period, region, or environment.

avocado [BOT] *Persea americana*. A subtropical evergreen tree of the order Magnoliales that bears a pulpy pear-shaped edible fruit.

awn [BOT] Any of the bristles at the ends of glumes or bracts on the spikelets of oats, barley, and some wheat and grasses. Also known as beard.

axenic culture [BIOL] The growth of organisms of a single species in the absence of cells or living organisms of any other species.

axial filament [CELL BIO] The central microtubule elements of a cilium or flagellum.

axial filament [INV ZOO] An organic fiber which serves as the core for deposition of mineral substance to form a ray of a sponge spicule.

axial gland [INV ZOO] A structure enclosing the stone canal in certain echinoderms; its function is uncertain.

axial gradient [EMBRYO] In some invertebrates, a graded difference in metobolic activity along the anterior-posterior, dorsal-ventral, and medial-lateral embryonic axes.

axial musculature [ANAT] The muscles that lie along the longitudinal axis of the vertebrate body.

axial skeleton [ANAT] The bones composing the skull, vertebral column, and associated structures of the vertebrate body.

axiation [EMBRYO] The formation or development of axial structures, such as the neural tube.

Axiidae [INV ZOO] A family of decapod crustaceans, including the hermit crabs, in the suborder Reptantia.

axil [BIOL] The angle between a structure and the axis from which it arises, especially for branches and leaves.

axilla [ANAT] The depression between the arm and the thoracic wall; the armpit. [BOT] An axil.

axillary [ANAT] Of, pertaining to, or near the axilla or armpit. [BOT] Placed or growing in the axis of a branch or leaf.

axillary bud [BOT] A lateral bud borne in the axil of a leaf.

axillary sweat gland [ANAT] An apocrine gland located in the axilla.

Axinellina [INV ZOO] A suborder of sponges in the order Clavaxinellida.

axis [ANAT] 1. The second cervical vertebra in higher vertebrates; the first vertebra of amphibians. 2. The center line of an organism, organ, or other body part.

axis cylinder [CELL BIO] 1. The central mass of a nerve fiber. 2. The core of protoplasm in a medullated nerve fiber.

axis of pelvis [ANAT] A curved line which forms right angles to the pelvic-cavity planes.

axoblast [INV ZOO] 1. The germ cell in mesozoans; cells are linearly arranged in the longitudinal axis and produce the primary nematogens. 2. The individual scleroblast of the axis epithelium which produces spicules in octocorals.

axocoel [INV ZOO] The anterior pair of coelomic sacs in the dipleurula larval ancestral stage of echinoderms.

axogamy [BOT] Having sex organs on a leafy stem.

axolemma [CELL BIO] The plasma membrane of an axon.

axolotl [VERT ZOO] The neotenous larva of some salamanders in the family Ambystomidae.

axolotl unit [BIOL] A unit for the standardization of thyroid extracts.

axon [ANAT] The process or nerve fiber of a neuron that carries the unidirectional nerve impulse away from the cell body. Also known as neuraxon; neurite.

axoneme [CELL BIO] A bundle of fibrils enclosed by a membrane that is continuous with the plasma membrane.

Axonolaimoidea [INV ZOO] A superfamily of free-living nematodes with species inhabiting marine and brackish-water environments.

axoplasm [CELL BIO] The protoplasm of an axon.

axopodium [INV ZOO] A semipermanent pseudopodium composed of axial filaments surrounded by a cytoplasmic envelope.

aye-aye [VERT ZOO] *Daubentonia madagascariensis*. A rare prosimian primate indigenous to eastern Madagascar; the single species of the family Daubentoniidae.

2-azetidinecarboxylic acid [BIOCHEM] $C_4H_7NO_2$ Crystals which discolor at 200°C and darken until 310°C; soluble in water; a specific antagonist of L-proline; used in the production of abnormally high-molecular-weight polypeptides.

Azomonas [MICROBIO] A genus of large, motile, oval to spherical bacteria in the family Axotobacteraceae; do not produce cysts, and secrete large quantities of capsular slime.

azomycin [MICROBIO] $C_3H_3O_2N_3$ An antimicrobial antibiotic produced by a strain of *Nocardia mesenterica*.

Azotobacter [MICROBIO] A genus of large, usually motile, rod-shaped, oval, or spherical bacteria in the family Azotobacteraceae; form thick-walled cysts, and may produce large quantities of capsular slime.

Azotobacteraceae [MICROBIO] A family of large, bluntly rod-shaped, gram-negative, aerobic bacteria capable of fixing molecular nitrogen.

azygospore [MYCOL] A spore which is morphologically similar to a zygospore but is formed parthenogenetically.

azygos vein [ANAT] A branch of the right pre-cava which drains the intercostal muscles and empties into the superior vena cava.

azygote [BIOL] An individual produced by haploid parthenogenesis.

B

Babesia [INV ZOO] The type genus of the Babesiidae, a protozoan family containing red blood cell parasites.

Babesiidae [INV ZOO] A family of protozoans in the suborder Haemosporina containing parasites of vertebrate red blood cells.

baboon [VERT ZOO] Any of five species of large African and Asian terrestrial primates of the genus *Papio*, distinguished by a doglike muzzle, a short tail, and naked callosities on the buttocks.

babuina [VERT ZOO] A female baboon.

baccate [BOT] 1. Bearing berries. 2. Having pulp like a berry.

bacciferous [BOT] Bearing berries.

Bacillaceae [MICROBIO] The single family of endospore-forming rods and cocci.

Bacillariophyceae [BOT] The diatoms, a class of algae in the division Chrysophyta.

Bacillariophyta [BOT] An equivalent name for the Bacillariophyceae.

bacillary [MICROBIO] 1. Rod-shaped. 2. Produced by, pertaining to, or resembling bacilli.

bacillus [MICROBIO] Any rod-shaped bacterium.

Bacillus [MICROBIO] A genus of bacteria in the family Bacillaceae; rod-shaped cells are aerobes or facultative anaerobes and usually produce catalase.

Bacillus anthracis [MICROBIO] A nonmotile pathogenic species of bacteria that causes anthrax.

Bacillus brevis [MICROBIO] A gram-variable, saprophytic species of bacteria important for production of the antibiotic tyrothricin.

Bacillus licheniformis [MICROBIO] A gram-positive species of bacteria; important for production of the antibiotic bacitracin.

Bacillus megaterium [MICROBIO] A gram-positive species of bacteria that can produce levan from sucrose.

Bacillus polymyxa [MICROBIO] A gram-variable species of bacteria that produces gas from carbohydrates; important for production of the antibiotic polymyxin B.

Bacillus subtilis [MICROBIO] A gram-positive species of bacteria important for production of the antibiotic subtilin; the type species of the genus.

bacitracin [MICROBIO] A group of polypeptide antibiotics produced by *Bacillus licheniformis*.

back [ANAT] The part of the human body extending from the neck to the base of the spine.

backbone [ANAT] *See* spine.

back bulb [BOT] A pseudobulb on certain orchid plants that remains on the plant after removal of the terminal growth, and that is used for propagation.

backcross [GEN] A cross between an F_1 heterozygote and an individual of P_1 genotype.

backmarsh [ECOL] Marshland formed in poorly drained areas of an alluvial floodplain.

back mutation *See* reverse mutation.

backswamp depression [ECOL] A low swamp found adjacent to river levees.

bacteria [MICROBIO] Extremely small, relatively simple prokaryotic microorganisms traditionally classified with the fungi as Schizomycetes.

Bacteriaceae [MICROBIO] A former designation for Brevibacteriaceae.

bacterial blight [PL PATH] Any blight disease of plants caused by bacteria, including common bacterial blight, halo blight, and fuscous blight.

bacterial brown spot [PL PATH] A bacterial blight disease of plants caused by *Pseudomonas syringae*; marked by water-soaked reddish-brown spots or cankers. Also known as bacterial canker.

bacterial canker *See* bacterial brown spot.

bacterial capsule [MICROBIO] A thick, mucous envelope, composed of polypeptides or carbohydrates, surrounding some bacteria.

bacterial coenzyme [MICROBIO] Organic molecules that participate directly in a bacterial enzymatic reaction and may be chemically altered during the reaction.

bacterial competence [MICROBIO] The ability of cells in a bacterial culture to accept and be transformed by a molecule of transforming deoxyribonucleic acid.

bacterial endoenzyme [MICROBIO] An enzyme produced and active within the bacterial cell.

bacterial endospore [MICROBIO] A body, resistant to extremes of temperature and to dehydration, produced within the cells of gram-positive, sporeforming rods of *Bacillus* and *Clostridium* and by the coccus *Sporosarcina*.

bacterial enzyme [MICROBIO] Any of the metabolic catalysts produced by bacteria.

bacterial genetics [GEN] The study of inheritance and variation patterns in bacteria.

bacterial leaf spot [PL PATH] A bacterial disease of plants characterized by spotty discolorations on the leaves; examples are angular leaf spot and leaf blotch.

bacterial luminescence [MICROBIO] A light-producing phenomenon exhibited by certain bacteria.

bacterial metabolism [MICROBIO] Total chemical changes carried out by living bacteria.

bacterial methanogenesis See methanogenesis.

bacterial motility [MICROBIO] Self-propulsion in bacteria, either by gliding on a solid surface or by moving the flagella.

bacterial photosynthesis [MICROBIO] Use of light energy to synthesize organic compounds in green and purple bacteria.

bacterial pigmentation [MICROBIO] The organic compounds produced by certain bacteria which give color to both liquid cultures and colonies.

bacterial pustule [PL PATH] A bacterial blight of plants caused by *Xanthomonas phaseoli*; characterized by blisters on the leaves.

bacterial soft rot [PL PATH] A bacterial disease of plants marked by disintegration of tissues.

bacterial speck [PL PATH] A bacterial disease of plants characterized by small lesions on plant parts.

bacterial spot [PL PATH] Any bacterial disease of plants marked by spotting of the infected part.

bacterial wilt disease [PL PATH] A common bacterial disease of cucumber and muskmelon, caused by *Erwinia tracheiphila*, characterized by wilting and shriveling of the leaves and stems.

bacteriochlorophyll [BIOCHEM] $C_{52}H_{70}O_6N_4Mg$ A tetrahydroporphyrin chlorophyll compound occurring in the forms *a* and *b* in photosynthetic bacteria; there is no evidence that *b* has the empirical formula given.

bacteriocyte [INV ZOO] A modified fat cell found in certain insects that contains bacterium-shaped rods believed to be symbiotic bacteria.

bacteriogenic [MICROBIO] Caused by bacteria.

bacteriologist [MICROBIO] A specialist in the study of bacteria.

bacteriology [MICROBIO] The science and study of bacteria; a specialized branch of microbiology.

bacteriolysin [MICROBIO] An antibody that is active against and causes lysis of specific bacterial cells.

bacteriolysis [MICROBIO] Dissolution of bacterial cells.

Bacterionema [MICROBIO] A genus of bacteria in the family Actinomycetaceae; characteristically cells are rods with filaments attached and produce filamentous microcolonies; facultative anaerobes; carbohydrates are fermented.

bacteriophage [VIROL] Any of the viruses that infect bacterial cells; each has a narrow host range. Also known as phage.

bacteriosis [PL PATH] Any bacterial disease of plants.

bacteriostasis [MICROBIO] Inhibition of bacterial growth and metabolism.

bacteriotoxin [MICROBIO] 1. Any toxin that destroys or inhibits growth of bacteria. 2. A toxin produced by bacteria.

bacterioviridin See chlorobium chlorophyll.

Bacterium enteritidis See Salmonella enteritidis.

Bacterium paratyphosum B See Salmonella schott-mülleri.

Bacterium paratyphosum C See Salmonella hirsch-feldii.

Bacterium typhosum See Salmonella typhosum.

bacteroid [MICROBIO] A strange bacterial form of irregular shape, frequently associated with special conditions.

Bacteroidaceae [MICROBIO] The single family of gram-negative anaerobic bacteria; cells are nonsporeforming rods; some species are pathogenic.

Bactrian camel [VERT ZOO] *Camelus bactrianus*. The two-humped camel.

baculum [VERT ZOO] The penis bone, or os priapi, in lower mammals.

badger [VERT ZOO] Any of eight species of carnivorous mammals in six genera comprising the subfamily Melinae of the weasel family (Mustelidae).

Bagridae [VERT ZOO] A family of semitropical catfishes in the suborder Siluroidei.

Bainbridge reflex [PHYSIO] A poorly understood reflex acceleration of the heart rate due to rise of pressure in the right atrium and vena cavae, possibly mediated through afferent vagal fibers.

Bairdiacea [INV ZOO] A superfamily of ostracod crustaceans in the suborder Podocopa.

Bakanae disease [PL PATH] A fungus disease of rice in Japan, caused by *Gibberella fujikurae*; a foot rot disease.

Balaenicipitidae [VERT ZOO] A family of wading birds composed of a single species, the shoebill stork (*Balaeniceps rex*), in the order Ciconiiformes.

Balaenidae [VERT ZOO] The right whales, a family of cetacean mammals composed of five species in the suborder Mysticeti.

balanced polymorphism [GEN] Maintenance in a population of two or more alleles in equilibrium at frequencies too high to be explained, particularly for the rarer of them, by mutation balanced by selection; for example, the selective advantage of heterozygotes over both homozygotes.

balanced translocation [GEN] Positional change of one or more chromosome segments in cells or gametes without alteration of the normal diploid or haploid complement of genetic material.

balancer See haltere.

balancer [VERT ZOO] Either of a pair of rodlike lateral appendages on the heads of some larval salamanders.

Balanidae [INV ZOO] A family of littoral, sessile barnacles in the suborder Balanomorpha.

Balanoglossus [INV ZOO] A cosmopolitan genus of tongue worms belonging to the class Enteropneusta.

Balanomorpha [INV ZOO] The symmetrical barnacles, a suborder of sessile crustaceans in the order Thoracica.

Balanopaceae [BOT] A small family of dioecious dicotyledonous plants in the order Fagales characterized by exstipulate leaves, seeds with endosperm, and the pistillate flower solitary in a multibracteate involucre.

Balanopales [BOT] An ordinal name suggested for the Balanopaceae in some classifications.

Balanophoraceae [BOT] A family of dicotyledonous terrestrial plants in the order Santalales characterized by dry nutlike fruit, one to five ovules, unisexual flowers, attachment to the stem of the host, and the lack of chlorophyll.

Balanopsidales [BOT] An order in some systems of classification which includes only the Balanopaceae of the Fagales.

Balantidium [INV ZOO] A genus of protozoans in the order Trichostomatida containing the only ciliated protozoan species parasitic in humans, *Balantidium coli*.

Balanus [INV ZOO] A genus of barnacles composed of sessile acorn barnacles; the type genus of the family Balanidae.

Balbiani rings [CELL BIO] Localized swellings of a polytene chromosome.

Baldwin spot *See* bitter pit.

baleen [VERT ZOO] A horny substance, growing as fringed filter plates suspended from the upper jaws of whalebone whales. Also known as whalebone.

Balfour's law [EMBRYO] The law that the speed with which any part of the ovum segments is roughly proportional to the protoplasm's concentration in that area; the segment's size is inversely proportional to the protoplasm's concentration.

ball-and-socket joint *See* enarthrosis.

ballistospore [MYCOL] A type of fungal spore that is forcibly discharged at maturity.

balsa [BOT] *Ochroma lagopus*. A tropical American tree in the order Malvales; its wood is strong and lighter than cork.

Balsaminaceae [BOT] A family of flowering plants in the order Geraniales, including touch-me-not (*Impatiens*); flowers are irregular with five stamens and five carpels, leaves are simple with pinnate venation, and the fruit is an elastically dehiscent capsule.

bamboo [BOT] The common name of various tropical and subtropical, perennial, ornamental grasses in five genera of the family Gramineae characterized by hollow woody stems up to 6 inches (15 centimeters) in diameter.

Bambusoideae [BOT] A subfamily of grasses, composed of bamboo species, in the family Gramineae.

banana [BOT] Any of the treelike, perennial plants of the genus *Musa* in the family Musaceae; fruit is a berry characterized by soft, pulpy flesh and a thin rind.

banana freckle [PL PATH] A fungus disease of the banana caused by *Macrophoma musae*, producing brown or black spots on the fruit and leaves.

banded anteater *See* marsupial anteater.

bandicoot [VERT ZOO] 1. Any of several large Indian rats of the genus *Nesokia* and related genera. 2. Any of several small insectivorous and herbivorous marsupials comprising the family Peramelidae and found in Tasmania, Australia, and New Guinea.

Bangiophyceae [BOT] A class of red algae in the plant division Rhodophyta.

banner [BOT] The fifth or posterior petal of a butterfly-shaped (papilionaceous) flower.

barb [VERT ZOO] A side branch on the shaft of a bird's feather.

barbel [VERT ZOO] 1. A slender, tactile process near the mouth in certain fishes, such as catfishes. 2. Any European fresh-water fish in the genus *Barbus*.

barbellate [BIOL] Having short, stiff, hooked bristles.

barbicel [VERT ZOO] One of the small, hook-bearing processes on a barbule of the distal side of a barb or a feather.

bark [BOT] The tissues external to the cambium in a stem or root.

bark graft [BOT] A graft made by slipping the scion beneath a slit in the bark of the stock.

bark-splitting disease *See* Armillaria root rot.

barley [BOT] A plant of the genus *Hordeum* in the order Cyperales that is cultivated as a grain crop; the seed is used to manufacture malt beverages and as a cereal.

barley scald [PL PATH] A fungus disease of barley caused by *Rhynchosporium secalis* and characterized by bluish-green to yellow blotches and blighting of the foliage.

barley smut [PL PATH] 1. A loose smut disease of barley caused by *Ustilago nuda*. 2. A covered smut disease of barley caused by *U. hordei*.

barley stripe [PL PATH] A fungus disease of barley characterized by light green or yellow stripes on the leaves; incited by the diffusible toxin of *Helminthosporium gramineum*.

barnacle [INV ZOO] The common name for a number of species of crustaceans which compose the subclass Cirripedia.

baroduric bacteria [MICROBIO] Bacteria that can tolerate conditions of high hydrostatic pressure.

barophile [MICROBIO] An organism that thrives under conditions of high hydrostatic pressure.

barotaxis [BIOL] Orientation movement of an organism in response to pressure changes.

barracuda [VERT ZOO] The common name for about 20 species of fishes belonging to the genus *Sphyraena* in the order Perciformes.

Barr body [CELL BIO] A condensed, inactivated X chromosome inside the nuclear membrane in interphase somatic cells of women and most female mammals.

barrier [ECOL] Any physical or biological factor that restricts the migration or free movement of individuals or populations.

barrier marsh [ECOL] A type of marsh that restricts or prevents invasion of the area beyond it by new species of animals.

barrier zone [BOT] In a tree, new tissue formed by the cambium after it has been wounded; serves as both an anatomical and a chemical wall.

Bartonella [MICROBIO] A genus of the family Bartonellaceae; parasites in or on red blood cells and within fixed tissue cells; found in humans and in the arthropod genus *Phlebotomus*.

Bartonellaceae [MICROBIO] A family of the order Rickettsiales; rod-shaped, coccoid, ring- or disk-shaped cells; parasites of human and other vertebrate red blood cells.

Barychilinidae [PALEON] A family of Paleozoic crustaceans in the suborder Platycopa.

Barylambdidae [PALEON] A family of late Paleocene and early Eocene aquatic mammals in the order Pantodonta.

Barytheriidae [PALEON] A family of extinct proboscidean mammals in the suborder Barytherioidea.

Barytherioidea [PALEON] A suborder of extinct mammals of the order Proboscidea, in some systems of classification.

basal [BIOL] Of, pertaining to, or located at the base. [PHYSIO] Being the minimal level for, or essential for maintenance of, vital activities of an organism, such as basal metabolism.

basal body [CELL BIO] A cellular organelle that induces the formation of cilia and flagella and is similar to and sometimes derived from a centriole. Also known as kinetosome.

basal disc [BIOL] The expanded basal portion of the stalk of certain sessile organisms, used for attachment to the substrate.

basal ganglia [ANAT] The corpus striatum, or the corpus striatum and the thalamus considered together as the important subcortical centers.

basalia [VERT ZOO] The cartilaginous rods that support the base of the pectoral and pelvic fins in elasmobranchs.

basalis [HISTOL] The basal portion of the endometrium; it is not shed during menstruation.

basal lamina [EMBRYO] The portion of the gray matter of the embryonic neural tube from which motor nerve roots develop.

basal membrane [ANAT] The tissue beneath the pigment layer of the retina that forms the outer layer of the choroid.

basal metabolic rate [PHYSIO] The amount of energy utilized per unit time under conditions of basal metabolism; expressed as calories per square meter of body surface or per kilogram of body weight per hour. Abbreviated BMR.

basal metabolism [PHYSIO] The sum total of anabolic and catabolic activities of an organism in the resting state providing just enough energy to maintain vital functions.

basal rot [PL PATH] Any rot that affects the basal parts of a plant, especially bulbs.

basal wall [BOT] The wall dividing the oospore into an anterior and a posterior half in plants bearing archegonia.

basement membrane [HISTOL] A delicate connective-tissue layer underlying the epithelium of many organs.

basendite [INV ZOO] In crustaceans, either of a pair of lobes at the end of each specialized paired appendage.

base pairing [MOL BIO] The hydrogen bonding of complementary purine and pyrimidine bases—adenine with thymine, guanine with cytosine—in double-stranded deoxyribonucleic acids (DNA) or ribonucleic acids (RNA) or in DNA/RNA hybrid molecules.

base sequence [GEN] The specific order of purine and pyrimidine bases in a polynucleotide.

basichromatic [BIOL] Staining readily with basic dyes.

basidiocarp [MYCOL] The fruiting body of a fungus in the class Basidiomycetes.

Basidiolichenes [BOT] A class of the Lichenes characterized by the production of basidia.

Basidiomycetes [MYCOL] A class of fungi in the subdivision Eumycetes; important as food and as causal agents of plant diseases.

basidiophore [MYCOL] A basidia-bearing sporophore.

basidiospore [MYCOL] A spore produced by a basidium.

basidium [MYCOL] A cell, usually terminal, occurring in Basidiomycetes and producing spores (basidiospores) by nuclear fusion followed by meiosis.

basifixed [BOT] Attached at or near the base.

basil [BOT] The common name for any of the aromatic plants in the genus *Ocimum* of the mint family; leaves of the plant are used for food flavoring.

basilar [BIOL] Of, pertaining to, or situated at the base.

basilar groove [ANAT] The cavity which is located on the upper surface of the basilar process of the brain and upon which the medulla rests.

basilar membrane [ANAT] A membrane of the mammalian inner ear supporting the organ of Corti and separating two cochlear channels, the scala media and scala tympani.

basilar papilla [ANAT] 1. A sensory structure in the lagenar portion of an amphibian's membranous labyrinth between the oval and round windows. 2. The organ of Corti in mammals.

basilar plate [EMBRYO] An embryonic cartilaginous plate in vertebrates that is formed from the parachordals and anterior notochord and gives rise to the ethmoid and other bones of the skull.

basilar process [ANAT] A strong, quadrilateral plate of bone forming the anterior portion of the occipital bone, in front of the foramen magnum.

basilic vein [ANAT] The large superficial vein of the arm on the medial side of the biceps brachii muscle.

basin swamp [ECOL] A fresh-water swamp at the margin of a small calm lake, or near a large lake protected by shallow water or a barrier.

basion [ANAT] In craniometry, the point on the anterior margin of the foramen magnum where the midsagittal plane of the skull intersects the plane of the foramen magnum.

basipetal [BIOL] Movement or growth from the apex toward the base.

basipodite [INV ZOO] The distal segment of the protopodite of a biramous appendage in arthropods.

basipterygium [VERT ZOO] A basal bone or cartilage supporting one of the paired fins in fishes.

basisternum [INV ZOO] In insects, the anterior one of the two sternal skeletal plates.

basistyle [INV ZOO] Either of a pair of flexible processes on the hypopygium of certain male Diptera.

basitarsus [INV ZOO] The basal segment of the tarsus in arthropods.

basket cell [HISTOL] A type of cell in the cerebellum whose axis-cylinder processes terminate in a basketlike network around the cells of Purkinje.

basket star [INV ZOO] The common name for ophiuroid echinoderms belonging to the family Gorgonocephalidae.

Basommatophora [INV ZOO] An order of mollusks in the subclass Pulmonata containing many aquatic snails.

basonym [SYST] The original, validly published name of a taxon.

basophil [HISTOL] A white blood cell with granules that stain with basic dyes and are water-soluble.

basophilia [BIOL] An affinity for basic dyes.

basophilous [BIOL] Staining readily with the basic dyes.

basophilous [ECOL] Of plants, growing best in alkaline soils.

bass [VERT ZOO] The common name for a number of fishes assigned to two families, Centrarchidae and Serranidae, in the order Perciformes.

basset [VERT ZOO] A French breed of short-legged hunting dogs with long ears and a typical hound coat.

basswood [BOT] A common name for trees of the genus *Tilia* in the linden family of the order Malvales. Also known as linden.

bast *See* phloem.

bast fiber [BOT] Any fiber stripped from the inner bark of plants, such as flax, hemp, jute, and ramie; used in textile and paper manufacturing.

bat [VERT ZOO] The common name for all members of the mammalian order Chiroptera.

Batales [BOT] A small order of dicotyledonous plants in the subclass Caryophillidae of the class Magnoliopsida containing a single family with only one genus, *Batis*.

Batesian mimicry [ECOL] Resemblance of an innocuous species to one that is distasteful to predators.

Bathornithidae [PALEON] A family of Oligocene birds in the order Gruiformes.

Bathyctenidae [INV ZOO] A family of bathypelagic coelenterates in the phylum Ctenophora.

Bathyergidae [VERT ZOO] A family of mammals, including the South African mole rats, in the order Rodentia.

Bathylaconoidei [VERT ZOO] A suborder of deep-sea fishes in the order Salmoniformes.

Bathynellacea [INV ZOO] An order of crustaceans in the superorder Syncarida found in subterranean waters in England and central Europe.

Bathynellidae [INV ZOO] The single family of the crustacean order Bathynellacea.

Bathypteroidae [VERT ZOO] A family of benthic, deep-sea fishes in the order Salmoniformes.

Bathysquillidae [INV ZOO] A family of mantis shrimps, with one genus (*Bathysquilla*) and two species, in the order Stomatopoda.

Batoidea [VERT ZOO] The skates and rays, an order of the subclass Elasmobranchii.

Batrachoididae [VERT ZOO] The single family of the order Batrachoidiformes.

Batrachoidiformes [VERT ZOO] The toadfishes, an order of teleostean fishes in the subclass Actinopterygii.

battery of genes [GEN] The set of producer genes which is activated when a particular sensor gene activates its set of integrator genes.

bay [BOT] *Laurus nobilis*. An evergreen tree of the laurel family.

bayberry [BOT] 1. *Pimenta acris*. A West Indian tree related to the allspice; a source of bay oil. Also known as bay-rum tree; Jamaica bayberry; wild cinnamon. 2. Any tree of the genus *Myrica*.

bay-rum tree *See* bayberry.

Bdelloidea [INV ZOO] An order of the class Rotifera comprising animals which resemble leeches in body shape and manner of locomotion.

Bdellomorpha [INV ZOO] An order of ribbonlike worms in the class Enopla containing the single genus *Malacobdella*.

Bdellonemertini [INV ZOO] An equivalent name for the Bdellomorpha.

Bdellovibrio [MICROBIO] A genus of bacteria of uncertain affiliation; parasites of other bacteria; curved, motile rods with a polar flagellum in parasitic state; in nonparasitic state, cells are helical.

beak [BOT] Any pointed projection, as on some fruits, that resembles a bird bill. [INV ZOO] The tip of the umbo in bivalves. [VERT ZOO] 1. The bill of a bird or some other animal, such as the turtle. 2. A projecting jawbone element of certain fishes, such as the sawfish and pike.

bean [BOT] The common name for various leguminous plants used as food for humans and livestock; important commercial beans are true beans (*Phaseolus*) and California blackeye (*Vigna sinensis*).

bean anthracnose [PL PATH] A fungus disease of the bean caused by *Colletotrichum lindemuthianum*, producing pink to brown lesions on the pod and seed and dark discolorations on the veins on the lower surface of the leaf.

bean blight [PL PATH] A bacterial disease of the bean caused by *Xanthomonas phaseoli*, producing water-soaked lesions that become yellowish-brown spots on all plant parts.

bear [VERT ZOO] The common name for a few species of mammals in the family Ursidae.

beard *See* awn.

beaver [VERT ZOO] The common name for two different and unrelated species of rodents, the mountain beaver (*Aplodontia rufa*) and the true or common beaver (*Castor canadensis*).

bedbug [INV ZOO] The common name for a number of species of household pests in the insect family Cimicidae that infest bedding, and by biting humans obtain blood for nutrition.

Bedsonia [MICROBIO] The psittacosis-lymphogranuloma-trachoma (PLT) group of bacteria belonging to the Chlamydozoaceae; all are obligatory intracellular parasites.

bee [INV ZOO] Any of the membranous-winged insects which compose the superfamily Apoidea in the order Hymenoptera characterized by a hairy body and by sucking and chewing mouthparts.

beech [BOT] Any of various deciduous trees of the genus *Fagus* in the beech family (Fagaceae) characterized by smooth gray bark, triangular nuts enclosed in burs, and hard wood with a fine grain.

beech bark disease [PL PATH] A disease of beech caused by the beech scale (*Cryptococcus fagi*) and a fungus (*Nectria coccinea faginata*) acting together; bark is destroyed, foliage wilts, and the tree eventually dies.

beehive [INV ZOO] A colony of bees.

beet [BOT] *Beta vulgaris.* The red or garden beet, a cool-season biennial of the order Caryophyllales grown for its edible, enlarged fleshy root.

beetle [INV ZOO] The common name given to members of the insect order Coleoptera.

Beggiatoa [MICROBIO] A genus of bacteria in the family Beggiatoaceae; filaments are individual, and cells contain sulfur granules when grown on media containing hydrogen sulfide.

Beggiatoaceae [MICROBIO] A family of bacteria in the order Cytophagales; cells are in chains in colorless, flexible, motile filaments; microcysts are not known.

Beggiatoales [MICROBIO] Formerly an order of motile, filamentous bacteria in the class Schizomycetes.

Begoniaceae [BOT] A family of dicotyledonous plants in the order Violales characterized by an inferior ovary, unisexual flowers, stipulate leaves, and two to five carpels.

Beijerinckia [MICROBIO] A genus of bacteria in the family Azotobacteraceae; slightly curved or pear-shaped rods with large, refractile lipoid bodies at the ends of the cell.

Belemnoidea [PALEON] An order of extinct dibranchiate mollusks in the class Cephalopoda.

Belinuracea [PALEON] An extinct group of horseshoe crabs; arthropods belonging to the Limulida.

belladonna [BOT] *Atropa belladonna.* A perennial poisonous herb that belongs to the family Solanaceae; atropine is produced from the roots and leaves; used as an antispasmodic, as a cardiac and respiratory stimulant, and to check secretions. Also known as deadly nightshade.

Bellerophontacea [PALEON] A superfamily of extinct gastropod mollusks in the order Aspidobranchia.

Bell's law [PHYSIO] 1. The law that in the spinal cord the ventral roots are motor and the dorsal roots sensory in function. 2. The law that in a reflex arc the nerve impulse can be conducted in one direction only.

belly [ANAT] 1. The abdominal cavity or the abdomen. 2. The most prominent, fleshy, central portion of a muscle.

Beloniformes [VERT ZOO] The former ordinal name for a group of fishes now included in the order Atheriniformes.

Belostomatidae [INV ZOO] The giant water bugs, a family of hemipteran insects in the subdivision Hydrocorisae.

belt [ECOL] 1. Any altitudinal vegetation zone or band from the base to the summit of a mountain. 2. Any benthic vegetation zone or band from sea level to the ocean depths. 3. Any of the concentric vegetation zones around bodies of fresh water.

Benger unit [BIOL] A unit for the standardization of hyaluronidase.

Bennettitales [PALEOBOT] An equivalent name for the Cycadeoidales.

Bennettitatae [PALEOBOT] A class of fossil gymnosperms in the order Cycadeoidales.

benthos [ECOL] Bottom-dwelling forms of marine life. Also known as bottom fauna.

2,3-benzopyrrole *See* indole.

benzyl penicillin potassium [MICROBIO] $C_{16}H_{17}KN_2O_4S$ Moderately hygroscopic crystals; soluble in water; inactivated by acids and alkalies; obtained from fermentation of *Penicillium chrysogenum*; used as an antimicrobial drug in human and animal disease. Also known as penicillin G_1 potassium; potassium benzyl penicillinate; potassium penicillin G_1.

benzyl penicillin sodium [MICROBIO] $C_{16}H_{17}N_2NaO_4S$ Crystals obtained from a methanolethyl acetate acidified extract of fermentation broth of *Penicillium chrysogenum*; used as an antimicrobial in human and animal disease. Also known as penicillin; sodium benzyl penicillinate; sodium penicillin G_1.

Berberidaceae [BOT] A family of dicotyledonous herbs and shrubs in the order Ranunculales characterized by alternate leaves, perfect, well-developed flowers, and a seemingly solitary carpel.

Bergmann's rule [ECOL] The principle that in a polytypic wide-ranging species of warm-blooded animals the average body size of members of each geographic race varies with the mean environmental temperature.

Bergman-Turner unit [BIOL] A unit for the standardization of thyroid extract.

Berkefeld filter [MICROBIO] A diatomaceous-earth filter used for sterilization of heat-labile liquids, such as blood serum, enzyme solutions, and antibiotics.

Bermuda grass [BOT] *Cynodon dactylon.* A long-lived perennial in the order Cyperales.

Beroida [INV ZOO] The single order of the class Nuda in the phylum Ctenophora.

berry [BOT] A usually small, simple, fleshy or pulpy fruit, such as a strawberry, grape, tomato, or banana.

Bertrand's rule [MICROBIO] The rule stating that in those compounds, and only in those compounds, having cis secondary alcoholic groups containing at least one carbon atom of D configuration which is subtended by a primary alcohol group, or having a methyl-substituted primary alcohol group of D configuration, the D-carbon atom will be dehydrogenated by the vinegar bacteria *Acetobacter suboxydans*, yielding a ketone.

Beryciformes [VERT ZOO] An order of actinopterygian fishes in the infraclass Teleostei.

Berycomorphi [VERT ZOO] An equivalent name for the Beryciformes.

Berytidae [INV ZOO] The stilt bugs, a small family of hemipteran insects in the superfamily Pentatomorpha.

Bessey unit [BIOL] A unit for the standardization of phosphatase.

beta blocker [PHYSIO] An adrenergic blocking agent capable of blocking nerve impulses to special sites (beta receptors) in the cerebellum; reduces the rate of heartbeats and the force of heart contractions.

beta carotene [BIOCHEM] $C_{40}H_{56}$ A carotenoid hydrocarbon pigment found widely in nature, always associated with chlorophylls; converted to vitamin A in the liver of many animals.

beta cell [HISTOL] 1. Any of the basophilic chromophiles in the anterior lobe of the adenohypophysis. 2. One of the cells of the islets of Langerhans which produce insulin.

betacyanin [BIOCHEM] A group of purple plant pigments found in leaves, flowers, and roots of members of the order Caryophyllales.

beta globulin [BIOCHEM] A heterogeneous fraction of serum globulins containing transferrin and various complement components.

beta hemolysis [MICROBIO] A sharply defined, clear, colorless zone of hemolysis surrounding certain streptococci colonies growing on blood agar.

betalain [BIOCHEM] The name for a group of 35 red or yellow compounds found only in plants of the family Caryophyllales, including red beets, red chard, and cactus fruits.

betanin [BIOCHEM] An anthocyanin that contains nitrogen and constitutes the principal pigment of garden beets.

beta rhythm [PHYSIO] An electric current of low voltage from the brain, with a pulse frequency of 13–30/sec, encountered in a person who is aroused and anxious.

beta taxonomy [SYST] The level of taxonomic study dealing with the arrangement of species into lower and higher taxa.

betaxanthin [BIOCHEM] The name given to any of the yellow pigments found only in plants of the family Caryophyllales; they always occur with betacyanins.

betel nut [BOT] A dried, ripe seed of the palm tree *Areca catechu* in the family Palmae; contains a narcotic.

Bethylidae [INV ZOO] A small family of hymenopteran insects in the superfamily Bethyloidea.

Bethyloidea [INV ZOO] A superfamily of hymenopteran insects in the suborder Apocrita.

Betula [BOT] The birches, a genus of deciduous trees composing the family Betulaceae.

Betulaceae [BOT] A small family of dicotyledonous plants in the order Fagales characterized by stipulate leaves, seeds without endosperm, and by being monoecious with female flowers mostly in catkins.

Betz cell [HISTOL] Any of the large conical cells composing the major histological feature of the precentral motor cortex in humans.

Beyrichacea [PALEON] A superfamily of extinct ostracods in the suborder Beyrichicopina.

Beyrichicopina [PALEON] A suborder of extinct ostracods in the order Paleocopa.

Beyrichiidae [PALEON] A family of extinct ostracods in the superfamily Beyrichacea.

Bibionidae [INV ZOO] The March flies, a family of orthorrhaphous dipteran insects in the series Nematocera.

bicameral [BIOL] Having two chambers, as the heart of a fish.

bicapsular [BIOL] 1. Having two capsules. 2. Having a capsule with two locules.

bicarinate [BIOL] Having two keellike projections.

bicaudal [ZOO] Having two tails.

bicellular [BIOL] Having two cells.

bicephalous [ZOO] Having two heads.

biceps [ANAT] 1. A bicipital muscle. 2. The large muscle of the front of the upper arm that flexes the forearm; biceps brachii. 3. The thigh muscle that flexes the knee joint and extends the hip joint; biceps femoris.

biciliate [BIOL] Having two cilia.

bicipital [ANAT] 1. Pertaining to muscles having two origins. 2. Pertaining to ribs having double articulation with the vertebrae. [BOT] Having two heads or two supports.

bicipital groove *See* intertubercular sulcus.

bicipital tuberosity [ANAT] An eminence on the anterior inner aspect of the neck of the radius; the tendon of the biceps muscle is inserted here.

bicornuate uterus [ANAT] A uterus with two hornshaped processes on the superior aspect.

Bicosoecida [INV ZOO] An order of colorless, free-living protozoans, each member having two flagella, in the class Zoomastigophorea.

bicostate [BOT] Of a leaf, having two principal longitudinal ribs.

bicuspid [ANAT] Any of the four double-pointed premolar teeth in humans. [BIOL] Having two points or prominences.

Bidder's organ [VERT ZOO] A structure in the males of some toad species that may develop into an ovary in older individuals.

bidentate [BIOL] Having two teeth or teethlike processes.

biennial plant [BOT] A plant that requires two growing seasons to complete its life cycle.

bifacial [BOT] Of a leaf, having dissimilar tissues on the upper and lower surfaces.

bifanged [ANAT] Of a tooth, having two roots.

bifid [BIOL] Divided into two equal parts by a median cleft.

Bifidobacterium [MICROBIO] A genus of bacteria in the family Actinomycetaceae; branched, bifurcated, club-shaped or spatulate rods forming smooth microcolonies; metabolism is saccharoclastic.

biflabellate [INV ZOO] The shape of certain insect antennae, characterized by short joints with long, flattened processes on opposite sides.

biflagellate [BIOL] Having two flagella.

bifoliate [BOT] Two-leaved.

biforate [BIOL] Having two perforations.

big bud [PL PATH] 1. A parasitic disease of currants caused by a gall mite (*Eriophyes ribis*) and characterized by abnormal swelling of the buds. 2. A virus disease of the tomato characterized by swelling of the buds.

bigeminal pulse [PHYSIO] A pulse that is characterized by a double impulse produced by coupled heartbeats, that is, an extra heartbeat occurs just after the normal beat.

Bignoniaceae [BOT] A family of dicotyledonous trees or shrubs in the order Scrophulariales characterized by a corolla with mostly five lobes, mature seeds with little or no endosperm and with wings, and opposite or whorled leaves.

big vein [PL PATH] A soil-borne virus disease of lettuce characterized by enlargement and yellowing of the leaf veins.

bijugate [BOT] Of a pinnate leaf, having two pairs of leaflets.

bilabiate [BOT] Having two lips, such as certain corollas.

bilateral [BIOL] Of or relating to both right and left sides of an area, organ, or organism.

bilateral cleavage [EMBRYO] The division pattern of a zygote that results in a bilaterally symmetrical embryo.

bilateral hermaphroditism [ZOO] The presence of an ovary and a testis on each side of the animal body.

bilateral symmetry [BIOL] Symmetry such that the body can be divided by one median, or sagittal, dorsoventral plane into equivalent right and left halves, each a mirror image of the other.

Bilateria [ZOO] A major division of the animal kingdom embracing all forms with bilateral symmetry.

bile [PHYSIO] An alkaline fluid secreted by the liver and delivered to the duodenum to aid in the emulsification, digestion, and absorption of fats. Also known as gall.

bile acid [BIOCHEM] Any of the liver-produced steroid acids, such as taurocholic acid and glycocholic acid, that appear in the bile as sodium salts.

bile duct [ANAT] Any of the major channels in the liver through which bile flows toward the hepatic duct.

bile pigment [BIOCHEM] Either of two colored organic compounds found in bile: bilirubin and biliverdin.

bile salt [BIOCHEM] The sodium salt of glycocholic and taurocholic acids found in bile.

biliary system [ANAT] The complex of canaliculi, or microscopic bile ducts, that empty into the larger intrahepatic bile ducts.

bilicyanin [BIOCHEM] A blue pigment found in gallstones; an oxidation product of biliverdin or bilirubin.

bilification [PHYSIO] Formation and excretion of bile.

biliprotein [BIOCHEM] The generic name for the organic compounds in certain algae that are composed of phycobilin and a conjugated protein.

bilirubin [BIOCHEM] $C_{33}H_{36}N_4O_6$ An orange, crystalline pigment occurring in bile; the major metabolic breakdown product of heme.

biliverdin [BIOCHEM] $C_{33}H_{34}N_4O_6$ A green, crystalline pigment occurring in the bile of amphibians, birds, and humans; oxidation product of bilirubin in humans.

bill [INV ZOO] A flattened portion of the shell margin of the broad end of an oyster. [VERT ZOO] The jaws, together with the horny covering, of a bird. [ZOO] Any jawlike mouthpart.

Billingsellacea [PALEON] A group of extinct articulate brachiopods in the order Orthida.

bilobate [BIOL] Divided into two lobes.

bilobular [BIOL] Having two lobules.

bilocular [BIOL] Having two cells or compartments.

bilophodont [ZOO] Having two transverse ridges, as the molar teeth of certain animals.

bimaxillary [ZOO] Pertaining to the two halves of the maxilla.

binary fission [BIOL] A method of asexual reproduction accomplished by the splitting of a parent cell into two equal, or nearly equal, parts, each of which grows to parental size and form.

binate [BOT] Growing in pairs.

binaural hearing [PHYSIO] The perception of sound by stimulation of two ears.

binding site See active site.

binocular [BIOL] 1. Of, pertaining to, or used by both eyes. 2. Of a type of visual perception which provides depth-of-field focus due to angular difference between the two retinal images.

binocular accommodation [PHYSIO] Automatic lens adjustment by both eyes simultaneously for focusing on distant objects.

binomen [SYST] A binomial name assigned to species, as *Canis familiaris* for the dog.

binomial nomenclature [SYST] The Linnean system of classification requiring the designation of a binomen, the genus and species name, for every species of plant and animal.

binuclear [CELL BIO] Having two nuclei.

binucleolate [CELL BIO] Having two nucleoli.

bioacoustics [BIOL] The study of the relation between living organisms and sound.

bioastronautics [BIOL] The study of biological, behavioral, and medical problems pertaining to astronautics.

biobubble [ECOL] A model concept of the ecosphere in which all living things are considered as particles held together by nonliving forces.

biocatalyst [BIOCHEM] A biochemical catalyst, especially an enzyme.

biocenology [ECOL] The study of natural communities and of interactions among the members of these communities.

biocenose See biotic community.

biochemical oxygen demand [MICROBIO] The amount of dissolved oxygen required to meet the metabolic needs of anaerobic microorganisms in water rich in organic matter, such as sewage. Abbreviated BOD. Also known as biological oxygen demand.

biochemical oxygen demand test [MICROBIO] A standard laboratory procedure for measuring biochemical oxygen demand; standard measurement is made for 5 days at 20°C. Abbreviated BOD test.

biochemorphology [BIOCHEM] The science dealing with the chemical structure of foods and drugs and their reactions on living organisms.

biochore [ECOL] A group of similar biotopes.

biochrome [BIOCHEM] Any naturally occurring plant or animal pigment.

biochron [PALEON] A fossil of relatively short range of time.

bioclation [ECOL] A subdivision of a biome distinguished by the predominant animal species.

bioclimatic law [ECOL] The law which states that phenological events are altered by about 4 days for each 5° change of latitude northward or longitude eastward; events are accelerated in spring and retreat in autumn.

bioclimatograph [ECOL] A climatograph showing the relation between climatic conditions and some living organisms.

bioclimatology [ECOL] The study of the effects of the natural environment on living organisms.

biocoenosis [ECOL] A group of organisms that live closely together and form a natural ecologic unit.

biocycle [ECOL] A group of similar biotopes composing a major division of the biosphere; there are three biocycles: terrestrial, marine, and freshwater.

biocytin [BIOCHEM] $C_{16}H_{28}N_4O_4S$ Crystals with a melting point of 241–243°C; obtained from dilute methanol or acetone solutions; characterized by its utilization by *Lactobacillus casei* and *L. delbrückii* LD5 as a biotin source, and by its unavailability as a biotin source to *L. arabinosus*. Also known as biotin complex of yeast.

biocytinase [BIOCHEM] An enzyme present in the blood and liver which hydrolyzes biocytin into biotin and lysine.

biodynamic [BIOPHYS] Of or pertaining to the dynamic relation between an organism and its environment.

biodynamics [BIOPHYS] The study of the effects of dynamic processes (motion, acceleration, weightlessness, and so on) on living organisms.

bioelectric current [PHYSIO] A self-propagating electric current generated on the surface of nerve and muscle cells by potential differences across excitable cell membranes.

bioelectricity [PHYSIO] The generation by and flow of an electric current in living tissue.

bioelectric model [PHYSIO] A conceptual model for the study of animal electricity in terms of physical principles.

bioelectrochemistry [PHYSIO] The study of the control of biological growth and repair processes by electrical stimulation.

bioelectronics [BIOPHYS] The application of electronic theories and techniques to the problems of biology.

bioenergetics [BIOCHEM] The branch of biology dealing with energy transformations in living organisms.

bioflavonoid [BIOCHEM] A group of compounds obtained from the rinds of citrus fruits and involved with the homeostasis of the walls of small blood vessels; in guinea pigs a marked reduction of bioflavonoids results in increased fragility and permeability of the capillaries; used to decrease permeability and fragility in capillaries in certain conditions. Also known as citrus flavonoid compound; vitamin P complex.

biogenesis [BIOL] Development of a living organism from a similar living organism.

biogenetic law *See* recapitulation theory.

biogenic [BIOL] 1. Essential to the maintenance of life. 2. Produced by actions of living organisms.

biogeography [ECOL] The science concerned with the geographical distribution of animal and plant life.

biohydrology [ECOL] Study of the interactions between water, plants, and animals, including the effects of water on biota as well as the physical and chemical changes in water or its environment produced by biota.

biological [BIOL] Of or pertaining to life or living organisms.

biological balance [ECOL] Dynamic equilibrium that exists among members of a stable natural community.

biological clock [PHYSIO] Any physiologic factor that functions in regulating body rhythms.

biological control [ECOL] Natural or applied regulation of populations of pest organisms, especially insects, through the role or use of natural enemies.

biological equilibrium [BIOPHYS] A state of body balance for an actively moving animal, when internal and external forces are in equilibrium.

biological half-life [PHYSIO] The time required by the body to eliminate half of the amount of an administered substance through normal channels of elimination.

biological oil-spill control [ECOL] The use of cultures of microorganisms capable of living on oil as a means of degrading an oil slick biologically.

biological oxidation [BIOCHEM] Energy-producing reactions in living cells involving the transfer of hydrogen atoms or electrons from one molecule to another.

biological oxygen demand *See* biochemical oxygen demand.

biological productivity [ECOL] The quantity of organic matter or its equivalent in dry matter, carbon, or energy content which is accumulated during a given period of time.

biological shield [MICROBIO] A structure designed to prevent the migration of living organisms from one part of a system to another; used on sterilized space probes.

biological specificity [BIOL] The principle that defines the orderly patterns of metabolic and developmental reactions giving rise to the unique characteristics of the individual and of its species.

biological value [BIOCHEM] A measurement of the efficiency of the protein content in a food for the maintenance and growth of the body tissues of an individual.

bioluminescence [BIOL] The emission of visible light by living organisms.

biolysis [BIOL] 1. Death and the following tissue disintegration. 2. Decomposition of organic materials, such as sewage, by living organisms.

biomass [ECOL] The dry weight of living matter, including stored food, present in a species population and expressed in terms of a given area or volume of the habitat.

biome [ECOL] A complex biotic community covering a large geographic area and characterized by the distinctive life-forms of important climax species.

biomechanics [BIOPHYS] The study of the mechanics of living things.

biomere [ECOL] A biostratigraphic unit bounded by abrupt nonevolutionary changes in the dominant elements of a single phylum.

biometeorology [BIOL] The study of the relationship between living organisms and atmospheric phenomena.

bion [ECOL] An independent, individual organism.

bionavigation [VERT ZOO] The ability of animals such as birds to find their way back to their roost, even if the landmarks on the outward-bound trip were effectively concealed from them.

biophagous [ZOO] Feeding on living organisms.

biophile [BIOCHEM] Any element concentrated or found in the bodies of living organisms and organic matter; examples are carbon, nitrogen, and oxygen.

biopolymer [BIOCHEM] A biological macromolecule such as a protein or nucleic acid.

biopotency [BIOCHEM] Capacity of a chemical substance, as a hormone, to function in a biological system.

biopotential [PHYSIO] Voltage difference measured between points in living cells, tissues, and organisms.

biorheology [BIOPHYS] The study of the deformation and flow of biological fluids, such as blood, mucus, and synovial fluid.

bioseries [EVOL] A historical sequence produced by the changes in a single hereditary character.

biosonar [PHYSIO] A guidance system in certain animals, such as bats, utilizing the reflection of sounds that they produce as they move about.

biosphere [ECOL] The life zone of the earth, including the lower part of the atmosphere, the hydrosphere, soil, and the lithosphere to a depth of about 2 kilometers.

biostasy [ECOL] Maximum development of organisms when, during tectonic repose, residual soils form extensively on the land and calcium carbonate deposition is widespread in the sea.

biostratigraphy [PALEON] A part of paleontology concerned with the study of the conditions and deposition order of sedimentary rocks.

biosynthesis [BIOCHEM] Production, by synthesis or degradation, of a chemical compound by a living organism.

biota [BIOL] 1. Animal and plant life characterizing a given region. 2. Flora and fauna, collectively.

biotic [BIOL] 1. Of or pertaining to life and living organisms. 2. Induced by the actions of living organisms.

biotic community [ECOL] An aggregation of organisms characterized by a distinctive combination of both animal and plant species in a particular habitat. Also known as biocenose.

biotic district [ECOL] A subdivision of a biotic province.

biotic environment [ECOL] That environment comprising living organisms, which interact with each other and their abiotic environment.

biotic isolation [ECOL] The occurrence of organisms in isolation from others of their species.

biotic potential [ECOL] The maximum possible growth rate of living things under ideal conditions.

biotic province [ECOL] A community, according to some systems of classification, occupying an area where similarity of climate, physiography, and soils leads to the recurrence of similar combinations of organisms.

biotin [BIOCHEM] $C_{10}H_{16}N_2O_3S$ A colorless, crystalline vitamin of the vitamin B complex occurring widely in nature, mainly in bound form.

biotin carboxylase [BIOCHEM] An enzyme which condenses bicarbonate with biotin to form carboxybiotin.

biotin complex of yeast *See* biocytin.

biotope [ECOL] An area of uniform environmental conditions and biota.

biotype [GEN] A group of organisms having the same genotype.

biozone [PALEON] The range of a single taxonomic entity in geologic time as reflected by its occurrence in fossiliferous rocks.

biparasitic [ECOL] Parasitic upon or in a parasite.

biparous [BOT] Bearing branches on dichotomous axes. [VERT ZOO] Bringing forth two young at a birth.

bipartite uterus [ANAT] A uterus divided into two parts almost to the base.

bipectinate [INV ZOO] Of the antennae of certain moths, having two margins with comblike teeth. [ZOO] Branching like a feather on both sides of a main shaft.

biped [VERT ZOO] 1. A two-footed animal. 2. Any two legs of a quadruped.

bipedal [BIOL] Having two feet.

bipedal dinosaur [PALEON] A dinosaur having two long, stout hindlimbs for walking and two relatively short forelimbs.

bipeltate [BOT] Having two shield-shaped parts. [ZOO] Having a shell or other covering resembling a double shield.

bipenniform [ANAT] Of the arrangement of muscle fibers, resembling a feather barbed on both sides.

biphasic [BOT] Possessing both a sporophyte and a gametophyte generation in the life cycle.

biphyletic [EVOL] Descended in two branches from a common ancestry.

Biphyllidae [INV ZOO] The false skin beetles, a family of coleopteran insects in the superfamily Cucujoidea.

bipinnaria [INV ZOO] The complex, bilaterally symmetrical, free-swimming larval stage of most asteroid echinoderms.

bipinnate [BOT] Pertaining to a leaf that is pinnate for both its primary and secondary divisions.

bipolar flagellation [MICROBIO] The presence of flagella at both poles in certain bacteria.

Bipolarina [INV ZOO] A suborder of protozoan parasites in the order Myxosporida.

bipotential [BIOL] Having the potential to develop in either of two mutually exclusive directions.

bipotentiality [BIOL] 1. Capacity to function either as male or female. 2. Hermaphroditism.

biradial symmetry [BIOL] Symmetry both radial and bilateral. Also known as disymmetry.

biramous [BIOL] Having two branches, such as an arthropod appendage.

birch [BOT] The common name for all deciduous trees of the genus *Betula* that compose the family Betulaceae in the order Fagales.

bird [VERT ZOO] Any of the warm-blooded vertebrates which make up the class Aves.

bird's eye rot [PL PATH] A fungus disease of the grape caused by *Elsinoe ampelina* and characterized by small, dark, sunken spots with light centers on the fruit.

bird's eye spot [PL PATH] 1. A plant disease characterized by dark, round spots surrounded by lighter tissue. 2. A fungus disease of tea leaves caused by *Orcospora theae*. 3. A leaf spot of the hevea rubber tree caused by the fungus *Helminthosporium heveae*.

bird-hipped dinosaur [PALEON] Any member of the order Ornithischia, distinguished by the birdlike arrangement of their hipbones.

bird louse [INV ZOO] The common name for any insect of the order Mallophaga. Also known as biting louse.

bird of prey [VERT ZOO] Any of various carnivorous birds of the orders Falconiformes and Strigiformes which feed on meat taken by hunting.

Bird unit [BIOL] Unit for the standardization of leuteotropin.

birimose [BOT] Opening by two slits, as an anther.

birotulate [INV ZOO] A sponge spicule characterized by two wheel-shaped ends.

birth [BIOL] The emergence of a new individual from the body of its parent.

birth canal [ANAT] The channel in mammals through which the fetus is expelled during parturition; consists of the cervix, vagina, and vulva.

birth rate [BIOL] The ratio between the number of live births and a specified number of people in a population over a given period of time.

biserial [BIOL] Arranged in two rows or series.

biserrate [BIOL] 1. Having serrated serrations. 2. Serrate on both sides.

bisexual [BIOL] Of or relating to two sexes.

bison [VERT ZOO] The common name for two species of the family Bovidae in the order Artiodactyla; the wisent or European bison (*Bison bonasus*), and the American species (*Bison bison*).

bisporangiate [BOT] Having two different types of sporangia.

bispore [BOT] In certain red algae, an asexual spore that is produced in pairs.

bite [BIOL] 1. To seize with the teeth. 2. Closure of the lower teeth against the upper teeth.

bitegmic [BOT] Having two integuments, especially in reference to ovules.

biternate [BOT] Of a ternate leaf, having each division ternate.

biting louse See bird louse.

bittern [VERT ZOO] Any of various herons of the genus *Botaurus* characterized by streaked and speckled plumage.

bitter pit [PL PATH] A disease of uncertain etiology affecting apple, pear, and quince; spots of dead brown tissue appear in the flesh of the fruit and discolored depressions are seen on its surface. Also known as Baldwin spot; stippen.

bitter rot [PL PATH] A fungus disease of apples, grapes, and other fruit caused by *Glomerella cingulata*.

bivalent chromosome [CELL BIO] The structure formed following synapsis of a pair of homologous chromosomes from the zygotene stage of meiosis up to the beginning of anaphase.

bivalve [INV ZOO] The common name for a number of diverse, bilaterally symmetrical animals, including mollusks, ostracod crustaceans, and brachiopods, having a soft body enclosed in a calcareous two-part shell.

Bivalvia [INV ZOO] A large class of the phylum Mollusca containing the clams, oysters, and other bivalves.

biventer [ANAT] A muscle having two bellies.

bivittate [ZOO] Having a pair of longitudinal stripes.

bivium [INV ZOO] The pair of starfish rays that extend on either side of the madreporite.

bivoltine [INV ZOO] 1. Having two broods in a season, used especially for silkworms. 2. Of insects, producing two generations a year.

blackberry [BOT] Any of the upright or trailing shrubs of the genus *Rubus* in the order Rosales; an edible berry is produced by the plant.

blackbird [VERT ZOO] Any bird species in the family Icteridae, of which the males are predominantly or totally black.

black blight [PL PATH] Any of several diseases of tropical plants caused by superficial sooty molds.

black canker See ink disease.

black chaff [PL PATH] A bacterial disease of wheat caused by *Xanthomonas translucens undulosa* and characterized by dark, longitudinal stripes on the chaff.

black coral [INV ZOO] The common name for antipatharian coelenterates having black, horny axial skeletons.

black end [PL PATH] 1. A disease of the pear marked by blackening of the epidermis and flesh in the region of the calyx; believed to be a result of a disturbed water relation. 2. A fungus disease of the banana caused by several species, especially *Gloesporium musarum*, characterized by discoloration of the stem of the fruit.

blackeye bean See cowpea.

blackfire [PL PATH] A bacterial disease of tobacco caused by *Pseudomonas angulata* and characterized by angular leaf spots which gradually darken and may fall out, leaving ragged holes.

blackhead disease [PL PATH] 1. A parasitic disease of the banana caused by eelworms of the family Tylenchidae. 2. A rot disease of the banana rootstock that is caused by the fungus *Thielaviopsis paradoxa*.

black kernel [PL PATH] A fungus disease of rice caused by *Curvularia lunata* and characterized by dark discoloration of the kernels.

black knot [PL PATH] A fungus disease of certain fruit and nut trees that is characterized by black excrescences on the branches; destructive to plum, cherry, gooseberry, filbert, and hazel.

black line [PL PATH] A disease of walnuts, especially of English varieties grafted to black walnuts, characterized by a black line of dead tissue at the graft union, eventually leading to death of the tree.

black measles [PL PATH] A disease of California grapevines of uncertain etiology; characterized by black spotting of the skin of the fruit, browning and dropping of the leaves, and dying back of the canes from the tip.

black mold [MYCOL] Any dark fungus belonging to the order Mucorales. [PL PATH] A fungus disease of rose grafts and onion bulbs marked by black appearance due to the mold.

blacknose [PL PATH] A physiological disease of the date, with the distal end of the fruit becoming dark, cracking, and shriveling.

black patch [PL PATH] A fungus disease of red clover characterized by simultaneous blackening of plants in groups.

black pod [PL PATH] A pod rot of cacao caused by the fungus *Phytophthora faveri*.

black point [PL PATH] A disease of wheat and other cereals characterized by blackening of the embryo ends of the grains.

black ring [PL PATH] 1. A virus disease of cabbage and other members of the family Cruciferae characterized by dark necrotic and often sunken rings on the surface of the leaf. 2. A virus disease of the tomato characterized in the early stage by small black rings on young leaves.

black root [PL PATH] Any plant disease characterized by black discolorations of the roots.

black root rot [PL PATH] 1. Any of several plant diseases characterized by dark lesions of the root. 2. A fungus disease of the apple caused by *Xylaria mali*. 3. A fungus disease of tobacco and other plants caused by *Thielaviopsis basicola*.

black rot [PL PATH] Any fungal or bacterial disease of plants characterized by dark brown discoloration and decay of a plant part.

black shank [PL PATH] A black rot disease of tobacco caused by *Phytophthora parasitica* var. *nicotianae*.

black spot [PL PATH] Any bacterial or fungal disease of plants characterized by black spots on a plant part.

black stem [PL PATH] Any of several fungal diseases of plants characterized by blackening of the stem.

black stripe See black thread.

black thread [PL PATH] A fungus disease affecting the para rubber tree at the point where the tree is tapped, caused by *Phytophthora meadii* and characterized by black stripes extending through the exposed bast into the cambium or wood. Also known as black stripe; stripe canker.

black tip [PL PATH] Any of several plant diseases characterized by dark necrotic areas at the tip of the seed or fruit.

bladder [ANAT] Any saclike structure in humans and animals, such as a swimbladder or urinary bladder, that contains a gas or functions as a receptacle for fluid.

bladder cell [INV ZOO] Any of the large vacuolated cells in the outer layers of the tunic in some tunicates.

blade [BOT] The broad, flat portion of a leaf. [VERT ZOO] A single plate of baleen.

blast cell [HISTOL] An undifferentiated precursor of a human blood cell in the reticuloendothelial tissue.

blastema [EMBRYO] 1. A mass of undifferentiated protoplasm capable of growth and differentiation. 2. See anlage.

blasto- [EMBRYO] A germ or bud, with reference to early embryonic stages of development.

Blastobacter [MICROBIO] A genus of budding bacteria; cells are rod-, wedge-, or club-shaped, and several attach at the narrow end to form a rosette; reproduce by budding at the rounded end.

Blastobasidae [INV ZOO] A family of lepidopteran insects in the superfamily Tineoidea.

blastocarpous [BOT] Germinating in the pericarp.

blastochyle [EMBRYO] The fluid filling the blastocoele.

Blastocladiales [MYCOL] An order of aquatic fungi in the class Phycomycetes.

blastocoele [EMBRYO] The cavity of a blastula. Also known as segmentation cavity.

blastocone [EMBRYO] An incomplete blastomere.

blastocyst [EMBRYO] A modified blastula characteristic of placental mammals.

blastocyte [EMBRYO] An embryonic cell that is undifferentiated. [INV ZOO] An undifferentiated cell capable of replacing damaged tissue in certain lower animals.

blastoderm [EMBRYO] The blastodisk of a fully formed vertebrate blastula.

blastodisk [EMBRYO] The embryo-forming, protoplasmic disk on the surface of a yolk-filled egg, such as in reptiles, birds, and some fish.

Blastoidea [PALEON] A class of extinct pelmatozoan echinoderms in the subphylum Crinozoa.

blastokinesis [INV ZOO] Movement of the embryo into the yolk in some insect eggs.

blastomere [EMBRYO] A cell of a blastula.

blastophore [CELL BIO] The cytoplasm that is detached from a spermatid during its transformation to a spermatozoon. [INV ZOO] An amorphose core of cytoplasm connecting cells of the male morula of developing germ cells in oligochaetes.

blastopore [EMBRYO] The opening of the archenteron. [MYCOL] A fungal resting spore that arises by budding.

blastostyle [INV ZOO] A zooid on certain hydroids that lacks a mouth and tentacles and functions to produce medusoid buds.

blastotomy [EMBRYO] Separation of cleavage cells during early embryogenesis.

blastozooid [INV ZOO] A zooid produced by budding.

blastula [EMBRYO] A hollow sphere of cells characteristic of the early metazoan embryo.

blastulation [EMBRYO] Formation of a blastula from a solid ball of cleaving cells.

Blattabacterium [MICROBIO] A genus of the tribe Wolbachiae; straight or slightly curved rod-shaped cells; symbiotic in cockroaches.

Blattidae [INV ZOO] The cockroaches, a family of insects in the order Orthoptera.

bleeding canker [PL PATH] A fungus disease of hardwoods caused by *Phytophthora cactorum* and characterized by cankers which exude a reddish ooze on the trunk and branches.

bleeding disease [PL PATH] A fungus disease of the coconut palm caused by *Ceratostomella paradoxa*, characterized by a rust-colored exudation from cracks in the stem.

bleeding time [PHYSIO] The time required for bleeding to stop after a small puncture wound.

blending inheritance [GEN] Inheritance in which the character of the offspring is a blend of those in the parents; a common feature for quantitative characters, such as stature, determined by large numbers of genes and affected by environmental variation.

Blenniidae [VERT ZOO] The blennies, a family of carnivorous marine fishes in the suborder Blennioidei.

Blennioidei [VERT ZOO] A large suborder of small marine fishes in the order Perciformes that live principally in coral and rock reefs.

Blephariceridae [INV ZOO] A family of dipteran insects in the suborder Orthorrhapha.

blepharoplast [MICROBIO] A cytoplasmic granule bearing a bacterial flagellum.

blight [PL PATH] Any plant disease or injury that results in general withering and death of the plant without rotting.

blight canker [PL PATH] A phase of fire blight characterized by cankers.

blind seed [PL PATH] A fungus disease of forage grasses caused by *Phealea temulenta*, resulting in abortion of the seed.

blind spot [PHYSIO] A place on the retina of the eye that is insensitive to light, where the optic nerve passes through the eyeball's inner surface.

blister blight [PL PATH] 1. A fungus disease of the tea plant caused by *Exobasidium vexans* and characterized by blisterlike lesions on the leaves. 2. A rust disease of Scotch pine caused by *Cronartium asclepiadeum* and characterized by blisterlike lesions on the twigs.

blister canker [PL PATH] A fungus disease of the apple tree caused by *Nummularia discreta* and characterized by rough, black cankers on the trunk and large branches. Also known as apple pox.

blister rust [PL PATH] Any of several diseases of pines caused by rust fungi of the genus *Cronartium;* the sapwood and inner bark are affected and blisters are produced externally.

blister spot [PL PATH] A bacterial disease of the apple caused by *Pseudomonas papulans* and characterized by dark-brown blisters on the fruit and cankers on the branches.

blocking [HISTOL] 1. The process of embedding tissue in a solid medium, such as paraffin. 2. A histochemical process in which a portion of a molecule is treated to prevent it from reacting with some other agent.

blood [HISTOL] A fluid connective tissue consisting of the plasma and cells that circulate in the blood vessels.

blood agar [MICROBIO] A nutrient microbiologic culture medium enriched with whole blood and used to detect hemolytic strains of bacteria.

blood cell [HISTOL] An erythrocyte or a leukocyte.

blood chimerism [GEN] Having red blood cells of two genetic types.

blood disease [PL PATH] A bacterial disease affecting the vascular tissues of the banana in the Celebes; believed to be caused by *Xanthomonas celebensis* and characterized by blighting of the leaves and reddish-brown rot of the fruit.

blood island [EMBRYO] One of the areas in the yolk sac of vertebrate embryos allocated to the production of the first blood cells.

blood-plate hemolysis [MICROBIO] Destruction of red blood cells in a blood agar medium by a bacterial toxin.

blood platelet *See* thrombocyte.

blood pressure [PHYSIO] Pressure exerted by blood on the walls of the blood vessels.

bloodstream [PHYSIO] The flow of blood in its circulation through the body.

blood sugar [BIOCHEM] The carbohydrate, principally glucose, of the blood.

blood vessel [ANAT] A tubular channel for blood transport.

bloom [BOT] 1. An individual flower. Also known as blossom. 2. To yield blossoms. 3. The waxy coating that appears as a powder on certain fruits, such as plums, and leaves, such as cabbage. [ECOL] A colored area on the surface of bodies of water caused by heavy planktonic growth.

blossom [BOT] *See* bloom.

blossom-end rot [PL PATH] 1. Any rot disease of fruit that originates at the blossom end. 2. A physiological disease of tomato believed to be caused by extreme fluctuations in available moisture; characterized by shallow leathery depressions with a water-soaked appearance around the tip end of the fruit.

blowball [BOT] A fluffy seed ball, as of the dandelion.

blowhole [VERT ZOO] The nostril on top of the head of cetacean mammals.

blowpipe [BIOL] A small tube, tapering to a straight or slightly curved tip, used in anatomy and zoology to reveal or clean a cavity.

blubber [INV ZOO] A large sea nettle or medusa. [VERT ZOO] A thick insulating layer of fat beneath the skin of whales and other marine mammals.

blueberry [BOT] Any of several species of plants in the genus *Vaccinium* of the order Ericales; the fruit, a berry, occurs in clusters on the plant.

bluefish [VERT ZOO] *Pomatomus saltatrix*. A predatory fish in the order Perciformes. Also known as skipjack.

bluegrass [BOT] The common name for several species of perennial pasture and lawn grasses in the genus *Poa* of the order Cyperales.

blue-green algae [BOT] The common name for members of the Cyanophyceae.

blue mold [MYCOL] Any fungus of the genus *Penicillium*.

blue rot [PL PATH] A fungus disease of conifers caused by members of the genus *Ceratostomella*, characterized by blue discoloration of the wood. Also known as bluing.

blue stain [PL PATH] A bluish stain of the sapwood of many trees that is caused by several fungi, especially of the genera *Fusarium*, *Ceratostomella*, and *Penicillium*.

bluestem grass [BOT] The common name for several species of tall, perennial grasses in the genus *Andropogon* of the order Cyperales.

bluing *See* blue rot.

BMR *See* basal metabolic rate.

boa [VERT ZOO] Any large, nonvenomous snake of the family Boidae in the order Squamata.

boar *See* wild boar.

Bobasatranidae [PALEON] A family of extinct palaeonisciform fishes in the suborder Platysomoidei.

BOD *See* biochemical oxygen demand.

Bodansky unit [BIOL] A unit for the standarization of phosphatase based on the activity of phosphatase toward β-glycerophosphate.

Bodonidae [INV ZOO] A family of protozoans in the order Kinetoplastida characterized by two unequally long flagella, one of them trailing.

BOD test *See* biochemical oxygen demand test.

body cavity [ANAT] The peritoneal, pleural, or pericardial cavities, or the cavity of the tunica vaginalis testis.

body rhythm [PHYSIO] Any bodily process having some degree of regular periodicity.

body-righting reflex [PHYSIO] A postural reflex, initiated by the asymmetric stimulation of the body surface by the weight of the body, so that the head tends to assume a horizontal position.

bog [ECOL] A plant community that develops and grows in areas with permanently waterlogged peat substrates. Also known as moor; quagmire.

bog moss [ECOL] Moss of the genus *Sphagnum* occurring as the characteristic vegetation of bogs.

Bohr effect [BIOCHEM] The effect of carbon dioxide and pH on the oxygen equilibrium of hemoglobin; increase in carbon dioxide prevents an increase in the release of oxygen from oxyhemoglobin.

Boidae [VERT ZOO] The boas, a family of nonvenomous reptiles of the order Squamata, having teeth on both jaws and hindlimb rudiments.

boil smut [PL PATH] A fungus disease of corn caused by *Ustilago maydis*, characterized by galls containing black spores.

boll [BOT] A pod or capsule (pericarp), as of cotton and flax.

boll rot [PL PATH] A fungus rot of cotton bolls caused by *Glomerella gossypii* and *Xanthomonas malvacearum*.

boll weevil [INV ZOO] A beetle, *Anthonomus grandis*, of the order Coleoptera; larvae destroy cotton plants and are the most important pests in agriculture.

bolus [PHYSIO] The mass of food prepared by the mouth for swallowing.

Bombacaceae [BOT] A family of dicotyledonous tropical trees in the order Malvales with dry or fleshy fruit usually having woolly seeds.

Bombidae [INV ZOO] A family of relatively large, hairy, black and yellow bumblebees in the hymenopteran superfamily Apoidea.

Bombycidae [INV ZOO] A family of lepidopteran insects of the superorder Heteroneura that includes only the silkworms.

Bombyliidae [INV ZOO] The bee flies, a family of dipteran insects in the suborder Orthorrhapha.

Bombyx [INV ZOO] The type genus of Bombycidae.

Bombyx mori [INV ZOO] The commercial silkworm.

bone [ANAT] One of the parts constituting a vertebrate skeleton. [HISTOL] A hard connective tissue that forms the major portion of the vertebrate skeleton.

bone conduction [BIOPHYS] Transmission of sound vibrations to the internal ear via the bones of the skull.

Bonellidae [INV ZOO] A family of wormlike animals belonging to the order Echiuroinea.

bone marrow [HISTOL] A vascular modified connective tissue occurring in the long bones and certain flat bones of vertebrates.

bony fish [VERT ZOO] The name applied to all members of the class Osteichthyes.

bony labyrinth [ANAT] The system of canals within the otic bones of vertebrates that houses the membranous labyrinth of the inner ear.

Boodleaceae [BOT] A family of green marine algae in the order Siphonocladales.

book gill [INV ZOO] A type of gill in king crabs consisting of folds of membranous tissue arranged like the leaves of a book.

book louse [INV ZOO] A common name for a number of insects belonging to the order Psocoptera; important pests in herbaria, museums, and libraries.

book lung [INV ZOO] A saccular respiratory organ in many arachnids consisting of numerous membranous folds arranged like the pages of a book.

Boopidae [INV ZOO] A family of lice in the order Mallophaga, parasitic on Australian marsupials.

Bopyridae [INV ZOO] A family of epicaridean isopods in the tribe Bopyrina known to parasitize decapod crustaceans.

Bopyrina [INV ZOO] A tribe of dioecious isopods in the suborder Epicaridea.

Bopyroidea [INV ZOO] An equivalent name for Epicaridea.

Boraginaceae [BOT] A family of flowering plants in the order Lamiales comprising mainly herbs and some tropical trees.

bordered [BOT] Having a margin with a distinctive color or texture; used especially of a leaf.

bordered pit [BOT] A wood-cell pit having the secondary cell wall arched over the cavity of the pit.

Bordetella [MICROBIO] A genus of gram-negative, aerobic bacteria of uncertain affiliation; minute coccobacilli, parasitic and pathogenic in the respiratory tract of mammals.

Bordetella parapertussis [MICROBIO] A small, nonmotile coccobacillus that causes parapertussis.

Bordetella pertussis [MICROBIO] A small, nonmotile coccobacillus that causes whooping cough.

Bordet-Gengou bacillus See Hemophilus pertussis.

boreal [ECOL] Of or relating to northern geographic regions.

Boreal life zone [ECOL] The zone comprising the climate and biotic communities between the Arctic and Transitional zones.

Borell unit [BIOL] A unit for the standardization of thyroid extracts.

borer [INV ZOO] Any insect or other invertebrate that burrows into wood, rock, or other substances.

Borhyaenidae [VERT ZOO] A family of carnivorous mammals in the superfamily Borhyaenoidea.

Borhyaenoidea [VERT ZOO] A superfamily of carnivorous mammals in the order Marsupialia.

boring sponge [INV ZOO] Marine sponge of the family Clionidae represented by species which excavate galleries in mollusks, shells, corals, limestone, and other calcareous matter.

Borrelia [MICROBIO] A genus of bacteria in the family Spirochaetaceae; helical cells with uneven coils and parallel fibrils coiled around the cell body for locomotion; many species cause relapsing fever in humans.

bosque See temperate and cold scrub.

Bostrichidae [INV ZOO] The powder-post beetles, a family of coleopteran insects in the superfamily Bostrichoidea.

Bostrichoidea [INV ZOO] A superfamily of beetles in the coleopteran suborder Polyphaga.

botanical garden [BOT] An institution for the culture of plants collected chiefly for scientific and educational purposes.

botany [BIOL] A branch of the biological sciences which embraces the study of plants and plant life.

bothridium [INV ZOO] A muscular holdfast organ, often with hooks, on the scolex of tetraphyllidean tapeworms.

Bothriocephaloidea [INV ZOO] The equivalent name for the Pseudophyllidea.

Bothriocidaroida [PALEON] An order of extinct echinoderms in the subclass Perischoechinoidea in which the ambulacra consist of two columns of plates, the interambulacra of one column, and the madreporite is placed radially.

bothrium [INV ZOO] A suction groove on the scolex of pseudophyllidean tapeworms.

Botrytis disease [PL PATH] Any of various fungus diseases of plants caused by fungi of the genus Botrytis; characterized by soft rotting.

bottle graft [BOT] A plant graft in which the scion is a detached branch and is protected from wilting by keeping the base of the branch in a bottle of water until union with the stock.

bottom break [BOT] A branch that arises from the base of a plant stem.

bottom rot [PL PATH] 1. A fungus disease of lettuce, caused by Pellicularia filamentosa, that spreads from the base upward. 2. A fungus disease of tree trunks caused by pore fungi.

botulin [MICROBIO] The neurogenic toxin which is produced by Clostridium botulinum and C. parabotulinum and causes botulism. Also known as botulinus toxin.

botulinus [MICROBIO] A bacterium that causes botulism.

botulinus toxin See botulin.

bough [BOT] A main branch on a tree.

Bourquin-Sherman unit [BIOL] A unit for the standardization of riboflavin.

bouton [ANAT] A club-shaped enlargement at the end of a nerve fiber. Also known as end bulb.

Bovidae [VERT ZOO] A family of pecoran ruminants in the superfamily Bovoidea containing the true antelopes, sheep, and goats.

bovine [VERT ZOO] 1. Any member of the genus Bos. 2. Resembling or pertaining to a cow or ox.

Bovoidea [VERT ZOO] A superfamily of pecoran ruminants in the order Artiodactyla comprising the pronghorns and bovids.

bowel [ANAT] The intestine.

bowfin [VERT ZOO] Amia calva. A fish recognized as the only living species of the family Amiidae. Also known as dogfish; grindle; mudfish.

Bowman's capsule [ANAT] A two-layered membranous sac surrounding the glomerulus and constituting the closed end of a nephron in the kidneys of all higher vertebrates.

brace root See prop root.

brachial [ZOO] Of or relating to an arm or armlike process.

brachial artery [ANAT] An artery which originates at the axillary artery and branches into the radial and ulnar arteries; it distributes blood to the various muscles of the arm, the shaft of the humerus, the elbow joint, the forearm, and the hand.

brachial cavity [INV ZOO] The anterior cavity which is located inside the valves of brachiopods and into which the brachia are withdrawn.

brachial plexus [ANAT] A plexus of nerves located in the neck and axilla and composed of the anterior rami of the lower four cervical and first thoracic nerves.

Brachiata [INV ZOO] A phylum of deuterostomous, sedentary bottom-dwelling marine animals that live encased in tubes.

brachiate [BOT] Possessing widely divergent branches. [ZOO] Having arms.

brachiolaria [INV ZOO] A transitional larva in the development of certain starfishes that is distinguished by three anterior processes homologous with those of the adult.

Brachiopoda [INV ZOO] A phylum of solitary, marine, bivalved coelomate animals.

brachioradialis [ANAT] The muscle of the arm that flexes the elbow joint; origin is the lateral supracondylar ridge of the humerus, and insertion is the lower end of the radius.

brachium [ANAT] The upper arm or forelimb, from the shoulder to the elbow. [INV ZOO] 1. A ray of a crinoid. 2. A tentacle of a cephalopod. 3. Either of the paired appendages constituting the lophophore of a brachiopod.

Brachyarchus [MICROBIO] A genus of bacteria of uncertain affiliation; rod-shaped cells bent in a bowlike configuration and usually arranged in groups of two, four, or more cells.

brachyblast [BOT] A short shoot often bearing clusters of leaves.

brachydont [ANAT] Of teeth, having short crowns, well-developed roots, and narrow root canals; characteristic of man.

Brachygnatha [INV ZOO] A subsection of brachyuran crustaceans to which most of the crabs are assigned.

Brachypsectridae [INV ZOO] A family of coleopteran insects in the superfamily Cantharoidea represented by a single species.

Brachypteraciidae [VERT ZOO] The ground rollers, a family of colorful Madagascan birds in the order Coraciiformes.

brachypterous [INV ZOO] Having rudimentary or abnormally small wings, referring to certain insects.

brachysclereid [BOT] A sclereid that is more or less isodiametric and is found in certain fruits and in the pith, cortex, and bark of many stems. Also known as stone cell.

brachysm [BOT] Plant dwarfing in which there is shortening of the internodes only.

Brachythoraci [PALEON] An order of the jointneck fishes, now extinct.

Brachyura [INV ZOO] The section of the crustacean order Decapoda containing the true crabs.

bracket fungus [MYCOL] A basidiomycete characterized by shelflike sporophores, sometimes seen on tree trunks.

Braconidae [INV ZOO] The braconid wasps, a family of hymenopteran insects in the superfamily Ichneumonoidea.

bract [BOT] A modified leaf associated with plant reproductive structures.

bracteolate [BOT] Having bracteoles.

bracteole [BOT] A small bract, especially if on the floral axis. Also known as bractlet.

bractlet *See* bracteole.

bradyauxesis [BIOL] Allometric growth in which a part lags behind the body as a whole in development.

bradykinin [BIOCHEM] $C_{50}H_{73}N_{15}O_{11}$ A polypeptide kinin; forms an amorphous precipitate in glacial acetic acid; released from plasma precursors by plasmin; acts as a vasodilator. Also known as callideic I; kallidin I.

Bradyodonti [PALEON] An order of Paleozoic cartilaginous fishes (Chondrichthyes), presumably derived from primitive sharks.

Bradypodidae [VERT ZOO] A family of mammals in the order Edentata comprising the true sloths.

bradytely [EVOL] Evolutionary change that is either arrested or occurring at a very slow rate over long geologic periods.

Bragg cell *See* acoustooptic modulator.

brain [ANAT] The portion of the vertebrate central nervous system enclosed in the skull. [ZOO] The enlarged anterior portion of the central nervous system in most bilaterally symmetrical animals.

braincase *See* cranium.

brain coral [INV ZOO] A reef-building coral resembling the human cerebrum in appearance.

brain hormone [INV ZOO] A neurohormone secreted by the insect brain that regulates the release of ecdysone from the prothoracic glands.

brainstem [ANAT] The portion of the brain remaining after the cerebral hemispheres and cerebellum have been removed.

brain wave [PHYSIO] A rhythmic fluctuation of voltage between parts of the brain, ranging from about 1 to 60 hertz and 10 to 100 microvolts.

bramble [BOT] 1. A plant of the genus *Rubus*. 2. A rough, prickly vine or shrub.

branch [BOT] A shoot or secondary stem on the trunk or a limb of a tree.

branched acinous gland [ANAT] A multicellular structure with saclike glandular portions connected to the surface of the containing organ or structure by a common duct.

branched tubular gland [ANAT] A multicellular structure with tube-shaped glandular portions connected to the surface of the containing organ or structure by a common secreting duct.

branchial [ZOO] Of or pertaining to gills.

branchial arch [VERT ZOO] One of the series of paired arches on the sides of the pharynx which support the gills in fishes and amphibians.

branchial basket [ZOO] A cartilaginous structure that supports the gills in protochordates and certain lower vertebrates such as cyclostomes.

branchial cleft [EMBRYO] A rudimentary groove in the neck region of air-breathing vertebrate embryos. [VERT ZOO] One of the openings between the branchial arches in fishes and amphibians.

branchial heart [INV ZOO] A muscular enlarged portion of a vein of a cephalopod that contracts and forces the blood into the gills.

branchial plume [INV ZOO] An accessory respiratory organ that extends out under the mantle in certain Gastropoda.

branchial pouch [ZOO] In cyclostomes and some sharks, one of the respiratory cavities occurring in the branchial clefts.

branchial sac [INV ZOO] In tunicates, the dilated pharyngeal portion of the alimentary canal that has vascular walls pierced with clefts and serves as a gill.

branchial segment [EMBRYO] Any of the paired pharyngeal segments indicating the visceral arches and clefts posterior to and including the third pair in air-breathing vertebrate embryos.

branchiate [VERT ZOO] Having gills.

branching adaptation See divergent adaptation.

branchiocranium [VERT ZOO] The division of the fish skull constituting the mandibular and hyal regions and the branchial arches.

branchiomere [EMBRYO] An embryonic metamere that will differentiate into a visceral arch and cleft; a branchial segment.

branchiomeric musculature [VERT ZOO] Those muscles derived from branchial segments in vertebrates.

Branchiopoda [INV ZOO] A subclass of crustaceans containing small or moderate-sized animals commonly called fairy shrimps, clam shrimps, and water fleas.

branchiostegite [INV ZOO] A gill cover and chamber in certain malacostracan crustaceans, formed by lateral expansion of the carapace.

Branchiostoma [ZOO] A genus of lancelets formerly designated as amphioxus.

Branchiotremata [INV ZOO] The hemichordates, a branch of the subphylum Oligomera.

Branchiura [INV ZOO] The fish lice, a subclass of fish ectoparasites in the class Crustacea.

Branhamella [MICROBIO] A genus of bacteria in the family Neisseriaceae; cocci occur in pairs with flattened adjacent sides; parasites of mammalian mucous membranes.

Brassica [BOT] A large genus of herbs in the family Cruciferae of the order Capparales, including cabbage, watercress, and sweet alyssum.

Brassicaceae [BOT] An equivalent name for the Cruciferae.

brassin [BIOCHEM] Any of a class of plant hormones characterized as long-chain fatty-acid esters; brassins act to induce both cell elongation and cell division in leaves and stems.

Brathinidae [INV ZOO] The grass root beetles, a small family of coleopteran insects in the superfamily Staphylinoidea.

Braulidae [INV ZOO] The bee lice, a family of cyclorrhaphous dipteran insects in the section Pupipara.

Brazil nut [BOT] *Bertholettia excelsa*. A large broad-leafed evergreen tree of the order Lecythidales; an edible seed is produced by the tree fruit.

breadfruit [BOT] *Artocarpus altilis*. An Indo-Malaysian tree, a species of the mulberry family (Moraceae). The tree produces a multiple fruit which is edible.

bread mold [MYCOL] Any fungus belonging to the family Mucoraceae in the order Mucorales.

breakage and reunion [CELL BIO] The classical model of crossing over by means of physical breakage and crossways reunion of completed chromatids during the process of meiosis.

breast [ANAT] The human mammary gland.

breathing [PHYSIO] Inhaling and exhaling.

breeding [GEN] Controlled mating and selection, or hybridization of plants and animals in order to improve the species.

bregma [ANAT] The point at which the coronal and sagittal sutures of the skull meet.

Brentidae [INV ZOO] The straight-snouted weevils, a family of coleopteran insects in the superfamily Curculionoidea.

Brevibacteriaceae [MICROBIO] Formerly a family of gram-positive, rod-shaped, schizomycetous bacteria in the order Eubacteriales.

Brevibacterium [MICROBIO] A genus of short, unbranched, rod-shaped bacteria in the coryneform group.

brevitoxin [BIOCHEM] One of several icthyotoxins produced by the dinoflagellate *Ptychodiscus brevis*.

Brewer anaerobic jar [MICROBIO] A glass container in which petri dish cultures are stacked and maintained under anaerobic conditions.

bridge graft [BOT] A plant graft in which each of several scions is grafted in two positions on the stock, one above and the other below an injury.

Brisingidae [INV ZOO] A family of deep-water echinoderms with as many as 44 arms, belonging to the order Forcipulatida.

bristle [BIOL] A short stiff hair or hairlike structure on an animal or plant.

brittle star [INV ZOO] The common name for all members of the echinoderm class Ophiuroidea.

broadleaf tree [BOT] Any deciduous or evergreen tree having broad, flat leaves.

broad-spectrum antibiotic [MICROBIO] An antibiotic that is effective against both gram-negative and gram-positive bacterial species.

broccoli [BOT] *Brassica oleracea* var. *italica*. A biennial crucifer of the order Capparales which is grown for its edible stalks and buds.

Brodmann's area 17 See visual projection area.

Brodmann's area 4 See motor area.

Brodmann's areas [PHYSIO] Numbered regions of the cerebral cortex used to identify cortical functions.

bromatium [ECOL] A swollen hyphal tip on fungi growing in ants nests that is eaten by the ants.

bromegrass [BOT] The common name for a number of forage grasses of the genus *Bromus* in the order Cyperales.

bromelain [BIOCHEM] An enzyme that digests protein and clots milk; prepared by precipitation by acetone from pineapple juice; used to tenderize meat, to chill-proof beer, and to make protein hydrolysates. Also spelled bromelin.

Bromeliaceae [BOT] The single family of the flowering plant order Bromeliales.

Bromeliales [BOT] An order of monocotyledonous plants in the subclass Commelinidae, including terrestrial xerophytes and some epiphytes.

bromelin *See* bromelain.

bromouracil [BIOCHEM] $C_4H_3N_2O_2Br$ 5-Bromouracil, an analog of thymine that can react with deoxyribonucleic acid to produce a polymer with increased susceptibility to mutation.

bromuration [HISTOL] A process in which a tissue section is treated with a solution of bromine or a bromine compound.

bronchial tree [ANAT] The arborization of the bronchi of the lung, considered as a structural and functional unit.

bronchiole [ANAT] A small, thin-walled branch of a bronchus, usually terminating in alveoli.

bronchus [ANAT] Either of the two primary branches of the trachea or any of the bronchi's pulmonary branches having cartilage in their walls.

Brontotheriidae [PALEON] The single family of the extinct mammalian superfamily Brontotherioidea.

Brontotherioidea [PALEON] The titanotheres, a superfamily of large, extinct perissodactyl mammals in the suborder Hippomorpha.

brood [BOT] Heavily infested by insects. [ZOO] 1. The young of animals. 2. To incubate eggs or cover the young for warmth. 3. An animal kept for breeding.

brood capsule [INV ZOO] A secondary scolex-containing cyst constituting the infective agent of a tapeworm.

brood parasitism [ECOL] A type of social parasitism among birds characterized by a bird of one species laying and abandoning its eggs in the nest of a bird of another species.

brood pouch [VERT ZOO] A pouch of an animal body where eggs or embryos undergo certain stages of development.

Brotulidae [VERT ZOO] A family of benthic teleosts in the order Perciformes.

brown algae [BOT] The common name for members of the Phaeophyta.

brown bast [PL PATH] A physiological disease of the para rubber tree characterized by grayish- or greenish-brown discolorations of the inner bark near the tapping cut.

brown blight [PL PATH] A virus disease of lettuce characterized by spots and streaks on the leaves, reduction in leaf size, and gradual browning of the foliage, beginning at the base.

brown blotch [PL PATH] 1. A bacterial disease of mushrooms caused by *Pseudomonas tolaasi* and characterized by brown blotchy discolorations. 2. A fungus disease of the pear characterized by brown blotches on the fruit.

brown canker [PL PATH] A fungus disease of roses caused by *Cryptosporella embrina* and characterized by lesions that are initially purple and gradually become buff.

brown fat cell [HISTOL] A moderately large, generally spherical cell in adipose tissue that has small fat droplets scattered in the cytoplasm.

brown felt blight [PL PATH] A fungus disease of conifers caused by several Ascomycetes, especially *Herpotrichia nigra* and *Neopeckia coul-*

teri; a dense felty growth of brown or black mycelia forms on the branches.

browning [PL PATH] Any plant disorder or disease marked by brown discoloration of a part. Also known as stem break.

brown leaf rust [PL PATH] A fungus disease of rye caused by *Puccinia dispersa.*

brown patch [PL PATH] A fungus disease of grasses in golf greens and lawns caused by various soil-inhabiting species, typically producing brown circular areas surrounded by a band of grayish-black mycelia.

brown root [PL PATH] A fungus disease of numerous tropical plants, such as coconut and rubber, caused by *Hymenochaete noxia* and characterized by defoliation and by incrustation of the roots with earth and stones held together by brown mycelia.

brown root rot [PL PATH] 1. A fungus disease of plants of the pea, cucumber, and potato families caused by *Thielavia basicola* and characterized by blackish discoloration and decay of the roots and stem base. 2. A disease of tobacco and other plants comparable to the fungus disease but believed to be caused by nematodes.

brown rot [PL PATH] Any fungus or bacterial plant disease characterized by browning and tissue decay.

brown seaweed [BOT] A common name for the larger algae of the division Phaeophyta.

brown spot [PL PATH] Any fungus disease of plants, especially Indian corn, characterized by brown leaf spots.

brown stem rot [PL PATH] A fungus disease of soybeans caused by *Cephalosporium gregatum* in which there is brownish internal stem rot followed by discoloration and withering of leaves.

brown stringy rot [PL PATH] A disease of conifers caused by the Indian point fungus; rusty or brown fibrous streaks appear in the heartwood.

browse [BIOL] 1. Twigs, shoots, and leaves eaten by livestock and other grazing animals. 2. To feed on this vegetation.

Brucella [MICROBIO] A genus of gram-negative, aerobic bacteria of uncertain affiliation; single, nonmotile coccobacilli or short rods, all of which are parasites and pathogens of mammals.

Brucella abortus [MICROBIO] The etiological agent of contagious abortion in cattle, brucellosis in humans, and a wasting disease in chickens.

Brucellaceae [MICROBIO] Formerly a family of small, coccoid to rod-shaped, gram-negative bacteria in the order Eubacteriales.

brucellergen [BIOCHEM] A nucleoprotein fraction of brucellae used in skin tests to detect the presence of *Brucella* infections.

Bruchidae [INV ZOO] The pea and bean weevils, a family of coleopteran insects in the superfamily Chrysomeloidea.

Bruch's membrane [ANAT] The membrane of the retina that separates the pigmented layer of the retina from the choroid coat of the eye.

Brunner's glands [ANAT] Simple, branched, tubular mucus-secreting glands in the submucosa of the duodenum in mammals. Also known as duodenal glands; glands of Brunner.

brush See tropical scrub.

brush border [CELL BIO] A superficial protoplasmic modification in the form of filiform processes or microvilli; present on certain absorptive cells in the intestinal epithelium and the proximal convolutions of nephrons.

brussels sprouts [BOT] *Brassica oleracea* var. *gemmifera* A biennial crucifer of the order Capparales cultivated for its small, edible, headlike buds.

bryology [BOT] The study of bryophytes.

Bryophyta [BOT] A small phylum of the plant kingdom, including mosses, liverworts, and hornworts, characterized by the lack of true roots, stems, and leaves.

Bryopsida [BOT] The mosses, a class of small green plants in the phylum Bryophyta. Also known as Musci.

Bryopsidaceae [BOT] A family of green algae in the order Siphonales.

Bryozoa [INV ZOO] The moss animals, a major phylum of sessile aquatic invertebrates occurring in colonies with hardened exoskeleton.

buccal cavity [ANAT] The space anterior to the teeth and gums in the mouths of all vertebrates having lips and cheeks. Also known as vestibule.

buccal gland [ANAT] Any of the mucous glands in the membrane lining the cheeks of mammals, except aquatic forms.

Buccinacea [INV ZOO] A superfamily of gastropod mollusks in the order Prosobranchia.

Buccinidae [INV ZOO] A family of marine gastropod mollusks in the order Neogastropoda containing the whelks in the genus *Buccinum*.

Bucconidae [VERT ZOO] The puffbirds, a family of neotropical birds in the order Piciformes.

Bucerotidae [VERT ZOO] The hornbills, a family of Old World tropical birds in the order Coraciiformes.

buck [VERT ZOO] A male deer.

bucket See calyx.

buckeye [BOT] The common name for deciduous trees composing the genus *Aesculus* in the order Sapindales; leaves are opposite and palmately compound, and the seed is large with a firm outer coat.

buckwheat [BOT] The common name for several species of annual herbs in the genus *Fagopyrum* of the order Polygonales; used for the starchy seed.

bud [BOT] An embryonic shoot containing the growing stem tip surrounded by young leaves or flowers or both and frequently enclosed by bud scales.

budbreak [BOT] Initiation of growth from a bud.

budding [BIOL] A form of asexual reproduction in which a new individual arises as an outgrowth of an older individual. Also known as gemmation. [BOT] A method of vegetative propagation in which a single bud is grafted laterally onto a stock.

budding bacteria [MICROBIO] Bacteria that reproduce by budding.

bud grafting [BOT] Grafting a plant by budding.

budling [BOT] The shoot that develops from the bud which was the scion of a bud graft.

bud rot [PL PATH] Any plant disease or symptom involving bud decay.

bud scale [BOT] One of the modified leaves enclosing and protecting buds in perennial plants.

buffalo [VERT ZOO] The common name for several species of artiodactyl mammals in the family Bovidae, including the water buffalo and bison.

buffer [ECOL] An animal that is introduced to serve as food for other animals to reduce the losses of more desirable animals.

Bufonidae [VERT ZOO] A family of toothless frogs in the suborder Procoela including the true toads (*Bufo*).

bug [INV ZOO] Any insect in the order Hemiptera.

bulb [BOT] A short, subterranean stem with many overlapping fleshy leaf bases or scales, such as in the onion and tulip.

bulbil [BOT] A secondary bulb usually produced on the aerial part of a plant.

bulbocavernosus See bulbospongiosus.

bulb of the penis [ANAT] The expanded proximal portion of the corpus spongiosum of the penis.

bulbospongiosus [ANAT] A muscle encircling the bulb and adjacent proximal parts of the penis in the male, and encircling the orifice of the vagina and covering the lateral parts of the vestibular bulbs in the female. Also known as bulbocavernosus.

bulbourethral gland [ANAT] Either of a pair of compound tubular glands, anterior to the prostate gland in males, which discharge into the urethra. Also known as Cowper's gland.

Buliminacea [INV ZOO] A superfamily of benthic, marine foraminiferans in the suborder Rotaliina.

bullate [BIOL] Appearing blistered or puckered, especially of certain leaves.

bull's-eye rot [PL PATH] A fungus disease of apples caused by either *Neofabraea malicorticis* or *Gloeosporium perennans* and characterized by spots resembling eyes on the fruit.

bulliform [BOT] Type of plant cell involved in tissue contraction or water storage, or of uncertain function.

bulliform cell [BOT] One of the large, highly vacuolated cells occurring in the epidermis of grass leaves. Also known as motor cell.

bumblebee [INV ZOO] The common name for several large, hairy social bees of the genus *Bombus* in the family Apidae.

bunchy top [PL PATH] Any viral disease of plants in which there is a shortening of the internodes with crowding of leaves and shoots at the stem apex.

bundle branch [ANAT] Either of the components of the atrioventricular bundle passing to the right and left ventricles of the heart.

bundle scar [BOT] A mark within a leaf scar that shows the point of an abscised vascular bundle.

bundle sheath [BOT] A sheath around a vascular bundle that consists of a layer of parenchyma.

bunodont [ANAT] Having tubercles or rounded cusps on the molar teeth, as in humans.

bunolophodont [VERT ZOO] 1. Of teeth, having the outer cusps in the form of blunt cones and the inner cusps as transverse ridges. 2. Having such teeth, as in tapirs.

bunoselenodont [VERT ZOO] 1. Of teeth, having the inner cusps in the form of blunt cones and the outer ones as longitudinal crescents. 2. Having such teeth, as in the extinct titanotheres.

bunt [PL PATH] A fungus disease of wheat caused by two *Tilletia* species and characterized by grain replacement with fishy-smelling smut spores.

Buprestidae [INV ZOO] The metallic wood-boring beetles, the large, single family of the coleopteran superfamily Buprestoidea.

Buprestoidea [INV ZOO] A superfamily of coleopteran insects in the suborder Polyphaga including many serious pests of fruit trees.

Burhinidae [VERT ZOO] The thick-knees or stone curlews, a family of the avian order Charadriiformes.

Burmanniaceae [BOT] A family of monocotyledonous plants in the order Orchidales characterized by regular flowers, three or six stamens opposite the petals, and ovarian nectaries.

burr [BOT] 1. A rough or prickly envelope on a fruit. 2. A fruit so characterized.

burr ball *See* lake ball.

burro [VERT ZOO] A small donkey used as a pack animal.

bursa [ANAT] A simple sac or cavity with smooth walls containing a clear, slightly sticky fluid and interposed between two moving surfaces of the body to reduce friction.

bursa of Fabricius [VERT ZOO] A thymuslike organ in the form of a diverticulum at the lower end of the alimentary canal in birds.

Burseraceae [BOT] A family of dicotyledonous plants in the order Sapindales characterized by an ovary of two to five cells, prominent resin ducts in the bark and wood, and an intrastaminal disk.

bursicle [BOT] A purse or pouchlike receptacle.

burster [BOT] An abnormally double flower having the calyx split or fragmented.

bush *See* tropical scrub.

bushbaby [VERT ZOO] Any of six species of African arboreal primates in two genera (*Galago* and *Euoticus*) of the family Lorisidae. Also known as galago; night ape.

butanol fermentation [MICROBIO] Butanol production as a result of the fermentation of corn and molasses by the anaerobic bacterium *Clostridium acetobutylicum*.

Butenandt unit [BIOL] A unit for the standardization of estrogens.

Butomaceae [BOT] A family of monocotyledonous plants in the order Alismatales characterized by secretory canals, linear leaves, and a straight embryo.

butterfly [INV ZOO] Any insect belonging to the lepidopteran suborder Rhopalocera, characterized by a slender body, broad colorful wings, and club-shaped antennae.

buttocks [ANAT] The two fleshy parts of the body posterior to the hip joints.

buttress [PALEON] A ridge on the inner surface of a pelecypod valve which acts as a support for part of the hinge.

butt rot [PL PATH] A fungus decay of the base of a tree trunk caused by polypores (such as *Fomea* species).

butyric fermentation [BIOCHEM] Fermentation in which butyric acid is produced by certain anaerobic bacteria acting on organic substances, such as butter; occurs in putrefaction and in digestion in herbivorous mammals.

butyrinase [BIOCHEM] An enzyme that hydrolyzes butyrin, found in the blood serum.

Butyrivibrio [MICROBIO] A genus of gram-negative, strictly anaerobic bacteria of uncertain affiliation; motile curved rods occur singly, in chains, or in filaments; ferment glucose to produce butyrate.

Buxbaumiales [BOT] An order of very small, atypical mosses (Bryopsida) composed of three genera and found on soil, rock, and rotten wood.

B virus [VIROL] An animal virus belonging to subgroup A of the herpesvirus group.

Byrrhidae [INV ZOO] The pill beetles, the single family of the coleopteran insect superfamily Byrrhoidea.

Byrrhoidea [INV ZOO] A superfamily of coleopteran insects in the superorder Polyphaga.

Byturidae [INV ZOO] The raspberry fruitworms, a small family of coleopteran insects in the superfamily Cucujoidea.

C

caatinga [ECOL] A sparse, stunted forest in areas of little rainfall in northeastern Brazil; trees are leafless in the dry season.

cabbage [BOT] *Brassica oleracea* var. *capitata*. A biennial crucifer of the order Capparales grown for its head of edible leaves.

cabbage yellows [PL PATH] A fungus disease of cabbage caused by *Fusarium conglutinans* and characterized by yellowing and dwarfing.

cabezon [VERT ZOO] *Scorpaenichthys marmoratus*. A fish that is the largest of the sculpin species, weighing as much as 25 pounds (11.3 kilograms) and reaching a length of 30 inches (76 centimeters).

Cabot's ring [CELL BIO] A ringlike body in immature erythrocytes that may represent the remains of the nuclear membrane.

cacao [BOT] *Theobroma cacao*. A small tropical tree of the order Theales that bears capsular fruits which are a source of cocoa powder and chocolate. Also known as chocolate tree.

cacomistle [VERT ZOO] *Bassariscus astutus*. A raccoonlike mammal that inhabits the southern and southwestern United States; distinguished by a bushy black-and-white ringed tail. Also known as civet cat; ringtail.

caconym [SYST] A taxonomic name that is linguistically unacceptable.

Cactaceae [BOT] The cactus family of the order Caryophyllales; represented by the American stem succulents, which are mostly spiny with reduced leaves.

cactus [BOT] The common name for any member of the family Cactaceae, a group characterized by a fleshy habit, spines and bristles, and large, brightly colored, solitary flowers.

cadang-cadang [PL PATH] An infectious virus disease of the coconut palm characterized by yellow-bronzing of the leaves.

cadaverine [BIOCHEM] $C_5H_{14}N_2$ A nontoxic, organic base produced as a result of the decarboxylation of lysine by the action of putrefactive bacteria on flesh.

caddis fly [INV ZOO] The common name for all members of the insect order Trichoptera; adults are mothlike and the immature stages are aquatic.

caducicorn [VERT ZOO] Having deciduous horns, as certain deer.

caducous [BOT] Lasting on a plant only a short time before falling off.

caecilian [VERT ZOO] The common name for members of the amphibian order Apoda.

caecum *See* cecum.

Caenolestidae [PALEON] A family of extinct insectivorous mammals in the order Marsupialia.

Caenolestoidea [VERT ZOO] A superfamily of marsupial mammals represented by the single living family Caenolestidae.

caenostylic [VERT ZOO] Having the first two visceral arches attached to the cranium and functioning in food intake; a condition found in sharks, amphibians, and chimaeras.

Caesalpinoideae [BOT] A subfamily of dicotyledonous plants in the legume family, Leguminosae.

3-caffeoylquinic acid *See* chlorogenic acid.

caiman [VERT ZOO] Any of five species of reptiles of the genus *Caiman* in the family Alligatoridae, differing from alligators principally in having ventral armor and a sharper snout.

Cainotheriidae [PALEON] The single family of the extinct artiodactyl superfamily Cainotherioidea.

Cainotherioidea [PALEON] A superfamily of extinct, rabbit-sized tylopod ruminants in the mammalian order Artiodactyla.

Calamitales [PALEOBOT] An extinct group of reedlike plants of the subphylum Sphenopsida characterized by horizontal rhizomes and tall, upright, grooved, articulated stems.

Calanoida [INV ZOO] A suborder of the crustacean order Copepoda, including the larger and more abundant of the pelagic species.

Calappidae [INV ZOO] The box crabs, a family of reptantian decapods in the subsection Oxystomata of the section Brachyura.

calathiform [BIOL] Cup-shaped, being almost hemispherical.

calcaneocuboid ligament [ANAT] The ligament that joins the calcaneus and the cuboid bones.

calcaneum [ANAT] 1. A bony projection of the metatarsus in birds. 2. *See* calcaneus.

calcaneus [ANAT] A bone of the tarsus, forming the heel bone in humans. Also known as calcaneum.

calcar [ZOO] A spur or spurlike process, especially on an appendage or digit.

calcarate [BOT] Having spurs.

Calcarea [INV ZOO] A class of the phylum Porifera, including sponges with a skeleton composed of calcium carbonate spicules.

calcareous algae [BOT] Algae that grow on limestone or in soil impregnated with lime.

calcarine fissure *See* calcarine sulcus.

calcarine sulcus [ANAT] A sulcus on the medial aspect of the occipital lobe of the cerebrum, between the lingual gyrus and the cuneus. Also known as calcarine fissure.

Calcaronea [INV ZOO] A subclass of sponges in the class Calcarea in which the larva are amphiblastulae.

calcicole [BOT] Requiring soil rich in calcium carbonate for optimum growth.

calciferous [BIOL] Containing or producing calcium or calcium carbonate.

calciferous gland [INV ZOO] One of a series of glands that secrete calcium carbonate into the esophagus of certain oligochaetes.

calcification [PHYSIO] The deposit of calcareous matter within the tissues of the body.

calcifuge [ECOL] A plant that grows in an acid medium that is poor in calcareous matter.

Calcinea [INV ZOO] A subclass of sponges in the class Calcarea in which the larvae are parenchymulae.

calcitonin [BIOCHEM] A polypeptide, calcium-regulating hormone produced by the ultimobranchial bodies in vertebrates. Also known as thyrocalcitonin.

calcium metabolism [BIOCHEM] Biochemical and physiological processes involved in maintaining the concentration of calcium in plasma at a constant level and providing a sufficient supply of calcium for bone mineralization.

Calclamnidae [PALEON] A family of Paleozoic echinoderms of the order Dendrochirotida.

calculus [ANAT] A small and cuplike structure.

calf [VERT ZOO] The young of the domestic cow, elephant, rhinoceros, hippopotamus, moose, whale, and others.

Caliciaceae [BOT] A family of lichens in the order Caliciales in which the disk of the apothecium is borne on a short stalk.

Caliciales [BOT] An order of lichens in the class Ascolichenes characterized by an unusual apothecium.

Caligidae [INV ZOO] A family of fish ectoparasites belonging to the crustacean suborder Caligoida.

Caligoida [INV ZOO] A suborder of the crustacean order Copepoda, including only fish ectoparasites and characterized by a sucking mouth with styliform mandibles.

Callichthyidae [VERT ZOO] A family of tropical catfishes in the suborder Siluroidei.

callideic I *See* bradykinin.

calling song [INV ZOO] A high-intensity insect sound which may play a role in habitat selection among certain species.

Callionymoidei [VERT ZOO] A suborder of fishes in the order Perciformes, including two families of colorful marine bottom fishes known as dragonets.

Callipallenidae [INV ZOO] A family of marine arthropods in the subphylum Pycnogonida lacking palpi and having chelifores and 10-jointed ovigers.

Calliphoridae [INV ZOO] The blow flies, a family of myodarian cyclorrhaphous dipteran insects in the subsection Calypteratae.

Callithricidae [VERT ZOO] The marmosets, a family of South American mammals in the order Primates.

Callorhinchidae [VERT ZOO] A family of ratfishes of the chondrichthyan order Chimaeriformes.

callose [BIOCHEM] A carbohydrate component of plant cell walls; associated with sieve plates where calluses are formed. [BIOL] Having hardened protuberances, as on the skin or on leaves and stems.

callus [BOT] **1.** A thickened callose deposit on sieve plates. **2.** A hard tissue that forms over a damaged plant surface.

caloreceptor [PHYSIO] A cutaneous sense organ that is stimulated by heat.

calotte [BIOL] A cap or caplike structure. [INV ZOO] **1.** The four-celled polar cap in Dicyemidae. **2.** A ciliated, retractile disc in certain bryozoan larva. **3.** A dark-colored anterior area in certain nematomorphs.

calsequestrin [BIOCHEM] An acidic protein, with a molecular weight of 44,000 daltons, which binds calcium inside the sarcoplasmic reticulum.

calthrop [INV ZOO] A sponge spicule having four axes in which the rays are equal or almost equal in length.

calvarium [ANAT] A skull lacking facial parts and the lower jaw.

calving [VERT ZOO] Giving birth to a calf.

calycanthemy [PL PATH] Abnormal development of calyx structures into petals or petaloid structures.

calyculate [BOT] Having bracts that imitate a second, external calyx.

calymma [INV ZOO] The outer, vacuolated protoplasmic layer of certain radiolarians.

Calymmatobacterium [MICROBIO] A genus of gram-negative, usually encapsulated, pleomorphic rods of uncertain affiliation; the single species causes granuloma inguinale in humans.

Calymnidae [INV ZOO] A family of echinoderms in the order Holasteroida characterized by an ovoid test with a marginal fasciole.

calypter [INV ZOO] A scalelike or lobelike structure above the haltere of certain two-winged flies. Also known as alula; squama.

Calyptoblastea [INV ZOO] A suborder of coelenterates in the order Hydroida, including the hydroids with protective cups around the hydranths and gonozooids.

calyptra [BOT] **1.** A membranous cap or hoodlike covering, especially the remains of the archegonium over the capsule of a moss. **2.** Tissue surrounding the archegonium of a liverwort. **3.** Root cap.

Calyptratae [INV ZOO] A subsection of dipteran insects in the suborder Cyclorrhapha characterized by calypters associated with the wings.

calyptrate [BOT] Having a calyptra.

calyptrogen [BOT] The specialized cell layer from which a root cap originates.

Calyssozoa [INV ZOO] The single class of the bryozoan subphylum Entoprocta.

calyx [BOT] The outermost whorl of a flower; composed of sepals. [INV ZOO] A cup-shaped structure to which the arms are attached in crinoids.

Camallanida [INV ZOO] An order of phasmid nematodes in the subclass Spiruria, including parasites of domestic animals.

Camarodonta [INV ZOO] An order of Euechinoidea proposed by R. Jackson and abandoned in 1957.

camarodont dentition [INV ZOO] In echinoderms, keeled teeth meeting the epiphyses so that the foramen magnum of the jaw is closed.

Cambaridae [INV ZOO] A family of crayfishes belonging to the section Macrura in the crustacean order Decapoda.

Cambarinae [INV ZOO] A subfamily of crayfishes in the family Astacidae, including all North American species east of the Rocky Mountains.

cambium [BOT] A layer of cells between the phloem and xylem of most vascular plants that is responsible for secondary growth and for generating new cells.

camel [VERT ZOO] The common name for two species of artiodactyl mammals, the bactrian camel (*Camelus bactrianus*) and the dromedary camel (*C. dromedarius*), in the family Camelidae.

Camelidae [VERT ZOO] A family of tylopod ruminants in the superfamily Cameloidea of the order Artiodactyla, including four species of camels and llamas.

Cameloidea [VERT ZOO] A superfamily of tylopod ruminants in the order Artiodiodactyla.

Camerata [PALEON] A subclass of extinct stalked echinoderms of the class Crinoidea.

cAMP *See* cyclic adenylic acid.

Campanulaceae [BOT] A family of dicotyledonous plants in the order Campanulales characterized by a style without an indusium but with well-developed collecting hairs below the stigmas, and by a well-developed latex system.

Campanulales [BOT] An order of dicotyledonous plants in the subclass Asteridae distinguished by a chiefly herbaceous habit, alternate leaves, and inferior ovary.

campanulate [BOT] Bell-shaped; applied particularly to the corolla.

campestrian [ECOL] Of or pertaining to the northern Great Plains area.

camphor tree [BOT] *Cinnamomum camphora*. A plant of the laurel family (Lauraceae) in the order Magnoliales from which camphor is extracted.

Campodeidae [INV ZOO] A family of primarily wingless insects in the order Diplura which are most numerous in the Temperate Zone of the Northern Hemisphere.

campos [ECOL] The savanna of South America.

Campylobacter [MICROBIO] A genus of bacteria in the family Spirillaceae; spirally curved rods that are motile by means of a polar flagellum at one or both poles.

campylotropous [BOT] Having the ovule symmetrical but half inverted, with the micropyle and funiculus at right angles to each other.

Canaceidae [INV ZOO] The seashore flies, a family of myodarian cyclorrhaphous dipteran insects in the subsection Acalypteratae.

Canadian life zone [ECOL] The zone comprising the climate and biotic communities of the portion of the Boreal life zone exclusive of the Hudsonian and Arctic-Alpine zones.

canal [BIOL] A tubular duct or passage in bone or soft tissues.

canal cell [BOT] One of the row of cells that make up the axial row within the neck of an archegonium.

canaliculate [BIOL] Having small channels, canals, or grooves.

canaliculus [HISTOL] 1. One of the minute channels in bone radiating from a Haversian canal and connecting lacunae with each other and with the canal. 2. A passage between the cells of the cell cords in the liver.

canalization [PHYSIO] The formation of new channels in tissues, such as the formation of new blood vessels through a thrombus.

canal of Schlemm [ANAT] An irregular channel at the junction of the sclera and cornea in the eye that drains aqueous humor from the anterior chamber.

canal valve [ANAT] The semilunar valve in the right atrium of the heart between the orifice of the inferior vena cava and the right atrioventricular orifice. Also known as eustachian valve.

canary-pox virus [VIROL] An avian poxvirus that causes canary pox, a disease closely related to fowl pox.

canavanine [BIOCHEM] $C_5H_{12}O_3N_4$ An amino acid found in the jack bean.

cancellate [BIOL] Lattice-shaped. Also known as clathrate.

cancellous [BIOL] Having a reticular or spongy structure.

cancellous bone [HISTOL] A form of bone near the ends of long bones having a cancellous matrix composed of rods, plates, or tubes; spaces are filled with marrow.

Candida [MYCOL] A genus of yeastlike, pathogenic imperfect fungi that produce very small mycelia.

Candida albicans [MYCOL] The fungus organism that causes thrush and other types of moniliasis. Also known as *Monilia albicans*.

cane [BOT] 1. A hollow, usually slender, jointed stem, such as in sugarcane or the bamboo grasses. 2. A stem growing directly from the base of the plant, as in most Rosaceae, such as blackberry and roses.

cane blight [PL PATH] A fungus disease affecting the canes of several bush fruits, such as currants and raspberries; caused by several species of fungi.

canescent [BOT] Having a grayish epidermal covering of short hairs.

Canidae [VERT ZOO] A family of carnivorous mammals in the superfamily Canoidea, including dogs and their allies.

canine [ANAT] A conical tooth, such as one located between the lateral incisor and first premolar in humans and many other mammals. Also known as cuspid. [VERT ZOO] Pertaining or related to dogs or to the family Canidae.

Canis [VERT ZOO] The type genus of the dog family (Canidae), including dogs, wolves, and jackals.

Canis familiaris [VERT ZOO] The scientific name for all breeds of domestic dogs.

canker [PL PATH] An area of necrosis on a woody stem resulting in shrinkage and cracking followed by the formation of callus tissue, ultimately killing the stem.

canker stain [PL PATH] A fungus disease of plane trees caused by *Endoconidiophora fimbriata platani* and characterized by bluish-black or reddish-brown discolorations beneath blackened cankers on the trunk and sometimes the branches.

cankerworm [INV ZOO] Any of several lepidopteran insect larvae in the family Geometridae which cause severe plant damage by feeding on buds and foliage.

Cannabaceae [BOT] A family of dicotyledonous herbs in the order Urticales, including Indian hemp (*Cannabis sativa*) and characterized by erect anthers, two styles or style branches, and the lack of milky juice.

Cannabis [BOT] A genus of tall annual herbs in the family Cannabaceae having erect stems, leaves with three to seven elongate leaflets, and pistillate flowers in spikes along the stem.

Cannabis sativa [BOT] Indian hemp, the source of a commercial fiber, hashish, and marijuana.

Cannaceae [BOT] A family of monocotyledonous plants in the order Zingiberales characterized by one functional stamen, a single functional pollen sac in the stamen, mucilage canals in the stem, and numerous ovules in each of the one to three locules.

Canoidea [VERT ZOO] A superfamily belonging to the mammalian order Carnivora, including all dogs and doglike species such as seals, bears, and weasels.

cantala [BOT] A fiber produced from agave (*Agave cantala*) leaves; used to make twine. Also known as Cebu maguey; maguey; Manila maguey.

cantaloupe [BOT] The fruit (pepo) of *Cucumis malo*, a small, distinctly netted, round to oval muskmelon of the family Cucurbitaceae in the order Violales.

Cantharidae [INV ZOO] The soldier beetles, a family of coleopteran insects in the superfamily Cantharoidea.

Cantharoidea [INV ZOO] A superfamily of coleopteran insects in the suborder Polyphaga.

canthus [ANAT] Either of the two angles formed by the junction of the eyelids, designated outer or lateral, and inner or medial.

cap [GEN] In many eukaryotic messenger ribonucleic acids, the structure at the 5' end consisting of 7'-methyl-guanosine-pppX, where X is the first nucleotide encoded in the deoxyribonucleic acid; it is added posttranscriptionally.

capillary [ANAT] The smallest vessel of both the circulatory and lymphatic systems; the walls are composed of a single cell layer.

capillary bed [ANAT] The capillaries, collectively, of a given area or organ.

capillary pressure [PHYSIO] Pressure exerted by blood against capillary walls.

capillitium [MYCOL] A network of threadlike tubes or filaments in which spores are embedded within sporangia of certain fungi, such as the slime molds.

capitate [BIOL] Enlarged and swollen at the tip. [BOT] Forming a head, as certain flowers of the Compositae.

capitellate [BOT] 1. Having a small knoblike termination. 2. Grouped to form a capitulum.

Capitellidae [INV ZOO] A family of mud-swallowing annelid worms, sometimes called bloodworms, belonging to the Sedentaria.

capitellum [ANAT] A small head or rounded process of a bone.

Capitonidae [VERT ZOO] The barbets, a family of pantropical birds in the order Piciformes.

capitulum [BIOL] A rounded, knoblike, usually terminal proturberance on a structure. [BOT] One of the rounded cells on the manubrium in the antheridia of lichens belonging to the Caliciales.

Caponidae [INV ZOO] A family of arachnid arthropods in the order Araneida characterized by having tracheae instead of book lungs.

capon unit [BIOL] A unit for the standardization of androgens.

Capparaceae [BOT] A family of dicotyledonous herbs, shrubs, and trees in the order Capparales characterized by parietal placentation; hypogynous, mostly regular flowers; four to many stamens; and simple to trifoliate or palmately compound leaves.

Capparales [BOT] An order of dicotyledonous plants in the subclass Dilleniidae.

Caprellidae [INV ZOO] The skeleton shrimps, a family of slender, cylindrical amphipod crustaceans in the suborder Caprellidea.

Caprellidea [INV ZOO] A suborder of marine and brackish-water animals of the crustacean order Amphipoda.

Caprifoliaceae [BOT] A family of dicotyledonous, mostly woody plants in the order Dipsacales, including elderberry and honeysuckle; characterized by distinct filaments and anthers, typically five stamens and five corolla lobes, more than one ovule per locule, and well-developed endosperm.

Caprimulgidae [VERT ZOO] A family of birds in the order Caprimulgiformes, including the nightjars, or goatsuckers.

Caprimulgiformes [VERT ZOO] An order of nocturnal and crepuscular birds, including nightjars, potoos, and frog-mouths.

Capsaloidea [INV ZOO] A superfamily of ectoparasitic trematodes in the subclass Monogenea characterized by a sucker-shaped holdfast with anchors and hooks.

capsanthin [BIOCHEM] $C_{40}H_{58}IO_3$ Carmine-red carotenoid pigment occurring in paprika.

capsicum [BOT] The fruit of a plant of the genus *Capsicum*, especially *C. frutescens*, cultivated in southern India and the tropics; a strong irritant to mucous membranes and eyes.

capsid [INV ZOO] The name applied to all members of the family Miridae. [VIROL] The protein coat of a virus particle.

capsomere [VIROL] An individual protein subunit of a capsid.

capsular ligament [ANAT] A saclike ligament surrounding the articular cavity of a freely movable joint and attached to the bones.

capsulate [BIOL] Enclosed in a capsule.

capsule [ANAT] A membranous structure enclosing a body part or organ. [BOT] A closed structure bearing seeds or spores; it is dehiscent at maturity. [MICROBIO] A thick, mucous envelope, composed of polypeptide or carbohydrate, surrounding certain microorganisms.

Captorhinomorpha [PALEON] An extinct subclass of primitive lizardlike reptiles in the order Cotylosauria.

capybara [VERT ZOO] *Hydrochoerus capybara*. An aquatic rodent (largest rodent in existence) found in South America and characterized by partly webbed feet, no tail, and coarse hair.

Carabidae [INV ZOO] The ground beetles, a family of predatory coleopteran insects in the suborder Adephaga.

Caracarinae [VERT ZOO] The caracaras, a subfamily of carrion-feeding birds in the order Falconiformes.

Carangidae [VERT ZOO] A family of perciform fishes in the suborder Percoidei, including jacks, scads, and pompanos.

carapace [INV ZOO] A dorsolateral, chitonous case covering the cephalothorax of many arthropods. [VERT ZOO] The bony, dorsal part of a turtle shell.

Carapidae [VERT ZOO] The pearlfishes, a family of sinuous, marine shore fishes in the order Gadiformes that live as commensals in the body cavity of holothurians.

caraway [BOT] *Carum carvi*. A white-flowered perennial herb of the family Umbelliferae; the fruit is used as a spice and flavoring agent.

carbamic acid [BIOCHEM] NH_2COOH An amino acid known for its salts, such as urea and carbamide. Also known as amidocarbonic acid; aminoformic acid.

carbamidine *See* guanidine.

carbamino [BIOCHEM] A compound formed by the combination of carbon dioxide with a free amino group in an amino acid or a protein.

carbamyl phosphate [BIOCHEM] $NH_2COPO_4H_2$ The ester formed from reaction of phosphoric acid and carbamyl acid.

carbohydrase [BIOCHEM] Any enzyme that catalyzes the hydrolysis of disaccharides and more complex carbohydrates.

carbohydrate [BIOCHEM] Any of the group of organic compounds composed of carbon, hydrogen, and oxygen, including sugars, starches, and celluloses.

carbohydrate metabolism [BIOCHEM] The sum of the biochemical and physiological processes involved in the breakdown and synthesis of simple sugars, oligosaccharides, and polysaccharides and in the transport of sugar across cell membranes.

carbomycin [MICROBIO] $C_{42}H_{67}O_{16}N$ Colorless, crystalline antibiotic produced by *Streptomyces halstedii;* principally active against gram-positive bacteria.

carbomycin B [MICROBIO] $C_{42}H_{67}O_{15}N$ A colorless, crystalline antibiotic differing from carbomycin only in having one less oxygen atom in its molecule.

carbonic anhydrase [BIOCHEM] An enzyme which aids carbon dioxide transport and release by catalyzing the synthesis, and the dehydration, of carbonic acid from, and to, carbon dioxide and water.

carbonmonoxyhemoglobin [BIOCHEM] A stable combination of carbon monoxide and hemoglobin formed in the blood when carbon monoxide is inhaled. Also known as carbonylhemoglobin and carboxyhemoglobin.

carbonylhemoglobin *See* carbonmonoxyhemoglobin.

carboxyhemoglobin *See* carbonmonoxyhemoglobin.

carboxylase [BIOCHEM] Any enzyme that catalyzes a carboxylation or decarboxylation reaction.

carboxyl terminal [BIOCHEM] The end of a polypeptide chain with a free carboxyl group.

carboxypeptidase [BIOCHEM] Any enzyme that catalyzes the hydrolysis of a peptide at the end containing the free carboxyl group.

Carcharhinidae [VERT ZOO] A large family of sharks belonging to the charcharinid group of galeoids, including the tiger sharks and blue sharks.

Carchariidae [VERT ZOO] A family of shallow-water predatory sharks belonging to the isurid group of galeoids.

carcharodont [VERT ZOO] Possessing sharp, flat, triangular teeth with serrated margins, like those of the human-eating sharks.

cardamom *See* cardamon.

cardamon [BOT] *Elettaria cardamomum*. A perennial herbaceous plant in the family Zingiberaceae; the seed of the plant is used as a spice. Also spelled cardamom.

cardia [ANAT] 1. The orifice where the esophagus enters the stomach. 2. The large, blind diverticulum of the stomach adjoining the orifice. [INV ZOO] Anterior enlargement of the ventriculus in some insects.

cardiac [ANAT] 1. Of, pertaining to, or situated near the heart. 2. Of or pertaining to the cardia of the stomach.

cardiac cycle [PHYSIO] The sequence of events in the heart between the start of one contraction and the start of the next.

cardiac electrophysiology [PHYSIO] The science that is concerned with the mechanism, spread, and interpretation of the electric currents which arise within heart muscle tissue and initiate each heart muscle contraction.

cardiac gland [ANAT] Any of the mucus-secreting, compound tubular structures near the esophagus or in the cardia of the stomach of vertebrates; capable of secreting digestive enzymes.

cardiac input [PHYSIO] The amount of venous blood returned to the heart during a specified period of time.

cardiac loop [EMBRYO] The embryonic heart formed by bending and twisting of the cardiac tube.

cardiac muscle [HISTOL] The principal tissue of the vertebrate heart; composed of a syncytium of striated muscle fibers.

cardiac output [PHYSIO] The total blood flow from the heart during a specified period of time.

cardiac plexus [ANAT] A network of visceral nerves situated at the base of the heart; contains both sympathetic and vagal nerve fibers.

cardiac sphincter [ANAT] The muscular ring at the orifice between the esophagus and stomach.

cardiac valve [ANAT] Any of the structures located within the orifices of the heart that maintain unidirectional blood flow.

cardinal teeth [INV ZOO] Ridges and grooves on the inner surfaces of both valves of a bivalve mollusk near the anterior end of the hinge.

cardinal vein [EMBRYO] Any of four veins in the vertebrate embryo which run along each side of the vertebral column; the paired veins on each side discharge blood to the heart through the duct of Cuvier.

Cardiobacterium [MICROBIO] A genus of gram-negative, rod-shaped bacteria of uncertain affiliation; facultative anaerobes that ferment fructose, glucose, mannose, sorbitol, and sucrose; the single species causes endocarditis in humans.

cardioblast [INV ZOO] Any of certain early embryonic cells in insects from which the heart develops.

cardiogenic plate [EMBRYO] An area of splanchnic mesoderm in the early mammalian embryo from which the heart develops.

cardiolipin [BIOCHEM] A complex phospholipid found in the ether alcohol extract of powdered beef heart; mixed with leutin and cholesterol, it functions as the antigen in the Wassermann complement-fixation test for syphilis. Also known as diphosphatidyl glycerol.

cardiovascular system [ANAT] Those structures, including the heart and blood vessels, which provide channels for the flow of blood.

Carettochelyidae [VERT ZOO] A family of reptiles in the order Chelonia containing only one species, the New Guinea plateless turtle (*Carettochelys insculpta*).

Cariamidae [VERT ZOO] The long-legged cariamas, a family of birds in the order Gruiformes.

Caribosireninae [VERT ZOO] A subfamily of trichechiform sirenean mammals in the family Dugongidae.

Caridea [INV ZOO] A large section of decapod crustaceans in the suborder Natantia including many diverse forms of shrimps and prawns.

carina [BIOL] A ridge or a keel-shaped anatomical structure. [VERT ZOO] *See* keel.

carinate [BIOL] Having a ridge or keel, as the breastbone of certain birds.

Carinomidae [INV ZOO] A monogeneric family of littoral ribbonlike worms in the order Palaeonemertini.

carnassial [ANAT] Of or pertaining to molar or premolar teeth specialized for cutting and shearing.

carnitine [BIOCHEM] $C_7H_{15}NO_3$ α-Amino-β-hydroxybutyric acid trimethylbetaine; a constituent of striated muscle and liver, identical with vitamin B_T (the L form of vitamin B).

Carnivora [VERT ZOO] A large order of placental mammals, including dogs, bears, and cats, that is primarily adapted for predation as evidenced by dentition and jaw articulation.

carnivorous [BIOL] Eating flesh or, as in plants, subsisting on nutrients obtained from animal protoplasm.

carnivorous plant *See* insectivorous plant.

Carnosauria [PALEON] A group of large, predacious saurischian dinosaurs in the suborder Theropoda having short necks and large heads.

carnosine [BIOCHEM] $C_9H_{14}N_4O_3$ A colorless, crystalline dipeptide occurring in the muscle tissue of vertebrates.

Carolinian life zone [ECOL] A zone comprising the climate and biotic communities of the oak savannas of eastern North America.

carotenase [BIOCHEM] An enzyme that effects the hydrolysis of carotenoid compounds, used in bleaching of flour.

carotene [BIOCHEM] $C_{40}H_{56}$ Any of several red, crystalline, carotenoid hydrocarbon pigments occurring widely in nature, convertible in the animal body to vitamin A, and characterized by preferential solubility in petroleum ether. Also known as carotin.

carotenoid [BIOCHEM] A class of labile, easily oxidizable, yellow, orange, red, or purple pigments that are widely distributed in plants and animals and are preferentially soluble in fats and fat solvents.

carotid artery [ANAT] Either of the two principal arteries on both sides of the neck that supply blood to the head and neck. Also known as common carotid artery.

carotid body [ANAT] Either of two chemoreceptors sensitive to changes in blood chemistry which lie near the bifurcations of the carotid arteries. Also known as glomus caroticum.

carotid ganglion [ANAT] A group of nerve cell bodies associated with each carotid artery.

carotid sinus [ANAT] An enlargement at the bifurcation of each carotid artery that is supplied with sensory nerve endings and plays a role in reflex control of blood pressure.

carotin *See* carotene.

carotol [BIOCHEM] $C_{15}H_{25}OH$ A sesquiterpenoid alcohol in carrots.

carp [VERT ZOO] The common name for a number of fresh-water, cypriniform fishes in the family Cyprinidae, characterized by soft fins, pharyngeal teeth, and a suckerlike mouth.

carpel [BOT] The basic specialized leaf of the female reproductive structure in angiosperms; a megasporophyll.

carpogonium [BOT] The basal, egg-bearing portion of the female reproductive organ in some thallophytes, especially red algae.

Carpoidea [PALEON] Former designation for a class of extinct homalozoan echinoderms.

carpoids [PALEON] An assemblage of three classes of enigmatic, rare Paleozoic echinoderms formerly grouped together as the class Carpoidea.

carpology [BOT] The study of the morphology of fruit and seeds.

carpophagous [ZOO] Feeding on fruits.

carpophore [BOT] The portion of a flower receptacle that extends between and attaches to the carpels. [MYCOL] The stalk of a fruiting body in fungi.

carpophyte [BOT] A thallophyte that forms a sporocarp following fertilization.

carposporangium [BOT] In red algae, a sporangium that forms the cystocarp and contains carpospores.

carpospore [BOT] In red algae, a diploid spore produced terminally by a gonimoblast, giving rise to the diploid tetrasporic plant.

carpus [ANAT] 1. The wrist in humans or the corresponding part in other vertebrates. 2. The eight bones of the human wrist. [INV ZOO] The fifth segment from the base of a generalized crustacean appendage.

carrageen [BOT] *Chondrus crispus*. A cartilaginous red algae harvested in the Northern Atlantic as a source of carrageenin.

carrier [GEN] An individual who is heterozygous for a recessive gene.

carrot [BOT] *Daucus carota*. A biennial umbellifer of the order Umbellales with a yellow or orange-red edible root.

Carr-Price unit [BIOL] A unit for the standardization of vitamin A.

carrying capacity [ECOL] The maximum population size that the environment can support without deterioration.

Carterinacea [INV ZOO] A monogeneric superfamily of marine, benthic foraminiferans in the suborder Rotaliina characterized by a test with monocrystal calcite spicules in a granular groundmass.

cartilage [HISTOL] A specialized connective tissue which is bluish, translucent, and hard but yielding.

cartilage bone [HISTOL] Bone formed by ossification of cartilage.

cartilaginous fish [VERT ZOO] The common name for all members of the class Chondrichthyes.

caruncle [ANAT] Any normal or abnormal fleshy outgrowth, such as the comb and wattles of fowl or the mass in the inner canthus of the eye. [BOT] A fleshy outgrowth developed from the seed coat near the hilum in some seeds, such as the castor bean.

Caryophanaceae [MICROBIO] Formerly a family of large, gram-negative bacteria belonging to the order Caryophanales and having disklike cells arranged in chains.

Caryophanales [MICROBIO] Formerly an order of bacteria in the class Schizomycetes occurring as trichomes which produce short structures that function as reproductive units.

Caryophanon [MICROBIO] A genus of gram-positive, large, rod-shaped or filamentous bacteria of uncertain affiliation.

Caryophyllaceae [BOT] A family of dicotyledonous plants in the order Caryophyllales differing from the other families in lacking betalains.

Caryophyllales [BOT] An order of dicotyledonous plants in the subclass Caryophyllidae characterized by free-central or basal placentation.

Caryophyllidae [BOT] A relatively small subclass of plants in the class Magnoliopsida characterized by trinucleate pollen, ovules with two integuments, and a multilayered nucellus.

caryopsis [BOT] A small, dry, indehiscent fruit having a single seed with such a thin, closely adherent pericarp that a single body, a grain, is formed.

casaba melon [BOT] *Cucumis melo*. A winter muskmelon with a yellow rind and sweet flesh belonging to the family Cucurbitaceae of the order Violales.

cashew [BOT] *Anacardium occidentale*. An evergreen tree of the order Sapindales grown for its kidney-shaped edible nuts and resinous oil.

Casparian strip [BOT] A thin band of suberin- or lignin-like deposition in the radial and transverse walls of certain plant cells during the primary development phase of the endodermis.

cassava [BOT] *Manihot esculenta*. A shrubby perennial plant grown for its starchy, edible tuberous roots. Also known as manihot; manioc.

Cassidulinacea [INV ZOO] A superfamily of marine, benthic foraminiferans in the suborder Rotaliina, characterized by a test of granular calcite with monolamellar septa.

Cassiduloida [INV ZOO] An order of exocyclic Euechinoidea possessing five similar ambulacra which form petal-shaped areas (phyllodes) around the mouth.

cassowary [VERT ZOO] Any of three species of large, heavy, flightless birds composing the family Casuariidae in the order Casuariiformes.

cast [PALEON] A fossil reproduction of a natural object formed by infiltration of a mold of the object by waterborne minerals. [PHYSIO] A mass of fibrous material or exudate having the form of the body cavity in which it has been molded; classified from its source, such as bronchial, renal, or tracheal.

castaneous [BIOL] Chestnut-colored.

caste [INV ZOO] One of the levels of mature social insects in a colony that carry out a specific function; examples are workers and soldiers.

Castle's intrinsic factor *See* intrinsic factor.

Castniidae [INV ZOO] The castniids; large diurnal, butterflylike moths composing the single, small family of the lepidopteran superfamily Castnioidea.

Castnioidea [INV ZOO] A superfamily of neotropical and Indo-Australian lepidopteran insects in the suborder Heteroneura.

castor bean [BOT] The seed of the castor oil plant (*Ricinus communis*), a coarse, erect annual herb in the spurge family (Euphorbiaceae) of the order Geraniales.

castoreum gland [VERT ZOO] A preputial scent gland in the beaver.

Casuariidae [VERT ZOO] The cassowaries, a family of flightless birds in the order Casuariiformes lacking head and neck feathers and having bony casques on the head.

Casuariiformes [VERT ZOO] An order of large, flightless, ostrichlike birds of Australia and New Guinea.

Casuarinaceae [BOT] The single, monogeneric family of the plant order Casuarinales characterized by reduced flowers and green twigs bearing whorls of scalelike, reduced leaves.

Casuarinales [BOT] A monofamilial order of dicotyledonous plants in the subclass Hamamelidae.

cat [VERT ZOO] The common name for all members of the carnivoran mammalian family Felidae, especially breeds of the domestic species, *Felis domestica*.

catabiosis [PHYSIO] Degenerative changes accompanying cellular senescence.

catabolism [BIOCHEM] That part of metabolism concerned with the breakdown of large protoplasmic molecules and tissues, often with the liberation of energy.

catabolite [BIOCHEM] Any product of catabolism.

catabolite repression [BIOCHEM] An intracellular regulatory mechanism in bacteria whereby glucose, or any other carbon source that is an intermediate in catabolism, prevents formation of inducible enzymes.

catadromous [VERT ZOO] Pertaining to fishes which live in fresh water and migrate to spawn in salt water.

catalase [BIOCHEM] An enzyme that catalyzes the decomposition of hydrogen peroxide into molecular oxygen and water.

catelectrotonus [PHYSIO] The negative electric potential during the passage of a current on the surface of a nerve or muscle in the region of the cathode.

catalytic site *See* activity site.

catamount *See* puma.

Catapochrotidae [INV ZOO] A monospecific family of coleopteran insects in the superfamily Cucujoidea.

catarobic [ECOL] Pertaining to a body of water characterized by the slow decomposition of organic matter, and oxygen utilization which is insufficient to prevent the activity of aerobic organisms.

catastrophism [PALEON] The theory that the differences between fossils in successive stratigraphic horizons resulted from a general catastrophe followed by creation of the different organisms found in the next-younger beds.

catecholamine [BIOCHEM] Any one of a group of sympathomimetic amines containing a catechol moiety, including especially epinephrine, norepinephrine (levarterenol), and dopamine.

catenulate [BIOL] Having a chainlike form.

Catenulida [INV ZOO] An order of threadlike, colorless fresh-water rhabdocoeles with a simple pharynx and a single, median protonephridium.

caterpillar [INV ZOO] 1. The wormlike larval stage of a butterfly or moth. 2. The larva of certain insects, such as scorpion flies and sawflies.

catfish [VERT ZOO] The common name for a number of fishes which constitute the suborder Siluroidei in the order Cypriniformes, all of which have barbels around the mouth.

Cathartidae [VERT ZOO] The New World vultures, a family of large, diurnal predatory birds in the order Falconiformes that lack a voice and have slightly webbed feet.

cathepsin [BIOCHEM] Any of several proteolytic enzymes occurring in animal tissue that hydrolyze high-molecular-weight proteins to proteoses and peptones.

Cathie unit [BIOL] A unit for the standardization of streptokinase.

cathomycin [MICROBIO] A trade name for novobiocin.

catkin [BOT] An indeterminate type of inflorescence that resembles a scaly spike and sometimes is pendant.

Catostomidae [VERT ZOO] The suckers, a family of cypriniform fishes in the suborder Cyprinoidei.

cauda equina [ANAT] The roots of the sacral and coccygeal nerves, collectively; so called because of their resemblance to a horse's tail.

caudal [ZOO] Toward, belonging to, or pertaining to the tail or posterior end.

caudal artery [VERT ZOO] The extension of the dorsal aorta in the tail of a vertebrate.

caudal vertebra [ANAT] Any of the small bones of the vertebral column that support the tail in vertebrates; in humans, three to five are fused to form the coccyx.

Caudata [VERT ZOO] An equivalent name for Urodela.

caudate [ZOO] 1. Having a tail or taillike appendage. 2. Any member of the Caudata.

caudate lobe [ANAT] The tailed lobe of the liver that separates the right extremity of the transverse fissure from the commencement of the fissure for the inferior vena cava.

caudate nucleus [ANAT] An elongated arched gray mass which projects into and forms part of the lateral wall of the lateral ventricle.

caudex [BOT] The main axis of a plant, including stem and roots.

caudicle [BOT] A slender appendage attaching pollen masses to the stigma in orchids.

Caulerpaceae [BOT] A family of green algae in the order Siphonales.

caulescent [BOT] Having an aboveground stem.

cauliflorous [BOT] Producing flowers on the older branches or main stem.

cauliflory [BOT] Of flowers, growth on the main stem of limbs of a tree.

cauliflower [BOT] *Brassica oleracea* var. *botrytis*. A biennial crucifer of the order Capparales grown for its edible white head or curd, which is a tight mass of flower stalks.

cauliflower disease [PL PATH] 1. A disease of the strawberry plant caused by the eelworm and manifested as clustered, puckered, and malformed leaves. 2. A bacterial disease of the strawberry and some other plants caused by *Corynebacterium fascians*.

cauline [BOT] Belonging to or arising from the stem, particularly if on the upper portion.

Caulobacter [MICROBIO] A genus of prosthecate bacteria; cells are rod-shaped, fusiform, or vibrioid and stalked, and reproduction is by binary fission of cells.

Caulobacteraceae [MICROBIO] Formerly a family of aquatic, stalked, gram-negative bacteria in the order Pseudomonadales.

caulocarpic [BOT] Having stems that bear flowers and fruit every year.

Caulococcus [MICROBIO] A genus of bacteria of uncertain affiliation; coccoid cells may be connected by threads; reproduces by budding.

caulome [BOT] The stem structure or stem axis of a plant as a whole.

Cavellinidae [PALEON] A family of Paleozoic ostracods in the suborder Platycopa.

caveolae [CELL BIO] Tiny indentations in the cell surface membrane which trap fluids during micropinocytosis.

cavernicolous [BIOL] Inhabiting caverns.

cavernous sinus [ANAT] Either of a pair of venous sinuses of the dura mater located on the side of the body of the sphenoid bone.

Caviidae [VERT ZOO] A family of large, hystricomorph rodents distinguished by a reduced number of toes and a rudimentary tail.

CA virus See croup-associated virus.

cavity [BIOL] A hole or hollow space in an organ, tissue, or other body part.

cavy [VERT ZOO] Any of the rodents composing the family Caviidae, which includes the guinea pig, rock cavies, mountain cavies, capybara, salt desert cavy, and mara.

Caytoniales [PALEOBOT] An order of Mesozoic plants.

Cebidae [VERT ZOO] The New World monkeys, a family of primates in the suborder Anthropoidea including the capuchins and howler monkeys.

Cebochoeridae [PALEON] A family of extinct palaeodont artiodactyls in the superfamily Entelodontoidae.

Cebrionidae [INV ZOO] The robust click beetles, a family of cosmopolitan coleopteran insects in the superfamily Elateroidea.

Cebu maguey See cantala.

cecidium [PL PATH] Plant gall produced either by insects in ovipositing or by fungi as a consequence of infection.

Cecropidae [INV ZOO] A family of crustaceans in the suborder Caligoida which are external parasites on fish.

cecum [ANAT] The blind end of a cavity, duct, or tube, especially the sac at the beginning of the large intestine. Also spelled caecum.

cedar [BOT] The common name for a large number of evergreen trees in the order Pinales having fragrant, durable wood.

ceiba See kapok.

Celastraceae [BOT] A family of dicotyledonous plants in the order Celastrales characterized by erect and basal ovules, a flower disk that surrounds the ovary at the base, and opposite or sometimes alternate leaves.

Celastrales [BOT] An order of dicotyledonous plants in the subclass Rosidae marked by simple leaves and regular flowers.

celery [BOT] *Apium graveolens* var. *dulce*. A biennial umbellifer of the order Umbellales with edible petioles or leaf stalks.

celiac [ANAT] Of, in, or pertaining to the abdominal cavity.

cell [BIOL] The microscopic functional and structural unit of all living organisms, consisting of a nucleus, cytoplasm, and a limiting membrane.

cell constancy [BIOL] The condition in which the entire body, or a part thereof, consists of a fixed number of cells that is the same for all adults of the species.

cell differentiation [CELL BIO] The series of events involved in the development of a specialized cell having specific structural, functional, and biochemical properties.

cell division [CELL BIO] The process by which living cells multiply; may be mitotic or a amitotic.

cell-free extract [CELL BIO] A fluid obtained by breaking open cells; contains most of the soluble molecules of a cell.

cell inclusion [CELL BIO] A small, nonliving intracellular particle, usually representing a form of stored food, not immediately vital to life processes.

cell lineage [EMBRYO] The developmental history of individual blastomeres from their first cleavage division to their ultimate differentiation into cells of tissues and organs.

cell membrane [CELL BIO] A thin layer of protoplasm, consisting mainly of lipids and proteins, which is present on the surface of all cells. Also known as plasmalemma; plasma membrane.

cell movement [CELL BIO] 1. Intracellular movement of cellular components. 2. The movement of a cell relative to its environment.

cell permeability [CELL BIO] The permitting or activating of the passage of substances into, out of, or through cells.

cell plate [CELL BIO] A membrane-bound disk formed during cytokinesis in plant cells which eventually becomes the middle lamella of the wall formed between daughter cells.

cell sap [CELL BIO] The liquid content of a plant cell vacuole.

cells of Paneth [HISTOL] Coarsely granular secretory cells found in the crypts of Lieberkühn in the small intestine. Also known as Paneth cells.

cell-surface differentiation [CELL BIO] The specialization or modification of the cell surface.

cell-surface ionization [PHYSIO] The presence of a negative charge on the surface of all living cells suspended in aqueous salt solutions at neutral pH.

cell theory [BIOL] 1. A principle that describes the cell as the fundamental unit of all living organisms. 2. A principle that describes the properties of an organism as the sum of the properties of its component cells.

cellular [BIOL] Characterized by, consisting of, or pertaining to cells.

cellular affinity [BIOL] The phenomenon of selective adhesiveness observed among the cells of certain sponges, slime molds, and vertebrates.

cellulase [BIOCHEM] Any of a group of extracellular enzymes, produced by various fungi, bacteria, insects, and other lower animals, that hydrolyze cellulose.

cellulolytic [BIOL] Having the ability to hydrolyze cellulose; applied to certain bacteria and protozoans.

Cellulomonas [MICROBIO] A genus of gram-positive, irregular rods in the coryneform group of bacteria; metabolism is respiratory; most strains produce acid from glucose, and cellulose is attacked by all strains.

cellulose [BIOCHEM] $(C_6H_{10}O_5)_n$ The main polysaccharide in living plants, forming the skeletal structure of the plant cell wall; a polymer of β-D-glucose units linked together, with the elimination of water, to form chains comprising 2000–4000 units.

cell wall [CELL BIO] A semirigid, permeable structure that is composed of cellulose, lignin, or other substances and that envelops most plant cells.

Celyphidae [INV ZOO] A family of myodarian cyclorrhaphous dipteran insects in the subsection Acalypteratae.

cement [HISTOL] Calcified tissue which fastens the roots of teeth to the alveolus. Also known as cementum. [INV ZOO] Any of the various adhesive secretions, produced by certain invertebrates, that harden on exposure to air or water and are used to bind objects.

cement gland [INV ZOO] A structure in many invertebrates that produces cement.

centimorgan [GEN] A unit of genetic map distance, equal to the distance along a chromosome that gives a recombination frequency of 1%.

centipede [INV ZOO] The common name for an arthropod of the class Chilopoda.

central apparatus [CELL BIO] The centrosome or centrosomes together with the surrounding cytoplasm. Also known as cytocentrum.

central canal [ANAT] The small canal running through the center of the spinal cord from the conus medullaris to the lower part of the fourth ventricle; represents the embryonic neural tube.

Centrales [BOT] An order of diatoms (Bacillariophyceae) in which the form is often circular and the markings on the valves are radial.

central nervous system [ANAT] The division of the vertebrate nervous system comprising the brain and spinal cord.

central placentation [BOT] Having the ovules located in the center of the ovary.

central pocket loop [ANAT] A whorl type of fingerprint pattern having two deltas and at least one ridge that make a complete circuit.

central sulcus [ANAT] A groove situated about the middle of the lateral surface of the cerebral hemisphere, separating the frontal from the parietal lobe.

Centrarchidae [VERT ZOO] A family of fishes in the order Perciformes, including the fresh-water or black basses and several sunfishes.

centric [ANAT] Having all teeth of both jaws meet normally with perfect distribution of forces in the dental arch.

centriole [CELL BIO] A complex cellular organelle forming the center of the centrosome in most cells; usually found near the nucleus in interphase cells and at the spindle poles during mitosis.

Centrohelida [INV ZOO] An order of protozoans in the subclass Heliozoia lacking a central capsule and having axopodia or filopodia, and siliceous scales and spines.

centrolecithal ovum [CELL BIO] An egg cell having the yolk centrally located; occurs in arthropods.

Centrolenidae [VERT ZOO] A family of arboreal frogs in the suborder Procoela characterized by green bones.

centromere [CELL BIO] A specialized chromomere to which the spindle fibers are attached during mitosis. Also known as kinomere; primary constriction.

Centronellidina [PALEON] A suborder of extinct articulate brachiopods in the order Terebratulida.

centrosome [CELL BIO] A spherical hyaline region of the cytoplasm surrounding the centriole in many cells; plays a dynamic part in mitosis as the focus of the spindle pole.

Centrospermae [BOT] An equivalent name for the Caryophyllales.

Centrospermales [BOT] An equivalent name for the Caryophyllales.

centrosphere [CELL BIO] The differentiated layer of cytoplasm immediately surrounding the centriole.

centrum [ANAT] The main body of a vertebra. [BOT] The central space in hollow-stemmed plants.

Cephalaspida [PALEON] An equivalent name for the Osteostraci.

Cephalaspidomorphi [VERT ZOO] An equivalent name for Monorhina.

cephalic [ZOO] Of or pertaining to the head or anterior end.

cephalic vein [ANAT] A superficial vein located on the lateral side of the arm which drains blood from the radial side of the hand and forearm into the axillary vein.

cephalin [BIOCHEM] Any of several acidic phosphatides whose composition is similar to that of lecithin but having ethanolamine, serine, and inositol instead of choline; found in many living tissues, especially nervous tissue of the brain.

Cephalina [INV ZOO] A suborder of protozoans in the order Eugregarinida that are parasites of certain invertebrates.

cephalization [ZOO] Anterior specialization resulting in the concentration of sensory and neural organs in the head.

Cephalobaenida [INV ZOO] An order of the arthropod class Pentastomida composed of primitive forms with six-legged larvae.

Cephalocarida [INV ZOO] A subclass of Crustacea erected to include the primitive crustacean *Hutchinsoniella macracantha*.

Cephalochordata [VERT ZOO] A subphylum of the Chordata comprising the lancelets, including *Branchiostoma*.

Cephaloidae [INV ZOO] The false longhorn beetles, a small family of coleopteran insects in the superfamily Tenebrionoidea.

cephalomere [INV ZOO] One of the somites that make up the head of an arthropod.

cephalont [INV ZOO] A sporozoan just prior to spore formation.

Cephalopoda [INV ZOO] Exclusively marine animals constituting the most advanced class of the Mollusca, including squids, octopuses, and *Nautilus*.

cephalosporin [MICROBIO] Any of a group of antibiotics produced by strains of the imperfect fungus *Cephalosporium*.

cephalothin [MICROBIO] An antibiotic derived from the fungus *Cephalosporium*, resembling penicillin units in structure and activity, and effective against many gram-positive cocci that are resistant to penicillin.

cephalothorax [INV ZOO] The body division comprising the united head and thorax of arachnids and higher crustaceans.

Cephalothrididae [INV ZOO] A family of ribbonlike worms in the order Palaeonemertini.

cephalotrichous flagellation [CELL BIO] Insertion of flagella in polar tufts.

Cephidae [INV ZOO] The stem sawflies, composing the single family of the hymenopteran superfamily Cephoidea.

Cephoidea [INV ZOO] A superfamily of hymenopteran insects in the suborder Symphyta.

Ceractinomorpha [INV ZOO] A subclass of sponges belonging to the class Demospongiae.

Cerambycidae [INV ZOO] The longhorn beetles, a family of coleopteran insects in the superfamily Chrysomeloidea.

Ceramoporidae [PALEON] A family of extinct, marine bryozoans in the order Cystoporata.

Cerapachyinae [INV ZOO] A subfamily of predacious ants in the family Formicidae, including the army ant.

Ceraphronidae [INV ZOO] A superfamily of hymenopteran insects in the superfamily Proctotrupoidea.

cerata [INV ZOO] Respiratory papillae of the mantle in certain nudibranchs.

ceratine [INV ZOO] A hornlike material secreted by some anthozoans.

Ceratiomyxaceae [MYCOL] The single family of the fungal order Ceratiomyxales.

Ceratiomyxales [MYCOL] An order of myxomycetous fungi in the subclass Ceratiomyxomycetidae.

Ceratiomyxomycetidae [MYCOL] A subclass of fungi belonging to the Myxomycetes.

ceratite [PALEON] A fossil ammonoid of the genus *Ceratites* distinguished by a type of suture in which the lobes are further divided into subordinate crenulations while the saddles are not divided and are smoothly rounded.

ceratitic [PALEON] Pertaining to a ceratite.

Ceratodontidae [PALEON] A family of Mesozoic lungfishes in the order Dipteriformes.

Ceratomorpha [VERT ZOO] A suborder of the mammalian order Perissodactyla including the tapiroids and the rhinoceratoids.

Ceratophyllaceae [BOT] A family of rootless, free-floating dicotyledons in the order Nymphaeales characterized by unisexual flowers and whorled, cleft leaves with slender segments.

Ceratopsia [PALEON] The horned dinosaurs, a suborder of Upper Cretaceous reptiles in the order Ornithischia.

cercaria [INV ZOO] The larval generation which terminates development of a digenetic trematode in the intermediate host.

Cercopidae [INV ZOO] A family of homopteran insects belonging to the series Auchenorrhyncha.

Cercopithecidae [VERT ZOO] The Old World monkeys, a family of primates in the suborder Anthropoidea.

cercopod [INV ZOO] 1. Either of two filamentous projections on the posterior end of notostracan crustaceans. 2. *See* cercus.

Cercospora [MYCOL] A genus of imperfect fungi having dark, elongate, multiseptate spores.

Cercospora leaf spot [PL PATH] Any of several fungus diseases of plants caused by *Cercospora* species and characterized by areas of discoloration on the leaves.

cercus [INV ZOO] Either of a pair of segmented sensory appendages on the last abdominal segment of many insects and certain other arthropods. Also known as cercopod.

cere [VERT ZOO] A soft, swollen mass of tissue at the base of the upper mandible through which the nostrils open in certain birds, such as parrots and birds of prey.

cereal [BOT] Any member of the grass family (Graminae) which produces edible, starchy grains usable as food by man and his livestock. Also known as grain.

cerebellum [ANAT] The part of the vertebrate brain lying below the cerebrum and above the pons, consisting of three lobes and concerned with muscular coordination and the maintenance of equilibrium.

cerebral cortex [ANAT] The superficial layer of the cerebral hemispheres, composed of gray matter and concerned with coordination of higher nervous activity.

cerebral hemisphere [ANAT] Either of the two lateral halves of the cerebrum.

cerebral localization [ANAT] Designation of a specific region of the brain as the area controlling a specific physiologic function or as the site of a lesion.

cerebral peduncle [ANAT] One of two large bands of white matter (containing descending axons of upper motor neurons) which emerge from the underside of the cerebral hemispheres and approach each other as they enter the rostral border of the pons.

cerebrose *See* galactose.

cerebroside [BIOCHEM] Any of a complex group of glycosides found in nerve tissue, consisting of a hexose, a nitrogenous base, and a fatty acid. Also known as galactolipid.

cerebrospinal axis [ANAT] The axis of the body composed of the brain and spinal cord.

cerebrospinal fluid [PHYSIO] A clear liquid that fills the ventricles of the brain and the spaces between the arachnoid mater and pia mater.

cerebrum [ANAT] The enlarged anterior or upper part of the vertebrate brain consisting of two lateral hemispheres.

cerelose *See* glucose.

Ceriantharia [INV ZOO] An order of the Zoantharia distinguished by the elongate form of the anemone-like body.

Ceriantipatharia [INV ZOO] A subclass proposed by some authorities to include the anthozoan orders Antipatharia and Ceriantharia.

Cerithiacea [INV ZOO] A superfamily of gastropod mollusks in the order Prosobranchia.

cernuous [BOT] Drooping or inclining.

Cerophytidae [INV ZOO] A small family of coleopteran insects in the superfamily Elateroidea.

ceruloplasmin [BIOCHEM] The copper-binding serum protein in human blood.

cerumen [PHYSIO] The waxy secretion of the ceruminous glands of the external ear. Also known as earwax.

ceruminous gland [ANAT] A modified sweat gland in the external ear that produces earwax.

cervical [ANAT] Of or relating to the neck, a necklike part, or the cervix of an organ.

cervical canal [ANAT] Canal of the cervix of the uterus.

cervical flexure [EMBRYO] A ventrally concave flexure of the embryonic brain occurring at the junction of hindbrain and spinal cord.

cervical ganglion [ANAT] Any ganglion of the sympathetic nervous system located in the neck.

cervical plexus [ANAT] A plexus in the neck formed by the anterior branches of the upper four cervical nerves.

cervical sinus [EMBRYO] A triangular depression caudal to the hyoid arch containing the posterior visceral arches and grooves.

cervical vertebra [ANAT] Any of the bones in the neck region of the vertebral column; the transverse process has a characteristic perforation by a transverse foramen.

Cervidae [VERT ZOO] A family of pecoran ruminants in the superfamily Cervoidea, characterized by solid, deciduous antlers; includes deer and elk.

cervix uteri [ANAT] The narrow outer end of the uterus.

Cervoidea [VERT ZOO] A superfamily of tylopod ruminants in infraorder Pecora, including deer, giraffes, and related species.

cespitose [BOT] 1. Tufted; growing in tufts, as grass. 2. Having short stems forming a dense turf.

Cestida [INV ZOO] An order of ribbon-shaped ctenophores having a very short tentacular axis and an elongated pharyngeal axis.

Cestoda [INV ZOO] A subclass of tapeworms including most members of the class Cestoidea; all are endoparasites of vertebrates.

Cestodaria [INV ZOO] A small subclass of worms belonging to the class Cestoidea; all are endoparasites of primitive fishes.

Cestoidea [INV ZOO] The tapeworms, endoparasites composing a class of the phylum Platyhelminthes.

Cetacea [VERT ZOO] An order of aquatic mammals, including the whales, dolphins, and porpoises.

cetology [VERT ZOO] The study of whales.

Cetomimiformes [VERT ZOO] An order of rare oceanic, deepwater, soft-rayed fishes that are structurally diverse.

Cetomimoidei [VERT ZOO] The whalefishes, a suborder of the Cetomimiformes, including bioluminescent, deep-sea species.

Cetorhinidae [VERT ZOO] The basking sharks, a family of large, galeoid elasmobranchs of the isurid line.

chaeta *See* seta.

Chaetetidae [PALEON] A family of Paleozoic corals of the order Tabulata.

Chaetodontidae [VERT ZOO] The butterflyfishes, a family of perciform fishes in the suborder Percoidei.

Chaetognatha [INV ZOO] A phylum of abundant planktonic arrowworms.

Chaetonotoidea [INV ZOO] An order of the class Gastrotricha characterized by two adhesive tubes connected with the distinctive paired, posterior tail forks.

Chaetophoraceae [BOT] A family of algae in the order Ulotrichales characterized as branched filaments which taper toward the apices, sometimes bearing terminal setae.

Chaetopteridae [INV ZOO] A family of spioniform polychaete annelids belonging to the Sedentaria.

chalaza [BOT] The region at the base of the nucellus of an ovule; gives rise to the integuments. [CELL BIO] One of the paired, spiral, albuminous bands in a bird's egg that attach the yolk to the shell lining membrane at the ends of the egg.

chalazogamy [BOT] A process of fertilization in which the pollen tube passes through the chalaza to reach the embryo sac.

Chalcididae [INV ZOO] The chalcids, a family of hymenopteran insects in the superfamily Chalcidoidea.

Chalcidoidea [INV ZOO] A superfamily of hymenopteran insects in the suborder Apocrita, including primarily insect parasites.

Chalicotheriidae [PALEON] A family of extinct perissodactyl mammals in the superfamily Chalicotherioidea.

Chalicotherioidea [PALEON] A superfamily of extinct, specialized perissodactyls having claws rather than hooves.

chalones [BIOCHEM] Substances thought to be molecules of the protein-polypeptide class that are produced as part of the growth-control systems of tissues; known to inhibit cell division by acting on several phases in the mitotic cycle.

Chamaeleontidae [VERT ZOO] The chameleons, a family of reptiles in the suborder Sauria.

Chamaemyidae [INV ZOO] The aphid flies, a family of myodarian cyclorrhaphous dipteran insects of the subsection Acalypteratae.

chamaephyte [ECOL] Any perennial plant whose winter buds are within 25 centimeters of the soil surface.

Chamaesiphonales [BOT] An order of blue-green algae of the class Cyanophyceae; reproduce by cell division, colony fragmentation, and endospores.

chameleon [VERT ZOO] The common name for about 80 species of small-to-medium-sized lizards composing the family Chamaeleontidae.

chamois [VERT ZOO] *Rupicapra rupicapra*. A goatlike mammal included in the tribe Rupicaprini of the family Bovidae.

Chanidae [VERT ZOO] A monospecific family of teleost fishes in the order Gonorynchiformes which contain the milkfish (*Chanos chanos*), distinguished by the lack of teeth.

Channidae [VERT ZOO] The snakeheads, a family of fresh-water perciform fishes in the suborder Anabantoidei.

Chaoboridae [INV ZOO] The phantom midges, a family of dipteran insects in the suborder Orthorrhapha.

chaparral [ECOL] A vegetation formation characterized by woody plants of low stature, impenetrable because of tough, rigid, interlacing branches, which have simple, waxy, evergreen, thick leaves.

Characeae [BOT] The single family of the order Charales.

Characidae [VERT ZOO] The characins, the single family of the suborder Characoidei.

Characoidei [VERT ZOO] A suborder of the order Cypriniformes including fresh-water fishes with toothed jaws and an adipose fin.

character displacement [ECOL] An outcome of competition in which two species living in the same area have evolved differences in morphology or other characteristics that lessen competition for food resources.

Charadrii [VERT ZOO] The shore birds, a suborder of the order Charadriiformes.

Charadriidae [VERT ZOO] The plovers, a family of birds in the superfamily Charadrioidea.

Charadriiformes [VERT ZOO] An order of cosmopolitan birds, most of which live near water.

Charadrioidea [VERT ZOO] A superfamily of the suborder Charadrii, including plovers, sandpipers, and phalaropes.

Charales [BOT] Green algae composing the single order of the class Charophyceae.

charcoal rot [PL PATH] A fungus disease of potato, corn, and other plants caused by *Macrophomina phaseoli*; tissues of the root and lower stem are destroyed and blackened.

Chareae [BOT] A tribe of green algae belonging to the family Characeae.

Charophyceae [BOT] A class of green algae, division Chlorophyta.

Charophyta [BOT] A group of aquatic plants, ranging in size from a few inches to several feet in height, that live entirely submerged in water.

chartaceous [BOT] Resembling paper.

chartreusin [MICROBIO] $C_{18}H_{18}O_{18}$ Crystalline, greenish-yellow antibiotic produced by a strain of *Streptomyces chartreusis*; active against gram-positive microorganisms, acid-fast bacilli, and phage of *Staphylococcus pyogenes*.

chasmophyte [ECOL] A plant that grows in rock crevices.

chE See cholinesterase.

check ligament [ANAT] A thickening of the orbital fascia running from the insertion of the lateral rectus muscle to the medial orbital wall (medial check ligament) or from the insertion of the lateral rectus muscle to the lateral orbital wall (lateral check ligament).

cheek [ANAT] The wall of the mouth in man and other mammals. [ZOO] The lateral side of the head in submammalian vertebrates and in invertebrates.

cheek pouch [VERT ZOO] A saclike dilation of the cheeks in certain animals, such as rodents, in which food is held.

cheetah [VERT ZOO] *Acinonyx jubatus*. A doglike carnivoran mammal belonging to the cat family, having nonretractile claws and long legs.

Cheilostomata [INV ZOO] An order of ectoproct bryozoans in the class Gymnolaemata possessing delicate erect or encrusting colonies composed of loosely grouped zooecia.

Cheiracanthidae [PALEON] A family of extinct acanthodian fishes in the order Acanthodiformes.

chela [INV ZOO] 1. A claw or pincer on the limbs of certain crustaceans and arachnids. 2. A sponge spicule with talonlike terminal processes.

chelicera [INV ZOO] Either appendage of the first pair in arachnids, usually modified for seizing, crushing, or piercing.

Chelicerata [INV ZOO] A subphylum of the phylum Arthropoda; chelicerae are characteristically modified as pincers.

Chelidae [VERT ZOO] The side-necked turtles, a family of reptiles in the suborder Pleurodira.

chelifore [INV ZOO] Either of the first pair of appendages on the cephalic segment of pycnogonids.

cheliform [INV ZOO] Having a forcepslike organ formed by a movable joint closing against an adjacent segment; referring especially to a crab's claw.

cheliped [INV ZOO] Either of the paired appendages bearing chelae in decapod crustaceans.

Chelonariidae [INV ZOO] A family of coleopteran insects in the superfamily Dryopoidea.

Chelonethida [INV ZOO] An equivalent name for the Pseudoscorpionida.

Chelonia [VERT ZOO] An order of the Reptilia, subclass Anapsida, including the turtles, terrapins, and tortoises.

Chelonlidae [VERT ZOO] A family of reptiles in the order Chelonia including the hawksbill, loggerhead, and green sea turtles.

Cheluridae [INV ZOO] A family of amphipod crustaceans in the suborder Gammaridea.

Chelydridae [VERT ZOO] The snapping turtles, a small family of reptiles in the order Chelonia.

chemical sense [PHYSIO] A process of the nervous system for reception of and response to chemical stimulation by excitation of specialized receptors.

chemoautotroph [MICROBIO] Any of a number of autotrophic bacteria and protozoans which do not carry out photosynthesis.

chemodifferentiation [EMBRYO] The process of cellular differentiation at the molecular level by which embryonic cells become specialized as tissues and organs.

chemoheterotroph [BIOL] An organism that derives energy and carbon from the oxidation of preformed organic compounds.

chemoorganotroph [BIOL] An organism that requires an organic source of carbon and metabolic energy.

chemoreception [PHYSIO] Reception of a chemical stimulus by an organism.

chemoreceptor [PHYSIO] Any sense organ that responds to chemical stimuli.

chemostat [MICROBIO] An apparatus, and a principle, for the continuous culture of bacterial populations in a steady state.

chemosynthesis [BIOCHEM] The synthesis of organic compounds from carbon dioxide by microorganisms using energy derived from chemical reactions.

chemotaxis [BIOL] The orientation movement of a motile organism with reference to a chemical agent.

chemotaxonomy [BOT] The classification of plants based on natural products.

chemotropism [BIOL] Orientation response of a sessile organism with reference to chemical stimuli.

chenic acid See chenodeoxycholic acid.

chenodeoxycholic acid [BIOCHEM] $C_{24}H_{40}O_4$ A constituent of bile; needlelike crystals with a melting point of 119°C; soluble in alcohol, methanol, and acetic acid; used on an experimental basis to prevent and dissolve gallstones. Also known as anthropodesoxycholic acid; chenic acid; gallodesoxycholic acid.

Chenopodiaceae [BOT] A family of dicotyledonous plants in the order Caryophyllales having reduced, mostly greenish flowers.

Chermidae [INV ZOO] A small family of minute homopteran insects in the superfamily Aphidoidea.

Cherminae [INV ZOO] A subfamily of homopteran insects in the family Chermidae; all forms have a beak and an open digestive tract.

cherry [BOT] 1. Any trees or shrub of the genus *Prunus* in the order Rosales. 2. The simple, fleshy, edible drupe or stone fruit of the plant.

cherry leaf spot [PL PATH] A fungus disease of the cherry caused by *Coccomyces hiemalis;* spotting and chlorosis of the leaves occurs, with consequent retardation of tree and fruit development.

chersophyte [ECOL] A plant that grows in dry waste lands.

chestnut [BOT] The common name for several species of large, deciduous trees of the genus *Castanea* in the order Fagales, which bear sweet, edible nuts.

chestnut blight [PL PATH] A fungus disease of the chestnut caused by *Endothia parasitica*, which attacks the bark and cambium, causing cankers that girdle the stem and kill the plant. Also known as chestnut canker.

chestnut canker See chestnut blight.

chevron [VERT ZOO] The bone forming the hemal arch of a caudal vertebra.

chevrotain [VERT ZOO] The common name for four species of mammals constituting the family Tragulidae in the order Artiodactyla. Also known as mouse deer.

chiasma [ANAT] A cross-shaped point of intersection of two parts, especially of the optic nerves. [CELL BIO] The point of junction and fusion between paired chromatids or chromosomes, first seen during diplotene of meiosis.

Chiasmodontidae [VERT ZOO] A family of deepsea fishes in the order Perciformes.

chicken [VERT ZOO] *Galus galus*. The common domestic fowl belonging to the order Galliformes.

chick unit [BIOL] A unit for the standardization of pantothenic acid.

chicory [BOT] *Cichorium intybus*. A perennial herb of the order Campanulales grown for its edible green leaves.

chief cell [HISTOL] 1. A parenchymal, secretory cell of the parathyroid gland. 2. A cell in the lumen of the gastric fundic glands.

chigger [INV ZOO] The common name for bloodsucking larval mites of the Trombiculidae which parasitize vertebrates.

chilarium [INV ZOO] One of a pair of processes between the bases of the fourth pair of walking legs in the king crab.

Chilobolbinidae [PALEON] A family of extinct ostracods in the superfamily Hollinacea showing dimorphism of the velar structure.

Chilopoda [INV ZOO] The centipedes, a class of the Myriapoda that is exclusively carnivorous and predatory.

Chimaeridae [VERT ZOO] A family of the order Chimaeriformes.

Chimaeriformes [VERT ZOO] The single order of the chondrichthyan subclass Holocephali comprising the ratfishes, marine bottom-feeders of the Atlantic and Pacific oceans.

chimera [BIOL] An organism or a part made up of tissues or cells exhibiting chimerism.

chimerism [BIOL] The admixture of cell populations from more than one zygote.

chimopelagic [ECOL] Pertaining to, belonging to, or being marine organisms living at great depths throughout most of the year; during the winter they move to the surface.

chimpanzee [VERT ZOO] Either of two species of Primates of the genus *Pan* indigenous to central-west Africa.

chin [ANAT] The lower part of the face, at or near the symphysis of the lower jaw.

China grass *See* ramie.

chinchilla [VERT ZOO] The common name for two species of rodents in the genus *Chinchilla* belonging to the family Chinchillidae.

Chinchillidae [VERT ZOO] A family of rodents comprising the chinchillas and viscachas.

Chionididae [VERT ZOO] The white sheathbills, a family of birds in the order Charadriiformes.

chionophile [ECOL] Having a preference for snow.

chipmunk [VERT ZOO] The common name for 18 species of rodents belonging to the tribe Marmotini in the family Sciuridae.

Chiridotidae [INV ZOO] A family of holothurians in the order Apodida having six-spoked, wheel-shaped spicules.

Chirodidae [PALEON] A family of extinct chondrostean fishes in the suborder Platysomoidei.

Chirognathidae [PALEON] A family of conodonts in the suborder Neurodontiformes.

Chiroptera [VERT ZOO] The bats, an order of mammals having the front limbs modified as wings.

chiropterophilous [BIOL] Pollinated by bats.

chiropterygium [VERT ZOO] A typical vertebrate limb, thought to have evolved from a finlike appendage.

Chirotheuthidae [INV ZOO] A family of mollusks comprising several deep-sea species of squids.

chitin [BIOCHEM] A white or colorless amorphous polysaccharide that forms a base for the hard outer integuments of crustaceans, insects, and other invertebrates.

chitinase [BIOCHEM] An externally secreted digestive enzyme produced by certain microorganisms and invertebrates that hydrolyzes chitin.

chitinivorous bacterium [MICROBIO] Any bacterium which secretes chitinase and can digest chitin; organisms extract chitin from lobster exoskeletons, causing an infection called soft-shell disease.

Chitinozoa [PALEON] An extinct group of unicellular microfossils of the kingdom Protista.

chiton [INV ZOO] The common name for over 600 extant species of mollusks which are members of the class Polyplacophora.

chlamydeous [BOT] 1. Pertaining to the floral envelope. 2. Having a perianth.

Chlamydia [MICROBIO] The single genus of the family Chylamydiaceae.

Chlamydiaceae [MICROBIO] The single family of the order Chlamydiales; characterized by a developmental cycle from a small elementary body to a larger initial body which divides, with daughter cells becoming elementary bodies.

Chlamydiales [MICROBIO] An order of coccoid rickettsias; gram-negative, obligate, intracellular parasites of vertebrates.

Chlamydobacteriaceae [MICROBIO] Formerly a family of gram-negative bacteria in the order Chlamydobacteriales possessing trichomes in which false branching may occur.

Chlamydobacteriales [MICROBIO] Formerly an order comprising colorless, gram-negative, algae-like bacteria of the class Schizomycetes.

Chlamydomonadidae [INV ZOO] A family of colorless, flagellated protozoans in the order Volvocida considered to be close relatives of protozoans that possess chloroplasts.

Chlamydoselachidae [VERT ZOO] The frilled sharks, a family of rare deep-water forms having a combination of hybodont and modern shark characteristics.

chlamydospore [MYCOL] A thick-walled, unicellular resting spore developed from vegetative hyphae in almost all parasitic fungi.

Chlamydozoaceae [MICROBIO] A family of small, gram-negative, coccoid bacteria in the order Rickettsiales; members are obligate intracytoplasmic parasites, or saprophytes.

Chloracea [MICROBIO] The green sulfur bacteria, a family of photosynthetic bacteria in the suborder Rhodobacteriineae.

chloragogen [INV ZOO] Of or pertaining to certain specialized cells forming the outer layer of the alimentary tract in earthworms and other annelids.

chloramphenicol [MICROBIO] $C_{11}H_{12}O_2N_2Cl_2$ A colorless, crystalline, broad-spectrum antibiotic produced by *Streptomyces venezuelae;* industrial production is by chemical synthesis. Also known as chloromycetin.

Chloranglaceae [BOT] A primitive family of colonial green algae belonging to the Tetrasporales in which the cells are directly attached to each other.

chloranthy [BOT] A reverting of normally colored floral leaves or bracts to green foliage leaves.

chlorenchyma [BOT] Chlorophyll-containing tissue in parts of higher plants, as in leaves.

chloride shift [PHYSIO] The reversible exchange of chloride and bicarbonate ions between erythrocytes and plasma to effect transport of carbon dioxide and maintain ionic equilibrium during respiration.

Chlorobacteriaceae [MICROBIO] The equivalent name for Chlorobiaceae.

Chlorobiaceae [MICROBIO] A family of bacteria in the suborder Chlorobiineae; cells are nonmotile and contain bacteriochlorophylls *c, d,* or *e* in chlorobium vesicles attached to the cytoplasmic membrane.

Chlorobiineae [MICROBIO] The green sulfur bacteria, a suborder of the order Rhodospirillales; contains the families Chlorobiaceae and Chloroflexaceae.

Chlorobium [MICROBIO] A genus of bacteria in the family Chlorobiaceae; cells are ovoid, rod- or vibrio-shaped, and nonmotile, do not have gas vacuoles, contain bacteriochlorophyll *cor d*, and are free-living.

chlorobium chlorophyll [BIOCHEM] $C_{51}H_{67}O_4$-N_4Mg Either of two spectral forms of chlorophyll occurring as esters of farnesol in certain (*Chlorobium*) photosynthetic bacteria. Also known as bacterioviridin.

Chlorococcales [BOT] A large, highly diverse order of unicellular or colonial, mostly fresh-water green algae in the class Chlorophyceae.

Chlorodendrineae [BOT] A suborder of colonial green algae in the order Volvocales comprising some genera with individuals capable of detachment and motility.

Chloroflexaceae [MICROBIO] A family of phototrophic bacteria in the suborder Chlorobiineae; cells possess chlorobium vesicles and bacteriochlorophyll *a* and *c*, are filamentous, and show gliding motility; capable of anaerobic, phototrophic growth or aerobic chemotrophic growth.

Chloroflexies [MICROBIO] The single genus of the family Chloroflexaceae.

chlorogenic acid [BIOCHEM] $C16H_{18}O_9$ An important factor in plant metabolism; isolated from green coffee beans; the hemihydrate crystallizes in needlelike crystals from water. Also known as 3-caffeoylquinic acid; 3-(3,4-dihydroxycinnamoyl)quinic acid.

Chloromonadida [INV ZOO] An order of flattened, grass-green or colorless, flagellated protozoans of the class Phytamastigophorea.

Chloromonadina [INV ZOO] The equivalent name for Chloromonadida.

Chloromonadophyceae [BOT] A group of algae considered by some to be a class of the division Chrysophyta.

Chloromonadophyta [BOT] A division of algae in the plant kingdom considered by some to be a class, Chloromonadophyceae.

chloromycetin *See* chloramphenicol.

Chlorophyceae [BOT] A class of microscopic or macroscopic green algae, division Chlorophyta, composed of fresh- or salt-water, unicellular or multicellular, colonial, filamentous or sheetlike forms.

chlorophyll [BIOCHEM] The generic name for any of several oil-soluble green tetrapyrrole plant pigments which function as photoreceptors of light energy for photosynthesis.

chlorophyll a [BIOCHEM] $C_{55}H_{72}O_5N_4Mg$ A magnesium chelate of dihydroporphyrin that is esterified with phytol and has a cyclopentanone ring; occurs in all higher plants and algae.

chlorophyllase [BIOCHEM] An enzyme that splits or hydrolyzes chlorophyll.

chlorophyll b [BIOCHEM] $C_{55}H_{70}O_6N_4Mg$ An ester similar to chlorophyll *a* but with a —CHO substituted for a —CH_3; occurs in small amounts in all green plants and algae.

Chlorophyta [BOT] The green algae, a highly diversified plant division characterized by chloroplasts, having chlorophyll *a* and *b* as the predominating pigments.

Chloropidae [INV ZOO] The chloropid flies, a family of myodarian cyclorrhaphous dipteran insects in the subsection Acalypteratae.

chloroplast [BOT] A type of cell plastid occurring in the green parts of plants, containing chlorophyll pigments, and functioning in photosynthesis and protein synthesis.

Chloropseudomonas [MICROBIO] An invalid genus of bacteria; originally described as a member of the family Chlorobiaceae, with motile rod-shaped cells, without gas vacuoles, containing bacteriochlorophyll *c*, and capable of photoheterotrophic growth; cultures now known to be symbiotic of one of a number of typical Chlorobiaceae and a chemoorganotrophic bacterium capable of reducing elemental sulfur to sulfide.

chlorosis [PL PATH] A disease condition of green plants seen as yellowing of green parts of the plant.

chlorotic streak [PL PATH] A systemic virus disease of sugarcane characterized by yellow or white streaks on the foliage.

chlortetracycline [MICROBIO] $C_{22}H_{23}O_8N_2Cl$ Yellow, crystalline, broad-spectrum antibiotic produced by a strain of *Streptomyces aureofaciens*.

choana [ANAT] A funnel-shaped opening, especially the posterior nares. [INV ZOO] A protoplasmic collar surrounding the basal ends of the flagella in certain flagellates and in the choanocytes of sponges.

choanate fish [PALEON] Any of the lobefins composing the subclass Crossopterygii.

Choanichthyes [VERT ZOO] An equivalent name for the Sarcopterygii.

choanocyte [INV ZOO] Any of the choanate, flagellate cells lining the cavities of a sponge. Also known as collar cell.

Choanoflagellida [INV ZOO] An order of single-celled or colonial, colorless flagellates in the class Zoomastigophorea; distinguished by a thin protoplasmic collar at the anterior end.

choanosome [INV ZOO] The inner layer of a sponge; composed of choanocytes.

chocolate spot [PL PATH] A fungus disease of legumes caused by species of *Botrytis* and characterized by brown spots on leaves and stems, with withering of shoots.

chocolate tree *See* cacao.

Choeropotamidae [PALEON] A family of extinct palaeodont artiodactyls in the superfamily Entelodontoidea.

cholagogic [PHYSIO] Inducing the flow of bile.

cholaic acid *See* taurocholic acid.

cholane [BIOCHEM] $C_{24}H_{42}$ A tetracyclic hydrocarbon which may be considered as the parent substance of sterols, hormones, bile acids, and digitalis aglycons.

cholate [BIOCHEM] Any salt of cholic acid.

cholecystokinin [BIOCHEM] A hormone produced by the mucosa of the upper intestine which stimulates contraction of the gallbladder.

choledochoduodenal junction [ANAT] The point where the common bile duct enters the duodenum.

choleglobin [BIOCHEM] Combined native protein (globin) and open-ring iron-porphyrin, which is bile pigment hemoglobin; a precursor of biliverdin.

cholera vibrio [MICROBIO] *Vibrio comma,* the bacterium that causes cholera.

cholesterol [BIOCHEM] $C_{27}H_{46}O$ A sterol produced by all vertebrate cells, particularly in the liver, skin, and intestine, and found most abundantly in nerve tissue.

cholic acid [BIOCHEM] $C_{24}H_{40}O_5$ An unconjugated, crystalline bile acid.

choline [BIOCHEM] $C_5H_{15}O_2N$ A basic hygroscopic substance constituting a vitamin of the B complex; used by most animals as a precursor of acetylcholine and a source of methyl groups.

cholinergic [PHYSIO] Liberating, activated by, or resembling the physiologic action of acetylcholine.

cholinergic nerve [PHYSIO] Any nerve, such as autonomic preganglionic nerves and somatic motor nerves, that releases a cholinergic substance at its terminal points.

cholinesterase [BIOCHEM] An enzyme found in blood and in various other tissues that catalyzes hydrolysis of choline esters, including acetylcholine. Abbreviated chE.

cholytaurine *See* taurocholic acid.

Chondrichthyes [VERT ZOO] A class of vertebrates comprising the cartilaginous, jawed fishes characterized by the absence of true bone.

chondrification [PHYSIO] Formation of or conversion into cartilage.

chondrin [BIOCHEM] A horny gelatinous protein substance obtainable from the collagen component of cartilage.

chondriome [CELL BIO] Referring collectively to the chondriosomes (mitochondria) of a cell as a functional unit.

chondriosome [CELL BIO] Any of a class of self-perpetuating lipoprotein complexes in the form of grains, rods, or threads in the cytoplasm of most cells; thought to function in cellular metabolism and secretion.

chondroblast [HISTOL] A cell that produces cartilage.

Chondrobrachii [VERT ZOO] The equivalent name for Ateleopoidei.

chondroclast [HISTOL] A cell that absorbs cartilage.

chondrocranium [ANAT] The part of the adult cranium derived from the cartilaginous cranium. [EMBRYO] The cartilaginous, embryonic cranium of vertebrates.

chondrocyte [HISTOL] A cartilage cell.

chondrogenesis [EMBRYO] The development of cartilage.

chondroitin [BIOCHEM] A nitrogenous polysaccharide occurring in cartilage in the form of condroitinsulfuric acid.

chondrology [ANAT] The anatomical study of cartilage.

chondromucoid [BIOCHEM] A mucoid found in cartilage; a glycoprotein in which chondroitinsulfuric acid is the prosthetic group.

Chondromyces [MICROBIO] A genus of bacteria in the family Polyangiaceae; sporangia are stalked, and vegetative cells are short rods or spheres.

chondrophone [INV ZOO] In bivalve mollusks, a structure or cavity supporting the internal hinge cartilage.

Chondrophora [INV ZOO] A suborder of polymorphic, colonial, free-floating coelenterates of the class Hydrozoa.

chondroprotein [BIOCHEM] A protein (glycoprotein) occurring normally in cartilage.

chondroskeleton [ANAT] 1. The parts of the bony skeleton which are formed from cartilage. 2. Cartilaginous parts of a skeleton. [VERT ZOO] A cartilaginous skeleton, as in Chondrostei.

Chondrostei [PALEON] The most archaic infraclass of the subclass Actinopterygii, or rayfin fishes.

Chondrosteidae [PALEON] A family of extinct actinopterygian fishes in the order Acipenseriformes.

Chonetidina [PALEON] A suborder of extinct articulate brachiopods in the order Strophomenida.

Chonotrichida [INV ZOO] A small order of vase-shaped ciliates in the subclass Holotrichia; commonly found as ectocommensals on marine crustaceans.

chordamesoderm [EMBRYO] The portion of the mesoderm in the chordate embryo from which the notochord and related structures arise, and which induces formation of ectodermal neural structures.

Chordata [ZOO] The highest phylum in the animal kingdom, characterized by a notochord, nerve cord, and gill slits; includes the urochordates, lancelets, and vertebrates.

Chordodidae [INV ZOO] A family of worms in the order Gordioidea distinguished by a rough cuticle containing thickenings called areoles.

chorioallantois [EMBRYO] A vascular fetal membrane that is formed by the close association or fusion of the chorion and allantois.

chorion [EMBRYO] The outermost of the extraembryonic membranes of amniotes, enclosing the embryo and all of its other membranes.

chorionic gonadotropin *See* human chorionic gonadotropin.

chorioretinal [ANAT] Pertaining to the choroid and retina of the eye.

choripetalous *See* polypetalous.

chorisepalous *See* polysepalous.

chorisis [BOT] Separation of a leaf or floral part into two or more parts during development.

Choristida [INV ZOO] An order of sponges in the class Demospongiae in which at least some of the megascleres are tetraxons.

Choristodera [PALEON] A suborder of extinct reptiles of the order Eosuchia composed of a single genus, *Champsosaurus.*

Chormobacterium [MICROBIO] A genus of gram-negative, aerobic or facultatively anaerobic, motile, rod-shaped bacteria of uncertain affiliation; they produce violet colonies and violacein, a violet pigment with antibiotic properties.

choroid [ANAT] The highly vascular layer of the vertebrate eye, lying between the sclera and the retina.

choroid plexus [ANAT] Any of the highly vascular, folded processes that project into the third, fourth, and lateral ventricles of the brain.

chorology [ECOL] The study of how organisms are distributed geographically.

Christensen unit [BIOL] A unit for the standardization of streptokinase and plasmin.

Christmas factor [BIOCHEM] A soluble protein blood factor involved in blood coagulation. Also known as factor IX; plasma thromboplastin component (PTC).

Chromadoria [INV ZOO] A subclass of nematode worms in the class Adenophorea.

Chromadorida [INV ZOO] An order of principally aquatic nematode worms in the subclass Chromadoria.

Chromadoridae [INV ZOO] A family of soil and fresh-water, free-living nematodes in the superfamily Chromadoroidea; generally associated with algal substances.

Chromadoroidea [INV ZOO] A superfamily of small to moderate-sized, free-living nematodes with spiral, transversely ellipsoidal amphids and a striated cuticle.

chromaffin [BIOL] Staining with chromium salts.

chromaffin body See paraganglion.

chromaffin cell [HISTOL] Any cell of the suprarenal organs in lower vertebrates, of the adrenal medulla in mammals, of the paraganglia, or of the carotid bodies that stains with chromium salts.

chromaffin system [PHYSIO] The endocrine organs and tissues of the body that secrete epinephrine; characterized by an affinity for chromium salts.

Chromatiaceae [MICROBIO] A family of bacteria in the suborder Rhodospirillineae; motile cells have polar flagella, photosynthetic membranes are continuous with the cytoplasmic membrane, all except one species are anaerobic, and bacteriochlorophyll a or b is present.

chromatic vision [PHYSIO] Vision pertaining to the color sense, that is, the perception and evaluation of the colors of the spectrum.

chromatid [CELL BIO] 1. One of the pair of strands formed by longitudinal splitting of a chromosome which are joined by a single centromere in somatic cells during mitosis. 2. One of a tetrad of strands formed by longitudinal splitting of paired chromosomes during diplotene of meiosis.

chromatin [BIOCHEM] The deoxyribonucleoprotein complex forming the major portion of the nuclear material and of the chromosomes.

Chromatium [MICROBIO] A genus of bacteria in the family Chromatiaceae; cells are ovoid to rod-shaped, are motile, do not have gas vacuoles, and contain bacteriochlorophyll a on vesicular photosynthetic membranes.

chromatophore [HISTOL] A type of pigment cell found in the integument and certain deeper tissues of lower animals that contains color granules capable of being dispersed and concentrated.

chromatophorotrophin [BIOCHEM] Any crustacean neurohormone which controls the movement of pigment granules within chromatophores.

chromatoplasm [BOT] The peripheral protoplasm in blue-green algae containing chlorophyll, accessory pigments, and stored materials.

chromocenter [CELL BIO] An irregular, densely staining mass of heterochromatin in the chromosomes, with six armlike extensions of euchromatin, in the salivary glands of *Drosophila*.

chromocyte [HISTOL] A pigmented cell.

chromogen [BIOCHEM] A pigment precursor. [MICROBIO] A microorganism capable of producing color under suitable conditions.

chromogenesis [BIOCHEM] Production of colored substances as a result of metabolic activity; characteristic of certain bacteria and fungi.

chromolipid See lipochrome.

chromomere [CELL BIO] Any of the linearly arranged chromatin granules in leptotene and pachytene chromosomes and in polytene nuclei.

chromomycin [MICROBIO] Any of five components of an antibiotic complex produced by a strain of *Streptomyces griseus*; components are designated A_1 to A_5, of which A_3 ($C_{51}H_{72}O_{32}$) is biologically active.

chromonema [CELL BIO] The coiled core of a chromatid; it is thought to contain the genes.

chromophile [BIOL] Staining readily.

chromophobe [BIOL] Not readily absorbing a stain.

chromophyll [BIOCHEM] Any plant pigment.

chromoplasm [BOT] The pigmented, peripheral protoplasm of blue-green algae cells; contains chlorophyll, carotenoids, and phycobilins.

chromoplast [CELL BIO] Any colored cell plastid, excluding chloroplasts.

chromoprotein [BIOCHEM] Any protein, such as hemoglobin, with a metal-containing pigment.

chromosomal hybrid sterility [GEN] Sterility caused by inability of homologous chromosomes to pair during meiosis due to a chromosome aberration.

chromosome [CELL BIO] Any of the complex, threadlike structures seen in animal and plant nuclei during karyokinesis which carry the linearly arranged genetic units.

chromosome aberration [GEN] Modification of the normal chromosome complement due to deletion, duplication, or rearrangement of genetic material.

chromosome complement [GEN] The species-specific, normal diploid set of chromosomes in somatic cells.

chromosome map See genetic map.

chromosome puff [CELL BIO] Chromatic material accumulating at a restricted site on a chromosome; thought to reflect functional activity of the gene at that site during differentiation.

chromosome walking [GEN] Sequential isolation of overlapping molecular clones in order to span large intervals on the chromosome.

chronaxie [PHYSIO] The time interval required to excite a tissue by an electric current of twice the galvanic threshold.

chronocline [PALEON] A cline shown by successive morphological changes in the members of a related group, such as a species, in successive fossiliferous strata.

Chroococcales [BOT] An order of blue-green algae (Cyanophyceae) that reproduce by cell division and colony fragmentation only.

Chryomyidae [INV ZOO] A family of myodarian cyclorrhaphous dipteran insects in the subsection Acalypteratae.

Chrysididae [INV ZOO] The cuckoo wasps, a family of hymenopteran insects in the superfamily Bethyloidea having brilliant metallic blue and green bodies.

chrysocarpous [BOT] Bearing yellow fruits.

Chrysochloridae [PALEON] The golden moles, a family of extinct lipotyphlan mammals in the order Insectivora.

Chrysomelidae [INV ZOO] The leaf beetles, a family of coleopteran insects in the superfamily Chrysomeloidea.

Chrysomeloidea [INV ZOO] A superfamily of coleopteran insects in the suborder Polyphaga.

Chrysomonadida [INV ZOO] An order of yellow to brown, flagellated colonial protozoans of the class Phytamastigophorea.

Chrysomonadina [INV ZOO] The equivalent name for the Chrysomonadida.

Chrysopetalidae [INV ZOO] A small family of scale-bearing polychaete worms belonging to the Errantia.

Chrysophyceae [BOT] Golden-brown algae making up a class of fresh- and salt-water unicellular forms in the division Chrysophyta.

Chrysophyta [BOT] The golden-brown algae, a division of plants with a predominance of carotene and xanthophyll pigments in addition to chlorophyll.

Chthamalidae [INV ZOO] A small family of barnacles in the suborder Thoracica.

chyle [PHYSIO] Lymph containing emulsified fat, present in the lacteals of the intestine during digestion of ingested fats.

chylomicron [BIOCHEM] One of the extremely small lipid droplets, consisting chiefly of triglycerides, found in blood after ingestion of fat.

chylophyllous [BOT] Having succulent or fleshy leaves.

chyme [PHYSIO] The semifluid, partially digested food mass that is expelled into the duodenum by the stomach.

chymosin See rennin.

chymotrypsin [BIOCHEM] A proteinase in the pancreatic juice that clots milk and hydrolyzes casein and gelatin.

chymotrypsinogen [BIOCHEM] An inactive proteolytic enzyme of pancreatic juice; converted to the active form, chymotrypsin, by trypsin.

Chytridiales [MYCOL] An order of mainly aquatic fungi of the class Phycomycetes having a saclike to rhizoidal thallus and zoospores with a single posterior flagellum.

Chytridiomycetes [MYCOL] A class of true fungi.

cibarium [INV ZOO] In insects, the space anterior to the mouth cavity in which food is chewed.

Cicadellidae [INV ZOO] Large family of homopteran insects belonging to the series Auchenorrhyncha; includes leaf hoppers.

Cicadidae [INV ZOO] A family of large homopteran insects belonging to the series Auchenorrhyncha; includes the cicadas.

cicatrix [BIOL] A scarlike mark, usually caused by previous attachment of a part or organ.

Cichlidae [VERT ZOO] The cichlids, a family of perciform fishes in the suborder Percoidei.

Cicindelidae [INV ZOO] The tiger beetles, a family of coleopteran insects in the suborder Adephaga.

Ciconiidae [VERT ZOO] The tree storks, a family of wading birds in the order Ciconiiformes.

Ciconiiformes [VERT ZOO] An order of predominantly long-legged, long-necked birds, including herons, storks, ibises, spoonbills, and their relatives.

Cidaroida [INV ZOO] An order of echinoderms in the subclass Perischoechinoidea in which the ambulacra comprise two columns of simple plates.

Ciereszko unit [BIOL] A unit for the standardization of thyroid extracts.

ciguatoxin [BIOCHEM] A toxin produced by the benthic dinoflagellate *Gambierdiscus toxicus*.

Ciidae [INV ZOO] The minute, tree-fungus beetles, a family of coleopteran insects in the superfamily Cucujoidea.

cilia [ANAT] Eyelashes. [CELL BIO] Relatively short, centriole-based, hairlike processes on certain anatomical cells and motile organisms.

ciliary body [ANAT] A ring of tissue lying just anterior to the retinal margin of the eye.

ciliary movement [BIOL] A type of cellular locomotion accomplished by the rhythmical beat of cilia.

ciliary muscle [ANAT] The smooth muscle of the ciliary body.

ciliary process [ANAT] Circularly arranged choroid folds continuous with the iris in front.

Ciliatea [INV ZOO] The single class of the protozoan subphylum Ciliophora.

ciliated epithelium [HISTOL] Epithelium composed of cells bearing cilia on their free surfaces.

ciliolate [BIOL] Ciliated to a very minute degree.

Ciliophora [INV ZOO] The ciliated protozoans, a homogeneous subphylum of the Protozoa distinguished principally by a mouth, ciliation, and infraciliature.

Cimbicidae [INV ZOO] The cimbicid sawflies, a family of hymenopteran insects in the superfamily Tenthredinoidea.

Cimex [INV ZOO] The type genus of Cimicidae, including bedbugs and related forms.

Cimex lectularius [INV ZOO] The common bedbug of temperate and subtropical regions.

Cimicidae [INV ZOO] The bat, bed, and bird bugs, a family of flattened, wingless, parasitic hemipteran insects in the superfamily Cimicimorpha.

Cimicimorpha [INV ZOO] A superfamily, or group according to some authorities, of hemipteran insects in the subdivision Geocorisae.

Cimicoidea [INV ZOO] A superfamily of the Cimicimorpha in some systems of classification.

cinchona [BOT] The dried, alkaloid-containing bark of trees of the genus *Cinchona*.

Cinclidae [VERT ZOO] The dippers, a family of insect-eating songbirds in the order Passeriformes.

cinclides [INV ZOO] Pores in the body wall of some sea anemones for the release of water and stinging cells.

cinclis [INV ZOO] Singular of cinclides.

cinereous [BIOL] 1. Ashen in color. 2. Having the inert and powdery quality of ashes.

Cingulata [VERT ZOO] A group of xenarthran mammals in the order Edentata, including the armadillos.

cingulate [BIOL] Having a girdle of bands or markings.

cingulum [ANAT] 1. The ridge around the base of the crown of a tooth. 2. The tract of association nerve fibers in the brain, connecting the callosal and the hippocampal convolutions.

cingulum [BOT] The part of a plant between stem and root. [INV ZOO] 1. Any girdlelike structure. 2. A band of color or a raised line on certain bivalve shells. 3. The outer zone of cilia on discs of certain rotifers. 4. The clitellum in annelids.

cinnamon [BOT] *Cinnamomum zeylanicum.* An evergreen shrub of the laurel family (Lauraceae) in the order Magnoliales; a spice is made from the bark.

circadian rhythm [PHYSIO] A rhythmic process within an organism occurring independently of external synchronizing signals.

circinate [BIOL] Having the form of a flat coil with the apex at the center.

circinate vernation [BOT] Uncoiling of new leaves from the base toward the apex, as in ferns.

circle of Willis [ANAT] A ring of arteries at the base of the cerebrum.

circular deoxyribonucleic acid [BIOCHEM] A single- or double-stranded ring of deoxyribonucleic acid found in certain bacteriophages and in human wart virus. Also known as ring deoxyribonucleic acid.

circulation [PHYSIO] The movement of blood through defined channels and tissue spaces; movement is through a closed circuit in vertebrates and certain invertebrates.

circulatory system [ANAT] The vessels and organs composing the lymphatic and cardiovascular systems.

circulin [MICROBIO] Any of a group of peptide antibiotics produced by *Bacillus circulans* which are related to polymixin and are active against both gram-negative and gram-positive bacteria.

circulus [BIOL] Any of various ringlike structures, such as the vascular circle of Willis or the concentric ridges on fish scales.

circumboreal distribution [ECOL] The distribution of a Northern Hemisphere organism whose habitat includes North American, European, and Asian stations.

circumduction [ANAT] Movement of the distal end of a body part in the form of an arc; performed at ball-and-socket and saddle joints.

circumflex artery [ANAT] Any artery that follows a curving or winding course.

circumpharyngeal connective [INV ZOO] One of a pair of nerve strands passing around the esophagus in annelids and anthropods, connecting the brain and subesophageal ganglia.

circumscissile [BOT] Dehiscing along the line of a circumference, as exhibited by a pyxidium.

circumvallate papilla See vallate papilla.

Cirolanidae [INV ZOO] A family of isopod crustaceans in the suborder Flabellifera composed of actively swimming predators and scavengers with biting mouthparts.

Cirratulidae [INV ZOO] A family of fringe worms belonging to the Sedentaria which are important detritus feeders in coastal waters.

cirriform [ZOO] Having the form of a cirrus; generally applied to a prolonged, slender process.

Cirripedia [INV ZOO] A subclass of the Crustacea, including the barnacles and goose barnacles; individuals are free-swimming in the larval stages but permanently fixed in the adult stage.

Cirromorpha [INV ZOO] A suborder of cephalopod mollusks in the order Octopoda.

cirrus [INV ZOO] 1. The conical locomotor structure composed of fused cilia in hypotrich protozoans. 2. Any of the jointed thoracic appendages of barnacles. 3. Any hairlike tuft on insect appendages. 4. The male copulatory organ in some mollusks and trematodes. [VERT ZOO] Any of the tactile barbels of certain fishes. [ZOO] A tendrillike animal appendage.

cirrus sac [INV ZOO] A pouch or channel containing the copulatory organ (cirrus) in certain invertebrates.

cistern [ANAT] A closed, fluid-filled sac or vesicle, such as the subarachnoid spaces or the vesicles comprising the dictyosomes of a Golgi apparatus.

cistron [MOL BIO] The genetic unit (deoxyribonucleic acid fragment) that codes for a particular polypeptide; mutants do not complement each other within a cistron.

Citheroniinae [INV ZOO] Subfamily of lepidopteran insects in the family Saturniidae, including the regal moth and the imperial moth.

citramalase [BIOCHEM] An enzyme that is involved in the fermentation of glutamate by *Clostridium tetanomorphum*; catalyzes the breakdown of citramalic acid to acetate and pyruvate.

citrate [BIOCHEM] A salt or ester of citric acid.

citrate test [MICROBIO] A differential cultural test to identify genera within the bacterial family Enterobacteriaceae that are able to utilize sodium citrate as a sole source of carbon.

citric acid [BIOCHEM] $C_6H_8O_7 \cdot H_2O$ A colorless crystalline or white powdery organic, tricarboxylic acid occurring in plants, especially citrus fruits, and used as a flavoring agent, as an antioxidant in foods, and as a sequestering agent; the commercially produced form melts at 153°C.

citric acid cycle See Krebs cycle.

citriculture [BOT] The cultivation of citrus fruits.

Citrobacter [MICROBIO] A genus of bacteria in the family Enterobacteriaceae; motile rods that utilize citrate as the only carbon source.

citron [BOT] *Citrus medica.* A shrubby, evergreen citrus tree in the order Sapindales cultivated for its edible, large, lemonlike fruit.

citronella [BOT] *Cymbopogon nardus*. A tropical grass; the source of citronella oil.

citrulline [BIOCHEM] $C_6H_{13}O_3N_3$ An amino acid formed in the synthesis of arginine from ornithine.

citrus anthracnose [PL PATH] A fungus disease of citrus plants caused by *Colletotrichum gloeosporioides* and characterized by tip blight, stains on the leaves, and spots, stains, or rot on the fruit.

citrus blast [PL PATH] A bacterial disease of citrus trees caused by *Pseudomonas syringae* and marked by drying and browning of foliage and twigs and black pitting of the fruit.

citrus canker [PL PATH] A bacterial disease of citrus plants caused by *Xanthomonas citri* and producing lesions on twigs, foliage, and fruit.

citrus fruit [BOT] Any of the edible fruits having a pulpy endocarp and a firm exocarp that are produced by plants of the genus *Citrus* and related genera.

citrus scab [PL PATH] A fungus disease of citrus plants caused by *Sphaceloma rosarum*, producing scablike lesions on all plant parts.

civet [PHYSIO] A fatty substance secreted by the civet gland; used as a fixative in perfumes. [VERT ZOO] Any of 18 species of catlike, nocturnal carnivores assigned to the family Viverridae, having a long head, pointed muzzle, and short limbs with nonretractile claws.

civet cat *See* cacomistle.

civet gland [VERT ZOO] A large anal scent gland in civet cats that secretes civet.

civetone [BIOCHEM] $C_{17}H_{30}O$ 9-Cycloheptadecen-1-one, a macrocyclic ketone component of civet used in perfumes because of its pleasant odor and lasting quality; believed to function as a sex attractant among civet cats.

cladism [SYST] A theory of taxonomy by which organisms are grouped and ranked on the basis of the most recent phylogenetic branching point.

Cladistia [VERT ZOO] The equivalent name for Polypteriformes.

Cladocera [INV ZOO] An order of small, freshwater branchiopod crustaceans, commonly known as water fleas, characterized by a transparent bivalve shell.

Cladocopa [INV ZOO] A suborder of the order Myodocopida including marine animals having a carapace that lacks a permanent aperture when the two valves are closed.

Cladocopina [INV ZOO] The equivalent name for Cladocopa.

cladode *See* cladophyll.

cladodont [PALEON] Pertaining to sharks of the most primitive evolutionary level.

cladogenesis [EVOL] Evolution associated with altered habit and habitat, usually in isolated species populations.

cladogenic adaptation *See* divergent adaptation.

cladogram [EVOL] A dendritic diagram which shows the evolution and descent of a group of organisms.

Cladoniaceae [BOT] A family of lichens in the order Lecanorales, including the reindeer mosses

and cup lichens, in which the main thallus is hollow.

Cladophorales [BOT] An order of coarse, wiry, filamentous, branched and unbranched algae in the class Chlorophyceae.

cladophyll [BOT] A branch arising from the axil of a true leaf and resembling a foliage leaf. Also known as cladode.

cladoptosis [BOT] The annual abscission of twigs or branches instead of leaves.

Cladoselachii [PALEON] An order of extinct elasmobranch fishes including the oldest and most primitive of sharks.

cladus [BOT] A branch of a ramose spicule.

clam [INV ZOO] The common name for a number of species of bivalve mollusks, many of which are important as food.

Clambidae [INV ZOO] The minute beetles, a family of coleopteran insects in the superfamily Dascilloidea.

clammy [BIOL] Moist and sticky, as the skin or a stem.

clam worm [INV ZOO] The common name for a number of species of dorsoventrally flattened annelid worms composing the large family Nereidae in the class Polychaeta; all have a distinct head, with numerous appendages.

clan [ECOL] A very small community, perhaps a few square yards in area, in climax formation, and dominated by one species.

Clariidae [VERT ZOO] A family of Asian and African catfishes in the suborder Siluroidei.

Clarkecarididae [PALEON] A family of extinct crustaceans in the order Anaspidacea.

clasper [VERT ZOO] A modified pelvic fin of male elasmobranchs and holocephalians used for the transmission of sperm.

class [SYST] A taxonomic category ranking above the order and below the phylum or division.

classification [SYST] A systematic arrangement of plants and animals into categories based on a definite plan, considering evolutionary, physiologic, cytogenetic, and other relationships.

clathrate *See* cancellate.

Clathrinida [INV ZOO] A monofamilial order of sponges in the subclass Calcinea having an asconoid structure and lacking a true dermal membrane or cortex.

Clathrinidae [INV ZOO] The single family of the order Clathrinida.

Clathrochloris [MICROBIO] A genus of bacteria in the family Chlorobiaceae; cells are spherical to ovoid and arranged in chains united in trellislike aggregates, are nonmotile, contain gas vacuoles, and are free-living.

Clauberg unit [BIOL] A unit for the standardization of progesterone.

claustrum [ANAT] A thin layer of gray matter in each cerebral hemisphere between the lenticular nucleus and the island of Reil.

clava [BIOL] A club-shaped structure, as the tip on the antennae of certain insects or the fruiting body of certain fungi.

clavate [BIOL] Club-shaped. Also known as claviform.

Clavatoraceae [PALEOBOT] A group of middle Mesozoic algae belonging to the Charophyta.

Clavaxinellida [INV ZOO] An order of sponges in the class Demospongiae; members have monaxonid megascleres arranged in radial or plumose tracts.

clavicle [ANAT] A bone in the pectoral girdle of vertebrates with articulation occurring at the sternum and scapula.

claviculate [ANAT] Having a clavicle.

claviform See clavate.

clavus [INV ZOO] Any of several rounded or fingerlike processes, such as the club of an insect antenna or the pointed anal portion of the hemelytron in hemipteran insects.

claw [ANAT] A sharp, slender, curved nail on the toe of an animal, such as a bird. [INV ZOO] A sharp-curved process on the tip of the limb of an insect.

cleavage [EMBRYO] The subdivision of activated eggs into blastomeres.

cleavage nucleus [EMBRYO] The nucleus of a zygote formed by fusion of male and female pronuclei.

cleft grafting [BOT] A top-grafting method in which the scion is inserted into a cleft cut into the top of the stock.

cleistocarp See cleistothecium.

cleistocarpous [BOT] Of mosses, having the capsule opening irregularly without an operculum. [MYCOL] Forming or having cleistothecia.

cleistogamy [BOT] The production of small closed flowers that are self-pollinating and contain numerous seeds.

cleistothecium [MYCOL] A closed sporebearing structure in Ascomycetes; asci and spores are freed of the fruiting body by decay or desiccation. Also known as cleistocarp.

cleithrum [VERT ZOO] A bone external and adjacent to the clavicle in certain fishes, stegocephalians, and primitive reptiles.

Cleridae [INV ZOO] The checkered beetles, a family of coleopteran insects in the superfamily Cleroidea.

Cleroidea [INV ZOO] A superfamily of coleopteran insects in the suborder Polyphaga.

climatic climax [ECOL] A climax community viewed, by some authorities, as controlled by climate.

Climatiidae [PALEON] A family of archaic toothbearing fishes in the suborder Climatioidei.

Climatiiformes [PALEON] An order of extinct fishes in the class Acanthodii having two dorsal fins and large plates on the head and ventral shoulder.

Climatioidei [PALEON] A suborder of extinct fishes in the order Climatiiformes.

climatophysiology [PHYSIO] The study of the interaction of the natural environment with physiologic factors.

climax [ECOL] A mature, relatively stable community in an area, which community will undergo no further change under the prevailing climate; represents the culmination of ecological succession.

climax plant formation [ECOL] A mature, stable plant population in a climax community.

climbing bog [ECOL] An elevated boggy area on a swamp margin, usually occurring where there is a short summer and considerable rainfall.

climbing stem [BOT] A long, slender stem that climbs up a support or along the tops of other plants by using spines, adventitious roots, or tendrils for attachment.

cline [BIOL] A graded series of morphological or physiological characters exhibited by a natural group (as a species) of related organisms, generally along a line of environmental or geographic transition.

clinical genetics [GEN] The study of biological inheritance by direct observation of the living patient.

Clionidae [INV ZOO] The boring sponges, a family of marine sponges in the class Demospongiae.

clisere [ECOL] The succession of ecological communities, especially climax formations, as a consequence of intense climatic changes.

clitellum [INV ZOO] The thickened, glandular, saddlelike portion of the body wall of some annelid worms.

clitoris [ANAT] The homolog of the penis in females, located in the anterior portion of the vulva.

cloaca [INV ZOO] The chamber which functions as a respiratory, excretory, and reproductive duct in certain invertebrates. [VERT ZOO] The chamber which receives the discharges of the intestine, urinary tract, and reproductive canals in monotremes, amphibians, birds, reptiles, and many fish.

cloacal bladder [VERT ZOO] A diverticulum of the cloacal wall in monotremes, amphibians, and some fish, into which urine is forced from the cloaca.

cloacal gland [VERT ZOO] Any of the sweat glands in the cloaca of lower vertebrates, as snakes or amphibians.

clone [BIOL] All individuals, considered collectively, produced asexually or by parthenogenesis from a single individual.

Clonothrix [MICROBIO] A genus of sheathed bacteria; cells are attached and encrusted with iron and manganese oxides, and filaments are tapered.

clonus [PHYSIO] Irregular, alternating muscular contractions and relaxations.

closed ecological system [ECOL] A community into which a new species cannot enter due to crowding and competition.

Clostridium [MICROBIO] A genus of bacteria in the family Bacillaceae; usually motile rods which form large spores that distend the cell; anaerobic and do not reduce sulfate.

Clostridium botulinum [MICROBIO] A species of human pathogenic bacteria that produce an exotoxin, botulinin, which causes botulism.

Clostridium chauvoei [MICROBIO] A species of pathogenic bacteria that produce an exotoxin causing black leg in cattle.

Clostridium perfringens [MICROBIO] A gas-producing species of bacteria that produce several toxins and are the principal cause of gas gangrene in humans. Also known as *Clostridium welchii*.

Clostridium tetani [MICROBIO] A species of pathogenic soil bacteria which cause tetanus in humans.

Clostridium welchii *See* Clostridium perfringens.

clot [PHYSIO] A semisolid coagulum of blood or lymph.

clotting time [PHYSIO] The length of time required for shed blood to coagulate under standard conditions. Also known as coagulation time.

cloud forest *See* temperate rainforest.

clove [BOT] 1. The unopened flower bud of a small, conical, symmetrical evergreen tree, *Eugenia caryophyllata*, of the myrtle family (Myrtaceae); the dried buds are used as a pungent, strongly aromatic spice. 2. A small bulb developed within a larger bulb, as in garlic.

clover [BOT] 1. A common name designating the true clovers, sweet clovers, and other members of the Leguminosa. 2. A herb of the genus *Trifolium*.

club fungi [MYCOL] The common name for members of the class Basidiomycetes.

club moss [BOT] The common name for members of the class Lycopodiatae.

clubroot [PL PATH] A disease principally of crucifers, such as cabbage, caused by the slime mold *Plasmodiophora brassicae* in which roots become enlarged and deformed, leading to plant death.

Clupeidae [VERT ZOO] The herrings, a family of fishes in the suborder Clupoidea composing the most primitive group of higher bony fishes.

Clupeiformes [VERT ZOO] An order of teleost fishes in the subclass Actinopterygii, generally having a silvery, compressed body.

clupeine [BIOCHEM] A protamine found in salmon sperm, mainly composed of arginine (74.1%) and small percentages of threonine, serine, proline, alanine, valine, and isoleucine.

Clupoidea [VERT ZOO] A suborder of fishes in the order Clupeiformes comprising the herrings and anchovies.

Clusiidae [INV ZOO] A family of myodarian cyclorrhaphous dipteran insects in the subsection Acalyptratae.

clutch [VERT ZOO] A nest of eggs or a brood of chicks.

Clypeasteroida [INV ZOO] An order of exocyclic Euechinoidea having a monobasal apical system in which all the genital plates fuse together.

clypeus [INV ZOO] An anterior medial plate on the head of an insect, commonly bearing the labrum on its anterior margin. [MYCOL] A disk of black tissue about the mouth of the perithecia in certain ascomycetes.

Clythiidae [INV ZOO] The flat-footed flies, a family of cyclorrhaphous dipteran insects in the series Aschiza characterized by a flattened distal end on the hind tarsus.

Cnidaria [INV ZOO] The equivalent name for Coelenterata.

cnidoblast [INV ZOO] A cell that produces nematocysts. Also known as nettle cell; stinging cell.

cnidocil [INV ZOO] The trigger on a cnidoblast that activates discharge of the nematocyst when touched.

cnidophore [INV ZOO] A modified structure bearing nematocysts in certain coelenterates.

Cnidospora [INV ZOO] A subphylum of spore-producing protozoans that are parasites in cells and tissues of invertebrates, fishes, a few amphibians, and turtles.

coagulase [BIOCHEM] Any enzyme that causes coagulation of blood plasma.

coagulation time *See* clotting time.

coal paleobotany [PALEOBOT] A branch of the paleobotanical sciences concerned with the origin, composition, mode of occurrence, and significance of fossil plant materials that occur in or are associated with coal seams.

coati [VERT ZOO] The common name for three species of carnivorous mammals assigned to the raccoon family (Procyonidae) characterized by their elongated snout, body, and tail.

cobalamin *See* vitamin B_{12}.

Cobb's disease [PL PATH] A bacterial disease of sugarcane caused by *Xanthomonas vascularum* and characterized by a slime in the vascular bundles, dwarfing, streaking of leaves, and decay. Also known as sugarcane gummosis.

Cobitidae [VERT ZOO] The loaches, a family of small fishes, many eel-shaped, in the suborder Cyprinoidei, characterized by barbels around the mouth.

cobra [VERT ZOO] Any of several species of venomous snakes in the reptilian family Elaphidae characterized by a hoodlike expansion of skin on the anterior neck that is supported by a series of ribs.

coca [BOT] *Erythroxylon coca*. A shrub in the family Erythroxylaceae; its leaves are the source of cocaine.

cocarboxylase *See* thiamine pyrophosphate.

Coccidia [INV ZOO] A subclass of protozoans in the class Telosporea; typically intracellular parasites of epithelial tissue in vertebrates and invertebrates.

Coccinellidae [INV ZOO] The ladybird beetles, a family of coleopteran insects in the superfamily Cucujoidea.

coccobacillus [MICROBIO] A short, thick, oval bacillus, midway between the coccus and the bacillus in appearance.

coccoid [MICROBIO] A spherical bacterial cell.

Coccoidea [INV ZOO] A superfamily of homopteran insects belonging to the Sternorrhyncha; includes scale insects and mealy bugs.

coccolith [BOT] One of the small, interlocking calcite plates covering members of the Coccolithophorida.

Coccolithophora [INV ZOO] An order of phytoflagellates in the protozoan class Phytamastigophorea.

Coccolithophorida [BOT] A group of unicellular, biflagellate, golden-brown algae characterized by a covering of coccoliths.

Coccomyxaceae [BOT] A family of algae belonging to the Tetrasporales composed of elongate cells which reproduce only by vegetative means.

coccosphere [PALEOBOT] The fossilized remains of a member of Coccolithophorida.

Coccosteomorphi [PALEON] An aberrant lineage of the joint-necked fishes.

coccus [MICROBIO] A form of eubacteria which are more or less spherical in shape.

coccygeal body [ANAT] A small mass of vascular tissue near the tip of the coccyx.

coccyx [ANAT] The fused vestige of caudal vertebrae forming the last bone of the vertebral column in man and certain other primates.

cochlea [ANAT] The snail-shaped canal of the mammalian inner ear; it is divided into three channels and contains the essential organs of hearing.

cochlear duct *See* scala media.

Cochlearlidae [VERT ZOO] A family of birds in the order Ciconiiformes composed of a single species, the boatbill.

cochlear nerve [ANAT] A sensory branch of the auditory nerve which receives impulses from the organ of Corti.

cochlear nucleus [ANAT] One of the two nuclear masses in which the fibers of the cochlear nerve terminate; located ventrad and dorsad to the inferior cerebellar peduncle.

cochleate [BIOL] Spiral; shaped like a snail shell.

Cochliodontidae [PALEON] A family of extinct chondrichthian fishes in the order Bradyodonti.

cock [VERT ZOO] The adult male of the domestic fowl and of gallinaceous birds.

cockle [INV ZOO] The common name for a number of species of marine mollusks in the class Bivalvia characterized by a shell having convex radial ribs.

cockroach *See* roach.

coconut [BOT] *Cocos nucifera*. A large palm in the order Arecales grown for its fiber and fruit, a large, ovoid, edible drupe with a fibrous exocarp and a hard, bony endocarp containing fleshy meat (endosperm).

coconut bud rot [PL PATH] A fungus disease of the coconut palm caused by *Phytophthora palmivora* and characterized by destruction of the terminal bud and adjacent leaves.

cocoon [INV ZOO] 1. A protective case formed by the larvae of many insects, in which they pass the pupa stage. 2. Any of the various protective egg cases formed by invertebrates.

cod [VERT ZOO] The common name for fishes of the subfamily Gadidae, especially the Atlantic cod (*Gadus morrhua*).

codecarboxylase [BIOCHEM] The prosthetic component of the enzyme carboxylase which catalyzes decarboxylation of D-amino acids. Also known as pyridoxal phosphate.

codehydrogenase I *See* diphosphopyridine nucleotide.

codehydrogenase II *See* triphosphopyridine nucleotide.

Codiaceae [BOT] A family of green algae in the order Siphonales having macroscopic thalli composed of aggregates of tubes.

codon [GEN] The basic unit of the genetic code, comprising three-nucleotide sequences of messenger ribonucleic acid, each of which is translated into one amino acid in protein synthesis.

coelacanth [VERT ZOO] Any member of the Coelacanthiformes, an order of lobefin fishes represented by a single living genus, *Latimeria*.

Coelacanthidae [PALEON] A family of extinct lobefin fishes in the order Coelacanthiformes.

Coelacanthiformes [VERT ZOO] An order of lobefin fishes in the subclass Crossopterygii which were common fresh-water animals of the Carboniferous and Permian; one genus, *Latimeria*, exists today.

Coelacanthini [VERT ZOO] The equivalent name for Coelacanthiformes.

Coelenterata [INV ZOO] A phylum of the Radiata whose members typically bear tentacles and possess intrinsic nematocysts.

coelenteron [INV ZOO] The internal cavity of coelenterates.

coeloblastula [EMBRYO] A simple, hollow blastula with a single-layered wall.

Coelolepida [PALEON] An order of extinct jawless vertebrates (Agnatha) distinguished by skin set with minute, close-fitting scales of dentine, similar to placoid scales of sharks.

coelom [ZOO] The mesodermally lined body cavity of most animals higher on the evolutionary scale than flatworms and nonsegmented roundworms.

Coelomata [ZOO] The equivalent name for Eucoelomata.

coelomocyte [INV ZOO] A corpuscle, including amebocytes and eleocytes, in the coelom of certain animals, especially annelids.

coelomoduct [INV ZOO] Either of a pair of ciliated excretory and reproductive channels passing from the coelom to the exterior in certain invertebrates, including annelids and mollusks.

Coelomomycetaceae [MYCOL] A family of entomophilic fungi in the order Blastocladiales which parasitize primarily mosquito larvae.

coelomostome [INV ZOO] The opening of a coelomoduct into the coelom.

Coelomycetes [MYCOL] A group set up by some authorities to include the Sphaerioidaceae and the Melanconiales.

Coelopidae [INV ZOO] The seaweed flies, a family of myodarian cyclorrhaphous dipteran insects in the subsection Acalypteratae whose larvae breed on decomposing seaweed.

coeloplanula [INV ZOO] A hollow planula having a wall of two layers of cells.

Coelurosauria [PALEON] A group of small, lightly built saurischian dinosaurs in the suborder Theropoda having long necks and narrow, pointed skulls.

Coenagrionidae [INV ZOO] A family of zygopteran insects in the order Odonata.

coenenchyme [INV ZOO] The mesagloea surrounding and uniting the polyps in compound anthozoans. Also known as coenosarc.

Coenobitidae [INV ZOO] A family of terrestrial decapod crustaceans belonging to the Anomura.

coenobium [INV ZOO] A colony of protozoans having a constant size, shape, and cell number, but with undifferentiated cells.

coenocyte [BIOL] A multinucleate mass of protoplasm formed by repeated nucleus divisions without cell fission.

Coenomyidae [INV ZOO] A family of orthorrhaphous dipteran insects in the series Brachycera.

Coenopteridales [PALEOBOT] A heterogeneous group of fernlike fossil plants belonging to the Polypodiophyta.

coenosarc [INV ZOO] 1. The living axial part of a hydroid colony. 2. *See* coenenchyme.

coenosteum [INV ZOO] The calcareous skeleton of a compound coral or bryozoan colony.

Coenothecalia [INV ZOO] An order of the class Alcyonaria that forms colonies; lacks spicules but has a skeleton composed of fibrocrystalline argonite.

coenotype [BIOL] An organism having the characteristic structure of the group to which it belongs.

coenzyme [BIOCHEM] The nonprotein portion of an enzyme; a prosthetic group which functions as an acceptor of electrons or functional groups.

coenzyme A [BIOCHEM] $C_{21}H_{36}O_{16}N_7P_3S$ A coenzyme in all living cells; required by certain condensing enzymes to act in acetyl or other acyl-group transfer and in fatty-acid metabolism. Abbreviated CoA.

coenzyme I *See* diphosphopyridine nucleotide.

coenzyme II *See* triphosphopyridine nucleotide.

coevolution [EVOL] An evolutionary pattern based on the interaction among major groups or organisms with an obvious ecological relationship; for example, plant and plant-eater, flower and pollinator.

coffee [BOT] Any of various shrubs or small trees of the genus *Coffea* (family Rubiaceae) cultivated for the seeds (coffee beans) of its fruit; most coffee beans are obtained from the Arabian species, *C. arabica*.

cogon [BOT] *Imperate cylindrica*. A grass found in rainforests. Also known as alang-alang.

cohesion [BOT] The union of similar plant parts or organs, as of the petals to form a corolla.

cohesive terminus [MOL BIO] Either of the ends of single-stranded deoxyribonucleic acid that are complementary in the nucleotide sequences and can join, by base pairing, to form circular molecules.

coiled tubular gland [ANAT] A structure having a duct interposed between the surface opening and the coiled glandular portion; an example is a sweat gland.

coincidence [GEN] A numerical value equal to the number of double crossovers observed, divided by the number expected.

coitus [ZOO] The act of copulation. Also known as intercourse.

cola [BOT] *Cola acuminata*. A tree of the sterculia family (Sterculiaceae) cultivated for cola nuts, the seeds of the fruit; extract of cola nuts is used in the manufacture of soft drinks.

cold-blooded [PHYSIO] Having body temperature approximating that of the environment and not internally regulated.

cold-sensitive mutation [GEN] An alteration that causes a gene to be inactive at low temperature.

cold torpor [PHYSIO] Condition of reduced body temperature in poikilotherms.

Coleochaetaceae [BOT] A family of green algae in the suborder Ulotrichineae; all occur as attached, disklike, or parenchymatous thalli.

Coleodontidae [PALEON] A family of conodonts in the suborder Neurodontiformes.

Coleoidea [INV ZOO] A subclass of cephalopod mollusks including all cephalopods except *Nautilus*, according to certain systems of classification.

Coleophoridae [INV ZOO] The case bearers, moths with narrow wings composing a family of lepidopteran insects in the suborder Heteroneura; named for the silk-and-leaf shell carried by larvae.

Coleoptera [INV ZOO] The beetles, holometabolous insects making up the largest order of the animal kingdom; general features of the Insecta are found in this group.

coleoptile [BOT] The first leaf of a monocotyledon seedling.

coleorhiza [BOT] The sheath surrounding the radicle in monocotyledons.

Coleorrhyncha [INV ZOO] A monofamilial group of homopteran insects in which the beak is formed at the anteroventral extremity of the face and the propleura form a shield for the base of the beak.

Coleosporaceae [MYCOL] A family of parasitic fungi in the order Uredinales.

colic artery [ANAT] Any of the three arteries that supply the colon.

colicin [MICROBIO] A highly specific protein, released by some enteric bacilli, which kills other enteric bacilli.

coliform bacteria [MICROBIO] Colon bacilli, or forms which resemble or are related to them.

Coliidae [VERT ZOO] The colies or mousebirds, composing the single family of the avian order Coliiformes.

Coliiformes [VERT ZOO] A monofamilial order of birds distinguished by long tails, short legs, and long toes, all four of which are directed forward.

coliphage [VIROL] Any bacteriophage able to infect *Escherichia coli*.

colistin [MICROBIO] $C_{45}H_{85}O_{10}N_{13}$ A basic polypeptide antibiotic produced by *Bacillus colistinus*; consists of an A and B component, active against a broad spectrum of gram-positive microorganisms and some gram-negative microorganisms.

collagen [BIOCHEM] A fibrous protein found in all multicellular animals, especially in connective tissue.

collagenase [BIOCHEM] Any proteinase that decomposes collagen and gelatin.

collar cell *See* choanocyte.

collard [BOT] *Brassica oleracea* var. *acephala*. A biennial crucifer of the order Capparales grown for its rosette of edible leaves.

collateral bud [BOT] An accessory bud produced beside an axillary bud.

collecting tubule [ANAT] One of the ducts conveying urine from the renal tubules (nephrons) to the minor calyces of the renal pelvis.

Collembola [INV ZOO] The springtails, an order of primitive insects in the subclass Apterygota having six abdominal segments.

collenchyma [BOT] A primary, or early-differentiated, subepidermal supporting tissue in leaf petioles and vein ribs formed before vascular differentiation.

collenchyme [INV ZOO] A loose mesenchyme that fills the space between ectoderm and endoderm in the body wall of many lower invertebrates, such as sponges.

collenia [PALEOBOT] A convex, slightly arched, or turbinate stromatolite produced by late Precambrian blue-green algae of the genus *Collenia*.

Colletidae [INV ZOO] The colletid bees, a family of hymenopteran insects in the superfamily Apoidea.

colliculus [ANAT] 1. Any of the four prominences of the corpora quadrigemina. 2. The elevation of the optic nerve where it enters the retina. 3. The anterolateral, apical elevation of the arytenoid cartilages.

Collip unit [BIOL] A unit for the standardization of parathyroid extract.

colloblast [INV ZOO] An adhesive cell on the tentacles of ctenophores.

colloidal osmotic pressure See oncotic pressure.

Collothecacea [INV ZOO] A monofamilial suborder of mostly sessile rotifers in the order Monogonata; many species are encased in gelatinous tubes.

Collothecidae [INV ZOO] The single family of the Collothecacea.

Collyritidae [PALEON] A family of extinct, small, ovoid, exocyclic Euechinoidea with fascioles or a plastron.

colon [ANAT] The portion of the human intestine extending from the cecum to the rectum; it is divided into four sections: ascending, transverse, descending, and sigmoid. Also known as large intestine.

colon bacillus See Escherichia coli.

colonization [ECOL] The establishment of an immigrant species in a peripherally unsuitable ecological area; occasional gene exchange with the parental population occurs, but generally the colony evolves in relative isolation and in time may form a distinct unit.

colony [BIOL] A localized population of individuals of the same species which are living either attached or separately. [MICROBIO] A cluster of microorganisms growing on the surface of or within a solid medium; usually cultured from a single cell.

colony count [MICROBIO] The number of colonies of bacteria growing on the surface of a solid medium.

color vision [PHYSIO] The ability to discriminate light on the basis of wavelength composition.

Colossendeidae [INV ZOO] A family of deep-water marine arthropods in the subphylum Pycnogonida, having long palpi and lacking chelifores, except in polymerous forms.

colostrum [PHYSIO] The first milk secreted by the mammary gland during the first days following parturition.

Colubridae [VERT ZOO] A family of cosmopolitan snakes in the order Squamata.

Columbia unit [BIOL] A unit for the standardization of bacitracin.

Columbidae [VERT ZOO] A family of birds in the order Columbiformes composed of the pigeons and doves.

Columbiformes [VERT ZOO] An order of birds distinguished by a short, pointed bill, imperforate nostrils, and short legs.

columella [ANAT] See stapes. [BIOL] Any part shaped like a column. [BOT] A sterile axial body within the capsules of certain mosses, liverworts, and many fungi.

columnar epithelium [HISTOL] Epithelium distinguished by elongated, columnar, or prismatic cells.

columnar stem [BOT] An unbranched, cylindrical stem bearing a set of large leaves at its summit, as in palms, or no leaves, as in cacti.

Colydiidae [INV ZOO] The cylindrical bark beetles, a large family of coleopteran insects in the superfamily Cucujoidea.

Comasteridae [INV ZOO] A family of radially symmetrical Crinozoa in the order Comatulida.

Comatulida [INV ZOO] The feather stars, an order of free-living echinoderms in the subclass Articulata.

comb [INV ZOO] 1. A system of hexagonal cells constructed of beeswax by a colony of bees. 2. A comblike swimming plate in ctenophores. [VERT ZOO] A crest of naked tissue on the head of many male fowl.

comb growth unit [BIOL] A unit for the standardization of male sex hormones.

Comesomatidae [INV ZOO] A family of free-living nematodes in the superfamily Chromadoroidea found as deposit feeders on soft bottom sediments.

Commelinaceae [BOT] A family of monocotyledonous plants in the order Commelinales characterized by differentiation of the leaves into a closed sheath and a well-defined, commonly somewhat succulent blade.

Commelinales [BOT] An order of monocotyledonous plants in the subclass Commelinidae marked by having differentiated sepals and petals but lacking nectaries and nectar.

Commelinidae [BOT] A subclass of flowering plants in the class Liliopsida.

commensal [ECOL] An organism living in a state of commensalism.

commensalism [ECOL] An interspecific, symbiotic relationship in which two different species are associated, wherein one is benefited and the other neither benefited nor harmed.

commissure [BIOL] A joint, seam, or closure line where two structures unite.

common bile duct [ANAT] The duct formed by the union of the hepatic and cystic ducts.

common carotid artery *See* carotid artery.

common hepatic duct *See* hepatic duct.

common iliac artery *See* iliac artery.

community [ECOL] Aggregation of organisms characterized by a distinctive combination of two or more ecologically related species; an example is a deciduous forest. Also known as ecological community.

community classification [ECOL] Arrangement of communities into classes with respect to their complexity and extent, their stage of ecological succession, or their primary production.

comose [BOT] Having a tuft of soft hairs.

companion cell [BOT] A specialized parenchyma cell occurring in close developmental and physiologic association with a sieve-tube member.

comparative embryology [EMBRYO] A branch of embryology that deals with the similarities and differences in the development of animals or plants of different orders.

compensation point [BOT] The light intensity at which the amount of carbon dioxide released in respiration equals the amount used in photosynthesis, and the amount of oxygen released in photosynthesis equals the amount used in respiration.

competence [EMBRYO] The ability of a reacting system to respond to the inductive stimulus during early developmental stages.

competition [ECOL] The inter- or intraspecific interaction resulting when several individuals share an environmental necessity.

competitive enzyme inhibition [BIOCHEM] Prevention of an enzymatic process resulting from the reversible interaction of an inhibitor with a free enzyme.

competitive exclusion [ECOL] The result of a competition in which one species is forced out of part of the available habitat by a more efficient species.

competitive exclusion principle *See* Gause's principle.

competitive inhibition [BIOCHEM] Enzyme inhibition in which the inhibitor competes with the natural substrate for the active site of the enzyme; may be overcome by increasing substrate concentration.

compital [BOT] 1. Of the vein of a leaf, intersecting at a wide angle. 2. Of a fern, bearing sori at the intersection of two veins.

complemental air [PHYSIO] The amount of air that can still be inhaled after a normal inspiration.

complementary deoxyribonucleic acid [GEN] Deoxyribonucleic acid that is complementary to messenger ribonucleic acid.

complementary genes [GEN] Nonallelic genes that complement one another's expression in a trait.

complementation [GEN] The action of complementary genes.

complete flower [BOT] A flower having all four floral parts, that is, having sepals, petals, stamens, and carpels.

complete leaf [BOT] A dicotyledon leaf consisting of three parts: blade, petiole, and a pair of stipules.

complicate [INV ZOO] Folded lengthwise several times, as applied to insect wings.

Compositae [BOT] The single family of the order Asterales; perhaps the largest family of flowering plants, it contains about 19,000 species.

composite nerve [PHYSIO] A nerve containing both sensory and motor fibers.

compound acinous gland [ANAT] A structure with spherical secreting units connected to many ducts that empty into a common duct.

compound eye [INV ZOO] An eye typical of crustaceans, insects, centipedes, and horseshoe crabs, constructed of many functionally independent photoreceptor units (ommatidia) separated by pigment cells.

compound gland [ANAT] A secretory structure with many ducts.

compound leaf [BOT] A type of leaf with the blade divided into two or more separate parts called leaflets.

compound sugar *See* oligosaccharide.

compound tubular-acinous gland [ANAT] A structure in which the secreting units are simple tubes with acinous side chambers and all are connected to a common duct.

compound tubular gland [ANAT] A structure having branched ducts between the surface opening and the secreting portion.

compression wood [BOT] Dense wood found at the base of some tree trunks and on the undersides of branches.

conarium *See* pineal body.

concentric bundle [BOT] A vascular bundle in which xylem surrounds phloem, or phloem surrounds xylem.

conceptacle [BOT] A cavity which is shaped like a flask with a pore opening to the outside, contains reproductive structures, and is bound in a thallus such as in the brown algae.

conception [BIOL] Fertilization of an ovum by the sperm resulting in the formation of a viable zygote.

conch [INV ZOO] The common name for several species of large, colorful gastropod mollusks of the family Strombidae; the shell is used to make cameos and porcelain.

conchiolin [BIOCHEM] A nitrogenous substance that is the organic basis of many molluscan shells.

Conchorhagae [INV ZOO] A suborder of benthonic wormlike animals in the class Kinorhyncha.

Conchostraca [INV ZOO] An order of mussellike crustaceans of moderate size belonging to the subclass Branchiopoda.

concordance [GEN] Similarity in appearance of members of a twin pair with respect to one or more specific traits.

concrescence [BIOL] Convergence and fusion of parts originally separate, as the lips of the blastopore in embryogenesis.

conditional lethal mutant [GEN] A mutant gene that has lethal expression only under particular growth conditions, such as a specific temperature range.

condor [VERT ZOO] *Vultur gryphus.* A large American vulture having a bare head and neck, dull black plumage, and a white neck ruff.

conduplicate [BOT] Folded lengthwise and in half with the upper faces together, applied to leaves and petals in the bud.

Condylarthra [PALEON] A mammalian order of extinct, primitive, hoofed herbivores with five-toed plantigrade to semidigitigrade feet.

condyle [ANAT] A rounded bone prominence that functions in articulation. [BOT] The antheridium of certain stoneworts. [INV ZOO] A rounded, articular process on arthropod appendages.

condyloid articulation [ANAT] A joint, such as the wrist, formed by an ovoid surface that fits into an elliptical cavity, permitting all movement except rotation.

cone [BOT] The ovulate or staminate strobilus of a gymnosperm. [HISTOL] A photoceptor of the vertebrate retina that responds differentially to light across the visible spectrum, providing both color vision and visual acuity in bright light.

congeneric [SYST] Referring to the species of a given genus.

congestin [BIOCHEM] A toxin produced by certain sea anemones.

Coniconchia [PALEON] A class name proposed for certain extinct organisms thought to have been mollusks; distinguished by a calcareous univalve shell that is open at one end and by lack of a siphon.

Conidae [INV ZOO] A family of marine gastropod mollusks in the order Neogastropoda containing the poisonous cone shells.

conidiophore [MYCOL] A specialized aerial hypha that produces conidia in certain ascomycetes and imperfect fungi.

conidiospore *See* conidium.

conidium [MYCOL] Unicellular, asexual reproductive spore produced externally upon a conidiophore. Also known as conidiospore.

conifer [BOT] The common name for plants of the order Pinales.

Coniferales [BOT] The equivalent name for Pinales.

Coniferophyta [BOT] The equivalent name for Pinicae.

coniferous forest [ECOL] An area of wooded land predominated by conifers.

conjoint tendon [ANAT] The common tendon of the transverse and internal oblique muscles of the abdomen.

Conjugales [BOT] An order of fresh-water green algae in the class Chlorophyceae distinguished by the lack of flagellated cells, and conjugation being the method of sexual reproduction.

conjugase [BIOCHEM] Any of a group of enzymes which catalyze the breakdown of pteroylglutamic acid.

conjugate division [MYCOL] Division of dikaryotic cells in certain fungi in which the two haploid nuclei divide independently, each daughter cell receiving one product of each nuclear division.

conjugated protein [BIOCHEM] A protein combined with a nonprotein group, other than a salt or a simple protein.

conjugation [BOT] Sexual reproduction by fusion of two protoplasts in certain thallophytes to form a zygote. [INV ZOO] Sexual reproduction by temporary union of cells with exchange of nuclear material between two individuals, principally ciliate protozoans. [MICROBIO] A process involving contact between two bacterial cells during which genetic material is passed from one cell to the other.

conjunctiva [ANAT] The mucous membrane covering the eyeball and lining the eyelids.

connate leaf [BOT] A leaf shaped as though the bases of two opposite leaves had fused around the stem.

connective tissue [HISTOL] A primary tissue, distinguished by an abundance of fibrillar and nonfibrillar extracellular components.

connivent [BIOL] Converging so as to meet, but not fused into a single part.

Conoclypidae [PALEON] A family of Cretaceous and Eocene exocyclic Euechinoidea in the order Holectypoida having developed aboral petals, internal partitions, and a high test.

Conocyeminae [PALEON] A subfamily of Mesozoan parasites in the family Dicyemidae.

conodont [PALEON] A minute, toothlike microfossil, composed of translucent amber-brown, fibrous or lamellar calcium phosphate; taxonomic identity is controversial.

Conodontiformes [PALEON] A suborder of conodonts from the Ordovician to the Triassic having a lamellar internal structure.

Conodontophoridia [PALEON] The ordinal name for the conodonts.

Conopidae [INV ZOO] The wasp flies, a family of dipteran insects in the suborder Cyclorrhapha.

consanguinity [GEN] Blood relationship arising from common parentage.

consensus sequence [GEN] An average nucleotide sequence; each nucleotide is the most frequent at its position in the sequence.

conservation [ECOL] Those measures concerned with the preservation, restoration, beneficiation, maximization, reutilization, substitution, allocation, and integration of natural resources.

consociation [ECOL] A climax community of plants which is dominated by a single species.

consortism *See* symbiosis.

conspecific [SYST] Referring to individuals or populations of a single species.

Constellariidae [PALEON] A family of extinct, marine bryozoans in the order Cystoporata.

constitutive enzyme [BIOCHEM] An enzyme whose concentration in a cell is constant and is not influenced by substrate concentration.

constriction disease [PL PATH] A fungus disease of peach trees caused by a species of *Phomopsis* and marked by death of peripheral structures.

consumer [ECOL] A nutritional grouping in the food chain of an ecosystem, composed of heterotrophic organisms, chiefly animals, which ingest other organisms or particulate organic matter.

contact inhibition [CELL BIO] Cessation of cell division when cultured cells are in physical contact with each other.

contamination [MICROBIO] The process or act of soiling with bacteria.

contorted [BOT] Twisted; applied to proximate leaves whose margins overlap.

contour feather [VERT ZOO] Any of the large flight feathers or long tail feathers of a bird. Also known as penna; vane feather.

contractile [BIOL] Displaying contraction; having the property of contracting.

contractile vacuole [CELL BIO] A tiny, intracellular, membranous bladder that functions in maintaining intra- and extracellular osmotic pressures in equilibrium, as well as excretion of water, such as occurs in protozoans.

contraction [PHYSIO] Shortening of the fibers of muscle tissue.

contralateral [PHYSIO] Opposite; acting in unison with a similar part on the opposite side of the body.

Conularida [PALEON] A small group of extinct invertebrates showing a narrow, four-sided, pyramidal-shaped test.

Conulata [INV ZOO] A subclass of free-living coelenterates in the class Scyphozoa; individuals are described as tetraramous cones to elongate pyramids having tentacles on the oral margin.

Conulidae [PALEON] A family of Cretaceous exocyclic Euechinoidea characterized by a flattened oral surface.

conus arteriosus [EMBRYO] The cone-shaped projection from which the pulmonary artery arises on the right ventricle of the heart in man and mammals.

convergence [ANAT] The coming together of a group of afferent nerves upon a motoneuron of the ventral horn of the spinal cord. [EVOL] Development of similarities between animals or plants of different groups resulting from adaptation to similar habitats.

convivium [ECOL] A population exhibiting differentiation within the species and isolated geographically, generally a subspecies or ecotype.

convolute [BIOL] Twisted or rolled together, specifically referring to leaves, mollusk shells, and renal tubules.

convolution [ANAT] A fold, twist, or coil of any organ, especially any one of the prominent convex parts of the brain, separated from each other by depressions or sulci.

Convolvulaceae [BOT] A large family of dicotyledonous plants in the order Polemoniales characterized by internal phloem, the presence of chlorophyll, two ovules per carpel, and plicate cotyledons.

Cooke unit [BIOL] A unit for the standardization of pollen antigenicity.

Copeognatha [INV ZOO] An equivalent name for Psocoptera.

Copepoda [INV ZOO] An order of Crustacea commonly included in the Entomostraca; contains free-living, parasitic, and symbiotic forms.

Copodontidae [PALEON] An obscure family of Paleozoic fishes in the order Bradyodonti.

copper blight [PL PATH] A leaf spot disease of tea caused by the fungus *Guignardia camelliae*.

copperhead [VERT ZOO] *Agkistrodon contortrix*. A pit viper of the eastern United States; grows to about 3 feet (90 centimeters) in length and is distinguished by its coppery-brown skin with dark transverse blotches.

copper spot [PL PATH] A fungus disease of lawn grasses caused by *Gloeocercospora sorghi* and marked by coppery-red areas.

coppice [ECOL] A growth of small trees that are repeatedly cut down at short intervals; the new shoots are produced by the old stumps.

coprophagy [ZOO] Feeding on dung or excrement.

coprophilous [ECOL] Living in dung.

copulation [ZOO] The sexual union of two individuals, resulting in insemination or deposition of the male gametes in close proximity to the female gametes.

copulatory bursa [INV ZOO] 1. A sac that receives the sperm during copulation in certain insects. 2. The caudal expansion of certain male nematodes that functions as a clasper during copulation.

copulatory organ [ANAT] An organ employed by certain male animals for insemination.

copulatory spicule *See* spiculum.

coquina [INV ZOO] A small marine clam of the genus *Donax*.

Coraciidae [VERT ZOO] The rollers, a family of Old World birds in the order Coraciiformes.

Coraciiformes [VERT ZOO] An order of predominantly tropical and frequently brightly colored birds.

coracoid [ANAT] One of the paired bones on the posterior-ventral aspect of the pectoral girdle in vertebrates.

coracoid ligament [ANAT] The transverse ligament of the scapula which crosses over the suprascapular notch.

coracoid process [ANAT] The beak-shaped process of the scapula.

coral [INV ZOO] The skeleton of certain solitary and colonial anthozoan coelenterates; composed chiefly of calcium carbonate.

Corallanidae [INV ZOO] A family of sometimes parasitic, but often free-living, isopod crustaceans in the suborder Flabellifera.

Corallidae [INV ZOO] A family of dimorphic coelenterates in the order Gorgonacea.

Corallimorpharia [INV ZOO] An order of solitary sea anemones in the subclass Zoantharia resembling coral in many aspects.

Corallinaceae [BOT] A family of red algae, division Rhodophyta, having compact tissue with lime deposits within and between the cell walls.

coralline [INV ZOO] Any animal that resembles coral, such as a bryozoan or hydroid.

coralline algae [BOT] Red algae belonging to the family Corallinaceae.

corallite [INV ZOO] Skeleton of an individual polyp in a compound coral.

coralloid [BIOL] Resembling coral, or branching like certain coral.

corallum [INV ZOO] Skeleton of a compound coral.

Corbiculidae [INV ZOO] A family of fresh-water bivalve mollusks in the subclass Eulamellibranchia; an important food in the Orient.

Cordaitaceae [PALEOBOT] A family of fossil plants belonging to the Cordaitales.

Cordaitales [PALEOBOT] An extensive natural grouping of forest trees of the late Paleozoic.

cordate [BOT] Heart-shaped; generally refers to a leaf base.

cord factor [MICROBIO] A toxic glycolipid found as a surface component of tubercle bacilli that is responsible for virulence and serpentine growth.

cordon [BOT] A plant trained to grow flat against a vertical structure, in a single horizontal shoot or two opposed horizontal shoots.

Cordulegasteridae [INV ZOO] A family of anisopteran insects in the order Odonata.

Coreidae [INV ZOO] The squash bugs and leaf-footed bugs, a family of hemipteran insects belonging to the superfamily Coreoidea.

coremium [MYCOL] A small bundle of conidiophores in certain imperfect fungi.

corepressor [MOL BIO] A certain metabolite which, through combination with a repressor apoprotein produced by a regulator gene, can cause the binding of the protein to the operator gene region of a DNA chain.

coriaceous [BIOL] Leathery, applied to leaves and certain insects.

coriander [BOT] *Coriandrum sativum*. A strong-scented perennial herb in the order Umbellales; the dried fruit is used as a flavoring.

Cori ester See glucose-1-phosphate.

Coriolis effect [PHYSIO] The physiological effects (nausea, vertigo, dizziness, and so on) felt by a person moving radially in a rotating system, as a rotating space station.

corium [ANAT] See dermis. [INV ZOO] Middle portion of the forewing of hemipteran insects.

Corixidae [INV ZOO] The water boatmen, the single family of the hemipteran superfamily Corixoidea.

Corixoidea [INV ZOO] A superfamily of hemipteran insects belonging to the subdivision Hydrocorisae that lack ocelli.

cork [BOT] A protective layer of cells that replaces the epidermis in older plant stems.

corm [BOT] A short, erect, fleshy underground stem, usually broader than high and covered with membranous scales.

cormatose [BOT] Having or producing a corm.

cormidium [INV ZOO] The assemblage of individuals dangling in clusters from the main stem of pelagic siphonophores.

corn [BOT] *Zea mays*. A grain crop of the grass order Cyperales grown for its edible seeds (technically fruits).

Cornaceae [BOT] A family of dicotyledonous plants in the order Cornales characterized by perfect or unisexual flowers, a single ovule in each locule, as many stamens as petals, and opposite leaves.

Cornales [BOT] An order of dicotyledonous plants in the subclass Rosidae marked by a woody habit, simple leaves, well-developed endosperm, and fleshy fruits.

cornea [ANAT] The transparent anterior portion of the outer coat of the vertebrate eye covering the iris and the pupil. [INV ZOO] The outer transparent portion of each ommatidium of a compound eye.

Corner-Allen unit [BIOL] A unit for the standardization of progesterone.

cornicle [INV ZOO] Either of two protruding horn-shaped dorsal tubes in aphids which secrete a waxy fluid.

corniculate [BIOL] Possessing small horns or hornlike processes.

corniculate cartilage [ANAT] The cartilaginous nodule on the tip of the arytenoid cartilage.

cornification [PHYSIO] Conversion of stratified squamous epithelial cells into a horny layer and into derivatives such as nails, hair, and feathers.

corn smut [PL PATH] A fungus disease of corn caused by *Ustilago maydis*.

cornu [ANAT] A horn or hornlike structure.

corolla [BOT] A collective term for the petals of a flower.

corollate [BOT] Having a corolla.

corolline [BOT] Relating to, resembling, or being borne on a corolla.

corona [BOT] 1. An appendage or series of fused appendages between the corolla and stamens of some flowers. 2. The region where stem and root of a seed plant merge. Also known as crown. [INV ZOO] 1. The anterior ring of cilia in rotifers. 2. A sea urchin test. 3. The calyx and arms of a crinoid.

coronal suture [ANAT] The union of the frontal with the parietal bones transversely across the vertex of the skull.

corona radiata [HISTOL] The layer of cells immediately surrounding a mammalian ovum.

coronary artery [ANAT] Either of two arteries arising in the aortic sinuses that supply the heart tissue with blood.

coronary sinus [ANAT] A venous sinus opening into the heart's right atrium which drains the cardiac veins.

coronary sulcus [ANAT] A groove in the external surface of the heart separating the atria from the ventricles, containing the trunks of the nutrient vessels of the heart.

coronary valve [ANAT] A semicircular fold of the endocardium of the right atrium at the orifice of the coronary sinus.

coronary vein [ANAT] 1. Any of the blood vessels that bring blood from the heart and empty into the coronary sinus. 2. A vein along the lesser curvature of the stomach.

Coronatae [INV ZOO] An order of the class Scyphozoa which includes mainly abyssal species having the exumbrella divided into two parts by a coronal furrow.

coronavirus [VIROL] A major group of animal viruses including avian infectious bronchitis virus and mouse hepatitis virus.

coronoid [BIOL] Shaped like a beak.

coronoid fossa [ANAT] A depression in the humerus into which the apex of the coronoid process of the ulna fits in extreme flexion of the forearm.

coronoid process [ANAT] 1. A thin, flattened process projecting from the anterior portion of the upper border of the ramus of the mandible, and serving for the insertion of the temporal muscle. 2. A triangular projection from the upper end of the ulna, forming the lower part of the radial notch.

coronule [INV ZOO] A peripheral ring of spines on some diatom shells.

Corophiidae [INV ZOO] A family of amphipod crustaceans in the suborder Gammaridea.

corpora quadrigemina [ANAT] The inferior and superior colliculi collectively. Also known as quadrigeminal body.

corpus albicans [HISTOL] The white fibrous scar in an ovary; produced by the involution of the corpus luteum.

corpus allatum [INV ZOO] An endocrine structure near the brain of immature arthropods that secretes a juvenile hormone, neotenin.

corpus callosum [ANAT] A band of nerve tissue connecting the cerebral hemispheres in humans and higher mammals.

corpus cavernosum [ANAT] The cylinder of erectile tissue forming the clitoris in the female and the penis in the male.

corpus cerebelli [ANAT] The central lobe or zone of the cerebellum; regulates reflex tonus of postural muscles in mammals.

corpuscle [ANAT] 1. A small, rounded body. 2. An encapsulated sensory-nerve end organ.

corpus luteum [HISTOL] The yellow endocrine body formed in the ovary at the site of a ruptured Graafian follicle.

corpus striatum [ANAT] The caudate and lenticular nuclei, together with the internal capsule which separates them.

corresponding points [PHYSIO] Any two retinal areas in the respective eyes so that the area in one eye has an identical direction in the opposite retina.

corridor [ECOL] A land bridge that allows free migration of fauna in both directions.

Corrodentia [INV ZOO] The equivalent name for Psocoptera.

cortex [ANAT] The outer portion of an organ or structure, such as of the brain and adrenal glands. [BOT] A primary tissue in roots and stems of vascular plants that extends inward from the epidermis to the phloem. [INV ZOO] The peripheral layer of certain protozoans.

corticoid See adrenal cortex hormone.

corticosteroid [BIOCHEM] 1. Any steroid hormone secreted by the adrenal cortex of vertebrates. 2. Any steroid with properties of an adrenal cortex steroid.

corticosterone [BIOCHEM] $C_{21}H_{30}O_4$ A steroid hormone produced by the adrenal cortex of vertebrates that stimulates carbohydrate synthesis and protein breakdown and is antagonistic to the action of insulin.

corticotrophic [PHYSIO] Having an effect on the adrenal cortex.

corticotropin [BIOCHEM] A hormonal preparation having adrenocorticotropic activity, derived from the adenohypophysis of certain domesticated animals.

cortin unit [BIOL] A unit for the standardization of adrenal cortical hormones.

cortisol See hydrocortisone.

cortisone [BIOCHEM] $C_{22}H_{28}O_8I$ A steroid hormone produced by the adrenal cortex of vertebrates that acts principally in carbohydrate metabolism.

Corvidae [VERT ZOO] A family of large birds in the order Passeriformes having stout, long beaks; includes the crows, jays, and magpies.

Corylophidae [INV ZOO] The equivalent name for Orthoperidae.

corymb [BOT] An inflorescence in which the flower stalks arise at different levels but reach the same height, resulting in a flat-topped cluster.

corymbose [BOT] Resembling or pertaining to a corymb.

Corynebacteriaceae [MICROBIO] Formerly a family of nonsporeforming, usually nonmotile rod-shaped bacteria in the order Eubacteriales including animal and plant parasites and pathogens.

corynebacteriophage [VIROL] Any bacteriophage able to infect *Corynebacterium* species.

Corynebacterium [MICROBIO] A genus of gram-positive, straight or slightly curved rods in the coryneform group of bacteria; club-shaped swellings are common; includes human and animal parasites and pathogens, and plant pathogens.

Corynebacterium diphtheriae [MICROBIO] A facultatively aerobic, nonmotile species of bacteria that causes diphtheria in humans. Also known as Klebs-Loeffler bacillus.

Coryphaenidae [VERT ZOO] A family of pelagic fishes in the order Perciformes characterized by a blunt nose and deeply forked tail.

Coryphodontidae [PALEON] The single family of the Coryphodontoidea, an extinct superfamily of mammals.

Coryphodontoidea [PALEON] A superfamily of extinct mammals in the order Pantodonta.

Cosmocercidae [INV ZOO] A group of nematodes assigned to the suborder Oxyurina by some authorities and to the suborder Ascaridina by others.

cosmoid scale [VERT ZOO] A structure in the skin of primitive rhipidistians and dipnoans that is composed of enamel, a dentine layer (cosmine), and laminated bone.

cosmopolitan [ECOL] Having a worldwide distribution wherever the habitat is suitable, with reference to the geographical distribution of a taxon.

Cossidae [INV ZOO] The goat or carpenter moths, a family of heavy-bodied lepidopteran insects in the superfamily Cossoidea having the abdomen extending well beyond the hindwings.

Cossoidea [INV ZOO] A monofamilial superfamily of lepidopteran insects belonging to suborder Heteroneura.

Cossuridae [INV ZOO] A family of fringe worms belonging to the Sedentaria.

Cossyphodidae [INV ZOO] The lively ant guest beetles, a small family of coleopteran insects in the superfamily Tenebrionoidea.

costa [BIOL] A rib or riblike structure. [BOT] The midrib of a leaf. [INV ZOO] The anterior vein of an insect's wing.

Costaceae [BOT] A family of monocotyledonous plants in the order Zingiberales distinguished by having one functional stamen with two pollen sacs and spirally arranged leaves and bracts.

costal cartilage [ANAT] The cartilage occupying the interval between the ribs and the sternum or adjacent cartilages.

costal process [ANAT] An anterior or ventral projection on the lateral part of a cervical vertebra. [EMBRYO] An embryonic rib primordium, the ventrolateral outgrowth of the caudal, denser half of a sclerotome.

costate [BIOL] Having ribs or ridges.

Cotingidae [VERT ZOO] The cotingas, a family of neotropical suboscine birds in the order Passeriformes.

Cottidae [VERT ZOO] The sculpins, a family of perciform fishes in the suborder Cottoidei.

Cottiformes [VERT ZOO] An order set up in some classification schemes to include the Cottoidei.

Cottoidei [VERT ZOO] The mail-cheeked fishes, a suborder of the order Perciformes characterized by the expanded third infraorbital bone.

cotton [BOT] Any plant of the genus *Gossypium* in the order Malvales; cultivated for the fibers obtained from its encapsulated fruits or bolls.

cotton anthracnose [PL PATH] A fungus disease of cotton caused by *Glomerella gossypii* and characterized by reddish-brown to light-colored or necrotic spots.

cotton root rot [PL PATH] A fungus disease of cotton caused by *Phymatotrichum omnivorum* and marked by bronzing of the foliage followed by sudden wilting and death of the plant.

cotton rust [PL PATH] A fungus disease of cotton caused by *Puccinia stakmanii* producing low, greenish-yellow or orange elevations on the undersurface of leaves.

cotton wilt [PL PATH] 1. A fungus disease of cotton caused by *Fusarium vasinfectum* growing in the water-conducting vessels and characterized by wilt, yellowing, blighting, and death. 2. A fungus blight of cotton caused by *Verticillium albo-atrum* and characterized by yellow mottling of the foliage.

cottonwood [BOT] Any of several poplar trees (*Populus*) having hairy, encapsulated fruit.

cottony rot [PL PATH] A fungus disease of many plants, especially citrus trees, marked by fluffy white growth caused by *Sclerotinia sclerotiorum*, in which there is stem wilt and rot.

cotyledon [BOT] The first leaf of the embryo of seed plants.

cotylocercous cercaria [INV ZOO] A digenetic trematode larva characterized by a sucker or adhesive gland on the tail.

Cotylosauria [PALEON] An order of primitive reptiles in the subclass Anapsida, including the stem reptiles, ancestors of all of the more advanced Reptilia.

cotype *See* syntype.

cougar *See* puma.

Couinae [VERT ZOO] The couas, a subfamily of Madagascan birds in the family Cuculidae.

Coulter counter [MICROBIO] An electronic device for counting the number of cells in a liquid culture.

coumarin glycoside [BIOCHEM] Any of several glycosidic aromatic principles in many plants; contains coumaric acid as the aglycon group.

counterstain [BIOL] A second stain applied to a biological specimen to color elements other than those demonstrated by the principal stain.

counting chamber [MICROBIO] An accurately dimensioned chamber in a microslide which can hold a specific volume of fluid and which is usually ruled into units to facilitate the counting under the microscope of cells, bacteria, or other structures in the fluid.

covered smut [PL PATH] A seed-borne smut of certain grain crops caused by *Ustilago hordei* in barley and *U. avenae* in oats.

covert [ECOL] A refuge or shelter, such as a coppice, for game animals.

covey [VERT ZOO] 1. A brood of birds. 2. A small flock of birds of one kind, used typically of partridge and quail.

cow [VERT ZOO] A mature female cattle of the genus *Bos*.

Cowdria [MICROBIO] A genus of the tribe Ehrlichieae; coccoid to ellipsoidal, pleomorphic, or rod-shaped cells; intracellular parasites in cytoplasm and vacuoles of vascular endothelium of ruminants.

cowpea [BOT] *Vigna sinensis*. An annual legume in the order Rosales cultivated for its edible seeds. Also known as blackeye bean.

Cowper's gland *See* bulbourethral gland.

cowpox virus [VIROL] The causative agent of cowpox in cattle.

coxa [INV ZOO] The proximal or basal segment of the leg of insects and certain other arthropods which articulates with the body.

coxal cavity [INV ZOO] A cavity in which the coxa of an arthropod limb articulates.

coxal gland [INV ZOO] One of certain paired glands with ducts opening in the coxal region of arthropods.

Coxiella [MICROBIO] A genus of the tribe Rickettsieae; short rods which grow preferentially in host cell vacuoles.

coxopodite [INV ZOO] The basal joint of a crustacean limb.

coxsackievirus [VIROL] A large subgroup of the enteroviruses in the picornavirus group including various human pathogens.

coyote [VERT ZOO] *Canis latrans*. A small wolf native to western North America but found as far eastward as New York State. Also known as prairie wolf.

crab [INV ZOO] 1. The common name for a number of crustaceans in the order Decapoda having five pairs of walking legs, with the first pair modified as chelipeds. 2. The common name for members of the Merostoma.

crabapple [BOT] Any of several trees of the genus *Malus*, order Rosales, cultivated for their small, edible pomes.

Cracidae [VERT ZOO] A family of New World tropical upland game birds in the order Galliformes; includes the chachalacas, guans, and curassows.

cracked stem [PL PATH] A boron-deficiency disease of celery characterized by brown mottling of leaves and brittleness and cracking of leaf stalks.

Crambiinae [INV ZOO] The snout moths, a subfamily of lepidopteran insects in the family Pyralididae containing small marshland and grassland forms.

cranberry [BOT] Any of several plants of the genus *Vaccinium*, especially *V. macrocarpon,* in the order Ericales, cultivated for its small, edible berries.

Cranchiidae [INV ZOO] A family of cephalopod mollusks in the subclass Dibranchia.

crane [VERT ZOO] The common name for the long-legged wading birds composing the family Gruidae of the order Gruiformes.

Craniacea [INV ZOO] A family of inarticulate branchiopods in the suborder Craniidina.

cranial capacity [ANAT] The volume of the cranial cavity.

cranial flexure [EMBRYO] A flexure of the embryonic brain.

cranial fossa [ANAT] Any of the three depressions in the floor of the interior of the skull.

cranial nerve [ANAT] Any of the paired nerves which arise in the brainstem of vertebrates and pass to peripheral structures through openings in the skull.

Craniata [VERT ZOO] A major subdivision of the phylum Chordata comprising the vertebrates, from cyclostomes to mammals, distinguished by a cranium.

Craniidina [INV ZOO] A subdivision of inarticulate branchiopods in the order Acrotretida known to possess a pedicle; all forms are attached by cementation.

craniobuccal pouch [EMBRYO] A diverticulum from the buccal cavity in the embryo from which the anterior lobe of the hypophysis is developed. Also known as Rathke's pouch.

cranium [ANAT] That portion of the skull enclosing the brain. Also known as braincase.

craspedon [INV ZOO] A coelenterate medusa stage possessing a velum.

craspedote [INV ZOO] Having a velum, used specifically for velate hydroid medusae.

Crassulaceae [BOT] A family of dicotyledonous plants in the order Rosales notable for their succulent leaves and resistance to desiccation.

craw [ZOO] 1. The crop of a bird or insect. 2. The stomach of a lower animal.

crayfish [INV ZOO] The common name for a number of lobsterlike fresh-water decapod crustaceans in the section Astacura.

creatine [BIOCHEM] $C_4H_9O_2N_3$ α-Methylguanidine-acetic acid; a compound present in verte-

brate muscle tissue, principally as phosphocreatine.

creatinine [BIOCHEM] $C_4H_7ON_3$ A compound present in urine, blood, and muscle that is formed from the dehydration of creatine.

creeping disk [INV ZOO] The smooth and adhesive undersurface of the foot or body of a mollusk or of certain other invertebrates, on which the animal creeps.

cremocarp [BOT] A dry dehiscent fruit consisting of two indehiscent one-seeded mericarps which separate at maturity and remain pendant from the carpophore.

crenate [BIOL] Having a scalloped margin; used specifically for foliar structures, shrunken erythrocytes, and shells of certain mollusks.

crenation [PHYSIO] A notched appearance of shrunken erythrocytes; seen when they are exposed to the air or to strong saline solutions.

Crenothrix [MICROBIO] A genus of sheathed bacteria; cells are nonmotile, sheaths are attached and encrusted with iron and manganese oxides, and filaments may have swollen tips.

Crenotrichaceae [MICROBIO] Formerly a family of bacteria in the order Chlamydobacteriales having trichomes that are differentiated at the base and tip and attached to a firm substrate.

crenulate [BIOL] Having a minutely crenate margin.

Creodonta [PALEON] A group formerly recognized as a suborder of the order Carnivora.

creosote bush [BOT] *Larrea divaricata.* A bronze-green, xerophytic shrub characteristic of all the American warm deserts.

crepuscular [ZOO] Active during the hours of twilight or preceding dawn.

cress [BOT] Any of several prostrate crucifers belonging to the order Capparales and grown for their flavorful leaves; includes watercress (*Nasturtium officinale*), garden cress (*Lepidium sativum*), and upland or spring cress (*Barbarea verna*).

cribellum [INV ZOO] 1. A small accessory spinning organ located in front of the ordinary spinning organ in certain spiders. 2. A chitinous plate perforated with the openings of certain gland ducts in insects.

Cribrariaceae [BOT] A family of true slime molds in the order Liceales.

cribriform [BIOL] Perforated, like a sieve.

cribriform fascia [ANAT] The sievelike covering of the fossa ovalis of the thigh.

cribriform plate [ANAT] 1. The horizontal plate of the ethmoid bone, part of the floor of the anterior cranial fossa. 2. The bone lining a dental alveolus.

Cricetidae [VERT ZOO] A family of the order Rodentia including hamsters, voles, and some mice.

Cricetinae [VERT ZOO] A subfamily of mice in the family Cricetidae.

cricket [INV ZOO] 1. The common name for members of the insect family Gryllidae. 2. The common name for any of several related species of orthopteran insects in the families Tettigoniidae, Gryllotalpidae, and Tridactylidae.

cricoid [ANAT] The signet-ring-shaped cartilage forming the base of the larynx in man and most other mammals.

Crinoidea [INV ZOO] A class of radially symmetrical crinozoans in which the adult body is flower-shaped and is either carried on an anchored stem or is free-living.

Crinozoa [INV ZOO] A subphylum of the Echinodermata comprising radially symmetrical forms that show a partly meridional pattern of growth.

crissum [VERT ZOO] 1. The region surrounding the cloacal opening in birds. 2. The vent feathers covering the circumcloacal region.

crista [BIOL] A ridge or crest.

cristate [BIOL] Having a crista.

Cristispira [MICROBIO] A genus of bacteria in the family Spirochaetaceae; helical cells with 3–10 complete turns; they have ovoid inclusion bodies and bundles of axial fibrils; commensals in mollusks.

crocodile [VERT ZOO] The common name for about 12 species of aquatic reptiles included in the family Crocodylidae.

Crocodilia [VERT ZOO] An order of the class Reptilia which is composed of large, voracious, aquatic species, including the alligators, caimans, crocodiles, and gavials.

Crocodylidae [VERT ZOO] A family of reptiles in the order Crocodilia including the true crocodiles, false gavial, alligators, and caimans.

Crocodylinae [VERT ZOO] A subfamily of reptiles in the family Crocodylidae containing the crocodiles, *Osteolaemus*, and the false gavial.

crocus [BOT] A plant of the genus *Crocus*, comprising perennial herbs cultivated for their flowers.

Cro-Magnon man [PALEON] 1. A race of tall, erect Caucasoid men having large skulls; identified from skeletons found in southern France. 2. A general term to describe all fossils resembling this race that belong to the upper Paleolithic (35,000–8000 B.C.) in Europe.

crop [VERT ZOO] A distensible saccular diverticulum near the lower end of the esophagus of birds which serves to hold and soften food before passage into the stomach.

crossbreed [BIOL] To propagate new individuals by breeding two distinctive varieties of a species.

cross-fertilization [BOT] Fertilization between two separate plants. [ZOO] Fertilization between different kinds of individuals.

crossing over [GEN] The exchange of genetic material between paired homologous chromosomes during meiosis. Also known as crossover.

Crossopterygii [PALEON] A subclass of the class Osteichthyes comprising the extinct lobefins or choanate fishes and represented by one extant species; distinguished by two separate dorsal fins.

Crossosomataceae [BOT] A monogeneric family of xerophytic shrubs in the order Dilleniales characterized by perigynous flowers, seeds with thin endosperm, and small, entire leaves.

crossover *See* crossing over.

cross-pollination [BOT] Transfer of pollen from the anthers of one plant to the stigmata of another plant.

Crotalidae [VERT ZOO] A family of proglyphodont venomous snakes in the reptilian suborder Serpentes.

croup-associated virus [VIROL] A virus belonging to subgroup 2 of the parainfluenza viruses and found in children with croup. Also known as CA virus; laryngotracheobronchitis virus.

crow [VERT ZOO] The common name for a number of predominantly black birds in the genus *Corvus* comprising the most advanced members of the family Corvidae.

crown [ANAT] 1. The top of the skull. 2. The portion of a tooth above the gum. [BOT] 1. The topmost part of a plant or plant part. 2. *See* corona.

crown gall [PL PATH] A bacterial disease of many plants induced by *Bacterium tumefaciens* and marked by abnormal enlargement of the stem near the root crown.

crown grafting [BOT] A method of vegetative propagation whereby a scion 3–6 inches (8–15 centimeters) long is grafted at the root crown, just below ground level.

crown rot [PL PATH] Any plant disease or disorder marked by deterioration of the stem at or near ground level.

crown rust [PL PATH] A rust disease of oats and certain other grasses caused by varieties of *Puccinia coronata* and marked by light-orange masses of fungi on the leaves.

cruciate [ANAT] Resembling a cross.

Cruciferae [BOT] A large family of dicotyledonous herbs in the order Capparales characterized by parietal placentation; hypogynous, mostly regular flowers; and a two-celled ovary with the ovules attached to the margins of the partition.

crura [ANAT] Plural of crus.

crus [ANAT] 1. The shank of the hindleg, that portion between the femur and the ankle. 2. Any of various parts of the body resembling a leg or root.

Crustacea [INV ZOO] A class of arthropod animals in the subphylum Mandibulata having jointed feet and mandibles, two pairs of antennae, and segmented, chitin-encased bodies.

crustecdysone [BIOCHEM] $C_{27}H_{44}O_7$ 20-Hydroxyecdysone, the molting hormone produced by Y organs in crustaceans.

crustose [BOT] Of a lichen, forming a thin crust-like thallus which adheres closely to the substratum of rock, bark, or soil.

crust vegetation [ECOL] Zonal growths of algae, mosses, lichens, or liverworts having variable coverage and a thickness of only a few centimeters.

cryobiology [BIOL] The use of low-temperature environments in the study of living plants and animals.

cryobiosis [PHYSIO] A type of cryptobiosis induced by low temperatures.

cryophilic *See* cryophilous.

cryophilous [ECOL] Having a preference for low temperatures. Also known as cryophilic.

cryophyte [ECOL] A plant that forms winter buds below the soil surface.

cryoprecipitate [BIOCHEM] The precipitate of a cryoglobulin.

Cryphaeaceae [BOT] A family of mosses in the order Isobryales distinguished by a rough calyptra.

crypt [ANAT] 1. A follicle or pitlike depression. 2. A simple glandular cavity.

cryptic behavior [ZOO] A behavior pattern that maximizes an organism's ability to conceal itself.

cryptic coloration [ZOO] A phenomenon of protective coloration by which an animal blends with the background through color matching or countershading.

Cryptobiidae [INV ZOO] A family of flagellate protozoans in the order Kinetoplastida including organisms with two flagella, one free and one with an undulating membrane.

cryptobiosis [PHYSIO] A state in which metabolic rate of the organism is reduced to an imperceptible level.

cryptobiotic [ECOL] Living in concealed or secluded situations.

Cryptobranchidae [VERT ZOO] The giant salamanders and hellbenders, a family of tailed amphibians in the suborder Cryptobranchoidea.

Cryptobranchoidea [VERT ZOO] A primitive suborder of amphibians in the order Urodela distinguished by external fertilization and aquatic larvae.

Cryptocerata [INV ZOO] A division of hemipteran insects in some systems of classification that includes the water bugs (Hydrocorisae).

Cryptochaetidae [INV ZOO] A family of myodarian cyclorrhaphous dipteran insects in the subsection Acalypteratae.

Cryptococcaceae [MYCOL] A family of imperfect fungi in the order Moniliales in some systems of classification; equivalent to the Cryptococcales in other systems.

Cryptococcales [MYCOL] An order of imperfect fungi, in some systems of classification, set up to include the yeasts or yeastlike organisms whose perfect or sexual stage is not known.

Cryptococcus [MYCOL] A genus of encapsulated pathogenic yeasts in the order Moniliales.

Cryptodira [VERT ZOO] A suborder of the reptilian order Chelonia including all turtles in which the cervical spines are uniformly reduced and the head folds directly back into the shell.

cryptogam [BOT] An old term for nonflowering plants.

cryptomedusa [INV ZOO] The final stage in the reduction of a hydroid medusa to a rudiment having sex cells within the gonophore.

cryptomitosis [INV ZOO] Cell division in certain protozoans in which a modified spindle forms, and chromatin assembles with no apparent chromosome differentiation.

Cryptomonadida [BIOL] An order of the class Phytamastigophorea considered to be protozoans by biologists and algae by botanists.

Cryptomonadina [BIOL] The equivalent name for Cryptomonadida.

Cryptophagidae [INV ZOO] The silken fungus beetles, a family of coleopteran insects in the superfamily Cucujoidea.

Cryptophyceae [BOT] A class of algae of the Pyrrhophyta in some systems of classification; equivalent to the division Cryptophyta.

Cryptophyta [BOT] A division of the algae in some classification schemes; equivalent to the Cryptophyceae.

cryptophyte [BOT] A plant that produces buds either underwater or underground on corms, bulbs, or rhizomes.

Cryptopidae [INV ZOO] A family of epimorphic centipedes in the order Scolopendromorpha.

Cryptostomata [PALEON] An order of extinct bryozoans in the class Gymnolaemata.

cryptoxanthin [BIOCHEM] $C_{40}H_{57}O$ A xanthophyll carotenoid pigment found in plants; convertible to vitamin A by many animal livers.

cryptozoon [PALEOBOT] A hemispherical or cabbagelike reef-forming fossil algae, probably from the Cambrian and Ordovician.

crypts of Lieberkühn [ANAT] Simple, tubular glands which arise as evaginations into the mucosa of the small intestine.

crystalliferous bacteria [MICROBIO] *Bacillus thuringiensis* and related species characterized by the formation of a protein crystal in the sporangium at the time of spore formation.

crystalline lens *See* lens.

ctenidium [INV ZOO] 1. The comb- or featherlike respiratory apparatus of certain mollusks. 2. A row of spines on the head or thorax of some fleas.

Ctenodrilidae [INV ZOO] A family of fringe worms belonging to the Sedentaria.

ctenoid scale [VERT ZOO] A thin, acellular structure composed of bonelike material and characterized by a serrated margin; found in the skin of advanced teleosts.

Ctenophora [INV ZOO] The comb jellies, a phylum of marine organisms having eight rows of comblike plates as the main locomotory structure.

Ctenostomata [INV ZOO] An order of bryozoans in the class Gymnolaemata recognized as inconspicuous, delicate colonies made up of relatively isolated, short, tubular zooecia with chitinous walls.

Ctenostomatida [INV ZOO] The equivalent name for Odontostomatida.

Ctenothrissidae [PALEON] A family of extinct teleostean fishes in the order Ctenothrissiformes.

Ctenothrissiformes [PALEON] A small order of extinct teleostean fishes; important as a group on the evolutionary line leading from the soft-rayed to the spiny-rayed fishes.

cubeb [BOT] The dried, nearly ripe fruit (berries) of a climbing vine, *Piper cubeba*, of the pepper family (Piperaceae).

cuboid [ANAT] The outermost distal tarsal bone in vertebrates. [INV ZOO] Main vein of the wing in many insects, particularly the flies (Diptera).

cuboidal epithelium [HISTOL] A single-layered epithelium made up of cubelike cells.

Cubomedusae [INV ZOO] An order of coelenterates in the class Scyphozoa distinguished by a cubic umbrella.

cuckoo [VERT ZOO] The common name for about 130 species of primarily arboreal birds in the family Cuculidae; some are social parasites.

Cucujidae [INV ZOO] The flat-back beetles, a family of predatory coleopteran insects in the superfamily Cucujoidea.

Cucujoidea [INV ZOO] A large superfamily of coleopteran insects in the suborder Polyphaga.

Cuculidae [VERT ZOO] A family of perching birds in the order Cuculiformes, including the cuckoos and the roadrunner, characterized by long tails, heavy beaks and conspicuous lashes.

Cuculiformes [VERT ZOO] An order of birds containing the cuckoos and allies, characterized by the zygodactyl arrangement of the toes.

Cucumariidae [INV ZOO] A family of dendrochirotacean holothurian echinoderms in the order Dendrochirotida.

cucumber [BOT] *Cucumis sativus*. An annual cucurbit, in the family Cucurbitaceae grown for its edible, immature fleshy fruit.

cucumber mildew [PL PATH] 1. A downy mildew of cucumbers and melons caused by *Peronoplasmopara cubensis*. 2. A powdery mildew of cucumbers and melons caused by *Erysiphe cichoracearum*.

cucumber mosaic [PL PATH] A virus disease of cucumbers and related fruits, producing mottling of terminal leaves and fruits and dwarfing of vines.

cucurbit wilt [PL PATH] A bacterial disease of cucumbers and related plants caused by *Erwinia tracheiphila*, characterized by sudden wilting of the plant.

cul-de-sac [ANAT] Blind pouch or diverticulum.

Culex [INV ZOO] A genus of mosquitoes important as vectors for malaria and several filarial parasites.

Culicidae [INV ZOO] The mosquitoes, a family of slender, orthorrhaphous dipteran insects in the series Nematocera having long legs and piercing mouthparts.

Culicinae [INV ZOO] A subfamily of the dipteran family Culicidae.

culm [BOT] 1. A jointed and usually hollow grass stem. 2. The solid stem of certain monocotyledons, such as the sedges.

culmen [VERT ZOO] The edge of the upper bill in birds.

cultigen [BIOL] A cultivated variety or species of organism for which there is no known wild ancestor. Also known as cultivar.

cultivar *See* cultigen.

culture [BIOL] A growth of living cells or microorganisms in a controlled artificial environment.

culture community [ECOL] A plant community which is established or modified through human intervention; for example, a fencerow, hedgerow, or windbreak.

cultured pearl [INV ZOO] A natural pearl grown by means of controlled stimulation of the oyster.

culture medium [MICROBIO] The nutrients and other organic and inorganic materials used for the growth of microorganisms and plant and animal tissue in culture.

Cumacea [INV ZOO] An order of the class Crustacea characterized by a well-developed carapace which is fused dorsally with at least the first three thoracic somites and overhangs the sides.

cumatophyte [ECOL] A plant that grows under surf conditions.

cumin [BOT] *Cuminum cyminum* An annual herb in the family Umbelliferae; the fruit is valuable for its edible, aromatic seeds.

cumulus oophorus [HISTOL] The layer of gelatinous, follicle cells surrounding the ovum in a Graafian follicle.

cuneate [BIOL] Wedge-shaped with the acute angle near the base, as in certain insect wings and the leaves of various plants.

cuneiform [ANAT] 1. Any of three wedge-shaped tarsal bones. 2. Either of a pair of cartilages lying dorsal to the thyroid cartilage of the larynx. 3. Wedge-shaped, chiefly referring to skeletal elements.

cunnus [ANAT] The vulva.

Cupedidae [INV ZOO] The reticulated beetles, the single family of the coleopteran suborder Archostemata.

cupule [BOT] 1. The cup-shaped involucre characteristic of oaks. 2. A cup-shaped corolla. 3. The gemmae cup of the Marchantiales. [INV ZOO] A small sucker on the feet of certain male flies.

Curculionidae [INV ZOO] The true weevils or snout beetles, a family of coleopteran insects in the superfamily Curculionoidea.

Curculionoidea [INV ZOO] A superfamily of coleopteran insects in the suborder Polyphaga.

Curcurbitaceae [BOT] A family of dicotyledonous herbs or herbaceous vines in the order Violales characterized by an inferior ovary, unisexual flowers, one to five stamens but typically three, and a sympetalous corolla.

Curcurbitales [BOT] The ordinal name assigned to the Cucurbitaceae in some systems of classification.

curd [BOT] The edible flower heads of members of the mustard family such as broccoli.

curling factor *See* griseofulvin.

curly top [PL PATH] A virus disease of sugarbeets and certain other plants that is transmitted by a leafhopper; affected plants are dwarfed and have curled, upturned leaves.

currant [BOT] A shrubby, deciduous plant of the genus *Ribes* in the order Rosales; the edible fruit, a berry, is borne in clusters on the plant.

currant leaf spot [PL PATH] 1. An angular leaf spot of currants caused by the fungus *Cercospora angulata*. 2. An anthracnose of currants caused by *Pseudopeziza ribis* and characterized by brown or black spots.

cursorial [VERT ZOO] Adapted for running.

Curtis-Dolsy unit [BIOL] A unit for the standardization of estrogens.

Cuscutaceae [BOT] A family of parasitic dicotyledonous plants in the order Polemoniales which lack internal phloem and chlorophyll, have capsular fruit, and are not rooted to the ground at maturity.

cusp [ANAT] 1. A pointed or rounded projection on the masticating surface of a tooth. 2. One of the flaps of a heart valve.

cuspid *See* canine.

cuspidate [BIOL] Having a cusp; terminating in a point.

cutaneous appendage [ANAT] Any of the epidermal derivatives, including the nails, hair, sebaceous glands, mammary glands, and sweat glands.

cutaneous pain [PHYSIO] A sensation of pain arising from the skin.

cutaneous sensation [PHYSIO] Any feeling originating in sensory nerve endings of the skin, including pressure, warmth, cold, and pain.

Cuterebridae [INV ZOO] The robust botflies, a family of myodarian cyclorrhaphous dipteran insects in the subsection Calypteratae.

cuticle [ANAT] The horny layer of the nail fold attached to the nail plate at its margin. [BIOL] A noncellular, hardened or membranous secretion of an epithelial sheet, such as the integument of nematodes and annelids, the exoskeleton of arthropods, and the continuous film of cutin on certain plant parts.

cutin [BIOCHEM] A mixture of fatty substances characteristically found in epidermal cell walls and in the cuticle of plant leaves and stems.

cutis *See* dermis.

cutting [BOT] A piece of plant stem with one or more nodes, which, when placed under suitable conditions, will produce roots and shoots resulting in a complete plant.

cuttlefish [INV ZOO] An Old World decapod mollusk of the genus *Sepia;* shells are used to manufacture dentifrices and cosmetics.

Cuvieroninae [PALEON] A subfamily of extinct proboscidean mammals in the family Gomphotheriidae.

Cyamidae [INV ZOO] The whale lice, a family of amphipod crustaceans in the suborder Caprellidea that bear a resemblance to insect lice.

cyanocobalamin *See* vitamin B₁₂.

cyanophilous [BIOL] Having an affinity for blue or green dyes.

Cyanophyceae [BOT] The blue-green algae, a class of plants in the division Schizophyta.

cyanophycin [BIOCHEM] A granular protein food reserve in the cells of blue-green algae, especially in the peripheral cytoplasm.

Cyanophyta [BOT] An equivalent name for the Cyanophyceae.

Cyatheaceae [BOT] A family of tropical and pantropical tree ferns distinguished by the location of sori along the veins.

cyathium [BOT] An inflorescence in which the flowers arise from the base of a cuplike involucre.

Cyathoceridae [INV ZOO] The equivalent name for the Lepiceridae.

Cycadales [BOT] An ancient order of plants in the class Cycadopsida characterized by tuberous or columnar stems that bear a crown of large, usually pinnate leaves.

Cycadeoidaceae [PALEOBOT] A family of extinct plants in the order Cycadeoidales characterized by sparsely branched trunks and a terminal crown of leaves.

Cycadeoidales [PALEOBOT] An order of extinct plants that were abundant during the Triassic, Jurassic, and Cretaceous periods.

Cycadicae [BOT] A subdivision of large-leaved gymnosperms with stout stems in the plant division Pinophyta; only a few species are extant.

Cycadofilicales [PALEOBOT] The equivalent name for the extinct Pteridospermae.

Cycadophyta [BOT] An equivalent name for Cycadicae elevated to the level of a division.

Cycadophytae [BOT] An equivalent name for Cycadicae.

Cycadopsida [BOT] A class of gymnosperms in the plant subdivision Cycadicae.

Cyclanthaceae [BOT] The single family of the order Cyclanthales.

Cyclanthales [BOT] An order of monocotyledonous plants composed of herbs; or, seldom, composed of more or less woody plants with leaves that usually have a bifid, expanded blade.

cyclic adenylic acid [BIOCHEM] $C_{10}H_{12}N_5O_6P$ An isomer of adenylic acid; crystal platelets with a melting point of 219–220°C; a key regulator which acts to control the rate of a number of cellular processes in bacteria, most animals, and some higher plants. Abbreviated cAMP. Also known as adenosine 3′,5′-cyclic monophosphate; adenosine 3′,5′-cyclic phosphate; adenosine 3′,5′-monophosphate; 3′,5′-AMP; cyclic AMP.

cyclic AMP *See* cyclic adenylic acid.

Cyclocystoidea [PALEON] A class of small, disk-shaped, extinct echinozoans in which the lower surface of the body probably consisted of a suction cup.

cycloheximide [MICROBIO] $C_{15}H_{23}NO_4$ Colorless crystals with a melting point of 119.5–121°C; soluble in water, in amyl acetate, and in common organic solvents such as ether, acetone, and chloroform; used as an agricultural fungicide. Also known as 3-[2-(3,5-dimethyl-2-oxocyclohexyl)2-hydroxyethyl]glutarimide; naramycin A.

cycloid scale [VERT ZOO] A thin, acellular structure which is composed of a bonelike substance and shows annual growth rings; found in the skin of soft-rayed fishes.

cyclomorphosis [ECOL] Cyclic recurrent polymorphism in certain planktonic fauna in response to seasonal temperature or salinity changes.

Cyclophoracea [INV ZOO] A superfamily of gastropod mollusks in the order Prosobranchia.

Cyclophoridae [INV ZOO] A family of land snails in the order Pectinibranchia.

Cyclophyllidea [INV ZOO] An order of platyhelminthic worms comprising most tapeworms of warm-blooded vertebrates.

Cyclopinidae [INV ZOO] A family of copepod crustaceans in the suborder Cyclopoida, section Gnathostoma.

Cyclopoida [INV ZOO] A suborder of small copepod crustaceans.

Cyclopteridae [VERT ZOO] The lumpfishes and snailfishes, a family of deep-sea forms in the suborder Cottoidei of the order Perciformes.

Cyclorhagae [INV ZOO] A suborder of benthonic, microscopic marine animals in the class Kinorhyncha of the phylum Aschelminthes.

Cyclorrhapha [INV ZOO] A suborder of true flies, order Diptera, in which developing adults are always formed in a puparium from which they emerge through a circular opening.

cycloserine [MICROBIO] $C_3H_6O_2N_2$ Broad-spectrum, crystalline antibiotic produced by several species of *Streptomyces;* useful in the treatment of tuberculosis and urinary-tract infections caused by resistant gram-negative bacteria.

cyclosis [CELL BIO] Massive rotational streaming of cytoplasm in certain vacuolated cells, such as the stonewort *Nitella* and *Paramecium*.

Cyclosporeae [BOT] A class of brown algae, division Phaeophyta, in which there is only a free-living diploid generation.

Cyclosteroidea [PALEON] A class of Middle Ordovician to Middle Devonian echinoderms in the subphylum Echinozoa.

Cyclostomata [INV ZOO] An order of bryozoans in the class Stenolaemata. [VERT ZOO] A subclass comprising the simplest and most primitive of living vertebrates characterized by the absence of jaws and the presence of a single median nostril and an uncalcified cartilaginous skeleton.

Cydippidea [INV ZOO] An order of the Ctenophora having well-developed tentacles.

Cydnidae [INV ZOO] The ground or burrower bugs, a family of hemipteran insects in the superfamily Pentatomorpha.

cylindrarthrosis [ANAT] A joint characterized by rounded articular surfaces.

Cylindrocapsaceae [BOT] A family of green algae in the suborder Ulotrichineae comprising thick-walled, sheathed cells having massive chloroplasts.

cyme [BOT] An inflorescence in which each main axis terminates in a single flower; secondary and tertiary axes may also have flowers, but with shorter flower stalks.

cymose [BOT] Of, pertaining to, or resembling a cyme.

Cymothoidae [INV ZOO] A family of isopod crustaceans in the suborder Flabellifera; members are fish parasites with reduced maxillipeds ending in hooks.

Cynipidae [INV ZOO] A family of hymenopteran insects in the superfamily Cynipoidea.

Cynipoidea [INV ZOO] A superfamily of hymenopteran insects in the suborder Apocrita.

Cynoglossidae [VERT ZOO] The tonguefishes, a family of Asiatic flatfishes in the order Pleuronectiformes.

Cyperaceae [BOT] The sedges, a family of monocotyledonous plants in the order Cyperales characterized by spirally arranged flowers on a spike or spikelet; a usually solid, often triangular stem; and three carpels.

Cyperales [BOT] An order of monocotyledonous plants in the subclass Commelinidae with reduced, mostly wind-pollinated or self-pollinated flowers that have a unilocular, two- or three-carpellate ovary bearing a single ovule.

Cyphellaceae [BOT] A family of typically crustose lichens with sessile apothecia in the order Caliciales.

cyphonautes [INV ZOO] The free-swimming bivalve larva of certain bryozoans.

Cyphophthalmi [INV ZOO] A family of small, mitelike arachnids in the order Phalangida.

Cypraecea [INV ZOO] A superfamily of gastropod mollusks in the order Prosobranchia.

Cypraeidae [INV ZOO] A family of colorful marine snails in the order Pectinibranchia.

cypress [BOT] The common name for members of the genus *Cupressus* and several related species in the order Pinales.

Cypridacea [INV ZOO] A superfamily of mostly fresh-water ostracods in the suborder Podocopa.

Cypridinacea [INV ZOO] A superfamily of ostracods in the suborder Myodocopa characterized by a calcified carapace and having a round back with a downward-curving rostrum.

Cyprinidae [VERT ZOO] The largest family of fishes, including minnows and carps in the order Cypriniformes.

Cypriniformes [VERT ZOO] An order of actinopterygian fishes in the suborder Ostariophysi.

Cyprinodontidae [VERT ZOO] The killifishes, a family of actinopterygian fishes in the order Atheriniformes that inhabit ephemeral tropical ponds.

Cyprinoidei [VERT ZOO] A suborder of primarily fresh-water actinopterygian fishes in the order Cypriniformes having toothless jaws, no adipose fin, and faliciform lower pharyngeal bones.

cypris [INV ZOO] An ostracod-like, free-swimming larval stage in the development of Cirripedia.

Cyrtophorina [INV ZOO] The equivalent name for Gymnostomatida.

cyrtopia [INV ZOO] A type of crustacean larva (Ostracoda) characterized by an elongation of the first pair of antennae and loss of swimming action in the second pair.

cyrtosis [PL PATH] A virus disease of cotton characterized by stunting, distortion, and abnormal branching and coloration.

cystacanth [INV ZOO] The infective larva of the Acanthocephala; lies in the hemocele of the intermediate host.

L-cystathionine [BIOCHEM] $C_7H_{14}N_2O_4S$ An amino acid formed by condensation of homocysteine with serine, catalyzed by an enzyme transsulfurase; found in high concentration in the brain of primates.

cysteine [BIOCHEM] $C_3H_7O_2NS$ A crystalline amino acid occurring as a constituent of glutathione and cystine.

cystic duct [ANAT] The duct of the gallbladder.

cysticercus [INV ZOO] A larva of tapeworms in the order Cyclophyllidea that has a bladder with a single invaginated scolex.

cystine [BIOCHEM] $C_6H_{12}N_2S_2$ A white, crystalline amino acid formed biosynthetically from cysteine.

Cystobacter [MICROBIO] A genus of bacteria in the family Cystobacteraceae; vegetative cells are tapered, sporangia are sessile, and microcysts are rigid rods.

Cystobacteraceae [MICROBIO] A family of bacteria in the order Myxobacterales; vegetative cells are tapered, and microcysts are rod-shaped and enclosed in sporangia.

cystocarp [BOT] A fruiting structure with a special protective envelope, produced after fertilization in red algae.

cystocercous cercariae [INV ZOO] A digenetic trematode larva that can withdraw the body into the tail.

Cystoidea [PALEON] A class of extinct crinozoans characterized by an ovoid body that was either sessile or attached by a short aboral stem.

cystolith [BOT] A concretion of calcium carbonate arising from the cell walls of modified epidermal cells in some flowering plants.

Cystoporata [PALEON] An order of extinct, marine bryozoans characterized by cystopores and minutopores.

cytase [BIOCHEM] Any of several enzymes in the seeds of cereals and other plants, which hydrolyze the cell-wall material.

Cytheracea [INV ZOO] A superfamily of ostracods in the suborder Podocopa comprising principally crawling and digging marine forms.

Cytherellidae [INV ZOO] The family comprising all living members of the ostracod suborder Platycopa.

cytidine [BIOCHEM] $C_9H_{13}N_3O_5$ Cytosine riboside, a nucleoside composed of one molecule each of cytosine and D-ribose.

cytidine monophosphate See cytidilic acid.

cytidylic acid [BIOCHEM] $C_9H_{14}O_8N_3P$ A nucleotide synthesized from the base cytosine and obtained by hydrolysis of nucleic acid. Also known as cytidine monophosphate.

cytochalasin [BIOCHEM] One of a series of structurally related fungal metabolic products which, among other effects on biological systems, selectively and reversibly block cytokinesis while not affecting karyokinesis; the molecule with minor variations consists of a benzyl-substituted hydroaromatic isoindolone system, which in turn is fused to a small macrolide-like cyclic ring.

cytochemistry [CELL BIO] The science concerned with the chemistry of cells and cell components, primarily with the location of chemical constituents and enzymes.

cytochrome [BIOCHEM] Any of the complex protein respiratory pigments occurring within plant and animal cells, usually in mitochondia, that function as electron carriers in biological oxidation.

cytochrome a_3 See cytochrome oxidase.

cytochrome oxidase [BIOCHEM] Any of a family of respiratory pigments that react directly with oxygen in the reduced state. Also known as cytochrome a_3.

cytocidal unit [BIOL] A unit for the standardization of adrenal cortical hormones.

cytocrine gland [CELL BIO] A cell, especially a melanocyte, that passes its secretion directly to another cell.

cytogenetics [CELL BIO] The comparative study of the mechanisms and behavior of chromosomes in populations and taxa, and the effect of chromosomes on inheritance and evolution.

cytogenous gland [PHYSIO] A structure that secretes living cells; an example is the testis.

cytokinesis [CELL BIO] Division of the cytoplasm following nuclear division.

cytokinin [BIOCHEM] Any of a group of plant hormones which elicit certain plant growth and development responses, especially by promoting cell division.

cytology [BIOL] A branch of the biological sciences which deals with the structure, behavior, growth, and reproduction of cells and the function and chemistry of cell components.

cytolysosome [CELL BIO] An enlarged lysosome that contains organelles such as mitochondria.

cytomegalovirus [VIROL] An animal virus belonging to subgroup B of the herpesvirus group; causes cytomegalic inclusion disease and pneumonia.

cytomorphosis [CELL BIO] All the structural alterations which cells or successive generations of cells undergo from the earliest undifferentiated stage to their final destruction.

Cytophaga [MICROBIO] A genus of bacteria in the family Cytophagaceae; cells are unsheathed, unbranched rods or filaments and are motile; microcysts are not known; decompose agar, cellulose, and chitin.

Cytophagaceae [MICROBIO] A family of bacteria in the order Cytophagales; cells are rods or filaments, unsheathed cells are motile, filaments are not attached, and carotenoids are present.

Cytophagales [MICROBIO] An order of gliding bacteria; cells are rods or filaments and motile by gliding, and fruiting bodies are not produced.

cytopharynx [INV ZOO] A channel connecting the surface with the protoplasm in certain protozoans; functions as a gullet in ciliates.

cytoplasm [CELL BIO] The protoplasm of an animal or plant cell external to the nucleus.

cytoplasmic inheritance [GEN] The control of genetic difference by hereditary units carried in cytoplasmic organelles. Also known as extrachromosomal inheritance.

cytoplasmic streaming [CELL BIO] Intracellular movement involving irreversible deformation of the cytoplasm produced by endogenous forces.

cytopyge [INV ZOO] A fixed point for waste discharge in the body of a protozoan, especially a ciliate.

cytosine [BIOCHEM] $C_4H_5ON_3$ A pyrimidine occurring as a fundamental unit or base of nucleic acids.

cytoskeleton [CELL BIO] Protein fibers composing the structural framework of a cell.

cytosome [CELL BIO] The cytoplasm of the cell, as distinct from the nucleus.

cytostome [INV ZOO] The mouth-like opening in many unicellular organisms, particularly Ciliophora.

cytotaxis [PHYSIO] Attraction of motile cells by specific diffusible stimuli emitted by other cells.

cytotrophoblast [EMBRYO] The inner, cellular layer of a trophoblast, covering the chorion and the chorionic villi during the first half of pregnancy.

cytotropism [BIOL] The tendency of individual cells and groups of cells to move toward or away from each other.

Czapek's agar [MICROBIO] A nutrient culture medium consisting of salt, sugar, water, and agar; used for certain mold cultures.

Czochralski method [ECOL] Alteration of the original state of a community by human agencies.

D

Dacromycetales [MYCOL] An order of jelly fungi in the subclass Heterobasidiomycetidae having branched basidia with the appearance of a tuning fork.

dacryocyst See lacrimal sac.

dacryon [ANAT] The point of the face where the frontomaxillary, the maxillolacrimal, and frontolacrimal sutures meet.

Dactylochirotida [INV ZOO] An order of dendrochirotacean holothurians in which there are 8–30 digitate or digitiform tentacles, which sometimes bifurcate.

dactylognathite [INV ZOO] The distal segment of a maxilliped in crustaceans.

Dactylogyroidea [INV ZOO] A superfamily of trematodes in the subclass Monogenea; all are fish ectoparasites.

dactylopodite [INV ZOO] The distal segment of ambulatory limbs in decapods and of certain limbs in other arthropods.

dactylopore [INV ZOO] Any of the small openings on the surface of Milleporina through which the bodies of the polyps are extended.

Dactylopteridae [VERT ZOO] The flying gurnards, the single family of the perciform suborder Dactylopteroidei.

Dactylopteroidei [VERT ZOO] A suborder of marine shore fishes in the order Perciformes, characterized by tremendously expansive pectoral fins.

Dactyloscopidae [VERT ZOO] The sand stargazers, a family of small tropical and subtropical perciform fishes in the suborder Blennioidei.

Dactylosporangium [MICROBIO] A genus of bacteria in the family Actinoplanaceae; fingerlike sporangia are formed in clusters, each containing a single row of three or four motile spores.

dactylosternal [VERT ZOO] Of turtles, having marginal fingerlike processes joining the plastron to the carapace.

dactylozooid [INV ZOO] One of the long, defensive polyps of the Milleporina, armed with stinging cells.

dactylus [INV ZOO] The structure of the tarsus of certain insects which follows the first joint; usually consists of one or more joints.

Dalatiidae [VERT ZOO] The spineless dogfishes, a family of modern sharks belonging to the squaloid group.

Dallis grass [BOT] The common name for the tall perennial forage grasses composing the genus *Paspalum* in the order Cyperales.

damping-off [PL PATH] A fungus disease of seedlings and cuttings in which the parasites invade the plant tissues near the ground level, causing wilting and rotting.

Danaidae [INV ZOO] A family of large tropical butterflies, order Lepidoptera, having the first pair of legs degenerate.

Dane particle [VIROL] The causative virus of type B viral hepatitis visualized ultrastructurally in its complete form.

DAP See diaminopimelate.

Daphoenidae [PALEON] A family of extinct carnivoran mammals in the superfamily Miacoidea.

dart [INV ZOO] A small sclerotized structure ejected from the dart sac of certain snails into the body of another individual as a stimulant before copulation.

dart sac [INV ZOO] A dart-forming pouch associated with the reproductive system of certain snails.

darwin [EVOL] A unit of evolutionary rate of change; if some dimension of a part of an animal or plant, or of the whole animal or plant, changes from l_o to l_t over a time of t years according to the formula $l_t = l_o \exp (Et/10^6)$, its evolutionary rate of change is equal to E darwins.

Darwin's finch [VERT ZOO] A bird of the subfamily Fringillidae; Darwin studied the variation of these birds and used his data as evidence for his theory of evolution by natural selection.

Darwinism [BIOL] The theory of the origin and perpetuation of new species based on natural selection of those offspring best adapted to their environment because of genetic variation and consequent vigor. Also known as Darwin's theory.

Darwin's theory See Darwinism.

Darwinulacea [INV ZOO] A small superfamily of nonmarine, parthenogenetic ostracods in the suborder Podocopa.

Dasyatidae [VERT ZOO] The stingrays, a family of modern sharks in the batoid group having a narrow tail with a single poisonous spine.

Dascillidae [INV ZOO] The soft-bodied plant beetles, a family of coleopteran insects in the superfamily Dascilloidea.

Dascilloidea [INV ZOO] Superfamily of coleopteran insects in the suborder Polyphaga.

dasheen [BOT] *Colocasia esculenta.* A plant in the order Arales, grown for its edible corm.

Dascycladaceae [BOT] A family of green algae in the order Dasycladales comprising plants formed of a central stem from which whorls of branches develop.

Dasycladales [BOT] An order of lime-encrusted marine algae in the division Chlorophyta, characterized by a thallus composed of nonseptate, highly branched tubes.

Dasyonygidae [INV ZOO] A family of biting lice, order Mallophaga, that are confined to rodents of the family Procaviidae.

Dasypodidae [VERT ZOO] The armadillos, a family of edentate mammals in the infraorder Cingulata.

Dasytidae [INV ZOO] An equivalent name for Melyridae.

Dasyuridae [VERT ZOO] A family of mammals in the order Marsupialia characterized by five toes on each hindfoot.

Dasyuroidea [VERT ZOO] A superfamily of marsupial mammals.

Daubentoniidae [VERT ZOO] A family of Madagascan prosimian primates containing a single species, the aye-aye.

Dawsoniales [BOT] An order of mosses comprising rigid plants with erect stems rising from a rhizomelike base.

day neutral [BOT] Reaching maturity regardless of relative length of light and dark periods.

dead arm [PL PATH] A fungus disease caused by *Cryptosporella viticola* in which the main lateral shoots are destroyed; common in grapes.

deadly nightshade *See* belladonna.

dead space [ANAT] The space in the trachea, bronchi, and other air passages which contains air that does not reach the alveoli during respiration, the amount of air being about 140 milliliters. Also known as anatomical dead space. [PHYSIO] A calculated expression of the anatomical dead space plus whatever degree of overventilation or underperfusion is present; it is alleged to reflect the relationship of ventilation to pulmonary capillary perfusion. Also known as physiological dead space.

deamidase [BIOCHEM] An enzyme that catalyzes the removal of an amido group from a compound.

deaminase [BIOCHEM] An enzyme that catalyzes the hydrolysis of amino compounds, removing the amino group.

death assemblage *See* thanatocoenosis.

death point [PHYSIO] The limit (as of extremes of temperature) beyond which an organism cannot survive.

debromoaplysiatoxin [BIOCHEM] A bislactone toxin related to aplysiatoxin and produced by the blue-green alga *Lyngbya majuscula*.

decanth larva *See* lycophore larva.

Decapoda [INV ZOO] **1.** A diverse order of the class Crustacea including the shrimps, lobsters, hermit crabs, and true crabs; all members have a carapace, well-developed gills, and the first three pairs of thoracic appendages specialized as maxillipeds. **2.** An order of dibranchiate cephalopod mollusks containing the squids and cuttle fishes, characterized by eight arms and two long tentacles.

decarboxylase [BIOCHEM] An enzyme that hydrolyzes the carboxyl radical, COOH.

deciduous [BIOL] Falling off or being shed at the end of the growing period or season.

deciduous teeth [ANAT] Teeth of a young mammal which are shed and replaced by permanent teeth. Also known as milk teeth.

deckzelle [INV ZOO] In certain hydroids, one of the supporting or epithelial cells which are usually columnar or cuboidal.

declinate [BIOL] Curved toward one side or downward.

declining population [ECOL] A population in which old individuals outnumber young individuals.

decomposer [ECOL] A heterotrophic organism (including bacteria and fungi) which breaks down the complex compounds of dead protoplasm, absorbs some decomposition products, and releases substances usable by consumers. Also known as microcomposer; microconsumer; reducer.

decompound [BOT] Divided or compounded several times, with each division being compound.

decorticate [BIOL] Lacking a cortical layer.

decumbent [BOT] Lying down on the ground but with an ascending tip, specifically referring to a stem.

decurrent [BOT] Running downward, especially of a leaf base extended past its insertion in the form of a winged expansion.

decussate [BOT] Of the arrangement of leaves, occurring in alternating pairs at right angles.

dedifferentiation [BIOL] Disintegration of a specialized habit or adaptation. [PHYSIO] Return of a specialized cell or structure to a more general or primitive condition.

deep fascia [ANAT] The fibrous tissue between muscles and forming the sheaths of muscles, or investing other deep, definitive structures, as nerves and blood vessels.

deep hibernation [PHYSIO] Profound decrease in metabolic rate and physiological function during winter, with a body temperature near 0°C, in certain warm-blooded vertebrates. Also known as hibernation.

deep pain [PHYSIO] Pattern of somesthetic sensation of pain, usually indefinitely localized, originating in the viscera, muscles, and other deep tissues.

deep palmar arch [ANAT] The anastomosis between the terminal part of the radial artery and the deep palmar branch of the ulnar artery. Also known as deep volar arch; palmar arch.

deep volar arch *See* deep palmar arch.

deer [VERT ZOO] The common name for 41 species of even-toed ungulates that compose the family Cervidae in the order Artiodactyla; males have antlers.

defecation [PHYSIO] The process by which fecal wastes that reach the lower colon and rectum are evacuated from the body.

defective virus [VIROL] A virus, such as adeno-associated satellite virus, that can grow and reproduce only in the presence of another virus.

defeminization [PHYSIO] Loss or reduction of feminine attributes, usually caused by ovarian dysfunction or removal.

definitive host [BIOL] The host in which a parasite reproduces sexually.

deflexed [BIOL] Turned sharply downward.

defoliate [BOT] To remove leaves or cause leaves to fall, especially prematurely.

degenerate code [GEN] A genetic code in which more than one triplet sequence of nucleotides (codon) can specify the insertion of the same amino acid into a polypeptide chain.

Degeneriaceae [BOT] A family of dicotyledonous plants in the order Magnoliales characterized by laminar stamens; a solitary, pluriovulate, unsealed carpel; and ruminate endosperm.

deglutition [PHYSIO] Act of swallowing.

dehiscence [BOT] Spontaneous bursting open of a mature plant structure, such as fruit, anther, or sporangium, to discharge its contents.

dehydrase [BIOCHEM] An enzyme which catalyzes the removal of water from a substrate.

dehydrocholesterol [BIOCHEM] $C_{27}H_{43}OH$ A provitamin of animal origin found in the skin of man, in milk, and elsewhere, which upon irradiation with ultraviolet rays becomes vitamin D.

dehydrogenase [BIOCHEM] An enzyme which removes hydrogen atoms from a substrate and transfers it to an acceptor other than oxygen.

Deinotheriidae [PALEON] A family of extinct proboscidean mammals in the suborder Deinotherioidea; known only by the genus *Deinotherium*.

Deinotherioidea [PALEON] A monofamilial suborder of extinct mammals in the order Proboscidea.

delamination [BIOL] The separation of cells into layers. [EMBRYO] Gastrulation in which the endodermal layer splits off from the inner surface of the blastoderm and the space between this layer and the yolk represents the archenteron.

deletion [GEN] Loss of a chromosome segment of any size, down to a part of a single gene.

deliquescence [BOT] The condition of repeated divisions ending in fine divisions; seen especially in venation and stem branching.

delomorphous cell *See* parietal cell.

Delphinidae [VERT ZOO] A family of aquatic mammals in the order Cetacea; includes the dolphins.

delphinidin [BIOCHEM] $C_{15}H_{11}O_7Cl$ A purple or brownish-red anthocyanin compound occurring widely in plants.

Delphinus [VERT ZOO] A genus of cetacean mammals, including the dolphin.

delta rhythm [PHYSIO] An electric current generated in slow waves with frequencies of 0.5–3 per second from the forward portion of the brain of normal subjects when asleep.

Deltatheridia [PALEON] An order of mammals that includes the dominant carnivores of the early Cenozoic.

deltoid [ANAT] The large triangular shoulder muscle; originates on the pectoral girdle and inserts on the humerus.

deltoid [BIOL] Triangular in shape.

deltoid ligament [ANAT] The ligament on the medial side of the ankle joint; the fibers radiate from the medial malleolus to the talus, calcaneus, and navicular bones.

demarcation potential *See* injury potential.

Dematiaceae [MYCOL] A family of fungi in the order Moniliales; sporophores are not grouped, hyphae are always dark, and the spores are hyaline or dark.

deme [ECOL] A local population in which the individuals freely interbreed among themselves but not with those of other demes.

demersal [BIOL] Living at or near the bottom of the sea.

demethylchlortetracycline [MICROBIO] $C_{21}H_{21}O_8N_2Cl$ A broad-spectrum tetracycline antibiotic produced by a mutant strain of *Streptomyces aureofaciens*.

demilune [BIOL] Crescent-shaped.

Demodicidae [INV ZOO] The pore mites, a family of arachnids in the suborder Trombidiformes.

demography [ECOL] The statistical study of populations with reference to natality, mortality, migratory movements, age, and sex, among other social, ethnic, and economic factors.

Demospongiae [INV ZOO] A class of the phylum Porifera, including sponges with a skeleton of one- to four-rayed siliceous spicules, or of spongin fibers, or both.

dendrite [ANAT] The part of a neuron that carries the unidirectional nerve impulse toward the cell body. Also known as dendron.

Dendrobatinae [VERT ZOO] A subfamily of anuran amphibians in the family Ranidae, including the colorful poisonous frogs of Central and South America.

dendrobranchiate gill [INV ZOO] A respiratory structure of certain decapod crustaceans, characterized by extensive branching of the two primary series.

Dendroceratida [INV ZOO] A small order of sponges of the class Demospongiae; members have a skeleton of spongin fibers or lack a skeleton.

Dendrochirotacea [INV ZOO] A subclass of echinoderms in the class Holothuroidea.

Dendrochirotida [INV ZOO] An order of dendrochirotacean holothurian echinoderms with 10–30 richly branched tentacles.

Dendrocolaptidae [VERT ZOO] The woodcreepers, a family of passeriform birds belonging to the suboscine group.

dendrogram [BIOL] A genealogical tree; the trunk represents the oldest common ancestor, and the branches indicate successively more recent divisions of a lineage for a group.

dendroid [BIOL] Branched or treelike in form.

Dendroidea [PALEON] An order of extinct sessile, branched colonial animals in the class Graptolithina occurring among typical benthonic fauna.

Dendromurinae [VERT ZOO] The African tree mice and related species, a subfamily of rodents in the family Muridae.

dendron See dendrite.

dendrophagous [ZOO] Feeding on trees, referring to insects.

dendrophysis [MYCOL] A hyphal thread with arboreal branching in certain fungi.

denervation hypersensitivity [PHYSIO] Extreme sensitivity of an organ that has recovered from the removal or interruption of its nerve supply.

denitrification [MICROBIO] The reduction of nitrate or nitrite to gaseous products such as nitrogen, nitrous oxide, and nitric oxide; brought about by denitrifying bacteria.

denitrifying bacteria [MICROBIO] Bacteria that reduce nitrates to nitrites or nitrogen gas; most are found in soil.

denitrogenate [PHYSIO] To remove nitrogen from the body by breathing nitrogen-free gas.

dense connective tissue [HISTOL] A fibrous connective tissue with an abundance of enlarged collagenous fibers which tend to crowd out the cells and ground substance.

dental [ANAT] Pertaining to the teeth.

dental arch [ANAT] The parabolic curve formed by the cutting edges and masticating surfaces of the teeth.

dental epithelium [HISTOL] The cells forming the boundary of the enamel organ.

dental follicle See dental sac.

dental formula [VERT ZOO] An expression of the number and kind of teeth in each half jaw, both upper and lower, in mammals.

Dentaliidae [INV ZOO] A family of mollusks in the class Scaphopoda; members have pointed feet.

dental pad [VERT ZOO] A firm ridge that replaces incisors in the maxilla of cud-chewing herbivores.

dental papilla [EMBRYO] The mass of connective tissue located inside the enamel organ of a developing tooth, and forming the dentin and dental pulp of the tooth.

dental plate [INV ZOO] A flat plate that replaces teeth in certain invertebrates, such as some worms. [VERT ZOO] A flattened plate that represents fused teeth in parrot fishes and related forms.

dental pulp [HISTOL] The vascular connective tissue of the roots and pulp cavity of a tooth.

dental ridge [EMBRYO] An elevation of the embryonic jaw that forms a cusp or margin of a tooth.

dental sac [EMBRYO] The connective tissue that encloses the developing tooth. Also known as dental follicle.

dentate [BIOL] 1. Having teeth. 2. Having toothlike or conical marginal projections.

dentate fissure See hippocampal sulcus.

dentate nucleus [ANAT] An ovoid mass of nerve cells located in the center of each cerebellar hemisphere, which give rise to fibers found in the superior cerebellar peduncle.

denticle [ZOO] A small tooth or toothlike projection, as the type of scale of certain elasmobranchs.

denticulate [ZOO] Having denticles; serrate.

dentigerous [BIOL] Having teeth or toothlike structures.

dentin [HISTOL] A bonelike tissue composing the bulk of a vertebrate tooth; consists of 70% inorganic materials and 30% water and organic matter.

dentinoblast [HISTOL] A mesenchymal cell that forms dentin.

dentinogenesis [PHYSIO] The formation of dentin.

dentition [VERT ZOO] The arrangement, type, and number of teeth which are variously located in the oral or in the pharyngeal cavities, or in both, in vertebrates.

deoperculate [BOT] Of mosses and liverworts, to shed the operculum.

deoxycholate [BIOCHEM] A salt or ester of deoxycholic acid.

deoxycholic acid [BIOCHEM] $C_{24}H_{40}O_4$ One of the unconjugated bile acids; in bile it is largely conjugated with glycine or taurine.

deoxycorticosterone [BIOCHEM] $C_{21}H_{30}O_3$ A steroid hormone secreted in small amounts by the adrenal cortex.

6-deoxy-L-galactose See L-fucose.

deoxyribonuclease [BIOCHEM] An enzyme that catalyzes the hydrolysis of deoxyribonucleic acid to nucleotides.

deoxyribonucleic acid [BIOCHEM] A linear polymer made up of deoxyribonucleotide repeating units (composed of the sugar 2-deoxyribose, phosphate, and a purine or pyrimidine base) linked by the phosphate group joining the 3' position of one sugar to the 5' position of the next; most molecules are double-stranded and antiparallel, resulting in a right-handed helix structure kept together by hydrogen bonds between a purine on one chain and a pyrimidine on another; carrier of genetic information, which is encoded in the sequence of bases; present in chromosomes and chromosomal material of cell organelles such as mitochondria and chloroplasts, and also present in some viruses. Abbreviated DNA.

deoxyribonucleic acid–directed RNA polymerase [BIOCHEM] An enzyme which transcribes a ribonucleic acid molecule complementary to DNA; required for initiation of DNA replication as well as transcription of RNA.

deoxyribonucleic acid ligase [BIOCHEM] An enzyme which joins the ends of two DNA chains by catalyzing the synthesis of a phosphodiester bond between a 3'-hydroxyl group at the end of one chain and a 5'-phosphate at the end of the other.

deoxyribonucleic acid polymerase I [BIOCHEM] An enzyme which catalyzes the addition of deoxyribonucleotide residues to the end of a DNA strand; generally considered to function in the repair of damaged DNA.

deoxyribonucleic acid polymerase II [BIOCHEM] An enzyme similar in action to DNA polymerase I but with lower activity.

deoxyribonucleic acid polymerase III [BIOCHEM] An enzyme thought to be the primary enzyme involved in DNA replication.

deoxyribonucleoprotein [BIOCHEM] A protein containing molecules of deoxyribonucleic acid in close association with protein molecules.

deoxyribose [BIOCHEM] $C_5H_{10}O_4$ A pentose sugar in which the hydrogen replaces the hydroxyl groups of ribose; a major constituent of deoxyribonucleic acid.

deoxy sugar [BIOCHEM] A substance which has the characteristics of a sugar, but which shows a deviation from the required hydrogen-to-oxygen ratio.

depauperate [BIOL] Inferiority of natural development or size.

Depertellidae [PALEON] A family of extinct perissodactyl mammals in the superfamily Tapiroidea.

depletion [ECOL] Using a resource, such as water or timber, faster than it is replenished.

deposit feeder [INV ZOO] Any animal that feeds on the detritus that collects on the substratum at the bottom of water. Also known as detritus feeder.

depressor [ANAT] A muscle that draws a part down.

depressor nerve [PHYSIO] A nerve which, upon stimulation, lowers the blood pressure either in a local part or throughout the body.

depth perception [PHYSIO] Ability to judge spatial relationships.

depurination [BIOCHEM] Detachment of guanine from sugar in a deoxyribonucleic acid molecule.

derelict land [ECOL] Land that, because of mining, drilling, or other industrial processes, or by serious neglect, is unsightly and cannot be beneficially utilized without treatment.

derepression [MICROBIO] Transfer of microbial cells from an enzyme-repressing medium to a nonrepressing medium.

Dermacentor [INV ZOO] A genus of ticks, important as vectors of disease.

Dermacentor andersoni [INV ZOO] The wood tick, which is the vector of Rocky Mountain spotted fever and tularemia.

Dermacentor variabilis [INV ZOO] A North American tick, parasitic primarily on dogs but may attack man and other mammals.

dermal [ANAT] Pertaining to the dermis.

dermal bone [ANAT] A type of bone that ossifies directly from membrane without a cartilaginous predecessor; occurs only in the skull and shoulder region. Also known as investing bone; membrane bone.

dermal denticle [VERT ZOO] A toothlike scale composed mostly of dentine with a large central pulp cavity, found in the skin of sharks.

dermalia [INV ZOO] Dermal microscleres in sponges.

dermal pore [INV ZOO] One of the minute openings on the surface of poriferans leading to the incurrent canals.

Dermaptera [INV ZOO] An order of small or medium-sized, slender insects having incomplete metamorphosis, chewing mouthparts, short forewings, and cerci.

Dermatemydinae [VERT ZOO] A family of reptiles in the order Chelonia; includes the river turtles.

Dermatocarpaceae [BOT] A family of lichens in the order Pyrenulales having an umbilicate or squamulose growth form; most members grow on limestone or calcareous soils.

dermatocranium [ANAT] Bony parts of the skull derived from ossifications in the dermis of the skin.

dermatogen [BOT] The outer layer of primary meristem or the primordial epidermis in embryonic plants. Also known as protoderm.

dermatoglyphics [ANAT] 1. The integumentary patterns on the surface of the fingertips, palms, and soles. 2. The study of these patterns.

dermatome [ANAT] An area of skin delimited by the supply of sensory fibers from a single spinal nerve. [EMBRYO] Lateral portion of an embryonic somite from which the dermis will develop.

Dermatophilaceae [MICROBIO] A family of bacteria in the order Actinomycetales; cells produce mycelial filaments or muriform thalli; includes human and mammalian pathogens.

Dermatophilus [MICROBIO] A genus of bacteria in the family Dermatophilaceae; mycelial filaments are long, tapering, and branched, and are divided transversely and longitudinally (in two planes) by septa; spherical spores are motile.

dermatophyte [MYCOL] A fungus parasitic on skin or its derivatives.

Dermestidae [INV ZOO] The skin beetles, a family of coleopteran insects in the superfamily Dermestoidea, including serious pests of stored agricultural grain products.

Dermestoidea [INV ZOO] A superfamily of coleopteran insects in the suborder Polyphaga.

dermis [ANAT] The deep layer of the skin, a dense connective tissue richly supplied with blood vessels, nerves, and sensory organs. Also known as corium; cutis.

Dermochelidae [VERT ZOO] A family of reptiles in the order Chelonia composed of a single species, the leatherback turtle.

dermoepidermal junction [HISTOL] The area of separation between the stratum basale of the epidermis and the papillary layer of the dermis.

Dermoptera [VERT ZOO] The flying lemurs, an ancient order of primatelike herbivorous and frugivorous gliding mammals confined to southeastern Asia and eastern India.

de Robertis unit [BIOL] A unit for the standardization of thyroid extracts.

Derodontidae [INV ZOO] The tooth-necked fungus beetles, a small family of coleopteran insects in the superfamily Dermestoidea.

derris [BOT] Any of certain tropical shrubs in the genus *Derris* in the legume family (Leguminosae), having long climbing branches.

Derxia [MICROBIO] A genus of bacteria in the family Azotobacteraceae; rod-shaped, pleomorphic, motile cells; older cells contain large refractive bodies.

Descemet's membrane [HISTOL] A layer of the cornea between the posterior surface of the stroma and the anterior surface of the endothelium which contains collagen arranged on a crystalline lattice.

descending [ANAT] Extending or directed downward or caudally, as the descending aorta. [PHYSIO] In the nervous system, efferent; conducting impulses or progressing down the spinal cord or from central to peripheral.

descriptive anatomy [ANAT] Study of the separate and individual portions of the body, with regard to form, size, character, and position.

descriptive botany [BOT] The branch of botany that deals with diagnostic characters or systematic description of plants.

deserticolous [ECOL] Living in a desert.

desertification [ECOL] The creation of desiccated, barren, desertlike conditions due to natural changes in climate or possibly through mismanagement of the semiarid zone.

desexualization [PHYSIO] Depriving an organism of sexual characters or power, as by spaying or castration.

desma [INV ZOO] A branched, knobby spicule in some Demospongiae.

desmacyte [INV ZOO] A bipolar collencyte found in the cortex of certain sponges.

Desmanthos [MICROBIO] A genus of bacteria in the family Pelonemataceae; unbranched, relatively straight filaments with a thickened base which are arranged in bundles partially enclosed in a sheath.

Desmidiaceae [BOT] A family of desmids, mostly unicellular algae in the order Conjugales.

desmin [BIOCHEM] The muscle protein forming the Z lines in striated muscle.

desmochore [ECOL] A plant having sticky or barbed disseminules.

Desmodonta [PALEON] An order of extinct bivalve, burrowing mollusks.

Desmodontidae [VERT ZOO] A small family of chiropteran mammals comprising the true vampire bats.

Desmodoroidea [INV ZOO] A superfamily of marine- and brackish-water-inhabiting nematodes with an annulated, usually smooth cuticle.

Desmokontae [BOT] The equivalent name for Desmophyceae.

desmolase [BIOCHEM] Any of a group of enzymes which catalyze rupture of atomic linkages that are not cleaved through hydrolysis, such as the bonds in the carbon chain of D-glucose.

desmoneme [INV ZOO] A nematocyst having a long coiled tube which is extruded and wrapped around the prey.

desmopelmous [VERT ZOO] A type of bird foot in which the hindtoe cannot be bent independently because planter tendons are united.

Desmophyceae [BOT] A class of rare, mostly marine algae in the division Pyrrhophyta.

Desmoscolecida [INV ZOO] An order of the class Nematoda.

Desmoscolecidae [INV ZOO] A family of nematodes in the superfamily Desmoscolecoidea; individuals resemble annelids in having coarse annulation.

Desmoscolecoidea [INV ZOO] A small superfamily of free-living nematodes characterized by a ringed body, an armored head set, and hemispherical amphids.

desmose [INV ZOO] A fibril connecting the centrioles during mitosis in certain protozoans.

desmosome [CELL BIO] A surface modification of stratified squamous epithelium formed by the apposition of short cytoplasmic processes of neighboring cells.

Desmostylia [PALEON] An extinct order of large hippopotamuslike, amphibious, gravigrade, shellfish-eating mammals.

Desmostylidae [PALEON] A family of extinct mammals in the order Desmostylia.

Desmothoracida [INV ZOO] An order of sessile and free-living protozoans in the subclass Heliozoia having a spherical body with a perforate, chitinous test.

Desor's larva [INV ZOO] An oval, ciliated larva of certain nemertineans in which the gastrula remains inside the egg membrane.

desquamation [PHYSIO] Shedding; a peeling and casting off, as of the superficial epithelium, mucous membranes, renal tubules, and the skin.

Desulfotomaculum [MICROBIO] A genus of bacteria in the family Bacillaceae; motile, straight or curved rods with terminal to subterminal spores; anaerobic and reduce sulfate.

Desulfovibrio [MICROBIO] A genus of gram-negative, strictly anaerobic bacteria of uncertain affiliation; motile, curved rods reduce sulfates and other sulfur compounds to hydrogen sulfide.

detached meristem [BOT] A meristematic region originating from apical meristem but becoming discontinuous with it because of differentiation of intervening tissue.

determinate cleavage [EMBRYO] A type of cleavage which separates portions of the zygote with specific and distinct potencies for development as specific parts of the body.

determinate growth [BOT] Growth in which the axis, or central stem, being limited by the development of the floral reproductive structure, does not grow or lengthen indefinitely.

detorsion [INV ZOO] Untwisting of the 180° visceral twist imposed by embryonic torsion on many gastropod mollusks.

detoxification [BIOCHEM] The act or process of removing a poison or the toxic properties of a substance in the body.

detritus feeder *See* deposit feeder.

detrivorous [BIOL] Referring to an organism that feeds on dead animals or partially decomposed organic matter.

deutencephalon *See* epichordal brain.

deuterogamy [BOT] Secondary pairing of sexual cells or nuclei replacing direct copulation in many fungi, algae, and higher plants.

Deuteromycetes [MYCOL] The equivalent name for Fungi Imperfecti.

Deuterophlebiidae [INV ZOO] A family of dipteran insects in the suborder Cyclorrhapha.

Deuterostomia [ZOO] A division of the animal kingdom which includes the phyla Echinodermata, Chaetognatha, Hemichordata, and Chordata.

deutocerebrum [INV ZOO] The median lobes of the insect brain.

deutoplasm [EMBRYO] The nutritive yolk granules in egg cells.

devernalization [BOT] Annulment of the vernalization effect.

deviation [EVOL] Evolutionary differentiation involving interpolation of new stages in the ancestral pattern of morphogenesis.

dewclaw [VERT ZOO] 1. A vestigial digit on the foot of a mammal which does not reach the ground. 2. A claw or hoof terminating such a digit.

dewlap [ANAT] A fleshy or fatty fold of skin on the throat of some humans. [BOT] One of a pair of hinges at the joint of a sugarcane leaf blade. [VERT ZOO] A fold of skin hanging from the neck of some reptiles and bovines.

Dexaminidae [INV ZOO] A family of amphipod crustaceans in the suborder Gammeridea.

dexterotropic [BIOL] Turning toward the right; applied to cleavage, shell formation, and whorl patterns.

dextran [BIOCHEM] Any of the several polysaccharides, $(C_5H_{10}O_5)_n$, that yield glucose units on hydrolysis.

dextrin [BIOCHEM] A polymer of D-glucose which is intermediate in complexity between starch and maltose.

dextrorse [BOT] Twining toward the right.

dextrose [BIOCHEM] $C_6H_{12}O_6 \cdot H_2O$ A dextrorotatory monosaccharide obtained as a white, crystalline, odorless, sweet powder, which is soluble in about one part of water; an important intermediate in carbohydrate metabolism; used for nutritional purposes, for temporary increase of blood volume, and as a diuretic. Also known as corn sugar; grape sugar.

dextrotopic cleavage [EMBRYO] A clockwise spiral cleavage pattern.

Diacodectidae [PALEON] A family of extinct artiodactyl mammals in the suborder Palaeodonta.

diactine [INV ZOO] A type of sponge spicule which develops in two directions from a central point.

diadelphous stamen [BOT] A stamen that has its filaments united into two sets.

Diadematacea [INV ZOO] A superorder of Euchinoidea having a rigid or flexible test, perforate tubercles, and branchial slits.

Diadematidae [INV ZOO] A family of large euechinoid echinoderms in the order Diadematoida having crenulate tubercles and long spines.

Diadematoida [INV ZOO] An order of echinoderms in the superorder Diadematacea with hollow primary radioles and crenulate tubercles.

diadromous [BOT] Having venation in the form of fanlike radiations. [VERT ZOO] Of fish, migrating between salt and fresh waters.

Diadumenidae [INV ZOO] A family of anthozoans in the order Actiniaria.

diageotropism [BIOL] Growth orientation of a sessile organism or structure perpendicular to the line of gravity.

diagnosis [SYST] In taxonomic study, a statement of the characters that distinguish a taxon from coordinate taxa.

diaheliotropism [BOT] Movement of plant leaves which follow the sun such that they remain perpendicular to the sun's rays throughout the day.

diakinesis [CELL BIO] The last stage of meiotic prophase, when the chromatids attain maximum contraction and the bivalents move apart and position themselves against the nuclear membrane.

diamine oxidase [BIOCHEM] A flavoprotein which catalyzes the aerobic oxidation of amines to the corresponding aldehyde and ammonia.

diaminopimelate [BIOCHEM] $C_7H_{14}O_4N_2$ A compound that serves as a component of cell wall mucopeptide in some bacteria and as a source of lysine in all bacteria. Abbreviated DAP. Also known as diaminopimelic acid.

diaminopimelic acid *See* diaminopimelate.

diamond canker [PL PATH] A virus disease that affects the bark of certain stone-fruit trees, resulting in weakening of the trunk and limbs.

diandrous [BOT] Having two stamens.

Dianemaceae [MICROBIO] A family of slime molds in the order Trichales.

Dianulitidae [PALEON] A family of extinct, marine bryozoans in the order Cystoporata.

diapause [PHYSIO] A period of spontaneously suspended growth or development in certain insects, mites, crustaceans, and snails.

Diapensiaceae [BOT] The single family of the Diapensiales, an order of flowering plants.

Diapensiales [BOT] A monofamilial order of dicotyledonous plants in the subclass Dilleniidae comprising certain herbs and dwarf shrubs in temperate and arctic regions of the Northern Hemisphere.

Diaphanocephalidae [INV ZOO] A family of parasitic roundworms belonging to the Strongyloidea; snakes are the principal host.

diaphorase [BIOCHEM] Mitochondrial flavoprotein enzymes which catalyze the reduction of dyes, such as methylene blue, by reduced pyridine nucleotides such as reduced diphosphopyridine nucleotide.

diaphragm [ANAT] The dome-shaped partition composed of muscle and connective tissue that separates the abdominal and thoracic cavities in mammals.

diaphragmatic respiration [PHYSIO] Respiration effected primarily by movement of the diaphragm, changing the intrathoracic pressure.

diaphysis [ANAT] The shaft of a long bone.

diapophysis [ANAT] The articular portion of a transverse process of a vertebra.

Diapriidae [INV ZOO] A family of hymenopteran insects in the superfamily Proctotrupoidea.

diarthrosis [ANAT] A freely moving articulation, characterized by a synovial cavity between the bones.

diastase [BIOCHEM] An enzyme that catalyzes the hydrolysis of starch to maltose. Also known as vegetable diastase.

diastasis [PHYSIO] The final phase of diastole, the phase of slow ventricular filling.

diastema [ANAT] A space between two types of teeth, as between an incisor and premolar. [CYTOL] Modified cytoplasm of the equatorial plane prior to cell division.

diastole [PHYSIO] The rhythmic relaxation and dilation of a heart chamber, especially a ventricle.

diastolic pressure [PHYSIO] The lowest arterial blood pressure during the cardiac cycle; reflects relaxation and dilation of a heart chamber.

diatom [INV ZOO] The common name for algae composing the class Bacillariophyceae; noted for the symmetry and sculpturing of the siliceous cell walls.

diatropism [BOT] Growth orientation of certain plant organs that is transverse to the line of action of a stimulus.

Diatrymiformes [PALEON] An order of extinct large, flightless birds having massive legs, tiny wings, and large heads and beaks.

diauxic growth [MICROBIO] The diphasic response of a culture of microorganisms based on a phenotypic adaptation to the addition of a second substrate; characterized by a growth phase followed by a lag after which growth is resumed.

diazotroph [MICROBIO] An organism that carries out nitrogen fixation; examples are *Clostridium* and *Azotobacter*.

Dibamidae [VERT ZOO] The flap-legged skinks, a small family of lizards in the suborder Sauria comprising three species confined to southeastern Asia.

Dibothriocephalus See Diphyllobothrium.

Dibranchia [INV ZOO] A subclass of the Cephalopoda containing all living cephalopods except *Nautilus*; members possess two gills and, when present, an internal shell.

dicarpellate [BOT] Having two carpels.

Dice's life zones [ECOL] Biomes proposed by L.R. Dice based on the concept of the biotic province.

dicentric [CELL BIO] Having two centromeres.

dicerous [INV ZOO] Having two tentacles or two antennae.

dichasium [BOT] A cyme producing two main axes from the primary axis or shoot.

Dichelesthiidae [INV ZOO] A family of parasitic copepods in the suborder Caligoida; individuals attach to the gills of various fishes.

dichlamydeous [BOT] Having both calyx and corolla.

Dichobunidae [PALEON] A family of extinct artiodactyl mammals in the superfamily Dichobunoidea.

Dichobunoidea [PALEON] A superfamily of extinct artiodactyl mammals in the suborder Paleodonta composed of small- to medium-size forms with tri- to quadritubercular bunodont upper teeth.

dichogamous [BOT] Referring to a type of flower in which the pistils and stamens reach maturity at different times.

dichogamy [BIOL] Producing mature male and female reproductive structures at different times.

dichoptous [INV ZOO] Having the margins of the compound eyes separate.

dichotomy [BIOL] 1. Divided in two parts. 2. Repeated branching or forking.

dichotriaene [INV ZOO] A type of sponge spicule with three rays.

dichromatic [BIOL] Having or exhibiting two color phases independently of age or sex.

Dickinsoniidae [PALEON] A family that comprises extinct flat-bodied, multisegmented coelomates; identified as ediacaran fauna.

Dicksoniaceae [BOT] A family of tree ferns characterized by marginal sori which are terminal on the veins and protected by a bivalved indusium.

diclinous [BOT] Having stamens and pistils on different flowers.

dicoccous [BOT] Composed of two adherent one-seeded carpels.

dicotyledon [BOT] Any plant of the class Magnoliopsida, all having two cotyledons.

Dicotyledoneae [BOT] The equivalent name for Magnoliopsida.

Dicranales [BOT] An order of mosses having erect stems, dichotomous branching, and dense foliation.

dictyoblastospore [MYCOL] A blastospore with both cross and longitudinal septa.

Dictyoceratida [INV ZOO] An order of sponges of the class Demospongiae; includes the bath sponges of commerce.

Dictyonellidina [PALEON] A suborder of extinct articulate brachiopods.

dictyosome [CELL BIO] A stack of two or more cisternae; a component of the Golgi apparatus.

Dictyospongiidae [PALEON] A family of extinct sponges in the subclass Amphidiscophora having spicules resembling a one-ended amphidisc (paraclavule).

Dictyosporae [MYCOL] A spore group of the imperfect fungi characterized by multicelled spores with cross and longitudinal septae.

dictyospore [MYCOL] A multicellular spore in certain fungi characterized by longitudinal walls and cross septa.

dictyostele [BOT] A modified siphonostele in which the vascular tissue is dissected into a network of distinct strands; found in certain fern stems.

Dictyostellaceae [MICROBIO] A family of microorganisms belonging to the Acrasiales and characterized by strongly differentiated fructifications.

Dicyemida [INV ZOO] An order of mesozoans comprising minute, wormlike parasites of the renal organs of cephalopod mollusks.

didelphic [ANAT] Having a double uterus or genital tract.

Didelphidae [VERT ZOO] The opossums, a family of arboreal mammals in the order Marsupialia.

Didolodontidae [PALEON] A family consisting of extinct medium-sized herbivores in the order Condylarthra.

Didymiaceae [MICROBIO] A family of slime molds in the order Physarales.

Didymosporae [MYCOL] A spore group of the imperfect fungi characterized by two-celled spores.

didymous [BIOL] Occurring in pairs.

didynamous [BOT] Having four stamens occurring in two pairs, one pair long and the other short.

dieback [ECOL] A large area of exposed, unprotected swamp or marsh deposits resulting from the salinity of a coastal lagoon. [PL PATH] Of a plant, to die from the top or peripheral parts.

die down [BOT] Normal seasonal death of aboveground parts of herbaceous perennials.

diencephalon [EMBRYO] The posterior division of the embryonic forebrain in vertebrates.

diesterase [BIOCHEM] An enzyme such as a nuclease which splits the linkages binding individual nucleotides of a nucleic acid.

diestrus [PHYSIO] The long, quiescent period following ovulation in the estrous cycle in mammals; the stage in which the uterus prepares for the reception of a fertilized ovum.

diet [BIOL] The food or drink regularly consumed.

diethylstilbesterol [BIOCHEM] $C_{18}H_{20}O_2$ A white, crystalline, nonsteroid estrogen that is used therapeutically as a substitute for natural estrogenic hormones. Also known as stilbestrol.

differential centrifugation [CELL BIO] The separation of mixtures such as cellular particles in a medium at various centrifugal forces to separate particles of different density, size, and shape from each other.

differential diagnosis [SYST] In taxonomic study, a statement of the characters that distinguish a given taxon from other, specifically mentioned equivalent taxa.

diffuse placenta [EMBRYO] A placenta having villi diffusely scattered over most of the surface of the chorion; found in whales, horses, and other mammals.

diffusion respiration [PHYSIO] Exchange of gases through the cell membrane, between the cells of unicellular or other simple organisms and the environment.

digastric [ANAT] Of a muscle, having a fleshy part at each end and a tendinous part in the middle.

Digenea [INV ZOO] A group of parasitic flatworms or flukes constituting a subclass or order of the class Trematoda and having two types of generations in the life cycle.

digenesis [BIOL] Sexual and asexual reproduction in succession.

digestion [PHYSIO] The process of converting food to an absorbable form by breaking it down to simpler chemical compounds.

digestive enzyme [BIOCHEM] Any enzyme that causes or aids in digestion.

digestive gland [PHYSIO] Any structure that secretes digestive enzymes.

digestive system [ANAT] A system of structures in which food substances are digested.

digestive tract [ANAT] The alimentary canal.

digicitrin [BIOCHEM] $C_{21}H_{21}O_{10}$ A flavone compound that is found in foxglove leaves.

Digitalis [BOT] A genus of herbs in the figwort family, Scrophulariaceae.

digitate [ANAT] Having digits or digitlike processes.

digitellum [INV ZOO] A tentaclelike gastric filament in scyphozoans.

digitigrade [VERT ZOO] Pertaining to animals, such as dogs and cats, which walk on the digits with the posterior part of the foot raised from the ground.

digitinervate [BOT] Having straight veins extending from the petiole like fingers.

digitipinnate [BOT] Having digitate leaves with pinnate leaflets.

digitus [INV ZOO] In insects, the claw-bearing terminal segment of the tarsus.

diglucoside [BIOCHEM] A compound containing two glucose molecules.

dihydrostreptomycin [MICROBIO] $C_{21}H_{41}O_{12}N_7$ A hydrogenated derivative of streptomycin having the same action as streptomycin.

dihydroxyacetonephosphoric acid [BIOCHEM] $C_3H_7O_6P$ A phosphoric acid ester of dehydroxyacetone, produced as an intermediate substance in the conversion of glycogen to lactic acid during muscular contraction. Also known as dihydroxyacetone phosphate.

3-(3,4-dihydroxycinnamoyl)quinic acid See chlorogenic acid.

dihydroxyphenylalanine [BIOCHEM] $C_9H_{11}NO_4$ An amino acid that can be formed by oxidation of tyrosine; it is converted by a series of biochemical transformations, utilizing the enzyme dopa oxidase, to melanins. Also known as dopa.

dikaryon [MYCOL] Also spelled dicaryon. 1. A pair of distinct, unfused nuclei in the same cell brought together by union of plus and minus hyphae in certain mycelia. 2. Mycelium containing dikaryotic cells.

dilator [PHYSIO] Any muscle, instrument, or drug causing dilation of an organ or part.

dill [BOT] *Anethum graveolens*. A small annual or biennial herb in the family Umbelliferae; the aromatic leaves and seeds are used for food flavoring.

Dilleniaceae [BOT] A family of dicotyledonous trees, woody vines, and shrubs in the order Dilleniales having hypogynous flowers and mostly entire leaves.

Dilleniales [BOT] An order of dicotyledonous plants in the subclass Dilleniidae characterized by separate carpels and numerous stamens.

Dilleniidae [BOT] A subclass of plants in the class Magnoliopsida distinguished by being syncarpous, having centrifugal stamens, and usually having bitegmic ovules and binucleate pollen.

dilution gene [GEN] Any modifier gene that acts to reduce the effect of another gene.

dilution method [MICROBIO] A technique in which a series of cultures is tested with various concentrations of an antibiotic to determine the minimum inhibiting concentration of antibiotic.

dimerous [BIOL] Composed of two parts.

diminution [BOT] Increasing simplification of inflorescences on successive branches.

Dimylidae [PALEON] A family of extinct lipotyphlan mammals in the order Insectivora; a side branch in the ancestry of the hedgehogs.

Dinidoridae [INV ZOO] A family of hemipteran insects in the superfamily Pentatomoidea.

Dinocerata [PALEON] An extinct order of large, herbivorous mammals having semigraviportal limbs and hoofed, five-toed feet; often called uintatheres.

Dinoflagellata [INV ZOO] The equivalent name for Dinoflagellida.

Dinoflagellida [INV ZOO] An order of flagellate protozoans in the class Phytamastigophorea; most members have fixed shapes determined by thick covering plates.

Dinophilidae [INV ZOO] A family of annelid worms belonging to the Archiannelida.

Dinophyceae [BOT] The dinoflagellates, a class of thallophytes in the division Pyrrhophyta.

Dinornithiformes [PALEON] The moas, an order of extinct birds of New Zealand; all had strong legs with four-toed feet.

dinosaur [PALEON] The name, meaning terrible lizard, applied to the fossil bones of certain large, ancient bipedal and quadripedal reptiles placed in the orders Saurischia and Ornithischia.

diocoel [EMBRYO] The cavity of the diencephalon, which becomes the third brain ventricle.

Dioctophymatida [INV ZOO] An order of parasitic nematode worms in the subclass Enoplia.

Dioctophymoidea [INV ZOO] An order or superfamily of parasitic nematodes characterized by the peculiar structure of the copulatory bursa of the male.

dioecious [BIOL] Having the male and female reproductive organs on different individuals. Also known as dioic.

dioic See dioecious.

Diomedeidae [VERT ZOO] The albatrosses, a family of birds in the order Procellariiformes.

Diopsidae [INV ZOO] The stalk-eyed flies, a family of myodarian cyclorrhaphous dipteran insects in the subsection Acalypteratae.

diorchism [ANAT] Having two testes.

Dioscoreaceae [BOT] A family of monocotyledonous, leafy-stemmed, mostly twining plants in the order Liliales, having an inferior ovary and septal nectaries and lacking tendrils.

dioxygenase [BIOCHEM] Any of a group of enzymes which catalyze the insertion of both atoms of an oxygen molecule into an organic substrate according to the generalized formula $AH_2 + O_2 \rightarrow A(OH)_2$.

dipeptidase [BIOCHEM] An enzyme that hydrolyzes a dipeptide.

diphosphatidyl glycerol See cardiolipin.

diphosphopyridine nucleotide [BIOCHEM] $C_{21}H_{27}O_{14}N_7P_2$ An organic coenzyme that functions in enzymatic systems concerned with oxidation-reduction reactions. Abbreviated DPN. Also known as codehydrogenase 1; coenzyme 1; nicotinamide adenine dinucleotide (NAD).

diphycercal [VERT ZOO] Pertaining to a tail fin, having symmetrical upper and lower parts, and with the vertebral column extending to the tip without upturning.

diphyletic [EVOL] Originating from two lines of descent.

Diphyllidea [INV ZOO] A monogeneric order of tapeworms in the subclass Cestoda; all species live in the intestine of elasmobranch fishes.

Diphyllobothrium [INV ZOO] A genus of tapeworms; including parasites of man, dogs, and cats. Formerly known as Dibothriocephalus.

Diphyllobothrium latum [INV ZOO] A large tapeworm that infects humans, dogs, and cats; causes anemia and disorders of the nervous and digestive systems in humans.

diphyllous [BOT] Having two leaves.

diphyodont [ANAT] Having two successive sets of teeth, deciduous followed by permanent, as in man.

dipicolinic acid [BIOCHEM] $C_7H_5O_4N \cdot 1\frac{1}{2}H_2O$ A chelating agent composing 5–15% of the dry weight of bacterial spores.

Diplacanthidae [PALEON] A family of extinct acanthodian fishes in the suborder Diplacanthoidei.

Diplacanthoidei [PALEON] A suborder of extinct acanthodian fishes in the order Climatiiformes.

Diplasiocoela [VERT ZOO] A suborder of amphibians in the order Anura typically having the eighth vertebra biconcave.

dipleurula [INV ZOO] 1. A hypothetical bilaterally symmetrical larva postulated to be an ancestral form of echinoderms and chordates. 2. Any bilaterally symmetrical, ciliated echinoderm larva.

Diplobathrida [PALEON] An order of extinct, camerate crinoids having two circles of plates beneath the radials.

diplobiont [BIOL] An organism characterized by alternating, morphologically dissimilar haploid and diploid generations.

diploblastic [ZOO] Having two germ layers, referring to embryos and certain lower invertebrates.

diploblastula [INV ZOO] A two-layered, flagellated larva of certain ceractinomorph sponges. Also known as parenchymella.

diplococci [MICROBIO] A pair of micrococci.

diploglossate [VERT ZOO] Pertaining to certain lizards, having the ability to retract the end of the tongue into the basal portion.

diplohaplont [BIOL] An organism characterized by alternating, morphologically similar haploid and diploid generations.

diploidization [GEN] The process of attaining the diploid state.

diploid merogony [EMBRYO] Development of a part of an egg in which the nucleus is the normal diploid fusion product of egg and sperm nuclei.

diploid state [GEN] A condition in which a chromosome set is present in duplicate in a nucleus (2N).

diplolepidious [BOT] Double-scaled, specifically referring to the peristome of mosses with two rows of scales on the outside and one row on the inner.

Diplomonadida [INV ZOO] An order of small, colorless protozoans in the class Zoomastigophorea, having a bilaterally symmetrical body with four flagella on each side.

Diplomystidae [VERT ZOO] A family of catfishes in the suborder Siluroidei confined to the waters of Chile and Argentina.

diplont [BIOL] An organism with diploid somatic cells and haploid gametes.

Diplopoda [INV ZOO] The millipeds, a class of terrestrial tracheate, oviparous arthropods; each body segment except the first few bears two pairs of walking legs.

Diploporita [PALEON] An extinct order of echinoderms in the class Cystoidea in which the thecal canals were associated in pairs.

Diplorhina [VERT ZOO] The subclass of the class Agnatha that includes the jawless vertebrates with paired nostrils.

diplosome [CELL BIO] A double centriole.

diplospondyly [ANAT] Having two centra in one vertebra.

diplotene [CELL BIO] The stage of meiotic prophase during which pairs of nonsister chromatids of each bivalent repel each other and are kept from falling apart by the chiasmata.

Diplura [INV ZOO] An order of small, primarily wingless insects of worldwide distribution.

Dipneumonomorphae [INV ZOO] A suborder of the order Araneida comprising the spiders common in the United States, including grass spiders, hunting spiders, and black widows.

Dipneusti [VERT ZOO] The equivalent name for Dipnoi.

Dipnoi [VERT ZOO] The lungfishes, a subclass of the Osteichthyes having lungs that arise from a ventral connection in the gut.

Dipodidae [VERT ZOO] The Old World jerboas, a family of mammals in the order Rodentia.

diporpa larva [INV ZOO] A developmental stage of a monogenean trematode.

Diprionidae [INV ZOO] The conifer sawflies, a family of hymenopteran insects in the superfamily Tenthredinoidea.

Diprotodonta [VERT ZOO] A proposed order of marsupial mammals to include the phalangers, wombats, koalas, and kangaroos.

Diprotodontidae [PALEON] A family of extinct marsupial mammals.

Dipsacales [BOT] An order of dicotyledonous herbs and shrubs in the subclass Asteridae characterized by an inferior ovary and usually opposite leaves.

Dipsocoridae [INV ZOO] A family of hemipteran insects in the superfamily Dipsocoroidea; members are predators on small insects under bark or in rotten wood.

Dipsocoroidea [INV ZOO] A superfamily of minute, ground-inhabiting hemipteran insects belonging to the subdivision Geocorisae.

Diptera [INV ZOO] The true flies, an order of the class Insecta characterized by possessing only two wings and a pair of balancers.

Dipteriformes [VERT ZOO] The single order of the subclass Dipnoi, the lungfishes.

Dipterocarpaceae [BOT] A family of dicotyledonous plants in the order Theales having mostly stipulate, alternate leaves, a prominently exserted connective, and a calyx that is mostly winged in fruit.

dipterous [BIOL] 1. Of, related to, or characteristic of Diptera. 2. Having two wings or winglike structures.

directive [INV ZOO] Any of the dorsal and ventral paired mesenteries of certain anthozoan coelenterates.

disaccharide [BIOCHEM] Any of the class of compound sugars which yield two monosaccharide units upon hydrolysis.

Disasteridae [PALEON] A family of extinct burrowing, exocyclic Euechinoidea in the order Holasteroida comprising mainly small, ovoid forms without fascioles or a plastron.

disc See disk.

Discellaceae [MYCOL] A family of fungi of the order Sphaeropsidales, including saprophytes and some plant pathogens.

discifloral [BOT] Having flowers with enlarged, disklike receptacles.

disciform [BIOL] Disk-shaped.

Discinacea [INV ZOO] A family of inarticulate brachiopods in the suborder Acrotretidina.

disclimax [ECOL] A climax community that includes foreign species following a disturbance of the natural climax by man or domestic animals. Also known as disturbance climax.

discoaster [BOT] A star-shaped coccolith.

discoblastula [EMBRYO] A blastula formed by cleavage of a meroblastic egg; the blastoderm is disk-shaped.

discocephalous [INV ZOO] Having a sucker on the head.

discoctaster [INV ZOO] A type of spicule with eight rays terminating in discs in hexactinellid sponges.

discodactylous [VERT ZOO] Having sucking disks on the toes.

discogastrula [EMBRYO] A gastrula formed from a blastoderm.

Discoglossidae [VERT ZOO] A family of anuran amphibians in and typical of the suborder Opisthocoela.

discoid [BIOL] 1. Being flat and circular in form. 2. Any structure shaped like a disc.

discoidal cleavage [EMBRYO] A type of cleavage producing a disc of cells at the animal pole.

Discoidiidae [PALEON] A family of extinct conical or globular, exocyclic Euechinoidea in the order Holectypoida distinguished by the rudiments of internal skeletal partitions.

Discolichenes [BOT] The equivalent name for Lecanorales.

Discolomidae [INV ZOO] The tropical log beetles, a family of coleopteran insects in the superfamily Cucujoidea.

Discomycetes [MYCOL] A group of fungi in the class Ascomycetes in which the surface of the fruiting body is exposed during maturation of the spores.

discopodous [INV ZOO] Having a disk-shaped foot.

Discorbacea [INV ZOO] A superfamily of foraminiferan protozoans in the suborder Rotaliina characterized by a radial, perforate, calcite test and a monolamellar septa.

disjunct endemism [PALEON] A type of regionally restricted distribution of a fossil taxon in which two or more component parts are separated by a major physical barrier and hence not readily explicable in terms of present-day geography.

disjunction [CELL BIO] Separation of chromatids or homologous chromosomes during anaphase.

disjunctor [MYCOL] A small cellulose body between the conidia of certain fungi, which eventually breaks down and thus frees the conidia.

disk Also spelled disc. [BIOL] Any of various rounded and flattened animal and plant structures.

disk flower [BOT] One of the flowers on the disk of a composite plant.

disomaty [CELL BIO] Duplication of chromosomes unaccompanied by nuclear division.

Disomidae [INV ZOO] A family of spioniform annelid worms belonging to the Sedentaria.

dispermy [PHYSIO] Entrance of two spermatozoa into an ovum.

dissect [BIOL] To divide, cut, and separate into different parts.

disseminule [BIOL] An individual organism or part of an individual adapted for the dispersal of a population of the same organisms.

dissepiment [BOT] A partition which divides a fruit or an ovary into chambers. [PALEON] One of the vertically positioned thin plates situated between the septa in extinct corals of the order Rugosa.

dissociation [MICROBIO] The appearance of a novel colony type on solid media after one or more subcultures of the microorganism in liquid media.

dissogeny [ZOO] Having two sexually mature stages, larva and adult, in the life of an individual.

Distacodidae [PALEON] A family of conodonts in the suborder Conodontiformes characterized as simple curved cones with deeply excavated attachment scars.

distal [BIOL] Located away from the point of origin or attachment.

distal convoluted tubule [ANAT] The portion of the nephron in the vertebrate kidney lying between the loop of Henle and the collecting tubules.

distichous [BIOL] Occurring in two vertical rows.

distome [INV ZOO] A digenetic trematode characterized by possession of an oral and a ventral sucker.

disturbance climax See disclimax.

ditokous [VERT ZOO] Producing two eggs or giving birth to two young at one time.

diuretic hormone [BIOCHEM] A neurohormone that promotes water loss in insects by increasing the volume of fluid secreted into the Malpighian tubules.

diurnal [BIOL] Active during daylight hours.

diurnal migration [BIOL] The daily rhythmic movements of organisms in the sea from deeper water to the surface at the approach of darkness and their return to deeper water before dawn.

divaricate [BIOL] Broadly divergent and spread apart.

divaricator [ZOO] A muscle that causes separation of parts, as of brachiopod shells.

divergent adaptation [EVOL] Adaptation to different kinds of environment that results in divergence from a common ancestral form. Also known as branching adaptation; cladogenic adaptation.

diving bird [VERT ZOO] Any bird adapted for diving and swimming, including loons, grebes, and divers.

Dixidae [INV ZOO] A family of orthorrhaphous dipteran insects in the series Nematocera.

dizygotic twins [BIOL] Twins derived from two eggs. Also known as fraternal twins.

Docodonta [PALEON] A primitive order of Jurassic mammals of North America and England.

dodecamerous [BOT] Having the whorls of floral parts in multiples of 12.

dodo [VERT ZOO] *Raphus calcullatus*. A large, flightless, extinct bird of the family Raphidae.

doe [VERT ZOO] The adult female deer, antelope, goat, rabbit, or any other mammal of which the male is referred to as buck.

dog [VERT ZOO] Any of various wild and domestic animals identified as *Canis familiaris* in the family Canidae; all are carnivorous and digitigrade, are adapted to running, and have four toes with nonretractable claws on each foot.

dogfish See bowfin.

Doisy unit [BIOL] A unit for standardization of vitamin K.

dolabriform [BIOL] Shaped like an ax head.

dolichol [BIOCHEM] Any of a group of long-chain unsaturated isoprenoid alcohols containing up to 84 carbon atoms; found free or phosphorylated in membranes of the endoplasmic reticulum and Golgi apparatus.

Dolichopodidae [INV ZOO] The long-legged flies, a family of orthorrhaphous dipteran insects in the series Brachycera.

Dolichothoraci [PALEON] A group of joint-necked fishes assigned to the Arctolepiformes in which the pectoral appendages are represented solely by large fixed spines.

dolioform [BIOL] Barrel-shaped.

doliolaria larva [INV ZOO] A free-swimming larval stage of crinoids and holothurians having an apical tuft and four or five bands of cilia.

Doliolida [INV ZOO] An order of pelagic tunicates in the class Thaliacea; transparent forms, partly or wholly ringed by muscular bands.

dollar spot [PL PATH] A fungus disease of lawn grasses caused by *Sclerotinia homeocarpa* and characterized by small, round, brownish areas which gradually coalesce.

dolphin [VERT ZOO] The common name for about 33 species of cetacean mammals included in the family Delphinidae and characterized by the pronounced beak-shaped mouth.

domestication [BIOL] The adaptation of an animal or plant through breeding in captivity to a life intimately associated with and advantageous to humans.

dominance [ECOL] The influence that a controlling organism has on numerical composition or internal energy dynamics in a community. [GEN] The expression of a heritable trait in the heterozygote such as to make it phenotypically indistinguishable from the homozygote.

dominant allele [GEN] The member of a pair of alleles which is phenotypically indistinguishable in both the homozygous and heterozygous condition.

dominant hemisphere [PHYSIO] The cerebral hemisphere which controls certain motor activities; usually the left hemisphere in right-handed individuals.

dominant species [ECOL] A species of plant or animal that is particularly abundant or controls a major portion of the energy flow in a community.

donkey [VERT ZOO] A domestic ass (*Equus asinus*); a perissodactyl mammal in the family Equidae.

doodlebug [INV ZOO] The larva of an ant lion.

dopa *See* dihydroxyphenylalanine.

dopamine [BIOCHEM] $C_8H_{11}O_2N$ An intermediate in epinephrine and norepinephrine biosynthesis; the decarboxylation product of dopa.

dopa oxidase [BIOCHEM] An enzyme that catalyzes the oxidation of dihydroxyphenylalanine to melanin; occurs in the skin.

Doradidae [VERT ZOO] A family of South American catfishes in the suborder Siluroidei.

Dorilaidae [INV ZOO] The big-headed flies, a family of cyclorrhaphous dipteran insects in the series Aschiza.

Dorippidae [INV ZOO] The mask crabs, a family of brachyuran decapods in the subsection Oxystomata.

dormancy [BOT] A state of quiescence during the development of many plants characterized by their inability to grow, though continuing their morphological and physiological activities.

dormant bud *See* latent bud.

dormouse [VERT ZOO] The common name applied to members of the family Gliridae; they are Old World arboreal rodents intermediate between squirrels and rats.

Dorngeholz *See* thornbush.

Dorngestrauch *See* thornbush.

dornveld *See* thornbush.

dorsal [ANAT] Located near or on the back of an animal or one of its parts.

dorsal aorta [ANAT] The portion of the aorta extending from the left ventricle to the first branch. [INV ZOO] The large, dorsal blood vessel in many invertebrates.

dorsal column [ANAT] A column situated dorsally in each lateral half of the spinal cord which receives the terminals of some afferent fibers from the dorsal roots of the spinal nerves.

dorsal fin [VERT ZOO] A median longitudinal vertical fin on the dorsal aspect of a fish or other aquatic vertebrate.

dorsal lip [EMBRYO] In an amphibian embryo, the margin or lip of the fold of blastula wall marking the dorsal limit of the blastopore during gastrulation and constituting the primary organizer, is necessary to the development of neural tissue, and forms the originating point of chordamesoderm.

dorsiferous [BOT] Of ferns, bearing sori on the back of the frond. [ZOO] Bearing the eggs or young on the back.

dorsiflex [ZOO] To flex or cause to flex in a dorsal direction.

dorsigrade [VERT ZOO] Walking on the back of the toes.

dorsocaudad [ANAT] To or toward the dorsal surface and caudal end of the body.

dorsomedial [ANAT] Located on the back, toward the midline.

dorsoposteriad [ANAT] To or toward the dorsal surface and posterior end of the body.

dorsum [ANAT] 1. The entire dorsal surface of the animal body. 2. The upper part of the tongue, opposite the velum.

Dorvilleidae [INV ZOO] A family of minute errantian annelids in the superfamily Eunicea.

Dorylaimoidea [INV ZOO] An order or superfamily of nematodes inhabiting soil and fresh water.

Dorylinae [INV ZOO] A subfamily of predacious ants in the family Formicidae, including the army ant (*Eciton hamatum*).

Dorypteridae [PALEON] A family of Permian palaeonisciform fishes sometimes included in the suborder Platysomoidei.

dosage [GEN] The number of genes with a similar action that control a given character.

dosage compensation [GEN] A mechanism that equalizes the phenotypic effects of genes located on the X chromosome, which genes therefore exist in two doses in the homogametic sex and one dose in the heterogametic sex.

double blossom [PL PATH] A fungus disease of dewberry and blackberry caused by *Fusarium rubi* and characterized by witches'-brooms and enlargement and malformation of the flowers.

double circulation [PHYSIO] A circulatory system in which blood flows through two separate circuits, as pulmonary and systemic.

double fertilization [BOT] In most seed plants, fertilization involving fusion between the egg nucleus and one sperm nucleus, and fusion between the other sperm nucleus and the polar nuclei.

double-loop pattern [ANAT] A whorl type of fingerprint pattern consisting of two separate loop formations and two deltas.

double square *See* adjustable square.

double-work [BOT] In plant propagation, to graft or bud a scion to an intermediate variety that is itself grafted on a stock of still another variety.

Douglas fir [BOT] *Pseudotsuga menziesii*. A large coniferous tree in the order Pinales; cones are characterized by bracts extending beyond the scales. Also known as red fir.

Dounce homogenizer [BIOL] An apparatus consisting of a glass tube with a tight-fitting glass pestle used manually to disrupt tissue suspensions to obtain single cells or subcellular fractions.

dove [VERT ZOO] The common name for a number of small birds of the family Columbidae.

downy mildew [PL PATH] A fungus disease of higher plants caused by members of the family Peronosporaceae and characterized by a white, downy growth on the diseased plant parts.

DPN See diphosphopyridine nucleotide.

Dracunculoidea [INV ZOO] An order or superfamily of parasitic nematodes characterized by their habitat in host tissues and by the way larvae leave the host through a skin lesion.

dragonfly [INV ZOO] Any of the insects composing six families of the suborder Anisoptera and having four large, membranous wings and compound eyes that provide keen vision.

Drepanellacea [PALEON] A monomorphic superfamily of extinct paleocopan ostracods in the suborder Beyrichicopina having a subquadrate carapace, many with a marginal rim.

Drepanellidae [PALEON] A monomorphic family of extinct ostracods in the superfamily Drepanellacea.

Drepanidae [INV ZOO] The hooktips, a small family of lepidopteran insects in the suborder Heteroneura.

Drilidae [INV ZOO] The false firefly beetles, a family of coleopteran insects in the superfamily Cantharoidea.

Dromadidae [VERT ZOO] A family of the avian order Charadriiformes containing a single species, the crab plover (*Dromas ardeola*).

dromedary [VERT ZOO] *Camelus dromedarius* The Arabian camel, distinguished by a single hump.

Dromiacea [INV ZOO] The dromiid crabs, a subsection of the Brachyura in the crustacean order Decapoda.

Dromiceidae [VERT ZOO] The emus, a monospecific family of flightless birds in the order Casuariiformes.

drone [INV ZOO] A haploid male bee or ant; one of the three castes in a colony.

drop [PL PATH] A fungus disease of various vegetables caused by *Sclerotinia sclerotiorum* and characterized by wilt and stem rot.

Droseraceae [BOT] A family of dicotyledonous plants in the order Sarraceniales, distinguished by leaves that do not form pitchers, parietal placentation, and several styles.

Drosophilidae [INV ZOO] The vinegar flies, a family of myodarian cyclorrhaphous dipteran insects in the subsection Acalyptratae, including the fruit fly (*Drosophila melanogaster*).

drug resistance [MICROBIO] A decreased reactivity of living organisms to the injurious actions of certain drugs and chemicals.

drupaceous [BOT] Of, pertaining to, or characteristic of a drupe.

drupe [BOT] A fruit, such as a cherry, having a thin or leathery exocarp, a fleshy mesocarp, and a single seed with a stony endocarp. Also known as stone fruit.

drupelet [BOT] An individual drupe of an aggregate fruit. Also known as grain.

Dryinidae [INV ZOO] A family of hymenopteran insects in the superfamily Bethyloidea.

Dryomyzidae [INV ZOO] A family of myodarian cyclorrhaphous dipteran insects in the subsection Acalypteratae.

Dryopidae [INV ZOO] The long-toed water beetles, a family of coleopteran insects in the superfamily Dryopoidea.

Dryopoidea [INV ZOO] A superfamily of coleopteran insects in the suborder Polyphaga, including the nonpredatory aquatic beetles.

dry rot [MICROBIO] A rapid decay of seasoned timber caused by certain fungi which cause the wood to be reduced to a dry, friable texture. [PL PATH] Any of various rot diseases of plants characterized by drying of affected tissues.

duck [VERT ZOO] The common name for a number of small waterfowl in the family Anatidae, having short legs, a broad, flat bill, and a dorsoventrally flattened body.

duck-billed dinosaur [PALEON] Any of several herbivorous, bipedal ornithopods having the front of the mouth widened to form a ducklike beak.

duckbill platypus See platypus.

duck wheat See tartary buckwheat.

duct [ANAT] An enclosed tubular channel for conducting a glandular secretion or other body fluid.

duct of Cuvier [EMBRYO] Either of the paired common cardinal veins in a vertebrate embryo.

duct of Santorini [ANAT] The dorsal pancreatic duct in a vertebrate embryo; persists in adult life in some species and serves as the pancreatic duct in the adult elasmobranch, pig, and ox.

ductus arteriosus [EMBRYO] Blood shunt between the pulmonary artery and the aorta of the mammalian embryo.

ductus deferens See vas deferens.

ductus venosus [EMBRYO] Blood shunt between the left umbilical vein and the right sinus venosus of the heart in the mammalian embryo.

Dugongidae [VERT ZOO] A family of aquatic mammals in the order Sirenia comprising two species, the dugong and the sea cow.

Dugonginae [VERT ZOO] The dugongs, a subfamily of sirenian mammals in the family Dugongidae characterized by enlarged, sharply deflected premaxillae and the absence of nasal bones.

dulse [BOT] Any of several species of red algae of the genus *Rhodymenia* found below the intertidal zone in northern latitudes; an important food plant.

duodenal glands See Brunner's glands.

duodenum [ANAT] The first section of the small intestine of mammals, extending from the pylorus to the jejunum.

duplex uterus [ANAT] A condition in certain primitive mammals, such as rodents and bats, that have two distinct uteri opening separately into the vagina.

dura mater [ANAT] The fibrous membrane forming the outermost covering of the brain and spinal cord. Also known as endocranium.

Durham fermentation tube [MICROBIO] A test tube containing lactose or lauryl tryptose and an inverted vial for gas collection; used to test for the presence of coliform bacteria.

Dutch elm disease [PL PATH] A lethal fungus disease of elm trees caused by *Graphium ulmi*, which releases a toxic substance that destroys vascular tissue; transmitted by a bark beetle.

dwarf [BIOL] Being an atypically small form or variety of something.

dwarf disease [PL PATH] A virus disease marked by the inhibition of fruit production; common in plum trees.

dwarf mouse unit [BIOL] A unit for the standardization of somatotropin.

dyad [CELL BIO] Either of the two pair of chromatids produced by separation of a tetrad during the first meiotic division.

Dysideidae [INV ZOO] A family of sponges in the order Dictyoceratida.

Dysodonta [PALEON] An order of extinct bivalve mollusks with a nearly toothless hinge and a ligament in grooves or pits.

dystonia [PHYSIO] Disorder or lack of muscle tonicity.

dystophic [BIOL] Pertaining to an environment that does not supply adequate nutrition.

Dytiscidae [INV ZOO] The predacious diving beetles, a family of coleopteran insects in the suborder Adephaga.

E

eagle [VERT ZOO] Any of several large, strong diurnal birds of prey in the family Accipitridae.

Eagle's medium [MICROBIO] A tissue-culture medium, developed by H. Eagle, containing vitamins, amino acids, inorganic salts and serous enrichments, and dextrose.

ear [ANAT] The receptor organ that sends both auditory information and space orientation information to the brain in vertebrates.

earlobe [ANAT] The pendulous, fleshy lower portion of the auricle or external ear.

ear rot [PL PATH] Any of several fungus diseases of corn, occurring both in the field and in storage and marked by decay and molding of the ears.

earthstar [MYCOL] A fungus of the genus *Geastrum* that resembles a puffball with a double peridium, the outer layer of which splits into the shape of a star.

earthworm [INV ZOO] The common name for certain terrestrial members of the class Oligochaeta, especially forms belonging to the family Lumbricidae.

earwig [INV ZOO] The common name for members of the insect order Dermaptera.

Eaton agent [MICROBIO] The name applied to *Mycoplasma pneumoniae* when it was regarded as a virus.

Ebenaceae [BOT] A family of dicotyledonous plants in the order Ebenales, in which a latex system is absent and flowers are mostly unisexual with the styles separate, at least distally.

Ebenales [BOT] An order of woody, sympetalous dicotyledonous plants in the subclass Dilleniidae, having axile placentation and usually twice as many stamens as corolla lobes.

ebony [BOT] Any of several African and Asian trees of the genus *Diospyros*, providing a hard, durable wood.

ebracteate [BOT] Without bracts, or much reduced leaves.

ebracteolate [BOT] Without bracteoles.

Ebriida [INV ZOO] An order of flagellate protozoans in the class Phytamastigophorea characterized by a solid siliceous skeleton.

ebullism [PHYSIO] The formation of bubbles, especially of water vapor bubbles in biological fluids, owing to reduced ambient pressure.

ecad [ECOL] A type of plant which is altered by its habitat and possesses nonheritable characteristics.

eccrine gland [PHYSIO] One of the small sweat glands distributed all over the human body surface; they are tubular coiled merocrine glands that secrete clear aqueous sweat.

ecdysis [INV ZOO] Molting of the outer cuticular layer of the body, as in insects and crustaceans.

ecdysone [BIOCHEM] The molting hormone of insects.

ecesis [ECOL] Successful naturalization of a plant or animal population in a new environment.

Echeneidae [VERT ZOO] The remoras, a family of perciform fishes in the suborder Percoidei.

echidna [VERT ZOO] A spiny anteater; any member of the family Tachyglossidae.

Echinacea [INV ZOO] A suborder of echinoderms in the order Euechinoidea; individuals have a rigid test, keeled teeth, and branchial slits.

echinate [ZOO] Having a dense covering of spines or bristles.

Echinidae [INV ZOO] A family of echinacean echinoderms in the order Echinoida possessing trigeminate or polyporous plates with the pores in a narrow vertical zone.

Echiniscoidea [INV ZOO] A suborder of tardigrades in the order Heterotardigrada characterized by terminal claws on the legs.

Echinococcus [INV ZOO] A genus of tapeworms.

echinococcus cyst [INV ZOO] A cyst formed in host tissues by the larva of *Echinococcus granulosus*.

Echinocystitoida [PALEON] An order of extinct echinoderms in the subclass Perischoechinoidea.

Echinodera [INV ZOO] The equivalent name for Kinorhyncha.

Echinodermata [INV ZOO] A phylum of exclusively marine coelomate animals distinguished from all others by an internal skeleton composed of calcite plates, and a water-vascular system to serve the needs of locomotion, respiration, nutrition, or perception.

Echinoida [INV ZOO] An order of Echinacea with a camarodont lantern, smooth test, and imperforate noncrenulate tubercles.

Echinoidea [INV ZOO] The sea urchins, a class of Echinozoa having a compact body enclosed in a hard shell, or test, formed by regularly arranged plates which bear movable spines.

Echinometridae [INV ZOO] A family of echinoderms in the order Echinoida, including polyporous types with either an oblong or a spherical test.

echinomycin [MICROBIO] $C_{50}H_{60}O_{12}N_{12}S_2$ A toxic polypeptide antibiotic produced by species of *Streptomyces*.

echinopluteus [INV ZOO] The bilaterally symmetrical larva of sea urchins.

Echinostellaceae [MYCOL] A family of slime molds in the order Echinosteliales.

Echinosteliales [MYCOL] An order of slime molds in the subclass Myxogastromycetidae.

echinostome cercaria [INV ZOO] A digenetic trematode larva characterized by the large anterior acetabulum and a collar with spines.

Echinothuriidae [INV ZOO] A family of deep-water echinoderms in the order Echinothurioida in which the large, flexible test collapses into a disk at atmospheric pressure.

Echinothurioida [INV ZOO] An order of echinoderms in the superorder Diadematacea with solid or hollow primary radioles, diademoid ambulacral plates, noncrenulate tubercles, and the anus within the apical system.

Echinozoa [INV ZOO] A subphylum of free-living echinoderms having the body essentially globoid with meridional symmetry and lacking appendages.

Echiurida [INV ZOO] A small group of wormlike organisms regarded as a separate phylum of the animal kingdom; members have a saclike or sausage-shaped body with an anterior, detachable prostomium.

Echiuridae [INV ZOO] A small family of the order Echiuroinea characterized by a flaplike prostomium.

Echiuroidea [INV ZOO] A phylum of schizocoelous animals.

Echiuroinea [INV ZOO] An order of the Echiurida.

echo ranging [VERT ZOO] An auditory feedback mechanism in bats, porpoises, seals, and certain other animals whereby reflected ultrasonic sounds are utilized in orientation.

echovirus [VIROL] A division of enteroviruses in the picornavirus group; the name is derived from the group designation enteric cytopathogenic human orphan virus.

eclipse period [VIROL] A phase in the proliferation of viral particles during which the virus cannot be detected in the host cell.

eclosion [INV ZOO] The process of an insect hatching from its egg.

ecocline [ECOL] A genetic gradient of adaptability to an environmental gradient; formed by the merger of ecotypes.

ecological association [ECOL] A complex of communities, such as an elm-hackberry association, which develops in accord with variations in physiography, soil, and successional history within the major subdivision of a biotic realm.

ecological climatology [BIOL] A branch of bioclimatology, including the physiological adaptation of plants and animals to their climate, and the geographical distribution of plants and animals in relation to climate.

ecological interaction [ECOL] The relation between species that live together in a community; specifically, the effect an individual of one species may exert on an individual of another species.

ecological pyramid [ECOL] A pyramid-shaped diagram representing quantitatively the numbers of organisms, energy relationships, and biomass of an ecosystem; numbers are high for the lowest trophic levels (plants) and low for the highest trophic level (carnivores).

ecological succession [ECOL] A gradual process incurred by the change in the number of individuals of each species of a community and by establishment of new species populations that may gradually replace the original inhabitants.

ecology [BIOL] A study of the interrelationships which exist between organisms and their environment. Also known as environmental biology.

economic entomology [BIOL] A branch of entomology concerned with the study of economic losses of commercially important animals and plants due to insect predation.

ecosystem [ECOL] A functional system which includes the organisms of a natural community together with their environment. Derived from ecological system.

ecosystem mapping [ECOL] The drawing of maps that locate different ecosystems in a geographic area.

ecotone [ECOL] A zone of intergradation between ecological communities.

ecotype [ECOL] A subunit, race, or variety of a plant ecospecies that is restricted to one habitat; equivalent to a taxonomic subspecies.

Ecterocoelia [INV ZOO] The equivalent name for Protostomia.

ectethmoid [ANAT] Either one of the lateral cellular masses of the ethmoid bone.

ectocommensal [ECOL] An organism living on the outer surface of the body of another organism, without affecting its host.

ectocornea [ANAT] The outer layer of the cornea.

ectocyst [INV ZOO] 1. The outer layer of the wall of a zooecium. 2. *See* epicyst.

ectoderm [EMBRYO] The outer germ layer of an animal embryo. Also known as epiblast. [INV ZOO] The outer layer of a diploblastic animal.

ectoenzyme [BIOCHEM] An enzyme which is located on the external surface of a cell.

ectogenesis [EMBRYO] Development of an embryo or embryonic tissue outside the body in an artificial environment.

ectogony [BOT] The influence of pollination and fertilization on structures outside the embryo and endosperm; effect may be on color, chemical composition, ripening, or abscission.

ectomere [EMBRYO] A blastomere that will differentiate into ectoderm.

ectomesoblast [EMBRYO] An undifferentiated layer of embryonic cells from which arises the epiblast and mesoblast.

ectomesoderm [EMBRYO] Mesoderm which is derived from ectoderm and is always mesenchymal; a type of primitive connective tissue.

ectoparasite [ECOL] A parasite that lives on the exterior of its host.

ectophagous [INV ZOO] The larval stage of a parasitic insect which is in the process of development externally on a host.

ectophloic siphonostele [BOT] A type of stele with pith that has the phloem only on the outside of the xylem.

ectophyte [ECOL] A plant which lives externally on another organism.

ectopic pairing [CELL BIO] Pairing between nonhomologous segments of the salivary gland chromosomes in *Drosophila*, presumably involving mainly heterochromatic regions.

ectoplasm [CELL BIO] The outer, gelled zone of the cytoplasmic ground substance in many cells. Also known as ectosarc.

Ectoprocta [INV ZOO] A subphylum of colonial bryozoans having eucoelomate visceral cavities and the anus opening outside the circlet of tentacles.

ectopterygold [VERT ZOO] A membrane bone located ventrally on the skull, situated behind the palate and extending to the quadrate; found in some fishes and reptiles.

ectosome [INV ZOO] The outer, cortical layer of a sponge.

ectostosis [PHYSIO] Formation of bone immediately beneath the perichondrium and surrounding and replacing underlying cartilage.

ectosymbiont [ECOL] A symbiont that lives on the surface of or is physically separated from its host.

ectotherm [PHYSIO] An animal that obtains most of its heat from the environment and therefore has a body temperature very close to that of its environment.

Ectothiorhodospira [MICROBIO] A genus of bacteria in the family Chromatiaceae; cells are spiral to slightly bent rods, are motile, contain bacteriochlorophyll *a* on lamellar stock membranes, and produce and deposit sulfur as globules outside the cells.

ectotrophic [BIOL] Obtaining nourishment from outside; applied to certain parasitic fungi that live on and surround the roots of the host plant.

ectozoa [ECOL] Animals which live externally on other organisms.

Ectrephidae [INV ZOO] An equivalent name for Ptinidae.

ectromelia virus [VIROL] A member of subgroup I of the poxvirus group; causes mousepox.

edaphic community [ECOL] A plant community that results from or is influenced by soil factors such as salinity and drainage.

edaphon [BIOL] Flora and fauna in soils.

Edaphosuria [PALEON] A suborder of extinct, lowland, terrestrial, herbivorous reptiles in the order Pelycosauria.

Edentata [VERT ZOO] An order of mammals characterized by the absence of teeth or the presence of simple prismatic, unspecialized teeth with no enamel.

edentate [VERT ZOO] 1. Lacking teeth. 2. Any member of the Edentata.

edentulous [VERT ZOO] Having no teeth; especially, having lost teeth that were present.

edge effect [ECOL] The influence of adjacent plant communities on the number of animal species present in the direct vicinity.

Ediacaran fauna [PALEON] The oldest known assemblage of fossil remains of soft-bodied marine animals; first discovered in the Ediacara Hills, Australia.

Edman degradation technique [BIOCHEM] In protein analysis, an approach to amino-end-group determination involving the use of a reagent, phenylisothiocyanate, that can be applied to the liberation of a derivative of the amino-terminal residue without hydrolysis of the remainder of the peptide chain.

Edrioasteroidea [PALEON] A class of extinct Echinozoa having ambulacral radial areas bordered by tube feet, and the mouth and anus located on the upper side of the theca.

Edwardsiella [MICROBIO] A genus of bacteria in the family Enterobacteriaceae; motile rods that produce hydrogen sulfide from TSI agar.

eel [VERT ZOO] The common name for a number of unrelated fishes included in the orders Anguilliformes and Cypriniformes; all have an elongate, serpentine body.

effector [BIOCHEM] An activator of an allosteric enzyme. [PHYSIO] A structure that is sensitive to a stimulus and causes an organism or part of an organism to react to the stimulus, either positively or negatively.

effector organ [PHYSIO] Any muscle or gland that mediates overt behavior, that is, movement or secretion.

effector system [PHYSIO] A system of effector organs in the animal body.

efferent [PHYSIO] Carrying or conducting away, as the duct of an exocrine gland or a nerve.

efflorescence [BOT] The period or process of flowering.

effuse [BOT] Expanded; spread out in a definite form.

egest [PHYSIO] 1. To discharge indigestible matter from the digestive tract. 2. To rid the body of waste.

egg [CELL BIO] 1. A large, female sex cell enclosed in a porous, calcareous or leathery shell, produced by birds and reptiles. 2. *See* ovum.

egg apparatus [BOT] A group of three cells, consisting of the egg and two synergid cells, in the micropylar end of the embryo sac in seed plants.

egg case [INV ZOO] 1. A protective capsule containing the eggs of certain insects and mollusks. Also known as egg capsule. 2. A silk pouch in which certain spiders carry their eggs. Also known as egg sac.

egg case [VERT ZOO] A soft, gelatinous (amphibians) or strong, horny (skates) envelope containing the egg of certain vertebrates.

eggplant [BOT] *Solanum melongena*. A plant of the order Polemoniales grown for its edible eggshaped, fleshy fruit.

egg raft [ZOO] A floating mass of eggs; produced by a variety of aquatic organisms.

egg sac [INV ZOO] 1. The structure containing the eggs of certain microcrustaceans. 2. *See* egg case.

egg tooth [VERT ZOO] A toothlike prominence on the tip of the beak of a bird embryo and the tip of the nose of an oviparous reptile, which is used to break the eggshell.

eglandular [BIOL] Without glands.

Egyptian cotton [BOT] Long-staple, high-quality cotton grown in Egypt.

Ehrlichia [MICROBIO] A genus of the tribe Ehrlichieae; coccoid to ellipsoidal or pleomorphic cells; intracellular parasites in cytoplasm of host leukocytes.

Ehrlichieae [MICROBIO] A tribe of the family Rickettsiaceae; spherical and occasionally pleomorphic cells; pathogenic for some mammals, not including humans.

Eimerina [INV ZOO] A suborder of coccidian protozoans in the order Eucoccida in which there is no syzygy and the microgametocytes produce a large number of microgametes.

ejaculation [PHYSIO] The act or process of suddenly discharging a fluid from the body; specifically, the ejection of semen during orgasm.

ejaculatory duct [ANAT] The terminal part of the ductus deferens after junction with the duct of a seminal vesicle, embedded in the prostate gland and opening into the urethra.

ejecta [PHYSIO] Excrement.

Elaeagnaceae [BOT] A family of dicotyledonous plants in the order Proteales, noted for peltate leaf scales which often give the leaves a silvery-gray appearance.

elaioplast [HISTOL] An oil-secreting leucoplast.

Elaphomycetaceae [MYCOL] A family of underground, saprophytic or mycorrhiza-forming fungi in the order Eurotiales characterized by ascocarps with thick, usually woody walls.

Elapidae [VERT ZOO] A family of poisonous reptiles, including cobras, kraits, mambas, and coral snakes; all have a pteroglyph fang arrangement.

Elasipodida [INV ZOO] An order of deep-sea aspidochirotacean holothurians in which there are no respiratory trees and bilateral symmetry is often quite conspicuous.

Elasmidae [INV ZOO] A family of hymenopteran insects in the superfamily Chalcidoidea.

Elasmobranchii [VERT ZOO] The sharks and rays, a subclass of the class Chondrichthyes distinguished by separate gill openings, amphistylic or hyostylic jaw suspension, and ampullae of Lorenzini in the head region.

Elassomatidae [VERT ZOO] The pygmy sunfishes, a family of the order Perciformes.

elastase [BIOCHEM] An enzyme which acts on elastin to change it chemically and render it soluble.

elastic cartilage [HISTOL] A type of cartilage containing elastic fibers in the matrix.

elastic fiber [HISTOL] A homogeneous, fibrillar connective tissue component that is highly refractile and appears yellowish when arranged in bundles.

elastic tissue [HISTOL] A type of connective tissue having a predominance of elastic fibers, bands, or lamellae.

elastin [BIOCHEM] An elastic protein composing the principal component of elastic fibers.

elater [BOT] A spiral, filamentous structure that functions in the dispersion of spores in certain plants, such as liverworts and slime molds.

Elateridae [INV ZOO] The click beetles, a large family of coleopteran insects in the superfamily Elateroidea; many have light-producing organs.

Elateroidea [INV ZOO] A superfamily of coleopteran insects in the suborder Polyphaga.

elaterophore [BOT] A tissue bearing elaters, found in some liverworts.

elbow [ANAT] The arm joint formed at the junction of the humerus, radius, and ulna.

elective culture [MICROBIO] A type of microorganism grown selectively from a mixed culture by culturing in a medium and under conditions selective for only one type of organism.

electric eel [VERT ZOO] *Electrophorus electricus*. An eellike cypriniform electric fish of the family Gymnotidae.

electric fish [VERT ZOO] Any of several fishes capable of producing electric discharges from an electric organ.

electric organ [VERT ZOO] An organ consisting of rows of electroplaques which produce an electric discharge.

electric shock [PHYSIO] The sudden pain, convulsion, unconsciousness, or death produced by the passage of electric current through the body.

electrogram [PHYSIO] The graphic representation of electric events in living tissues; commonly, an electrocardiogram or electroencephalogram.

electron transport system [BIOCHEM] The components of the final sequence of reactions in biological oxidations; composed of a series of oxidizing agents arranged in order of increasing strength and terminating in oxygen.

electrophonic effect [BIOPHYS] The sensation of hearing produced when an alternating current of suitable frequency and magnitude is passed through a person.

electrophoretic mobility [BIOCHEM] A characteristic of living cells in suspension and biological compounds (proteins) in solution to travel in an electric field to the positive or negative electrode, because of the charge on these substances.

electrophoretic variants [BIOCHEM] Phenotypically different proteins that are separable into distinct electrophoretic components due to differences in mobilities; an example is erythrocyte acid phosphatase.

electrophysiology [PHYSIO] The branch of physiology concerned with determining the basic mechanisms by which electric currents are generated within living organisms.

electroplax [VERT ZOO] One of the structural units of an electric organ of some fishes, composed of thin, flattened plates of modified muscle that appear as two large, waferlike, roughly circular or rectangular surfaces.

electrotaxis [BIOL] Movement of an organism in response to stimulation by electric charges.

electrotonus [PHYSIO] The change of condition in a nerve or a muscle during the passage of a current of electricity.

electrotropism [BIOL] Orientation response of a sessile organism to stimulation by electric charges.

elephant [VERT ZOO] The common name for two living species of proboscidean mammals in the family Elephantidae; distinguished by the elongation of the nostrils and upper lip into a sensitive, prehensile proboscis.

Elephantidae [VERT ZOO] A family of mammals in the order Proboscidea containing the modern elephants and extinct mammoths.

elfinwood *See* krummholz.

elk [VERT ZOO] *Alces alces.* A mammal (family Cervidae) in Europe and Asia that resembles the North American moose but is smaller; it is the largest living deer.

elm [BOT] The common name for hardwood trees composing the genus *Ulmus*, characterized by simple, serrate, deciduous leaves.

Elmidae [INV ZOO] The drive beetles, a small family of coleopteran insects in the superfamily Dryopoidea.

elongation factor [BIOCHEM] Any of several proteins required for elongation of growing polypeptide chains during protein synthesis.

Elopidae [VERT ZOO] A family of fishes in the order Elopiformes, including the tarpon, ladyfish, and machete.

Elopiformes [VERT ZOO] A primitive order of actinopterygian fishes characterized by a single dorsal fin composed of soft rays only, cycloid scales, and toothed maxillae.

El Tor vibrio [MICROBIO] Any of the rod-shaped paracholera vibrios; many strains can be agglutinated with anticholera serum.

elytron [INV ZOO] 1. One of the two sclerotized or leathery anterior wings of beetles which serve to cover and protect the membranous hindwings. 2. A dorsal scale of certain Polychaeta.

emarginate [BIOL] Having a margin that is notched or slightly forked.

EMB agar [MICROBIO] A culture medium containing sugar, eosin, and methylene blue, used in the confirming test for coliform bacteria.

Emballonuridae [VERT ZOO] The sheath-tailed bats, a family of mammals in the order Chiroptera.

Embden-Meyerhof pathway *See* glycolytic pathway.

embed Also spelled imbed. [BIOL] To prepare a specimen for sectioning for microscopic examination by infiltrating with or enclosing in paraffin or other supporting material.

Emblidina [INV ZOO] An equivalent name for Embioptera.

Embioptera [INV ZOO] An order of silk-spinning, orthopteroid insects resembling the grasshoppers; commonly called the embiids or web spinners.

Embiotocidae [VERT ZOO] The surfperches, a family of perciform fishes in the suborder Percoidei.

Embolomeri [PALEON] An extinct side branch of slender-bodied, fish-eating aquatic anthracosaurs in which intercentra as well as centra form complete rings.

emboly [EMBRYO] Formation of a gastrula by the process of invagination.

Embrithopoda [PALEON] An order established for the unique Oligocene mammal *Arsinoitherium*, a herbivorous animal that resembled the modern rhinoceros.

embryo [BOT] The young sporophyte of a seed plant. [EMBRYO] 1. An early stage of development in multicellular organisms. 2. The product of conception up to the third month of human pregnancy.

Embryobionta [BOT] The land plants, a subkingdom of the Plantae characterized by having specialized conducting tissue in the sporophyte (except bryophytes), having multicellular sex organs, and producing an embryo.

embryogenesis [EMBRYO] The formation and development of an embryo from an egg.

embryology [BIOL] The study of the development of the organism from the zygote, or fertilized egg.

embryonate [EMBRYO] 1. To differentiate into a zygote. 2. Containing an embryo.

embryonated egg culture [VIROL] Embryonated hen's eggs inoculated with animal viruses for the purpose of identification, isolation, titration, or for quantity cultivation in the production of viral vaccines.

embryonic differentiation [EMBRYO] The process by which specialized and diversified structures arise during embryogenesis.

embryonic inducer [EMBRYO] The acting system in embryos, which contributes to the formation of specialized tissues by controlling the mode of development of the reacting system.

embryonic induction [EMBRYO] The influence of one cell group (inducer) over a neighboring cell group (induced) during embryogenesis. Also known as induction.

Embryophyta [BOT] The equivalent name for Embryobionta.

embryo sac [BOT] The female gametophyte of a seed plant, containing the egg, synergids, and polar and antipodal nuclei; fusion of the antipodals and a pollen generative nucleus forms the endosperm.

emerged bog [ECOL] A bog which grows vertically above the water table by drawing water up through the mass of plants.

emigration [ECOL] The movement of individuals or their disseminules out of a population or population area.

emiocytosis [CELL BIO] Fusion of intracellular granules with the cell membrane, followed by discharge of the granules outside of the cell; applied chiefly to the mechanism of insulin secretion. Also known as reverse pinocytosis.

Empididae [INV ZOO] The dance flies, a family of orthorrhaphous dipteran insects in the series Nematocera.

empodium [INV ZOO] A small peripheral part located between the claws of the tarsi of many insects and arachnids.

emu [VERT ZOO] *Dromiceius novae-hollandiae*. An Australian ratite bird, the second largest living bird, characterized by rudimentary wings and a feathered head and neck without wattles.

Emydidae [VERT ZOO] A family of aquatic and semiaquatic turtles in the suborder Cryptodira.

Enaliornithidae [PALEON] A family of extinct birds assigned to the order Hesperornithiformes, having well-developed teeth found in grooves in the dentary and maxillary bones of the jaws.

enamel organ [EMBRYO] The epithelial ingrowth from the dental lamina which covers the dental papilla, furnishes a mold for the shape of a developing tooth, and forms the dental enamel.

Enantiozoa [INV ZOO] The equivalent name for Parazoa.

enarthrosis [ANAT] A freely movable joint that allows a wide range of motion on all planes. Also known as ball-and-socket joint.

enchymatous [PHYSIO] Of gland cells, distended with secreted material.

encrinite [PALEON] One of certain fossil crinoids, especially of the genus *Encrinus*.

Encyrtidae [INV ZOO] A family of hymenopteran insects in the superfamily Chalcidoidea.

encystment [BIOL] The process of forming or becoming enclosed in a cyst or capsule.

Endamoeba [INV ZOO] The type genus of the Endamoebidae comprising insect parasites and, in some systems of classification, certain vertebrate parasites.

Endamoeba coli [INV ZOO] A nonpathogenic ameba that inhabits the human intestinal tract.

endarch [BOT] Formed outward from the center, referring to xylem or its development.

end bulb of Krause See Krause's corpuscle.

Endeidae [INV ZOO] A family of marine arthropods in the subphylum Pycnogonida.

endergonic [BIOCHEM] Of or pertaining to a biochemical reaction in which the final products possess more free energy than the starting materials; usually associated with anabolism.

endite [INV ZOO] 1. One of the appendages on the inner aspect of an arthropod limb. 2. A ridgelike chewing surface on the inner part of the pedipalpus or maxilla of many arachnids.

endobasion [ANAT] The anteriormost point of the margin of the foramen magnum at the level of its smallest diameter.

endobiotic [ECOL] Referring to an organism living in the cells or tissues of a host.

endobranchiate [ZOO] Animal form with endodermal gills.

endocardium [ANAT] The membrane lining the heart.

endocarp [BOT] The inner layer of the wall of a fruit or pericarp.

endocervix [ANAT] The glandular mucous membrane of the cervix uteri.

endochondral ossification [PHYSIO] The conversion of cartilage into bone. Also known as intracartilaginous ossification.

endocommensal [ECOL] A commensal that lives within the body of its host.

endocorpuscular [CELL BIO] Located within an erythrocyte.

endocranium [ANAT] 1. The inner surface of the cranium. 2. See dura mater. [INV ZOO] The processes on the inner surface of the head capsule of certain insects.

endocrine gland [PHYSIO] A ductless structure whose secretion (hormone) is passed into adjacent tissue and then to the bloodstream either directly or by way of the lymphatics. Also known as ductless gland.

endocrine system [PHYSIO] The chemical coordinating system in animals, that is, the endocrine glands that produce hormones.

endocrinology [PHYSIO] The study of the endocrine glands and the hormones that they synthesize and secrete.

endocuticle [INV ZOO] The inner, elastic layer of an insect cuticle.

endocyst [INV ZOO] The soft layer consisting of ectoderm and mesoderm, lining the ectocyst of bryozoans.

endocytic vacuole [CELL BIO] A membrane-bound cellular organelle containing extracellular particles engulfed by the mechanisms of endocytosis.

endocytosis [CELL BIO] 1. An active process in which extracellular materials are introduced into the cytoplasm of cells by either phagocytosis or pinocytosis. 2. The process by which animal cells internalize large molecules and large collections of fluid.

endoderm [EMBRYO] The inner, primary germ layer of an animal embryo; sometimes referred to as the hypoblast. Also known as entoderm; hypoblast.

endodermis [BOT] The innermost tissue of the cortex of most plant roots and certain stems consisting of a single layer of at least partly suberized or cutinized cells; functions to control the movement of water and other substances into and out of the stele.

endoenzyme [BIOCHEM] An intracellular enzyme, retained and utilized by the secreting cell.

endogamy [BIOL] Sexual reproduction between organisms which are closely related. [BOT] Pollination of a flower by another flower of the same plant.

endogenote [MICROBIO] The genetic complement of the partial zygote formed as a result of gene transfer during the process of recombination in bacteria.

endogenous [BIOCHEM] Relating to the metabolism of nitrogenous tissue elements.

endogenous pyrogen [BIOCHEM] A fever-inducing substance (protein) produced by cells of the host body, such as leukocytes and macrophages.

endognath [INV ZOO] The inner and main branch of a crustacean's oral appendage.

endolecithal [INV ZOO] A type of egg found in turbellarians with yolk granules in the cytoplasm of the egg. Also spelled entolecithal.

endolithic [ECOL] Living within rocks, as certain algae and coral.

endolymph [PHYSIO] The lymph fluid found in the membranous labyrinth of the ear.

endomeninx [EMBRYO] The internal part of the meninx primitiva that differentiates into the pia mater and arachnoid membrane.

endomere [EMBRYO] A blastomere that forms endoderm.

endometrium [ANAT] The mucous membrane lining the uterus.

endomitosis [CELL BIO] Division of the chromosomes without dissolution of the nuclear membrane; results in polyploidy or polyteny.

endomixis [INV ZOO] Periodic division and reorganization of the nucleus in certain ciliated protozoans.

Endomycetales [MICROBIO] Former designation for Saccharomycetales.

Endomycetoideae [MICROBIO] A subfamily of ascosporogenous yeasts in the family Saccharomycetaceae.

Endomychidae [INV ZOO] The handsome fungus beetles, a family of coleopteran insects in the superfamily Cucujoidea.

endomysium [HISTOL] The connective tissue layer surrounding an individual skeletal muscle fiber.

endoneurium [HISTOL] Connective tissue fibers surrounding and joining the individual fibers of a nerve trunk.

endonuclease [BIOCHEM] Any of a group of enzymes which degrade deoxyribonucleic acid or ribonucleic acid molecules by attaching nucleotide linkages within the polynucleotide chain.

endoparasite [ECOL] A parasite that lives inside its host.

endopeptidase [BIOCHEM] An enzyme that acts upon the centrally located peptide bonds of a protein molecule.

endophagous [INV ZOO] Of an insect larva, living within and feeding upon the host tissues.

endophallus [INV ZOO] Inner wall of the phallus of insects.

endophyte [ECOL] A plant that lives within, but is not necessarily parasitic on, another plant.

endoplasm [CELL BIO] The inner, semifluid portion of the cytoplasm.

endoplasmic reticulum [CELL BIO] A vacuolar system of the cytoplasm in differentiated cells that functions in protein synthesis and sequestration. Abbreviated ER.

endopleurite [INV ZOO] 1. The portion of a crustacean apodeme which develops from the interepimeral membrane. 2. One of the laterally located parts on the thorax of an insect which fold inward, extending into the body cavity.

endopodite [INV ZOO] The inner branch of a biramous crustacean appendage.

Endoprocta [INV ZOO] The equivalent name for Entoprocta.

endopterygoid [VERT ZOO] A paired dermal bone of the roof of the mouth in fishes.

Endopterygota [INV ZOO] A division of the insects in the subclass Pterygota, including those orders which undergo a holometabolous metamorphosis.

endoreduplication [CELL BIO] Appearance in mitotic cells of certain chromosomes or chromosome sets in the form of multiples.

end organ [ANAT] The expanded termination of a nerve fiber in muscle, skin, mucous membrane, or other structure.

β-endorphin [BIOCHEM] A 31–amino acid peptide fragment of pituitary β-lipotropic hormone having morphinelike activity.

endosalpinx [ANAT] The mucous membrane that lines the fallopian tube.

endosarc [INV ZOO] The inner, relatively fluid part of the protoplasm of certain unicellular organisms.

endosepsis [PL PATH] A fungus disease of figs caused by *Fusarium moniliforme fici*; fruits rot internally.

endoskeleton [ZOO] An internal skeleton or supporting framework in an animal.

endosmosis [PHYSIO] The passage of a liquid inward through a cell membrane.

endosome [CELL BIO] A mass of chromatin near the center of a vesicular nucleus. [INV ZOO] The inner layer of certain sponges.

endosperm [BOT] 1. The nutritive protein material within the embryo sac of seed plants. 2. Storage tissue in the seeds of gymnosperms.

endosperm nucleus [BOT] The triploid nucleus formed within the embryo sac of most seed plants by fusion of the polar nuclei with one sperm nucleus.

endospore [BIOL] An asexual spore formed within a cell.

endostome [BOT] The opening in the inner integument of a bitegmic ovule.

endostyle [INV ZOO] A ciliated groove or pair of grooves in the pharynx of lower chordates.

endosymbiont [ECOL] A symbiont that lives within the body of the host without deleterious effect on the host.

endotergite [INV ZOO] A dorsal plate to which muscles are attached in the insect skeleton.

endothecium [BOT] The middle of three layers that make up an immature anther; becomes the inner layer of a mature anther.

endothelial cell [HISTOL] A type of squamous epithelial cell composing the endothelium.

endotheliochorial placenta [EMBRYO] A type of placenta in which the maternal blood is separated from the chorion by the maternal capillary endothelium; occurs in dogs.

endothelium [HISTOL] The epithelial layer of cells lining the heart and vessels of the circulatory system.

Endotheriidae [PALEON] A family of Cretaceous insectivores from China belonging to the Proteutheria.

endotherm [PHYSIO] An animal that produces enough heat from its own metabolism and employs devices to retard heat loss so that it is able to keep its body temperature higher than that of its environment.

Endothyracea [PALEON] A superfamily of extinct benthic marine foraminiferans in the suborder Fusulinina, having a granular or fibrous wall.

endotoxin [MICROBIO] A toxin that is produced within a microorganism and can be isolated only after the cell is disintegrated.

endotracheal [ANAT] Within the trachea.

endotrophic [BIOL] Obtaining nourishment from within; applied to certain parasitic fungi that live in the root cortex of the host plant.

energy balance [PHYSIO] The relation of the amount of utilizable energy taken into the body to that which is employed for internal work, external work, and the growth and repair of tissues.

energy metabolism [BIOCHEM] The chemical reactions involved in energy transformations within cells.

energy pyramid [ECOL] An ecological pyramid illustrating the energy flow within an ecosystem.

engram [PHYSIO] A memory imprint; the alteration that has occurred in nervous tissue as a result of an excitation from a stimulus, which hypothetically accounts for retention of that experience. Also known as memory trace.

Engraulidae [VERT ZOO] The anchovies, a family of herringlike fishes in the suborder Clupoidea.

enhancer gene [GEN] Any modifier gene that acts to enhance the action of a nonallelic gene.

Enicocephalidae [INV ZOO] The gnat bugs, a family of hemipteran insects in the superfamily Enicocephaloidea.

Enicocephaloidea [INV ZOO] A superfamily of the Hemiptera in the subdivision Geocorisae containing a single family.

enkephalin [BIOCHEM] A mixture of two polypeptides isolated from the brain; central mode of action is an inhibition of neurotransmitter release.

enolase [BIOCHEM] An enzyme that catalyzes the reversible dehydration of phosphoglyceric acid to phosphopyruvic acid.

Enopla [INV ZOO] A class or subclass of ribbonlike worms of the phylum Rhynchocoela.

Enoplia [INV ZOO] A subclass of nematodes in the class Adenophorea.

Enoplida [INV ZOO] An order of nematodes in the subclass Enoplia.

Enoplidae [INV ZOO] A family of free-living marine nematodes in the superfamily Enoploidea, characterized by a complex arrangement of teeth and mandibles.

Enoploidea [INV ZOO] A superfamily of small to very large free-living marine nematodes having pocketlike amphids opening to the exterior via slitlike apertures.

Enoploteuthidae [INV ZOO] A molluscan family of deep-sea squids in the class Cephalopoda.

enphytotic [PL PATH] 1. A disease that occurs regularly among plants of a specific region. 2. An outbreak of such a disease.

enrichment culture [MICROBIO] A medium of known composition and specific conditions of incubation which favors the growth of a particular type or species of bacterium.

ensiform [BIOL] Sword-shaped.

Entamoeba [INV ZOO] A genus of parasite amebas in the family Endamoebidae, including some

species of the genus *Endamoeba* which are parasites of humans and other vertebrates.

Entamoeba histolytica [INV ZOO] A pathogenic ameba, causing amebic dysentery.

Enteletacea [PALEON] A group of extinct articulate brachiopods in the order Orthida.

Entelodontidae [PALEON] A family of extinct palaeodont artiodactyls in the superfamily Entelodontoidea.

Entelodontoidea [PALEON] A superfamily of extinct piglike mammals in the suborder Palaeodonta having huge skulls and enlarged incisors.

enteric bacilli [MICROBIO] Microorganisms, especially the gram-negative rods, found in the intestinal tract of man and animals.

Enterobacter [MICROBIO] A genus of bacteria in the family Enterobacteriaceae; motile rods found in the intestine of humans and other animals; some strains are encapsulated.

Enterobacteriaceae [MICROBIO] A family of gram-negative, facultatively anaerobic rods; cells are nonsporeforming and may be nonmotile or motile with peritrichous flagella; includes important human and plant pathogens.

enterocoel [ZOO] A coelom that arises by mesodermal outpocketing of the archenteron.

Enterocoela [SYST] A section of the animal kingdom that includes the Echinodermata, Chaetognatha, Hemichordata, and Chordata.

enterohydrocoel [INV ZOO] In crinoids, an anterior cavity derived from the archenteron.

enterokinase [BIOCHEM] An enzyme which catalyzes the conversion of trypsinogen to trypsin.

enteron [ANAT] The alimentary canal.

Enteropneusta [INV ZOO] The acorn worms or tongue worms, a class of the Hemichordata; free-living solitary animals with no exoskeleton and with numerous gill slits and a straight gut.

enterotoxin [MICROBIO] A toxin produced by *Micrococcus pyogenes* var. *aureus* (*Staphylococcus aureus*) which gives rise to symptoms of food poisoning in humans and monkeys.

enterovirus [VIROL] One of the two subgroups of human picornaviruses; includes the polioviruses, the coxsackieviruses, and the echoviruses.

Enterozoa [ZOO] Animals with a digestive tract or cavity; includes all animals except Protozoa, Mesozoa, and Parazoa.

entire [BIOL] Having a continuous, unimpaired margin.

Entner-Doudoroff pathway [BIOCHEM] A sequence of reactions for glucose degradation, with the liberation of energy; the distinguishing feature is the formation of 2-keto-3-deoxy-6-phosphogluconate from 6-phosphogluconate and the cleaving of this compound to yield pyruvate and glyceraldehyde-3-phosphate.

entoblast [EMBRYO] A blastomere that differentiates into endoderm.

entoderm *See* endoderm.

Entodiniomorphida [INV ZOO] An order of highly evolved ciliated protozoans in the subclass Spirotrichia, characterized by a smooth, firm pellicle and the lack of external ciliature.

Entomoconchacea [PALEON] A superfamily of extinct marine ostracods in the suborder Myodocopa that are without a rostrum above the permanent aperture.

entomogenous [BIOL] Growing on or in an insect body, as certain fungi.

entomology [INV ZOO] A branch of the biological sciences that deals with the study of insects.

entomophagous [ZOO] Feeding on insects.

entomophilic fungi [MYCOL] Species of fungi that are insect pathogens.

entomophilous [ECOL] Pollinated by insects.

Entomophthoraceae [MYCOL] The single family of the order Entomophthorales.

Entomophthorales [MYCOL] An order of mainly terrestrial fungi in the class Phycomycetes having a hyphal thallus and nonmotile sporangiospores, or conidia.

Entomostraca [INV ZOO] A group of Crustacea comprising the orders Cephalocarida, Branchiopoda, Ostracoda, Copepoda, Branchiura, and Cirripedia.

Entoniscidae [INV ZOO] A family of isopod crustaceans in the tribe Bopyrina that are parasitic in the visceral cavity of crabs and porcellanids.

entoplastron [VERT ZOO] The anterior median bony plate of the plastron of chelonians.

Entoprocta [INV ZOO] A group of bryozoans, sometimes considered to be a subphylum, having a pseudocoelomate visceral cavity and the anus opening inside the circlet of tentacles.

entypy [EMBRYO] The formation of the amnion in certain mammals by the invagination of the embryonic knob into the yolk sac, without the formation of any amniotic folds.

environment [ECOL] The sum of all external conditions and influences affecting the development and life of organisms.

environmental biology *See* ecology.

environmental resistance [ECOL] All the limiting factors in the environment that act on a particular population.

enzyme [BIOCHEM] Any of a group of catalytic proteins that are produced by living cells and that mediate and promote the chemical processes of life without themselves being altered or destroyed.

enzyme induction [MICROBIO] The process by which a microbial cell synthesizes an enzyme in response to the presence of a substrate or of a substance closely related to a substrate in the medium.

enzyme inhibition [BIOCHEM] Prevention of an enzymic process as a result of the interaction of some substance with the enzyme so as to decrease the rate of reaction.

enzyme repression [BIOCHEM] The process by which the rate of synthesis of an enzyme is reduced in the presence of a metabolite, often the end product of a chain of reactions in which the enzyme in question operates near the beginning.

enzyme unit [BIOCHEM] The amount of an enzyme that will catalyze the transformation of 10^{-6} mole of substrate per minute or, when more than one bond of each substrate is attacked, 10^{-6} of

1 gram equivalent of the group concerned, under specified conditions of temperature, substrate concentration, and pH number.

enzymology [BIOCHEM] A branch of science dealing with the chemical nature, biological activity, and biological significance of enzymes.

Eoacanthocephala [INV ZOO] An order of the Acanthocephala characterized by the presence of a small number of giant subcuticular nuclei.

Eocrinoidea [PALEON] A class of extinct echinoderms in the subphylum Crinozoa that had biserial brachioles like those of cystoids combined with a theca like that of crinoids.

Eohippus [PALEON] The earliest, primitive horse, included in the genus *Hyracotherium;* described as a small, four-toed species.

Eomoropidae [PALEON] A family of extinct perissodactyl mammals in the superfamily Chalicotherioidea.

Eosentomidae [INV ZOO] A family of primitive wingless insects in the order Protura that possess spiracles and tracheae.

eosinophil [HISTOL] A granular leukocyte having cytoplasmic granules that stain with acid dyes and a nucleus with two lobes connected by a thin thread of chromatin.

Eosuchia [PALEON] The oldest, most primitive, and only extinct order of lepidosaurian reptiles.

Epacridaceae [BOT] A family of dicotyledonous plants in the order Ericales, distinguished by palmately veined leaves, and stamens equal in number with the corolla lobes.

epaulette [INV ZOO] 1. Any of the branched or knobbed processes on the oral arms of many Scyphozoa. 2. The first haired scale at the base of the costal vein in Diptera.

epaxial [BIOL] Above or dorsal to an axis.

epaxial muscle [ANAT] Any of the dorsal trunk muscles of vertebrates.

ependyma [HISTOL] The layer of epithelial cells lining the cavities of the brain and spinal cord. Also known as ependymal layer.

Eperythrozoon [MICROBIO] A genus of the family Anaplasmataceae; rings and coccoids occur on erythrocytes and in the plasma of various vertebrates.

ephapse [ANAT] A contact point between neurons.

ephaptic transmission [PHYSIO] Electrical transfer of activity to a postephaptic unit by the action current of a preephaptic cell.

Ephedra [BOT] A genus of low, leafless, green-stemmed shrubs belonging to the order Ephedrales; source of the drug ephedrine.

Ephedrales [BOT] A monogeneric order of gymnosperms in the subdivision Gneticae.

ephemeral plant [BOT] An annual plant that completes its life cycle in one short moist season; desert plants are examples.

Ephemerida [INV ZOO] An equivalent name for the Ephemeroptera.

Ephemeroptera [INV ZOO] The mayflies, an order of exopterygote insects in the subclass Pterygota.

Ephydridae [INV ZOO] The shore flies, a family of myodarian cyclorrhaphous dipteran insects in the subsection Acalypteratae.

ephyra [INV ZOO] A larval, free-swimming medusoid stage of scyphozoans; arises from the scyphistoma by transverse fission. Also known as ephyrula.

ephyrula See ephyra.

epiandrum [INV ZOO] The genital orifice of a male arachnid.

epibasidium [MYCOL] A lengthening of the upper part of each cell of the basidium of various heterobasidiomycetes.

epibiotic [ECOL] Living, usually parasitically, on the surface of plants or animals; used especially of fungi.

epiblast See ectoderm.

epiblem [BOT] A tissue that replaces the epidermis in most roots and in stems of submerged aquatic plants.

epiboly [EMBRYO] The growing or extending of one part, such as the upper hemisphere of a blastula, over and around another part, such as the lower hemisphere, in embryogenesis.

epibranchial [ANAT] Of or pertaining to the segment below the pharyngobranchial region in a branchial arch.

epicalyx [BOT] A ring of fused bracts below the calyx forming a structure that resembles the calyx.

epicardium [ANAT] The inner, serous portion of the pericardium that is in contact with the heart. [INV ZOO] A tubular prolongation of the branchial sac in certain ascidians which takes part in the process of budding.

Epicaridea [INV ZOO] A suborder of the Isopoda whose members are parasitic on various marine crustaceans.

epicarp [BOT] The outer layer of the pericarp. Also known as exocarp.

epichordal [VERT ZOO] Located upon or above the notochord.

epichordal brain [EMBRYO] The area of origin of the hindbrain or rhombencephalon, located on the dorsal side of the notochord. Also known as deutencephalon.

epicnemial [ANAT] Of or pertaining to the anterior portion of the tibia.

epicondyle [ANAT] An eminence on the condyle of a bone.

epicone [INV ZOO] The part anterior to the equatorial groove in a dinoflagellate.

epicotyl [BOT] The embryonic plant stem above the cotyledons.

epicranium [INV ZOO] The dorsal wall of an insect head. [VERT ZOO] The structures covering the cranium in vertebrates.

epicuticle [INV ZOO] The outer, waxy layer of an insect cuticle or exoskeleton.

epicyst [INV ZOO] The outer layer of a cyst wall in encysted protozoans. Also known as ectocyst.

epidermal ridge [ANAT] Any of the minute corrugations of the skin on the palmar and plantar surfaces of humans and other primates.

epidermis [BOT] The outermost layer (sometimes several layers) of cells on the primary plant body.

[HISTOL] The outer nonsensitive, nonvascular portion of the skin comprising two strata of cells, the stratum corneum and the stratum germinativum.

epididymis [ANAT] The convoluted efferent duct lying posterior to the testis and connected to it by the efferent ductules of the testis.

epidural [ANAT] Located on or over the dura mater.

epigaster [EMBRYO] The portion of the intestine in vertebrate embryos which gives rise to the colon.

epigastric region [ANAT] The upper and middle part of the abdominal surface between the two hypochondriac regions. Also known as epigastrium.

epigastrium [ANAT] See epigastric region. [INV ZOO] The ventral side of mesothorax and metathorax in insects.

epigean [BOT] Pertaining to a plant or plant part that grows above the ground surface. [ZOO] Living near or on the ground surface, applied especially to insects.

epigenesis [EMBRYO] Development in gradual stages of differentiation.

epigenetics [GEN] The study of those processes by which genetic information ultimately results in distinctive physical and behavioral characteristics.

epigenous [BOT] Developing or growing on a surface, especially of a plant or plant part.

epiglottis [ANAT] A flap of elastic cartilage covered by mucous membrane that protects the glottis during swallowing.

epigynous [BOT] Having the perianth and stamens attached near the top of the ovary; that is, the ovary is inferior.

epigynum [INV ZOO] 1. The genital pore of female arachnids. 2. The plate covering this opening.

epilemma [HISTOL] The perineurium of very small nerves.

epimerase [BIOCHEM] A type of enzyme that catalyzes the rearrangement of hydroxyl groups on a substrate.

epimere [ANAT] The dorsal muscle plate of the lining of a coelomic cavity. [EMBRYO] The dorsal part of a mesodermal segment in the embryo of chordates.

epimeron [INV ZOO] 1. The posterior plate of the pleuron in insects. 2. The portion of a somite between the tergum and the insertion of a limb in arthropods.

epimorphosis [PHYSIO] Regeneration in which cell proliferation precedes differentiation.

epimyocardium [EMBRYO] The layer of the embryonic heart from which both the myocardium and epicardium develop.

epimysium [ANAT] The connective-tissue sheath surrounding a skeletal muscle.

epinasty [BOT] Growth changes in which the upper surface of a leaf grows, thus bending the leaf downward.

epinephrine [BIOCHEM] $C_9H_{13}O_3N$ A hormone secreted by the adrenal medulla that acts to increase blood pressure due to stimulation of heart action and constriction of peripheral blood vessels. Also known as adrenaline.

epineural [ANAT] 1. Arising from the neural arch. 2. Any process arising from the neural arch.

epineural [INV ZOO] The nervous tissue dorsal to the ventral nerve cord in arthropods.

epineural canal [INV ZOO] A canal that runs between the radial nerve and the epithelium in echinoids and ophiuroids.

epineurium [ANAT] The connective-tissue sheath of a nerve trunk.

epipetalous [BOT] Having stamens located on the corolla.

epiphallus [INV ZOO] A sclerite in some orthopterans in the floor of the genital chamber.

epipharynx [INV ZOO] An organ attached beneath the labrium of many insects.

epiphragm [BOT] A membrane covering the aperture of the capsule in certain mosses. [INV ZOO] A membranous or calcareous partition that covers the aperture of certain hibernating land snails.

epiphyll [ECOL] A plant that grows on the surface of leaves.

epiphyseal arch [EMBRYO] The arched structure in the third ventricle of the embryonic brain, which marks the site of development of the pineal body.

epiphyseal plate [ANAT] 1. The broad, articular surface on each end of a vertebral centrum. 2. The thin layer of cartilage between the epiphysis and the shaft of a long bone. Also known as metaphysis.

epiphysis [ANAT] 1. The end portion of a long bone in vertebrates. 2. *See* pineal body.

epiphyte [ECOL] A plant which grows nonparasitically on another plant or on some nonliving structure, such as a building or telephone pole, deriving moisture and nutrients from the air. Also known as aerophyte.

epiphytotic [PL PATH] 1. Any infectious plant disease that occurs sporadically in epidemic proportions. 2. Of or pertaining to an epidemic plant disease.

epiplankton [BIOL] Plankton occurring in the sea from the surface to a depth of about 100 fathoms.

epipleural [ANAT] Arising from a rib. [VERT ZOO] An intramuscular bone arising from and extending between some of the ribs in certain fishes.

epiploic foramen [ANAT] An aperture of the peritoneal cavity, formed by folds of the peritoneum and located between the liver and the stomach. Also known as foramen of Winslow.

epipodite [INV ZOO] A branch of the basal joint of the protopodite of thoracic limbs of many arthropods.

epipodium [BOT] The apical portion of an embryonic phyllopodium. [INV ZOO] 1. A ridge or fold on the lateral edges of each side of the foot of certain gastropod mollusks. 2. The elevated ring on an ambulacral plate in Echinoidea.

Epipolasina [INV ZOO] A suborder of sponges in the order Clavaxinellida having radially arranged monactinal or diactinal megascleres.

epiproct [INV ZOO] A plate above the anus forming the dorsal part of the tenth or eleventh somite of certain insects.

epipubis [VERT ZOO] A single cartilage or bone located in front of the pubis in some vertebrates, particularly in some amphibians.

episclera [ANAT] The loose connective tissue lying between the conjunctiva and the sclera.

episepalous [BOT] Having stamens growing on or adnate to the sepals.

episome [GEN] A circular genetic element in bacteria, presumably a deoxyribonucleic acid fragment, which is not necessary for survival of the organism and which can be integrated in the bacterial chromosome or remain free.

episperm *See* testa.

epistasis [GEN] The suppression of the effect of one gene by another.

episternum [VERT ZOO] A dermal bone or pair of bones ventral to the sternum of certain fishes and reptiles.

epistome [INV ZOO] 1. The area between the mouth and the second antennae in crustaceans. 2. The plate covering this region. 3. The area between the labrum and the epicranium in many insects. 4. A flap covering the mouth of certain bryozoans. 5. The area just above the labrum in certain dipterans.

epithalamus [ANAT] A division of the vertebrate diencephalon including the habenula, the pineal body, and the posterior commissure.

epitheca [INV ZOO] 1. An external, calcareous layer around the basal portion of the theca of many corals. 2. A protective covering of the epicone. 3. The outer portion of a diatom frustule.

epitheliochorial placenta [EMBRYO] A type of placenta in which the maternal epithelium and fetal epithelium are in contact. Also known as villous placenta.

epithelioid cell [HISTOL] A macrophage that resembles an epithelial cell. Also known as alveolated cell.

epitheliomuscular cell [INV ZOO] An epithelial cell with an elongate base that contains contractile fibrils; common among coelenterates.

epithelium [HISTOL] A primary animal tissue, distinguished by cells being close together with little intercellular substance; covers free surfaces and lines body cavities and ducts.

epithema [VERT ZOO] A horny outgrowth on the beak of certain birds.

epitoke [INV ZOO] The posterior portion of marine polychaetes; contains the gonads.

epitrichium [EMBRYO] The outer layer of the fetal epidermis of many mammals.

epitrochlear [ANAT] Of or pertaining to a lymph node that lies above the trochlea of the elbow joint.

epitympanum [ANAT] The attic of the middle ear, or tympanic cavity.

epivalve [INV ZOO] 1. The upper or apical shell of certain dinoflagellates. 2. The upper shell of a diatom.

epixylous [ECOL] Growing on wood; used especially of fungi.

epizoic [BIOL] Living on the body of an animal.

eponychium [ANAT] The horny layer of the nail fold attached to the nail plate at its margin; represents the remnant of the embryonic condition. [EMBRYO] A horny condition of the epidermis from the second to the eighth month of fetal life, indicating the position of the future nail.

epoophoron [ANAT] A blind longitudinal duct and 10–15 transverse ductules in the mesosalpinx near the ovary which represent remnants of the reproductive part of the mesonephros in the female; homolog of the head of the epididymis in the male. Also known as parovarium; Rosenmueller's organ.

Epstein-Barr virus [VIROL] Herpeslike virus particles first identified in cultures of cells from Burkett's malignant lymphoma.

equatorial plane [CELL BIO] The plane in a cell undergoing mitosis that is midway between the centrosomes and perpendicular to the spindle fibers.

Equidae [VERT ZOO] A family of perissodactyl mammals in the superfamily Equoidea, including the horses, zebras, and donkeys.

equine [VERT ZOO] 1. Resembling a horse. 2. Of or related to the Equidae.

Equisetales [BOT] The horsetails, a monogeneric order of the class Equisetopsida; the only living genus is *Equisetum*.

Equisetineae [BOT] The equivalent name for the Equisetophyta.

Equisetophyta [BOT] A division of the subkingdom Embryobionta represented by a single living genus, *Equisetum*.

Equisetopsida [BOT] A class of the division Equisetophyta whose members made up a major part of the flora, especially in moist or swampy places, during the Carboniferous Period.

equitant [BOT] Of leaves, overlapping transversely at the base.

Equoidea [VERT ZOO] A superfamily of perissodactyl mammals in the suborder Hippomorpha comprising the living and extinct horses and their relatives.

Equus [VERT ZOO] The genus comprising the large, one-toed modern horses, including donkeys and zebras.

ER *See* endoplasmic reticulum.

erection [PHYSIO] The enlarged state of erectile tissue when engorged with blood, as of the penis or clitoris.

erector [PHYSIO] Any muscle that produces erection of a part.

erect stem [BOT] A stem that stands, having a vertical or upright habit.

Eremascoideae [BOT] A monogeneric subfamily of ascosporogenous yeasts characterized by mostly septate mycelia, and spherical asci with eight oval to round ascospores.

Erethizontidae [VERT ZOO] The New World porcupines, a family of rodents characterized by sharply pointed, erectile hairs and four functional digits.

Ergasilidae [INV ZOO] A family of copepod crustaceans in the suborder Cyclopoida in which the females are parasitic on aquatic animals, while the males are free-swimming.

ergastic [CELL BIO] Pertaining to the nonliving components of protoplasm.

ergastoplasm [CELL BIO] A cytoplasm component which shows an affinity for basic dyes; a form of the endoplasmic reticulum.

ergosterin *See* ergosterol.

ergosterol [BIOCHEM] $C_{28}H_{44}O$ A crystalline, water-insoluble, unsaturated sterol found in ergot, yeast, and other fungi, and which may be converted to vitamin D_2 on irradiation with ultraviolet light or activation with electrons. Also known as ergosterin.

ergot [MYCOL] The dark purple or black sclerotium of the fungus *Claviceps purpurea*.

Ericaceae [BOT] A large family of dicotyledonous plants in the order Ericales distinguished by having twice as many stamens as corolla lobes.

Ericales [BOT] An order of dicotyledonous plants in the subclass Dilleniidae; plants are generally sympetalous with unitegmic ovules and they have twice as many stamens as petals.

ericophyte [ECOL] A plant that grows on a heath or moor.

Erinaceidae [VERT ZOO] The hedgehogs, a family of mammals in the order Insectivora characterized by dorsal and lateral body spines.

erineum [PL PATH] An abnormal growth of hairs induced on the epidermis of a leaf by certain mites.

Erinnidae [INV ZOO] A family of orthorrhaphous dipteran insects in the series Brachycera.

Eriocaulaceae [BOT] The single family of the order Eriocaulales.

Eriocaulales [BOT] An order of monocotyledonous plants in the subclass Commelinidae, having a perianth reduced or lacking and having unisexual flowers aggregated on a long peduncle.

Eriococcinae [INV ZOO] A family of homopteran insects in the superfamily Coccoidea; adult females and late instar nymphs have an anal ring.

Eriocraniidae [INV ZOO] A small family of lepidopteran insects in the superfamily Eriocranioidea.

Eriocranioidea [INV ZOO] A superfamily of lepidopteran insects in the suborder Homoneura comprising tiny moths with reduced, untoothed mandibles.

Eriophyidae [INV ZOO] The bud mites or gall mites, a family of economically important plant-feeding mites in the suborder Trombidiformes.

eriophyllous [BOT] Having leaves covered by a cottony pubescence.

erose [BIOL] Having an irregular margin.

Erotylidae [INV ZOO] The pleasing fungus beetles, a family of coleopteran insects in the superfamily Cucujoidea.

Errantia [INV ZOO] A group of 34 families of polychaete annelids in which the anterior region is exposed and the linear body is often long and is dorsoventrally flattened.

Erwinia [MICROBIO] A genus of motile, rod-shaped bacteria in the family Enterobacteriaceae; these organisms invade living plant tissues and cause dry necroses, galls, wilts, and soft rots.

Erwinieae [MICROBIO] Formerly a tribe of phytopathogenic bacteria in the family Enterobacteriaceae, including the single genus *Erwinia*.

Erysipelothrix [MICROBIO] A genus of gram-positive, rod-shaped bacteria of uncertain affiliation; cells have a tendency to form long filaments.

Erysiphaceae [MYCOL] The powdery mildews, a family of ascomycetous fungi in the order Erysiphales with light-colored mycelia and conidia.

Erysiphales [MYCOL] An order of ascomycetous fungi which are obligate parasites of seed plants, causing powdery mildew and sooty mold.

erythroblast [HISTOL] A nucleated cell occurring in bone marrow as the earliest recognizable cell of the erythrocytic series.

erythrocruorin [BIOCHEM] Any of the iron-porphyrin protein respiratory pigments found in the blood and tissue fluids of certain invertebrates; corresponds to hemoglobin in vertebrates.

erythrocyte [HISTOL] A type of blood cell that contains a nucleus in all vertebrates but humans and that has hemoglobin in the cytoplasm. Also known as red blood cell.

erythrocytopoiesis *See* erythropoiesis.

erythromycin [MICROBIO] A crystalline antibiotic produced by *Streptomyces erythreus* and used in the treatment of gram-positive bacterial infections.

D-erythropentose *See* ribulose.

erythrophilous [BIOL] Having an affinity for red dyes and other coloring matter.

erythrophore [ZOO] A chromatophore containing a red pigment, especially a carotenoid.

erythropoiesis [PHYSIO] The process by which erythrocytes are formed. Also known as erythrocytopoiesis.

erythropoietin [BIOCHEM] A hormone, thought to be produced by the kidneys, that regulates erythropoiesis, at least in higher vertebrates.

Erythroxylaceae [BOT] A homogeneous family of dicotyledonous woody plants in the order Linales characterized by petals that are internally appendiculate, three carpels, and flowers without a disk.

erythrulose [BIOCHEM] $C_4H_8O_4$ A ketose sugar occurring as an oxidation product of erythritol due to the action of certain bacteria.

Escherichia [MICROBIO] A genus of bacteria in the family Enterobacteriaceae; straight rods occurring singly or in pairs.

Escherichia coli [MICROBIO] The type species of the genus, occurring as part of the normal intestinal flora in vertebrates. Also known as colon bacillus.

Escherichieae [MICROBIO] Formerly a tribe of bacteria in the family Enterobacteriaceae defined by the ability to ferment lactose, with the rapid production of acid and visible gas.

Esocidae [VERT ZOO] The pikes, a family of fishes in the order Clupeiformes characterized by an elongated beaklike snout and sharp teeth.

Esocoidei [VERT ZOO] A small suborder of freshwater fishes in the order Salmoniformes; includes the pikes, mudminnows, and pickerels.

esophageal gland [ANAT] Any of the digestive glands within the submucosa of the esophagus; secretions are chiefly mucus and serve to lubricate the esophagus.

esophageal hiatus [ANAT] The opening in the diaphragm for passage of the esophagus.

esophageal teeth [VERT ZOO] The enamel-tipped hypapophyses of the posterior cervical vertebrae of certain snakes, which penetrate the esophagus and function to break eggshells.

esophagus [ANAT] The tubular portion of the alimentary canal interposed between the pharynx and the stomach. Also known as gullet.

essential amino acid [BIOCHEM] Any of eight of the 20 naturally occurring amino acids that are indispensable for optimum animal growth but cannot be formed in the body and must be supplied in the diet.

essential fatty acid [BIOCHEM] Any of the polyunsaturated fatty acids which are required in the diet of mammals; they are probably precursors of prostaglandins.

esterase [BIOCHEM] Any of a group of enzymes that catalyze the synthesis and hydrolysis of esters.

esthacyte [INV ZOO] A simple sensory cell occurring in certain lower animals, such as sponges. Also spelled aesthacyte.

esthesia [PHYSIO] The capacity for sensation, perception, or feeling. Also spelled aesthesia.

estivation [PHYSIO] 1. The adaptation of certain animals to the conditions of summer, or the taking on of certain modifications, which enables them to survive a hot, dry summer. 2. The dormant condition of an organism during the summer.

estradiol [BIOCHEM] $C_{18}H_{24}O_2$ An estrogenic hormone produced by follicle cells of the vertebrate ovary; provokes estrus and proliferation of the human endometrium, and stimulates ICSH (interstitial-cell-stimulating hormone) secretion.

estriol [BIOCHEM] $C_{18}H_{24}O_3$ A crystalline estrogenic hormone obtained from human pregnancy urine.

estrogen [BIOCHEM] Any of various natural or synthetic substances possessing the biologic activity of estrus-producing hormones.

estrogenic hormone [BIOCHEM] A hormone, found principally in ovaries and also in the placenta, which stimulates the accessory sex structures and the secondary sex characteristics in the female.

estrone [BIOCHEM] $C_{18}H_{22}O_2$ An estrogenic hormone produced by follicle cells of the vertebrate ovary; functions the same as estradiol.

estrous cycle [PHYSIO] The physiological changes that take place between periods of estrus in the female mammal.

estrus [PHYSIO] The period in female mammals during which ovulation occurs and the animal is receptive to mating.

ethionine [BIOCHEM] $C_5H_{13}O_2N$ An amino acid that is the ethyl analog of and the biological antagonist of methionine.

Ethiopian zoogeographic region [ECOL] A geographic unit of faunal homogeneity including all of Africa south of the Sahara.

ethmoid bone [ANAT] An irregularly shaped cartilage bone of the skull, forming the medial wall of each orbit and part of the roof and lateral walls of the nasal cavities.

ethmoturbinate [ANAT] Of or pertaining to the masses of ethmoid bone which form the lateral and superior portions of the turbinate bones in mammals.

ethology [VERT ZOO] The study of animal behavior in a natural context.

ethyl chlorophyllide [BIOCHEM] A compound formed by replacing the phytyl ($C_{20}H_{39}$) tail of the chlorophyll molecule with a short ethyl (C_2H_5) tail; crystallizes easily and has an absorption spectrum and electrochemical properties similar to those of chlorophyll.

etioallocholane *See* androstane.

etioblast [BOT] An immature chloroplast, containing prolamellar bodies.

etiolation [BOT] The yellowing or whitening of green plant parts grown in darkness.

Eubacteriales [MICROBIO] Formerly an order of the class Schizomycetes; considered the true bacteria and characterized by simple, undifferentiated, rigid cells of either spherical or straight, rod-shaped form.

Eubacterium [MICROBIO] A genus of bacteria in the family Propionibacteriaceae; obligate anaerobes producing a mixture of organic acids (butyric, acetic, formic, and lactic) from carbohydrates and peptone.

Eubasidiomycetes [MYCOL] An equivalent name for Homobasidiomycetidae.

Eubrya [BOT] A subclass of the mosses (Bryopsida); the leafy gametophytes arise from buds on the protonemata, which are nearly always filamentous or branched green threads attached to the substratum by rhizoids.

Eubryales [BOT] An order of mosses (Bryatae); plants have the sporophyte at the end of a stem, vary in size from small to robust, and generally grow in tufts.

Eucalyptus [BOT] A large genus of evergreen trees belonging to the myrtle family (Myrtaceae) and occurring in Australia and New Guinea.

Eucarida [INV ZOO] A large superorder of the decapod crustaceans, subclass Malacostraca, including shrimps, lobsters, hermit crabs, and crabs; characterized by having the shell and thoracic segments fused dorsally and the eyes on movable stalks.

Eucaryota [BIOL] Primitive, unicellular organisms having a well-defined nuclear membrane, chromosomes, and mitotic cell division.

Eucestoda [INV ZOO] The true tapeworms, a subclass of the class Cestoda.

Eucharitidae [INV ZOO] A family of hymenopteran insects in the superfamily Chalcidoidea.

euchromatin [CELL BIO] The portion of the chromosomes that stains with low intensity, uncoils during interphase, and condenses during cell division.

Eucinetidae [INV ZOO] The plate thigh beetles, a family of coleopteran insects in the superfamily Dascilloidea.

Euclasterida [INV ZOO] An order of asteroid echinoderms in which the arms are sharply distinguished from a small, central disk-shaped body.

Eucleidae [INV ZOO] The slug moths, a family of lepidopteran insects in the suborder Heteroneura.

Euclymeninae [INV ZOO] A subfamily of annelids in the family Maldonidae of the Sedentaria, having well-developed plaques and an anal pore within the plaque.

Eucnemidae [INV ZOO] The false click beetles, a family of coleopteran insects in the superfamily Elateroidea.

Eucoccida [INV ZOO] An order of parasitic protozoans in the subclass Coccidia characterized by alternating sexual and asexual phases; stages of the life cycle occur intracellularly in vertebrates and invertebrates.

Eucoelomata [ZOO] A large sector of the animal kingdom including all forms in which there is a true coelom or body cavity; includes all phyla above Aschelminthes.

Eucommiales [BOT] A monotypic order of dicotyledonous plants in the subclass Hamamelidae; plants have two, unitegmic ovules and lack stipules.

Eudactylinidae [INV ZOO] A family of parasitic copepod crustaceans in the suborder Caligoida; found as ectoparasites on the gills of sharks.

eudoxid *See* eudoxome.

eudoxome [INV ZOO] Cormidium of most calycophoran siphonophores which lead a free existence. Also known as eudoxid.

Euechinoidea [INV ZOO] A subclass of echinoderms in the class Echinoidea; distinguished by the relative stability of ambulacra and interambulacra.

eugenics [GEN] The use of practices that influence the hereditary qualities of future generations, with the aim of improving the genetic future of humanity.

Euglena [BIOL] A genus of organisms with one or two flagella, chromatophores in most species, and a generally elongate, spindle-shaped body; classified as algae by botanists (Euglenophyta) and as protozoans by zoologists (Euglenida).

Euglenida [INV ZOO] An order of protozoans in the class Phytamastigophorea, including the largest green, noncolonial flagellates.

Euglenidae [INV ZOO] The antlike leaf beetles, a family of coleopteran insects in the superfamily Tenebrionoidea.

Euglenoidina [INV ZOO] The equivalent name for Euglenida.

Euglenophyceae [BOT] The single class of the plant division Euglenophyta.

Euglenophyta [BOT] A division of the plant kingdom including one-celled, chiefly aquatic flagellate organisms having a spindle-shaped or flattened body, naked or with a pellicle.

euglobulin [BIOCHEM] True globulin; a simple protein that is soluble in distilled water and dilute salt solutions.

Eugregarinida [INV ZOO] An order of protozoans in the subclass Gregarinia; parasites of certain invertebrates.

eukaryote [BIOL] A cell with a definitive nucleus. Also spelled eucaryote.

Eulamellibranchia [INV ZOO] The largest subclass of the molluscan class Bivalvia, having a heterodont shell hinge, leaflike gills, and well-developed siphons.

Eulophidae [INV ZOO] A family of hymenopteran insects in the superfamily Chalcidoidea including species that are parasitic on the larvae of other insects.

Eumalacostraca [INV ZOO] A series of the class Crustacea comprising shrimplike crustaceans having eight thoracic segments, six abdominal segments, and a telson.

Eumetazoa [ZOO] A section of the animal kingdom that includes the phyla above the Porifera; contains those animals which have tissues or show some tissue formation and organ systems.

eumitosis [CELL BIO] Typical mitosis.

Eumycetes [MYCOL] The true fungi, a large group of microorganisms characterized by cell walls, lack of chlorophyll, and mycelia in most species; includes the unicellular yeasts.

Eumycetozoida [INV ZOO] An order of protozoans in the subclass Mycetozoia; includes slime molds which form a plasmodium.

Eumycophyta [MYCOL] An equivalent name for the Eumycetes.

Eumycota [MYCOL] An equivalent name for Eumycetes.

Eunicea [INV ZOO] A superfamily of polychaete annelids belonging to the Errantia.

Eunicidae [INV ZOO] A family of polychaete annelids in the superfamily Eunicea having characteristic pharyngeal armature consisting of maxillae and mandibles.

Euomphalacea [PALEON] A superfamily of extinct gastropod mollusks in the order Aspidobranchia characterized by shells with low spires, some approaching bivalve symmetry.

Eupelmidae [INV ZOO] A family of hymenopteran insects in the superfamily Chalcidoidea.

Euphausiacea [INV ZOO] An order of planktonic malacostracans in the class Crustacea possessing photophores which emit a brilliant blue-green light.

euphenics [GEN] The production of a satisfactory phenotype by means other than eugenics.

Eupheterochlorina [INV ZOO] A suborder of flagellate protozoans in the order Heterochlorida.

Euphorblaceae [BOT] A family of dicotyledonous plants in the order Euphorbiales characterized by dehiscent fruit having more than one seed and by epitropous ovules.

Euphorblales [BOT] An order of dicotyledonous plants in the subclass Rosidae having simple leaves and unisexual flowers that are aggregated and reduced.

Euphrosinidae [INV ZOO] A family of amphinomorphan polychaete annelids with short, dorsolaterally flattened bodies.

Euplexoptera [INV ZOO] The equivalent name for Dermaptera.

euploid [GEN] Having a chromosome complement that is an exact multiple of the haploid complement.

eupnea [PHYSIO] Normal or easy respiration rhythm.

Eupodidae [INV ZOO] A family of mites in the suborder Trombidiformes.

Euproopacea [PALEON] A group of Paleozoic horseshoe crabs belonging to the Limulida.

European boreal faunal region [ECOL] A zoogeographic region describing marine littoral faunal regions of the northern Atlantic Ocean between Greenland and the northwestern coast of Europe.

European canker [PL PATH] 1. A fungus disease of apple, pear, and other fruit and shade trees caused by *Nectria galligena* and characterized by cankers with concentric rings of callus on the trunk and branches. 2. A fungus disease of poplars caused by *Dothichiza populea*.

Eurotiaceae [MYCOL] A family of ascomycetous fungi of the order Eurotiales in which the asci are borne in cleistothecia or closed fruiting bodies.

Eurotiales [MYCOL] An order of fungi in the class Ascomycetes bearing ascospores in globose or broadly oval, delicate asci which lack a pore.

Euryalae [INV ZOO] The basket fishes, a family of echinoderms in the subclass Ophiuroidea.

Euryalina [INV ZOO] A suborder of ophiuroid echinoderms in the order Phrynophiurida characterized by a leathery integument.

Euryapsida [PALEON] A subclass of fossil reptiles distinguished by an upper temporal opening on each side of the skull.

eurybathic [ECOL] Living at the bottom of a body of water.

Eurychilinidae [PALEON] A family of extinct dimorphic ostracods in the superfamily Hollinacea.

eurygamous [INV ZOO] Mating in flight, as in many insect species.

euryhaline [ECOL] Pertaining to the ability of marine organisms to tolerate a wide range of saline conditions, and therefore a wide variation of osmotic pressure, in the evironment.

Eurylaimi [VERT ZOO] A monofamilial suborder of suboscine birds in the order Passeriformes.

Eurylaimidae [VERT ZOO] The broadbills, the single family of the avian suborder Eurylaimi.

Eurymylidae [PALEON] A family of extinct mammals presumed to be the ancestral stock of the order Lagomorpha.

euryon [ANAT] One of the two lateral points functioning as end points to measure the greatest transverse diameter of the skull.

Euryphoridae [INV ZOO] A family of copepod crustaceans in the order Caligoida; members are fish ectoparasites.

euryplastic [BIOL] Referring to an organism with a marked ability to change and adapt to a wide spectrum of environmental conditions.

Eurypterida [PALEON] A group of extinct aquatic arthropods in the subphylum Chelicerata having elongate-lanceolate bodies encased in a chitinous exoskeleton.

Eurypygidae [VERT ZOO] The sun bitterns, a family of tropical and subtropical New World birds belonging to the order Gruiformes.

eurypylous [INV ZOO] Having a wide opening; applied to sponges with wide apopyles opening directly into excurrent canals, and wide prosopyles opening directly from incurrent canals.

eurytherm [BIOL] An organism that is tolerant of a wide range of temperatures.

Eurytomidae [INV ZOO] The seed and stem chalcids, a family of hymenopteran insects in the superfamily Chalcidoidea.

eurytopic [ECOL] Referring to organisms which are widely distributed.

Eusiridae [INV ZOO] A family of pelagic amphipod crustaceans in the suborder Gammaridea.

eusporangiate [BOT] Having sporogenous tissue derived from a group of epidermal cells.

eustachian tube [ANAT] A tube composed of bone and cartilage that connects the nasopharynx with the middle ear cavity.

eustachian valve See canal valve.

eustele [BOT] A modified siphonostele containing collateral or bicollateral vascular bundles; found in most gymnosperm and angiosperm stems.

eusternum [INV ZOO] The anterior sternal plate in insects.

Eusuchia [VERT ZOO] The modern crocodiles, a suborder of the order Crocodilia characterized by a fully developed secondary palate and procoelous vertebrae.

Eusyllinae [INV ZOO] A subfamily of polychaete annelids in the family Syllidae having a thick body and unsegmented cirri.

Eutardigrada [INV ZOO] An order of tardigrades which lack both a sensory cephalic appendage and a club-shaped appendage.

eutely [BIOL] Having the body composed of a constant number of cells, as in certain rotifers.

Euthacanthidae [PALEON] A family of extinct acanthodian fishes in the order Climatiiformes.

euthenics [BIOL] The science that deals with the improvement of the future of man by changing his environment.

Eutheria [VERT ZOO] An infraclass of therian mammals including all living forms except the monotremes and marsupials.

Eutrichosomatidae [INV ZOO] Small family of hymenopteran insects in the superfamily Chalcidoidea.

eutrophication [ECOL] Of bodies of water, the process of becoming better nourished either naturally by processes of maturation or artificially by fertilization.

Evaniidae [INV ZOO] The ensign flies, a family of hymenopteran insects in the superfamily Proctotrupoidea.

Evans-Burr unit [BIOL] A unit for the standardization of vitamin E.

evaporative heat regulation [PHYSIO] The composite process by which an animal body is cooled by evaporation of sensible perspiration; this avenue of heat loss serves as a physical means of regulating the body temperature.

Eventognathi [VERT ZOO] The equivalent name for Cypriniformes.

evergreen [BOT] Pertaining to a perennially green plant. Also known as aiophyllous.

evoked potential [PHYSIO] Electrical response of any neuron to stimuli.

evolution [BIOL] The processes of biological and organic change in organisms by which descendants come to differ from their ancestors.

ewe [VERT ZOO] A mature female sheep, goat, or related animal, as the smaller antelopes.

exalate [BOT] Being without winglike appendages.

exalbuminous See exendospermous.

exarch [BOT] A vascular bundle in which the primary wood is centripetal.

exasperate [BIOL] Having a surface roughened by stiff elevations or bristles.

exaspidean [VERT ZOO] Of the tarsal envelope of birds, being continuous around the outer edge of the tarsus.

Excipulaceae [MYCOL] The equivalent name for Discellaceae.

excision [GEN] Recombination involving removal of a genetic element.

excision enzyme [BIOCHEM] A bacterial enzyme that removes damaged dimers from the deoxyribonucleic acid molecule of a bacterial cell following light or ultraviolet radiation or nitrogen mustard damage.

excitable [BIOL] Describing a tissue or organism that exhibits irritability.

exclusive species [ECOL] A species which is completely or nearly limited to one community.

Excorallanidae [INV ZOO] A family of free-living and parasitic isopod crustaceans in the suborder Flabellifera which have mandibles and first maxillae modified as hooklike piercing organs.

excrement [PHYSIO] An excreted substance; the feces.

excrescence [BIOL] 1. Abnormal or excessive increase in growth. 2. An abnormal outgrowth.

excretion [PHYSIO] The removal of unusable or excess material from a cell or a living organism.

excretory system [ANAT] Those organs concerned with solid, fluid, or gaseous excretion.

excurrent [BIOL] Flowing out. [BOT] 1. Having an undivided main stem or trunk. 2. Having the midrib extending beyond the apex.

exendospermous [BOT] Lacking endosperm. Also known as exalbuminous.

exergonic [BIOCHEM] Of or pertaining to a biochemical reaction in which the end products possess less free energy than the starting materials; usually associated with catabolism.

exhalation [PHYSIO] The giving off or sending forth in the form of vapor; expiration.

exine See exosporium.

exite [INV ZOO] A movable appendage or lobe located on the external side of the limb of a generalized arthropod.

exobiology [BIOL] The search for and study of extraterrestrial life.

exocarp See epicarp.

exoccipital [ANAT] Lying to the side of the foramen magnum, as the exoccipital bone.

exochorion [INV ZOO] The outer of two layers forming the covering of an insect egg.

exocoel [INV ZOO] The space between pairs of adjacent mesenteries in anthozoan polyps.

Exocoetidae [VERT ZOO] The halfbeaks, a family of actinopterygian fishes in the order Atheriniformes.

exocrine gland [PHYSIO] A structure whose secretion is passed directly or by ducts to its exterior surface, or to another surface which is continuous with the external surface of the gland.

exocuticle [INV ZOO] The middle layer of the cuticle of insects.

exocytosis [CELL BIO] The extrusion of material from a cell.

exodermis *See* hypodermis.

exoenzyme [BIOCHEM] An enzyme that functions outside the cell in which it was synthesized.

exogamy [GEN] Union of gametes from organisms that are not closely related. Also known as outbreeding.

exogastrula [EMBRYO] An abnormal gastrula that is unable to undergo invagination or further development because of a quantitative increase of presumptive endoderm.

exogenote [GEN] The genetic fragment transferred from the donor to the recipient cell during the process of recombination in bacteria.

exogenous [BIOL] 1. Due to an external cause; not arising within the organism. 2. Growing by addition to the outer surfaces. [PHYSIO] Pertaining to those factors in the metabolism of nitrogenous substances obtained from food.

exognathite [INV ZOO] The external branch of an oral appendage of a crustacean.

Exogoninae [INV ZOO] A subfamily of polychaete annelids in the family Syllidae having a short, small body of few segments.

exogynous [BOT] Having the style longer than and exserted beyond the corolla.

exon [GEN] That portion of deoxyribonucleic acid which codes for the final messenger ribonucleic acid.

exonephric [INV ZOO] Having the excretory organs discharge through the body wall.

exonuclease [BIOCHEM] Any of a group of enzymes which catalyze hydrolysis of single nucleotide residues from the end of a deoxyribonucleic acid chain.

exopathogen [PL PATH] An external, nonparasitic plant pathogen.

exopathogenesis [PL PATH] The external incitement of disease by a nonparasitic pathogen.

exopeptidase [BIOCHEM] An enzyme that acts on the terminal peptide bonds of a protein chain.

exopodite [INV ZOO] The outer branch of a biramous crustacean appendage.

Exopterygota [INV ZOO] A division of the insect subclass Pterygota including those insects which undergo a hemimetabolous metamorphosis.

exoskeleton [INV ZOO] The external supportive covering of certain invertebrates, such as arthropods. [VERT ZOO] Bony or horny epidermal derivatives, such as nails, hoofs, and scales.

exosmosis [PHYSIO] Passage of a liquid outward through a cell membrane.

exospore [MYCOL] An asexual spore formed by abstriction, as in certain Phycomycetes.

exosporium [BOT] The outer of two layers forming the wall of spores such as pollen and bacterial spores. Also known as exine.

exostome [BOT] The opening through the outer integument of a bitegmic ovule.

exotheca [INV ZOO] The tissue external to the theca of corals.

exotic [ECOL] Not endemic to an area.

exotoxin [MICROBIO] A toxin that is excreted by a microorganism.

expanding population [ECOL] A population containing a large proportion of young individuals.

expectorate [PHYSIO] To eject phlegm or other material from the throat or lungs.

expiratory reserve volume [PHYSIO] At the end of a normal expiration, the quantity of air that can be expelled by forcible expiration.

expiratory standstill [PHYSIO] Suspension of action at the end of expiration.

explosive evolution [EVOL] Rapid diversification of a group of fossil organisms in a short geological time.

exponential growth [MICROBIO] The period of bacterial growth during which cells divide at a constant rate. Also known as logarithmic growth.

exserted [BIOL] Protruding beyond the enclosing structure, such as stamens extending beyond the margin of the corolla.

exsheath [INV ZOO] To escape from the residual membrane of a previous developmental stage, used of the larva of certain nematodes, microfilaria, and so on.

exstipulate [BOT] Lacking stipules.

extension [PHYSIO] A movement which has the effect of straightening a limb.

external auditory meatus [ANAT] The external passage of the ear, leading to the tympanic membrane in reptiles, birds, and mammals.

external carotid artery [ANAT] An artery which originates at the common carotid and distributes blood to the anterior part of the neck, face, scalp, side of the head, ear, and dura mater.

external ear [ANAT] The portion of the ear that receives sound waves, including the pinna and external auditory meatus.

external fertilization [PHYSIO] Those processes involved in the union of male and female sex cells outside the body of the female.

external gill [ZOO] A gill that is external to the body wall, as in certain larval fishes and amphibians, and in many aquatic insects.

external respiration [PHYSIO] The processes by which oxygen is carried into living cells from the outside environment and by which carbon dioxide is carried in the reverse direction.

exteroceptor [PHYSIO] Any sense receptor at the surface of the body that transmits information about the external environment.

extinction [EVOL] The worldwide death and disappearance of a specific organism or group of organisms.

extirpate [BIOL] To uproot, destroy, make extinct, or exterminate.

extracellular [BIOL] Outside the cell.

extrachromosomal inheritance *See* cytoplasmic inheritance.

extraembryonic coelom [EMBRYO] The cavity in the extraembryonic mesoderm; it is continuous with the embryonic coelom in the region of the umbilicus, and is obliterated by growth of the amnion.

extraembryonic membrane *See* fetal membrane.

extrajunctional receptor [PHYSIO] An acetylcholine receptor which occurs randomly over a muscle fiber surface outside the area of the neuromuscular junction.

extrapyramidal system [ANAT] Descending tracts of nerve fibers arising in the cortex and subcortical motor areas of the brain.

extrinsic factor *See* vitamin B_{12}.

extrorse [BIOL] Directed outward or away from the axis of growth.

extroversion [BIOL] A turning outward.

exumbrella [INV ZOO] The outer, convex surface of the umbrella of jellyfishes.

eye [ZOO] Photoreceptive sense organ that can form an image in vertebrates and in some invertebrates such as squids and crayfishes.

eyeball [ANAT] The globe of the eye.

eyeball potential [PHYSIO] Very small electrical potentials at the eyeball surface resulting from depolarization of muscles controlling eye position.

eyelid [ANAT] A movable, protective section of skin that covers and uncovers the eyeball of many terrestrial animals.

eye socket *See* orbit.

eyespot [BOT] 1. A small photosensitive pigment body in certain unicellular algae. 2. A dark area around the hilum of certain seeds, as some beans. [INV ZOO] A simple organ of vision in many invertebrates consisting of pigmented cells overlying a sensory termination. [PL PATH] A fungus disease of sugarcane and certain other grasses which is caused by *Helminthosporium sacchari* and characterized by yellowish oval lesions on the stems and leaves.

eyestalk [INV ZOO] A movable peduncle bearing a terminal eye in decapod crustaceans.

F

F₁ [GEN] Notation for the first filial generation resulting from a cross.

F₂ [GEN] Notation for the progeny produced by intercrossing members of the F_1. Also known as second generation.

Fabriclinae [INV ZOO] A subfamily of small to minute, colonial, sedentary polychaete annelids in the family Sabellidae.

face [ANAT] The anterior portion of the head, including the forehead and jaws.

facet [ANAT] A small plane surface, especially on a bone or a hard body; may be produced by wear, as a worn spot on the surface of a tooth. [INV ZOO] The surface of a simple eye in the compound eye of arthropods and certain other invertebrates.

facial artery [ANAT] The external branch of the external carotid artery.

facial bone [ANAT] The bone comprising the nose and jaws, formed by the maxilla, zygoma, nasal, lacrimal, palatine, inferior nasal concha, vomer, mandible, and parts of the ethmoid and sphenoid.

facial nerve [ANAT] The seventh cranial nerve in vertebrates; a paired composite nerve, with motor elements supplying muscles of facial expression and with sensory fibers from the taste buds of the anterior two-thirds of the tongue and from other sensory endings in the anterior part of the throat.

facies [ANAT] Characteristic appearance of the face in association with a disease or abnormality. [ECOL] The makeup or appearance of a community or species population.

factor I See fibrinogen.

factor III See thromboplastin.

factor IV [BIOCHEM] Calcium ions involved in the mechanism of blood coagulation.

factor V See proaccelerin.

factor VII [BIOCHEM] A procoagulant, related to prothrombin, that is involved in the formation of a prothrombin-converting principle which transforms prothrombin to thrombin. Also known as stable factor.

factor VIII See antihemophilic factor.

factor IX See Christmas factor.

factor X See Stuart factor.

factor XI [BIOCHEM] A procoagulant present in normal blood but deficient in hemophiliacs. Also known as plasma thromboplastin antecedent (PTA).

factor XII [BIOCHEM] A blood clotting factor effective experimentally only in vitro; deficient in hemophiliacs. Also known as Hageman factor.

facultative aerobe [MICROBIO] An anaerobic microorganism which can grow under aerobic conditions.

facultative anaerobe [MICROBIO] A microorganism that grows equally well under aerobic and anaerobic conditions.

facultative parasite [ECOL] An organism that can exist independently but may be parasitic on certain occasions, such as the flea.

facultative photoheterotroph [MICROBIO] Any bacterium that usually grows anaerobically in light but can also grow aerobically in the dark.

FAD See flavin adenine dinucleotide.

Fagaceae [BOT] A family of dicotyledonous plants in the order Fagales characterized by stipulate leaves, seeds without endosperm, female flowers generally not in catkins, and mostly three styles and locules.

Fagales [BOT] An order of dicotyledonous woody plants in the subclass Hamamelidae having simple leaves and much reduced, mostly unisexual flowers.

fairy ring spot [PL PATH] A fungus disease of carnations caused by *Heterosporium echinulatum*, producing bleached spots with concentric dark zones on the leaves.

falcate [BIOL] Shaped like a sickle.

falciform [BIOL] Sickle-shaped.

falciform ligament [ANAT] The ventral mesentery of the liver; its peripheral attachment extends from the diaphragm to the umbilicus and contains the round ligament of the liver.

falcon [VERT ZOO] Any of the highly specialized diurnal birds of prey composing the family Falconidae; these birds have been captured and trained for hunting.

Falconidae [VERT ZOO] The falcons, a family consisting of long-winged predacious birds in the order Falconiformes.

Falconiformes [VERT ZOO] An order of birds containing the diurnal birds of prey, including falcons, hawks, vultures, and eagles.

falculate [ZOO] Curved and with a sharp point.

Fallopian tube [ANAT] Either of the paired oviducts that extend from the ovary to the uterus for conduction of the ovum in mammals.

false blossom [PL PATH] 1. A fungus disease of the cranberry caused by *Exobasidium oxycocci;* erect flower buds are formed which produce malformed flowers that set no fruit. Also known as rosebloom. 2. A similar virus disease of the cranberry transmitted by the leafhopper, *Scleroracus vaccinii.* Also known as Wisconsin false blossom.

false ligament [ANAT] Any peritoneal fold which is not a true supporting ligament.

false rib [ANAT] A rib that is not attached to the sternum directly; any of the five lower ribs on each side in humans.

false ring [BOT] A layer of wood that is less than a full season's growth and often does not form a complete ring.

false smut [PL PATH] 1. A fungus disease of palm caused by *Graphiola phoenicis* and characterized by small cylindrical protruding pustules, often surrounded by yellowish leaf tissue. 2. *See* green smut.

falx [ANAT] A sickle-shaped structure.

familial [BIOL] Of, pertaining to, or occurring among the members of a family.

family [SYST] A taxonomic category based on the grouping of related genera.

fan [BIOL] Any structure, such as a leaf or the tail of a bird, resembling an open fan.

fang [ANAT] The root of a tooth. [VERT ZOO] A long, pointed tooth, especially one of a venomous serpent.

Fanti unit [BIOL] A unit for the standardization of thrombin.

faradization [PHYSIO] Use of a faradic current to stimulate muscles and nerves.

farinaceous [BIOL] Having a mealy surface covering.

Farinales [BOT] An order that includes several groups regarded as orders of the Commelinidae in other systems of classification.

Farinosae [BOT] The equivalent name for Farinales.

farinose [BIOL] Covered with a white powdery substance.

farnesol [BIOCHEM] $C_{1}H_{25}OH$ A colorless liquid extracted from oils of plants such as citronella, neroli, cyclamen, and tuberose; it has a delicate floral odor, and is an intermediate step in the biological synthesis of cholesterol from mevalonic acid in vertebrates; used in perfumery.

fascia [HISTOL] Layers of areolar connective tissue under the skin and between muscles, nerves, and blood vessels.

fasciate [BOT] Having bands or stripes.

fasciation [PL PATH] Malformation of plant parts resulting from disorganized tissue growth.

fascicle [BOT] A small bundle, as of fibers or leaves.

fasciculate [BOT] Arranged in tufts or fascicles.

fasciculation potential [PHYSIO] An action potential which is quantitatively comparable to that

of a motor unit and which represents spontaneous contraction of a bundle of muscle fibers.

fasciculus [ANAT] A bundle or tract of nerve, muscle, or tendon fibers isolated by a sheath of connective tissues and having common origins, innervation, and functions.

Fasciola hepatica [INV ZOO] A digenetic trematode which parasitizes sheep, cattle, and occasionally humans.

fasciole [INV ZOO] A band of cilia on the test of certain sea urchins.

Fasciolopsis buski [INV ZOO] A large, fleshy trematode, native to eastern Asia and the southwestern Pacific, which parasitizes humans.

fastigiate [BOT] 1. Having erect branches that are close to the stem. 2. Becoming narrower at the top. [ZOO] Arranged in a conical bundle.

fat [ANAT] Pertaining to an obese person. [BIOCHEM] Any of the glyceryl esters of fatty acids which form a class of neutral organic compounds. [PHYSIO] The chief component of fat cells and other animal and plant tissues.

fat body [INV ZOO] A nutritional reservoir of fatty tissue surrounding the viscera or forming a layer beneath the integument in the immature larval stages of many insects. [VERT ZOO] A mass of adipose tissue attached to each genital gland in amphibians.

fat cell [HISTOL] The principal component of adipose connective tissue; two types are yellow fat cells and brown fat cells.

fate map [EMBRYO] A graphic scheme indicating the definite spatial arrangement of undifferentiated embryonic cells in accordance with their destination to become specific tissues.

fatigue [PHYSIO] Exhaustion of strength or reduced capacity to respond to stimulation following a period of activity.

fat-metabolizing hormone *See* ketogenic hormone.

fatty acid peroxidase [BIOCHEM] An enzyme present in germinating plant seeds which catalyzes the oxidation of the carboxyl carbon of fatty acids to carbon dioxide.

fatty acyl carnitine [BIOCHEM] Transport form of fatty acids which allows them to cross the mitochondrial membrane; formed by reaction of fatty acyl-coenzyme A with carnitine by employing the enzyme carnitine acyltransferase. Also known as acyl carnitine.

fatty acyl-coenzyme A [BIOCHEM] Activated form of fatty acids formed by the enzyme acyl-coenzyme A synthetase at the expense of adenosinetriphosphate. Also known as acyl-coenzyme A.

fatty infiltration [PHYSIO] Infiltration of an organ or tissue with excessive amounts of fats.

faucal [BIOL] Of or pertaining to the fauces. [INV ZOO] The opening of a spiral shell.

fauces [ANAT] The passage in the throat between the soft palate and the base of the tongue. [BOT] The throat of a calyx, corolla, or similar part.

faucial tonsil *See* palatine tonsil.

fauna [ZOO] 1. Animals. 2. The animal life characteristic of a particular region or environment.

faunal extinction [EVOL] The worldwide death and disappearance of diverse animal groups under circumstances that suggest common and related causes. Also known as mass extinction.

faunal region [ECOL] A division of the zoosphere, defined by geographic and environmental barriers, to which certain animal communities are bound.

faunule [PALEON] The localized stratigraphic and geographic distribution of a particular taxon.

Favositidae [PALEON] A family of extinct Paleozoic corals in the order Tabulata.

feather [VERT ZOO] An ectodermal derivative which is a specialized keratinous outgrowth of the epidermis of birds; functions in flight and in providing insulation and protection.

feathering [VERT ZOO] Plumage.

feather rot [PL PATH] A fungus rot of both dead and living tree trunks caused by *Poria subacida* and characterized by the white stringy or spongy nature of the rotted tissue.

feces [PHYSIO] The waste material eliminated by the gastrointestinal tract.

Fechner fraction [PHYSIO] The smallest difference in the brightness of two sources that can be detected by the human eye divided by the brightness of one of them.

Fechner law [PHYSIO] The intensity of a sensation produced by a stimulus varies directly as the logarithm of the numerical value of that stimulus.

fecundity [BIOL] The innate potential reproductive capacity of the individual organism, as denoted by its ability to form and separate from the body the mature germ cells.

feedback inhibition [BIOCHEM] A cellular control mechanism by which the end product of a series of metabolic reactions inhibits the activity of the first enzyme in the sequence.

feeding mechanism [ZOO] A mechanism by which an animal obtains and utilizes food materials.

Felidae [VERT ZOO] The cats and saber-toothed cats, a family of mammals in the superfamily Feloidea.

feline [VERT ZOO] 1. Of or relating to the genus *Felis*. 2. Catlike.

Felis [VERT ZOO] The type genus of the Felidae, comprising the true or typical cats, both wild and domestic.

fell-field [ECOL] A culture community of dwarfed, scattered plants or grasses above the timberline.

Feloidea [VERT ZOO] A superfamily of catlike mammals in the order Carnivora.

Felon's unit [BIOL] A unit for the standardization of antipneumococcic serum.

female [BOT] A flower lacking stamens. [ZOO] An individual that bears young or produces eggs.

female heterogamety [GEN] The occurrence, in females of a species, of an unequal pair of sex chromosomes.

female homogamety [GEN] The occurrence, in females of a species, of an equal pair of sex chromosomes.

femoral artery [ANAT] The principal artery of the thigh; originates as a continuation of the external iliac artery.

femoral nerve [ANAT] A mixed nerve of the leg; the motor portion innervates muscles of the thigh, and the sensory portion innervates portions of the skin of the thigh, leg, hip, and knee.

femoral ring [ANAT] The abdominal opening of the femoral canal.

femoral vein [ANAT] A vein accompanying the femoral artery.

femur [ANAT] 1. The proximal bone of the hind or lower limb in vertebrates. 2. The thigh bone in humans, articulating with the acetabulum and tibia.

Fenestellidae [PALEON] A family of extinct fenestrated, cryptostomatous bryozoans which abounded during the Silurian.

fenestra [ANAT] An opening in the medial wall of the middle ear.

fenestrated membrane [HISTOL] One of the layers of elastic tissue in the tunica media and tunica intima of large arteries.

fenestration [BIOL] 1. A transparent or windowlike break or opening in the surface. 2. The presence of windowlike openings.

fennel [BOT] *Foeniculum vulgare*. A tall perennial herb of the family Umbelliferae; a spice is derived from the fruit.

ferment [BIOCHEM] An agent that can initiate fermentation and other metabolic processes.

fermentation [MICROBIO] An enzymatic transformation of organic substrates, especially carbohydrates, generally accompanied by the evolution of gas; a physiological counterpart of oxidation, permitting certain organisms to live and grow in the absence of air; used in various industrial processes for the manufacture of products such as alcohols, acids, and cheese by the action of yeasts, molds, and bacteria; alcoholic fermentation is the best-known example. Also known as zymosis.

fermentation tube [MICROBIO] A culture tube with a vertical closed arm to collect gas formed in a broth culture by microorganisms.

fern [BOT] Any of a large number of vascular plants composing the division Polypodiophyta.

ferredoxins [BIOCHEM] Iron-containing proteins that transfer electrons, usually at a low potential, to flavoproteins; the iron is not present as a heme.

ferret [VERT ZOO] *Mustela nigripes*. The largest member of the weasel family, Mustelidae, and a relative of the European polecat; has yellowish fur with black feet, tail, and mask.

ferrichrome [MICROBIO] A cyclic hexapeptide that is a microbial hydroxamic acid and is involved in iron transport and metabolism in microorganisms.

ferrihemoglobin [BIOCHEM] Hemoglobin in the oxidized state. Also known as methemoglobin.

ferrimycin [MICROBIO] The representative antibiotic of the sideromycin group; a hydroxamic acid compound.

ferriporphyrin [BIOCHEM] A red-brown to black complex of iron and porphyrin in which the iron is in the $3+$ oxidation state.

ferritin [BIOCHEM] An iron-protein complex occurring in tissues, probably as a storage form of iron.

ferrochelatase [BIOCHEM] A mitochondrial enzyme which catalyzes the incorporation of iron into the protoporphyrin molecule.

ferroporphyrin [BIOCHEM] A red complex of porphyrin and iron in which the iron is in the 2+ oxidation state.

fertility [BIOL] The state of or capacity for abundant productivity.

fertility factor [GEN] An episomal bacterial sex factor which determines the role of a bacterium as either a male donor or as a female recipient of genetic material. Also known as F factor; sex factor.

fertilization [PHYSIO] The physicochemical processes involved in the union of the male and female gametes to form the zygote.

fertilization membrane [CELL BIO] A membrane that separates from the surface of and surrounds many eggs following activation by the sperm; prevents multiple fertilization.

fertilizin [BIOCHEM] A mucopolysaccharide, derived from the jelly coat of an egg, that plays a role in sperm recognition and the stimulation of sperm motility and metabolic activity.

fervenulin [MICROBIO] $C_7H_7N_5O_2$ An antibiotic from culture filtrates of *Streptomyces fervens*; yellow, orthorhombic crystals are formed; melting point is 178–179°C. Also known as planomycin.

fescue [BOT] A group of grasses of the genus *Festuca*, used for both hay and pasture.

fetal hemoglobin [BIOCHEM] A normal embryonic hemoglobin having alpha chains identical to those of normal adult human hemoglobin, and gamma chains similar to adult beta chains.

fetal membrane [EMBRYO] Any one of the membranous structures which surround the embryo during its development period. Also known as extraembryonic membrane.

fetometamorphism [INV ZOO] A life cycle variation in the Cantharidae (Coleoptera); the larvae hatch prematurely as legless, immature prelarvae.

fetus [EMBRYO] 1. The unborn offspring of viviparous mammals in the later stages of development. 2. In human beings, the developing body in utero from the beginning of the ninth week after fertilization through the fortieth week of intrauterine gestation, or until birth.

Feylinildae [VERT ZOO] The limbless skinks, a family of reptiles in the suborder Sauria represented by four species in tropical Africa.

F factor See fertility factor.

fiber [BOT] 1. An elongate, thick-walled, tapering plant cell that lacks protoplasm and has a small lumen. 2. A very slender root.

fiber flax [BOT] The flax plant grown in fertile, well-drained, well-prepared soil and cool, humid climate; planted in the early spring and harvested when half the seed pods turn yellow; used in the manufacture of linen.

fibril [BIOL] A small thread or fiber, as a root hair or one of the structural units of a striated muscle.

fibrillation [PHYSIO] An independent, spontaneous, local twitching of muscle fibers.

fibrillose [BIOL] Having fibrils.

fibrin [BIOCHEM] The fibrous, insoluble protein that forms the structure of a blood clot; formed by the action of thrombin.

fibrinase [BIOCHEM] An enzyme that catalyzes the formation of covalent bonds between fibrin molecules. Also known as fibrin-stabilizing factor.

fibrinogen [BIOCHEM] A plasma protein synthesized by the parenchymal cells of the liver; the precursor of fibrin. Also known as factor I.

fibrinoid [BIOCHEM] A homogeneous, refractile, oxyphilic substance occurring in degenerating connective tissue, as in term placentas, rheumatoid nodules, and Aschoff bodies, and in pulmonary alveoli in some prolonged pneumonitides.

fibrinolysin See plasmin.

fibrinolysis [PHYSIO] Liquefaction of coagulated blood by the action of plasmin on fibrin.

fibrin-stabilizing factor See fibrinase.

fibroblast [HISTOL] A stellate connective tissue cell found in fibrous tissue. Also known as a fibrocyte.

fibrocartilage [HISTOL] A form of cartilage rich in dense, closely opposed bundles of collagen fibers; occurs in intervertebral disks, in the symphysis pubis, and in certain tendons.

fibroid [HISTOL] Composed of fibrous tissue.

fibroid deoxyribonucleic acid [MOL BIO] Sections of relatively uncoiled double-stranded deoxyribonucleic acid thought to be regions of specific base sequences for coding rather than gene control.

fibroin [BIOCHEM] A protein secreted by spiders and silkworms which rapidly solidifies into strong, insoluble thread that is used to form webs or cocoons.

fibrous protein [BIOCHEM] Any of a class of highly insoluble proteins representing the principal structural elements of many animal tissues.

fibula [ANAT] The outer and usually slender bone of the hind or lower limb below the knee in vertebrates; it articulates with the tibia and astragalus in humans, and is ankylosed with the tibia in birds and some mammals.

Ficus [BOT] A genus of tropical trees in the family Moraceae including the rubber tree and the fig tree. [INV ZOO] A genus of gastropod mollusks having pear-shaped, spirally ribbed sculptured shells.

fig [BOT] *Ficus carica*. A deciduous tree of the family Moraceae cultivated for its edible fruit, which is a syconium, consisting of a fleshy hollow receptacle lined with pistillate flowers.

Figitidae [INV ZOO] A family of hymenopteran insects in the superfamily Cynipoidea.

Fiji disease [PL PATH] A virus disease of sugarcane; elongated swellings on the underside of leaves precede death of the plant.

filament [BOT] 1. The stalk of a stamen which supports the anther. 2. A chain of cells joined end to end, as in certain algae. [INV ZOO] A single silk fiber in the cocoon of a silkworm.

filamentous bacteria [MICROBIO] Bacteria, especially in the order Actinomycetales, whose cells resemble filaments and are often branched.

filaria [INV ZOO] A parasitic filamentous nematode belonging to the order Filaroidea.

Filarioidea [INV ZOO] An order of the class Nematoda comprising highly specialized parasites of humans and domestic animals.

filbert [BOT] Either of two European plants belonging to the genus *Corylus* and producing a thick-shelled, edible nut. Also known as hazelnut.

Filicales [BOT] The equivalent name for Polypodiales.

Filicineae [BOT] The equivalent name for Polypodiatae.

Filicornia [INV ZOO] A group of hyperiid amphipod crustaceans in the suborder Genuina having the first antennae inserted anteriorly.

filiform [BIOL] Threadlike or filamentous.

filiform papilla [ANAT] Any one of the papillae occurring on the dorsum and margins of the oral part of the tongue, consisting of an elevation of connective tissue covered by a layer of epithelium.

film [BIOL] A thin, membranous skin, such as a pellicle.

filoplume [VERT ZOO] A specialized feather that may be decorative, sensory, or both; it is always associated with papillae of contour feathers.

filopodia [INV ZOO] Filamentous pseudopodia.

filoreticulopodia [INV ZOO] Branched, filamentous pseudopodia.

Filosia [INV ZOO] A subclass of the class Rhizopodea characterized by slender filopodia which rarely anastomose.

filterable virus [VIROL] Virus particles that remain in a fluid after passing through a diatomite or glazed porcelain filter with pores too minute to allow the passage of bacterial cells.

filter feeder [INV ZOO] A microphagous organism that uses complex filtering mechanisms to trap particles suspended in water.

fimbriate [BIOL] Having a fringe along the edge.

fin [VERT ZOO] A paddle-shaped appendage on fish and other aquatic animals that is used for propulsion, balance, and guidance.

final common pathway *See* lower motor neuron.

finch [VERT ZOO] The common name for birds composing the family Fringillidae.

fin fold [EMBRYO] A median integumentary fold extending along the body of a fish embryo which gives rise to the dorsal, caudal, and anal fins.

finger [ANAT] Any of the four digits on the hand other than the thumb.

fingerprint [ANAT] A pattern of distinctive epidermal ridges on the bulbs of the inside of the end joints of fingers and thumbs.

fin spine [VERT ZOO] A bony process that supports the fins of certain fishes.

fir [BOT] The common name for any tree of the genus *Abies* in the pine family; needles are characteristically flat.

fire blight [PL PATH] A bacterial disease of apple, pear, and related pomaceous fruit trees caused by *Erwinia amylovora*; leaves are blackened, cankers form on the trunk, and flowers and fruits become discolored.

fire disclimax [ECOL] A community that is perpetually maintained at an early stage of succession through recurrent destruction by fire followed by regeneration.

firefly [INV ZOO] Any of various flying insects which produce light by bioluminescence.

first filial generation [GEN] The first generation resulting from a cross with all members being heterozygous for characters which differ from those of the parents. Symbolized F_1.

fish [VERT ZOO] The common name for the cold-blooded aquatic vertebrates belonging to the groups Cyclostomata, Chondrichthyes, and Osteichthyes.

fisher [VERT ZOO] *Martes pennanti*. An arboreal, carnivorous mammal of the family Mustelidae; a relatively large weasellike animal with dark fur, found in northern North America.

fisheries conservation [ECOL] Those measures concerned with the protection and preservation of fish and other aquatic life, particularly in sea waters.

fishery [ECOL] A place for harvesting fish or other aquatic life, particularly in sea waters.

fish lice [INV ZOO] The common name for all members of the crustacean group Arguloida.

Fissidentales [BOT] An order of the Bryopsida having erect to procumbent, simple or branching stems and two rows of leaves arranged in one plane.

fission [BIOL] A method of asexual reproduction among bacteria, algae, and protozoans by which the organism splits into two or more parts, each part becoming a complete organism.

fission fungi [MICROBIO] A misnomer once used to describe the Schizomycetes.

fissiped [VERT ZOO] 1. Having the toes separated to the base. 2. Of or relating to the Fissipeda.

Fissipeda [VERT ZOO] Former designation for a suborder of the Carnivora.

Fissurellidae [INV ZOO] The keyhole limpets, a family of gastropod mollusks in the order Archeogastropoda.

Fistuliporidae [PALEON] A diverse family of extinct marine bryozoans in the order Cystoporata.

fix [BIOL] To kill, harden, or preserve a tissue, organ, or organism by immersion in dilute acids, alcohol, or solutions of coagulants.

fixator [PHYSIO] A muscle whose action tends to hold a body part in a certain position or limit its movement.

flabellate [BIOL] Fan-shaped.

Flabellifera [INV ZOO] The largest and morphologically most generalized suborder of isopod crustaceans; the biramous uropods are attached to the sides of the abdomen and may form, with the last abdominal fragment, a caudal fan.

Flabelligeridae [INV ZOO] The cage worms, a family of spioniform worms belonging to the Sedentaria; the anterior part of the body is often concealed by a cage of setae arising from the first few segments.

flabellum [INV ZOO] Any structure resembling a fan, as the epipodite of certain crustacean limbs.

flaccid [BOT] Deficient in turgor. [PHYSIO] Soft, flabby, or relaxed.

flacherie [INV ZOO] A fatal bacterial disease of caterpillars, especially silkworms, marked by loss of appetite, dysentery, and flaccidity of the body; after death the body darkens and liquefies.

Flacourtiaceae [BOT] A family of dicotyledonous plants in the order Violales having the characteristics of the more primitive members of the order.

flagella [BIOL] Relatively long, whiplike, centriole-based locomotor organelles on some motile cells.

Flagellata [INV ZOO] The equivalent name for Mastigophora.

flagellate [BIOL] 1. Having flagella. 2. An organism that propels itself by means of flagella. 3. Resembling a flagellum. [INV ZOO] Any member of the protozoan superclass Mastigophora.

flagellated chamber [INV ZOO] An outpouching of the wall of the central cavity in Porifera that is lined with choanocytes; connects with incurrent canals through prosophyles.

flagellation [BIOL] The arrangement of flagella on an organism.

flagellin [MICROBIO] The protein component of bacterial flagella.

flagilliflory [BOT] Of flowers, hanging down freely from ropelike twigs.

flag smut [PL PATH] A smut affecting the leaves and stems of cereals and other grasses, characterized by formation of sori within the tissues, which rupture releasing black spore masses and causing fraying of the infected area.

flame bulb [INV ZOO] The enlarged terminal part of the flame cell of a protonephridium, consisting of a tuft of cilia.

flame cell [INV ZOO] A hollow cell that contains the terminal branches of excretory vessels in certain flatworms and rotifers and some other invertebrates.

flamingo [VERT ZOO] Any of various long-legged and long-necked aquatic birds of the family Phoenicopteridae characterized by a broad bill resembling that of a duck but abruptly bent downward and rosy-white plumage with scarlet coverts.

flash pasteurization [MICROBIO] A pasteurization method in which a heat-labile liquid, such as milk, is briefly subjected to temperatures of 230°F (110°C).

flatfish [VERT ZOO] Any of a number of asymmetrical fishes which compose the order Pleuronectiformes; the body is laterally compressed, and both eyes are on the same side of the head.

flatworm [INV ZOO] The common name for members of the phylum Platyhelminthes; individuals are dorsoventrally flattened.

flavan [BIOCHEM] $C_{15}H_{14}O$ 2-Phenylbenzopyran, an aromatic heterocyclic compound from which all flavonoids are derived.

flavanol [BIOCHEM] Yellow needles with a melting point of 169°C, derived from flavanone; a flavanoid pigment used as a dye. Also known as 3-hydroxyflavone.

flavanone [BIOCHEM] $C_{15}H_{12}O_2$ A colorless crystalline derivative of flavone.

flavescence [PL PATH] Yellowing or blanching of green plant parts due to diminution of chlorophyll accompanying certain virus disease.

flavin [BIOCHEM] 1. A yellow dye obtained from the bark of quercitron trees. 2. Any of several water-soluble yellow pigments occurring as coenzymes of flavoproteins.

flavin adenine dinucleotide [BIOCHEM] $C_{27}H_{33}$-$N_9O_{15}P_2$ A coenzyme that functions as a hydrogen acceptor in aerobic dehydrogenases (flavoproteins). Abbreviated FAD.

flavin mononucleotide *See* riboflavin 5′-phosphate.

flavin phosphate *See* riboflavin 5′-phosphate.

Flavobacterium [MICROBIO] A genus of bacterium of uncertain affiliation; gram-negative coccobacilli or slender rods producing pigmented (yellow, red, orange, or brown) growth on solid media.

flavone [BIOCHEM] 1. Any of a number of ketones composing a class of flavonoid compounds. 2. $C_{15}H_{10}O_2$ A colorless crystalline compound occurring as dust on the surface of many primrose plants.

flavonoid [BIOCHEM] Any of a series of widely distributed plant constituents related to the aromatic heterocyclic skeleton of flavan.

flavonol [BIOCHEM] 1. Any of a class of flavonoid compounds that are hydroxy derivatives of flavone. 2. $C_{16}H_{10}O_2$ A colorless, crystalline compound from which many yellow plant pigments are derived.

flavoprotein [BIOCHEM] Any of a number of conjugated protein dehydrogenases containing flavin that play a role in biological oxidations in both plants and animals; a yellow enzyme.

flax [BOT] *Linum usitatissimum*. An erect annual plant with linear leaves and blue flowers; cultivated as a source of flaxseed and fiber.

flax rust [PL PATH] A disease of flax caused by the rust fungus *Melampsora lini*.

flaxseed [BOT] The seed obtained from the seed flax plant; a source of linseed oil.

flax wilt [PL PATH] A fungus disease of flax caused by *Fusarium oxysporum lini*; diseased plants wilt, yellow, and die.

flea [INV ZOO] Any of the wingless insects composing the order Siphonaptera; most are ectoparasites of mammals and birds.

fleece [VERT ZOO] Coat of wool shorn from sheep; usually taken off the animal in one piece.

flesh [ANAT] The soft parts of the body of a vertebrate, especially the skeletal muscle and associated connective tissue and fat.

fleshy fruit [BOT] A fruit having a fleshy pericarp that is usually soft and juicy, but sometimes hard and tough.

Flexibacter [MICROBIO] A genus of bacteria in the family Cytophagaceae; cells are unsheathed rods or filaments and are motile; microcysts are not known.

Flexibilia [PALEON] A subclass of extinct stalked or creeping Crinoidea; characteristics include a flexible tegmen with open ambulacral grooves, uniserial arms, a cylindrical stem, and five conspicuous basals and radials.

flexion [BIOL] Act of bending, especially of a joint.

flexion reflex [PHYSIO] An unconditioned, segmental reflex elicited by noxious stimulation and consisting of contraction of the flexor muscles of all joints on the same side. Also known as the nocioceptive reflex.

Flexithrix [MICROBIO] A genus of bacteria in the family Cytophagaceae; cells are usually sheathed filaments, and unsheathed cells are motile; microcysts are not known.

flexor [PHYSIO] A muscle that bends or flexes a limb or a part.

flexuous [BIOL] 1. Flexible. 2. Bending in a zigzag manner. 3. Wavy.

flexure [EMBRYO] A sharp bend of the anterior part of the primary axis of the vertebrate embryo. [VERT ZOO] The last joint of a bird's wing.

flight feather [VERT ZOO] Any of the long contour feathers on the wing of a bird. Also known as remex.

flipper [VERT ZOO] A broad, flat appendage used for locomotion by aquatic mammals and sea turtles.

float [BIOL] An air-filled sac in many pelagic flora and fauna that serves to buoy up the body of the organism.

floating rib [ANAT] One of the last two ribs in humans which have the anterior end free.

floatoblast [INV ZOO] A free-floating statoblast having a float of air cells.

floccose [BOT] Covered with tufts of woollike hairs.

flocculate [BIOL] Having small tufts of hairs.

flocculonodular lobes [ANAT] The pair of lateral cerebellar lobes in vertebrates which function to regulate vestibular reflexes underlying posture; referred to functionally as the vestibulocerebellum.

flocculus [ANAT] A prominent lobe of the cerebellum situated behind and below the middle cerebellar peduncle on each side of the median fissure.

floccus [BOT] A tuft of woolly hairs.

flora [BOT] 1. Plants. 2. The plant life characterizing a specific geographic region or environment.

floral axis [BOT] A flower stalk.

floral diagram [BOT] A diagram of a flower in cross section showing the number and arrangement of floral parts.

floret [BOT] A small individual flower that is part of a compact group of flowers, such as the head of a composite plant or inflorescence.

Florey unit [BIOL] A unit for the standardization of penicillin.

floricome [INV ZOO] A type of branched hexaster spicule.

Florideophyceae [BOT] A class of red algae, division Rhodophyta, having prominent pit connections between cells.

floriferous [BOT] Blooming freely, used principally of ornamental plants.

florigen [BIOCHEM] A plant hormone that stimulates buds to flower.

florivorous [ZOO] Feeding on flowers.

florula [ECOL] Plants which grow in a small, confined habitat, for example, a pond.

floscelle [INV ZOO] A flowerlike structure around the mouth of some echinoids.

Flosculariacea [INV ZOO] A suborder of rotifers in the order Monogononta having a malleoramate mastax.

Flosculariidae [INV ZOO] A family of sessile rotifers in the suborder Flosculariacea.

flosculous [BOT] 1. Composed of florets. 2. Of a floret, tubular in form.

flosculus [BOT] A floret.

flounder [VERT ZOO] Any of a number of flatfishes in the families Pleuronectidae and Bothidae of the order Pleuronectiformes.

flow bog [ECOL] A peat bog with a surface level that fluctuates in accordance with rain and tides.

flower [BOT] The characteristic reproductive structure of a seed plant, particularly if some or all of the parts are brightly colored.

fluctuation test [MICROBIO] A method of demonstrating that bacterial mutations preexist in a population before they are selected; a large parent population is divided into small parts which are grown independently and the number of mutants in each subculture determined; the number of mutants in the subculture will fluctuate because in some a mutant arises early (giving a large number of progeny), while in others the mutant arises late and gives few progeny.

fluke [INV ZOO] The common name for more than 40,000 species of parasitic flatworms that form the class Trematoda. [VERT ZOO] A flatfish, especially summer flounder.

fluorescent staining [CELL BIO] The use of fluorescent dyes to mark specific cell structures, such as chromosomes.

fluorochromasia [CELL BIO] The immediate appearance of fluorescence inside viable cells on exposure to a fluorogenic substrate.

flush [ECOL] An evergreen herbaceous or nonflowering vegetation growing in habitats where seepage water causes the surface to be constantly wet but rarely flooded.

fly [INV ZOO] The common name for a number of species of the insect order Diptera characterized by a single pair of wings, antennae, compound eyes, and hindwings modified to form knoblike balancing organs, the halters.

flying fish [VERT ZOO] Any of about 65 species of marine fishes which form the family Exocoetidae in the order Atheriniformes; characteristic enlarged pectoral fins are used for gliding.

flyway [VERT ZOO] A geographic migration route for birds, including the breeding and wintering areas that it connects.

FMN See riboflavin 5'-phosphate.

foal [VERT ZOO] A young horse, especially one under 1 year of age.

fog climax [ECOL] A community that deviates from a climatic climax because of the persistent occurrence of a controlling fog blanket.

fog forest [ECOL] The dense, rich forest growth which is found at high or medium-high altitudes on tropical mountains; occurs when the tropical rain forest penetrates altitudes of cloud formation, and the climate is excessively moist and not too cold to prevent plant growth.

fold [ANAT] A plication or doubling, as of various parts of the body such as membranes and other flat surfaces.

foliaceous [BOT] Consisting of or having the form or texture of a foliage leaf. [ZOO] Resembling a leaf in growth form or mode.

foliage [BOT] The leaves of a plant.

foliar [BOT] Of, pertaining to, or consisting of leaves.

foliate papilla [VERT ZOO] One of the papillae found on the posterolateral margin of the tongue of many mammals, but vestigial or absent in humans.

foliation [BOT] 1. The process of developing into a leaf. 2. The state of being in leaf.

folic acid [BIOCHEM] $C_{19}H_{19}N_7O_6$ A yellow, crystalline vitamin of the B complex; it is slightly soluble in water, usually occurs in conjugates containing glutamic acid residues, and is found especially in plant leaves and vertebrate livers. Also known as pteroylglutamic acid (PGA).

foliferous [BOT] Producing leaves.

folicolous [BIOL] Growing or parasitic upon leaves, as certain fungi.

foliobranchiate [VERT ZOO] Having leaflike gills.

foliolate [BOT] Having leaflets.

follicle [BIOL] A deep, narrow sheath or a small cavity. [BOT] A type of dehiscent fruit composed of one carpel opening along a single suture.

follicle-stimulating hormone [BIOCHEM] A protein hormone released by the anterior pituitary of vertebrates which stimulates growth and secretion of the Graafian follicle and also promotes spermatogenesis. Abbreviated FSH.

folliculate [BIOL] Having or composed of follicles.

fontanelle [ANAT] A membrane-covered space between the bones of a fetal or young skull. [INV ZOO] A depression on the head of termites.

Fontéchevade man [PALEON] A fossil man representing the third interglacial *Homo sapiens* and having browridges and a cranial vault similar to those of modern *Homo sapiens*.

food [BIOL] A material that can be ingested and utilized by the organism as a source of nutrition and energy.

food chain [ECOL] The scheme of feeding relationships by trophic levels which unites the member species of a biological community.

food pyramid [ECOL] An ecological pyramid representing the food relationship among the animals in a community.

food vacuole [CELL BIO] A membrane-bound organelle in which digestion occurs in cells capable of phagocytosis. Also known as heterophagic vacuole; phagocytic vacuole.

food web [ECOL] A modified food chain that expresses feeding relationships at various, changing trophic levels.

foot [ANAT] Terminal portion of a vertebrate leg. [INV ZOO] An organ for locomotion or attachment.

foot gland [INV ZOO] A glandular structure which secretes an adhesive substance in many animals. Also known as pedal gland.

foot rot [PL PATH] Any disease that involves rotting of the stem or trunk of a plant.

foramen [BIOL] A small opening, orifice, pore, or perforation.

foramen magnum [ANAT] A large oval opening in the occipital bone at the base of the cranium that allows passage of the spinal cord, accessory nerves, and vertebral arteries.

foramen of Magendie [ANAT] The median aperture of the fourth ventricle of the brain.

foramen of Monro *See* interventricular foramen.

foramen of Winslow *See* epiploic foramen.

foramen ovale [ANAT] An opening in the sphenoid for the passage of nerves and blood vessels. [EMBRYO] An opening in the fetal heart partition between the two atria.

foramen primum [EMBRYO] A temporary embryonic interatrial opening.

Foraminiferida [INV ZOO] An order of dominantly marine protozoans in the subclass Granuloreticulosia having a secreted or agglutinated shell enclosing the ameboid body.

forb [BOT] A weed or broadleaf herb.

forceps [INV ZOO] A pair of curved, hard, movable appendages at the end of the abdomen of certain insects, for example, the earwig.

forcipate [BIOL] Shaped like forceps; deeply forked.

forcipate trophus [INV ZOO] A type of masticatory apparatus in certain predatory rotifers which resembles forceps and is used for grasping.

Forcipulatida [INV ZOO] An order of echinoderms in the subclass Asteroidea characterized by crossed pedicellariae.

forearm [ANAT] The part of the upper extremity between the wrist and the elbow. Also known as antebrachium.

forebrain [EMBRYO] The most anterior expansion of the neural tube of a vertebrate embryo. [VERT ZOO] The part of the adult brain derived from the embryonic forebrain; includes the cerebrum, thalamus, and hypothalamus.

forefinger [ANAT] The index finger; the first finger next to the thumb.

forefoot [VERT ZOO] An anterior foot of a quadruped.

foregut [EMBRYO] The anterior alimentary canal in a vertebrate embryo, including those parts which will develop into the pharynx, esophagus, stomach, and anterior intestine.

forehead [ANAT] The part of the face above the eyes.

forelimb [ANAT] An appendage (as a wing, fin, or arm) of a vertebrate that is, or is homologous to, the foreleg of a quadruped.

forest [ECOL] An ecosystem consisting of plants and animals and their environment, with trees as the dominant form of vegetation.

forest conservation [ECOL] Those measures concerned with the protection and preservation of forest lands and resources.

forest ecology [ECOL] The science that deals with the relationship of forest trees to their environment, to one another, and to other plants and to animals in the forest.

forestry [ECOL] The management of forest lands for wood, forages, water, wildlife, and recreation.

forest-tundra [ECOL] A temperate and cold savanna which occurs at high altitudes and consists of scattered or clumped trees and a shrub layer of varying coverage.

formamidase [BIOCHEM] An enzyme involved in tryptophane catabolism; catalyzes the conversion of N-formylkynurenine to kynurenine and formate.

Formicariidae [VERT ZOO] The antbirds, a family of suboscine birds in the order Passeriformes.

Formicidae [INV ZOO] The ants, social insects composing the single family of the hymenopteran superfamily Formicoidea.

formicivorous [ZOO] Feeding on ants.

Formicoidea [INV ZOO] A monofamilial superfamily of hymenopteran insects in the suborder Apocrita, containing the ants.

formyl methionine [BIOCHEM] Formylated methionine; initiates peptide chain synthesis in bacteria.

fornix [ANAT] A structure that is folded or arched. [BOT] A small scale, especially in the corolla tube of some plants.

fossa [ANAT] A pit or depression. [VERT ZOO] *Cryptoprocta ferox.* A Madagascan carnivore related to the civets.

fossil [PALEON] The organic remains, traces, or imprint of an organism preserved in the earth's crust since some time in the geologic past.

fossil man [PALEON] An ancient human identified from prehistoric skeletal remains which are archeologically earlier than the Neolithic.

fossorial [VERT ZOO] Adapted for digging.

foulbrood [INV ZOO] The common name for three destructive bacterial diseases of honeybee larvae.

fouling organism [ECOL] Any aquatic organism with a sessile adult stage that attaches to and fouls underwater structures of ships.

fourré *See* temperate and cold scrub; tropical scrub.

fovea [BIOL] A small depression or pit.

fovea centralis [ANAT] A small, rodless depression of the retina in line with the visual axis, which affords acute vision.

foveal vision [PHYSIO] Vision achieved by looking directly at objects in the daylight so that the image falls on or near the fovea centralis. Also known as photopic vision.

foveola [BIOL] A small pit, especially one in the embryonic gastric mucosa from which gastric glands develop.

foveolate [BIOL] Having small depressions; pitted.

fox [VERT ZOO] The common name for certain members of the dog family (Canidae) having relatively short legs, long bodies, large erect ears, pointed snouts, and long bushy tails.

fragmentation [CELL BIO] Amitotic division; a type of asexual reproduction.

frameshift mutation [GEN] A mutation caused by addition or deletion of nucleotides in numbers other than three which shifts the translation reading frame so a new set of codons beyond the point of abnormality in the messenger ribonucleic acid is read. Also known as phase-shift mutation.

Francisella [MICROBIO] A genus of gram-negative, aerobic bacteria of uncertain affiliation; cells are small, coccoid to ellipsoidal, pleomorphic rods and can be parasitic on mammals, birds, and arthropods.

Frankia [MICROBIO] The single genus of the family Frankiaceae.

Frankiaceae [MICROBIO] A family of bacteria in the order Actinomycetales; filamentous cells form true mycelia; they are symbiotic and found in active, nitrogen-fixing root nodules.

fraternal twins *See* dizygotic twins.

freemartin [VERT ZOO] An intersexual, usually sterile female calf twinborn with a male.

free recombination [GEN] Genetic recombination having a frequency of 50, that is, occurring by independent reassortment.

freestone [BOT] A fruit stone to which the fruit does not cling, as in certain varieties of peach.

Fregatidae [VERT ZOO] Frigate birds or man-o'-war birds, a family of fish-eating birds in the order Pelecaniformes.

Frenatae [INV ZOO] The equivalent name for Heteroneura.

frenulum [ANAT] 1. A small fold of integument or mucous membrane. 2. A small ridge on the upper part of the anterior medullary velum. [INV ZOO] A spine on most moths that projects from the hindwings and is held to the forewings by a clasp, thus coupling the wings together.

frenum [ANAT] A fold of tissue that restricts the movements of an organ.

frequency coding [PHYSIO] A means by which the central nervous system analyzes the content of a receptor message; the frequency of discharged impulses is a function of the rate of rise of the generator current and indirectly of the stimulus strength; the greater the stimulus intensity, the higher the impulse frequency of the message.

frequency theory [PHYSIO] A theory of human hearing according to which every specific frequency of sound energy is represented by nerve impulses of the same frequency, and pitch differentiation and analysis are carried out by the brain centers. Also known as telephone theory.

fresh-water ecosystem [ECOL] The living organisms and nonliving materials of an inland aquatic environment.

friar's cowl *See* aconite.

friction ridge [ANAT] One of the integumentary ridges on the plantar and palmar surfaces of primates.

Friedlander's bacillus See Klebsiella pneumoniae.

frigidoreceptor [PHYSIO] A cutaneous sense organ which is sensitive to cold.

Fringillidae [VERT ZOO] The finches, a family of oscine birds in the order Passeriformes.

fritillary [BOT] The common name for plants of the genus *Fritillaria*. [INV ZOO] The common name for butterflies in several genera of the subfamily Nymphalinae.

frog [VERT ZOO] The common name for a number of tailless amphibians in the order Anura; most have hindlegs adapted for jumping, scaleless skin, and large eyes.

frogeye [PL PATH] Any of various leaf diseases characterized by formation of concentric rings around the diseased spots.

frond [BOT] 1. The leaf of a palm or fern. 2. A foliaceous thallus or thalloid shoot.

frontal bone [ANAT] Either of a pair of flat membrane bones in vertebrates, and a single bone in humans, forming the upper frontal portion of the cranium; the forehead bone.

frontal crest [ANAT] A median ridge on the internal surface of the frontal bone in humans.

frontal eminence [ANAT] The prominence of the frontal bone above each superciliary ridge in humans.

frontal lobe [ANAT] The anterior portion of a cerebral hemisphere, bounded behind by the central sulcus and below by the lateral cerebral sulcus.

frontal nerve [ANAT] A somatic sensory nerve, attached to the ophthalmic nerve, which innervates the skin of the upper eyelid, the forehead, and the scalp.

frontal plane [ANAT] Any plane parallel with the long axis of the body and perpendicular to the sagittal plane.

frontal sinus [ANAT] Either of a pair of air spaces within the frontal bone above the nasal bridge.

frost cracks [BOT] Cracks in wood that have split outward from ray shakes.

frost ring [BOT] A false annual growth ring in the trunk of a tree due to out-of-season defoliation by frost and subsequent regrowth of foliage.

frosty mildew [PL PATH] A leaf spot caused by fungi of the genus *Cercosporella* and characterized by pale to white lesions.

frozen section [BIOL] A thin slice of material cut from a frozen sample of tissue or organ.

fructescence [BOT] The period of fruit maturation.

fructification [BOT] 1. The process of producing fruit. 2. A fruit and its appendages. [MYCOL] A sporogenous structure.

fructivorous See frugivorous.

D-fructopyranose See fructose.

fructose [BIOCHEM] $C_6H_{12}O_5$ The commonest of ketoses and the sweetest of sugars, found in the free state in fruit juices, honey, and nectar of plant glands. Also known as D-fructopyranose.

frugivorous [ZOO] Fruit-eating. Also known as fructivorous.

fruit [BOT] A fully matured plant ovary with or without other floral or shoot parts united with it at maturity.

fruit bud [BOT] A fertilized flower bud that matures into a fruit.

fruit fly [INV ZOO] 1. The common name for those acalyptrate insects composing the family Tephritidae. 2. Any insect whose larvae feed on fruit or decaying vegetable matter.

fruiting body [BOT] A specialized, spore-producing organ.

frustule [INV ZOO] 1. The shell and protoplast of a diatom. 2. A nonciliated planulalike bud in some hydrozoans.

frutescent [BIOL] See fruticose. [BOT] Shrublike in habit.

fruticose [BIOL] Resembling a shrub; applied especially to lichens. Also known as frutescent.

FSH See follicle-stimulating hormone.

Fucales [BOT] An order of brown algae composing the class Cyclosporeae.

fuchsinophile [BIOL] Having an affinity for the dye fuchsin.

fucoidin [BIOCHEM] A gum composed of L-fucose and sulfate acid ester groups obtained from *Fucus* species and other brown algae.

Fucophyceae [BOT] A class of brown algae.

L-fucopyranose See L-fucose.

L-fucose [BIOCHEM] $C_6H_{12}O_5$ A methyl pentose present in some algae and a number of gums and identified in the polysaccharides of blood groups and certain bacteria. Also known as 6-deoxy-L-galactose; L-fucopyranose; L-galactomethylose; L-rhodeose.

fucoxanthin [BIOCHEM] $C_{40}H_{60}O_6$ A carotenoid pigment; a partial xanthophyll ester found in diatoms and brown algae.

Fucus [BOT] A genus of dichotomously branched brown algae; it is harvested in the kelp industry as a source of algin.

fugacious [BOT] Lasting a short time; used principally to describe plant parts that fall soon after being formed.

fulcrate [BIOL] Having a fulcrum.

fulcrate trophus [INV ZOO] A type of masticatory apparatus in certain rotifers characterized by an elongate fulcrum.

Fuld-Gross unit [BIOL] A unit for the standardization of trypsin.

Fulgoroidea [INV ZOO] The lantern flies, a superfamily of homopteran insects in the series Auchenorrhyncha distinguished by the anterior and middle coxae being of equal length and joined to the body at some distance from the median line.

fulmar [VERT ZOO] Any of the oceanic birds composing the family Procellariidae; sometimes referred to as foul gulls because of the foul-smelling substance spat at intruders upon their nests.

fumagillin [MICROBIO] $C_{26}H_{34}O_7$ An insoluble, crystalline antibiotic produced by a strain of the fungus *Aspergillus fumigatus*.

fumarase [BIOCHEM] An enzyme that catalyzes the hydration of fumaric acid to malic acid, and the reverse dehydration.

Fumariaceae [BOT] A family of dicotyledonous plants in the order Papaverales having four or six stamens, irregular flowers, and no latex system.

Funariales [BOT] An order of mosses; plants are usually annual, are terrestrial, and have stems that are erect, short, simple, or sparingly branched.

functional residual capacity [PHYSIO] The volume of gas which remains within the lungs at expiratory standstill.

fundic gland [ANAT] Any of the glands of the corpus and fundus of the stomach.

fundus [ANAT] The bottom of a hollow organ.

fungi [MYCOL] Nucleated, usually filamentous, sporebearing organisms devoid of chlorophyll.

fungiform [BIOL] Mushroom-shaped.

fungiform papilla [ANAT] One of the low, broad papillae scattered over the dorsum and margins of the tongue.

Fungi Imperfecti [MYCOL] A class of the subdivision Eumycetes; the name is derived from the lack of a sexual stage.

Fungivoridae [INV ZOO] The fungus gnats, a family of orthorrhaphous dipteran insects in the series Nematocera; the larvae feed on fungi.

fungivorous [ZOO] Feeding on or in fungi.

fungus [MYCOL] Singular of fungi.

fungus gall [PL PATH] A plant gall resulting from an attack of a parasitic fungus.

funiculus [ANAT] Also known as funicle. 1. Any structure in the form of a chord. 2. A column of white matter in the spinal cord. [BOT] The stalk of an ovule. [INV ZOO] A band of tissue extending from the adoral end of the coelom to the adoral body wall in bryozoans.

fur [VERT ZOO] The coat of a mammal.

furanose [BIOCHEM] A sugar whose cyclic or ring structure resembles that of furan.

furca [INV ZOO] A forked process as the last abdominal segment of certain crustaceans, and as part of the spring in collembolans.

furcate [BIOL] Forked.

furcocercous cercaria [INV ZOO] A free-swimming, digenetic trematode larva with a forked tail.

furcula [ZOO] A forked structure, especially the wishbone of fowl.

Furipteridae [VERT ZOO] The smoky bats, a family of mammals in the order Chiroptera having a vestigial thumb and small ears.

Furnariidae [VERT ZOO] The oven birds, a family of perching birds in the superfamily Furnarioidea.

Furnarioidea [VERT ZOO] A superfamily of birds in the order Passeriformes characterized by a predominance of gray, brown, and black plumage.

Fusarium [MYCOL] A genus of fungi in the family Tuberculariaceae having sickle-shaped, multicelled conidia; includes many important plant pathogens.

Fusarium oxysporum [MYCOL] A pathogenic fungus causing a variety of plant diseases, including cabbage yellows and wilt of tomato, flax, cotton, peas, and muskmelon.

Fusarium solani [MYCOL] A pathogenic fungus implicated in root rot and wilt diseases of several plants, including sisal and squash.

fusiform [BIOL] Spindle-shaped; tapering toward the ends.

fusiform bacillus [MICROBIO] A bacillus having one blunt and one pointed end, as *Fusobacterium fusiforme*.

fusiform initial cell [BOT] A cell type of the vascular cambium that gives rise to all cells in the vertical system of secondary xylem and phloem.

fusimotoneuron [PHYSIO] One of the small motor fibers, composing about 30% of the fibers in the ventral root of the spinal cord, which innervate intrafusal fibers.

fusion nucleus [BOT] The triploid, or $3n$, nucleus which results from double fertilization and which produces the endosperm in some seed plants.

fusula [INV ZOO] A spindle-shaped, terminal projection of the spinneret of a spider.

Fusulinacea [PALEON] A superfamily of large, marine extinct protozoans in the order Foraminiferida characterized by a chambered calcareous shell.

Fusulinidae [PALEON] A family of extinct protozoans in the superfamily Fusulinacea.

Fusulinina [PALEON] A suborder of extinct rhizopod protozoans in the order Foraminiferida having a monolamellar, microgranular calcite wall.

G

Gadidae [VERT ZOO] A family of fishes in the order Gadiformes, including cod, haddock, pollock, and hake.

Gadiformes [VERT ZOO] An order of actinopterygian fishes that lack fin spines and a swim bladder duct and have cycloid scales and many-rayed pelvic fins.

galactan [BIOCHEM] Any of a number of polysaccharides composed of galactose units. Also known as galactosan.

galactogen [BIOCHEM] A polysaccharide, in snails, that yields galactose on hydrolysis.

galactoglucomannan [BIOCHEM] Any of a group of polysaccharides which are prominent components of coniferous woods; they are soluble in alkali and consist of D-glucopyranose and D-mannopyranose units.

galactokinase [BIOCHEM] An enzyme which reacts D-galactose with adenosinetriphosphate to give D-galactose-1-phosphate and adenosinediphosphate.

galactolipid See cerebroside.

galactomannan [BIOCHEM] Any of a group of polysaccharides which are composed of D-galactose and D-mannose units, are soluble in water, and form highly viscous solutions; they are plant mucilages existing as reserve carbohydrates in the endosperm of leguminous seeds.

L-galactomethylose See L-fucose.

galactonic acid [BIOCHEM] $C_6H_{12}O_7$ A monobasic acid derived from galactose, occurring in three optically different forms, and melting at 97°C. Also known as pentahydroxyhexoic acid.

galactophore [ANAT] A duct that carries milk.

galactopoiesis [PHYSIO] Formation of the components of milk by the cells composing the lobuloalveolar glandular structure.

galactosamine [BIOCHEM] $C_6H_{14}O_5N$ A crystalline amino acid derivative of galactose; found in bacterial cell walls.

galactosan See galactan.

galactose [BIOCHEM] $C_6H_{12}O_6$ A monosaccharide occurring in both levo and dextro forms as a constituent of plant and animal oligosaccharides (lactose and raffinose) and polysaccharides (agar and pectin). Also known as cerebrose.

galactosidase [BIOCHEM] An enzyme that hydrolyzes galactosides.

galactoside [BIOCHEM] A glycoside formed by the reaction of galactose with an alcohol; yields galactose on hydrolysis.

galacturonic acid [BIOCHEM] The monobasic acid resulting from oxidation of the primary alcohol group of D-galactose to carboxyl; it is widely distributed as a constituent of pectins and many plant gums and mucilages.

galago See bushbaby.

Galatheidea [INV ZOO] A group of decapod crustaceans belonging to the Anomura and having a symmetrical abdomen bent upon itself and a well-developed tail fan.

Galaxioidei [VERT ZOO] A suborder of mostly small, fresh-water fishes in the order Salmoniformes.

Galbulidae [VERT ZOO] The jacamars, a family of highly iridescent birds of the order Piciformes that resemble giant hummingbirds.

galea [ANAT] The epicranial aponeurosis linking the occipital and frontal muscles. [BIOL] A helmet-shaped structure. [BOT] A helmet-shaped petal near the axis. [INV ZOO] **1.** The endopodite of the maxilla of certain insects. **2.** A spinning organ on the movable digit of chelicerae of pseudoscorpions.

galeate [BIOL] **1.** Shaped like a helmet. **2.** Having a galea.

Galen's vein [ANAT] One of the two veins running along the roof of the third ventricle that drain the interior of the brain.

Galeritidae [PALEON] A family of extinct exocyclic Euechinoidea in the order Holectypoida, characterized by large ambulacral plates with small, widely separated pore pairs.

gall [PHYSIO] See bile. [PL PATH] A large swelling on plant tissues caused by the invasion of parasites, such as fungi or bacteria, following puncture by an insect; insect oviposit and larvae of insects are found in galls.

gallbladder [ANAT] A hollow, muscular organ in humans and most vertebrates which receives dilute bile from the liver, concentrates it, and discharges it into the duodenum.

galleria forest [ECOL] A modified tropical deciduous forest occurring along stream banks.

Galleriinae [INV ZOO] A monotypic subfamily of lepidopteran insects in the family Pyralididae; contains the bee moth or wax worm (*Galleria* *mellonella*), which lives in beehives and whose larvae feed on beeswax.

gallicolous [BIOL] Producing or inhabiting galls.

Galliformes [VERT ZOO] An order of birds that includes important domestic and game birds, such as turkeys, pheasants, and quails.

gallinaceous [VERT ZOO] Of, pertaining to, or resembling birds of the order Galliformes.

Gallionella [MICROBIO] A genus of appendaged bacteria; cells are kidney-shaped or rounded and occur on stalks; reproduce by binary fission.

gallivorous [ZOO] Feeding on the tissues of galls, especially certain insect larvae.

gallnut [PL PATH] A gall resembling a nut.

gallodesoxycholic acid *See* chenodeoxycholic acid.

Galumnidae [INV ZOO] A family of oribatid mites in the suborder Sarcoptiformes.

galvanic skin response [PHYSIO] The electrical reactions of the skin to any stimulus as detected by a sensitive galvanometer; most often used experimentally to measure the resistance of the skin to the passage of a weak electric current.

galvanism [BIOL] The use of a galvanic current for medical or biological purposes.

galvanotaxis [BIOL] Movement of a free-living organism in response to an electrical stimulus.

galvanotropism [BIOL] Response of an organism to electrical stimulation.

game bird [BIOL] A bird that is legal quarry for hunters.

Gamella [MICROBIO] A genus of bacteria in the family Streptococcaceae; spherical cells occurring singly or in pairs with flattened adjacent sides; ferment glucose.

gametangial copulation [MYCOL] Direct fusion of certain fungal gametangia without differentiation of the gametes.

gamete [BIOL] A mature germ cell.

gametic copulation [MYCOL] The fusion of pairs of differentiated, uninucleate sexual cells or gametes formed in specialized gametangia.

gametocyte [HISTOL] An undifferentiated cell from which gametes are produced.

gametogenesis [BIOL] The formation of gametes, or reproductive cells such as ova or sperm.

gametophore [BOT] A branch that bears gametangia.

gametophyte [BOT] 1. The haploid generation producing gametes in plants exhibiting metagenesis. 2. An individual plant of this generation.

Gammaridea [INV ZOO] The scuds or sand hoppers, a suborder of amphipod crustaceans; individuals are usually compressed laterally, are poor walkers, and lack a carapace.

gamma taxonomy [SYST] The level of taxonomic study concerned with biological aspects of taxa, including intraspecific populations, speciation, and evolutionary rates and trends.

gamodeme [ECOL] An isolated breeding community.

gamogony [INV ZOO] Spore formation by multiple fission in sporozoans. [ZOO] Sexual reproduction.

gamont [INV ZOO] The gametocyte of sporozoans.

gamopetalous [BOT] Having petals united at their edges. Also known as sympetalous.

gamophyllous [BOT] Having the leaves of the perianth united.

gamosepalous [BOT] Having sepals united at their edges. Also known as synsepalous.

Gampsonychidae [PALEON] A family of extinct crustaceans in the order Palaeocaridacea.

gangliated cord [ANAT] One of the two main trunks of the sympathetic nervous system, one trunk running along each side of the spinal column.

ganglion [ANAT] A group of nerve cell bodies, usually located outside the brain and spinal cord.

ganglioside [BIOCHEM] One of a group of glycosphingolipids found in neuronal surface membranes and spleen; they contain an N-acyl fatty acid derivative of sphingosine linked to a carbohydrate (glucose or galactose); they also contain N-acetylglucosamine or N-acetylgalactosamine, and N-acetylneuraminic acid.

ganoid scale [VERT ZOO] A structure having several layers of enamellike material (ganoin) on the upper surface and laminated bone below.

ganoin [VERT ZOO] The enamellike covering of a ganoid scale.

gap [GEN] A short region that is missing in one strand of a double-stranded deoxyribonucleic acid.

gape [ANAT] The margin to margin distance between open jaws. [INV ZOO] The space between the margins of a closed mollusk valve.

gar [VERT ZOO] The common name for about seven species of bony fishes in the order Semionotiformes having a slim form, an elongate snout, and close-set ganoid scales.

garigue [ECOL] A low, open scrubland restricted to limestone sites in the Mediterranean area; characterized by small evergreen shrubs and low trees.

garlic [BOT] *Allium sativum.* A perennial plant of the order Liliales grown for its pungent, edible bulbs.

Gartner's duct [ANAT] The remnant of the embryonic Wolffian duct in the adult female mammal.

gas gland [VERT ZOO] A structure inside the swim bladder of many teleosts which secretes gas into the bladder.

Gasserian ganglion [ANAT] A group of nerve cells of the sensory root of the trigeminal nerve. Also known as semilunar ganglion.

gas sterilization [MICROBIO] Sterilization of heat and liquid-labile materials by means of gaseous agents, such as formaldehyde, ethylene oxide, and β-propiolactone.

Gasteromycetes [MYCOL] A group of basidiomycetous fungi in the subclass Homobasidiomycetidae with enclosed basidia and basidiospores borne symmetrically on long sterigmata and not forcibly discharged.

Gasterophilidae [INV ZOO] The horse bots, a family of myodarian cyclorrhaphous dipteran insects in the subsection Calypteratae, including individuals that cause myiasis in horses.

Gasterophilus [INV ZOO] A large genus of botflies in the family Gasterophilidae.

Gasterosteidae [VERT ZOO] The sticklebacks, a family of actinopterygian fishes in the order Gasterosteiformes.

Gasterosteiformes [VERT ZOO] An order of actinopterygian fishes characterized by a ductless swim bladder, a pelvic fin that is abdominal in subthoracic in position, and an elongate snout.

Gasteruptiidae [INV ZOO] A family of hymenopteran insects in the superfamily Proctotrupoidea.

gastralium [INV ZOO] A microsclere located just beneath the inner cell layer of hexactinellid sponges. [VERT ZOO] One of the riblike structures in the abdomen of certain reptiles.

gastric acid [BIOCHEM] Hydrochloric acid secreted by parietal cells in the fundus of the stomach.

gastric cecum [INV ZOO] One of the elongated pouchlike projections of the upper end of the stomach in insects.

gastric enzyme [BIOCHEM] Any digestive enzyme secreted by cells lining the stomach.

gastric filament [INV ZOO] In scyphozoans, a row of filaments on the surface of the gastric cavity which function to kill or paralyze live prey taken into the stomach. Also known as phacella.

gastric gland [ANAT] Any of the glands in the wall of the stomach that secrete components of the gastric juice.

gastric juice [PHYSIO] The digestive fluid secreted by gastric glands; contains gastric acid and enzymes.

gastric mill [INV ZOO] A grinding apparatus consisting of calcareous or chitinous plates in the pharynx or stomach of certain invertebrates.

gastric ostium [INV ZOO] The opening into the gastric pouch in scyphozoans.

gastric pouch [INV ZOO] One of the pouchlike diversions of a scyphozoan stomach.

gastric shield [INV ZOO] A thickening of the stomach wall in some mollusks for mixing the contents.

gastrin [BIOCHEM] A polypeptide hormone secreted by the pyloric mucosa which stimulates the pancreas to release pancreatic fluid and the stomach to release gastric acid.

gastroblast [INV ZOO] A feeding zooid of a tunicate colony.

gastrocnemius [ANAT] A large muscle of the posterior aspect of the leg, arising by two heads from the posterior surfaces of the lateral and medial condyles of the femur, and inserted with the soleus muscle into the calcaneal tendon, and through this into the back of the calcaneus.

gastrocoele *See* archenteron.

gastrodermis [INV ZOO] The cellular lining of the digestive cavity of certain invertebrates.

gastroepiploic artery [ANAT] Either of two arteries arising from the gastroduodenal and splenic arteries respectively and forming an anastomosis along the greater curvature of the stomach.

gastrointestinal hormone [BIOCHEM] Any hormone secreted by the gastrointestinal system.

gastrointestinal system [ANAT] The portion of the digestive system including the stomach, intestine, and all accessory organs.

gastrointestinal tract [ANAT] The stomach and intestine.

gastrolith [VERT ZOO] A pebble swallowed by certain animals and retained in the gizzard or stomach, where it serves to grind food.

Gastromyzontidae [VERT ZOO] A small family of actinopterygian fishes of the suborder Cyprinoidei found in southeastern Asia.

Gastropoda [INV ZOO] A large, morphologically diverse class of the phylum Mollusca, containing the snails, slugs, limpets, and conchs.

gastropore [INV ZOO] A pore containing a gastrozooid in hydrozoan corals.

gastrosplenic ligament [ANAT] The fold of peritoneum passing from the stomach to the spleen. Also known as gastrosplenic omentum.

gastrostome [INV ZOO] The opening of a gastropore.

gastrostyle [INV ZOO] A spiculated projection that extends into the gastrozooid from the base of the gastropore.

Gastrotricha [INV ZOO] A group of microscopic, pseudocoelomate animals considered either to be a class of the Aschelminthes or to constitute a separate phylum.

gastrozooid [INV ZOO] A nutritive polyp of colonial coelenterates, characterized by having tentacles and a mouth.

gastrula [EMBRYO] The stage of development in animals in which the endoderm is formed and invagination of the blastula has occurred.

gastrulation [EMBRYO] The process by which the endoderm is formed during development.

gas vacuole [BIOL] A membrane-bound, gas-filled cavity in some algae and protozoans; thought to control buoyancy.

Gaultheria [BOT] A genus of upright or creeping evergreen shrubs (Ericaceae).

Gause's principle [ECOL] A statement that two species cannot occupy the same niche simultaneously. Also known as competitive exclusion principle.

gavial [VERT ZOO] The name for two species of reptiles composing the family Gavialidae.

Gavialidae [VERT ZOO] The gavials, a family of reptiles in the order Crocodilia distinguished by an extremely long, slender snout with an enlarged tip.

Gaviidae [VERT ZOO] The single, monogeneric family of the order Gaviiformes.

Gaviiformes [VERT ZOO] The loons, a monofamilial order of diving birds characterized by webbed feet, compressed, bladelike tarsi, and a heavy, pointed bill.

Gecarcinidae [INV ZOO] The true land crabs, a family of decapod crustaceans belonging to the Brachygnatha.

gecko [VERT ZOO] The common name for more than 300 species of arboreal and nocturnal reptiles composing the family Gekkonidae.

geitonogamy [BOT] Pollination and fertilization of one flower by another on the same plant.

Gekkonidae [VERT ZOO] The geckos, a family of small lizards in the order Squamata distinguished by a flattened body, a long sensitive tongue, and adhesive pads on the toes of many species.

Gelastocoridae [INV ZOO] The toad bugs, a family of tropical and subtropical hemipteran insects in the subdivision Hydrocorisae.

gelatinase [BIOCHEM] An enzyme, found in some yeasts and molds, that liquefies gelatin.

gelatin liquefaction [MICROBIO] Reduction of a gelatin culture medium to the liquid state by enzymes produced by bacteria in a stab culture; used in identifying bacteria.

Gelechiidae [INV ZOO] A large family of minute to small moths in the lepidopteran superfamily Tineoidea, generally having forewings and trapezoidal hindwings.

Gelocidae [PALEON] A family of extinct pecoran ruminants in the superfamily Traguloidea.

geminate [BIOL] Growing in pairs or couples.

geminiflorous [BOT] Having flowers in pairs.

gemma [BOT] A small, multicellular, asexual reproductive body of some liverworts and mosses.

gemmation See budding.

gemmiform [BOT] Resembling a gemma or bud.

gemmiparous [BIOL] Producing a bud or reproducing by a bud.

gemmule [ANAT] A minute dendritic process functioning as a synaptic contact point. [BIOL] Any bud formed by gemmation. [INV ZOO] A cystlike, asexual reproductive structure of many Porifera that germinates when proper environmental conditions exist; it is a protective, overwintering structure which germinates the following spring.

Gempylidae [VERT ZOO] The snake mackerels, a family of the suborder Scombroidei comprising compressed, elongate, or eel-shaped spiny-rayed fishes with caniniform teeth.

Gemuendinoidei [PALEON] A suborder of extinct raylike placoderm fishes in the order Rhenanida.

gena [ANAT] Cheek, or side of the head.

gene [GEN] The basic unit of inheritance.

gene action [GEN] The functioning of a gene in determining the phenotype of an individual.

genecology [BIOL] The study of species and their genetic subdivisions, their place in nature, and the genetic and ecological factors controlling speciation.

gene conversion [GEN] A situation in which gametocytes of an individual that is heterozygous for a pair of alleles undergo meiosis, and the gametes produced are in a 3:1 ratio rather than the expected 2:2 ratio, implying that one allele was converted to the other.

gene flow [GEN] The passage and establishment of genes characteristic of a breeding population into the gene complex of another population through hybridization and backcrossing.

gene frequency [GEN] The number of occurrences of a specific gene within a population.

gene library [GEN] A random collection of cloned deoxyribonucleic acid fragments in a vector; includes all the genetic information of the species.

gene pool [GEN] The totality of the genes of a specific population at a given time.

generation [BIOL] A group of organisms having a common parent or parents and comprising a single level in line of descent.

generation time [MICROBIO] The time interval required for a bacterial cell to divide or for the population to double.

gene redundancy [GEN] The presence of many copies of one gene within a cell.

generic [BIOL] Pertaining to or having the rank of a biological genus.

gene suppression [GEN] The development of a normal phenotype in a mutant individual or cell due to a second mutation either in the same gene or in a different gene.

genet [VERT ZOO] The common name for nine species of small, arboreal African carnivores in the family Viverridae.

genetic code [MOL BIO] The genetic information in the nucleotide sequences in deoxyribonucleic acid represented by a four-letter alphabet that makes up a vocabulary of 64 three-nucleotide sequences, or codons; a sequence of such codons (averaging about 100 codons) constructs a message for a polypeptide chain.

genetic drift [GEN] The random fluctuation of gene frequencies from generation to generation that occurs in small populations.

genetic engineering [GEN] The intentional production of new genes and alteration of genomes by the substitution or addition of new genetic material.

genetic fingerprinting [MOL BIO] Identification of chemical entities in animal tissues as indicative of the presence of specific genes.

genetic homeostasis [GEN] The tendency of Mendelian populations to maintain a constant genetic composition.

genetic load [GEN] The abnormalities, deformities, and deaths produced in every generation by defective genetic material carried in the gene pool of the human race.

genetic map [GEN] A graphic presentation of the linear arrangement of genes on a chromosome; gene positions are determined by percentages of recombination in linkage experiments. Also known as chromosome map.

genetic material [GEN] The ultramicroscopic particles or genes, first defined by H. J. Muller, the influences of which permeate the cell and play a fundamental role in determining the nature of all cell substances, cell structures, and cell effects; the genes have properties of self-propagation and variation.

genetics [BIOL] The science that is concerned with the study of biological inheritance.

genial See mental.

genic hybrid sterility [GEN] Sterility resulting from the interaction of genes in a hybrid to cause disturbances of sex-cell formation or meiosis.

geniculate body [ANAT] Any of the four oval, flattened prominences on the posterior inferior aspect of the thalamus; functions as the synaptic center for fibers leading to the cerebral cortex.

geniculate ganglion [ANAT] A mass of sensory and sympathetic nerve cells located along the facial nerve.

geniculum [ANAT] 1. A small, kneelike, anatomical structure. 2. A sharp bend in any small organ.

genioglossus [ANAT] An extrinsic muscle of the tongue, arising from the superior mental spine of the mandible.

Geniohyidae [PALEON] A family of extinct ungulate mammals in the order Hyracoidea; all members were medium to large-sized animals with long snouts.

genital atrium [ZOO] A common chamber receiving openings of male, female, and accessory organs.

genital coelom [INV ZOO] In mollusks, the lumina of the gonads.

genital cord [EMBRYO] A mesenchymal shelf bridging the coeloms in mammalian embryos, produced by fusion of the caudal part of the urogenital folds; fuses with the urinary bladder in the male, and is the primordium of the broad ligament and the uterine walls in the female.

genital cord [INV ZOO] Strands of cells located in the genital canal which are primordial sex cells in crinoids. Also known as genital rachis.

genitalia [ANAT] The organs of reproduction, especially those which are external.

genital orifice *See* genital pore.

genital pore [INV ZOO] A small opening on the side of the head in some gastropods through which the penis is protruded. Also known as genital orifice.

genital recess [INV ZOO] A depression between the calyx surface and anal cone in entoprocts which serves as a brood chamber.

genital ridge [EMBRYO] A medial ridge or fold on the ventromedial surface of the mesonephros in the embryo, produced by growth of the peritoneum; the primordium of the gonads and their ligaments.

genital scale [INV ZOO] Any of the small calcareous plates in ophiuroids associated with the buccal shields.

genital segment *See* gonosomite.

genital shield [INV ZOO] In ophiuroids, a support of a bursal slit in the arms located near the arm base.

genital stolon [INV ZOO] Part of the axial complex in ophiuroids.

genital sucker [INV ZOO] In some trematodes, a suckerlike structure surrounding the gonopore.

genital tract [ANAT] The ducts of the reproductive system.

genital tube [INV ZOO] A blood lacuna in crinoids, connected with the subtegminal plexus and suspended in the genital canal.

genitourinary system *See* urogenital system.

genome [GEN] 1. The genetic endowment of a species. 2. The haploid set of chromosomes.

genotype [GEN] The genetic constitution of an organism, usually in respect to one gene or a few genes relevant in a particular context. [SYST] The type species of a genus.

gentamicin [MICROBIO] A broad-spectrum antibiotic produced by a species of *Micromonospora*.

Gentianaceae [BOT] A family of dicotyledonous herbaceous plants in the order Gentianales distinguished by lacking stipules and having parietal placentation.

Gentianales [BOT] A family of dicotyledonous plants in the subclass Asteridae having well-developed internal phloem and opposite, simple, mostly entire leaves.

genu *See* knee.

genus [SYST] A taxonomic category that includes groups of closely related species; the principal subdivision of a family.

geobotany [BOT] The study of plants as related to their geologic environment.

Geocorisae [INV ZOO] A subdivision of hemipteran insects containing those land bugs with conspicuous antennae and an ejaculatory bulb in the male.

Geodermatophilus [MICROBIO] A genus of bacteria in the family Dermatophilaceae; the mycelium is rudimentary and a muriform thallus is produced; motile spores are elliptical to lanceolate.

geographic speciation [EVOL] Evolution of two or more species from a single species following geographic isolation.

Geometridae [INV ZOO] A large family of lepidopteran insects in the superfamily Geometroidea that have slender bodies and relatively broad wings; includes measuring worms, loopers, and cankerworms.

Geometroidea [INV ZOO] A superfamily of lepidopteran insects in the suborder Heteroneura comprising small to large moths with reduced maxillary palpi and tympanal organs at the base of the abdomen.

Geomyidae [VERT ZOO] The pocket gophers, a family of rodents characterized by fur-lined cheek pouches which open outward, a stout body with short legs, and a broad, blunt head.

geophagous [ZOO] Feeding on soil, as certain worms.

Geophilomorpha [INV ZOO] An order of centipedes in the class Chilopoda including specialized forms that are blind, epimorphic, and dorsoventrally flattened.

geophilous [ECOL] Living or growing in or on the ground.

geophyte [ECOL] A perennial plant that is deeply embedded in the soil substrata.

Georyssidae [INV ZOO] The minute mud-loving beetles, a family of coleopteran insects belonging to the Polyphaga.

Geosiridaceae [BOT] A monotypic family of monocotyledonous plants in the order Orchidales characterized by regular flowers with three stamens that are opposite the sepals.

Geospizinae [VERT ZOO] Darwin finches, a subfamily of perching birds in the family Fringillidae.

geotaxis [PHYSIO] Movement of a free-living organism in response to the stimulus of gravity.

geotropism [BOT] Response of a plant to the force of gravity.

Gephyrea [INV ZOO] A class of burrowing worms in the phylum Annelida.

gephyrocercal [VERT ZOO] Having the dorsal and anal fins coming together smoothly at the aborted end of the vertebral column of a fish's tail.

Geraniaceae [BOT] A family of dicotyledonous plants in the order Geraniales in which the fruit is beaked, styles are usually united, and the leaves have stipules.

Geraniales [BOT] An order of dicotyledonous plants in the subclass Rosidae comprising herbs or soft shrubs with a superior ovary and with compound or deeply cleft leaves.

Geranium [BOT] A genus of plants in the family Geraniaceae characterized by regular flowers, and glands alternating with the petals.

Gerardiidae [INV ZOO] A family of anthozoans in the order Zoanthidea.

gerbil [VERT ZOO] The common name for about 100 species of African and Asian rodents composing the subfamily Gerbillinae.

Gerbillinae [VERT ZOO] The gerbils, a subfamily of rodents in the family Muridae characterized by hindlegs that are longer than the front ones, and a long, slightly haired, usually tufted tail.

germ [BIOL] A primary source, especially one from which growth and development are expected. [MICROBIO] General designation for a microorganism.

germarium [INV ZOO] The egg-producing portion of an ovary and the sperm-producing portion of a testis in Platyhelminthes and Rotifera.

germ ball [INV ZOO] A group of cells in digenetic trematode miracidial larvae which are embryos.

germ cell [BIOL] An egg or sperm or one of their antecedent cells.

germfree animal [MICROBIO] An animal having no demonstrable, viable microorganisms living in intimate association with it.

germfree isolator [MICROBIO] An apparatus that provides a mechanical barrier surrounding the area in which germfree vertebrates and accessory equipment are housed.

germinal epithelium [EMBRYO] The region of the dorsal coelomic epithelium lying between the dorsal mesentery and the mesonephros.

germinal vesicle [CELL BIO] The enlarged nucleus of the primary oocyte before reduction divisions are complete.

germination [BOT] The beginning or the process of development of a spore or seed.

germ layer [EMBRYO] One of the primitive cell layers which appear in the early animal embryo and from which the embryo body is constructed.

germ-layer theory [EMBRYO] The theory that three primary germ layers, ectoderm, mesoderm, and endoderm, are established in the early embryo and all organs and structures are derived from a specific germ layer.

germovitellarium [INV ZOO] A sex gland which differentiates into a yolk-producing or egg-producing region.

gerontology [PHYSIO] The scientific study of aging processes in biological systems, particularly in humans.

Gerrhosauridae [VERT ZOO] A small family of lizards in the suborder Sauria confined to Africa and Madagascar.

Gerridae [INV ZOO] The water striders, a family of hemipteran insects in the subdivision Amphibicorisae having long middle and hind legs and a median scent gland opening on the metasternum.

Gerroidea [INV ZOO] The single superfamily of the hemipteran subdivision Amphibicorisae; all members have conspicuous antennae and hydrofuge hairs covering the body.

Gesneriaceae [BOT] A family of dicotyledonous plants in the order Scrophulariales characterized by parietal placentation, mostly opposite or whorled leaves, and a well-developed embryo.

gestate [EMBRYO] To carry the young in the uterus from conception to delivery.

gestation period [EMBRYO] The period in mammals from fertilization to birth.

ghost spot [PL PATH] A disease of tomato characterized by small white rings on the fruit.

Giardia [INV ZOO] A genus of zooflagellates that inhabit the intestine of numerous vertebrates, and may cause diarrhea in humans.

gibberellic acid [BIOCHEM] $C_{18}H_{22}O_6$ A crystalline acid occurring in plants that is similar to the gibberellins in its growth-promoting effects.

gibberellin [BIOCHEM] Any member of a family of naturally derived compounds which have a gibbane skeleton and a broad spectrum of biological activity but are noted as plant growth regulators.

gibbon [VERT ZOO] The common name for seven species of large, tailless primates belonging to the genus *Hylobates*; the face and ears are hairless, and the arms are longer than the legs.

Giganturoidei [VERT ZOO] A suborder of small, mesopelagic actinopterygian fishes in the order Cetomimiformes having large mouths and strong teeth.

Gila monster [VERT ZOO] The common name for two species of reptiles in the genus *Heloderma* (Helodermatidae) distinguished by a rounded body that is covered with multicolored beaded tubercles, and a bifid protrusible tongue.

gill [VERT ZOO] The respiratory organ of water-breathing animals. Also known as branchia.

gill cover [VERT ZOO] The fold of skin providing external protection for the gill apparatus of most fishes; it may be stiffened by bony plates and covered with scales.

gill raker [VERT ZOO] One of the bony processes on the inside of the branchial arches of fishes which prevents the passage of solid substances through the branchial clefts.

ginger [BOT] *Zingiber officinale*. An erect perennial herb of the family Zingiberaceae having thick, scaly branched rhizomes; a spice oleoresin is made by an organic solvent extraction of the ground dried rhizome.

gingiva [ANAT] The mucous membrane surrounding the teeth sockets.

gingival crevice [ANAT] The space between the free margin of the gingiva and the surface of a tooth. Also known as gingival sulcus.

gingival sulcus *See* gingival crevice.

ginglymoarthrodia [ANAT] A composite joint consisting of one hinged and one gliding element.

Ginglymodi [VERT ZOO] An equivalent name for Semionotiformes.

ginglymus [ANAT] A type of diarthrosis permitting motion only in one plane. Also known as hinge joint.

Ginkgoales [BOT] An order of gymnosperms composing the class Ginkgoopsida with one living species, the dioecious maidenhair tree (*Ginkgo biloba*).

Ginkgoopsida [BOT] A class of the subdivision Pinicae containing the single, monotypic order Ginkgoales.

Ginkgophyta [BOT] The equivalent name for Ginkgoopsida.

ginseng [BOT] The common name for plants of the genus *Panax*, a group of perennial herbs in the family Araliaceae; the aromatic root of the plant has been used medicinally in China.

giraffe [VERT ZOO] *Giraffa camelopardalis*. An artiodactyl mammal in the family Giraffidae characterized by extreme elongation of the neck vertebrae, and two prominent horns on the head.

Giraffidae [VERT ZOO] A family of pecoran ruminants in the superfamily Bovoidea including giraffe, okapi, and relatives.

girdle [ANAT] Either of the ringlike groups of bones supporting the forelimbs (arms) and hindlimbs (legs) in vertebrates. [INV ZOO] 1. Either of the hooplike bands constituting the sides of the two valves of a diatom. 2. The peripheral portion of the mantle in chitons.

gizzard [VERT ZOO] The muscular portion of the stomach of most birds where food is ground with the aid of ingested pebbles.

glabella [ANAT] The bony prominence on the frontal bone joining the supraorbital ridges.

glabrous [BIOL] Having a smooth surface; specifically, having the epidermis devoid of hair or down.

gladiate [BOT] Sword-shaped.

gladiolus *See* mesosternum.

Gladiolus [BOT] A genus of chiefly African plants in the family Iridaceae having erect, sword-shaped leaves and spikes of brightly colored irregular flowers.

gland [ANAT] A structure which produces a substance essential and vital to the existence of the organism.

glands of Brunner *See* Brunner's glands.

glands of Leydig [VERT ZOO] Unicellular, epidermal structures of urodele larvae and the adult *Necturus* that secrete a substance which digests the egg capsule and permits hatching.

glandulomuscular [ANAT] Of or pertaining to glands and muscles.

glans [ANAT] The conical body forming the distal end of the clitoris or penis.

Glareolidae [VERT ZOO] A family of birds in the order Charadriiformes including the ploverlike coursers and the swallowlike pratincoles.

glareous [ECOL] Growing in gravelly soil; refers specifically to plants.

glass sponge [INV ZOO] A siliceous sponge belonging to the class Hyalospongiae.

glaucous [BOT] Having a white or grayish powdery coating that gives a frosty appearance and rubs off easily.

gleba [MYCOL] The central, sporogenous tissue of the sporophore in certain basidiomycetous fungi.

glenoid [ANAT] A smooth, shallow, socketlike depression, particularly of the skeleton.

glenoid cavity [ANAT] The articular surface on the scapula for articulation with the head of the humerus.

gliding bacteria [MICROBIO] The descriptive term for members of the orders Beggiatoales and Myxobacterales; they are motile by means of creeping movements.

gliding joint *See* arthrodia.

gliding motility [MICROBIO] A means of bacterial self-propulsion by slow gliding or creeping movements on the surface of a substrate.

gliotoxin [MICROBIO] $C_{13}H_{14}O_4N_2S_2$ A heat-labile, bacteriostatic antibiotic produced by species of *Trichoderma* and *Cliocladium* and by *Aspergillus fumigatus*.

Gliridae [VERT ZOO] The dormice, a family of mammals in the order Rodentia.

Glisson's capsule [ANAT] The membranous sheet of collagenous and elastic fibers covering the liver.

Globigerinacea [INV ZOO] A superfamily of foraminiferan protozoans in the suborder Rotaliina characterized by a radial calcite test with bilamellar septa and a large aperture.

globin [BIOCHEM] Any of a class of soluble histone proteins obtained from animal hemoglobins.

globoside [BIOCHEM] A glycoside of ceramide containing several sugar residues, but not neuraminic acid; obtained from human, sheep, and hog erythrocytes.

globular deoxyribonucleic acid [MOL BIO] A compact arrangement of double-stranded deoxyribonucleic acid formed by additional twisting of the fiber into a helical double helix.

globular protein [BIOCHEM] Any protein that is readily soluble in aqueous solvents.

globulin [BIOCHEM] A heat-labile serum protein precipitated by 50% saturated ammonium sulfate and soluble in dilute salt solutions.

glochid *See* glochidium.

glochidium [BOT] A barbed hair. Also known as glochid. [INV ZOO] The larva of fresh-water mussels in the family Unionidae.

gloea [INV ZOO] An adhesive mucoid substance secreted by certain protozoans and other lower organisms.

glomerulus [ANAT] A tuft of capillary loops projecting into the lumen of a renal corpuscle.

glomus [ANAT] 1. A fold of the mesothelium arising near the base of the mesentery in the pronephros and containing a ball of blood vessels.

2. A prominent portion of the choroid plexus of the lateral ventricle of the brain.

glomus aorticum See paraaortic body.

glomus caroticum See carotid body.

glossa [INV ZOO] A tongue or tonguelike structure in insects, especially the median projection of the labium.

glossate [INV ZOO] Having a glossa or tonguelike structure.

Glossinidae [INV ZOO] The tsetse flies, a family of cyclorrhaphous dipteran insects in the section Pupipara.

Glossiphoniidae [INV ZOO] A family of small leeches with flattened bodies in the order Rhynchobdellae.

glossopalatine nerve [ANAT] The intermediate branch of the facial nerve.

glossopharyngeal nerve [ANAT] The ninth cranial nerve in vertebrates; a paired mixed nerve that supplies autonomic innervation to the parotid gland and contains sensory fibers from the posterior one-third of the tongue and the anterior pharynx.

glossopterid flora [PALEOBOT] Permian and Triassic fossil ferns of the genus *Glossopteris.*

glottis [ANAT] The opening between the margins of the vocal folds.

glucagon [BIOCHEM] The protein hormone secreted by α-cells of the pancreas which plays a role in carbohydrate metabolism. Also known as hyperglycemic factor; hyperglycemic glycogenolytic factor.

glucamine [BIOCHEM] $C_6H_{15}O_4N$ An amine formed by reduction of glucosylamine or of glucose oxime.

glucan [BIOCHEM] A polysaccharide composed of the hexose sugar D-glucose.

glucocerebroside [BIOCHEM] A glycoside of ceramide that contains glucose.

glucocorticoid [BIOCHEM] A corticoid that affects glucose metabolism; secreted principally by the adrenal cortex.

glucogenesis [BIOCHEM] Formation of glucose within the animal body from products of glycolysis.

glucokinase [BIOCHEM] An enzyme that catalyzes the phosphorylation of D-glucose to glucose-6-phosphate.

glucolipid [BIOCHEM] A glycolipid that yields glucose on hydrolysis.

glucomannan [BIOCHEM] A polysaccharide composed of D-glucose and D-mannose; a prominent component of coniferous trees.

gluconeogenesis [BIOCHEM] Formation of glucose within the animal body from substances other than carbohydrates, particularly proteins and fats.

Gluconobacter [MICROBIO] A genus of bacteria in the family Pseudomonadaceae; ellipsoidal to rod-shaped cells having three to eight polar flagella and occurring singly, in pairs, or in chains.

D-glucopyranose See glucose.

glucopyranoside [BIOCHEM] Any glucoside that contains a six-membered ring.

glucosamine [BIOCHEM] $C_6H_{13}O_5$ An amino sugar; the most abundant in nature, occurring in glycoproteins and chitin.

glucose [BIOCHEM] $C_6H_{12}O_6$ A monosaccharide; occurs free or combined and is the most common sugar. Also known as cerelose; D-glucopyranose.

glucose-6-phosphatase [BIOCHEM] An enzyme found in liver which catalyzes the hydrolysis of glucose-6-phosphate to free glucose and inorganic phosphate.

glucose phosphate [BIOCHEM] A phosphoric derivative of glucose, as glucose-1-phosphate.

glucose-1-phosphate [BIOCHEM] $C_6H_{12}O_8P$ An ester of glucopyranose in which a phosphate group is attached to carbon atom 1; there are two types: α-D- and β-D-glucose-1-phosphates. Also known as Cori ester.

glucose-6-phosphate [BIOCHEM] $C_6H_{13}O_9P$ An ester of glucose with phosphate attached to carbon atom 6. Also known as Robisonester.

glucose-6-phosphate dehydrogenase [BIOCHEM] The mammalian enzyme that catalyzes the oxidation of glucose-6-phosphate by TPN+ (triphosphopyridine nucleotide).

glucosidase [BIOCHEM] An enzyme that hydrolyzes glucosidices.

glucoside [BIOCHEM] One of a group of compounds containing the cyclic forms of glucose, in which the hydrogen of the hemiacetal hydroxyl has been replaced by an alkyl or aryl group.

glucosyltransferase [BIOCHEM] An enzyme that catalyzes the glucosylation of hydroxymethyl cytosine; a constituent of bacteriophage deoxyribonucleic acid.

glucuronic acid [BIOCHEM] $C_6H_{10}O_7$ An acid resulting from oxidation of the CH_2OH radical of D-glucose to COOH; a component of many polysaccharides and certain vegetable gums. Also known as glycuronic acid.

glucuronidase [BIOCHEM] An enzyme that catalyzes hydrolysis of glucuronides. Also known as glycuronidase.

glucuronide [BIOCHEM] A compound resulting from the interaction of glucuronic acid with a phenol, an alcohol, or an acid containing a carboxyl group. Also known as glycuronide.

D-glucuronolactone [BIOCHEM] $C_6H_8O_6$ A water-soluble crystalline compound found in plant gums in polymers with other carbohydrates, and an important structural component of almost all fibrous and connective tissues in animals; used in medicine as an antiarthritic.

glue cell See adhesive cell.

glume [BOT] One of two bracts at the base of a spikelet of grass.

glumiferous [BOT] Bearing glumes.

Glumiflorae [BOT] An equivalent name for Cyperales.

glutamate [BIOCHEM] A salt or ester of glutamic acid.

glutamic acid [BIOCHEM] $C_5H_9O_4N$ A dicarboxylic amino acid of the α-ketoglutaric acid family occurring widely in proteins.

glutaminase [BIOCHEM] The enzyme which catalyzes the conversion of glutamine to glutamic acid and ammonia.

glutamine [BIOCHEM] $C_5H_{10}O_3N_2$ An amino acid; the monamide of glutamic acid; found in the juice of many plants and essential to the development of certain bacteria.

glutamine synthetase [BIOCHEM] An enzyme which catalyzes the formation of glutamine from glutamic acid and ammonia, using adenosinetriphosphate as a source of energy.

glutarate [BIOCHEM] The salt or ester of glutaric acid.

glutaric acid [BIOCHEM] $C_5H_5O_4$ A water-soluble, crystalline acid that occurs in green sugarbeets and in water extracts of crude wool.

glutathione [BIOCHEM] $C_{10}H_{17}O_6N_3S$ A widely distributed tripeptide that is important in plant and animal tissue oxidation reactions.

glutelin [BIOCHEM] A class of simple, heat-labile proteins occurring in seeds of cereals; soluble in dilute acids and alkalies.

gluten [BIOCHEM] 1. A mixture of proteins found in the seeds of cereals; gives dough elasticity and cohesiveness. 2. An albuminous element of animal tissue.

glutenin [BIOCHEM] A glutelin of wheat.

gluteus maximus [ANAT] The largest and most superficial muscle of the buttocks.

gluteus medius [ANAT] The muscle of the buttocks lying between the gluteus maximus and gluteus minimus.

gluteus minimus [ANAT] The smallest and deepest muscle of the buttocks.

glutinant nematocyst [INV ZOO] A nematocyst characterized by an open, sticky tube used for anchoring the coelenterate when walking on its tentacles.

glutinous [BOT] Having a sticky surface.

glycemia [PHYSIO] The presence of glucose in the blood.

glyceraldehyde [BIOCHEM] $CH_2OHCOHCHO$ A colorless solid, isomeric with dehydroxyacetone; soluble in water and insoluble in organic solvents; an important intermediate in carbohydrate metabolism; used as a chemical intermediate in biochemical research and nutrition. Also known as 2,3-dihydroxypropanal; glyceric aldehyde.

glycerate [BIOCHEM] A salt or ester of glyceric acid.

glyceric acid [BIOCHEM] $C_3H_6O_4$ A hydroxy acid obtained by oxidation of glycerin.

glyceric aldehyde See glyceraldehyde.

Glyceridae [INV ZOO] A family of polychaete annelids belonging to the Errantia and characterized by an enormous eversible proboscis.

glyceride [BIOCHEM] An ester of glycerin and an organic acid radical; fats are glycerides of certain long-chain fatty acids.

glycerokinase [BIOCHEM] An enzyme that catalyzes the phosphorylation of glycerol to glycerophosphate during microbial fermentation of propionic acid.

glycerophosphate [BIOCHEM] Any salt of glycerophosphoric acid.

glycerophosphoric acid [BIOCHEM] C_3H_5-$(OH)_2OPO_3H_2$ Either of two pale-yellow, water-soluble, isomeric dibasic acids occurring in nature in combined form as cephalin and lecithin.

glycine [BIOCHEM] $C_2H_5O_2N$ A white, crystalline amino acid found as a constituent of many proteins. Also known as aminoacetic acid.

glycocalyx [CELL BIO] The outer component of a cell surface, outside the plasmalemma; usually contains strongly acidic sugars, hence it carries a negative electric charge.

glycocholic acid [BIOCHEM] $C_{26}H_{43}NO_6$ A bile obtained by the conjugation of cholic acid with glycine.

glycocyamine [BIOCHEM] $C_3H_7N_3O_2$ A product of interaction of aminocetic acid and arginine, which on transmethylation with methionine is converted to creatine. Also known as guanidineacetic acid.

glycogen [BIOCHEM] A nonreducing, white, amorphous polysaccharide found as a reserve carbohydrate stored in muscle and liver cells of all higher animals, as well as in cells of lower animals.

glycogenesis [BIOCHEM] The metabolic formation of glycogen from glucose.

glycogenolysis [BIOCHEM] The metabolic breakdown of glycogen.

glycogen synthetase [BIOCHEM] An enzyme that catalyzes the synthesis of the amylose chain of glycogen.

glycolipid [BIOCHEM] Any of a class of complex lipids which contain carbohydrate residues.

glycolysis [BIOCHEM] The enzymatic breakdown of glucose or other carbohydrate, with the formation of lactic acid or pyruvic acid and the release of energy in the form of adenosinetriphosphate.

glycolytic pathway [BIOCHEM] The principal series of phosphorylative reactions involved in pyruvic acid production in phosphorylative fermentations. Also known as Embden-Meyerhof pathway; hexose diphosphate pathway.

glyconeogenesis [BIOCHEM] The metabolic process of glycogen formation from noncarbohydrate precursors.

glycopeptide See glycoprotein.

glycophyte [BOT] A plant requiring more than 0.5% sodium chloride solution in the substratum.

glycoprotein [BIOCHEM] Any of a class of conjugated proteins containing both carbohydrate and protein units. Also known as glycopeptide.

glycosidase [BIOCHEM] An enzyme that hydrolyzes a glycoside.

glycoside [BIOCHEM] A compound that yields on hydrolysis a sugar (glucose, galactose) and an aglycon; many of the glycosides are therapeutically valuable.

glycotropic [BIOCHEM] Acting to antagonize the action of insulin.

glycuresis [PHYSIO] Excretion of sugar seen normally in urine.

glycuronic acid See glucuronic acid.

glycuronidase See glucuronidase.

glycuronide See glucuronide.

glyoxalase [BIOCHEM] An enzyme present in various body tissues which catalyzes the conversion of methylglyoxal into lactic acid.

glyoxylate cycle [BIOCHEM] A sequence of biochemical reactions related to respiration in germinating fatty seeds by which acetyl coenzyme A is converted to succinic acid and then to hexose.

glyoxylic acid [BIOCHEM] $CH(OH)_2COOH$ An aldehyde acid found in many plant and animal tissues, especially unripe fruit.

Glyphocyphidae [PALEON] A family of extinct echinoderms in the order Temnopleuroida comprising small forms with a sculptured test, perforate crenulate tubercles, and diademoid ambulacral plates.

Glyptocrinina [PALEON] A suborder of extinct crinoids in the order Monobathrida.

GMP See guanylic acid.

gnat [INV ZOO] The common name for a large variety of biting insects in the order Diptera.

Gnathiidea [INV ZOO] A suborder of isopod crustaceans characterized by a much reduced second thoracomere, short antennules and antennae, and a straight pleon.

gnathion [VERT ZOO] The most anterior point of the premaxillae on or near the middle line in certain lower mammals.

gnathite [INV ZOO] A mouth appendage in arthropods.

Gnathobdellae [INV ZOO] A suborder of leeches in the order Arhynchobdellae having jaws and a conspicuous posterior sucker; contains most of the important blood-sucking leeches of humans and other warm-blooded animals.

Gnathobelodontinae [PALEON] A subfamily of extinct elephantoid proboscideans containing the shovel-jawed forms of the family Gomphotheriidae.

gnathocephalon [INV ZOO] The part of the insect head lying behind the protocephalon; bears the maxillae and mandibles.

gnathochilarium [INV ZOO] The lower lip of certain arthropods; thought to be fused maxillae.

Gnathodontidae [PALEON] A family of extinct conodonts having platforms with large, cup-shaped attachment scars.

gnathopod [INV ZOO] Any of the crustacean paired thoracic appendages modified for manipulation of food but sometimes functioning in copulatory amplexion.

gnathopodite [INV ZOO] A segmental, modified appendage which serves as a jaw in arthropods.

gnathos [INV ZOO] A mid-ventral plate on the ninth tergum in lepidopterans.

gnathostegite [INV ZOO] One of a pair of broad plates formed from the outer maxillipeds of some crustaceans, which function to cover other mouthparts.

Gnathostomata [INV ZOO] A suborder of echinoderms in the order Echinoidea characterized by a rigid, exocyclic test and a lantern or jaw apparatus. [VERT ZOO] A group of the subphylum Vertebrata which possess jaws and usually have paired appendages.

Gnathostomidae [INV ZOO] A family of parasitic nematodes in the superfamily Spiruroidea; sometimes placed in the superfamily Physalopteroidea.

Gnathostomulida [INV ZOO] Microscopic marine worms of uncertain systematic relationship, mainly characterized by cuticular structures in the pharynx and a monociliated skin epithelium.

gnathothorax [INV ZOO] The thorax and part of the head bearing feeding organs in arthropods, regarded as a primary region of the body.

Gnetales [BOT] A monogeneric order of the subdivision Gneticae; most species are lianas with opposite, oval, entire-margined leaves.

Gneticae [BOT] A subdivision of the division Pinophyta characterized by vessels in the secondary wood, ovules with two integuments, opposite leaves, and an embryo with two cotyledons.

Gnetophyta [BOT] The equivalent name for Gnetopsida.

Gnetopsida [BOT] A class of gymnosperms comprising the subdivision Gneticae.

Gnostidae [INV ZOO] An equivalent name for Ptinidae.

gnotobiology [BIOL] That branch of biology dealing with known living forms; the study of higher organisms in the absence of all demonstrable, viable microorganisms except those known to be present.

gnotobiote [MICROBIO] An individual (host) living in intimate association with another known species (microorganism). 2. The known microorganism living on a host.

gnu [VERT ZOO] Any of several large African antelopes of the genera *Connochaetes* and *Gorgon* having a large oxlike head with horns that characteristically curve downward and outward and then up, with the bases forming a frontal shield in older individuals.

goat [VERT ZOO] The common name for a number of artiodactyl mammals in the genus *Capra*; closely related to sheep but differing in having a lighter build and hollow, swept-back, sometimes spiral or twisted horns.

Goblatherlinae [PALEON] A subfamily of extinct herbivorous mammals in the family Uintatheriidae known from one late Eocene genus; characterized by extreme reduction of anterior dentition and by lack of horns.

Gobiesocidae [VERT ZOO] The single family of the order Gobiesociformes.

Gobiesociformes [VERT ZOO] The clingfishes, a monofamilial order of scaleless bony fishes equipped with a thoracic sucking disk which serves for attachment.

Gobiidae [VERT ZOO] A family of perciform fishes in the suborder Gobioidei characterized by pelvic fins united to form a sucking disk on the breast.

Gobioidei [VERT ZOO] The gobies, a suborder of morphologically diverse actinopterygian fishes in the order Perciformes; all lack a lateral line.

goblet cell [HISTOL] A unicellular, mucus-secreting intraepithelial gland that is distended on the free surface. Also known as chalice cell. [INV ZOO] Any of the unicellular choanocytes of the genus *Monosiga*.

Goldblatt unit [BIOL] A unit for the standardization of angiotonin.

golden algae [BOT] The common name for members of the class Chrysophyceae.

golden-brown algae [BOT] The common name for members of the division Chrysophyta.

goldfish [VERT ZOO] *Crassius auratus*. An orange cypriniform fish of the family Cyprinidae that can grow to over 18 inches (46 centimeters); closely related to the carps.

Golgi apparatus [CELL BIO] A cellular organelle that is part of the cytoplasmic membrane system; it is composed of regions of stacked cisternae and it functions in secretory processes.

Golgi cell [ANAT] 1. A nerve cell with long axons. 2. A nerve cell with short axons that branch repeatedly and terminate near the cell body.

Golgi-Mazzoni's corpuscle [ANAT] A small sensory lamellar corpuscle located in the parietal pleura.

Golgi tendon organ [PHYSIO] Any of the kinesthetic receptors situated near the junction of muscle fibers and a tendon which act as muscle-tension recorders.

Gomphidae [INV ZOO] A family of dragonflies belonging to the Anisoptera.

gomphosis [ANAT] An immovable articulation, as that formed by the insertion of teeth into the bony sockets.

Gomphotheriidae [PALEON] A family of extinct proboscidean mammals in the suborder Elephantoidea consisting of species with shoveling or digging specializations of the lower tusks.

Gomphotheriinae [PALEON] A subfamily of extinct elephantoid proboscideans in the family Gomphotheriidae containing species with long jaws and bunomastodont teeth.

gonad [ANAT] A primary sex gland; an ovary or a testis.

gonadotropic hormone [BIOCHEM] Either of two adenohypophyseal hormones, FSH (follicle-stimulating hormone) or ICSH (interstitial-cell-stimulating hormone), that act to stimulate the gonads.

gonadotropin [BIOCHEM] A substance that acts to stimulate the gonads.

gonapophysis [INV ZOO] A paired, modified appendage of the anal region in insects that functions in copulation, oviposition, or stinging.

Goniadidae [INV ZOO] A family of marine polychaete annelids belonging to the Errantia.

gonidium [BIOL] An asexual reproductive cell or group of cells arising in a special organ on or in a gametophyte.

gonimoblast [BOT] A filament arising from the fertilized carpogonium of most red algae.

Gonodactylidae [INV ZOO] A family of mantis shrimp in the order Stomatopoda.

gonodendrum [INV ZOO] A branched structure which bears clusters of gonophores.

gonopalpon [INV ZOO] Tentaclelike, sensitive structures associated with cnidarian gonophores.

gonophore [BOT] An elongation of the receptacle extending between the stamens and corolla. [INV ZOO] Reproductive zooid of a hydroid colony.

gonopodium [VERT ZOO] Anal fin modified as a copulatory organ in certain fishes.

Gonorhynchiformes [VERT ZOO] A small order of soft-rayed teleost fishes having fusiform or moderately compressed bodies, single short dorsal and anal fins, a forked caudal fin, and weak toothless jaws.

gonosome [INV ZOO] Aggregate of gonophores in a hydroid colony.

gonosomite [INV ZOO] The ninth segment of the abdomen of the male insect. Also known as genital segment.

gonostome [INV ZOO] The part of the genital duct of a coelomate invertebrate known as the coelomic funnel. Also known as coelomostome.

gonostyle [INV ZOO] Gonapophysis of dipteran insects.

gonotome [EMBRYO] The part of an embryonic somite involved in gonad formation.

gonozooid [INV ZOO] A zooid of bryozoans and tunicates which produces gametes.

gonyautoxin [BIOCHEM] One of a group of saxitoxin-related compounds that are produced by the dinoflagellates *Gonyaulax catenella* and *tamarensis*.

gonys [VERT ZOO] A ridge along the mid-ventral line of the lower mandible of certain birds.

goose [VERT ZOO] The common name for a number of waterfowl in the subfamily Anatinae; they are intermediate in size and features between ducks and swans.

gooseberry [BOT] The common name for about six species of thorny, spreading bushes of the genus *Ribes* in the order Rosales, producing small, acidic, edible fruit.

gooseneck barnacle [INV ZOO] Any stalked barnacle, especially of the genus *Lepas*.

gopher [VERT ZOO] The common name for North American rodents composing the family Geomyidae. Also known as pocket gopher.

Gordiidae [INV ZOO] A monogeneric family of worms in the order Gordioidea distinguished by a smooth cuticle.

Gordioidea [INV ZOO] An order of worms belonging to the Nematomorpha in which there is one ventral epidermal cord, a body cavity filled with mesenchymal tissue, and paired gonads.

gordioid larva [INV ZOO] The developmental stage of nematomorphs, free-living for a short time.

Gorgonacea [INV ZOO] The horny corals, an order of the coelenterate subclass Alcyonaria; colonies are fanlike or featherlike with branches spread radially or oppositely in one plane.

gorgonin [BIOCHEM] The protein, frequently containing iodine and bromine, composing the horny skeleton of members of the Gorgonacea; contains iodine and bromine.

Gorgonocephalidae [INV ZOO] A family of ophiuroid echinoderms in the order Phrynophiurida in which the individuals often have branched arms.

gorilla [VERT ZOO] *Gorilla gorilla*. An anthropoid ape, the largest living primate; the two African subspecies are the lowland gorilla and the mountain gorilla.

gossypose *See* raffinose.

Graafian follicle [HISTOL] The mature mammalian ovum with its surrounding epithelial cells.

Gracilariidae [INV ZOO] A family of small moths in the superfamily Tineoidea; both pairs of wings are lanceolate and widely fringed.

gracilis [ANAT] A long slender muscle on the medial aspect of the thigh.

graded topocline [ECOL] A topocline having a wide range, or ranging into different kinds of environment, thus subjecting its members to differential selection so that divergence between local races may become sufficient to warrant creation of varietal, or even specific, names.

graft [BIOL] **1.** To unite to form a graft. **2.** A piece of tissue transplanted from one individual to another or to a different place on the same individual. **3.** An individual resulting from the grafting of parts. [BOT] To unite a scion to an understock in such manner that the two grow together and continue development as a single plant without change in scion or stock.

Grahamella [MICROBIO] A genus of the family Bartonellaceae; intracellular parasites in red blood cells of rodents and other mammals.

grain [BOT] **1.** A rounded, granular prominence on the back of a sepal. **2.** *See* cereal; drupelet.

grain sorghum [BOT] *Sorghum bicolor.* A grass plant cultivated for its grain and to a lesser extent for forage. Also known as nonsaccharine sorghum.

gramagrass [BOT] Any grass of the genus *Bouteloua*; pasture grass.

gramicidin [MICROBIO] A polypeptide antibacterial antibiotic produced by *Bacillus brevis*; active locally against gram-positive bacteria.

Graminales [BOT] The equivalent name for Cyperales.

Gramineae [BOT] The grasses, a family of monocotyledonous plants in the order Cyperales characterized by distichously arranged flowers on the axis of the spikelet.

graminicolous [ECOL] Living upon grass.

graminivorous [ZOO] Feeding on grasses.

graminoid [BOT] Of or resembling the grasses.

gram-negative [MICROBIO] Of bacteria, decolorizing and staining with the counterstain when treated with Gram's stain.

gram-negative diplococci [MICROBIO] Three bacteriologic genera composing the family Neisseriaceae: *Gemella*, *Veillonella*, and *Neisseria*.

gram-positive [MICROBIO] Of bacteria holding the color of the primary stain when treated with Gram's stain.

Gram's stain [MICROBIO] A differential bacteriological stain; a fixed smear is stained with a slightly alkaline solution of basic dye, treated with a solution of iodine in potassium iodide, and then with a neutral decolorizing agent, and usually counterstained; bacteria stain either blue (gram-positive) or red (gram-negative).

gram-variable [MICROBIO] Pertaining to staining inconsistently with Gram's stain.

grana [CELL BIO] A multilayered membrane unit formed by stacks of the lobes or branches of a chloroplast thylakoid.

granite moss [BOT] The common name for a group of the class Bryatae represented by two

Arctic genera and distinguished by longitudinal splitting of the mature capsule into four valves.

Grantiidae [INV ZOO] A family of calcareous sponges in the order Sycettida.

granular gland [PHYSIO] A gland that produces and secretes a granular material.

granular leukocyte *See* granulocyte.

granulocyte [HISTOL] A leukocyte containing granules in the cytoplasm. Also known as granular leukocyte; polymorph; polymorphonuclear leukocyte.

Granuloreticulosia [INV ZOO] A subclass of the protozoan class Rhizopodea characterized by reticulopodia which often fuse into networks.

granulosis [INV ZOO] A virus disease of lepidopteran larvae characterized by the accumulation of small granular inclusion bodies (capsules) in the infected cells.

Granville wilt [PL PATH] A bacterial wilt of tobacco caused by *Pseudomonas solanacearum*.

grape [BOT] The common name for plants of the genus *Vitis* characterized by climbing stems with cylindrical-tapering tendrils and polygamodioecious flowers; grown for the edible, pulpy berries.

grapefruit [BOT] *Citrus paradisi.* An evergreen tree with a well-rounded top cultivated for its edible fruit, a large, globose citrus fruit characterized by a yellow rind and white, pink, or red pulp.

Graphidaceae [BOT] A family of mosses formerly grouped with lichenized Hysteriales but now included in the order Lecanorales; individuals have true paraphyses.

Graphiolaceae [MYCOL] A family of parasitic fungi in the order Ustilaginales in which teleutospores are produced in a cuplike fruiting body.

Grapsidae [INV ZOO] The square-backed crabs, a family of decapod crustaceans in the section Brachyura.

Graptolithina [PALEON] A class of extinct colonial animals believed to be related to the class Pterobranchia of the Hemichordata.

Graptoloidea [PALEON] An order of extinct animals in the class Graptolithina including branched, planktonic forms described from black shales.

Graptozoa [PALEON] The equivalent name for Graptolithina.

grass [BOT] The common name for all members of the family Gramineae; monocotyledonous plants having leaves that consist of a sheath which fits around the stem like a split tube, and a long, narrow blade.

grasserie [INV ZOO] A polyhedrosis disease of silkworms characterized by spotty yellowing of the skin and internal liquefaction. Also known as jaundice.

grasshopper [INV ZOO] The common name for a number of plant-eating orthopteran insects composing the subfamily Saltatoria; individuals have hindlegs adapted for jumping, and mouthparts adapted for biting and chewing.

grassland [ECOL] Any area of herbaceous terrestrial vegetation dominated by grasses and graminoid species.

gravid [ZOO] 1. Of the uterus, containing a fetus. 2. Pertaining to female animals when carrying young or eggs.

Gravigrada [VERT ZOO] The sloths, a group of herbivorous xenarthran mammals in the order Edentata; members are completely hairy and have five upper and four lower prismatic teeth without enamel.

gray blight [PL PATH] A fungus disease of tea caused by *Pestalotia (Pestalozzia) theae*, which invades the tissues and causes the formation of black dots on the leaves.

gray leaf spot [PL PATH] A fungus disease of tomatoes caused by *Stemphylium solani* and characterized by water-soaked brown spots on the leaves that become gray with age.

gray matter [HISTOL] The part of the central nervous system composed of nerve cell bodies, their dendrites, and the proximal and terminal unmyelinated portions of axons.

gray mold [PL PATH] Any fungus disease characterized by a gray surface appearance of the affected part.

gray scab [PL PATH] A fungus disease of willow caused by *Sphaceloma murrayae* and characterized by irregular raised leaf spots having grayish-white centers and dark-brown margins.

gray speck [PL PATH] A manganese-deficiency disease of oats characterized by light-green to grayish leaf spots, and later by the buff or light-brown discoloration of the blades.

graywall [PL PATH] A disease of tomatoes thought to be caused by excess sunlight and characterized by translucent grayish-brown streaks or blotches on the fruit and browning of the vascular strands.

graze [VERT ZOO] To feed by browsing on, cropping, and eating grass.

grease spot [PL PATH] A fungus disease of turf grasses caused by *Pythium aphanidermatum* and characterized by spots that have a greasy border of blackened leaves and intermingled cottony mycelia. Also known as spot blight.

greasewood [BOT] Any plant of the genus *Sarcobatus*, especially *S. vermiculatus*, which is a low shrub that grows in alkali soils of the western United States.

greater omentum [ANAT] A fold of peritoneum that is attached to the greater curvature of the stomach and hangs down over the intestine and fuses with the mesocolon.

grebe [VERT ZOO] The common name for members of the family Podicipedidae; these birds have legs set far posteriorly, compressed bladelike tarsi, individually broadened and lobed toes, and a rudimentary tail.

Greeffiellidae [INV ZOO] A superfamily of free-living nematodes in the order Desmoscolecoidea.

green algae [BOT] The common name for members of the plant division Chlorophyta.

green gland *See* antennal gland.

greenhouse [BOT] Glass-enclosed, climate-controlled structure in which young or out-of-season plants are cultivated and protected.

green mold [MYCOL] Any fungus, especially *Penicillium* and *Aspergillus* species, that is green or has green spores.

green rosette [PL PATH] A virus disease of the peanut characterized by bunching and yellowing of the leaves with severe stunting of the plant.

green rot [PL PATH] A decay of fallen deciduous trees in which the wood is colored a malachite green by the fungus *Peziza aeruginosa*.

green smut [PL PATH] A fungus disease of rice characterized by enlarged grains covered with a green powder consisting of conidia, and caused by *Ustilaginoidea virens*. Also known as false smut.

green sulfur bacteria [MICROBIO] A physiologic group of green photosynthetic bacteria of the Chloraceae that are capable of using H_2S and other inorganic electron donors.

Gregarinia [INV ZOO] A subclass of the protozoan class Telosporea occurring principally as extracellular parasites of invertebrates.

gressorial [VERT ZOO] Adapted for walking, as certain birds' feet.

Grimmiales [BOT] An order of mosses commonly growing upon rock in dense tufts or cushions and having hygroscopic, costate, usually lanceolate leaves arranged in many rows on the stem.

grindle *See* bowfin.

grisein [MICROBIO] $C_{40}H_{61}O_{20}N_{10}SFe$ A red, crystalline, water-soluble antibiotic produced by strains of *Streptomyces griseus*.

griseofulvin [MICROBIO] $C_{17}H_{17}O_6Cl$ A colorless, crystalline antifungal antibiotic produced by several species of *Penicillium*. Also known as curling factor.

griseolutein [MICROBIO] Either of two fractions, A or B, of broad-spectrum antibiotics produced by *Streptomyces griseoluteus*; more active against gram-positive than gram-negative microorganisms.

griseomycin [MICROBIO] A white, crystalline antibiotic produced by an actinomycete resembling *Streptomyces griseolus*.

grizzly bear [VERT ZOO] The common name for a number of species of large carnivorous mammals in the genus *Ursus*, family Ursidae.

Groeberiidae [PALEON] A family of extinct rodentlike marsupials.

groin [ANAT] Depression between the abdomen and the thigh.

Gromiida [INV ZOO] An order of protozoans in the subclass Filosia; the test, which is chitinous in some species and thin and somewhat flexible in others, is reinforced with sand grains or siliceous particles.

groove [BIOCHEM] Any of a group of depressions in the double helix of deoxyribonucleic acid that are believed to be sites occupied by nuclear proteins.

gross anatomy [ANAT] Anatomy that deals with the naked-eye appearance of tissues.

Grossberg unit [BIOL] A unit for the standardization of lipase.

gross primary production [ECOL] The incorporation of organic matter or biocontent by a grassland community over a given period of time.

gross production rate [ECOL] The speed of assimilation of organisms belonging to a specific trophic level.

ground cover [BOT] Prostrate or low plants that cover the ground instead of grass.

grouse [VERT ZOO] Any of a number of game birds in the family Tetraonidae having a plump body and strong, feathered legs.

growth [PHYSIO] Increase in the quantity of metabolically active protoplasm, accompanied by an increase in cell number or cell size, or both.

growth curve [MICROBIO] A graphic representation of the growth of a bacterial population in which the log of the number of bacteria or the actual number of bacteria is plotted against time.

growth factor [PHYSIO] Any factor, genetic or extrinsic, which affects growth.

growth form [ECOL] The habit of a plant determined by its appearance of branching and periodicity.

growth hormone [BIOCHEM] 1. A polypeptide hormone secreted by the anterior pituitary which promotes an increase in body size. Abbreviated GH. 2. Any hormone that regulates growth in plants and animals.

growth rate [MICROBIO] Increase in the number of bacteria in a population per unit time.

growth regulator [BIOCHEM] A synthetic substance that produces the effect of a naturally occurring hormone in stimulating plant growth; an example is dichlorophenoxyacetic acid.

Gruidae [VERT ZOO] The cranes, a family of large, tall, cosmopolitan wading birds in the order Gruiformes.

Gruiformes [VERT ZOO] A heterogeneous order of generally cosmopolitan birds including the rails, coots, limpkins, button quails, sun grebes, and cranes.

Gryllidae [INV ZOO] The true crickets, a family of orthopteran insects in which individuals are dark-colored and chunky with long antennae and long, cylindrical ovipositors.

Grylloblattidae [INV ZOO] A monogeneric family of crickets in the order Orthoptera; members are small, slender, wingless insects with hindlegs not adapted for jumping.

Gryllotalpidae [INV ZOO] A family of North American insects in the order Orthoptera which live in sand or mud; they eat the roots of seedlings growing in moist, light soils.

guanidine [BIOCHEM] CH_5N_2 Aminomethanamidine, a product of protein metabolism found in urine. Also known as carbamidine; iminourea.

guanidine-acetic acid *See* glycocyamine.

guanine [BIOCHEM] $C_5H_5ON_5$ A purine base; occurs naturally as a fundamental component of nucleic acids.

guanophore *See* iridocyte.

guanosine [BIOCHEM] $C_{10}H_{13}O_5N_5$ Guanine riboside, a nucleoside composed of guanine and ribose. Also known as vernine.

guanosine monophophosphate *See* guanylic acid.

guanosine phosphoric acid *See* guanylic acid.

guanosine tetraphosphate [BIOCHEM] A nucleotide which participates in the regulation of gene transcription in bacteria by turning off the synthesis of ribosomal ribonucleic acid.

guanylic acid [BIOCHEM] A nucleotide composed of guanine, a pentose sugar, and phosphoric acid and formed during the hydrolysis of nucleic acid. Abbreviated GMP. Also known as guanosine monophosphate; guanosine phosphoric acid.

guard cell [BOT] Either of two specialized cells surrounding each stoma in the epidermis of plants; functions in regulating stoma size.

guava [BOT] *Psidium guajava.* A shrub or low tree of tropical America belonging to the family Myrtaceae; produces an edible, aromatic, sweet, juicy berry.

guayule [BOT] *Parthenium argentatum.* A subshrub of the family Compositae that is native to Mexico and the southwestern United States; it has been cultivated as a source of rubber.

gubernaculum [ANAT] A guiding structure, as the fibrous cord extending from the fetal testes to the scrotal swellings. [INV ZOO] 1. A posterior flagellum of certain protozoans. 2. A sclerotized structure associated with the copulatory spicules of certain nematodes.

Guest unit [BIOL] A unit for the standardization of plasmin.

guinea fowl [VERT ZOO] The common name for plump African game birds composing the family Numididae; individuals have few feathers on the head and neck, but may have a crest of feathers and various fleshy appendages.

guinea pig [VERT ZOO] The common name for several species of wild and domestic hystricomorph rodents in the genus *Cavia*, family Caviidae; individuals are stocky, short-eared, short-legged, and nearly tailless.

guinea worm [INV ZOO] *Dracunculus medinensis.* A parasitic nematode that infects the subcutaneous tissues of humans and other mammals.

guitarfish [VERT ZOO] The common name for fishes composing the family Rhinobatidae.

gular [ANAT] Of, pertaining to, or situated in the gula or upper throat. [VERT ZOO] A horny shield on the plastron of turtles.

gulfweed [BOT] Brown algae of the genus *Sargassum.*

gull [VERT ZOO] The common name for a number of long-winged swimming birds in the family Laridae having a stout build, a thick, somewhat hooked bill, a short tail, and webbed feet.

gullet [ANAT] *See* esophagus. [INV ZOO] A canal between the cytostome and reservoir that functions in food intake in ciliates.

gumbo [BOT] *See* okra.

gummosis [PL PATH] Production of gummy exudates in diseased plants as a result of cell degeneration.

gum vein [BOT] Local accumulation of resin occurring as a wide streak in certain hardwoods.

Gunneraceae [BOT] A family of dicotyledonous terrestrial herbs in the order Haloragales, distinguished by two to four styles, a unilocular bitegmic ovule, large inflorescences with no petals, and drupaceous fruit.

gustation [PHYSIO] The act or the sensation of tasting.

gustatoreceptor [ANAT] A taste bud. [PHYSIO] Any sense organ that functions as a receptor for the sense of taste.

gut [ANAT] The intestine. [EMBRYO] The embryonic digestive tube.

guttation [BOT] The discharge of water from a plant surface, especially from a hydathode.

Guttiferae [BOT] A family of dicotyledonous plants in the order Theales characterized by extipulate leaves and conspicuous secretory canals or cavities in all organs.

Guttulinaceae [MICROBIO] A family of microorganisms in the Acrasiales characterized by simple fruiting structures with only slightly differentiated component cells containing little or no cellulose.

Gymnarchidae [VERT ZOO] A monotypic family of electrogenic fishes in the order Osteoglossiformes in which individuals lack pelvic, anal, and caudal fins.

Gymnarthridae [PALEON] A family of extinct lepospondylous amphibians that have a skull with only a single bone representing the tabular and temporal elements of the primitive skull roof.

Gymnoascaceae [MYCOL] A family of ascomycetous fungi in the order Eurotiales including dermatophytes and forms that grow on dung, soil, and feathers.

Gymnoblastea [INV ZOO] A suborder of coelenterates in the order Hydroida comprising hydroids without protective cups around the hydranths and gonozooids.

gymnoblastic [INV ZOO] Having naked medusa buds, referring to anthomedusan hydroids.

gymnocarpous [BOT] Having the hymenium uncovered on the surface of the thallus or fruiting body of lichens or fungi.

gymnocephalous cercaria [INV ZOO] A type of digenetic trematode larva.

Gymnocerata [INV ZOO] An equivalent name for Hydrocorisae.

Gymnocodiaceae [PALEOBOT] A family of fossil red algae.

Gymnodinia [INV ZOO] A suborder of flagellate protozoans in the order Dinoflagellida that are naked or have thin pellicles.

gymnogynous [BOT] Having a naked ovary.

Gymnolaemata [INV ZOO] A class of ectoproct bryozoans possessing lophophores which are circular in basal outline and zooecia which are short, wide, and vaselike or boxlike.

Gymnonoti [VERT ZOO] An equivalent name for Cypriniformes.

Gymnophiona [VERT ZOO] An equivalent name for Apoda.

Gymnopleura [INV ZOO] A subsection of brachyuran decapod crustaceans including the primitive burrowing crabs with trapezoidal or elongate carapaces, the first pereiopods subchelate, and some or all of the remaining pereiopods flattened and expanded.

gymnosperm [BOT] The common name for members of the division Pinophyta; seed plants having naked ovules at the time of pollination.

Gymnospermae [BOT] The equivalent name for Pinophyta.

Gymnostomatida [INV ZOO] An order of the protozoan subclass Holotrichia containing the most primitive ciliates, distinguished by the lack of ciliature in the oral area.

Gymnotidae [VERT ZOO] The single family of the suborder Gymnotoidei; eel-shaped fishes having numerous vertebrae, and anus located far forward, and lacking pelvic and developed dorsal fins.

Gymnotoidei [VERT ZOO] A monofamilial suborder of actinopterygian fishes in the order Cypriniformes.

gynaecandrous [BOT] Having staminate and pistillate flowers on the same spike.

gynander [BIOL] A mosaic individual composed of diploid female portions derived from both parents and haploid male portions derived from an extra egg or sperm nucleus.

gynandry [PHYSIO] A form of pseudohermaphroditism in which the external sexual characteristics are partly or wholly of the male aspect, but internal female genitalia are present. Also known as female pseudohermaphroditism; virilism.

gynobase [BOT] A gynoecium-bearing elongation of the receptacle in certain plants.

gynodioecious [BOT] Dioecious but with some perfect flowers on a plant bearing pistillate flowers.

gynoecium [BOT] The aggregate of carpels in a flower.

gynogenesis [EMBRYO] Development of a fertilized egg through the action of the egg nucleus, without participation of the sperm nucleus.

gynomerogony [EMBRYO] Development of a fragment of a fertilized egg containing the haploid egg nucleus.

gynomonoecious [BOT] Having complete and pistillate flowers on the same plant.

gynophore [BOT] 1. A stalk that bears the gynoecium. 2. An elongation of the receptacle between pistil and stamens.

gynostemium [BOT] The column composed of the united gynoecia and androecium.

gypsophilous [ECOL] Flourishing on a gypsum-rich substratum.

gypsy moth [INV ZOO] *Porthetria dispar.* A large lepidopteran insect of the family Lymantriidae that was accidentally imported into New England from Europe in the late 19th century; larvae are economically important as pests of deciduous trees.

Gyracanthidae [PALEON] A family of extinct acanthodian fishes in the suborder Diplacanthoidei.

Gyrinidae [INV ZOO] The whirligig beetles, a family of large coleopteran insects in the suborder Adephaga.

Gyrinocheilidae [VERT ZOO] A monogeneric family of cypriniform fishes in the suborder Cyprinoidei.

Gyrocotylidae [INV ZOO] An order of tapeworms of the subclass Cestodaria; species are intestinal parasites of chimaeroid fishes and are characterized by an anterior eversible proboscis and a posterior ruffled adhesive organ.

Gyrocotyloidea [INV ZOO] A class of trematode worms according to some systems of classification.

Gyrodactyloidea [INV ZOO] A superfamily of ectoparasitic trematodes in the subclass Monoge-

nea; the posterior holdfast is solid and is armed with central anchors and marginal hooks.

gyrogonite [PALEOBOT] A minute, ovoid body that is the residue of the calcareous encrustation about the female sex organs of a fossil stonewort.

Gyropidae [INV ZOO] A family of biting lice in the order Mallophaga; members are ectoparasites of South American rodents.

gyrus [ANAT] One of the convolutions (ridges) on the surface of the cerebrum.

habenula [ANAT] 1. Stalk of the pineal body. 2. A ribbonlike structure.

habenular commissure [ANAT] The commissure connecting the habenular ganglia in the roof of the diencephalon.

habenular ganglia [ANAT] Olfactory centers anterior to the pineal body.

habenular nucleus [ANAT] Either of a pair of nerve centers that are located at the base of the pineal body on either side and serve as an olfactory correlation center.

habitat [ECOL] The part of the physical environment in which a plant or animal lives.

habitus [BIOL] General appearance or constitution of an organism.

hackberry [BOT] 1. *Celtis occidentalis*. A tree of the eastern United States characterized by corky or warty bark, and by alternate, long-pointed serrate leaves unequal at the base; produces small, sweet, edible drupaceous fruit. 2. Any of several other trees of the genus *Celtis*.

hackmarack *See* tamarack.

haddock [VERT ZOO] *Melanogrammus aeglefinus*. A fish of the family Gadidae characterized by a black lateral line and a dark spot behind the gills.

Hadromerina [INV ZOO] A suborder of sponges in the class Clavaxinellida having monactinal megascleres, usually with a terminal knob at one end.

hadromycosis [PL PATH] Any plant disease resulting from infestation of the xylem by a fungus.

hadrosaur [PALEON] A duck-billed dinosaur.

Haeckel's law *See* recapitulation theory.

haematodocha [INV ZOO] A sac in the palpus of male spiders that fills with hemolymph and becomes distended during pairing.

Haemobartonella [MICROBIO] A genus of bacteria in the family Anaplasmataceae; parasites in or on red blood cells of many vertebrates.

Haemophilus [MICROBIO] A genus of gram-negative coccobacilli or rod-shaped bacteria of uncertain affiliation; cells may form threads and filaments and are aerobic or facultatively anaerobic; strictly blood parasites.

Haemosporina [INV ZOO] A suborder of sporozoan protozoans in the subclass Coccidia; all are parasites of vertebrates, and human malarial parasites are included.

haerangium [MYCOL] The fruiting body of *Fugascus* and *Ceratostomella*.

Hafnia [MICROBIO] A genus of bacteria in the family Enterobacteriaceae; motile rods that can utilize citrate as the only source of carbon.

Haftplatte [INV ZOO] An adhesive plate or disk in some turbellarians; it is a glanduloepidermal organ.

Hageman factor *See* factor XII.

hagfish [VERT ZOO] The common name for the jawless fishes composing the order Myxinoidea.

hair [ZOO] 1. A threadlike outgrowth of the epidermis of animals, especially a keratinized structure in mammalian skin. 2. The hairy coat of a mammal, or of a part of the animal.

hair ball *See* lake ball.

hair cell [HISTOL] The basic sensory unit of the inner ear of vertebrates; a columnar, polarized structure with specialized cilia on the free surface.

hair cycle [PHYSIO] The formation and growth of a new hair, followed by a resting stage, and ending with growth of another new hair from the same follicle.

hair follicle [ANAT] An epithelial ingrowth of the dermis that surrounds a hair.

hair gland [ANAT] Sebaceous gland associated with hair follicles.

hairworm [INV ZOO] The common name for about 80 species of worms composing the class Nematomorpha.

Halacaridae [INV ZOO] A family of marine arachnids in the order Acarina.

Haldane's rule [GEN] The rule that if one sex in a first generation of hybrids is rare, absent, or sterile, then it is the heterogametic sex.

Halecomorphi [VERT ZOO] The equivalent name for Amiiformes.

Halecostomi [VERT ZOO] The equivalent name for Pholidophoriformes.

halibut [VERT ZOO] Either of two large species of flatfishes in the genus *Hippoglossus;* commonly known as a right-eye flounder.

Halichondrida [INV ZOO] A small order of sponges in the class Demospongiae with a skeleton of diactinal or monactinal, siliceous megascleres (or both), a skinlike dermis, and small amounts of spongin.

Halictidae [INV ZOO] The halictid and sweat bees, a family of hymenopteran insects in the superfamily Apoidea.

Hallmeda [BOT] A genus of small, bushy green algae in the family Codiaceae composed of thick, leaflike segments; important as a fossil and as a limestone builder.

Haliotis [INV ZOO] A genus of gastropod mollusks commonly known as the abalones.

Haliplidae [INV ZOO] The crawling water beetles, a family of coleopteran insects in the suborder Adephaga.

Halitherinae [PALEON] A subfamily of extinct sirenian mammals in the family Dugongidae.

Haller's organ [INV ZOO] A chemoreceptor on the tarsus of certain ticks.

hallux [ANAT] The first digit of the hindlimb; the big toe of man.

halmophagous [ZOO] Pertaining to organisms which infest and eat stalks or culms of plants.

Halobacteriaceae [MICROBIO] A family of gramnegative, aerobic rods and cocci which require high salt (sodium chloride) concentrations for maintenance and growth.

Halobacterium [MICROBIO] A genus of bacteria in the family Halobacteriaceae; single, rod-shaped cells which may be pleomorphic when media are deficient.

halo blight [PL PATH] A bacterial blight of beans and sometimes other legumes caused by *Pseudomonas phaseolicola* and characterized by watersoaked lesions surrounded by a yellow ring on the leaves, stems, and pods.

Halococcus [MICROBIO] A genus of bacteria in the family Halobacteriaceae; nonmotile cocci which occur in pairs, tetrads, or clusters of tetrads.

Halocypridacea [INV ZOO] A superfamily of ostracods in the suborder Myodocopa; individuals are straight-backed with a very thin, usually calcified carapace.

halonate [MYCOL] Pertaining to a spore surrounded by a colored circle. [PL PATH] A leaf spot surrounded by a halo.

halophile [BIOL] An organism that requires high salt concentrations for growth and maintenance.

halophilism [BIOL] The phenomenon of demand for high salt concentrations for growth and maintenance.

halophyte [ECOL] A plant or microorganism that grows well in soils having a high salt content.

Haloragaceae [BOT] A family of dicotyledonous plants in the order Haloragales distinguished by an apical ovary of 2–4 loculi, small inflorescences, and small, alternate or opposite or whorled, exstipulate leaves.

Haloragales [BOT] An order of dicotyledonous plants in the subclass Rosidae containing herbs with perfect or often unisexual, more or less reduced flowers, and a minute or vestigial perianth.

Halosauridae [VERT ZOO] A family of mostly extinct deep-sea teleost fishes in the order Notacanthiformes.

halosere [ECOL] The series of communities succeeding one another, from the pioneer stage to the climax, and commencing in salt water or on saline soil.

haltere [INV ZOO] Either of a pair of capitate filaments representing rudimentary hindwings in Diptera. Also known as balancer.

Halysitidae [PALEON] A family of extinct Paleozoic corals of the order Tabulata.

Hamamelidaceae [BOT] A family of dicotyledonous trees or shrubs in the order Hamamelidales characterized by united carpels, alternate leaves, perfect or unisexual flowers, and free filaments.

Hamamelidae [BOT] A small subclass of plants in the class Magnoliopsida having strongly reduced, often unisexual flowers with poorly developed or no perianth.

Hamamelidales [BOT] A small order of dicotyledonous plants in the subclass Hamamelidae characterized by vessels in the wood and a gynoecium consisting either of separate carpels or of united carpels that open at maturity.

hamate [BIOL] Hook-shaped or hooked.

Hamoproteidae [INV ZOO] A family of parasitic protozoans in the suborder Haemosporina; only the gametocytes occur in blood cells.

hamster [VERT ZOO] The common name for any of 14 species of rodents in the family Cricetidae characterized by scent glands in the flanks, large cheek pouches, and a short tail.

hamstring muscles [ANAT] The biceps femoris, semitendinosus, and semimembranosus collectively.

hamulus [VERT ZOO] A hooklike process, especially a small terminal hook on the barbicel of a feather.

hamus [BIOL] A hook or a curved process.

hand [ANAT] The terminal part of the upper extremity modified for grasping.

hanging-drop preparation [MICROBIO] A technique used in microscopy in which a specimen is placed in a drop of a suitable fluid on a cover slip and the cover slip is inverted over a concavity on a slide.

Hanson unit [BIOL] A unit for the standardization of parathyroid hormone.

H antigen [MICROBIO] A general term for microbial flagellar antigens; former designation for species-specific flagellar antigens of *Salmonella*.

haploblont [BOT] A plant that produces only sexual haploid individuals.

haplocaulescent [BOT] Having a simple axis with the reproductive organs on the principal axis.

Haplodoci [VERT ZOO] The equivalent name for Batrachoidiformes.

haploid [GEN] Having half of the diploid or full complement of chromosomes, as in mature gametes.

Haplolepidae [PALEON] A family of Carboniferous chondrostean fishes in the suborder Palaeoniscoidei having a reduced number of fin rays and a vertical jaw suspension.

Haplomi [VERT ZOO] An equivalent name for Salmoniformes.

haplomitosis [CELL BIO] Type of primitive mitosis in which the nuclear granules form into threadlike masses rather than clearly differentiated chromosomes.

haplont [BOT] A plant with only haploid somatic cells; the zygote is diploid.

haplophase [BIOL] Haploid stage in the life cycle of an organism.

haplopore [PALEON] Any randomly distributed pore on the surface of fossil cystoid echinoderms.

Haplosclerida [INV ZOO] An order of sponges in the class Demospongiae including species with a skeleton made up of siliceous megascleres embedded in spongin fibers or spongin cement.

haplosis [CELL BIO] Reduction of the chromosome number to half during meiosis.

Haplosporea [INV ZOO] A class of Protozoa in the subphylum Sporozoa distinguished by the production of spores lacking polar filaments.

Haplosporida [INV ZOO] An order of Protozoa in the class Haplosporea distinguished by the production of uninucleate spores that lack both polar capsules and filaments.

haplostele [BOT] A type of protostele with the core of xylem characterized by a smooth outline.

hapteron [BOT] A disklike holdfast on the stem of certain algae.

haptochlamydeous [BOT] Having the sporophylls protected by rudimentary perianth leaves.

haptoglobin [BIOCHEM] An alpha globulin that constitutes 1–2% of normal blood serum; contains about 5% carbohydrate.

Haptophyceae [BOT] A class of the phylum Chrysophyta that contains the Coccolithophorida.

haptor [INV ZOO] The posterior organ of attachment in certain monogenetic trematodes characterized by multiple suckers and the presence of hooks.

haptotropism [BIOL] Movement of sessile organisms in response to contact, especially in plants.

Harderian gland [VERT ZOO] An accessory lacrimal gland associated with lower eyelid structures in all vertebrates except land mammals.

hard fiber [BOT] A heavily lignified leaf fiber used in making cordage, twine, and textiles.

hard palate [ANAT] The anterior portion of the roof of the mouth formed by paired palatine processes of the maxillary bones and by the horizontal part of each palate bone.

hard rot [PL PATH] 1. Any plant disease characterized by lesions with hard surfaces. 2. A fungus disease of gladiolus caused by *Septoria gladioli* which produces hard-surfaced lesions on the leaves and corms.

hardwood forest [ECOL] 1. An ecosystem having deciduous trees as the dominant form of vegetation. 2. An ecosystem consisting principally of trees that yield hardwood.

hare [VERT ZOO] The common name for a number of lagomorphs in the family Leporidae; they differ from rabbits in being larger with longer ears, legs, and tails.

Harpacticoida [INV ZOO] An order of minute copepod crustaceans of variable form, but generally being linear and more or less cylindrical.

harpago [INV ZOO] Part of the clasper on the copulatory organ of certain male insects.

Harpidae [INV ZOO] A family of marine gastropod mollusks in the order Neogastropoda.

Hartman unit [BIOL] A unit for the standardization of adrenal cortical hormone.

Hart-Park virus [VIROL] A ribonucleic acid–containing animal virus of the rhabdovirus group.

Hassal's body *See* thymic corpuscle.

hastate [BIOL] Shaped like an arrowhead with divergent barbs.

Hatch-Slack pathway [BIOCHEM] A metabolic cycle involved in the non-light-requiring phase of photosynthesis in certain plants having specific metabolic and anatomical modifications in their mesophyll and bundle sheath cells which facilitate the temporary fixation of carbon dioxide (CO_2) into four-carbon organic acid; these acids are next broken down to three-carbon organic acids plus CO_2 in bundle sheath cells, where this freed CO_2 is then fixed into carbohydrates in a normal Calvin cycle pathway.

haustellum [INV ZOO] A proboscis modified for sucking.

haustorium [BOT] 1. An outgrowth of certain parasitic plants which serves to absorb food from the host. 2. Food-absorbing cell of the embryo sac in nonparasitic plants.

haustrum [ANAT] An outpocketing or pouch of the colon.

Haversian canal [HISTOL] The central, longitudinal channel of an osteon containing blood vessels and connective tissue.

Haversian lamella [HISTOL] One of the concentric layers of bone composing a Haversian system.

Haversian system *See* osteon.

HA virus *See* hemadsorption virus.

hawk [VERT ZOO] Any of the various smaller diurnal birds of prey in the family Accipitridae; some species are used for hunting hare and partridge in India and other parts of Asia.

hazelnut *See* filbert.

H-B virus [VIROL] A subgroup-A picornavirus associated with diseases in rodents.

HCG *See* human chorionic gonadotropin.

head [ANAT] The region of the body consisting of the skull, its contents, and related structures.

head bulb [INV ZOO] A structure armed with spines behind the lips of spiruroid nematodes.

head fold [EMBRYO] A ventral fold formed by rapid growth of the head of the embryo over the embryonic disk, resulting in the formation of the foregut accompanied by anteroposterior reversal of the anterior part of the embryonic disk.

head organ [INV ZOO] One of the bulbous structures in the prohaptor of monogenetic trematodes which are openings for adhesive glands.

head process [EMBRYO] The notochord or notochordal plate formed as an axial outgrowth of the primitive node.

head shield [INV ZOO] A conspicuous structure arching over the lips of certain nematodes.

head smut [PL PATH] A fungus disease of corn and sorghum caused by *Sphacelotheca reiliana* which destroys the head of the plant.

hearing [PHYSIO] The general perceptual behavior and the specific responses made in relation to sound stimuli.

heart [ANAT] The hollow muscular pumping organ of the cardiovascular system in vertebrates.

heartbeat [PHYSIO] Pulsation of the heart coincident with ventricular systole.

heart rate [PHYSIO] The number of heartbeats per minute.

heartrot [PL PATH] 1. A rot involving disintegration of the heartwood of a tree. 2. A fungus disease of beets and rutabagas caused by *Mycosphaerella tabifica* which results in decay of the central tissues of the plant. 3. A boron-deficiency disease of sugarbeets that causes rot. 4. A fatal disease of palms associated with a trypanosomatid flagellate *Phytomonas*. Also known as cedros wilt; marchitez sorpresiva.

heart valve [ANAT] Flaps of tissue that prevent reflux of blood from the ventricles to the atria or from the pulmonary arteries or aorta to the atria.

heartwood [BOT] Xylem of an angiosperm.

heart worm [INV ZOO] *Dirofilaria immitis*. A filarial nematode parasitic on dogs and other carnivores.

heath *See* temperate and cold scrub.

heather [BOT] *Calluna vulgaris*. An evergreen heath of northern and alpine regions distinguished by racemes of small purple-pink flowers.

heat stress index [PHYSIO] Relation of the amount of evaporation or perspiration required for particular job conditions as related to the maximum evaporative capacity of an average person. Abbreviated HSI.

heavy meromyosin [BIOCHEM] The larger of two fragments obtained from the muscle protein myosin following limited proteolysis by trypsin or chymotrypsin.

Hebrovelildae [INV ZOO] A family of hemipteran insects in the subdivision Amphibicorisae.

hectocotylus [INV ZOO] A specialized appendage of male cephalopods adapted for the transference of sperm.

hedgehog [VERT ZOO] The common name for members of the insectivorous family Erinaceidae characterized by spines on their back and sides.

hedonic gland [VERT ZOO] One of the mucus-secreting scent glands in many urodeles; functions in courtship.

Hedwigiaceae [BOT] A family of mosses in the order Isobryales.

Heidelberg man [PALEON] An early type of European fossil man known from an isolated lower jaw; considered a variant of *Homo erectus* or an early stock of Neanderthal man.

hekistotherm [ECOL] Plant adapted for conditions of minimal heat; can withstand long dark periods.

Helaletidae [PALEON] A family of extinct perissodactyl mammals in the superfamily Tapiroidea.

Helcionellacea [PALEON] A superfamily of extinct gastropod mollusks in the order Aspidobranchia.

Heleidae [INV ZOO] The biting midges, a family of orthorrhaphous dipteran insects in the series Nematocera.

Helferich unit [BIOL] A unit for the standardization of phosphatase.

Heliasteridae [INV ZOO] A family of echinoderms in the subclass Asteroidea lacking pentameral symmetry but structurally resembling common asteroids.

Helicinidae [INV ZOO] A family of gastropod mollusks in the order Archeogastropoda containing tropical terrestrial snails.

helicoid [INV ZOO] Of a gastropod shell, shaped like a flat coil or flattened spiral.

helicoid cyme [BOT] A type of determinate inflorescence having a coiled cluster, with flowers on only one side of the axis.

Heliconiaceae [BOT] A family of monocotyledonous plants in the order Zingiberales characterized by perfect flowers with a solitary ovule in each locule, schizocarpic fruit, and capitate stigma.

Helicoplacoidea [PALEON] A class of free-living, spindle- or pear-shaped, plated echinozoans known only from the Lower Cambrian of California.

Helicosporae [MYCOL] A spore group of the Fungi Imperfecti characterized by spirally coiled, septate spores.

helicospore [INV ZOO] Mature spore of the Helicosporida characterized by a peripheral spiral filament.

Helicosporida [INV ZOO] An order of protozoans in the class Myxosporidea characterized by production of spores with a relatively thick, single intrasporal filament and three uninucleate sporoplasms.

helicotrema [ANAT] The opening at the apex of the cochlea through which the scala tympani and the scala vestibuli communicate with each other.

Heligmosomidae [INV ZOO] A family of parasitic roundworms belonging to the Strongyloidea.

Heliodinidae [INV ZOO] A family of lepidopteran insects in the suborder Heteroneura.

Heliolitidae [PALEON] A family of extinct corals in the order Tabulata.

heliophilous [ECOL] Attracted by and adapted for a high intensity of sunlight.

heliophyte [ECOL] A plant that thrives in full sunlight.

Heliornithidae [VERT ZOO] The lobed-toed sun grebes, a family of pantropical birds in the order Gruiformes.

heliotaxis [BIOL] Orientation movement of an organism in response to the stimulus of sunlight.

heliotrope [BOT] A plant whose flower or stem turns toward the sun.

heliotropism [BIOL] Growth or orientation movement of a sessile organism or part, such as a plant, in response to the stimulus of sunlight.

Heliozoia [INV ZOO] A subclass of the protozoan class Actinopodea; individuals lack a central capsule and have either axopodia or filopodia.

heliozooid [BIOL] Ameboid, but with distinct filamentous pseudopodia.

Helix [INV ZOO] A genus of pulmonate land mollusks including many of the edible snails; individuals have a coiled shell with a low conical spire.

hellbender [VERT ZOO] *Cryptobranchus alleganiensis*. A large amphibian of the order Urodela which is the most primitive of the living salamanders, retaining some larval characteristics.

Helmholtz theory *See* Young-Helmholtz theory.

helminth [INV ZOO] Any parasitic worm.

helminthoid [BIOL] Resembling a helminth.

helminthologist [BIOL] One who studies helminths.

helminthosporin [BIOCHEM] $C_{15}H_{10}O_5$ A maroon, crystalline pigment formed by certain fungi growing on a sugar substrate.

Helminthosporium [MYCOL] A genus of parasitic fungi of the family Dematiaceae having conidiophores which are more or less irregular or bent and bear conidia successively on new growing tips.

Helminthosporium leaf spot [PL PATH] Any leaf spot, commonly of grasses, caused by *Helminthosporium* species.

Helobiae [BOT] The equivalent name for Helobiales.

Helobiales [BOT] An order embracing most of the Alismatidae in certain systems of classification.

Heloderma [VERT ZOO] The single genus in the reptilian family Helodermatidae; contains the only known poisonous lizards, the Gila monster (*H. suspectum*) and the beaded lizard (*H. horridum*).

Helodermatidae [VERT ZOO] A family of lizards in the suborder Sauria.

Helodidae [INV ZOO] The marsh beetles, a family of coleopteran insects in the superfamily Dascilloidea.

Helodontidae [PALEON] A family of extinct ratfishes conditionally placed in the order Bradyodonti.

Helomyzidae [INV ZOO] The sun flies, a family of myodarian cyclorrhaphous dipteran insects in the subsection Acalypteratae.

helophyte [ECOL] A marsh plant; buds overwinter underwater.

helophytia [ECOL] Differences in ecological control by fluctuations in water level such as in marshes.

Heloridae [INV ZOO] A family of hymenopteran insects in the superfamily Proctotrupoidea.

Helotiales [MYCOL] An order of fungi in the class Ascomycetes.

Helotidae [INV ZOO] The metallic sap beetles, a family of coleopteran insects in the superfamily Cucujoidea.

helotism [ECOL] Symbiosis in which one organism is a slave to the other, as between certain species of ants.

Helotrephidae [INV ZOO] A family of true aquatic, tropical hemipteran insects in the subdivision Hydrocorisae.

helper virus [VIROL] A virus that, by its infection of a cell, enables a defective virus to multiply by supplying one or more functions that the defective virus lacks.

hem-, hema-, hemo-, haem- [HISTOL] Combining form for blood.

hemadsorption virus [VIROL] A descriptive term for myxoviruses that agglutinate red blood cells and cause the cells to adsorb to each other. Abbreviated HA virus.

hemal arch [ANAT] 1. A ventral loop on the body of vertebrate caudal vertebrae surrounding the blood vessels. 2. In man, the ventral vertebral process formed by the centrum together with the ribs.

hemal ring [INV ZOO] A vessel in certain echinoderms, variously located, associated with the coelom and axial gland.

hemal sinus [INV ZOO] The two principal lacunae along the digestive tube in certain echinoderms.

hemal tuft [INV ZOO] Series of fine vessels in echioderms arising from the axial gland.

hemapodium [INV ZOO] The dorsal lobe of a parapodium.

hematein [BIOCHEM] $C_{16}H_{12}O_6$ A brownish stain and chemical indicator obtained by oxidation of hematoxylin.

hematoblast [HISTOL] An immature erythrocyte.

hematochrome [BIOCHEM] A red pigment occurring in green algae, especially when plants are exposed to intense light on subaerial habitats.

hematogenous [PHYSIO] 1. Pertaining to the production of blood or of its fractions. 2. Carried by way of the bloodstream. 3. Originating in blood.

hematophagous [ZOO] Feeding on blood.

hematopoiesis [PHYSIO] The process by which the cellular elements of the blood are formed. Also known as hemopoiesis.

hematopoietic system *See* reticuloendothelial system.

hematopoietic tissue [HISTOL] Blood-forming tissue, consisting of reticular fibers and cells. Also known as hemopoietic tissue.

hematopoietin [BIOCHEM] A substance which is produced by the juxtaglomerular apparatus in the kidney and controls the rate of red cell production. Also known as hemopoietin.

hematoporphyrin [BIOCHEM] $C_{34}H_{38}O_6N$ Iron-free heme, a porphyrin obtained by treating hemoglobin with sulfuric acid in vitro. Also known as hemoporphyrin.

hematoxylon [BOT] The heartwood of *Haematoxylon campechianum*. Also known as logwood.

heme [BIOCHEM] $C_{34}H_{32}O_4N_4Fe$ An iron-protoporphyrin complex associated with each polypeptide unit of hemoglobin.

hemerythrin *See* hemoerythrin.

heme synthetase [BIOCHEM] An enzyme which combines protoporphyrin IX, ferrous iron, and globin to form the intact hemoglobin molecule.

hemi- [BIOL] 1. Prefix for half. 2. Prefix denoting one side of the body.

Hemiascomycetes [MYCOL] The equivalent name for Hemiascomycetidae.

Hemiascomycetidae [MYCOL] A subclass of fungi in the class Ascomycetes.

hemiazygous vein [ANAT] A vein on the left side of the vertebral column which drains blood from the left ascending lumbar vein to the azygos vein.

Hemibasidiomycetes [MYCOL] The equivalent name for Heterobasidiomycetidae.

hemicellulose [BIOCHEM] $(C_6H_{10}O_5)_{2n}$ A type of polysaccharide found in plant cell walls in association with cellulose and lignin; it is soluble in and extractable by dilute alkaline solutions. Also known as hexosan.

Hemichordata [SYST] A group of marine animals categorized as either a phylum of deuterostomes or a subphylum of chordates; includes the Enteropneusta, Pterobranchia, and Graptolithina.

Hemicidaridae [PALEON] A family of extinct Echinacea in the order Hemicidaroida distinguished by a stirodont lantern, and ambulacra abruptly widened at the ambitus.

Hemicidaroida [PALEON] An order of extinct echinoderms in the superorder Echinacea characterized by one very large tubercle on each interambulacral plate.

hemicryptophyte [ECOL] A plant having buds at the soil surface and protected by scales, snow, or litter.

hemicyclic [BOT] Of flowers, having the floral leaves arranged partly in whorls and partly in spirals.

hemidiaphragm [ANAT] A lateral half of a diaphragm.

Hemidiscosa [INV ZOO] An order of sponges in the subclass Amphidiscophora distinguished by birotulates that are hemidiscs with asymmetrical ends.

Hemileucinae [INV ZOO] A subfamily of lepidopteran insects in the family Saturnidae consisting of the buck moths and relatives.

Hemimetabola [INV ZOO] A division of the insect subclass Pterygota; members are characterized by hemimetabolous metamorphosis.

hemimetabolous metamorphosis [INV ZOO] An incomplete metamorphosis; gills are present in aquatic larvae, or naiads.

hemin [BIOCHEM] $C_{34}H_{32}O_4N_4FeCl$ The crystalline salt of ferriheme, containing iron in the ferric state.

hemiparasite [ECOL] A parasite capable of a saprophytic existence, especially certain parasitic plants containing some chlorophyll. Also known as semiparasite.

hemipelagic [ECOL] Of the biogeographic environment of the hemipelagic region with both neritic and pelagic qualities.

hemipenis [VERT ZOO] Either of a pair of nonerectile, evertible sacs that lie on the floor of the cloaca in snakes and lizards; used as intromittent organs.

Hemipeplidae [INV ZOO] An equivalent name for Cucujidae.

Hemiprocnidae [VERT ZOO] The crested swifts, a family comprising three species of perching birds found only in southeastern Asia.

Hemiptera [INV ZOO] The true bugs, an order of the class Insecta characterized by forewings differentiated into a basal area and a membranous apical region.

Hemisphaeriales [MYCOL] A group of ascomycetous fungi characterized by the wall of the fruit body being a stroma.

hemithorax [ANAT] One side of the chest.

Hemizonida [PALEON] A Paleozoic order of echinoderms of the subclass Asteroidea having an ambulacral groove that is well defined by adambulacral ossicles, but with restricted or undeveloped marginal plates.

hemizygous [GEN] Pertaining to the condition or state of having a gene present in a single dose; for instance, in the X chromosome of male mammals.

hemlock [BOT] The common name for members of the genus *Tsuga* in the pine family characterized by two white lines beneath the flattened, needlelike leaves.

hemobilirubin [BIOCHEM] Bilirubin in normal blood serum before passage through the liver.

hemoblast See hemocytoblast.

hemochorial placenta [EMBRYO] A type of placenta having the maternal blood in direct contact with the chorionic trophoblast. Also known as labyrinthine placenta.

hemocoel [INV ZOO] An expanded portion of the blood system in arthropods that replaces a portion of the coelom.

hemoconia [BIOCHEM] Round or dumbbell-shaped, refractile, colorless particles found in blood plasma.

hemocyanin [BIOCHEM] A blue respiratory pigment found only in mollusks and in arthropods other than insects.

hemocyte [INV ZOO] A cellular element of blood, especially in invertebrates.

hemocytoblast [HISTOL] A pluripotential blast cell thought to be capable of giving rise to all other blood cells. Also known as hemoblast; stem cell.

hemocytolysis [PHYSIO] The dissolution of blood cells.

hemodichorial placenta [EMBRYO] A placenta with a double trophoblastic layer.

hemodynamics [PHYSIO] A branch of physiology concerned with circulatory movements of the blood and the forces involved in circulation.

hemoendothelial placenta [EMBRYO] A placenta having the endothelium of vessels of chorionic villi in direct contact with the maternal blood.

hemoerythrin [BIOCHEM] A red respiratory pigment found in a few annelid and sipunculid worms and in the brachiopod *Lingula*. Also known as hemerythrin.

hemoflagellate [INV ZOO] A parasitic, flagellate protozoan that lives in the blood of the host.

hemoglobin [BIOCHEM] The iron-containing, oxygen-carrying molecule of the red blood cells of vertebrates comprising four polypeptide subunits in a heme group.

hemoglobin A [BIOCHEM] The type of hemoglobin found in normal adults, which moves as a single component in an electrophoretic field, is rapidly denatured by highly alkaline solutions, and contains two titratable sulfhydryl groups per molecule.

hemohistioblast [HISTOL] The hypothetical reticuloendothelial cell from which all the cells of the blood are eventually differentiated.

hemolymph [INV ZOO] The circulating fluid of the open circulatory systems of many invertebrates.

hemolysis [PHYSIO] The lysis, or destruction, of erythrocytes with the release of hemoglobin.

hemomonochorial placenta [EMBRYO] A placenta with a single trophoblastic layer.

hemoparasite [INV ZOO] A parasitic animal that lives in the blood of a vertebrate.

hemopexin [BIOCHEM] A heme-binding protein in human plasma that may be a regulator of heme and drug metabolism, and a distributor of heme.

hemophilic bacteria [MICROBIO] Bacteria of the genera Hemophilus, Bordetella, and Moraxella; all are small, gram-negative, nonmotile, parasitic rods, dependent upon blood factors for growth.

Hemophilus [MICROBIO] A genus of hemophilic bacteria in the family Brucellaceae requiring hemin and nicotinamide nucleoside for growth.

Hemophilus aegyptius [MICROBIO] A nonhemolytic hemophilic bacterium that causes pinkeye. Also known as Koch-Weeks bacillus.

Hemophilus ducreyi [MICROBIO] A hemolytic hemophilic bacterium that causes chancroid in man. Also known as Ducrey bacillus.

Hemophilus influenzae [MICROBIO] A hemophilic bacterium that causes serious infections of man, especially infants, including influenza, purulent meningitis, and pneumonia.

Hemophilus parainfluenzae [MICROBIO] A nonpathogenic hemophilic bacterium found in the upper respiratory tract of man.

Hemophilus pertussis [MICROBIO] A pathogenic hemophilic bacterium that causes whooping cough. Also known as Bordet-Gengou bacillus.

hemopoietic tissue See hematopoietic tissue.

hemopoietin See hematopoietin.

hemoporphyrin See hematoporphyrin.

hemorrhagic fever virus [VIROL] Any of several arboviruses causing acute infectious human diseases characterized by fever, prostration, vomiting, and hemorrhage.

hemorrhagic unit [BIOL] A unit for the standardization of snake venom.

hemosiderin [BIOCHEM] An iron-containing glycoprotein found in most tissues and especially in liver.

hemosiderosis [PHYSIO] Deposition of hemosiderin in body tissues without tissue damage, reflecting an increase in body iron stores.

hemotrichorial placenta [EMBRYO] A placenta with a triple trophoblastic layer.

hemotrophe [BIOCHEM] The nutritive substance supplied via the placenta to embryos of viviparous animals.

hen [VERT ZOO] The female of several bird species, especially gallinaceous species.

henbane [BOT] Hyoscyamus niger. A poisonous herb containing the toxic alkaloids hyoscyamine

and hyoscine; extracts have properties similar to belladonna.

Henicocephalidae [INV ZOO] A family of hemipteran insects of uncertain affinities.

Henle's loop See loop of Henle.

henna [BOT] Lawsonia inermis. An Old World plant having small opposite leaves and axillary panicles of white flowers; a reddish-brown dye extracted from the leaves is used in hair dyes. Also known as Egyptian henna.

Henry unit [BIOL] A unit for the standardization of thyroid extracts.

Hensen's node [EMBRYO] Thickening formed by a group of cells at the anterior end of the primitive streak in vertebrate gastrulas.

heparin [BIOCHEM] An acid mucopolysaccharide acting as an antithrombin, antithromboplastin, and antiplatelet factor to prolong the clotting time of whole blood; occurs in a variety of tissues, most abundantly in liver.

Hepaticae [BOT] The equivalent name for Marchantiatae.

hepatic artery [ANAT] A branch of the celiac artery that carries blood to the stomach, pancreas, great omentum, liver, and gallbladder.

hepatic cecum [INV ZOO] A hollow outpocketing of the foregut of Branchiostoma; receives veins from the intestine.

hepatic duct [ANAT] The common duct draining the liver. Also known as common hepatic duct.

hepatic duct system [ANAT] The biliary tract including the hepatic ducts, gallbladder, cystic duct, and common bile duct.

hepatic plexus [ANAT] Nerve network accompanying the hepatic artery to the liver.

hepatic portal system [ANAT] A system of veins in vertebrates which collect blood from the digestive tract and spleen and pass it through capillaries in the liver.

hepatic vein [ANAT] A blood vessel that drains blood from the liver into the inferior vena cava.

hepatitis virus [VIROL] Any of several viruses causing hepatitis in man and lower mammals.

hepatocyte [HISTOL] An epithelial cell constituting the major cell type in the liver.

hepatopancreas [INV ZOO] A gland in crustaceans and certain other invertebrates that combines the digestive functions of the liver and pancreas of vertebrates.

Hepialidae [INV ZOO] A family of lepidopteran insects in the superfamily Hepialoidea.

Hepialoidea [INV ZOO] A superfamily of lepidopteran insects in the suborder Homoneura including medium- to large-sized moths which possess rudimentary mouthparts.

Hepsogastridae [INV ZOO] A family of parasitic insects in the order Mallophaga.

heptose [BIOCHEM] Any member of the group of monosaccharides containing seven carbon atoms.

heptulose [BIOCHEM] The generic term for a ketose formed from a seven-carbon monosaccharide.

herb [BOT] 1. A seed plant that lacks a persistent, woody stem aboveground and dies at the end of the season. 2. An aromatic plant or plant part used medicinally or for food flavoring.

herbaceous [BOT] 1. Resembling or pertaining to a herb. 2. Pertaining to a stem with little or no woody tissue.

herbaceous dicotyledon [BOT] A type of dicotyledon in which the primary vascular cylinder forms an ectophloic siphonostele with widely separated vascular strands.

herbaceous monocotyledon [BOT] A type of monocotyledon with a vascular system composed of widely spaced strands arranged in one of four ways.

herbarium [BOT] A collection of plant specimens, pressed and mounted on paper or placed in liquid preservatives, and systematically arranged.

herbicolous [ECOL] Living on herbs.

herbivore [VERT ZOO] An animal that eats only vegetation.

Herbst corpuscle [VERT ZOO] A cutaneous sense organ found in the mucous membrane of the tongue of the duck.

herd [VERT ZOO] A number of one kind of wild, semidomesticated, or domesticated animals grouped or kept together under human control.

hereditary [GEN] Of or pertaining to heredity or inheritance.

heredity [GEN] The sum of genetic endowment obtained from the parents.

Hering theory [PHYSIO] A theory of color vision which assumes that three qualitatively different processes are present in the visual system, and that each of the three is capable of responding in two opposite ways.

hermaphrodite [BIOL] An individual (animal, plant, or higher vertebrate) exhibiting hermaphroditism. [PHYSIO] An abnormal condition, especially in humans and other higher vertebrates, in which both male and female reproductive organs are present in the individual.

hermatype See hermatypic coral.

hermatypic coral [INV ZOO] Reef-building coral characterized by the presence of symbiotic algae within their endodermal tissue. Also known as hermatype.

hermit crab [INV ZOO] The common name for a number of marine decapod crustaceans of the families Paguridae and Parapaguridae; all lack right-sided appendages and have a large, soft, coiled abdomen.

heron [VERT ZOO] The common name for wading birds composing the family Ardeidae characterized by long legs and neck, a long tapered bill, large wings, and soft plumage.

herpes simplex virus [VIROL] Either of two types of subgroup A herpesviruses that are specific for humans; given the binomial designation *Herpesvirus hominis*.

herpesvirus [VIROL] A major group of deoxyribonucleic acid–containing animal viruses, distinguished by a cubic capsid, enveloped virion, and affinity for the host nucleus as a site of maturation.

Herpetosiphon [MICROBIO] A genus of bacteria in the family Cytophagaceae; cells are unbranched, sheathed rods or filaments; un-

sheathed segments are motile; microcysts are not known.

herring [VERT ZOO] The common name for fishes composing the family Clupeidae; fins are softrayed and have no supporting spines, there are usually four gill clefts, and scales are on the body but absent on the head.

Herring body [HISTOL] Any of the distinct colloid masses in the vertebrate pituitary gland, possibly representing greatly dilated endings of nerve fibers.

Hesionidae [INV ZOO] A family of small polychaete worms belonging to the Errantia.

hesperidium [BOT] A modified berry, with few seeds, a leathery rind, and membranous extensions of the endocarp dividing the pulp into chambers; an example is the orange.

Hesperiidae [INV ZOO] The single family of the superfamily Hesperioidea comprising butterflies known as skippers because of their rapid, erratic flight.

Hesperioidea [INV ZOO] A monofamilial superfamily of lepidopteran insects in the suborder Heteroneura including heavy-bodied, mostly diurnal insects with clubbed antennae that are bent, curved, or reflexed at the tip.

Hesperornithidae [PALEON] A family of extinct North American birds in the order Hesperornithiformes.

Hesperornithiformes [PALEON] An order of ancient extinct birds; individuals were large, flightless, aquatic diving birds with the shoulder girdle and wings much reduced and the legs specialized for strong swimming.

Heteractinida [PALEON] A group of Paleozoic sponges with calcareous spicules; probably related to the Calcarea.

Heterakidae [INV ZOO] A group of nematodes assigned either to the suborder Oxyurina or the suborder Ascaridina.

heterandrous [BOT] Having stamens differing from each other in length or form.

heterauxesis See allometry.

heteroallele [GEN] An allele that carries mutational alterations at different sites.

heteroauxin [BIOCHEM] $C_{10}H_9O_2N$ A plant growth hormone with an indole skeleton.

Heterobasidiomycetidae [MYCOL] A class of fungi in which the basidium either is branched or is divided into cells by cross walls.

heteroblastic [EMBRYO] Arising from different tissues or germ layers, in referring to similar organs in different species.

Heterocapsina [BOT] An order of green algae in the class Xanthophyceae. [INV ZOO] A suborder of yellow-green to green flagellate protozoans in the order Heterochlorida.

heterocarpous [BOT] Producing two distinct types of fruit.

Heterocera [INV ZOO] A formerly recognized suborder of Lepidoptera including all forms without clubbed antennae.

heterocercal [VERT ZOO] Pertaining to the caudal fin of certain fishes and indicating that the upper lobe is larger, with the vertebral column terminating in this lobe.

Heteroceridae [INV ZOO] The variegated mud-loving beetles, a family of coleopteran insects in the superfamily Dryopoidea.

Heterocheilidae [INV ZOO] A family of parasitic roundworms in the superfamily Ascaridoidea.

heterochlamydeous [BOT] Having the perianth differentiated into a distinct calyx and a corolla.

Heterochlorida [INV ZOO] An order of yellow-green to green flagellate oraganisms of the class Phytamastigophorea.

heterochromatin [CELL BIO] Specialized chromosome material which remains tightly coiled even in the nondividing nucleus and stains darkly in interphase.

heterochromia [PHYSIO] A condition in which the two irises of an individual have different colors, or in which one iris has two colors.

heterochronism [EMBRYO] Deviation from the normal sequence of organ formation; a factor in evolution.

heterococcolith [BIOL] A coccolith with crystals arranged into boat, trumpet, or basket shapes.

heterocoelous [ANAT] Pertaining to vertebrae with centra having saddle-shaped articulations.

Heterocorallia [PALEON] An extinct small, monofamilial order of fossil corals with elongate skeletons; found in calcareous shales and in limestones.

Heterocotylea [INV ZOO] The equivalent name for Monogenea.

heterocyst [BOT] Clear, thick-walled cell occurring at intervals along the filament of certain blue-green algae.

heterodactylous [VERT ZOO] Having the first two toes turned backward.

Heterodera [INV ZOO] The cyst nematodes, a genus of phytoparasitic worms that live in the internal root systems of many plants.

heterodont [ANAT] Having teeth that are variable in shape and differentiated into incisors, canines, and molars. [INV ZOO] In bivalves, having two types of teeth on one valve which fit into depressions on the other valve.

Heterodonta [INV ZOO] An order of bivalve mollusks in some systems of classification; hinge teeth are few in number and variable in form.

Heterodontoidea [VERT ZOO] A suborder of sharks in the order Selachii which is represented by the single living genus *Heterodontus*.

heteroduplex [GEN] A double-stranded deoxyribonucleic molecule comprising strands from different individuals. [MOL BIO] A double-stranded molecule of deoxyribonucleic acid in which the two strands show noncomplementary sections.

heteroecious [BIOL] Pertaining to forms that pass through different stages of a life cycle in different hosts.

heterogamete [BIOL] A gamete that differs in size, appearance, structure, or sex chromosome content from the gamete of the opposite sex. Also known as anisogamete.

heterogametic sex [GEN] That sex of some species in which the two sex chromosomes are different in gene content or size and which there-fore produces two or more different kinds of gametes.

heterogamety [GEN] The production of different kinds of gametes by one sex of a species.

heterogamous [BIOL] Of or pertaining to heterogamy.

heterogamy [BIOL] 1. Alternation of a true sexual generation with a parthenogenetic generation. 2. Sexual reproduction by fusion of unlike gametes. Also known as anisogamy. [BOT] Condition of producing two kinds of flowers.

heterogeneity [BIOL] The condition or state of being different in kind or nature.

heterogeneous ribonucleic acid [MOL BIO] A large molecule of ribonucleic acid that is believed to be the precursor of messenger ribonucleic acid. Abbreviated H-RNA.

Heterogeneratae [BOT] A class of brown algae distinguished by a heteromorphic alteration of generations.

heterogenesis [BIOL] Alternation of generations in a complete life cycle, especially the alternation of a dioecious generation with one or more parthenogenetic generations.

heterogenous [BIOL] Not originating within the body of the organism.

Heterognathi [VERT ZOO] An equivalent name for Cypriniformes.

heterogony [BIOL] 1. Alteration of generations in a complete life cycle, especially of a dioecious and hermaphroditic generation. 2. See allometry. [BOT] Having heteromorphic perfect flowers with respect to lengths of the stamens or styles.

heterokaryon [MYCOL] A bi- or multinucleate cell having genetically different kinds of nuclei.

heterokaryosis [MYCOL] The condition of a bi- or multinucleate cell having nuclei of genetically different kinds.

heterokont [BIOL] An individual, especially among certain algae, having unequal flagella.

heterolactic fermentation [MICROBIO] A type of lactic acid fermentation by which small yields of lactic acid are produced and much of the sugar is converted to carbon dioxide and other products.

heterolateral [ANAT] Of, pertaining to, or located on the opposite side.

heterolecithal [CELL BIO] Of an egg, having the yolk distributed unevenly throughout the cytoplasm.

heterologous stimulus [PHYSIO] A form of energy capable of exciting any sensory receptor or form of nervous tissue.

heteromedusoid [INV ZOO] A styloid type of sessile gonophore.

Heteromera [INV ZOO] The equivalent name for Tenebrionoidea.

heteromerous [BOT] Of a flower, having one or more whorls made up of a different number of members than the remaining whorls.

Heteromi [VERT ZOO] An equivalent name for Notacanthiformes.

heteromixis [MYCOL] In Fungi, sexual reproduction which involves the fusion of genetically different nuclei, each from a different thallus.

heteromorphic [CELL BIO] Having synoptic or sex chromosomes that differ in size or form. [ZOO] Having a different form at each stage of the life history.

heteromorphosis [BIOL] Regeneration of an organ or part that differs from the original structure at the site. [EMBRYO] Formation of an organ at an abnormal site. Also known as homeosis.

Heteromyidae [VERT ZOO] A family of the mammalian order Rodentia containing the North American kangaroo mice and the pocket mice.

Heteromyinae [VERT ZOO] The spiny pocket mice, a subfamily of the rodent family Heteromyidae.

Heteromyota [INV ZOO] A monospecific order of wormlike animals in the phylum Echiurida.

Heterodontidae [VERT ZOO] The Port Jackson sharks, a family of aberrant modern elasmobranchs in the suborder Heterodontoidea.

Heteronemertini [INV ZOO] An order of the class Anopla; individuals have a middorsal blood vessel and a body wall composed of three muscular layers.

Heteroneura [INV ZOO] A suborder of Lepidoptera; individuals are characterized by fore- and hindwings that differ in shape and venation and by sucking mouthparts.

heteropelmous [VERT ZOO] Having bifid flexor tendons of the toes.

heterophagic vacuole *See* food vacuole.

heterophile leukocyte [HISTOL] A neutrophile of vertebrates other than humans.

Heterophyllidae [PALEON] The single family of the extinct coelenterate order Heterocorallia.

heterophyllous [BOT] Having more than one form of foliage leaves on the same plant or stem.

heterophyte [BOT] A plant that depends upon living or dead plants or their products for food materials.

Heteroplidae [INV ZOO] A family of calcareous sponges in the order Sycettida.

heteroploidy [GEN] The condition of a chromosome complement in which one or more chromosomes, or parts of chromosomes, are present in number different from the numbers of the rest.

heteropolysaccharide [BIOCHEM] A polysaccharide which is a polymer consisting of two or more different monosaccharides.

Heteroporidae [INV ZOO] A family of trepostomatous-like bryozoans in the order Cyclostomata.

Heteroptera [INV ZOO] The equivalent name for Hemiptera.

heteropycnosis [CYTOL] Differential condensation of certain chromosomes, such as sex chromosomes, or chromosome parts.

heterosis [GEN] The increase in size, yield, and performance found in some hybrids, especially of inbred parents. Also known as hybrid vigor.

Heterosomata [VERT ZOO] The equivalent name for Pleuronectiformes.

Heterosoricinae [PALEON] A subfamily of extinct insectivores in the family Soricidae distinguished by a short jaw and hedgehoglike teeth.

Heterospionidae [INV ZOO] A monogeneric family of spioniform worms found in shallow and abyssal depths of the Atlantic and Pacific oceans.

heterospory [BOT] Development of more than one type of spores, especially relating to the microspores and megaspores in ferns and seed plants.

heterostemony [BOT] Presence of two or more different types of stamens in the same flower.

Heterostraci [PALEON] An extinct group of ostracoderms, or armored, jawless vertebrates; armor consisted of bone lacking cavities for bone cells.

heterostyly [BOT] Condition or state of flowers having unequal styles.

Heterotardigrada [INV ZOO] An order of the tardigrades exhibiting wide morphologic variations.

heterothallic [BOT] Pertaining to a mycelium with genetically incompatible hyphae, therefore requiring different hyphae to form a zygospore; refers to fungi and some algae.

heterotopia [ECOL] An abnormal habitat.

heterotopic transplantation [BIOL] A graft transplanted to an abnormal anatomical location on the host.

Heterotrichida [INV ZOO] A large order of large ciliates in the protozoan subclass Spirotrichia; buccal ciliature is well developed and some species are pigmented.

Heterotrichina [INV ZOO] A suborder of the protozoan order Heterotrichida.

heterotroph [BIOL] An organism that obtains nourishment from the ingestion and breakdown of organic matter.

heterotrophic effect [BIOCHEM] The interaction between different ligands, such as the effect of an inhibitor or activator on the binding of a substrate by an enzyme.

heterotropic enzyme [BIOCHEM] A type of allosteric enzyme in which a small molecule other than the substrate serves as the allosteric reflector.

heteroxenous [BIOL] Requiring more than one host to complete a life cycle.

heterozooid [INV ZOO] Any of the specialized, nonfeeding zooids in a bryozoan colony.

heterozygote [GEN] An individual that has different alleles at one or more loci and therefore produces gametes of two or more different kinds.

heterozygous [GEN] Of or pertaining to a heterozygote.

hexacanth [INV ZOO] Having six hooks; refers specifically to the embryo of certain tapeworms.

Hexacorallia [INV ZOO] The equivalent name for Zoantharia.

hexactin [INV ZOO] A spicule, especially in Porifera, having six equal rays at right angles to each other.

Hexactinellida [INV ZOO] A class of the phylum Porifera which includes sponges with a skeleton made up basically of hexactinal siliceous spicules.

Hexactinosa [INV ZOO] An order of sponges in the subclass Hexasterophora; parenchymal megascleres form a rigid framework and consist of simple hexactins.

Hexanchidae [VERT ZOO] The six- and seven-gill sharks, a group of aberrant modern elasmobranchs in the suborder Notidanoidea.

hexapetalous [BOT] Having or being a perianth comprising six petaloid divisions.

Hexapoda [INV ZOO] An equivalent name for Insecta.

hexaster [INV ZOO] A type of hexactin with branching rays that form star-shaped figures.

Hexasterophora [INV ZOO] A subclass of sponges of the class Hexactinellida in which parenchymal microscleres are typically hexasters.

hexenbesen See witches'-broom disease.

hexokinase [BIOCHEM] Any enzyme that catalyzes the phosphorylation of hexoses.

hexosamine [BIOCHEM] A primary amine derived from a hexose by replacing the hydroxyl with an amine group.

hexosaminidase A [BIOCHEM] An enzyme which catalyzes the hydrolysis of the N-acetylgalactosamine residue from certain gangliosides.

hexosan See hemicellulose.

hexose [BIOCHEM] Any monosaccharide that contains six carbon atoms in the molecule.

hexose diphosphate pathway See glycolytic pathway.

hexose monophosphate cycle [BIOCHEM] A pathway for carbohydrate metabolism in which one molecule of hexose monophosphate is completely oxidized.

hexose phosphate [BIOCHEM] Any one of the phosphoric acid esters of a hexose, notably glucose, formed during the metabolism of carbohydrates by living organisms.

hexulose [BIOCHEM] A ketose made from a six-carbon-chain monosaccharide.

Hfr See high-frequency recombination.

hiascent [BIOL] Gaping.

hiatus [ANAT] A space or a passage through an organ.

hibernaculum [BIOL] A winter shelter for plants or dormant animals. [BOT] A winter bud or other winter plant part. [INV ZOO] A winter resting bud produced by a few fresh-water bryozoans which grows into a new colony in the spring.

hibernation [PHYSIO] 1. Condition of dormancy and torpor found in cold-blooded vertebrates and invertebrates. 2. See deep hibernation.

hickory [BOT] The common name for species of the genus *Carya* in the order Fagales; tall deciduous tree with pinnately compound leaves, solid pith, and terminal, scaly winter buds.

hide [VERT ZOO] Outer covering of an animal.

high-frequency recombination [MICROBIO] A bacterial cell type, especially *Escherichia coli*, having an integrated F factor and characterized by a high frequency of recombination. Abbreviated Hfr.

highmoor bog [ECOL] A bog whose surface is covered by sphagnum mosses and is not dependent upon the water table.

Hill plot [BIOCHEM] A graphic representation of the Hill reaction.

Hill reaction [BIOCHEM] The release of molecular oxygen by isolated chloroplasts in the presence of a suitable electron receptor, such as ferricyanide.

hilum [ANAT] See hilus. [BOT] Scar on a seed marking the point of detachment from the funiculus.

hilus [ANAT] An opening or recess in an organ, usually for passage of a vessel or duct. Also known as hilum.

Himantandraceae [BOT] A family of dicotyledonous plants in the order Magnoliales characterized by several, uniovulate carpels and laminar stamens.

himantioid [MYCOL] Pertaining to a mycelium arranged in spreading fanlike cords.

Himantopterinae [INV ZOO] A subfamily of lepidopteran insects in the family Zygaenidae including small, brightly colored moths with narrow hindwings, ribbonlike tails, and long hairs covering the body and wings.

hindbrain See rhombencephalon.

hindgut [EMBRYO] The caudal portion of the embryonic digestive tube in vertebrates.

hinge plate [INV ZOO] 1. In bivalve mollusks, the portion of a valve that supports the hinge teeth. 2. The socket-bearing part of the dorsal valve in brachiopods.

hinge tooth [INV ZOO] A projection on a valve of a bivalve mollusk near the hinge line.

Hiodontidae [VERT ZOO] A family of tropical, fresh-water actinopterygian fishes in the order Osteoglossiformes containing the mooneyes of North America.

hip [ANAT] 1. The region of the junction of thigh and trunk. 2. The hip joint, formed by articulation of the femur and hipbone.

hipbone [ANAT] A large broad bone consisting of three parts, the ilium, ischium, and pubis; makes up a lateral half of the pelvis in mammals. Also known as innominate.

Hippidea [INV ZOO] A group of decapod crustaceans belonging to the Anomura and including cylindrical or squarish burrowing crustaceans in which the abdomen is symmetrical and bent under the thorax.

Hippoboscidae [INV ZOO] The louse flies, a family of cyclorrhaphous dipteran insects in the section Pupipara.

hippocampal sulcus [ANAT] A fissure on the brain situated between the para hippocampal gyrus and the fimbria hippocampi. Also known as dentate fissure.

hippocampus [ANAT] A ridge that extends over the floor of the descending horn of each lateral ventricle of the brain.

Hippocampus [VERT ZOO] A genus of marine fishes in the order Gasterosteiformes which contains the sea horses.

Hippocrateaceae [BOT] A family of dicotyledonous plants in the order Celastrales distinguished by an extrastaminal disk, mostly opposite leaves, seeds without endosperm, and a well-developed latex system.

hippocrepiform [BIOL] Horseshoe-shaped.

Hippoglossidae [VERT ZOO] A family of actinopterygian fishes in the order Pleuronectiformes composed of the flounders and plaice.

Hippomorpha [VERT ZOO] A suborder of the mammalian order Perissodactyla containing horses, zebras, and related forms.

Hippopotamidae [VERT ZOO] The hippopotamuses, a family of palaeodont mammals in the superfamily Anthracotherioidea.

hippopotamus [VERT ZOO] The common name for two species of artiodactyl ungulates composing the family Hippopotamidae.

Hipposideridae [VERT ZOO] The Old World leaf-nosed bats, a family of mammals in the order Chiroptera.

hirsute [BIOL] Shaggy; hairy.

Hirudinea [INV ZOO] A class of parasitic or predatory annelid worms commonly known as leeches; all have 34 body segments and terminal suckers for attachment and locomotion.

Hirudinidae [VERT ZOO] The swallows, a family of passeriform birds in the suborder Oscines.

his operon [GEN] A sequence of nine genes in the chromosomes of many bacteria which code for all the enzymes of histidine biosynthesis.

hispid [BIOL] Having a covering of bristles or minute spines.

hispidulous [BIOL] Hispid to a minute degree.

histamine [BIOCHEM] $C_5H_9N_3$ An amine derivative of histadine which is widely distributed in human tissues.

Histeridae [INV ZOO] The clown beetles, a large family of coleopteran insects in the superfamily Histeroidea.

Histeroidea [INV ZOO] A superfamily of coleopteran insects in the suborder Polyphaga.

histidase [BIOCHEM] An enzyme found in the liver of higher vertebrates that catalyzes the deamination of histidine to urocanic acid.

histidine [BIOCHEM] $C_6H_9O_2N_3$ A crystalline basic amino acid present in large amounts in hemoglobin and resulting from the hydrolysis of most proteins.

Histioteuthidae [INV ZOO] A family of cephalopod mollusks containing several species of squids.

histochemistry [BIOCHEM] A science that deals with the distribution and activities of chemical components in tissues.

histodifferentiation [EMBRYO] Differentiation of cell groups into tissues.

histogen [BOT] A clearly delimited region or primary tissue from which the specific parts of a plant organ are thought to be produced.

histogenesis [EMBRYO] The developmental process by which the definite cells and tissues which make up the body of an organism arise from embryonic cells.

histologist [ANAT] An individual who specializes in histology.

histology [ANAT] The study of the structure and chemical composition of animal and plant tissues as related to their function.

histone [BIOCHEM] Any of the strong, soluble basic proteins of cell nuclei that are precipitated by ammonium hydroxide.

histophysiology [PHYSIO] The science of tissue functions.

Histoplasma [MYCOL] A genus of parasitic fungi.

Histoplasma capsulatum [MYCOL] The parasitic fungus that causes histoplasmosis in humans.

historadiography [BIOPHYS] A technique for taking x-ray pictures of cells, tissues, or sometimes whole small organisms.

histotome [BIOL] A microtome used to cut tissue sections for microscopic examination.

Histriobdellidae [INV ZOO] A small family of errantian polychaete worms that live as ectoparasites on crayfishes.

hoarding behavior [VERT ZOO] The carrying of food to the home nest for storage, in quantities exceeding daily need.

hoarhound See marrubium.

hoary [BOT] Having grayish or whitish color, referring to leaves.

Hodotermitidae [INV ZOO] A family of lower (primitive) termites in the order Isoptera.

Hofbauer cell [HISTOL] A large, possibly phagocytic cell found in chorionic villi.

hoja blanca [PL PATH] A major virus disease of rice in Cuba and Venezuela.

holarctic zoogeographic region [ECOL] A major unit of the earth's surface extending from the North Pole to 30–45°N latitude and characterized by faunal homogeneity.

Holasteridae [INV ZOO] A family of exocyclic Euechinoidea in the order Holasteroida; individuals are oval or heart-shaped, with fully developed pore pairs.

Holasteroida [INV ZOO] An order of exocyclic Euechinoidea in which the apical system is elongated along the anteroposterior axis and teeth occur only in juvenile stages.

holcodont [VERT ZOO] Having the teeth fixed in a long, continuous groove.

holdfast [BOT] 1. A suckerlike base which attaches the thallus of certain algae to the support. 2. A disklike terminal structure on the tendrils of various plants used for attachment to a flat surface. [INV ZOO] An organ by which parasites such as tapeworms attach themselves to the host.

Holectypidae [PALEON] A family of extinct exocyclic Euechinoidea in the order Holectypoida; individuals are hemispherical.

Holectypoida [INV ZOO] An order of exocyclic Euechinoidea with keeled, flanged teeth, with distinct genital plates, and with the ambulacra narrower than the interambulacra on the adoral side.

holism [BIOL] The view that the whole of a complex system, such as a cell or organism, is functionally greater than the sum of its parts. Also known as organicism.

Hollinacea [PALEON] A dimorphic superfamily of extinct ostracods in the suborder Beyrichicopina including forms with sulci, lobation, and some form of velar structure.

Hollinidae [PALEON] An extinct family of ostracods in the superfamily Hollinacea distinguished by having a bulbous third lobe on the valve.

hollow stalk [PL PATH] Any plant disease characterized by deterioration of the pith in the stalk.

holly [BOT] The common name for the trees and shrubs composing the genus *Ilex*; distinguished by spiny leaves and small berries.

hollywood lignumvitae *See* lignumvitae.

Holobasidiomycetes [MYCOL] An equivalent name for Homobasidiomycetidae.

holoblastic [EMBRYO] Pertaining to eggs that undergo total cleavage due to the absence of a mass of yolk.

holobranch [VERT ZOO] A gill with a row of filaments on each side of the branchial arch.

holocarpic [BOT] 1. Having the entire thallus developed into a fruiting body or sporangium. 2. Lacking rhizoids and haustoria.

holocellulose [BIOCHEM] The total polysaccharide fraction of wood, straw, and so on, that is composed of cellulose and all of the hemicelluloses and that is obtained when the extractives and the lignin are removed from the natural material.

Holocentridae [VERT ZOO] A family of nocturnal beryciform fishes found in shallow tropical and subtropical reefs; contains the squirrelfishes and soldierfishes.

Holocephali [VERT ZOO] The chimaeras, a subclass of the Chondrichthyes, distinguished by four pairs of gills and gill arches, an erectile dorsal fin and spine, and naked skin.

holococcolith [BIOL] A coccolith with simple rhombic or hexagonal crystals arranged like a mosaic.

holocoenosis [ECOL] The nature of the action of the environment on living organisms.

holocrine gland [PHYSIO] A structure whose cells undergo dissolution and are entirely extruded, together with the secretory product.

holoenzyme [BIOCHEM] A complex, fully active enzyme, containing an apoenzyme and a coenzyme.

hologamy [BIOL] Condition of having gametes similar in size and form to somatic cells. [BOT] Condition of having the whole thallus develop into a gametangium.

hologony [INV ZOO] Condition of having the germinal area extend the full length of a gonad; refers specifically to certain nematodes.

Holometabola [INV ZOO] A division of the insect subclass Pterygota whose members undergo holometabolous metamorphosis during development.

holometabolous metamorphosis [INV ZOO] Complete metamorphosis, during which there are four stages; the egg, larva, pupa, and imago or adult.

holomorphosis [BIOL] Complete regeneration of a lost body structure.

holomyarian [INV ZOO] Having zones of muscle layers but no muscle cells; refers specifically to certain nematodes.

holonephros [VERT ZOO] Type of kidney having one nephron beside each somite along the entire length of the coelom; seen in larvae of myxinoid cyclostomes.

holophyte [BIOL] An organism that obtains food in the manner of a green plant, that is, by synthesis of organic substances from inorganic substances using the energy of light.

holoplankton [ZOO] Organisms that live their complete life cycle in the floating state.

Holoptychidae [PALEON] A family of extinct lobefin fishes in the order Osteolepiformes.

holorhinal [VERT ZOO] Among birds, having a rounded anterior margin on the nasal bones.

Holostei [VERT ZOO] An infraclass of fishes in the subclass Actinopterygii descended from the Chondrostei and ancestral to the Teleostei.

holostome [INV ZOO] A type of adult digenetic trematode having a portion of the ventral surface modified as a complex adhesive organ.

Holothuriidae [VERT ZOO] A family of aspidochirotacean echinoderms in the order Aspidochirotida possessing tentacular ampullae and only the left gonad.

Holothuroidea [INV ZOO] The sea cucumbers, a class of the subphylum Echinozoa characterized by a cylindrical body and smooth, leathery skin.

Holothyridae [INV ZOO] The single family of the acarine suborder Holothyrina.

Holothyrina [INV ZOO] A suborder of mites in the order Acarina which are large and hemispherical with a deep-brown, smooth, heavily sclerotized cuticle.

Holotrichia [INV ZOO] A major subclass of the protozoan class Ciliatea; body ciliation is uniform with cilia arranged in longitudinal rows.

holotype [SYST] A nomenclatural type for the single specimen designated as "the type" by the orginal author at the time of publication of the original description.

holozoic [ZOO] Obtaining food in the manner of most animals, by ingesting complex organic matter.

Holuridae [PALEON] A group of extinct chondrostean fishes in the suborder Palaeoniscoidei distinguished in having lepidotrichia of all fins articulated but not bifurcated, fins without fulcra, and the tail not cleft.

Homacodontidae [PALEON] A family of extinct palaeodont mammals in the superfamily Dichobunoidea.

Homalopteridae [VERT ZOO] A small family of cypriniform fishes in the suborder Cyprinoidei.

Homalorhagae [INV ZOO] A suborder of the class Kinorhyncha having a single dorsal plate covering the neck and three ventral plates on the third zonite.

Homalozoa [INV ZOO] A subphylum of echinoderms characterized by the complete absence of radial symmetry.

Homaridae [INV ZOO] A family of marine decapod crustaceans containing the lobsters.

Homarus [INV ZOO] A genus of the family Homaridae comprising most species of lobsters.

homaxial [BIOL] Having all axes equal.

homeomorph [BIOL] An organism which exhibits a superficial resemblance to another organism even though they have different ancestors.

homeostasis [BIOL] In higher animals, the maintenance of an internal constancy and an independence of the environment.

homeotherm [PHYSIO] An endotherm that maintains a constant body temperature, as do most mammals and birds.

homeothermia [PHYSIO] The condition of being warm-blooded.

home range [ECOL] The physical area of an organism's normal activity.

Hominidae [VERT ZOO] A family of primates in the superfamily Hominoidea containing one living species, *Homo sapiens*.

Hominoidea [VERT ZOO] A superfamily of the order Primates comprising apes and humans.

Homo [VERT ZOO] The genus of human beings, including modern humans and many extinct species.

Homobasidiomycetidae [MYCOL] A subclass of basidiomycetous fungi in which the basidium is not divided by cross walls.

homocercal [VERT ZOO] Pertaining to the caudal fin of certain fishes which has almost equal lobes, with the vertebral column terminating near the middle of the base.

homochlamydeous [BIOL] Having all members of the perianth similar or not differentiated into calyx or corolla.

homochromy [ZOO] A form of protective coloration whereby the individual blends into the background.

homocysteine [BIOCHEM] $C_4H_9O_2NS$ An amino acid formed in animals by demethylation of methionine.

homodont [VERT ZOO] Having all teeth similar in form; characteristic of nonmammalian vertebrates.

homodynamic [INV ZOO] Developing through continuous successive generations without a diapause; applied to insects.

homoecious [BIOL] Having one host for all stages of the life cycle.

homoeomerous [BOT] Having algae distributed uniformly throughout the thallus of a lichen.

Homo erectus [PALEON] A type of fossil human from the Pleistocene of Java and China representing a specialized side branch in human evolution.

homofermentative lactobacilli [MICROBIO] Bacteria that produce a single end product, lactic acid, from fermentation of carbohydrates.

homogametic sex [GEN] The sex of a species in which the paired sex chromosomes are of equal size and which therefore produces homogametes.

homogamety [GEN] The production of homogametes by one sex of a species.

homogamous [BIOL] Of or pertaining to homogamy.

homogamy [BIOL] Inbreeding due to isolation. [BOT] Condition of having all flowers alike.

homogenate [BIOL] A tissue that has been finely divided and mixed.

homogentisase [BIOCHEM] The enzyme that catalyzes the conversion of homogentisic acid to fumaryl acetoacetic acid.

homogentisic acid [BIOCHEM] $C_8H_8O_4$ An intermediate product in the metabolism of phenylalanine and tyrosine; found in excess in persons with phenylketonuria and alkaptonuria.

homogony [BOT] Condition of having one type of flower, with stamens and pistil of uniform length.

homoiochlamydeous [BOT] Having perianth leaves alike, not differentiated into sepals and petals.

homologenetic [EMBRYO] Of a determined part of an embryo, capable of inducing formation of a similar part when grafted into an undetermined field.

homolothermal [PHYSIO] Referring to an organism which maintains a constant internal temperature which is often higher than that of the environment; common among birds and mammals. Also known as warm-blooded.

Homoistela [PALEON] A class of extinct echinoderms in the subphylum Homalozoa.

homokaryon [MYCOL] A bi- or multinucleate cell having nuclei all of the same kind.

homokaryosis [MYCOL] The condition of a bi- or multinucleate cell having nuclei all of the same kind.

homolecithal [CELL BIO] Referring to eggs having small amounts of evenly distributed yolk. Also known as isolecithal.

homologous [BIOL] Pertaining to a structural relation between parts of different organisms due to evolutionary development from the same or a corresponding part, such as the wing of a bird and the pectoral fin of a fish.

homologous stimulus [PHYSIO] A form of energy to which a specific sensory receptor is most sensitive.

homomorphism [BOT] Having perfect flowers consisting of only one type.

Homoneura [INV ZOO] A suborder of the Lepidoptera with mandibulate mouthparts, and fore- and hindwings that are similar in shape and venation.

homopetalous [BOT] Having all petals identical.

homoplasy [BIOL] Correspondence between organs or structures in different organisms acquired as a result of evolutionary convergence or of parallel evolution.

homopolysaccharide [BIOCHEM] A polysaccharide which is a polymer of one kind of monosaccharide.

Homoptera [INV ZOO] An order of the class Insecta including a large number of sucking insects of diverse forms.

Homo sapiens [VERT ZOO] Modern human species; a large, erect, omnivorous terrestrial biped of the primate family Hominidae.

Homosclerophorida [INV ZOO] An order of primitive sponges of the class Demospongiae with a skeleton consisting of equirayed, tetraxonid, siliceous spicules.

homoserine [BIOCHEM] $C_4H_9O_3N$ An amino acid formed as an intermediate product in animals in the metabolic breakdown of cystathionine to cysteine.

homosexual [BIOL] Of, pertaining to, or being the same sex.

homospory [BOT] Production of only one kind of asexual spore.

homothallic [MYCOL] Having genetically compatible hyphae and therefore forming zygospores from two branches of the same mycelium.

homotropic enzyme [BIOCHEM] A type of allosteric enzyme in which the substrate serves as the allosteric reflector.

homotropous [BOT] Having the radicle directed toward the hilum.

homotype [SYST] A taxonomic type for a specimen which has been compared with the holotype by another than the author of the species and determined by him to be conspecific with it.

homotypy [BIOL] Protective device based on resemblance of shape to the background.

homovanillic acid [BIOCHEM] $HOC_6H_3(OCH_3)-CH_2CO_2H$ A major metabolite of 3-O-methyl dopa; used in enzyme determination. Abbreviated HVA. Also known as 4-hydroxy-3-methoxyphenylacetic acid.

homozygote [GEN] An individual that has identical alleles at one or more loci and therefore produces gametes which are all identical.

homozygous [GEN] Of or pertaining to a homozygote.

honeybee [INV ZOO] *Apis mellifera.* The bee kept for the commercial production of honey; a member of the dipterous family Apidae.

honeycomb [INV ZOO] A mass of wax cells in the form of hexagonal prisms constructed by honeybees for their brood and honey.

honeycomb coral [PALEON] The common name for members of the extinct order Tabulata; has prismatic sections arranged like the cells of a honeycomb.

honeydew [INV ZOO] The viscous secretion deposited on leaves by many aphids and scale insects; an attractant for ants.

Honey Dew melon [BOT] A variety of muskmelon (*Cucumis melo*) belonging to the Violales; fruit is large, oval, smooth, and creamy yellow to ivory, without surface markings.

honey tube [INV ZOO] Either of a pair of cornicles on the dorsal aspect of one abdominal segment in certain aphids.

hoof [VERT ZOO] 1. Horny covering for terminal portions of the digits of ungulate mammals. 2. A hoofed foot, as of a horse.

Hookeriales [BOT] An order of the mosses with irregularly branched stems and leaves that appear to be in one plane.

hookworm [INV ZOO] The common name for parasitic roundworms composing the family Ancylostomidae.

hop [BOT] *Humulus lupulus.* A dioecious liana of the order Urticales distinguished by herbaceous vines produced from a perennial crown; the inflorescence, a catkin, of the female plant is used commercially for beer production.

hophornbeam [BOT] Any tree of the genus *Ostrya* in the birch family recognized by its very scaly bark and the fruit which closely resembles that of the hopvine.

Hoplocarida [INV ZOO] A superorder of the class Crustacea with the single order Stomatopoda.

Hoplonemertini [INV ZOO] An order of unsegmented, ribbonlike worms in the class Enopla; all species have an armed proboscis.

Hoplophoridae [INV ZOO] A family of prawns containing numerous bathypelagic representatives.

hopperburn [PL PATH] A disease of potato and peanut plants caused by a leafhopper which secretes a toxic substance on the leaves, causing browning and shriveling.

Hordeum [BOT] A genus of the order Cyperales containing all species of barley.

horehound *See* marrubium.

horizontal plane [ANAT] A transverse plane at right angles to the longitudinal axis of the body.

hormesis [BIOL] Providing stimulus by nontoxic amounts of a toxic agent.

hormogonium [BOT] Portion of a filament between heterocysts in certain algae; detaches as a reproductive body.

hormone [BIOCHEM] 1. A chemical messenger produced by endocrine glands and secreted directly into the bloodstream to exert a specific effect on a distant part of the body. 2. An organic compound that is synthesized in minute quantities in one part of a plant and translocated to another part, where it influences a specific physiological process.

hornbeam [BOT] Any tree of the genus *Carpinus* in the birch family distinguished by doubly serrate leaves and by small, pointed, angular winter buds with scales in four rows.

horned dinosaur [PALEON] Common name for extinct reptiles of the suborder Ceratopsia.

horned liverwort [BOT] The common name for bryophytes of the class Anthocerotae. Also known as hornwort.

horned toad [VERT ZOO] The common name for any of the lizards of the genus *Phrynosoma;* a reptile that resembles a toad but is less bulky.

horned-toad dinosaur [PALEON] The common name for extinct reptiles composing the suborder Ankylosauria.

hornet [INV ZOO] The common name for a number of large wasps in the hymenopteran family Vespidae.

hornwort *See* horned liverwort.

horny coral [INV ZOO] The common name for coelenterate members of the order Gorgonacea.

horse [VERT ZOO] *Equus caballus.* A herbivorous mammal in the family Equidae; the feet are characterized by a single functional digit.

horse chestnut [BOT] *Aesculus hippocastanum.* An ornamental buckeye tree in the order Sapindales, usually with seven leaflets per leaf and resinous buds.

horsehair blight [PL PATH] A fungus disease of tea and certain other tropical plants caused by *Marasmius equicrinis* and characterized by black festoons of mycelia hanging from the branches.

horseradish [BOT] *Armoracia rusticana.* A perennial crucifer belonging to the order Capparales and grown for its pungent roots, used as a condiment.

horseshoe crab [INV ZOO] The common name for arthropods composing the subclass Xiphosurida, especially the subgroup Limulida.

horsetail [BOT] The common name for plants of the genus *Equisetum* composing the order Equisetales.

horticulture [BOT] The art and science of growing plants.

host [BIOL] 1. An organism on or in which a parasite lives. 2. The dominant partner of a symbiotic or commensal pair.

hot flash [PHYSIO] A sudden transitory sensation of heat, often involving the whole body, due to cessation of ovarian function; a symptom of the climacteric.

hot spot [MOL BIO] A site in a gene at which there is an unusually high frequency of mutation.

housefly [INV ZOO] *Musca domestica*. A dipteran insect with lapping mouthparts commonly found near human habitations; a vector in the transmission of many disease pathogens.

Howell's unit [BIOL] A unit for the standardization of heparin.

Howship's lacuna [HISTOL] Minute depressions in the surface of a bone undergoing resorption.

H-RNA See heterogeneous ribonucleic acid.

HSI See heat stress index.

H substance [BIOCHEM] An agent similar to histamine and believed to play a role in local blood vessel response in tissue damage.

huarizo [VERT ZOO] A hybrid offspring of a male llama and a female alpaca, bred for its fine fleece.

huckleberry [BOT] The common name for shrubs of the genus *Gaylussacia* in the family Ericaceae distinguished by an ovary with 10 locules and 10 ovules; the dark-blue berries are edible.

Hudsonian life zone [ECOL] A zone comprising the climate and biotic communities of the northern portions of North American coniferous forests and the peaks of high mountains.

Huggins-Talalay unit [BIOL] A unit for the standardization of phosphatase.

hull [BOT] The outer, usually hard, covering of a fruit or seed.

hulless buckwheat See tartary buckwheat.

human biogeography [ECOL] The science concerned with the distribution of human populations on the earth.

human chorionic gonadotropin [BIOCHEM] A gonadotropic and luteotropic hormone secreted by the chorionic vesicle. Abbreviated HCG. Also known as chorionic gonadotropin.

human community [ECOL] That portion of a human ecosystem composed of human beings and associated plant and animal species.

human ecology [ECOL] The branch of ecology that considers the relations of individual persons and of human communities with their particular environment.

human genetics [GEN] The study of human heredity and variation, including the physical basis, mechanisms of inheritance, inheritance patterns, and population analysis.

human threadworm See pinworm.

humeral [ANAT] Of or pertaining to the humerus or the shoulder region.

humeroglandular effector system [PHYSIO] Glandular effector system in which the activating agent is a blood-borne chemical.

humeromuscular effector system [PHYSIO] Muscular effector system in which the activating agent is a blood-borne chemical.

humerus [ANAT] The proximal bone of the forelimb in vertebrates; the bone of the upper arm in humans, articulating with the glenoid fossa and the radius and ulna.

humicolous [ECOL] Of or pertaining to plant species inhabiting medium-dry ground.

humid transition life zone [ECOL] A zone comprising the climate and biotic communities of the northwest moist coniferous forest of the north-central United States.

humifuse [BIOL] Spread over the ground surface.

Humiriaceae [BOT] A family of dicotyledonous plants in the order Linales characterized by exappendiculate petals, usually five petals, flowers with an intrastaminal disk, and leaves lacking stipules.

humivore [ECOL] An organism that feeds on humus.

hummingbird [VERT ZOO] The common name for members of the family Trochilidae; fast-flying, short-legged, weak-footed insectivorous birds with a tubular, pointed bill and a fringed tongue.

hummock [ECOL] A rounded or conical knoll frequently formed of earth and covered with vegetation.

humor [PHYSIO] A fluid or semifluid part of the body.

husk [BOT] The outer coat of certain seeds, particularly if it is a dry, membranous structure.

Huxley's anastomosis [HISTOL] Polyhedral cells forming the middle layer of a hair root sheath.

HVA See homovanillic acid.

Hyaenidae [VERT ZOO] A family of catlike carnivores in the superfamily Feloidea including the hyenas and aardwolf.

Hyaenodontidae [PALEON] A family of extinct carnivorous mammals in the order Deltatheridia.

Hyalellidae [INV ZOO] A family of amphipod crustaceans in the suborder Gammaridea.

hyaline [BIOCHEM] A clear, homogeneous, structureless material found in the matrix of cartilage, vitreous body, mucin, and glycogen.

hyaline cartilage [HISTOL] A translucent connective tissue comprising about two-thirds clear, homogeneous matrix with few or no collagen fibrils.

hyaline membrane [HISTOL] 1. A basement membrane. 2. A membrane of a hair follicle between the inner fibrous layer and the outer root sheath.

hyaline test [INV ZOO] A translucent wall or shell of certain foraminiferans composed of layers of calcite interspersed with separating membranes.

Hyalodictyae [MYCOL] A subdivision of the spore group Dictyosporae characterized by hyaline spores.

Hyalodidymae [MYCOL] A subdivision of the spore group Didymosporae characterized by hyaline spores.

Hyalohelicosporae [MYCOL] A subdivision of the spore group Helicosporae characterized by hyaline spores.

hyaloid membrane [ANAT] The limiting membrane surrounding the vitreous body of the eyeball, and forming the suspensory ligament.

Hyalophragmiae [MYCOL] A subdivision of the spore group Phragmosporae characterized by hyaline spores.

hyaloplasm [CELL BIO] The optically clear, viscous to gelatinous ground substance of cytoplasm in which formed bodies are suspended.

Hyaloscolecosporae [MYCOL] A subdivision of the spore group Scalecosporae characterized by hyaline spores.

Hyalospongia [PALEON] A class of extinct glass sponges, equivalent to the living Hexactinellida, having siliceous spicules made of opaline silica.

Hyalosporae [MYCOL] A subdivision of the spore group Amerosporae characterized by hyaline spores.

Hyalostaurosporae [MYCOL] A subdivision of the spore group Staurosporae characterized by hyaline spores.

hyaluronate [BIOCHEM] A salt or ester of hyaluronic acid.

hyaluronate lyase See hyaluronidase.

hyaluronic acid [BIOCHEM] A polysaccharide found as an integral part of the gellike substance of animal connective tissue.

hyaluronidase [BIOCHEM] Any one of a family of enzymes which catalyze the breakdown of hyaluronic acid. Also known as hyaluronate lyase; spreading factor.

Hybodontoidea [PALEON] An ancient suborder of extinct fossil sharks in the order Selachii.

hybrid [GEN] The offspring of genetically dissimilar parents.

hybrid enzyme [BIOCHEM] A form of polymeric enzyme occurring in heterozygous individuals that shows a hybrid molecular form made up of subunits differing in one or more amino acids.

hybridization [GEN] The act or process of producing hybrids.

hybrid merogony [EMBRYO] The fertilization of cytoplasmic fragments of the egg of one species by the sperm of a related species.

hybrid molecule [BIOCHEM] A single molecule, usually protein, peculiar to heterozygotes and containing two structurally different polypeptide chains determined by two different alleles.

hybrid sterility [GEN] Inability to form functional gametes in a hybrid due to disturbances in sex-cell development or in meiosis, caused by incompatible genetic constitution.

hybrid vigor See heterosis.

hydathode [BOT] An opening of the epidermis of higher plants specialized for exudation of water.

hydra [INV ZOO] Any species of *Hydra* or related genera, consisting of a simple, tubular body with a mouth at one end surrounded by tentacles, and a foot at the other end for attachment.

Hydra [INV ZOO] A common genus of coelenterates in the suborder Anthomedusae.

Hydrachnellae [INV ZOO] A family of generally fresh-water predacious mites in the suborder Trombidiformes, including some parasitic forms.

Hydraenidae [INV ZOO] The equivalent name for Limnebiidae.

hydranth [INV ZOO] Nutritive individual in a hydroid colony.

hydrase [BIOCHEM] An enzyme that catalyzes removal or addition of water to a substrate without hydrolyzing it.

hydric [ECOL] Characterized by or thriving in abundance of moisture.

Hydrobatidae [VERT ZOO] The storm petrels, a family of oceanic birds in the order Procellariiformes.

hydrocaulus [INV ZOO] Branched, upright stem of a hydroid colony.

Hydrocharitaceae [BOT] The single family of the order Hydrocharitales, characterized by an inferior, compound ovary with laminar placentation.

Hydrocharitales [BOT] A monofamilial order of aquatic monocotyledonous plants in the subclass Alismatidae.

hydrochory [BIOL] Dispersal of disseminules by water.

hydrocladium [INV ZOO] Branchlet of a hydrocaulus.

hydrocoele [INV ZOO] 1. Water vascular system in Echinodermata. 2. Embryonic precursor of the system.

Hydrocorallina [INV ZOO] An order in some systems of classification set up to include the coelenterate groups Milleporina and Stylasterina.

Hydrocorisae [INV ZOO] A subdivision of the Hemiptera containing water bugs with concealed antennae and without a bulbus ejaculatorius in the male.

hydrocortisone [BIOCHEM] $C_{21}H_{30}O_5$ The generic name for 17-hydroxycorticosterone; an adrenocortical steroid occurring naturally and prepared synthetically; its effects are similar to cortisone, but it is more active. Also known as cortisol.

Hydrodamalinae [VERT ZOO] A monogeneric subfamily of sirenian mammals in the family Dugongidae.

hydroecium [INV ZOO] The closed, funnel-shaped tube at the upper end of coelenterates belonging to the Siphonophora.

hydrofuge [ZOO] Of a structure, shedding water, as the hair on certain animals.

hydrogenase [BIOCHEM] Enzyme that catalyzes the oxidation of hydrogen.

hydrogen bacteria [MICROBIO] Bacteria capable of obtaining energy from the oxidation of molecular hydrogen.

hydroid [INV ZOO] 1. The polyp form of a hydrozoan coelenterate. Also known as hydroid polyp; hydropolyp. 2. Any member of the Hydroida.

Hydroida [INV ZOO] An order of coelenterates in the class Hydrozoa including usually colonial forms with a well-developed polyp stage.

hydrolase [BIOCHEM] Any of a class of enzymes which catalyze the hydrolysis of proteins, nucleic acids, starch, fats, phosphate esters, and other macromolecular substances.

hydrolytic enzyme [BIOCHEM] A catalyst that acts like a hydrolase.

Hydrometridae [INV ZOO] The marsh treaders, a family of hemipteran insects in the subdivision Amphibicorisae.

Hydrophiidae [VERT ZOO] A family of proglyphodont snakes in the suborder Serpentes found in Indian-Pacific oceans.

Hydrophilidae [INV ZOO] The water scavenger beetles, a large family of coleopteran insects in the superfamily Hydrophiloidea.

Hydrophiloidea [INV ZOO] A superfamily of coleopteran insects in the suborder Polyphaga.

hydrophilous [ECOL] Inhabiting moist places.

Hydrophyllaceae [BOT] A family of dicotyledonous plants in the order Polemoniales distinguished by two carpels, parietal placentation, and generally imbricate corolla lobes in the bud.

hydrophyllium [INV ZOO] A transparent body partly covering the spore sacs of siphonophoran coelenterates.

hydrophyte [BOT] 1. A plant that grows in a moist habitat. 2. A plant requiring large amounts of water for growth. Also known as hygrophyte.

hydroplanula [INV ZOO] A coelenterate larval stage between the planula and actinula stages.

hydroponics [BOT] Growing of plants in a nutrient solution with the mechanical support of an inert medium such as sand.

hydropore [INV ZOO] In certain asteroids and echinoids, an opening on the aboral surface of a canal which extends from the ring canal in one of the interradii.

hydrorhiza [INV ZOO] Rootlike structure of a hydroid colony.

Hydroscaphidae [INV ZOO] The skiff beetles, a small family of coleopteran insects in the suborder Myxophaga.

hydrosere [ECOL] Community in which the pioneer plants invade open water, eventually forming some kind of soil such as peat or muck.

hydroskeleton [INV ZOO] Water contained within the coelenteron and serving a skeletal function in most coelenterate polyps.

hydrospire [INV ZOO] Either of a pair of flattened tubes composing part of the respiratory system in blastoids.

hydrospore [INV ZOO] Opening into the hydrocoele on the right side in echinoderm larvae.

hydrotheca [INV ZOO] Cup-shaped portion of the perisarc in some coelenterates that serves to hold and protect a withdrawn hydranth.

hydrotropism [BIOL] Orientation involving growth or movement of a sessile organism or part, especially plant roots, in response to the presence of water.

2-hydroxy-3-amylene-α-naphthoquinone See lapachol.

β-hydroxybutyric dehydrogenase [BIOCHEM] The enzyme that catalyzes the conversion of L-β-hydroxybutyric acid to acetoacetic acid by dehydrogenation.

hydroxylase [BIOCHEM] Any of several enzymes that catalyze certain hydroxylation reactions involving atomic oxygen.

4-hydroxy-3-methoxyphenylacetic acid See homovanillic acid.

hydroxyproline [BIOCHEM] $C_5H_9O_3N$ An amino acid that is essentially limited to structural proteins of the collagen type.

2-hydroxy-1,2,3-propane-tricarboxylic acid See isocitric acid.

α-hydroxypropanoic acid See lactic acid.

2-hydroxypropanoic acid See lactic acid.

5-hydroxytryptamine See serotonin.

5-hydroxytryptophan [BIOCHEM] $C_{11}H_{12}N_2O_3$ Minute rods or needlelike crystals; the biological precursor of serotonin.

8-hydroxyxanthine See uric acid.

Hydrozoa [INV ZOO] A class of the phylum Coelenterata which includes the fresh-water hydras, the marine hydroids, many small jellyfish, a few corals, and the Portuguese man-of-war.

hyena [VERT ZOO] An African carnivore represented by three species of the family Hyaenidae that resemble dogs but are more closely related to cats.

Hyeniales [PALEOBOT] An order of Devonian plants characterized by small, dichotomously forked leaves borne in whorls.

Hyeniopsida [PALEOBOT] An extinct class of the division Equisetophyta.

Hygrobiidae [INV ZOO] The squeaker beetles, a small family of coleopteran insects in the suborder Adephaga.

hygromycin [MICROBIO] $C_{25}H_{33}O_{12}N$ A weakly acidic, soluble antibiotic with a fairly broad spectrum, produced by a strain of *Streptomyces hygroscopicus*.

hygrophyte See hydrophyte.

hygroscopic [BOT] Being sensitive to moisture, such as certain tissues.

hylaea See tropical rainforest.

Hylidae [VERT ZOO] The tree frogs, a large amphibian family in the suborder Procoela; many are adapted to arboreal life, having expanded digital disks.

Hylobatidae [VERT ZOO] A family of anthropoid primates in the superfamily Hominoidea including the gibbon and the siamang of southeastern Asia.

hylophagous [ZOO] Feeding on wood, as termites.

hylotomous [ZOO] Cutting wood, as wood-boring insects.

hymen [ANAT] A mucous membrane partly closing off the vaginal orifice. Also known as maidenhead.

hymenium [MYCOL] The outer, sporebearing layer of certain fungi or their fruiting bodies.

Hymenolepis [INV ZOO] A genus of tapeworms parasitic in humans, birds, and mammals.

Hymenolepis nana [INV ZOO] The dwarf tapeworm that infests humans.

Hymenomycetes [MYCOL] A group of the Homobasidiomycetidae including forms such as mushrooms and pore fungi in which basidia are formed in an exposed layer (hymenium) and basidiospores are borne asymmetrically on slender stalks.

hymenophore [MYCOL] Portion of a sporophore that bears the hymenium.

hymenopodium [MYCOL] 1. Tissue beneath the hymenium in certain fungi. 2. A genus of the Moniliales.

Hymenoptera [INV ZOO] A large order of insects including ants, wasps, bees, sawflies, and related forms; head, thorax and abdomen are clearly differentiated; wings, when present, and legs are attached to the thorax.

Hymenostomatida [INV ZOO] An order of ciliated protozoans in the subclass Holotrichia having fairly uniform ciliation and a definite buccal ciliature.

Hynobiidae [VERT ZOO] A family of salamanders in the suborder Cryptobranchoidea.

hyobranchium [VERT ZOO] A Y-shaped bone supporting the tongue and tongue muscles in a snake.

Hyocephalidae [INV ZOO] A monospecific family of hemipteran insects in the superfamily Pentatomorpha.

hyoglossus [ANAT] An extrinsic muscle of the tongue arising from the hyoid bone.

hyoid [ANAT] 1. A bone or complex of bones at the base of the tongue supporting the tongue and its muscles. 2. Of or pertaining to structures derived from the hyoid arch.

hyoid arch [EMBRYO] Either of the second pair of pharyngeal segments or gill arches in vertebrate embryos.

hyoid tooth [VERT ZOO] One of a number of teeth on the tongue of fishes.

hyomandibular [VERT ZOO] The upper portion of the hyoid arch in fishes.

hyomandibular cleft [EMBRYO] The space between the hyoid arch and the mandibular arch in the vertebrate embryo.

hyomandibular pouch [EMBRYO] A portion of the endodermal lining of the pharyngeal cavity which separates the paired hyoid and mandibular arches in vertebrate embryos.

Hyopssodontidae [PALEON] A family of extinct mammalian herbivores in the order Condylarthra.

hyostylic [VERT ZOO] Having the jaws and cranium connected by the hyomandibular, as certain fishes.

hypalgesia [PHYSIO] Diminished sensitivity to pain.

hypandrium [INV ZOO] A plate covering the genitalia on the ninth abdominal segment of certain male insects.

hypanthium [BOT] Expanded receptacle margin to which the sepals, petals, and stamens are attached in some flowers.

hypantrum [VERT ZOO] In reptiles, a notch on the anterior portion of the neural arch that articulates with the hyposphene.

hypaxial musculature [ANAT] The ventral portion of the axial musculature of vertebrates including subvertebral flank and ventral abdominal muscle groups.

hyperacid [PHYSIO] Containing more than the normal concentration of acid in the gastric juice.

hyperactivity [PHYSIO] Excessive or pathologic activity.

hyperalgesia [PHYSIO] Increased or heightened sensitivity to pain stimulation.

hyperchromatic [BIOL] Staining more intensely than normal.

hypercoracoid [VERT ZOO] The upper of two bones at the base of the pectoral fin in teleosts.

hyperesthesia [PHYSIO] Increased sensitivity or sensation.

hyperglycemic factor *See* glucagon.

hyperglycemic glycogenolytic factor *See* glucagon.

Hyperiidea [INV ZOO] A suborder of amphipod crustaceans distinguished by large eyes which cover nearly the entire head.

Hypermastigida [INV ZOO] An order of the multiflagellate protozoans in the class Zoomastigophorea; all inhabit the alimentary canal of termites, cockroaches, and woodroaches.

hypermetamorphism [INV ZOO] Type of embryological development in certain insects in which one or more stages have been interpolated between the full-grown larva and the adult.

Hyperoartii [VERT ZOO] A superorder in the subclass Monorhina distinguished by the single median dorsal nasal opening leading into a blind hypophyseal sac.

Hyperotreti [VERT ZOO] A suborder in the subclass Monorhina distinguished by the nasal opening which is located at the tip of the snout and communicates with the pharynx by a long duct.

hyperparasite [ECOL] An organism that is parasitic on other parasites.

hyperploid [GEN] Having one or more chromosomes or parts of chromosomes in excess of the haploid number, or of a whole multiple of the haploid number.

hyperploidy [GEN] The condition or state of being hyperploid.

hypertelorism [ANAT] An unusually large distance between paired body parts or organs.

hypertely [EVOL] An extreme overdevelopment of an organ or body part during evolution that is disadvantageous to the organism. [ZOO] An extreme degree of imitative coloration, beyond the aspect of utility.

hypertensin *See* angiotensin.

hyperthermia [PHYSIO] A condition of elevated body temperature.

hypertonic [PHYSIO] 1. Excessive or above normal in tone or tension, as a muscle. 2. Having an osmotic pressure greater than that of physiologic salt solution or of any other solution taken as a standard.

Hypertragulidae [PALEON] A family of extinct chevrotainlike pecoran ruminants in the superfamily Traguloidea.

hypha [MYCOL] One of the filaments composing the mycelium of a fungus.

hyphidium [MYCOL] A sterile hymenial structure of hyphal origin.

Hyphochytriales [MYCOL] An order of aquatic fungi in the class Phycomycetes having a saclike to limited hyphal thallus and zoospores with two flagella.

Hyphochytridiomycetes [MYCOL] A class of the true fungi; usually grouped with other classes under the general term Phycomycetes.

hyphoid [MYCOL] Hyphalike.

Hyphomicrobiaceae [MICROBIO] Formerly a family of bacteria in the order Hyphomicrobiales; cells occurring in free-floating groups with individual cells attached to each other by a slender filament.

Hyphomicrobiales [MICROBIO] Formerly an order of bacteria in the class Schizomycetes containing forms that multiply by budding.

Hyphomicrobium [MICROBIO] A genus of prosthecate bacteria; they reproduce by budding at hyphal tips; cells are rod-shaped with pointed ends, ovoid, or bean-shaped; hyphae are not septate.

Hyphomonas [MICROBIO] A genus of prosthecate bacteria; cells are oval or pear-shaped, and reproduction is by budding of the hyphae or by direct budding of cells.

hyphopodium [MYCOL] Hypha with a haustorium in certain ectoparasitic fungi.

Hypnineae [BOT] A suborder of the Hypnobryales characterized by complanate, glossy plants with ecostate or costate leaves and paraphyllia rarely present.

Hypnobryales [BOT] An order of mosses composed of procumbent and pleurocumbent plants with usually symmetrical leaves arranged in more than two rows.

hypnotoxin [BIOCHEM] A supposed hormone produced by brain tissue and inducing sleep.

hypobasal [BOT] Located posterior to the basal wall.

hypoblast *See* endoderm.

hypobranchial musculature [ANAT] The ventral musculature in vertebrates extending from the pectoral girdle forward to the hyoid arch, chin, and tongue.

hypochil [BOT] Lower portion of the lip in orchids. Also known as hypochillium.

Hypochilidae [INV ZOO] A family of true spiders in the order Araneida.

hypochillium *See* hypochil.

Hypochilomorphae [INV ZOO] A monofamilial suborder of spiders in the order Araneida.

hypochnoid [MYCOL] Having generally compacted hyphae.

hypochondriac region [ANAT] The upper, lateral abdominal region just below the ribs on each side of the body.

hypocleidium [ANAT] The median, ventral bone between clavicles. [VERT ZOO] Median process on the wishbone of birds.

hypocone [ANAT] The posterior inner cusp of an upper molar. [INV ZOO] Region of a dinoflagellate posterior to the girdle.

Hypocopridae [INV ZOO] A small family of coleopteran insects in the superfamily Cucujoidea.

hypocoracoid [VERT ZOO] The lower of two bones at the base of the pectoral fin in teleosts.

hypocotyl [BOT] The portion of the embryonic plant axis below the cotyledon.

hypocrateriform [BIOL] Saucer-shaped.

Hypocreales [MYCOL] An order of fungi belonging to the Ascomycetes and including several entomophilic fungi.

Hypodermatidae [INV ZOO] The warble flies, a family of myodarian cyclorrhaphous dipteran insects in the subsection Calypteratae.

hypodermis [BOT] The outermost cell layer of the cortex of plants. Also known as exodermis. [INV ZOO] The layer of cells that underlies and secretes the cuticle in arthropods and some other invertebrates.

hypogeous [BIOL] Living or maturing below the surface of the ground.

hypoglossal nerve [ANAT] The twelfth cranial nerve; a paired motor nerve in tetrapod vertebrates innervating tongue muscles; corresponds to the hypobranchial nerve in fishes.

hypoglossal nucleus [ANAT] A long nerve nucleus throughout most of the length of the medulla oblongata; cells give rise to the hypoglossal nerve fibers.

hypogynium [BOT] Structure that supports the ovary in plants such as sedges.

hypogynous [BOT] Having all flower parts attached to the receptacle below the pistil and free from it.

hypokalemia [PHYSIO] A reduction in the normal amount of potassium in the blood.

hypomere [EMBRYO] The lateral or lower mesodermal plate zone in vertebrate embryos. [INV ZOO] The basal portion of certain sponges that contain no flagellated chambers.

hypomorph [GEN] An allele having an effect similar to the normal allele, but being less active.

hypomorphic allele [GEN] An allele that has reduced levels of gene activity.

hyponasty [BOT] A nastic movement involving inward and upward bending of a plant part.

hyponeural sinus [INV ZOO] Tubular portion of the coelom containing hemal vessels and motor nerves in certain echinoderms.

hyponychium [HISTOL] The thickened stratum corneum of the epidermis, which lies under the free edge of the nail.

hypopharynx [ANAT] *See* laryngopharynx. [INV ZOO] A sensory, tonguelike structure on the floor of the mouth of many insects; sometimes modified for piercing.

hypophysis [ANAT] A small rounded endocrine gland which lies in the sella turcica of the sphenoid bone and is attached to the floor of the third ventricle of the brain in all craniate vertebrates. Also known as pituitary gland.

hypoplankton [BIOL] Forms of marine life whose swimming ability lies somewhere between that of the plankton and the nekton; includes some mysids, amphipods, and cumacids.

hypoplastron [VERT ZOO] Either of the third pair of lateral bony plates in the plastron of most turtles.

hypopleura [INV ZOO] Sclerite above and in front of the hind coxa in Diptera.

hypoploid [GEN] Having one or more less chromosomes, or parts of chromosomes, than a whole multiple of the haploid number.

hypoploidy [GEN] The condition or state of being hypoploid.

hypopus [INV ZOO] The resting larval stage of certain mites.

hypopygium [INV ZOO] A modified ninth abdominal segment together with the copulatory apparatus in Diptera.

hypostatic [GEN] Subject to being suppressed, as a gene that can be suppressed by a nonallelic gene.

hypostome [INV ZOO] 1. Projection surrounding the oral aperture in many coelenterate polyps. 2. Anteroventral part of the head in Diptera. 3. Median ventral mouthpart in ticks. 4. Raised area on the posterior oral margin in crustaceans.

hypostracum [INV ZOO] The innermost layer of the cuticle of ticks lying above the hypodermis.

hyposulculus [INV ZOO] A groove of the siphonoglyph below the pharynx in anthozoans.

hypotarsus [VERT ZOO] A process on the tarsometatarsal bone in birds.

hypothalamic center [ANAT] Any of the neural centers which regulate autonomic functions.

hypothalamic releasing factor [BIOCHEM] Any of the hormones secreted by the hypothalamus which travel by way of nerve fibers to the anterior pituitary, where they cause selective release of specific pituitary hormones.

hypothalamoneurohypophyseal system [PHYSIO] The hormones and neurosecretory structures involved in the endocrine activity of the adenohypophysis, neurohypophysis, and hypothalamus.

hypothalamoneurohypophyseal tract [ANAT] A bundle of nerve fibers connecting the supraoptic and paraventricular neurons of the hypothalamus with the infundibular stem and neurohypophysis.

hypothalamus [ANAT] The floor of the third brain ventricle; site of production of several substances that act on the adenohypophysis.

hypotheca [INV ZOO] 1. The lower valve of a diatom frustule. 2. Covering on the hypocone in dinoflagellates.

hypothenar [ANAT] Of or pertaining to the prominent portion of the palm above the base of the little finger.

hypothermia [PHYSIO] Condition of reduced body temperature in homeotherms.

hypotonic [PHYSIO] 1. Pertaining to subnormal muscle strength or tension. 2. Referring to a solution with a lower osmotic pressure than physiological saline.

Hypotrichida [INV ZOO] An order of highly specialized protozoans in the subclass Spirotrichia characterized by cirri on the ventral surface and a lack of ciliature on the dorsal surface.

hypotype [SYST] A specimen of a species, which, though not a member of the original type series, is known from a published description or listing.

hypoxanthine [BIOCHEM] $C_5H_4ON_4$ An intermediate product derived from adenine in the hydrolysis of nucleic acid.

hypozygal [INV ZOO] In comatulids, the proximal member of adjacent brachials in an articulation.

hypsodont [VERT ZOO] Of teeth, having crowns that are high or deep and roots that are short.

hypural [VERT ZOO] Of or pertaining to the bony structure formed by fusion of the hemal spines of the last few vertebrae in most teleost fishes.

Hyracodontidae [PALEON] The running rhinoceroses, an extinct family of perissodactyl mammals in the superfamily Rhinoceratoidea.

Hyracoidea [VERT ZOO] An order of ungulate mammals represented only by the conies of Africa, Arabia, and Syria.

hysteriaceous [MYCOL] Of, belonging to, or resembling the Hysteriales.

Hysteriales [BOT] An order of lichens in the class Ascolichenes including those species with an ascolocular structure.

hysterochroic [MYCOL] Having fruiting bodies which discolor progressively from base to apex with age.

hysterosoma [INV ZOO] A body division of an acarid mite composed of the metapodosoma and opisthosoma.

Hystrichospherida [PALEON] A group of protistan microfossils.

Hystricidae [VERT ZOO] The Old World porcupines, a family of Rodentia ranging from southern Europe to Africa and eastern Asia and into the Philippines.

Hystricomorpha [VERT ZOO] A superorder of the class Rodentia.

H zone [HISTOL] The central portion of an A band in a sarcomere; characterized by the presence of myosin filaments.

I

IAA *See* indoleacetic acid.

Iballidae [INV ZOO] A small family of hymenopteran insects in the superfamily Cynipoidea.

I band [HISTOL] The band on either side of a Z line; encompasses portions of two adjacent sarcomeres and is characterized by the presence of actin filaments.

ibis [VERT ZOO] The common name for wading birds making up the family Threskiornithidae and distinguished by a long, slender, downward-curving bill.

Icacinaceae [BOT] A family of dicotyledonous plants in the order Celastrales characterized by haplostemonous flowers, pendulous ovules, stipules wanting or vestigial, a polypetalous corolla, valvate petals, and usually one (sometimes three) locules.

ichneumon [INV ZOO] The common name for members of the family Ichneumonidae.

Ichneumonidae [INV ZOO] The ichneumon flies, a large family of cosmopolitan, parasitic wasps in the superfamily Ichneumonoidea.

Ichneumonoidea [INV ZOO] A superfamily of hymenopteran insects; members are parasites of other insects.

Ichthyobdellidae [INV ZOO] A family of leeches in the order Rhynchobdellae distinguished by cylindrical bodies with conspicuous, powerful suckers.

Ichthyodectidae [PALEON] A family of Cretaceous marine osteoglossiform fishes.

ichthyology [VERT ZOO] A branch of vertebrate zoology that deals with the study of fishes.

ichthyophagous [ZOO] Subsisting on a diet of fish.

Ichthyopterygia [PALEON] A subclass of extinct Mesozoic reptiles composed of predatory fish-finned and sea-swimming forms with short necks and a porpoiselike body.

Ichthyornis [PALEON] The type genus of Ichthyornithidae.

Ichthyornithes [PALEON] A superorder of fossil birds of the order Ichthyornithiformes according to some systems of classification.

Ichthyornithidae [PALEON] A family of extinct birds in the order Ichthyornithiformes.

Ichthyornithiformes [PALEON] An order of ancient fossil birds including strong flying species from the Upper Cretaceous that possessed all skeletal characteristics of modern birds.

Ichthyosauria [PALEON] The only order of the reptilian subclass Ichthyopterygia, comprising the extinct predacious fish-lizards; all were adapted to a sea life in having tail flukes, paddles, and dorsal fins.

Ichthyostegalia [PALEON] An extinct Devonian order of labyrinthodont amphibians, the oldest known representatives of the class.

Ichthyotomidae [INV ZOO] A monotypic family of errantian annelids in the superfamily Eunicea.

icosahedral virus [VIROL] A virion in the form of an icosahedron.

Icosteidae [VERT ZOO] The ragfishes, a family of perciform fishes in the suborder Stromateoidei found in high seas.

icotype [SYST] A typical, accurately identified specimen of a species, but not the basis for a published description.

Icteridae [VERT ZOO] The troupials, a family of New World perching birds in the suborder Oscines.

Ictidosauria [PALEON] An extinct order of mammallike reptiles in the subclass Synapsida including small carnivorous and herbivorous terrestrial forms.

ID₅₀ *See* infective dose 50.

identical twins *See* monozygotic twins.

ideomotor [PHYSIO] **1.** Pertaining to involuntary movement resulting from or accompanying some mental activity, as moving the lips while reading. **2.** Pertaining to both ideation and motor activity.

ideotype [SYST] A specimen identified as belonging to a specific taxon but collected from other than the type locality.

idioblast [BOT] A plant cell that differs markedly in shape or function from neighboring cells within the same tissue.

idiochromatin [CELL BIO] The portion of the nuclear chromatin thought to function as the physical carrier of genes.

idiomuscular [PHYSIO] Pertaining to any phenomenon occurring in a muscle which is independent of outside stimuli.

idiosome [CELL BIO] **1.** A hypothetical unit of a cell, such as the region of modified cytoplasm surrounding the centriole or centrosome. **2.** A sex chromosome.

idiostolidae [INV ZOO] A small family of hemipteran insects in the superfamily Pentatomorpha.

Idoteidae [INV ZOO] A family of isopod crustaceans in the suborder Valvifera having a flattened body and seven pairs of similar walking legs.

Iguana [VERT ZOO] The common name for a number of species of herbivorous, arboreal reptiles in the family Iguanidae characterized by a dorsal crest of soft spines and a dewlap; there are only two species of true iguanas.

Iguanid [VERT ZOO] The common name for members of the reptilian family Iguanidae.

Iguanidae [VERT ZOO] A family of reptiles in the order Squamata having teeth fixed to the inner edge of the jaws, a nonretractile tongue, a compressed body, five clawed toes, and a long but rarely prehensile tail.

Ileocecal valve [ANAT] A muscular structure at the junction of the ileum and cecum which prevents reflex of the cecal contents.

Ileocolic artery [ANAT] A branch of the superior mesenteric artery that supplies blood to the terminal part of the ileum and the beginning of the colon.

Ileum [ANAT] The last portion of the small intestine, extending from the jejunum to the large intestine.

Iliac artery [ANAT] Either of the two large arteries arising by bifurcation of the abdominal aorta and supplying blood to the lower trunk and legs (or hind limbs in quadrupeds). Also known as common iliac artery.

Iliac fascia [ANAT] The fascia covering the pelvic surface of the iliacus muscle.

Iliac region See inguinal region.

Iliacus [ANAT] The portion of the iliopsoas muscle arising from the iliac fossa and sacrum.

Iliac vein [ANAT] Any of the three veins on each side of the body which correspond to and accompany the iliac artery.

Iliocostalis [ANAT] The lateral portion of the erector spinal muscle that extends the vertebral column and assists in lateral movements of the trunk.

Iliofemoral ligament [ANAT] A strong band of dense fibrous tissue extending from the anterior inferior iliac spine to the lesser trochanter and the intertrochanteric line. Also known as Y ligament.

Iliolumbar ligament [ANAT] A fibrous band that radiates laterally from the transverse processes of the fourth and fifth lumbar vertebrae and attaches to the pelvis by two main bands.

Iliopsoas [ANAT] The combined iliacus and psoas muscles.

Iliotibial tract [ANAT] A thickened portion of the fascia lata extending from the lateral condyle of the tibia to the iliac crest.

Ilium [ANAT] Either of a pair of bones forming the superior portion of the pelvis bone in vertebrates.

Imaginal disk [INV ZOO] Any of the thickened areas within the sac of the body wall in holometabolous insects which give rise to specific organs in the adult.

Imago [INV ZOO] The sexually mature, usually winged stage of insect development.

Imbed See embed.

Imbricate [BIOL] Having overlapping edges, such as scales, or the petals of a flower.

Iminourea See guanidine.

Immarginate [BIOL] Lacking a clearly defined margin.

Immigrant [ECOL] An organism that settles in a zone where it was previously unknown.

Immigration [ECOL] The one-way inward movement of individuals or their disseminules into a population or population area.

Immunology [BIOL] A branch of biological science concerned with the native or acquired resistance of higher animal forms and humans to infection with microorganisms.

Imparipinnate See odd-pinnate.

Impennes [VERT ZOO] A superorder of birds for the order Sphenisciformes in some systems of classification.

Imperfect flower [BOT] A flower lacking either stamens or carpels.

Imperforate [BIOL] Lacking a normal opening.

Implexed [INV ZOO] In insects, having the integument infolded for muscle attachment.

Impunctate [BIOL] Lacking pores.

IMVIC test [MICROBIO] A group of four cultural tests used to differentiate genera of bacteria in the family Enterobacteriaceae and to distinguish them from other bacteria; tests are indole, methyl red, Voges-Proskauer, and citrate.

Inadunata [PALEON] An extinct subclass of stalked Paleozoic Crinozoa characterized by branched or simple arms that were free and in no way incorporated into the calyx.

Inadunate [BIOL] Not united. [INV ZOO] In crinoids, having the arms free from the calyx.

Inaperturate [BIOL] Lacking apertures.

Inarching [BOT] A kind of repair grafting in which two plants growing on their own roots are grafted together and one plant is severed from its roots after the graft union is established.

Inarticulata [INV ZOO] A class of the phylum Brachiopoda; valves are typically not articulated and are held together only by soft tissue of the living animal.

Inborn [BIOL] Of or pertaining to a congenital or hereditary characteristic.

Inbreeding [GEN] Breeding of closely related individuals; self-fertilization, as in some plants, is the most extreme form.

Incertae sedis [SYST] Placed in an uncertain taxonomic position.

Incirrata [INV ZOO] A suborder of cephalopod mollusks in the order Octopoda.

Incised [BIOL] Having a deeply and irregularly notched margin.

Incisive canal [ANAT] The bifurcated bony passage from the floor of the nasal cavity to the incisive fossa.

Incisive foramen [ANAT] One of the two to four openings of the incisive canal on the floor of the incisive fossa.

Incisive fossa [ANAT] 1. A bony pit behind the upper incisors into which the incisive canals open. 2. A depression on the maxilla at the origin of the depressor muscle of the nose. 3. A depression of the mandible at the origin of the mentalis muscle.

Incisor [ANAT] A tooth specialized for cutting, especially those in front of the canines on the upper jaw of mammals.

Inclusion [CELL BIO] A visible product of cellular metabolism within the protoplasm.

Inclusion body [VIROL] Any of the abnormal structures appearing within the cell nucleus or the cytoplasm during the course of virus multiplication.

Incomplete flower [BOT] A flower lacking one or more modified leaves, such as petals, sepals, pistils, or stamens.

Incrassate [BIOL] State of being swollen or thickened.

Incretion [PHYSIO] An internal secretion.

Incubation [VERT ZOO] The act or process of brooding or incubating.

Incubation period [VERT ZOO] The brooding period required to bring an egg to hatching.

Incubator [MICROBIO] A laboratory cabinet with controlled temperature for the cultivation of bacteria, or for facilitating biologic tests.

Incubous [BOT] The juxtaposition of leaves such that the anterior margins of older leaves overlap the posterior margins of younger leaves.

Incudate [BIOL] Of, pertaining to, or having an incus.

Incumbent [BIOL] Lying on or down.

Incurrent canal [INV ZOO] A canal through which water enters a sponge.

Incurvariidae [INV ZOO] A family of lepidopteran insects in the superfamily Incurvarioidea; includes yucca moths and relatives.

Incurvarioidea [INV ZOO] A monofamilial superfamily of lepidopteran insects in the suborder Heteroneura having wings covered with microscopic spines, a single genital opening in the female, and venation that is almost complete.

Incus [ANAT] The middle one of three ossicles in the middle ear. Also known as anvil.

Indeciduate placenta [EMBRYO] A placenta having the maternal and fetal elements associated but not fused.

Indehiscent [BOT] 1. Remaining closed at maturity, as certain fruits. 2. Not splitting along regular lines.

Independent assortment [GEN] The random assortment of the alleles at two or more loci on different chromosome pairs or far apart on the same chromosome pair which occurs at meiosis; first discovered by G. Mendel.

Indeterminate cleavage [EMBRYO] Cleavage in which all the early cells have the same potencies with respect to development of the entire zygote.

Indeterminate growth [BOT] Growth of a plant in which the axis is not limited by development of a reproductive structure, and therefore growth continues indefinitely.

Index fossil [PALEON] The ancient remains and traces of an organism that lived during a particular geologic time period and that geologically date the containing rocks.

Indican [BIOCHEM] C_8H_6NOSOK The potassium salt of indoxylsulfate found in urine as a result of bacterial action on tryptophan in the bowel.

Indicator medium [MICROBIO] A usually solid culture medium containing substances capable of undergoing a color change in the vicinity of a colony which has effected a particular chemical change, such as fermenting a certain sugar.

Indicator plant [BOT] A plant used in geobotanical prospecting as an indicator of a certain geological phenomenon.

Indole Also known as 2,3-benzopyrrole. [BIOCHEM] C_6H_4 (CHNH)CH A decomposition product of tryptophan formed in the intestine during putrefaction and by certain cultures of bacteria.

Indoleacetic acid [BIOCHEM] $C_{10}H_9O_2N$ A decomposition product of tryptophan produced by bacteria and occurring in urine and feces; used as a hormone to promote plant growth. Abbreviated IAA.

Indole test [MICROBIO] A test for the production of indole from tryptophan by microorganisms; a solution of para-dimethylaminobenzaldehyde, amyl alcohol, and hydrochloric acid added to the incubated culture of bacteria shows a red color in the alcoholic layer if indole is present.

Indo-Pacific faunal region [ECOL] A marine littoral faunal region extending eastward from the east coast of Africa, passing north of Australia and south of Japan, and ending in the east Pacific south of Alaska.

Indriidae [VERT ZOO] A family of Madagascan prosimians containing wholly arboreal vertical clingers and leapers.

Inducer [EMBRYO] The cell group that functions as the acting system in embryonic induction by controlling the mode of development of the reacting system. Also known as inductor.

Inducible enzyme [BIOCHEM] An enzyme which is present in trace quantities within a cell but whose concentration increases dramatically in the presence of substrate molecules.

Induction [EMBRYO] See See embryonic induction.

Inductor See inducer.

Inductura [INV ZOO] A layer of lamellar shell material along the inner lip of the aperture in gastropods.

Indumentum [BOT] A covering, such as one that is woolly. [MYCOL] A covering of hairs. [VERT ZOO] The plumage covering a bird.

Induplicate [BOT] Having the edges turned or rolled inward without twisting or overlapping; applied to the leaves of a bud.

Induration [BIOL] The process of hardening, especially by increasing the fibrous elements.

Indusium [ANAT] A covering membrane such as the amnion. [BOT] An epidermal outgrowth covering the sori in many ferns. [MYCOL] The annulus of certain fungi.

Industrial microbiology [MICROBIO] The study, utilization, and manipulation of those microorganisms capable of economically producing desirable substances or changes in substances, and the control of undesirable microorganisms.

industrial microorganism [MICROBIO] Any microorganism utilized for industrial microbiology.

industrial yeast [MICROBIO] Any yeast used for the production of fermented foods and beverages, for baking, or for the production of vitamins, proteins, alcohol, glycerol, and enzymes.

inequilateral [BIOL] Having the two sides or ends unequal, as the ends of a bivalve mollusk on either side of a line from umbo to gape.

inermous [BIOL] Lacking mechanisms for defense or offense, especially spines.

infantile genitalia [ANAT] The genital organs of an infant.

infauna [ZOO] Aquatic animals which live in the bottom sediment of a body of water.

infect [MICROBIO] To cause a phage infection of bacteria.

infectious chlorosis [PL PATH] A virus disease of plants characterized by yellowing of the green parts.

infectious drug resistance [MICROBIO] A type of drug resistance that is transmissible from one bacterium to another by infectivelike agents referred to as resistance factors.

infective dose 50 [MICROBIO] The dose of microorganisms required to cause infection in 50% of the experimental animals; a special case of the median effective dose. Abbreviated ID_{50}. Also known as median infective dose.

inferior [BIOL] The lower of two structures.

inferior alveolar artery [ANAT] A branch of the internal maxillary artery supplying the mucous membrane of the mouth and teeth of the lower jaw.

inferior alveolar nerve [ANAT] A branch of the mandibular nerve that innervates the teeth of the lower jaw.

inferior cerebellar peduncle [ANAT] A large bundle of nerve fibers running from the medulla oblongata to the cerebellum. Also known as restiform body.

inferior colliculus [ANAT] One of the posterior pair of rounded eminences arising from the dorsal portion of the mesencephalon.

inferior ganglion [ANAT] 1. The lower sensory ganglion in the glossopharyngeal nerve. 2. The lower sensory ganglion on the vagus.

inferior hypogastric plexus [ANAT] A network of nerves in the pelvic fascia containing autonomic nerve elements.

inferior mesenteric ganglion [ANAT] A sympathetic ganglion within the inferior mesenteric plexus at the origin of the inferior mesenteric artery.

inferior temporal gyrus [ANAT] A convolution on the temporal lobe of the cerebral hemispheres lying below the middle temporal sulcus and extending to the inferior sulcus.

inferior vena cava [ANAT] A large vein which drains blood from the iliac veins, lower extremities, and abdomen into the right atrium.

inferior vermis [ANAT] The inferior portion of the vermis of the brain.

inferior vestibular nucleus [ANAT] The terminal nucleus for the spinal vestibular nerve tract.

inflated [BIOL] 1. Distended, applied to a hollow structure. 2. Open and enlarged.

inflected [BOT] Curved or bent sharply inward, downward, or toward the axis. Also known as inflexed.

inflexed See inflected.

inflorescence [BOT] 1. A flower cluster. 2. The arrangement of flowers on a plant.

influent [ECOL] An organism that disturbs the ecological balance of a community.

influenza virus [VIROL] Any of three immunological types, designated A, B, and C, belonging to the myxovirus group which cause influenza.

informosome [CELL BIO] A type of cellular particle that is thought to be a complex of messenger ribonucleic acid with ribonucleoprotein.

infrabasal [BIOL] Inferior to a basal structure.

infrabranchial [VERT ZOO] Situated below the gills.

infracentral [ANAT] Located below the centrum.

infracerebral gland [INV ZOO] A structure lying ventral to the brain in annelids which is thought to produce a hormone that inhibits maturation of the gametes.

infraciliature [INV ZOO] The neuromotor apparatus, silverline system, or neuroneme system of ciliates.

infraclass [SYST] A subdivision of a subclass; equivalent to a superorder.

infraclavicle [VERT ZOO] A bony element of the shoulder girdle located below the cleithrum in some ganoid and crossopterygian fishes.

infrafoliar [BOT] Located below the leaves.

infraglenoid [ANAT] Below the glenoid cavity of the scapula.

infraglenoid tubercle [ANAT] A rough impression below the glenoid cavity, from which the long head of the triceps muscle arises.

infraorbital [ANAT] Located beneath the orbit.

infraspinous [ANAT] Below the spine of the scapula.

infraspinous fossa [ANAT] The recess on the posterior surface of the scapula occupied by the infraspinatus muscle.

infratemporal [ANAT] Situated below the temporal fossa.

infratemporal fossa [ANAT] An irregular space situated below and medial to the zygomatic arch, behind the maxilla and medial to the upper part of the ramus of the mandible.

infructescence [BOT] An inflorescence's fruiting stage.

infundibular canal [INV ZOO] A pathway from the mantle cavity through the funnel for water in cephalopods.

infundibular ganglion [INV ZOO] A branch of pedal ganglion which supplies the funnel in cephalopods.

infundibular process [ANAT] The distal portion of the neural lobe of the pituitary.

infundibulum [ANAT] 1. A funnel-shaped passage or part. 2. The stalk of the neurohypophysis.

Infusoriform larva [INV ZOO] The final larval stage, arising from germ cells within the infusorigen, in the life cycle of dicyemid mesozoans.

Infusorigen [INV ZOO] An individual that gives rise to the infusoriform larva in dicyemid mesozoans.

Ingesta [BIOL] Food and other substances taken into an animal body.

Ingestion [BIOL] The act or process of taking food and other substances into the animal body.

Ingolfiellidea [INV ZOO] A suborder of amphipod crustaceans in which both abdomen and maxilliped are well developed and the head often bears a separate ocular lobe lacking eyes.

Inguinal canal [ANAT] A short, narrow passage between the abdominal ring and the inguinal ring in which lies the spermatic cord in males and the round ligament in females.

Inguinal fold [EMBRYO] A fold of embryonic tissue on the urogenital ridge in which the gubernaculum testis develops.

Inguinal gland [ANAT] Any of the superficial lymphatic glands in the groin.

Inguinal ligament [ANAT] The thickened lower portion of the aponeurosis of the external oblique muscle extending from the anterior superior spine of the ileum to the tubercle of the pubis and the pectineal line. Also known as Poupart's ligament.

Inguinal region [ANAT] The abdominal region occurring on each side of the body as a depression between the abdomen and the thigh. Also known as iliac region.

Inhalant canal [INV ZOO] The incurrent canal in sponges and mollusks.

Inhalant siphon [INV ZOO] A channel for water intake in the mantle of bivalve mollusks. Also known as incurrent siphon.

Inhalation [PHYSIO] The process of breathing in.

Inheritance [GEN] 1. The acquisition of characteristics by transmission of germ plasm from ancestor to descendant. 2. The sum total of characteristics dependent upon the constitution of the fertilized ovum.

Inhibition index [BIOCHEM] The amount of antimetabolite that will overcome the biological effect of a unit weight of metabolite.

Iniomi [VERT ZOO] An equivalent name for Salmoniformes.

Initiation codon [GEN] A codon that signals the first amino acid in a protein sequence; usually *AUG*, but sometimes *GUG*. Also known as start codon.

Initiator codon [MOL BIO] A codon that acts as a start signal for the synthesis of a polypeptide.

Injury current *See* injury potential.

Injury potential [PHYSIO] The potential difference observed between the injured and the noninjured regions of an injured tissue or cell. Also known as demarcation potential; injury current.

Ink disease [PL PATH] A fungus disease of the chestnut in Europe caused by *Phytophthora cambivora* which produces black cankers and a black exudate in the trunk. Also known as black canker.

Ink sac [INV ZOO] An organ attached to the rectum in many cephalopods which secretes and ejects an inky fluid.

Inlet of the pelvis [ANAT] The space within the brim of the pelvis.

Innate [BIOL] Pertaining to a natural or inborn character dependent on genetic constitution. [BOT] Positioned at the apex of a supporting structure. [MYCOL] Embedded in, especially of an organ such as the fruiting body embedded in the thallus of some fungi.

Inner cell mass [EMBRYO] The cells at the animal pole of a blastocyst which give rise to the embryo and certain extraembryonic membranes.

Inner ear [ANAT] The part of the vertebrate ear concerned with labyrinthine sense and sound reception; consists generally of a bony and a membranous labyrinth, made up of the vestibular apparatus, three semicircular canals, and the cochlea. Also known as internal ear.

Innervation [ANAT] The distribution of nerves to a part.

Innervation [PHYSIO] The amount of nerve stimulation received by a part.

Innominate *See* hip bone.

Innominate artery [ANAT] The first artery branching from the aortic arch; distributes blood to the head, neck, shoulder, and arm on the right side of the body.

Inoculation [BIOL] Introduction of a disease agent into an animal or plant to produce a mild form of disease and render the individual immune. [MICROBIO] Introduction of microorganisms onto or into a culture medium.

Inoculum [MICROBIO] A small amount of substance containing bacteria from a pure culture which is used to start a new culture or to infect an experimental animal.

Inoperculate [BIOL] Lacking an operculum.

Inosine [BIOCHEM] $C_{10}H_{12}N_4O_5$ A compound occurring in muscle; a hydrolysis product of inosinic acid.

Inosinic acid [BIOCHEM] $C_{10}H_{13}N_4O_8P$ A nucleotide constituent of muscle, formed by deamination of adenylic acid; on hydrolysis it yields hypoxanthine and D-ribose-5-phosphoric acid. Also known as hypoxanthine riboside-5-phosphoric acid; hypoxanthylic acid; inosine monophosphate (IMP).

Inquiline [ZOO] An animal that inhabits the nest of another species.

Insect [INV ZOO] 1. A member of the Insecta. 2. An invertebrate that resembles an insect, such as a spider, mite, or centipede.

Insecta [INV ZOO] A class of the Arthropoda typically having a segmented body with an external, chitinous covering, a pair of compound eyes, a pair of antennae, three pairs of mouthparts, and two pairs of wings.

Insect control [ECOL] Regulation of insect populations by biological or chemical means.

Insectistasis [ECOL] The use of pheromones to trap, confuse, or inhibit insects in order to hold populations below a level where they can cause significant economic damage.

Insectivora [VERT ZOO] An order of mammals including hedgehogs, shrews, moles, and other forms, most of which have spines.

Insectivorous [BIOL] Feeding on a diet of insects.

Insectivorous plant [BOT] A plant that captures and digests insects as a source of nutrients by using specialized leaves. Also known as carnivorous plant.

Insect pathology [INV ZOO] A biological discipline embracing the general principles of pathology as applied to insects.

Insect physiology [INV ZOO] The study of the functional properties of insect tissues and organs.

Insemination [BIOL] The planting of seed. [PHYSIO] 1. The introduction of sperm into the vagina. 2. Impregnation.

Inserted [BIOL] United or attached to the supporting structure by natural growth.

Insertion [MOL BIO] The addition of an extranumerary base pair to double-stranded deoxyribonucleic acid; causes errors in transcription.

Inspiration [PHYSIO] The drawing in of the breath.

Inspiratory capacity [PHYSIO] Commencing from expiratory standstill, the maximum volume of gas which can be drawn into the lungs.

Inspiratory reserve volume [PHYSIO] The amount of air that can be inhaled by forcible inspiration after completion of a normal inspiration.

Instar [INV ZOO] A stage between molts in the life of arthropods, especially insects.

Instep [ANAT] The arch on the medial side of the foot.

Instinct [ZOO] A precise form of behavior in which there is an invariable association of a particular series of responses with specific stimuli; an unconditioned compound reflex.

Instinctive behavior [ZOO] Any species-typical pattern of responses not clearly acquired through training.

Instinctual [ZOO] Of or pertaining to instincts.

Insulin [BIOCHEM] A protein hormone produced by the beta cells of the islets of Langerhans which participates in carbohydrate and fat metabolism.

Insulinase [BIOCHEM] An enzyme produced by the liver which is able to inactivate insulin.

Integration [GEN] Recombination involving insertion of a genetic element.

Integument [ANAT] An outer covering, especially the skin, together with its various derivatives.

Integumentary musculature [VERT ZOO] Superficial skeletal muscles which are spread out beneath the skin and are inserted into it in some terrestrial vertebrates.

Integumentary pattern [ANAT] Any of the features of the skin and its derivatives that are arranged in designs, such as scales, epidermal ridges, feathers coloration, or hair.

Integumentary system [ANAT] A system encompassing the integument and its derivatives.

Interambulacrum [INV ZOO] In echinoderms, an area between two ambulacra.

Interarticular [ANAT] Situated between articulating surfaces.

Interatrial [ANAT] Located between the atria of the heart.

Interatrial septum *See* atrial septum.

Interaxillary [BOT] Located within or between the axils of leaves.

Intercalary [BOT] Referring to growth occurring between the apex and leaf.

Intercalary meristem [BOT] A meristem that is forming between regions of permanent or mature meristem.

Intercalated disc [HISTOL] A dense region at the junction of cellular units in cardiac muscle.

Intercalated nucleus [ANAT] A nucleus of the medulla oblongata in the central gray matter of the ventricular floor located between the hypoglossal nucleus and the dorsal motor nucleus of the vagus.

Intercapillary [ANAT] Located between capillaries.

Intercarpal [ANAT] Located between the carpal bones.

Intercavernous sinuses [ANAT] Venous sinuses located on the median line of the dura mater, connecting the cavernous sinuses of each side.

Intercellular [HISTOL] Of or pertaining to the region between cells.

Intercellular cement [HISTOL] A substance bonding epithelial cells together.

Intercellular plexus [HISTOL] A network of neuronal processes surrounding the cells in a sympathetic ganglion.

Intercellular space [HISTOL] A space between adjacent cells.

Intercellular substance [HISTOL] Tissue component that lies between cells.

Intercentrum [VERT ZOO] A type of crescentic intervertebral structure between successive centra in certain reptilian and mammalian tails.

Interclavicle [VERT ZOO] A membrane bone in front of the sternum and between the clavicles in monotremes and most reptiles.

Intercostal [ANAT] Situated or occurring between adjacent ribs.

Intercostal muscles [ANAT] Voluntary muscles between adjacent ribs.

Intercostal nerve [ANAT] Any of the branches of the thoracic nerves in the intercostal spaces.

Intercourse *See* coitus.

Intercrescence [BIOL] A growing together of tissues.

Interference phenomenon [VIROL] Inhibition by a virus of the simultaneous infection of host cells by some other virus.

Interferon [BIOCHEM] A protein produced by intact animal cells when infected with viruses; acts to inhibit viral reproduction and to induce resistance in host cells.

Interferonogen [VIROL] A preparation made of inactivated virus particles used as an inoculant to stimulate formation of interferon.

Interfoliaceous [BOT] Between a pair of leaves, such as between those which are opposite or verticillate.

Intergenic crossing-over [MOL BIO] Recombination between distinct genes or cistrons.

Intergenic suppression [GEN] The restoration of a suppressed function or character by a second mutation that is located in a different gene than the original or first mutation.

Interkinesis *See* interphase.

Interlabium [INV ZOO] A small lobe situated between the lips in certain nematodes.

Intermediary metabolism [BIOCHEM] Intermediate steps in the chemical synthesis and breakdown of foodstuffs within body cells.

Intermediate ganglion [ANAT] Any of certain small groups of nerve cells found along communicating branches of spinal nerves.

Intermediate host [BIOL] The host in which a parasite multiplies asexually.

Intermediate lobe [ANAT] The intermediate portion of the adenohypophysis.

Intermedin [BIOCHEM] A hormonal substance produced by the intermediate portion of the hypophysis of certain animal species which influences pigmentation; similar to melanocyte-stimulating hormone in humans.

Intermembranous ossification [HISTOL] Ossification within connective tissue with no prior formation of cartilage.

Intermeningeal [ANAT] Between any two of the three meninges covering the brain and spinal cord.

Intermenstrual [PHYSIO] Between periods of menstruation.

Intermetameric [ANAT] Between adjacent metameres.

Intermetatarsal [ANAT] Between adjacent bones of the metatarsus.

Intermitotic [CELL BIO] Of or pertaining to a stage of the cell cycle between two successive mitoses.

Intermural [ANAT] Between the walls of an organ.

Intermuscular [ANAT] Between muscles.

Intermuscular septum [ANAT] A connective-tissue partition between muscles.

Internal acoustic meatus [ANAT] An opening in the hard portion of the temporal bone for passage of the facial and acoustic nerves and internal auditory vessels.

Internal capsule [ANAT] A layer of nerve fibers on the outer side of the thalamus and caudate nucleus, which it separates from the lenticular nucleus.

Internal carotid [ANAT] A main division of the common carotid artery, distributing blood through three sets of branches to the cerebrum, eye, forehead, nose, internal ear, trigeminal nerve, dura mater, and hypophysis.

Internal carotid nerve [ANAT] A sympathetic nerve which forms networks of branches around the internal carotid artery and its branches.

Internal ear *See* inner ear.

Internal elastic membrane [HISTOL] A sheet of elastin found between the tunica intima and the tunica media in medium-and small-caliber arteries.

Internal fertilization [PHYSIO] Fertilization of the egg within the body of the female.

Internal fistula [ANAT] A fistula which has no opening through the skin.

Internal granular layer [HISTOL] The fourth layer of the cerebral cortex.

Internal iliac artery [ANAT] The medial terminal division of the common iliac artery.

Internal respiration [PHYSIO] The gas exchange which occurs between the blood and tissues of an organism.

Internal secretion [PHYSIO] A secreted substance that is absorbed directly into the blood.

International unit [BIOL] A quantity of a vitamin, hormone, antibiotic, or other biological that produces a specific internationally accepted biological effect.

Internode [BIOL] The interval between two nodes, as on a stem or along a nerve fiber.

Internuncial neuron [HISTOL] A neuron located in the spinal cord which connects motor and sensory neurons.

Interoceptor [PHYSIO] A sense receptor located in visceral organs and yielding diffuse sensations.

Interocular distance [ANAT] The distance between the centers of rotation of the human eyes.

Interorbital [ANAT] Between the orbits of the eyes.

Interparietal [ANAT] Between the parietal bones.

Interphase [CELL BIO] Also known as interkinesis. **1.** The period between succeeding mitotic divisions. **2.** The period between the first and second meiotic divisions in those organisms where nuclei are reconstituted at the end of the first division.

Interproglottid gland [INV ZOO] Any of a number of cell clusters or glands arranged transversely along the posterior margin of the proglottids of certain tapeworms.

Interpterygoid [ZOO] A space between palatal plates in certain chordates.

Interpulmonary [ANAT] Located between the lungs.

Interradial canal [INV ZOO] Any of the radially arranged gastrovascular canals in certain jellyfishes and ctenophores.

Interradius [INV ZOO] The area between two adjacent arms in echinoderms.

Interray [INV ZOO] A division of the radiate body of echinoderms.

Interrenal [ANAT] Located between the kidneys.

Interrupted gene *See* split gene.

Interscapular [ANAT] Between the shoulders or shoulder blades.

Intersegmental [BIOL] Situated between or involving segments. [EMBRYO] Situated between the primordial segments of the embryo.

Intersegmental reflex [PHYSIO] An unconditioned reflex arc connecting input and output by means of afferent pathways in the dorsal spinal roots and efferent pathways in the ventral spinal roots.

Intersex [PHYSIO] An individual who is intermediate in sexual constitution between male and female.

Interspace [ANAT] An interval between the ribs or the fibers or lobules of a tissue or organ.

Interspersion [ECOL] **1.** An intermingling of different organisms within a community. **2.** The level or degree of intermingling of one kind of organism with others in the community.

interspinal [ANAT] Situated between or connecting spinous processes; interspinous.

intersternite [INV ZOO] An intersegmental plate on the ventral surface of the abdomen in insects.

interstitial cell [HISTOL] A cell that is not peculiar to or characteristic of a particular organ or tissue but which comprises fibrous tissue binding other cells and tissue elements; examples are neuroglial cells and Leydig cells.

interstitial-cell–stimulating hormone See luteinizing hormone.

interstitial gland [HISTOL] 1. Groups of Leydig cells which secrete angiogens. 2. Groups of epithelioid cells in the ovarian medulla of some lower animals.

interstitial lamella [HISTOL] Any of the layers of bone between adjacent Haversian systems.

intertergite [INV ZOO] One of the small plates between the tergites of certain insects.

intertubercular sulcus [ANAT] A deep groove on the anterior surface of the upper end of the humerus, separating the greater and lesser tubercles; contains the tendon of the long head of the biceps brachii muscle. Also known as bicipital groove.

intervallum [INV ZOO] The space between the walls of pleosponges.

intervascular [ANAT] Located between or surrounded by blood vessels.

intervening sequence [GEN] A region of a gene that is transcribed but is not included in the final transcript of a ribonucleic acid.

interventricular foramen [ANAT] Either one of the two foramens that connect the third ventricle of the brain with each lateral ventricle. Also known as foramen of Monro.

interventricular septum [ANAT] The muscular wall between the heart ventricles. Also known as ventricular septum.

intervertebral [ANAT] Being or located between the vertebrae.

intervillous spaces [HISTOL] Spaces in the placenta which communicate with the maternal blood vessels.

intestinal crura [INV ZOO] The main intestinal branches in certain trematodes.

intestinal digestion [PHYSIO] Conversion of food to an assimilable form by the action of intestinal juices.

intestinal hormone [BIOCHEM] Either of two hormones, secretin and cholecystokinin, secreted by the intestine.

intestinal juice [PHYSIO] An alkaline fluid composed of the combined secretions of all intestinal glands.

intestinal villi [ANAT] Fingerlike projections of the small intestine, composed of a core of vascular tissue covered by epithelium and containing smooth muscle cells and an efferent lacteal end capillary.

intestine [ANAT] The tubular portion of the vertebrate digestive tract, usually between the stomach and the cloaca or anus.

intima [HISTOL] The innermost coat of a blood vessel. Also known as tunica intima.

intorsion [BIOL] Inward rotation of a structure about a fixed point or axis.

intraabdominal [ANAT] Occurring or being within the cavity of the abdomen.

intracartilaginous ossification See endochondral ossification.

intracellular [CELL BIO] Within a cell.

intracellular canaliculi [CELL BIO] A system of minute canals within certain gland cells which are thought to drain the glandular secretions.

intracellular digestion [PHYSIO] Digestion which takes place within the cytoplasm of the organism, as in many unicellular protozoans.

intracellular enzyme [BIOCHEM] An enzyme that remains active only within the cell in which it is formed. Also known as organized ferment.

intracellular symbiosis [CELL BIO] Existence of a self-duplicating unit within the cytoplasm of a cell, such as a kappa particle in *Paramecium*, which seems to be an infectious agent and may influence cell metabolism.

intracervical [ANAT] Located within the cervix of the uterus.

intracistron complementation [GEN] The process whereby two different mutant alleles, each of which determines in homozygotes an inactive enzyme, determine the formation of the active enzyme when present in the same nucleus.

intracortical [ANAT] Occurring or located within the cortex.

intracranial [ANAT] Within the cranium.

intracytoplasmic [CELL BIO] Being or occurring within the cytoplasm of a cell.

intradermal [ANAT] Within the skin.

intraductal [ANAT] Within a duct.

intradural [ANAT] Within the dura mater.

intraembryonic [EMBRYO] Within the embryo.

intraepidermal [ANAT] Within the epidermis.

intraepithelial [ANAT] Within the epithelium.

intraesophageal [ANAT] Within the esophagus.

intrafascicular [BOT] Located or occurring within a vascular bundle.

intrafusal fiber [HISTOL] Any of the striated muscle fibers contained in a muscle spindle.

intragenic [MOL BIO] Within a gene, in referring to certain events.

intragenic recombination [MOL BIO] Recombination occurring between the mutons of one cistron.

intragenic suppression [GEN] The restoration of a suppressed function or character as a consequence of a second mutation located within the same gene as the original or first mutation.

intrahepatic [ANAT] Within the liver.

intrajugular process [ANAT] 1. A small, curved process on some occipital bones which partially or completely divides the jugular foramen into lateral and medial parts. 2. A small process on the hard portion of the temporal bone which completely or partly separates the jugular foramen into medial and lateral parts.

intralaminar nuclei [ANAT] A diffuse group of nuclei located in the internal medullary lamina of the thalamus.

Intraluminal [ANAT] Within the lumen of a structure.

Intramarginal [BIOL] Within a margin.

Intramedullary [ANAT] 1. Within the tissues of the spinal cord or medulla oblongata. 2. Within the bone marrow. 3. Within the adrenal medulla.

Intramembranous [HISTOL] Formed or occurring within a membrane.

Intramembranous ossification [HISTOL] Formation of bone tissue directly from connective tissue without a preliminary cartilage stage.

Intramural [ANAT] Within the substance of the walls of an organ.

Intramuscular [ANAT] Lying within or going into the substance of a muscle.

Intraocular [ANAT] Occurring within the globe of the eye.

Intraocular pressure [PHYSIO] The hydrostatic pressure within the eyeball.

Intraparietal [ANAT] 1. Within the wall of an organ or cavity. 2. Within the parietal region of the cerebrum. 3. Within the body wall.

Intraperitoneal [ANAT] 1. Within the peritoneum. 2. Within the peritoneal cavity.

Intrapetiolar [BOT] 1. Enclosed by the base of the petiole. 2. Between the petiole and the stem.

Intrapulmonic [ANAT] Being or occurring within the lungs.

Intraspecific [BIOL] Being within or occurring among the members of the same species.

Intrathecal [ANAT] Within the subarachnoid space.

Intrathoracic [ANAT] Within the thoracic cavity.

Intratracheal [ANAT] Being or occurring within the trachea.

Intrauterine [ANAT] Being or occurring within the uterus.

Intravaginal [ANAT] 1. Being or occurring within the vagina. 2. Located within a tendon sheath. [BOT] Located within a sheath, referring to branches of grass.

Intravenous [ANAT] Located within, or going into, the veins.

Intravesical [ANAT] Within the urinary bladder.

Intravital [BIOL] Occurring while the cell or organism is alive.

Intravital stain [BIOL] A nontoxic dye injected into the body to selectively stain certain cells or tissues.

Intrinsic factor [BIOCHEM] A substance, produced by the stomach, which combines with the extrinsic factor (vitamin B_{12}) in food to yield an antianemic principle; lack of the intrinsic factor is believed to be a cause of pernicious anemia. Also known as Castle's intrinsic factor.

Intrinsic nerve supply [ANAT] The nerves contained entirely within an organ or structure.

Introgressive hybridization [GEN] The spreading of genes of a species into the gene complex of another due to hybridization between numerically dissimilar populations, the extensive backcrossing preventing formation of a single stable population.

Introitus [ANAT] An opening or entryway, especially the opening into the vagina.

Intromission [ZOO] The act or process of inserting one body into another, specifically, of the penis into the vagina.

Intromittent [ZOO] Adapted for intromission; applied to a copulatory organ.

Intron [GEN] A noncoding segment of a gene.

Introrse [BIOL] Turned inward or toward the axis.

Introspective diplopia See physiologic diplopia.

Introvert [ZOO] 1. A structure capable of introversion. 2. To turn inward.

Inulase [BIOCHEM] An enzyme produced by certain molds that catalyzes the conversion of inulin to levulose.

Inulin [BIOCHEM] A polysaccharide made up of polymerized fructofuranose units.

In utero [EMBRYO] Within the uterus, referring to the fetus.

Invagination [EMBRYO] The enfolding of a part of the wall of the blastula to form a gastrula. [PHYSIO] 1. The act of ensheathing or becoming ensheathed. 2. The process of burrowing or enfolding to form a hollow space within a previously solid structure, as the invagination of the nasal mucosa within a bone of the skull to form a paranasal sinus.

Inversion [GEN] A type of chromosomal rearrangement in which two breaks take place in a chromosome and the fragment between breaks rotates 180° before rejoining.

Invertase See saccharase.

Invertebrata [INV ZOO] A division of the animal kingdom including all animals which lack a spinal column; has no taxonomic status.

Invertebrate [INV ZOO] An animal lacking a backbone and internal skeleton.

Invertebrate pathology [INV ZOO] All studies having to do with the principles of pathology as applied to invertebrates.

Invertebrate zoology [ZOO] A branch of biology that deals with the study of Invertebrata.

Invertin See saccharase.

In vitro [BIOL] Pertaining to a biological reaction taking place in an artificial apparatus.

In vivo [BIOL] Pertaining to a biological reaction taking place in a living cell or organism.

Involucrate [BOT] Having an involucre.

Involucre [BOT] Bracts forming one or more whorls at the base of an inflorescence or fruit in certain plants.

Involucrum [ANAT] 1. The covering of a part. 2. New bone laid down by periosteum around a sequestrum in osteomyelitis.

Involuntary fiber See smooth muscle fiber.

Involuntary muscle [PHYSIO] Muscle not under the control of the will; usually consists of smooth muscle tissue and lies within a vescus, or is associated with skin.

Involute [BIOL] Being coiled, curled, or rolled in at the edge.

Involution [BIOL] A turning or rolling in. [EMBRYO] Gastrulation by ingrowth of blastomeres around the dorsal lip.

Involution form [CELL BIO] A cell with a bizarre configuration caused by abnormal culture conditions.

Involvucel [BOT] A secondary involucre.

Involvucellate [BOT] Possessing an involvucel.

Iodopsin [BIOCHEM] The visual pigment found in the retinal cones, consisting of retinene, combined with photopsin.

Ionophore [BIOCHEM] Any of a class of compounds, generally cyclic, having the ability to carry ions across lipid barriers due to the property of cation selectivity; examples are valinomycin and nonactin.

Iospilidae [INV ZOO] A small family of pelagic polychaetes assigned to the Errantia.

Ipecac [BOT] Any of several low, perennial, tropical South American shrubs or half shrubs in the genus *Cephaelis* of the family Rubiaceae; the dried rhizome and root, containing emetine, cephaeline, and other alkaloids, is used as an emetic and expectorant.

Ipidae [INV ZOO] The equivalent name for Scolytidae.

Iridaceae [BOT] A family of monocotyledonous herbs in the order Liliales distinguished by three stamens and an inferior ovary.

Iridocyte [HISTOL] A specialized cell in the integument of certain animal species which is filled with iridescent crystals of guanine and a variety of lipophores. Also known as guanophore; iridophore.

Iridophore *See* iridocyte.

Iris [ANAT] A pigmented diaphragm perforated centrally by an adjustable pupil which regulates the amount of light reaching the retina in vertebrate eyes. [BOT] Any plant of the genus *Iris*, the type genus of the family Iridaceae, characterized by linear or sword-shaped leaves, erect stalks, and bright-colored flowers with the three inner perianth segments erect and the outer perianth segments drooping.

Irish potato *See* potato.

Iron bacteria [MICROBIO] The common name for bacteria capable of oxidizing ferrous iron to the ferric state.

Iron-binding protein [BIOCHEM] A serum protein, such as hemoglobin, for the transport of iron ions.

Iron metabolism [BIOCHEM] The chemical and physiological processes involved in absorption of iron from the intestine and in its role in erythrocytes.

Iron-porphyrin protein [BIOCHEM] Any protein containing iron and porphyrin; examples are hemoglobin, the cytochromes, and catalase.

Ironwood [BOT] Any of a number of hardwood trees in the United States, including the American hornbeam, the buckwheat, and the eastern hophornbeam.

Irradiation [BIOPHYS] Subjection of a biological system to sound waves of sufficient intensity to modify their structure or function.

Irregular [BOT] Lacking symmetry, as of a flower having petals unlike in size or shape.

Irregular cleavage [EMBRYO] Division of a zygote into random masses of cells, as in certain coelenterates.

Irregular connective tissue [HISTOL] A loose or dense connective tissue with fibers irregularly woven and irregularly distributed; collagen is the dominant fiber type.

Irregularia [INV ZOO] An artificial assemblage of echinoderms in which the anus and periproct lie outside the apical system, the ambulacral plates remain simple, the primary radioles are hollow, and the rigid test shows some degree of bilateral symmetry.

Irritability [PHYSIO] 1. A condition or quality of being excitable; the power of responding to a stimulus. 2. A condition of abnormal excitability of an organism, organ, or part, when it reacts excessively to a slight stimulation.

Isanthous [BOT] Having regular flowers.

Ischiopodite [INV ZOO] The segment nearest the basipodite of walking legs in certain crustaceans. Also known as ischium.

Ischiorectal region [ANAT] The region between the ischium and the rectum.

Ischium [ANAT] Either of a pair of bones forming the dorsoposterior portion of the vertebrate pelvis; the inferior part of the human pelvis upon which the body rests in sitting. [INV ZOO] *See* ischiopodite.

Ischium-pubis index [ANAT] The ratio (length of pubis × 100/length of ischium) by which the sex of an adult pelvis may usually be determined; the index is greater than 90 in females, and less than 90 in males.

Ischnacanthidae [PALEON] The single family of the acanthodian order Ischnacanthiformes.

Ischnacanthiformes [PALEON] A monofamilial order of extinct fishes of the order Acanthodii; members were slender, lightly armored predators with sharp teeth, deeply inserted fin spines, and two dorsal fins.

Isectolophidae [PALEON] A family of extinct ceratomorph mammals in the superfamily Tapiroidea.

Island of Langerhans *See* islet of Langerhans.

Island of Reil [ANAT] The insula of the cerebral hemisphere.

Islet of Langerhans [HISTOL] A mass of cell cords in the pancreas that is of an endocrine nature, secreting insulin and a minor hormone like lipocaic. Also known as island of Langerhans; islet of the pancreas.

Islet of the pancreas *See* islet of Langerhans.

Isoacceptor [MOL BIO] Any of several species of transfer ribonucleic acid that can accept the same amino acid.

Isoallele [GEN] An allele that carries mutational alterations at the same site.

Isoalloxazine mononucleotide *See* riboflavin 5'-phosphate.

Isochore [ECOL] A boundary line on a map connecting world environments that have similar floral and faunal constituents.

Isobryales [BOT] An order of mosses in which the plants are slender to robust and up to 90 centimeters in length.

Isocarpic [BOT] Having the same number of carpels and perianth divisions.

Isocercal [VERT ZOO] Of the tail fin of a fish, having the upper and lower lobes symmetrical and the vertebral column gradually tapering.

Isochela [INV ZOO] 1. A chela having two equally developed parts. 2. A chelate spicule with both ends identical.

Isochromosome [CELL BIO] An abnormal chromosome with a medial centromere and identical arms formed as a result of transverse, rather than longitudinal, splitting of the centromere.

Isocitric acid [BIOCHEM] HOOCCH$_2$CH-(COOH)CH (OH)COOH An isomer of citric acid that is involved in the Krebs tricarboxylic acid cycle in bacteria and plants. Also known as 2-hydroxy-1,2,3-propanetricarboxylic acid.

Isocrinida [INV ZOO] An order of stalked articulate echinoderms with nodal rings of cirri.

Isodiametric [BIOL] Having equal diameters or dimensions.

Isodont [VERT ZOO] 1. Having all teeth alike. 2. Of a snake, having the maxillary teeth of equal length.

Isodulcitol *See* rhamnose.

Isoenzyme [BIOCHEM] Any of the electrophoretically distinct forms of an enzyme, representing different polymeric states but having the same function. Also known as isozyme.

Isoetaceae [BOT] The single family assigned to the order Isoetales in some systems of classification.

Isoetales [BOT] A monotypic order of the class Isoetopsida containing the single genus *Isoetes*, characterized by long, narrow leaves with a spoonlike base, spirally arranged on an underground cormlike structure.

Isoetopsida [BOT] A class of the division Lycopodiophyta; members are heterosporous and have a distinctive appendage, the ligule, on the upper side of the leaf near the base.

Isoflavone [BIOCHEM] C$_{15}$H$_{10}$O$_2$ A colorless, crystalline ketone, occurring in many plants, generally in the form of a hydroxy derivative.

Isogamete [BIOL] A reproductive cell that is morphologically similar in both male and female and cannot be distinguished on form alone.

Isogamy [BIOL] Sexual reproduction by union of gametes or individuals of similar form or structure.

Isogeneic [GEN] Having the same origin and thus being genetically identical, as an inbred strain. Also known as isogenic; syngeneic.

Isogeneratae [BOT] A class of brown algae distinguished by having an isomorphic alternation of generations.

Isogenic *See* isogeneic.

Isogony [BIOL] Growth of parts at such a rate as to maintain relative size differences.

Isograft [BIOL] A tissue transplant from one organism to another organism which is genetically identical.

Isolation [MICROBIO] Separation of an individual or strain from a natural, mixed population. [PHYSIO] Separation of a tissue, organ, system, or other part of the body for purposes of study.

Isolecithal *See* homolecithal.

Isoleucine [BIOCHEM] C$_6$H$_{13}$O$_2$ An essential monocarboxylic amino acid occurring in most dietary proteins.

Isomerase [BIOCHEM] An enzyme that catalyzes isomerization reactions.

Isomerism [BIOL] The condition of having two or more comparable parts made up of identical numbers of similar segments.

Isomerous [BIOL] Characterized by isomerism.

Isometopidae [INV ZOO] A family of hemipteran insects in the superfamily Cimicimorpha.

Isometric contraction [PHYSIO] A contraction in which muscle tension is increased, but the muscle is not shortened because the resistance cannot be overcome. Also known as static contraction.

Isometric particle [VIROL] A plant virus particle that appears at first sight to be spherical when viewed in the electron microscope, but which is actually an icosahedron, possessing 20 sides.

Isophene [BIOL] A line on a chart connecting those places within a given region where a particular biological phenomenon (as the flowering of a certain plant) occurs at the same time.

Isophyllous [BOT] Having foliage leaves of similar form on a plant or stem.

Isopoda [INV ZOO] An order of malacostracan crustaceans characterized by a cephalon bearing one pair of maxillipeds in addition to the antennae, mandibles, and maxillae.

Isoptera [INV ZOO] An order of Insecta containing morphologically primitive forms characterized by gradual metamorphosis, lack of true larval and pupal stages, biting and prognathous mouthparts, two pairs of subequal wings, and the abdomen joined broadly to the thorax.

Isopygous [INV ZOO] Having a pygidium and a cephalon of equal size, as in certain trilobites.

Isospondyli [VERT ZOO] A former equivalent name for Clupeiformes.

Isospore [BIOL] A spore that does not display sexual dimorphism.

Isostemonous [BOT] Having the number of stamens of a flower equal to the number of perianth divisions.

Isotonic [PHYSIO] 1. Having uniform tension, as the fibers of a contracted muscle. 2. Of a solution, having the same osmotic pressure as the fluid phase of a cell or tissue.

Isotonic sodium chloride solution *See* normal saline.

Isotope farm [BOT] A carbon-14 growth chamber, or greenhouse, arranged as a closed system in which plants can be grown in a carbon-14 dioxide (CO_2^{14}) atmosphere and thus become labeled with C^{14}; isotope farms also can be used with other materials, such as heavy water (D_2O), phosphorus-35 (P^{35}), and so forth, to produce biochemically labeled compounds.

Isotropic [BIOL] Having a tendency for equal growth in all directions. [CELL BIO] An ovum lacking any predetermined axis.

Isotypes [GEN] A series of antigens, for example, blood types, common to all members of a species but differentiating classes and subclasses within the species.

Isozyme *See* isoenzyme.

Isthmus [BIOL] A passage or constricted part connecting two parts of an organ.

Istiophoridae [VERT ZOO] The billfishes, a family of oceanic perciform fishes in the suborder Scombroidei.

Isuridae [VERT ZOO] The mackerel sharks, a family of pelagic, predacious galeoids distinguished by a heavy body, nearly symmetrical tail, and sharp, awllike teeth.

Itch [PHYSIO] An irritating cutaneous sensation allied to pain.

Ithomiinae [INV ZOO] The glossy-wings, a subfamily of weak-flying lepidopteran insects having on the wings broad, transparent areas in which the scales are reduced to short hairs.

Itonididae [INV ZOO] The gall midges, a family of orthorrhaphous dipteran insects in the series Nematocera; most are plant pests.

Ixodides [INV ZOO] The ticks, a suborder of the Acarina distinguished by spiracles behind the third or fourth pair of legs.

J

Jacanidae [VERT ZOO] The jacanas or lily-trotters, the single family of the avian superfamily Jacanoidea.

Jacanoidea [VERT ZOO] A monofamilial superfamily of colorful marshbirds distinguished by greatly elongated toes and claws, long legs, a short tail, and a straight bill.

jackal [VERT ZOO] 1. *Canis aureus*. A wild dog found in southeastern Europe, southern Asia, and northern Africa. 2. Any of various similar Old World wild dogs; they resemble wolves but are smaller and more yellowish.

Jacobson's cartilage *See* vomeronasal cartilage.

Jacobsonlidae [INV ZOO] The false snout beetles, a small family of coleopteran insects in the superfamily Dermestoidea.

Jacobson's organ [VERT ZOO] An olfactory canal in the nasal mucosa which ends in a blind pouch; it is highly developed in reptiles and vestigial in humans.

jaguar [VERT ZOO] *Felis onca*. A large, wild cat indigenous to Central and South America; it is distinguished by a buff-colored coat with black spots, and has a relatively large head and short legs.

Jamaica bayberry *See* bayberry.

Japygidae [INV ZOO] A family of wingless insects in the order Diplura with forcepslike anal appendages; members attack and devour small soil arthropods.

jaundice [INV ZOO] *See* grasserie.

Java black rot [PL PATH] A fungus disease of stored sweet potatoes caused by *Diplodia tubericola*; the inside of the root becomes black and brittle.

Java cotton *See* kapok.

Java man [PALEON] An overspecialized, apelike form of *Homo sapiens* from the middle Pleistocene having a small brain capacity, low cranial vault, and massive browridges.

jaw [ANAT] Either of two bones forming the skeleton of the mouth of vertebrates: the upper jaw or maxilla, and the lower jaw or mandible.

jawless vertebrate [VERT ZOO] The common name for members of the Agnatha.

jejunum [ANAT] The middle portion of the small intestine, extending between the duodenum and the ileum.

jellyfish [INV ZOO] Any of various free-swimming marine coelenterates belonging to the Hydrozoa or Scyphozoa and having a bell- or bowl-shaped body. Also known as medusa.

jelly fungus [MYCOL] The common name for many members of the Heterobasidiomycetidae, especially the orders Tremallales and Dacromycetales, distinguished by a jellylike appearance or consistency.

jenny [VERT ZOO] 1. A female animal, as a jenny wren. 2. A female donkey.

jerboa [VERT ZOO] The common name for 25 species of rodents composing the family Dipodidae; all are adapted for jumping, having extremely long hindlegs and feet.

jimsonweed [BOT] *Datura stramonium*. A tall, poisonous annual weed having large white or violet trumpet-shaped flowers and globose prickly fruits. Also known as apple of Peru.

jird [VERT ZOO] Any one of the diminutive rodents composing related species of the genus *Meriones* which are inhabitants of northern Africa and southwestern Asia; they serve as experimental hosts for studies of schistosomiasis.

joint [ANAT] A contact surface between two individual bones. Also known as articulation.

joint capsule [ANAT] A sheet of fibrous connective tissue enclosing a synovial joint.

Jonathan freckle [PL PATH] A storage disease of apples characterized by small circular discolorations in the skin.

Jonathan spot [PL PATH] A disease of apples characterized by circular depressed necrotic areas around the lenticels.

Joppelcidae [INV ZOO] A monospecific family of hemipteran insects included in the Pentatomorpha; found in the Mediterranean regions.

Jordan's rule [EVOL] The rule that organisms which are closely related tend to occupy adjacent rather than identical or distant ranges. [VERT ZOO] The rule that fishes in areas of low temperatures tend to have more vertebrae than those in warmer waters.

jugal [ANAT] Pertaining to the zygomatic bone. [VERT ZOO] In lower vertebrates, a bone lying below the orbit of the eye.

Jugatae [INV ZOO] The equivalent name for Homoneura.

jugate [BIOL] Structures which are joined together.

Juglandaceae [BOT] A family of dicotyledonous plants in the order Juglandales having unisexual flowers, a solitary basal ovule in a unilocular inferior ovary, and pinnately compound, exstipulate leaves.

Juglandales [BOT] An order of dicotyledonous plants in the subclass Hamamelidae distinguished by compound leaves; includes hickory, walnut, and butternut.

jugular [ANAT] Pertaining to the region of the neck above the clavicle.

jugular foramen [ANAT] An opening in the cranium formed by the jugular notches of the occipital and temporal bones for passage of an internal jugular vein, the ninth, tenth, and eleventh cranial nerves, and the inferior petrosal sinus.

jugular process [ANAT] A rough process external to the condyle of the occipital bone.

jugular vein [ANAT] The vein in the neck which drains the brain, face, and neck into the innominate.

jugum [BOT] One pair of opposite leaflets of a pinnate leaf. [INV ZOO] 1. The most posterior and basal portion of the wing of an insect. 2. A crossbar connecting the two arms of the brachidium in some brachiopods.

Juncaceae [BOT] A family of monocotyledonous plants in the order Juncales characterized by an inflorescence of diverse sorts, vascular bundles with abaxial phloem, and cells without silica bodies.

Juncales [BOT] An order of monocotyledonous plants in the subclass Commelinidae marked by reduced flowers and capsular fruits with one too many anatropous ovules per carpel.

junctional receptor [PHYSIO] An acetylcholine receptor which occurs in clusters in a muscle membrane at the nerve-muscle junction.

Jungermanniales [BOT] The leafy liverworts, an order of bryophytes in the class Marchantiatae characterized by chlorophyll-containing, ribbonlike or leaflike bodies and an undifferentiated thallus.

jungle [ECOL] An impenetrable thicket of second-growth vegetation replacing tropical rain forest that has been disturbed; lower growth layers are dense.

jute [BOT] Either of two Asiatic species of tall, slender, half-shrubby annual plants, *Corchorus capsularis* and *C. olitorius*, in the family Malvaceae, useful for their fiber.

juvenile cell *See* metamyelocyte.

Jynginae [VERT ZOO] The wrynecks, a family of Old World birds in the order Piciformes; a subfamily of the Picidae in some systems of classification.

kaempferol [BIOCHEM] A flavonoid with a structure similar to that of quercetin but with only one hydroxyl in the B ring; acts as an enzyme cofactor and causes growth inhibition in plants.

kairomone [PHYSIO] A chemical produced by an organism that benefits the recipient, which is an individual of a different species.

Kaiserling's method [BIOL] A method for preserving organ specimens and retaining their color by fixing in a solution of formalin, water, potassium nitrate, and potassium acetate, immersing in ethyl alcohol to restore color, and preserving in a solution of glycerin, aqueous arsenious acid, water, potassium acetate, and thymol.

kaki [BOT] *Diospyros kaki*. The Japanese persimmon; it provides a type of ebony wood that is black with gray, yellow, and brown streaks, has a close, even grain, and is very hard.

kale [BOT] Either of two biennial crucifers, *Brassica oleracea* var. *acephala* and *B. fimbriata*, in the order Capparales, grown for the nutritious curled green leaves.

kallidin I *See* bradykinin.

Kalotermitidae [INV ZOO] A family of relatively primitive, lower termites in the order Isoptera.

Kamptozoa [INV ZOO] An equivalent name for Entoprocta.

kanamycin [MICROBIO] $C_{18}H_{36}O_{11}N_4$ A water-soluble, basic antibiotic produced by strains of *Streptomyces kanamyceticus;* the sulfate salt is effective in infections caused by gram-negative bacteria.

kangaroo [VERT ZOO] Any of various Australian marsupials in the family Macropodidae generally characterized by a long, thick tail that is used as a balancing organ, short forelimbs, and enlarged hindlegs adapted for jumping.

kapok [BOT] Silky fibers that surround the seeds of the kapok or ceiba tree. Also known as ceiba; Java cotton; silk cotton.

kapok tree [BOT] *Ceiba pentandra*. A tree of the family Bombacaceae which produces pods containing seeds covered with silk cotton. Also known as silk cotton tree.

kappa particle [CELL BIO] A self-duplicating nucleoprotein particle found in various strains of *Paramecium* and thought to function as an infectious agent; classed as an intracellular symbiont, occupying a position between the viruses and the bacteria and organelles.

Karumiidae [INV ZOO] The termitelike beetles, a small family of coleopteran insects in the superfamily Cantharoidea distinguished by having a tenth tergum.

karyocyte *See* normoblast.

karyogamy [CELL BIO] Fusion of gametic nuclei, as in fertilization.

karyokinesis [CELL BIO] Nuclear division characteristic of mitosis.

karyolymph [CELL BIO] The clear material composing the ground substance of a cell nucleus.

karyolysis [CELL BIO] Dissolution of a cell nucleus.

karyomastigont [INV ZOO] Pertaining to members of the protozoan order Oxymonadida; individuals can be uni- or multinucleate, and unattached give rise to two pairs of flagella.

karyoplasm *See* nucleoplasm.

karyoplasmic ratio *See* nucleocytoplasmic ratio.

karyorrhexis [CELL BIO] Fragmentation of a nucleus with scattering of the pieces in the cytoplasm.

karyotype [CELL BIO] The normal diploid or haploid complement of chromosomes, with respect to size, form, and number, characteristic of an individual, species, genus, or other grouping.

kasugamycin [MICROBIO] $C_{14}H_{28}ClN_3O_{10}$ A white, crystalline antibiotic used as a fungicide for rice crops. Also known as kasumin; kasugamycin hydrochloride.

kasugamycin hydrochloride *See* kasugamycin.

kasumin *See* kasugamycin.

Kathlaniidae [INV ZOO] A family of nematodes assigned to the Ascaridina by some authorities and to the Oxyurina by others.

keel [VERT ZOO] The median ridge on the breastbone in certain birds. Also known as carina.

Keilor skull [PALEON] An Australian fossil type specimen of *Homo sapiens* from the Pleistocene.

kelp [BOT] The common name for brown seaweed belonging to the Laminariales and Fucales.

kelyphite *See* corona.

kenozooecium [INV ZOO] The outer, nonliving, hardened portion of a kenozooid.

kenozooid [INV ZOO] A type of bryozoan heterozooid possessing a slender tubular or boxlike chamber, completely enclosed and lacking an aperture.

Kentucky coffee tree [BOT] *Gymnocladus dioica*. An extremely tall, dioecious tree of the order Rosales readily recognized when in fruit by its leguminous pods containing heavy seeds, once used as a coffee substitute.

Kenyapithecus [PALEON] An early member of Hominidae from the Miocene.

keratin [BIOCHEM] Any of various albuminoids characteristic of epidermal derivatives, such as nails and feathers, which are insoluble in protein solvents, have a high sulfur content, and generally contain cystine and arginine as the predominating amino acids.

keratinized tissue [HISTOL] Any tissue with a high keratin content, such as the epidermis or its derivatives.

keratinocyte [HISTOL] A specialized epidermal cell that synthesizes keratin.

keratinous degeneration [CELL BIO] The occurrence of keratin granules in the cytoplasm of a cell, other than a keratinocyte.

keratohyalin [HISTOL] Granules in the stratum granulosum of keratinized stratified squamous epithelium which become keratin.

Kerguelen faunal region [ECOL] A marine littoral faunal region comprising a large area surrounding Kerguelen Island in the southern Indian Ocean.

kernel [BOT] 1. The inner portion of a seed. 2. A whole grain or seed of a cereal plant, such as corn or barley.

kernel blight [PL PATH] Any of several fungus diseases of barley caused chiefly by *Gibberella zeae*, *Helminthosporium sativum*, and *Alternaria* species shriveling and discoloring the grain.

kernel spot [PL PATH] A fungus disease of the pecan kernel caused by *Coniothyrium caryogenum* and characterized by dull-brown roundish spots.

ketoadipic acid [BIOCHEM] $C_6H_8O_5$ An intermediate product in the metabolism of lysine to glutaric acid.

ketogenesis [BIOCHEM] Production of ketone bodies.

ketogenic hormone [BIOCHEM] A factor originally derived from crude anterior hypophysis extract which stimulated fatty-acid metabolism; now known as a combination of adrenocorticotropin and the growth hormone. Also known as fat-metabolizing hormone.

ketogenic substance [BIOCHEM] Any foodstuff which provides a source of ketone bodies.

ketoglutaric acid [BIOCHEM] $C_5H_6O_5$ A dibasic keto acid occurring as an intermediate product in carbohydrate and protein metabolism.

ketohexose [BIOCHEM] Any monosaccharide composed of a six-carbon chain and containing one ketone group.

ketolase [BIOCHEM] A type of enzyme that catalyzes cleavage of carbohydrates at the carbonyl carbon position.

ketolysis [BIOCHEM] Dissolution of ketone bodies.

ketone body [BIOCHEM] Any of various ketones which increase in blood and urine in certain conditions, such as diabetic acidosis, starvation, and pregnancy. Also known as acetone body.

α-ketopropionic acid *See* pyruvic acid.

ketose [BIOCHEM] A carbohydrate that has a ketone group.

ketosteroid [BIOCHEM] One of a group of neutral steroids possessing keto substitution, which produces a characteristic red color with *m*-dinitrobenzene in an alkaline solution; these compounds are principally metabolites of adrenal cortical and gonadal steroids.

key [SYST] An arrangement of the distinguishing features of a taxonomic group to serve as a guide for establishing relationships and names of unidentified members of the group.

kidney [ANAT] Either of a pair of organs involved with the elimination of water and waste products from the body of vertebrates; in humans they are bean-shaped, about 5 inches (12.7 centimeters) long, and are located in the posterior part of the abdomen behind the peritoneum.

killer whale [VERT ZOO] *Orcinus orca*. A predatory, cosmopolitan cetacean mammal, about 30 feet (9 meters) long, found only in cold waters.

kinase [BIOCHEM] Any enzyme that catalyzes phosphorylation reactions.

kinesiology [PHYSIO] The study of human motion through anatomical and mechanical principles.

kinesis [PHYSIO] The general term for physical movement, including that induced by stimulation, for example, light.

kinesthesis [PHYSIO] The system of sensitivity present in the muscles and their attachments.

kinetin [BIOCHEM] $C_{10}H_9ON_5$ A cytokinin formed in many plants which has a stimulating effect on cell division.

kinetochore [CELL BIO] Within the centromere, the granule upon which the spindle fibers attach.

kinetoplast [CELL BIO] A genetically autonomous, membrane-bound organelle associated with the basal body at the base of flagella in certain flagellates, such as the trypanosomes. Also known as parabasal body.

Kinetoplastida [INV ZOO] An order of colorless protozoans in the class Zoomastigophorea having pliable bodies and possessing one or two flagella in some stage of their life.

kinetosome *See* basal body.

kingdom [SYST] One of the primary divisions that include all living organisms: most authorities recognize two, the animal kingdom and the plant kingdom, while others recognize three or more, such as Protista, Plantae, Animalia, and Mychota.

kingfisher [VERT ZOO] The common name for members of the avian family Alcedinidae; most are tropical Old World species characterized by short legs, long bills, bright plumage, and short wings.

kinocilium [CELL BIO] A type of cilium containing one central pair of microfibrils and nine peripheral pairs; they extend from the apex of hair cells in all vertebrate ears except mammals.

kinomere *See* centromere.

kinoplasm [CELL BIO] The substance of the protoplasm that is thought to form astral rays and spindle fibers.

Kinorhyncha [INV ZOO] A class of the phylum Aschelminthes consisting of superficially segmented microscopic marine animals lacking external ciliation.

Kinosternidae [VERT ZOO] The mud and musk turtles, a family of chelonian reptiles in the suborder Cryptodira found in North, Central, and South America.

Kirkbyacea [PALEON] A monomorphic superfamily of extinct ostracods in the suborder Beyrichicopina, all of which are reticulate.

Kirkbyidae [PALEON] A family of extinct ostracods in the superfamily Kirkbyacea in which the pit is reduced and lies below the middle of the valve.

Kitasatoa [MICROBIO] A genus of bacteria in the family Actinoplanaceae; club-shaped sporangia, each containing a single chain of diplococcuslike uniflagellate spores.

kiwi [VERT ZOO] The common name for three species of nocturnal ratites of New Zealand composing the family Apterygidae; all have small eyes, vestigial wings, a long slender bill, and short powerful legs.

Klebsiella [MICROBIO] A genus of bacteria in the family Enterobacteriaceae; nonmotile, encapsulated rods arranged singly, in pairs, or in chains; some species are human pathogens.

Klebsiella pneumoniae [MICROBIO] An encapsulated pathogenic bacterium that causes severe pneumonitis in humans. Formerly known as Friedlander's bacillus; pneumobacillus.

Klebs-Loeffler bacillus See Corynebacterium diphtheriae.

klendusity [BOT] The tendency of a plant to resist disease due to a protective covering, such as a thick cuticle, that prevents inoculation.

klinotaxis [BIOL] Positive orientation movement of a motile organism induced by a stimulus.

Kloedenellacea [PALEON] A dimorphic superfamily of extinct ostracods in the suborder Kloedenellocopina having the posterior part of one dimorph longer and more inflated than the other dimorph.

Kloedenellocopina [PALEON] A suborder of extinct ostracods in the order Paleocopa characterized by a relatively straight dorsal border with a gently curved or nearly straight ventral border.

knee [ANAT] **1.** The articulation between the femur and the tibia in humans. Also known as genu. **2.** The corresponding articulation in the hindlimb of a quadrupedal vertebrate.

Kneriidae [VERT ZOO] A small family of tropical African fresh-water fishes in the order Gonorynchiformes.

koala [VERT ZOO] Phascolarctos cinereus. An arboreal marsupial mammal of the family Phalangeridae having large hairy ears, gray fir, and two clawed toes opposing three others on each limb.

Koch's postulates [MICROBIO] A set of laws elucidated by Robert Koch: the microorganism identified as the etiologic agent must be present in every case of the disease; the etiologic agent must be isolated and cultivated in pure culture; the organism must produce the disease when inoculated in pure culture into susceptible animals; a microorganism must be observed in and recovered from the experimentally diseased animal. Also known as law of specificity of bacteria.

Koch-Weeks bacillus See Hemophilus aegyptus.

kohlrabi [BOT] A biennial crucifer, designated Brassica caulorapa and B. oleracea var. caulorapa, of the order Capparales grown for its edible turniplike, enlarged stem.

Komodo dragon [VERT ZOO] Varanus komodoensis. A predatory reptile of the family Varanidae found only on the island of Komodo; it is the largest living lizard and may grow to 10 feet (3 meters).

Koonungidae [INV ZOO] A family of Australian crustaceans in the order Anaspidacea with sessile eyes and the first thoracic limb modified for digging.

Krause's corpuscle [ANAT] One of the spheroid nerve-end organs resembling lamellar corpuscles, but having a more delicate capsule; found especially in the conjunctiva, the mucosa of the tongue, and the external genitalia; they are believed to be cold receptors. Also known as end bulb of Krause.

Krebs cycle [BIOCHEM] A sequence of enzymatic reactions involving oxidation of a two-carbon acetyl unit to carbon dioxide and water to provide energy for storage in the form of high-energy phosphate bonds. Also known as citric acid cycle; tricarboxylic acid cycle.

Krebs-Henseleit cycle [BIOCHEM] A cyclic reaction pathway involving the breakdown of arginine to urea in the presence of arginase.

Krebspest [INV ZOO] A fatal fungus disease of crayfish caused by Aphanomyces mystaci.

krill [INV ZOO] A name applied to planktonic crustaceans that constitute the diet of many whales, particularly whalebone whales.

krummholz [ECOL] Stunted alpine forest vegetation. Also known as elfinwood.

kudzu [BOT] Any of various perennial vine legumes of the genus Pueraria in the order Rosales cultivated principally as a forage crop.

Kuehneosauridae [PALEON] The gliding lizards, a family of Upper Triassic reptiles in the order Squamata including the earliest known aerial vertebrates.

kumquat [BOT] A citrus shrub or tree of the genus Fortunella in the order Sapindales grown for its small, flame- to orange-colored edible fruit having three to five locules filled with an acid pulp, and a sweet, pulpy rind.

Kupffer cell [HISTOL] One of the fixed macrophages lining the hepatic sinusoids.

Kurthia [MICROBIO] A genus of gram-positive, aerobic, rod-shaped to coccoid bacteria in the coryneform group; metabolism is respiratory.

Kurtoidei [VERT ZOO] A monogeneric suborder of perciform fishes having a unique ossification that encloses the upper part of the swim bladder, and an occipital hook in the male for holding eggs during brooding.

Kusnezovia [MICROBIO] A genus of bacteria of uncertain affiliation; coccoid, nonmotile cells attach to substrate and reproduce by budding.

Kutorginida [PALEON] An order of extinct brachiopod mollusks that is unplaced taxonomically.

K virus [VIROL] A group 2 papovavirus affecting rats and mice.

Kyasanur Forest virus [VIROL] A group B arbovirus recognized as an agent that causes hemorrhagic fever.

kynurenic acid [BIOCHEM] $C_{10}H_7O_3N$ A product of tryptophan metabolism found in the urine of mammals.

kynurenine [BIOCHEM] $C_{10}H_{12}O_3N_2$ An intermediate product of tryptophan metabolism occurring in the urine of mammals.

labellate [BIOL] Having a labellum.

labellum [BOT] The median membrane of the corolla of an orchid often differing in size and morphology from the other two petals. [INV ZOO] 1. A prolongation of the labrum in certain beetles and true bugs. 2. In Diptera, either of a pair of sensitive fleshy lobes consisting of the expanded end of the labium.

labial gland [ANAT] Any of the small, tubular mucous and serous glands underneath the mucous membrane of mammalian lips. [INV ZOO] A salivary gland, or modification thereof, opening at the base of the labium in certain insects.

labial palp [INV ZOO] 1. Either of a pair of fleshy appendages on either side of the mouth of certain bivalve mollusks. 2. A jointed appendage attached to the labium of certain insects.

labial papilla [INV ZOO] Any of the sensory bristles around the mouth of many nematodes; they are jointed projections of the cuticle.

Labiatae [BOT] A large family of dicotyledonous plants in the order Lamiales; members are typically aromatic and usually herbaceous or merely shrubby.

labiate [ANAT] Having liplike margins that are thick and fleshy. [BIOL] Having lips. [BOT] Having the limb of a tubular calyx or corolla divided into two unequal overlapping parts.

labile factor See proaccelerin.

labium [BIOL] 1. A liplike structure. 2. The lower lip, as of a labiate corolla or of an insect.

labium majus [ANAT] Either of the two outer folds surrounding the vulva in the female.

labium minus [ANAT] Either of the two inner folds, at the inner surfaces of the labia majora, surrounding the vulva in the female.

Laboulbeniales [MYCOL] An order of ascomycetous fungi made up of species that live primarily on the external surfaces of insects.

Labridae [VERT ZOO] The wrasses, a family of perciform fishes in the suborder Percoidei.

labrum [INV ZOO] 1. The upper lip of certain arthropods, lying in front of or above the mandibles. 2. The outer edge of a gastropod shell.

labyrinth [ANAT] 1. Any body structure full of intricate cavities and canals. 2. The inner ear.

labyrinthine placenta See hemochorial placenta.

labyrinthine reflex [PHYSIO] The involuntary response to stimulation of the vestibular apparatus in the inner ear.

Labyrinthodontia [PALEON] A subclass of fossil amphibians descended from crossopterygian fishes, ancestral to reptiles, and antecedent to at least part of other amphibian types.

Labyrinthulia [INV ZOO] A subclass of the protozoan class Rhizopoda containing mostly marine, ovoid to spindle-shaped, uninucleate organisms that secrete a network of filaments (slime tubes) along which they glide.

Labyrinthulida [INV ZOO] The single order of the protozoan subclass Labyrinthulia.

laccaic [BIOCHEM] $C_{17}H_{31}C_6H_3(OH)_2$ A phenol compound which is found in the sap of lacquer trees, and which can be isolated in crystalline form.

laccase [BIOCHEM] Any of a class of plant oxidases which catalyze the oxidation of phenols.

laccate [BIOL] Having a lacquered appearance.

Lacciferinae [INV ZOO] A subfamily of scale insects in the superfamily Coccoidea in which the male lacks compound eyes, the abdomen is without spiracles in all stages, and the apical abdominal segments of nymphs and females do not form a pygidium.

lacerated [BIOL] Having a deeply and irregularly incised margin or apex.

Lacertidae [VERT ZOO] A family of reptiles in the suborder Sauria, including all typical lizards, characterized by movable eyelids, a fused lower jaw, homodont dentition, and epidermal scales.

Lachnospira [MICROBIO] A genus of weakly grampositive, anaerobic bacteria of uncertain affiliation; motile, curved rods that ferment glucose and are found in the rumen of bovine animals.

laciniate [BIOL] 1. Having a fringed border. 2. Narrowly and deeply incised to form irregular lobes, which may be pointed.

lac operon [GEN] A sequence of three linked genes which code for the enzymes involved in lactose utilization in many bacteria.

lacquer tree See varnish tree.

lacrimal [ANAT] Pertaining to tears, tear ducts, or tear-secreting organs.

lacrimal apparatus [ANAT] The functional and structural mechanisms for secreting and draining tears; includes the lacrimal gland, lake, puncta, canaliculi, sac, and nasolacrimal duct.

lacrimal bone [ANAT] A small bone located in the anterior medial wall of the orbit, articulating with the frontal, ethmoid, maxilla, and inferior nasal concha.

lacrimal canal *See* nasolacrimal canal.

lacrimal canaliculus [ANAT] A small tube lined with stratified squamous epithelium which runs vertically a short distance from the punctum of each eyelid and then turns horizontally in the lacrimal part of the lid margin to the lacrimal sac. Also known as lacrimal duct.

lacrimal duct *See* lacrimal canaliculus.

lacrimal gland [ANAT] A compound tubuloalveolar gland that secretes tears. Also known as tear gland.

lacrimal sac [ANAT] The dilation at the upper end of the nasolacrimal duct within the medial canthus of the eye. Also known as dacryocyst.

lacrimation [PHYSIO] 1. Normal secretion of tears. 2. Excessive secretion of tears, as in weeping.

lactalbumin [BIOCHEM] A simple protein contained in milk which resembles serum albumin and is of high nutritional quality.

lactase [BIOCHEM] An enzyme that catalyzes the hydrolysis of lactose to dextrose and galactose.

lactate [PHYSIO] To secrete milk.

lactate dehydrogenase [BIOCHEM] A zinc-containing enzyme which catalyzes the oxidation of several α-hydroxy acids to corresponding α-keto acids.

lactation [PHYSIO] Secretion of milk by the mammary glands.

lacteal [ANAT] One of the intestinal lymphatics that absorb chyle. [PHYSIO] Pertaining to or resembling milk.

lactescent [BIOL] Having a milky appearance. [PHYSIO] Secreting milk or a milklike substance.

lactic acid [BIOCHEM] $C_3H_6O_3$ A hygroscopic α-hydroxy acid, occurring in three optically isomeric forms: L form, in blood and muscle tissue as a product of glucose and glycogen metabolism; D form, obtained by fermentation of sucrose; and DL form, a racemic mixture present in foods prepared by bacterial fermentation, and also made synthetically. Also known as 2-hydroxypropanoic acid; α-hydroxypropanoic acid.

lactic dehydrogenase [BIOCHEM] An enzyme that catalyzes the dehydrogenation of L-lactic acid to pyruvic acid. Abbreviated LDH.

lactic dehydrogenase virus [VIROL] A virus of the rubella group which infects mice.

lactin *See* lactose.

lactivorous [ZOO] Feeding on milk.

Lactobacillaceae [MICROBIO] The single family of gram-positive, asporogenous, rod-shaped bacteria; they are saccharoclastic, and produce lactate from carbohydrate metabolism.

Lactobacilleae [MICROBIO] Formerly a tribe of rod-shaped bacteria in the family Lactobacillaceae.

Lactobacillus [MICROBIO] Lactic acid bacteria, the single genus of the family Lactobacillaceae; found in dairy products, meat products, fruits, beer, wine, and other food products.

lactoferrin [BIOCHEM] An iron-binding protein found in milk, saliva, tears, and intestinal and respiratory secretions that interferes with the iron metabolism of bacteria; in conjunction with antibodies, it plays an important role in resistance to certain infectious diseases.

lactoflavin *See* riboflavin.

lactogenic hormone *See* prolactin.

lactoglobulin [BIOCHEM] A crystalline protein fraction of milk, which is soluble in half-saturated ammonium sulfate solution and insoluble in pure water.

lactonase [BIOCHEM] The enzyme that catalyzes the hydrolysis of 6-phosphoglucono-Δ-lactone to 6-phosphogluconic acid in the pentose phosphate pathway.

lactose [BIOCHEM] $C_{12}H_{22}O_{11}$ A disaccharide composed of D-glucose and D-galactose which occurs in milk. Also known as lactin; milk sugar.

lacuna [BIOL] A small space or depression. [HISTOL] A cavity in the matrix of bone or cartilage which is occupied by the cell body.

lacunar system [INV ZOO] A series of intercommunicating spaces branching from two longitudinal vessels in the hypodermis of many acanthocephalins.

Lacydonidae [INV ZOO] A benthic family of pelagic errantian polychaetes.

Laemobothridae [INV ZOO] A family of lice in the order Mallophaga including parasites of aquatic birds, especially geese and coots.

Lagenidiales [MYCOL] An order of aquatic fungi belonging to the class Phycomycetales characterized by a saclike to limited hyphal thallus and zoospores having two flagella.

lageniform [BIOL] Flask-shaped.

Lagomorpha [VERT ZOO] The order of mammals including rabbits, hares, and pikas; differentiated from rodents by two pairs of upper incisors covered by enamel, vertical or transverse jaw motion, three upper and two lower premolars, fused tibia and fibula, and a spiral valve in the cecum.

lag phase [MICROBIO] The period of physiological activity and diminished cell division following the addition of inoculum of bacteria to a new culture medium.

Lagriidae [INV ZOO] The long-jointed bark beetles, a family of coleopteran insects in the superfamily Tenebrionoidea.

Lagynacea [INV ZOO] A superfamily of foraminiferan protozoans in the suborder Allogromiina having a free or attached test that has a membranous to tectinous wall and a single, ovoid, tubular, or irregular chamber.

lake ball [ECOL] A spherical mass of tangled, waterlogged fibers and other filamentous material of living or dead vegetation, produced mechanically along a lake bottom by wave action, and usually impregnated with sand and fine-grained mineral fragments. Also known as burr ball; hair ball.

Lamarckism [EVOL] The theory that organic evolution takes place through the inheritance of modifications caused by the environment, and by the effects of use and disuse of organs.

lamb [VERT ZOO] A young sheep.

lamb's wool [VERT ZOO] The first fleece taken from a sheep up to 7 months old, having natural tapered fiber tip and spinning qualities superior to those of wool taken from previously shorn sheep.

lamella [ANAT] A thin scale or plate.

lamellar bone [HISTOL] Any bone with a microscopic structure consisting of thin layers or plates.

lamellar chloroplast [CELL BIO] A type of chloroplast in which the layered structure extends more or less uniformly through the whole chloroplast body.

Lamellibranchiata [INV ZOO] An equivalent name for Bivalvia.

Lamellisabellidae [INV ZOO] A family of marine animals in the order Thecanephria.

Lamiaceae [BOT] An equivalent name for Labiatae.

Lamiales [BOT] An order of dicotyledonous plants in the subclass Asteridae marked by its characteristic gynoecium, consisting of usually two biovulate carpels, with each carpel divided between the ovules by a false partition, or with the two halves of the carpel seemingly wholly separate.

lamina [ANAT] A thin sheet or layer of tissue; a scalelike structure.

lamina cribrosa [ANAT] 1. The portion of the sclera which is perforated for the passage of the optic nerve. 2. The fascia covering the saphenous opening in the thigh. 3. The anterior or posterior perforated space of the brain. 4. The perforated plates of bone through which pass branches of the cochlear part of the vestibulocochlear nerve.

laminal placentation [BOT] Condition in which the ovules occur on the inner surface of the carpels.

Laminariophyceae [BOT] A class of algae belonging to the division Phaeophyta.

lamina terminalis [ANAT] The layer of gray matter in the brain connecting the optic chiasma and the anterior commissure where the latter becomes continuous with the rostral lamina.

lampbrush chromosome [CELL BIO] An exceptionally large chromosome characterized by fine lateral projections which are associated with active ribonucleic acid and protein synthesis.

lamprey [VERT ZOO] The common name for all members of the order Petromyzonida.

Lampridiformes [VERT ZOO] An order of teleost fishes characterized by a compressed, often ribbonlike body, fins composed of soft rays, a ductless swim bladder, and protractile maxillae among other distinguishing features.

Lamprocystis [MICROBIO] A genus of bacteria in the family Chromatiaceae; cells are spherical and motile, have gas vacuoles, and contain bacteriochlorophyll *a* on vesicular photosynthetic membranes.

Lampropedia [MICROBIO] A genus of gram-negative, obligately anaerobic cocci of uncertain affiliation; cells form pairs, tetrads, or flat squared tablets.

Lampyridae [INV ZOO] The firefly beetles, a large cosmopolitan family of coleopteran insects in the superfamily Cantharoidea.

lanatoside [BIOCHEM] Any of three natural glycosides from the leaves of *Digitalis lanata*; on hydrolysis with acid, it yields one molecule of D-glucose, three molecules of digitoxose, and one molecule of acetic acid; all three glycosides are cardioactive.

Lancefield groups [MICROBIO] Antigenically determined categories for classification of β-hemolytic streptococci.

lancelet [ZOO] The common name for members of the subphylum Cephalochordata.

lanceolate [BIOL] Shaped like the head of a lance.

Lanceolidae [INV ZOO] A family of bathypelagic amphipod crustaceans in the suborder Hyperiidea.

Lange's nerve [INV ZOO] One of the paired cords of nervous tissue lying in the wall of the radial perihemal canal of asteroids.

Langerhans cell [HISTOL] 1. A type of cytotrophoblast in the human chorionic vesicle which is thought to secrete chorionic gonadotropin. 2. A highly branched dendritic cell of the mammalian epidermis showing a lobulated nucleus and a diagnostic organelle resembling a tennis racket.

Languriidae [INV ZOO] The lizard beetles, a cosmopolitan family of coleopteran insects in the superfamily Cucujoidea.

Lang's vesicle [INV ZOO] A seminal bursa in many polyclad flatworms.

Laniatores [INV ZOO] A suborder of arachnids in the order Phalangida having flattened, often colorful bodies and found chiefly in tropical areas.

lanosterol [BIOCHEM] $C_{30}H_{50}O$ An unsaturated sterol occurring in wool fat and yeast.

lantern fish [VERT ZOO] The common name for the deep-sea teleost fishes composing the family Myctophidae and distinguished by luminous glands that are widely distributed upon the body surface.

Lanthonotidae [VERT ZOO] A family of lizards (Sauria) belonging to the Anguimorpha line; restricted to North Borneo.

lanugo [ANAT] A downy covering of hair, especially that seen on the fetus or persisting on the adult body.

lapachoic acid *See* lapachol.

lapachol [BIOCHEM] $C_{15}H_{14}O_3$ A yellow crystalline compound obtained from lapacho, a hardwood in Argentina and Paraguay. Also known as 2-hydroxy-3-amylene-α-naphtho-quinone; lapachoic acid; targusic acid.

lapidicolous [ECOL] Living under a stone.

lappet [ZOO] A lobe or flaplike projection, such as on the margin of a jellyfish or the wattle of a bird.

larch [BOT] The common name for members of the genus *Larix* of the pine family, having deciduous needles and short, spurlike branches which annually bear a crown of needles.

larch canker [PL PATH] A destructive fungus disease of larch and sometimes pine and fir caused by *Dasyscypha willkommii* and characterized by flat, depressed cankers on the twigs and branches.

large intestine *See* colon.

Largidae [INV ZOO] A family of hemipteran insects in the superfamily Pentatomorpha.

Laridae [VERT ZOO] A family of birds in the order Charadriiformes composed of the gulls and terns.

Larinae [VERT ZOO] A subfamily of birds in the family Laridae containing the gulls and characterized by a thick, slightly hooked beak, a square tail, and a stout white body, with shades of gray on the back and the upper wing surface.

larva [INV ZOO] An independent, immature, often vermiform stage that develops from the fertilized egg and must usually undergo a series of form and size changes before assuming characteristic features of the parent.

Larvacea [INV ZOO] A class of the subphylum Tunicata consisting of minute planktonic animals in which the tail, with dorsal nerve cord and notochord, persists throughout life.

Larvaevoridae [INV ZOO] The tachina flies, a large family of dipteran insects in the suborder Cyclorrhapha distinguished by a thick covering of bristles on the body; most are parasites of arthropods.

larva migrans [INV ZOO] Fly larva, *Hypoderma* or *Gastrophilus*, that produces a creeping eruption in the dermis.

larviporous [INV ZOO] Feeding on larva, referring especially to insects.

laryngeal pouch [VERT-ZOO] A lateral saclike expansion of the cavity of the larynx that is greatly developed in certain monkeys.

laryngopharynx [ANAT] The lower portion of the pharynx, lying adjacent to the larynx. Also known as hypopharynx.

laryngotracheal groove [EMBRYO] A channel in the floor of the pharynx serving as the anlage of the respiratory system.

laryngotracheobronchitis virus *See* croup-associated virus.

larynx [ANAT] The complex of cartilages and related structures at the opening of the trachea into the pharynx in vertebrates; functions in protecting the entrance of the trachea, and in phonation in higher forms.

Lasiocampidae [INV ZOO] The tent caterpillars and lappet moths, a family of cosmopolitan (except New Zealand) lepidopteran insects in the suborder Heteroneura.

lasso cell *See* adhesive cell.

late blight [PL PATH] A fungus blight disease in which symptoms do not appear until late in the growing season and vary for different species.

latency [PHYSIO] The period between the introduction of and the response to a stimulus.

latent bud [BOT] An axillary bud whose development is inhibited, sometimes for many years, due to the influence of apical and other buds. Also known as dormant bud.

latent period [PHYSIO] The period between the introduction of a stimulus and the response to it. [VIROL] The initial period of phage growth after infection during which time virus nucleic acid is manufactured by the host cell.

laterad [ANAT] Toward the lateral aspect.

lateral [ANAT] At, pertaining to, or in the direction of the side; on either side of the medial vertical plane.

lateral bud [BOT] Any bud that develops on the side of a stem.

lateral lemniscus [ANAT] The secondary auditory pathway arising in the cochlear nuclei and terminating in the inferior colliculus and medial geniculate body.

lateral line [INV ZOO] A longitudinal lateral line along the sides of certain oligochaetes consisting of cell bodies of the layer of circular muscle. [VERT ZOO] A line along the sides of the body of most fishes, often distinguished by differently colored scales, which marks the lateral line organ.

lateral-line organ [VERT ZOO] A small, pear-shaped sense organ in the skin of many fishes and amphibians that is sensitive to pressure changes in the surrounding water.

lateral-line system [VERT ZOO] The complex of lateral-line end organs and nerves in skin on the sides of many fishes and amphibians.

lateral meristem [BOT] Strips or cylinders of dividing cells located parallel to the long axis of the organ in which they occur; the lateral meristem functions to increase the diameter of the organ.

lateral root [BOT] A root branch arising from the main axis.

lateral ventricle [ANAT] The cavity of a cerebral hemisphere; communicates with the third ventricle by way of the interventricular foramen.

Lathridiidae [INV ZOO] The minute brown scavenger beetles, a large cosmopolitan family of coleopteran insects in the superfamily Cucujoidea.

laticifer [BOT] A latex duct found in the midcortex of certain plants.

latiferous [BOT] Containing or secreting latex.

Latimeridae [VERT ZOO] A family of deep-sea lobefin fishes (Coelacanthiformes) known from a single living species, *Latimeria chalumnae*.

latissimus dorsi [ANAT] The widest muscle of the back; a broad, flat muscle of the lower back that adducts and extends the humerus, is used to pull the body upward in climbing, and is an accessory muscle of respiration.

Laugiidae [PALEON] A family of Mesozoic fishes in the order Coelacanthiformes.

Lauraceae [BOT] The laurel family of the order Magnoliales distinguished by definite stamens in series of three, a single pistil, and the lack of petals.

Lauratonematidae [INV ZOO] A family of marine nematodes of the superfamily Enoploidea; many females possess a cloaca.

laurel forest *See* temperate rainforest.

Laurer's canal [INV ZOO] In certain flukes, a canal which passes from the oviduct to the ventral surface of the body.

laurisilva *See* temperate rainforest.

Lauxaniidae [INV ZOO] A family of myodarian cyclorrhaphous dipteran insects in the subsection Acalypteratae; larvae are leaf miners.

law of minimum [BIOL] The law that those essential elements for which the ratio of supply to demand (A/N) reaches a minimum will be the first to be removed from the environment by life processes; it was proposed by J. von Liebig, who recognized phosphorus, nitrogen, and potassium as minimum in the soil; in the ocean the corresponding elements are phosphorus, nitrogen, and silicon. Also known as Liebig's law of minimum.

law of specificity of bacteria *See* Koch's postulate.

layering [BOT] A propagation method by which root formation is induced on a branch or a shoot attached to the parent stem by covering the part with soil. [ECOL] A stratum of plant forms in a community, such as mosses, shrubs, or trees in a bog area.

LDH *See* lactic dehydrogenase.

leaf [BOT] A modified aerial appendage which develops from a plant stem at a node, usually contains chlorophyll, and is the principal organ in which photosynthesis and transpiration occur.

leaf blight [PL PATH] Any of various blight diseases which cause browning, death, and falling of the leaves.

leaf blotch [PL PATH] A plant disease characterized by discolored areas in the leaves with indistinct or diffuse margins.

leaf bud [BOT] A bud that produces a leafy shoot.

leaf cast [PL PATH] Any of several diseases of conifers characterized by falling of the needles.

leaf curl [PL PATH] A fungus or viral disease of plants marked by the curling of leaves.

leaf cushion [BOT] The small part of the thickened leaf base that remains after abscission in various conifers, and also in some extinct plants.

leaf drop [PL PATH] Premature falling of leaves, associated with disease.

leaf fiber [BOT] A long, multiple-celled fiber extracted from the leaves of many plants that is used for cordage, such as sisal for binder, and abaca for manila hemp.

leafhopper [INV ZOO] The common name for members of the homopteran family Cicadellidae.

leaflet [BOT] 1. A division of a compound leaf. 2. A small or young foliage leaf.

leaf miner [INV ZOO] Any of the larvae of various insects which burrow into and eat the parenchyma of leaves.

leaf mottle [PL PATH] A fungus disease characterized by chlorotic mottling of the leaves; for example, caused by *Verticillium dahliae* in sunflower.

leaf-nosed [VERT ZOO] Having a leaflike membrane on the nose, as certain bats.

leaf roll [PL PATH] Any of several virus diseases characterized by upward or inward rolling of the leaf margins.

leaf rot [PL PATH] Any plant disease characterized by break-down of leaf tissues; for example, caused by *Pellicularia koleroga* in coffee.

leaf rust [PL PATH] Any rust disease that primarily affects leaves; common in coffee, alfalfa, and wheat, barley, and other cereals.

leaf scald [PL PATH] A bacterial disease of sugarcane caused by *Bacterium albilineans* which invades the vascular tissues, causing creamy or grayish streaking and withering of the leaves.

leaf scar [BOT] A mark on a stem, formed by secretion of suberin and a gumlike substance, showing where a leaf has abscised.

leaf scorch [BOT] Any of several disorders and fungus diseases marked by a burned appearance of the leaves; for example, caused by the fungus *Diplocarpon earliana* in strawberry.

leaf spot [PL PATH] Any of various diseases or disorders characterized by the appearance of well-defined discolored spots on the leaves.

leaf stripe [PL PATH] Any of various plant diseases characterized by striped discolorations on the foliage.

leak [PL PATH] A watery rot of fruits and vegetables caused by various fungi, such as *Rhizopus nigricans* in strawberry.

leaky mutant gene [GEN] An allele with reduced activity relative to that of the normal allele.

leather rot [PL PATH] A hard rot of strawberry caused by the fungus *Phytophthora cactorum*.

Lecanicephaloidea [INV ZOO] An order of tapeworms of the subclass Cestoda distinguished by having the scolex divided into two portions; all species are intestinal parasites of elasmobranch fishes.

Lecanoraceae [BOT] A temperate and boreal family of lichens in the order Lecanorales characterized by a crustose thallus and a distinct thalloid rim on the apothecia.

Lecanorales [BOT] An order of the Ascolichenes having open, discoid apothecia with a typical hymenium and hypothecium.

Lecideaceae [BOT] A temperate and boreal family of lichens in the order Lecanorales; members lack a thalloid rim around the apothecia.

lecithin [BIOCHEM] Any of a group of phospholipids having the general composition $CH_2OR_1 \cdot CHOR_2 \cdot CH_2OPO_2OHR_3$, in which R_1 and R_2 are fatty acids and R_3 is choline, and with emulsifying, wetting, and antioxidant properties.

lecithinase [BIOCHEM] An enzyme that catalyzes the breakdown of a lecithin into its constituents.

lecithinase A [BIOCHEM] An enzyme that catalyzes the removal of only one fatty acid from lecithin, yielding lipolecithin.

lecithinase C [BIOCHEM] An enzyme that catalyzes the removal of the nitrogenous base of lecithin to produce the base and a phosphatidic acid.

lecithinase D [BIOCHEM] An enzyme that catalyzes the removal of the phosphorylated base from lecithins, producing αβ-diglyceride.

lectin [BIOCHEM] Any of various proteins that agglutinate erythrocytes and other types of cells and also have other properties, including mitogenesis, agglutination of tumor cells, and toxicity toward animals; found widely in plants, predominantly in legumes, and also occurring in bacteria, fish, and invertebrates.

lectotype [SYST] A specimen selected as the type of a species or subspecies if the type was not designated by the author of the classification.

Lecythidaceae [BOT] The single family of the order Lecythidales.

Lecythidales [BOT] A monofamilial order of dicotyledonous tropical woody plants in the subclass Dilleniidae; distinguished by entire leaves, valvate sepals, separate petals, numerous centrifugal stamens, and a syncarpous, inferior ovary with axile placentation.

Lederberg technique [MICROBIO] A method for rapid isolation of individual bacterial cells for demonstrating the spontaneous origin of bacterial mutants.

Leeaceae [BOT] A family of dicotyledonous plants in the order Rhamnales distinguished by solitary ovules in each locule, simple to compound leaves, a small embryo, and hypogynous flowers.

leech [INV ZOO] The common name for members of the annelid class Hirudinea.

leek [BOT] *Allium porrum*. A biennial herb known only by cultivation; grown for its mildly pungent succulent leaves and thick cylindrical stalk.

leg [ANAT] The lower extremity of a human limb, between the knee and the ankle. [ZOO] An appendage or limb used for support and locomotion.

legena [VERT ZOO] An appendage of the sacculus containing sensory areas in the inner ear of tetrapods; termed the cochlea in humans.

legume [BOT] A dry, dehiscent fruit derived from a single simple pistil; common examples are alfalfa, beans, peanuts, and vetch.

Leguminosae [BOT] The legume family of the plant order Rosales characterized by stipulate, compound leaves, 10 or more stamens, and a single carpel; many members harbor symbiotic nitrogen-fixing bacteria in their roots.

Leiodidae [INV ZOO] The round carrion beetles, a cosmopolitan family of coleopteran insects in the superfamily Staphylinoidea; commonly found under decaying bark.

leiosporous [MYCOL] Having smooth spores.

Leishmania [INV ZOO] A genus of flagellated protozoan parasites that are the etiologic agents of several diseases of humans, such as leishmaniasis.

Leishmania donovani [INV ZOO] The protozoan parasite that causes kala-azar.

Leishmania infantum [INV ZOO] The protozoan parasite that causes infantile leishmaniasis.

Leitneriales [BOT] A monofamilial order of flowering plants in the subclass Hamamelidae; members are simple-leaved, dioecious shrubs with flowers in catkins, and have a superior, pseudomonomerous ovary with a single ovule.

lek [ZOO] A gathering place for courtship. Also known as arena.

Lelapiidae [INV ZOO] A family of calcaronean sponges in the order Sycettida characterized by a rigid skeleton composed of tracts or bundles of modified triradiates.

lemma [BOT] Either of the pair of bracts that are borne above the glumes and enclose the flower of a grass spikelet.

lemming [VERT ZOO] The common name for the small burrowing rodents composing the subfamily Microtinae.

Lemnaceae [BOT] The duckweeds, a family of monocotyledonous plants in the order Arales; members are small, free-floating, thalloid aquat-

ics with much reduced flowers that form a miniature spadix.

lemniscus [ANAT] A secondary sensory pathway of the central nervous system, usually terminating in the thalamus.

lemon [BOT] *Citrus limon*. A small evergreen tree belonging to the order Sapindales cultivated for its acid citrus fruit which is a modified berry called a hesperidium.

lemur [VERT ZOO] The common name for members of the primate family Lemuridae; characterized by long tails, foxlike faces, and scent glands on the shoulder region and wrists.

Lemuridae [VERT ZOO] A family of prosimian primates of Madagascar belonging to the Lemuroidea; all members are arboreal forest dwellers.

Lemuroidea [VERT ZOO] A suborder or superfamily of Primates including the lemurs, tarsiers, and lorises, or sometimes simply the lemurs.

lengthening reaction [PHYSIO] Sudden inhibition of the stretch reflex when extensor muscles are subjected to an excessive degree of stretching by forceful flexion of a limb.

lens [ANAT] A transparent, encapsulated, nearly spherical structure located behind the pupil of vertebrate eyes, and in the complex eyes of many invertebrates, that focuses light rays on the retina. Also known as crystalline lens.

lens placode [EMBRYO] The ectodermal anlage of the lens of the eye; its formation is induced by the presence of the underlying optic vesicle.

lentic [ECOL] Of or pertaining to still waters such as lakes, reservoirs, ponds, and bogs. Also spelled lenitic.

lenticel [BOT] A loose-structured opening in the periderm beneath the stomata in the stem of many woody plants that facilitates gas transport.

lentiginose [ANAT] Of or pertaining to pigment spots in the skin; freckled.

lentil [BOT] *Lens esculenta*. A seminvy annual legume having pinnately compound, vetchlike leaves; cultivated for its thin, lens-shaped, edible seed.

leopard [VERT ZOO] *Felis pardus*. A species of wildcat in the family Felidae found in Africa and Asia; the coat is characteristically buff-colored with black spots.

Leotichidae [INV ZOO] A small Oriental family of hemipteran insects in the superfamily Leptopodoidea.

Lepadomorpha [INV ZOO] A suborder of barnacles in the order Thoracica having a peduncle and a capitulum which is usually protected by calcareous plates.

Leperditicopida [PALEON] An order of extinct ostracods characterized by very thick, straight-backed valves which show unique muscle scars and other markings.

Leperditiiacea [PALEON] A superfamily of extinct paleocopan ostracods in the suborder Kloedenellocopina including the unisulcate, nondimorphic forms.

Lepiceridae [INV ZOO] Horn's beetle, a family of Central American coleopteran insects composed of two species.

Lepidocentroida [INV ZOO] The name applied to a polyphyletic assemblage of echinoids now regarded as members of the Echinocystitoida and Echinothurioida.

Lepidodendrales [PALEOBOT] The giant club mosses, an order of extinct lycopods (Lycopodiopsida) consisting primarily of arborescent forms characterized by dichotomous branching, small amounts of secondary vascular tissue, and heterospory.

lepidophyllous [BOT] Having scaly leaves.

Lepidoptera [INV ZOO] Large order of scaly-winged insects, including the butterflies, skippers, and moths; adults are characterized by two pairs of membranous wings and sucking mouthparts, featuring a prominent, coiled proboscis.

Lepidosirenidae [VERT ZOO] A family of slender, obligate air-breathing, eellike fishes in the order Dipteriformes having small thin scales, slender ribbonlike paired fins, and paired ventral lungs.

Lepidosaphinae [INV ZOO] A family of homopteran insects in the superfamily Coccoidea having dark-colored, noncircular scales.

Lepidosauria [VERT ZOO] A subclass of reptiles in which the skull structure is characterized by two temporal openings on each side which have reduced bony arcades, and by the lack of an antorbital opening in front of the orbit.

Lepidotrichidae [INV ZOO] A family of wingless insects in the order Thysanura.

Lepismatidae [INV ZOO] A family of silverfish in the order Thysanura characterized by small or missing compound eyes.

Lepisostei [VERT ZOO] An equivalent name for Semionotiformes.

Lepisosteidae [VERT ZOO] A family of fishes in the order Semionotiformes.

Lepisosteiformes [VERT ZOO] An equivalent name for Semionotiformes.

Leporidae [VERT ZOO] A family of mammals in the order Lagomorpha including the rabbits and hares.

Lepospondyli [PALEON] A subclass of extinct amphibians including all forms in which the vertebral centra are formed by ossification directly around the notochord.

lepospondylous [VERT ZOO] Having the notochord enclosed by cylindrical vertebrae shaped like an hourglass in longitudinal section.

Leptaleinae [INV ZOO] A subfamily of the Formicidae including largely arboreal ant forms which inhabit plants in tropical and subtropical regions.

Leptictidae [PALEON] A family of extinct North American insectivoran mammals belonging to the Proteutheria which ranged from the Cretaceous to middle Oligocene.

Leptinidae [INV ZOO] The mammal nest beetles, a small European and North American family of coleopteran insects in the superfamily Staphylinoidea.

Leptocardii [ZOO] The equivalent name for Cephalochordata.

leptocephalous larva [VERT ZOO] The marine larva of the fresh-water European eel *Anguilla vulgaris*.

leptocercal [VERT ZOO] Of the tail of a fish, tapering to a long, slender point.

Leptochoeridae [PALEON] An extinct family of palaeodont artiodactyl mammals in the superfamily Dichobunoidea.

Leptodactylidae [VERT ZOO] A large family of frogs in the suborder Procoela found principally in the American tropics and Australia.

leptodactylous [VERT ZOO] Having slender toes, as certain birds.

Leptodiridae [INV ZOO] The small carrion beetles, a cosmopolitan family of coleopteran insects in the superfamily Staphylinoidea.

Leptolepidae [PALEON] An extinct family of fishes in the order Leptolepiformes representing the first teleosts as defined on the basis of the advanced structure of the caudal skeleton.

Leptolepiformes [PALEON] An extinct order of small, ray-finned teleost fishes characterized by a relatively strong, ossified axial skeleton, thin cycloid scales, and a preopercle with an elongated dorsal portion.

Leptomedusae [INV ZOO] A suborder of hydrozoan coelenterates in the order Hydroida characterized by the presence of a hydrotheca.

leptomeninges [ANAT] The pia mater and arachnoid considered together.

Leptomitales [MYCOL] An order of aquatic Phycomycetes characterized by a hyphal thallus, or basal rhizoids and terminal hyphae, and zoospores with two flagella.

leptophyll [ECOL] A growth-form class of plants having a leaf surface area of 25 square millimeters or less; common in alpine and desert habitats.

Leptopodidae [INV ZOO] A tropical and subtropical family of hemipteran insects in the superfamily Leptopodoidea distinguished by the spiny body and appendages.

Leptopodoidea [INV ZOO] A superfamily of hemipteran insects in the subdivision Geocorisae.

Leptosomatidae [VERT ZOO] The cuckoo rollers, a family of Madagascan birds in the order Coraciiformes composed of a single species distinguished by the downy covering on the newly hatched young.

Leptospira [MICROBIO] A genus of bacteria in the family Spirochaetaceae; thin, helical cells with bent or hooked ends.

Leptospira icterohemorrhagiae [MICROBIO] The organism that causes spirochetal jaundice in humans.

Leptostraca [INV ZOO] A primitive group of crustaceans considered as one of a series of Malacostraca distinguished by an additional abdominal somite that lacks appendages, and a telson bearing two movable articulated prongs.

Leptostromataceae [MYCOL] A family of fungi of the order Sphaeropsidales; pycnidia are black and shield-shaped, circular or oblong, and slightly asymmetrical; included are some fruit-tree pathogens.

leptotene [CELL BIO] The first stage of meiotic prophase, when the chromosomes appear as thin threads having well-defined chromomeres.

Leptothrix [MICROBIO] A genus of sheathed bacteria; single cells are motile by means of polar or subpolar flagella, and sheaths are encrusted with iron or manganese oxides.

Leptotrichia [MICROBIO] A genus of bacteria in the family Bacteroidaceae; straight or slightly curved rods with pointed or rounded ends arranged in filaments.

Leptotyphlopidae [VERT ZOO] A family of small, harmless, burrowing circumtropical snakes (Serpentes) in the order Squamata; teeth are present only on the lower jaw and are few in number.

Lepus [VERT ZOO] The type genus of the family Leporidae, comprising the typical hares.

Lernaeidae [INV ZOO] A family of copepod crustaceans in the suborder Caligoida; all are fixed ectoparasites, that is, they penetrate the skin of fresh-water fish.

Lernaeopodidae [INV ZOO] A family of ectoparasitic crustaceans belonging to the Lernaeopodoida; individuals are attached to the walls of the fishes' gill chambers by modified second maxillae.

Lernaeopodoida [INV ZOO] The fish maggots, a group of ectoparasitic crustaceans characterized by a modified postembryonic development reduced to two or three stages, a free-swimming larva, and the lack of external signs of physical maturity in adults.

lesion [BIOL] A structural or functional alteration due to injury or disease.

Leskeineae [BOT] A suborder of mosses in the order Hypnobryales; plants are not complanate, paraphyllia are frequently present, leaves are costate, and alar cells are not generally differentiated.

lespedeza [BOT] Any of various legumes of the genus *Lespedeza* having trifoliate leaves, small purple pea-shaped blossoms, and one seed per pod.

lesser circulation *See* pulmonary circulation.

lesser omentum [ANAT] A fold of the peritoneum extending from the lesser curvature of the stomach to the transverse hepatic fissure.

Lestidae [INV ZOO] A family of odonatan insects belonging to the Zygoptera; distinguished by the wings being held in a V position while at rest.

Lestoniidae [INV ZOO] A monospecific family of hemipteran insects in the superfamily Pentatomorpha found only in Australia.

lethal gene [GEN] A gene mutation that causes premature death in heterozygotes if dominant, and in homozygotes if recessive. Also known as lethal mutation.

lettuce [BOT] *Lactuca sativa*. An annual plant of the order Asterales cultivated for its succulent leaves; common varieties are head lettuce, leaf or curled lettuce, romaine lettuce, and iceberg lettuce.

Leucaltidae [INV ZOO] A family of calcinean sponges in the order Leucettida having numerous small, interstitial, flagellated chambers.

Leucascidae [INV ZOO] A family of calcinean sponges in the order Leucettida having a radiate arrangement of flagellated chambers.

Leucettida [INV ZOO] An order of calcareous sponges in the subclass Calcinea having a leuconoid structure and a distinct dermal membrane or cortex.

leucine [BIOCHEM] $C_6H_{13}O_2N$ A monocarboxylic essential amino acid obtained by hydrolysis of protein-containing substances such as milk.

leucine amino peptidase [BIOCHEM] An enzyme that acts on peptides to catalyze the release of terminal amino acids, especially leucine residues, having free α-amino groups.

Leucodontineae [BOT] A family of mosses in the order Isobryales with foliated branches, often bearing catkins.

leucon [INV ZOO] A type of sponge having the choanocytes restricted to flagellated chambers inserted between the incurrent and excurrent canals, and a reduced or absent paragastric cavity.

Leuconostoc [MICROBIO] A genus of bacteria in the family Streptococcaceae; spherical or lenticular cells occurring in pairs or chains; ferment glucose with production of levorotatory lactic acid (heterofermentative), ethanol, and carbon dioxide.

leucophore [HISTOL] A white reflecting chromatophore.

leucoplast [BOT] A nonpigmented plastid; capable of developing into a chromoplast.

Leucosiidae [INV ZOO] The purse crabs, a family of true crabs belonging to the Oxystomata.

leucosin [BIOCHEM] A simple protein of the albumin type found in wheat and other cereals.

Leucosolenida [INV ZOO] An order of calcareous sponges in the subclass Calcaronea characterized by an asconoid structure and the lack of a true dermal membrane or cortex.

Leucospidae [INV ZOO] A small family of hymenopteran insects in the superfamily Chalcidoidea distinguished by a longitudinal fold in the forewings.

leucosporous [MYCOL] Having white spores.

Leucothoidae [INV ZOO] A family of amphipod crustaceans in the suborder Gammaridea including semiparasitic and commensal species.

Leucothrix [MICROBIO] The type genus of the family Leucotrichaceae; cells do not form sulfur deposits.

Leucotrichaceae [MICROBIO] A family of bacteria in the order Cytophagales; long, colorless, unbranched filaments having conspicuous cross-walls and containing cylindrical or ovoid cells; filaments attach to substrate.

leukocidin [BIOCHEM] A toxic substance released by certain bacteria which destroys leukocytes.

leukocyte [HISTOL] A colorless, ameboid blood cell having a nucleus and granular or nongranular cytoplasm. Also known as white blood cell; white corpuscle.

leukocytolysin [BIOCHEM] A leukocyte-disintegrating lysin.

leukocytopoiesis [PHYSIO] Formation of leukocytes.

leukotriene [BIOCHEM] Any of a family of oxidized metabolites of certain polyunsaturated fatty acids, predominantly arachidonic acid, that mediate responses in allergic reactions and inflammations, produced in specific cells upon stimulation.

leukovirus [VIROL] A major group of animal viruses including those causing leukemia in birds, mice, and rats. Also known as leukemia virus.

levan [BIOCHEM] $(C_6H_{10}O_5)_n$ A polysaccharide consisting of repeating units of D-fructose and produced by a range of microorganisms, such as *Bacillus mesentericus*.

levator [PHYSIO] Any muscle that raises or elevates a part.

level above threshold [PHYSIO] Also known as sensation level. 1. The pressure level of a sound in decibels above its threshold of audibility for the individual observer. 2. In general, the level of any psychophysical stimulus, such as light, above its threshold of perception.

leveret [VERT ZOO] A young hare.

levigate [BOT] *See* glabrous.

levotropic cleavage [EMBRYO] Spiral cleavage with the cells displaced counterclockwise.

levulose [BIOCHEM] Levorotatory D-fructose.

Leydig cell [HISTOL] One of the interstitial cells of the testes; thought to produce androgen.

liana [BOT] A woody or herbaceous climbing plant with roots in the ground.

Libellulidae [INV ZOO] A large family of odonatan insects belonging to the Anisoptera and distinguished by a notch on the posterior margin of the eyes and a foot-shaped anal loop in the hindwing.

Libytheidae [INV ZOO] The snout butterflies, a family of cosmopolitan lepidopteran insects in the suborder Heteroneura distinguished by long labial palps; represented in North America by a single species.

Liceaceae [MYCOL] A family of plasmodial slime molds in the order Liceales.

Liceales [MYCOL] An order of plasmodial slime molds in the subclass Myxogastromycetidae.

lichen [BOT] The common name for members of the Lichenes.

Lichenes [BOT] A group of organisms consisting of fungi and algae growing together symbiotically.

Lichenes Imperfecti [BOT] A class of the Lichenes containing species with no known method of sexual reproduction.

lichenology [BOT] The study of lichens.

lichenophagous [ZOO] Feeding on lichens.

Lichnophorina [INV ZOO] A suborder of ciliophoran protozoans belonging to the Heterotrichida.

licorice [BOT] *Glycyrrhiza glabra*. A perennial herb of the legume family (Leguminosae) cultivated for its roots, which when dried provide a product used as a flavoring in medicine, candy, and tobacco and in the manufacture of shoe polish.

Liebig's law of the minimum *See* law of minimum.

Lieskeela [MICROBIO] A genus of sheathed bacteria; cells are nonmotile, and sheaths are not attached and may be encrusted with iron and manganese oxides.

life cycle [BIOL] The functional and morphological stages through which an organism passes between two successive primary stages.

life expectancy [BIOL] The expected number of years that an organism will live based on statistical probability.

life form [ECOL] The form characteristically taken by a plant at maturity.

life zone [ECOL] A portion of the earth's land area having a generally uniform climate and soil, and a biota showing a high degree of uniformity in species composition and adaptation.

ligament [HISTOL] A flexible, dense white fibrous connective tissue joining, and sometimes encapsulating, the articular surfaces of bones.

ligamentum nuchae *See* nuchal ligament.

ligase [BIOCHEM] An enzyme that catalyzes the union of two molecules, involving the participation of a nucleoside triphosphate which is converted to a nucleoside diphosphate or monophosphate. Also known as synthetase.

light adaptation [PHYSIO] The disappearance of dark adaptation; the chemical processes by which the eyes, after exposure to a dim environment, become accustomed to bright illumination, which initially is perceived as quite intense and uncomfortable.

light meromyosin [BIOCHEM] The smaller of two fragments obtained from the muscle protein myosin following limited proteolysis by trypsin or chymotrypsin.

light reflex [PHYSIO] The postural orientation response of certain aquatic forms stimulated by the source of light; receptors may be on the ventral or dorsal surface.

Ligiidae [INV ZOO] A family of primitive terrestrial isopods in the suborder Oniscoidea.

ligneous [BIOL] Of, pertaining to, or resembling wood.

lignify [BOT] To convert cell wall constituents into wood or woody tissue by chemical and physical changes.

lignin [BIOCHEM] A substance that together with cellulose forms the woody cell walls of plants and cements them together; a colorless to brown substance removed from paper-pulp sulfite liquor.

lignocellulose [BIOCHEM] Any of a group of substances in woody plant cells consisting of cellulose and lignin.

lignosa [BOT] Woody vegetation.

lignumvitae [BOT] *Guaiacum sanctum*. A medium-sized evergreen tree in the order Sapindales that yields a resin or gum known as gum guaiac or resin of guaiac. Also known as hollywood lignumvitae.

ligulate [BOT] 1. Strap-shaped. 2. Having ligules.

ligule [BOT] 1. A small outgrowth in the axis of the leaves in Selaginellales. 2. A thin outgrowth of a foliage leaf or leaf sheath. [INV ZOO] A small lobe on the parapodium of certain poly-chaetes.

Liliaceae [BOT] A family of the order Liliales distinguished by six stamens, typically narrow, parallel-veined leaves, and a superior ovary.

Liliales [BOT] An order of monocotyledonous plants in the subclass Liliidae having the typical characteristics of the subclass.

Liliidae [BOT] A subclass of the Liliopsida; all plants are syncarpous and have a six-membered perianth, with all members petaloid.

Liliopsida [BOT] The monocotyledons, making up a class of the Magnoliophyta; characterized generally by a single cotyledon, parallel-veined leaves, and stems and roots lacking a well-defined pith and cortex.

lily [BOT] 1. Any of the perennial bulbous herbs with showy unscented flowers constituting the genus *Lilium*. 2. Any of various other plants having similar flowers.

Limacidae [INV ZOO] A family of gastropod mollusks containing the slugs.

limb [ANAT] An extremity or appendage used for locomotion or prehension, such as an arm or a leg. [BOT] A large primary tree branch.

limbate [BIOL] Having a part of one color bordered with a different color.

limb bud [EMBRYO] A mound-shaped lateral proliferation of the embryonic trunk; the anlage of a limb.

limbic system [ANAT] The inner edge of the cerebral cortex in the medial and temporal regions of the cerebral hemispheres.

limbus [BIOL] A border clearly defined by its color or structure, as the margin of a bivalve shell or of the cornea of the eye.

lime [BOT] *Citrus aurantifolia*. A tropical tree with elliptic oblong leaves cultivated for its acid citrus fruit which is a hesperidium.

limicolous [ECOL] Living in mud.

limivorous [ZOO] Feeding on mud, as certain annelids, for the organic matter it contains.

Limnebiidae [INV ZOO] The minute moss beetles, a family of coleopteran insects in the superfamily Hydrophiloidea.

limnetic [ECOL] Of, pertaining to, or inhabiting the pelagic region of a body of fresh water.

Limnichidae [INV ZOO] The minute false water beetles, a cosmopolitan family of coleopteran insects in the superfamily Dryopoidea.

Limnocharitaceae [BOT] A family of monocotyledonous plants in the order Alismatales characterized by schizogenous secretory canals, multiaperturate pollen, several or many ovules, and a horseshoe-shaped embryo.

limnology [ECOL] The science of the life and conditions for life in lakes, ponds, and streams.

Limnomedusae [INV ZOO] A suborder of hydrozoan coelenterates in the order Hydroida characterized by naked hydroids.

limnoplankton [BIOL] Plankton found in fresh water, especially in lakes.

Limnoriidae [INV ZOO] The gribbles, a family of isopod crustaceans in the suborder Flabellifera that burrow into submerged marine timbers.

limoniform [BOT] Lemon-shaped.

limpet [INV ZOO] Any of several species of marine gastropod mollusks composing the families Patellidae and Acmaeidae which have a conical and tentlike shell with ridges extending from the apex to the border.

Limulacea [INV ZOO] A group of horseshoe crabs belonging to the Limulida.

Limulida [INV ZOO] A subgroup of Xiphosurida including all living members of the subclass.

Limulodidae [INV ZOO] The horseshoe crab beetles, a family of coleopteran insects in the superfamily Staphylinoidea.

Limulus [INV ZOO] The horseshoe crab; the type genus of the Limulacea.

Linaceae [BOT] A family of herbaceous or shrubby dicotyledonous plants in the order Linales characterized by mostly capsular fruit, stipulate leaves, and exappendiculate petals.

Linales [BOT] An order of dicotyledonous plants in the subclass Orsidae containing simple-leaved herbs or woody plants with hypogynous, regular, syncarpous flowers having five to many stamens which are connate at the base.

lincomycin [MICROBIO] $C_{18}H_{34}O_6N_2S \cdot HCl$ Monobasic crystalline antibiotic, produced by *Streptomyces lincolnensis*, that is active as lincomycin hydrochloride mainly toward grampositive microorganisms.

linden *See* basswood.

line [BOT] A unit of length, equal to $\frac{1}{12}$ inch, or approximately 2.117 millimeters; it is most frequently used by botanists in describing the size of plants.

linea alba [ANAT] A tendinous ridge extending in the median line of the abdomen from the pubis to the tiphoid process and formed by the blending of aponeuroses of the oblique and transverse muscles of the abdomen.

lineage [GEN] Descent from a common progenitor.

Lineidae [INV ZOO] A family of the Heteronemertini.

Lineolaceae [MICROBIO] A family of bacteria in some systems of classification that includes coenocytic members (*Lineola*) of the Caryophanales.

lineolate [BIOL] Marked with fine lines.

lingual artery [ANAT] An artery originating in the external carotid and supplying the tongue.

lingual gland [ANAT] A serous, mucous, or mucoserous gland lying deep in the mucous membrane of the mammalian tongue.

lingual nerve [ANAT] A branch of the mandibular nerve having somatic sensory components and innervating the mucosa of the floor of the mouth and the anterior two-thirds of the tongue.

lingual tonsil [ANAT] An aggregation of lymphoid tissue composed of 35–100 separate tonsillar units occupying the posterior part of the tongue surface.

Linguatulida [INV ZOO] The equivalent name for Pentastomida.

Linguatuloidea [INV ZOO] A suborder of pentastomid arthropods in the order Porocephalida; characterized by an elongate, ventrally flattened, annulate, posteriorly attenuated body, simple hooks on the adult, and binate hooks in the larvae.

lingula [ANAT] A tongue-shaped organ, structure, or part thereof.

Lingulacea [INV ZOO] A superfamily of inarticulate brachiopods in the order Lingulida characterized by an elongate, biconvex calcium phosphate shell, with the majority having a pedicle.

lingulate [BIOL] Tongue- or strap-shaped.

Lingulida [INV ZOO] An order of inarticulate brachiopods represented by two living genera, *Lingula* and *Glottidia*.

linin net [CELL BIO] The reticulum composed of chromatinic or oxyphilic substances in a cell nucleus.

linkage [GEN] Failure of nonallelic genes to recombine at random as a result of their being located within the same chromosome or chromosome fragment.

linkage group [GEN] The genes located on a single chromosome.

linoleic acid [BIOCHEM] $C_{17}H_{31}COOH$ A yellow unsaturated fatty acid, boiling at 229°C (14 mm Hg), occurring as a glyceride in drying oils; obtained from linseed, safflower, and tall oils; a principal fatty acid in plants, and considered essential in animal nutrition; used in medicine, feeds, paints, and margarine. Also known as linolic acid; 9,12-octadecadienoic acid.

linolenate [BIOCHEM] A salt or ester of linolenic acid.

linolenic acid [BIOCHEM] $C_{17}H_{29}COOH$ One of the principal unsaturated fatty acids in plants and an essential fatty acid in animal nutrition; a colorless liquid that boils at 230°C (17 mmHg or 2266 newtons per square meter), soluble in many organic solvents; used in medicine and drying oils. Also known as 9,12,15-octadecatrienoic acid.

linolic acid *See* linoleic acid.

lion [VERT ZOO] *Felis leo.* A large carnivorous mammal of the family Felidae distinguished by a tawny coat and blackish tufted tail, with a heavy blackish or dark-brown mane in the male.

Liopteridae [INV ZOO] A small family of hymenopteran insects in the superfamily Cynipoidea.

lip [ANAT] A fleshy fold above and below the entrance to the mouth of mammals.

Liparidae [INV ZOO] The equivalent name for Lymantriidae.

lipase [BIOCHEM] An enzyme that catalyzes the hydrolysis of fats or the breakdown of lipoproteins.

Liphistiidae [INV ZOO] A family of spiders in the suborder Liphistiomorphae in which the abdomen shows evidence of true segmentation by the presence of tergal and sternal plates.

Liphistiomorphae [INV ZOO] A suborder of arachnids in the order Araneida containing families with a primitively segmented abdomen.

lipid [BIOCHEM] One of a class of compounds which contain long-chain aliphatic hydrocarbons and their derivatives, such as fatty acids, alcohols, amines, amino alcohols, and aldehydes; includes waxes, fats, and derived compounds. Also known as lipin; lipoid.

lipid metabolism [BIOCHEM] The physiologic and metabolic processes involved in the assimilation of dietary lipids and the synthesis and degradation of lipids.

lipin [BIOCHEM] **1.** A compound lipid, such as a cerebroside. **2.** *See* lipid.

lipochrome [BIOCHEM] Any of various fat-soluble pigments, such as carotenoid, occurring in natural fats. Also known as chromolipid.

lipofuscin [BIOCHEM] Any of a group of lipid pigments found in cardiac and smooth muscle cells, in macrophages, and in parenchyma and interstitial cells; differential reactions include sudanophilia, Nile blue staining, fatty acid, glycol, and ethylene.

lipoic acid [BIOCHEM] $C_8H_{14}O_2S_2$ A compound which participates in the enzymatic oxidative decarboxylation of α-keto acids in a stage between thiamine pyrophosphate and coenzyme A.

lipoid [BIOCHEM] **1.** A fatlike substance. **2.** *See* lipid.

Lipomycetoideae [MICROBIO] A subfamily of oxidative yeasts in the family Saccharomycetaceae characterized by budding cells and a saclike appendage which develops into an ascus.

lipophore [HISTOL] A chromatophore which contains lipochrome.

lipopolysaccharide [BIOCHEM] Any of a class of conjugated polysaccharides consisting of a polysaccharide combined with a lipid.

lipoprotein [BIOCHEM] Any of a class of conjugated proteins consisting of a protein combined with a lipid.

liposome [CELL BIO] One of the fatty droplets occurring in the cytoplasm, particularly of an egg.

Lipostraca [PALEON] An order of the subclass Branchiopoda erected to include the single fossil species *Lepidocaris rhyniensis*.

lipotropic [BIOCHEM] Having an affinity for lipid compounds.

lipotropic hormone [BIOCHEM] Any hormone having lipolytic activity on adipose tissue.

Lipotyphla [VERT ZOO] A group of insectivoran mammals composed of insectivores which lack an intestinal cecum and in which the stapedial artery is the major blood supply to the brain.

lipoxidase [BIOCHEM] An enzyme catalyzing the oxidation of the double bonds of an unsaturated fatty acid.

lirella [BOT] A long, narrow apothecium with a medial longitudinal furrow, occurring in certain lichens.

Liriopeidae [INV ZOO] The phantom craneflies, a family of dipteran insects in the suborder Orthorrhapha distinguished by black and white banded legs.

Lissamphibia [VERT ZOO] A subclass of Amphibia including all living amphibians; distinguished by pedicellate teeth and an operculum-plectrum complex of the middle ear.

Listeria [MICROBIO] A genus of small, gram-positive, motile coccoid rods of uncertain affiliation; found in animal and human feces.

litchi *See* lychee.

Lithistida [PALEON] An order of fossil sponges in the class Demospongia having a reticulate skeleton composed of irregular and knobby siliceous spicules.

Lithobiomorpha [INV ZOO] An order of chilopods in the subclass Pleurostigmophora; members are anamorphic and have 15 leg-bearing trunk segments, and when eyes are present, they are ocellar.

lithocholic acid [BIOCHEM] $C_{24}H_{40}O_3$ A crystalline substance with a melting point of 184–186°C; soluble in hot alcohol; found in ox, human, and rabbit bile.

lithocyst [BOT] Epidermal plant cell in which cytoliths are formed. [INV ZOO] One of the minute sacs containing lithites in many invertebrates; thought to function in audition and orientation.

lithocyte [INV ZOO] A special cell in anthomedusae containing a statolith.

Lithodidae [INV ZOO] The king crabs, a family of anomuran decapods in the superfamily Paguridea distinguished by reduced last pereiopods and by the asymmetrical arrangement of the abdominal plates in the female.

lithodomous [ZOO] Burrowing in rock.

lithophagous [ZOO] Feeding on stone, as certain mollusks.

lithophyte [ECOL] A plant that grows on rock.

lithosere [ECOL] A succession of plant communities that originate on rock.

lithostyle [INV ZOO] A static organ in Narcomedusae. Also known as tentaculocyst.

Litopterna [PALEON] An order of hoofed, herbivorous mammals confined to the Cenozoic of South America; characterized by a skull without expansion of the temporal or squamosal sinuses, a postorbital bar, primitive dentition, and feet that were three-toed or reduced to a single digit.

little cherry disease [PL PATH] A virus disease of sweet cherries characterized by small, angular pointed fruits which retain the bright red color of immaturity and never reach mature size.

little-drop technique [BIOL] A method for isolating single cells in which a drop of a cellular suspension containing a single cell, as determined by microscopic examination, is transferred with a capillary pipet to an appropriate culture medium.

little leaf [PL PATH] Any of various plant diseases and disorders characterized by chlorotic, underdeveloped, and sometimes distorted leaves.

little peach disease [PL PATH] A virus disease of the peach tree in which the fruit is dwarfed and delayed in ripening, the leaves yellow, and the tree dies.

littoral zone [ECOL] Of or pertaining to the biogeographic zone between the high- and low-water marks.

Littorinacea [PALEON] An extinct superfamily of gastropod mollusks in the order Prosobranchia.

Littorinidae [INV ZOO] The periwinkles, a family of marine gastropod mollusks in the order Pectinibranchia distinguished by their spiral, globular shells.

lituate [BOT] Having a forked member or part with the ends turned slightly outward, as in certain fungi.

Lituolacea [INV ZOO] A superfamily of benthic marine foraminiferans in the suborder Textulariina having a multilocular, rectilinear, enrolled or uncoiled test with a simple to labyrinthic wall.

liver [ANAT] A large vascular gland in the body of vertebrates, consisting of a continuous parenchymal mass covered by a capsule; secretes bile, manufactures certain blood proteins and enzymes, and removes toxins from the systemic circulation.

liver fluke [INV ZOO] Any trematode, especially *Clonorchis sinensis*, that lodges in the biliary passages within the liver.

liver phosphorylase [BIOCHEM] An enzyme that catalyzes the breakdown of liver glycogen to glucose-1-phosphate.

liverwort [BOT] The common name for members of the Marchantiatae.

living fossil [BIOL] A living species belonging to an ancient stock otherwise known only as fossils.

lizard [VERT ZOO] Any reptile of the suborder Sauria.

lizard-hipped dinosaur [PALEON] The name applied to members of the Saurichia because of the comparatively unspecialized three-pronged pelvis.

LK virus [VIROL] A type of equine herpesvirus.

llama [VERT ZOO] Any of three species of South American artiodactyl mammals of the genus *Lama* in the camel family; differs from the camel in being smaller and lacking a hump.

llano [ECOL] A savannah of Spanish America and the southwestern United States generally having few trees.

loach [VERT ZOO] The common name for fishes composing the family Cobitidae; most are small and many are eel-shaped.

Lobata [INV ZOO] An order of the Ctenophora in which the body is helmet-shaped.

lobate [BIOL] Having lobes. [VERT ZOO] Of a fish, having the skin of the fin extend onto the bases of the fin rays.

lobe [BIOL] A rounded projection on an organ or body part.

lobefin fish [VERT ZOO] The common name for members composing the subclass Crossopterygii.

loblolly pine [BOT] *Pinus taeda*. A hard yellow pine of the central and southeastern United States having a reddish-brown fissured bark, needles in groups of three, and a full bushy top.

lobopodia [INV ZOO] Broad, thick pseudopodia.

Lobosia [INV ZOO] A subclass of the protozoan class Rhizopodea generally characterized by lobopodia.

lobster [INV ZOO] The common name for several bottom-dwelling decapod crustaceans making up the family Homaridae which are commercially important as a food item.

lobule [BIOL] 1. A small lobe. 2. A division of a lobe.

locellus [BOT] 1. In some legumes, a secondary compartment of a unilocular ovary that is formed by a false partition. 2. One of the two cavities of a pollen sac.

lociation [ECOL] One of the subunits of a faciation, distinguished by the relative abundance of a dominant species.

locomotor system [ZOO] Appendages and associated parts, such as muscles, joints, and bones, concerned with motor activities and locomotion of the animal body.

loco weed [BOT] Any species of *Astragalus* containing selenium taken up from the soil.

loculate [BIOL] Having, or divided into, loculi.

loculus [BIOL] A small cavity or chamber.

locus [GEN] The fixed position of a gene in a chromosome.

locust [BOT] Either of two species of commercially important trees, black locust (*Robinia pseudoacacia*) and honey locust (*Gladitsia triacanthos*), in the family Leguminosae. [INV ZOO] The common name for various migratory grasshoppers of the family Locustidae.

Locustidae [INV ZOO] A family of insects in the order Orthoptera; antennae are usually less than half the body length, hindlegs are adapted for jumping, and the ovipositor is multipartite.

Loganiaceae [BOT] A family of mostly woody dicotyledonous plants in the order Gentianales; members lack a latex system and have fully united carpels and axile placentation.

logarithmic growth *See* exponential growth.

logotype [SYST] The selection or designation of a genotype after the generic name was published.

logwood *See* hematoxylon.

loment [BOT] A dry, indehiscent single-celled fruit that is formed from a single superior ovary; splits transversely in numerous segments at maturity.

Lonchaeidae [INV ZOO] A family of minute myodarian cyclorrhaphous dipteran insects in the subsection Acalyptreatae.

long bone [ANAT] A bone in which the length markedly exceeds the width, as the femur or the humerus.

long-day plant [BOT] A plant that flowers in response to a long photoperiod.

longicollous [BIOL] Having a long beak or neck.

Longidorinae [INV ZOO] A subfamily of nematodes belonging to the Dorylaimoidea including economically important plant parasites.

Longipennes [VERT ZOO] An equivalent name for Charadriiformes.

loon [VERT ZOO] The common name for birds composing the family Gaviidae, all of which are fish-eating diving birds.

loop of Henle [ANAT] The U-shaped portion of a renal tubule formed by a descending and an ascending tubule. Also known as Henle's loop.

loop pattern [ANAT] A type of fingerprint pattern in which one or more of the ridges enter on either side of the impression, recurve, touch, or pass an imaginary line from the delta to the core and terminate on the entering side.

loose connective tissue [HISTOL] A type of irregularly arranged connective tissue having a relatively large amount of ground substance.

loose kernel smut [PL PATH] A type of kernel smut disease distinguished by the ruptured spore-containing gall.

Lopadorrhynchidae [INV ZOO] A small family of pelagic polychaete annelids belonging to the Errantia.

Lophialetidae [PALEON] A family of extinct perissodactyl mammals in the superfamily Tapiroidea.

Lophiiformes [VERT ZOO] A modified order of actinopterygian fishes distinguished by the reduction of the first dorsal fin to a few flexible rays, the first of which is on the head and bears a terminal bulb; includes anglerfish and allies.

Lophiodontidae [PALEON] An extinct family of perissodactyl mammals in the superfamily Tapiroidea.

lophocercous [VERT ZOO] Having a ridgelike caudal fin that lacks rays.

lophocyte [INV ZOO] A specialized cell of uncertain function beneath the dermal membrane of certain Demospongiae which bears a process terminating in a tuft of fibrils.

lophodont [VERT ZOO] Having molar teeth whose grinding surfaces have transverse ridges.

Lophogastrida [INV ZOO] A suborder of free-swimming marine crustaceans in the order Mysidacea characterized by imperfect fusion of the sixth and seventh abdominal somites, seven pairs of gills and brood lamellae, and natatory, biramous pleopods.

lophophore [INV ZOO] A food-gathering organ consisting of a fleshy basal ridge or lobe, from which numerous ciliated tentacles arise; found in Bryozoa, Phoronida, and Brachiopoda.

lophotrichous [CELL BIO] Having a polar tuft of flagella.

Loranthaceae [BOT] A family of dicotyledonous plants in the order Santalales in which the ovules have no integument and are embedded in a large, central placenta.

lorate [BIOL] Strap-shaped.

L organisms [MICROBIO] Pleomorphic forms of bacteria occurring spontaneously, or favored by agents such as penicillin, which lack cell walls and grow in minute colonies; transition may be reversible under certain conditions.

lorica [INV ZOO] A hard shell or case in certain invertebrates, as in many rotifers and protozoans; functions as an exoskeleton.

Loricariidae [VERT ZOO] A family of catfishes in the suborder Siluroidei found in the Andes.

Loricata [INV ZOO] An equivalent name for Polyplacophora.

loricate [INV ZOO] Of, pertaining to, or having a lorica.

loris [VERT ZOO] Either of two slow-moving, nocturnal, arboreal primates included in the family Lorisidae: the slender loris (*Loris tardigradus*) and slow loris (*Nycticebus coucang*).

Lorisidae [VERT ZOO] A family of prosimian primates comprising the lorises of Asia and the galagos of Africa.

lotic [ECOL] Of or pertaining to swiftly moving waters.

louping-ill virus [VIROL] A group B arbovirus that is infectious in sheep, monkeys, mice, horses, and cattle.

louse [INV ZOO] The common name for the apterous ectoparasites composing the orders Anoplura and Mallophaga.

Lower Austral life zone [ECOL] A term used by C.H. Merriam to describe the southern portion of the Austral life zone, characterized by accumulated temperatures of 18,000°F (10,000°C).

lower motor neuron [ANAT] An efferent neuron which has its body located in the anterior gray column of the spinal cord or in the brainstem nuclei, and its axon passing by way of a peripheral nerve to skeletal muscle. Also known as final common pathway.

Lower Sonoran life zone [ECOL] A term used by C.H. Merriam to describe the climate and biotic communities of subtropical deserts and thorn savannas in the southwestern United States.

loxodont [VERT ZOO] Having molar teeth with shallow hollows between the ridges.

loxolophodont [VERT ZOO] Having crests on the molar teeth that connect three of the tubercles and with the fourth or posterior inner tubercle being rudimentary or absent.

Loxonematacea [PALEON] An extinct superfamily of gastropod mollusks in the order Prosobranchia.

Lucanidae [INV ZOO] The stag beetles, a cosmopolitan family of coleopteran insects in the superfamily Scarabaeoidea.

lucerne See alfalfa.

Lucibacterium [MICROBIO] A genus of light-emitting bacteria in the family Vibrionaceae; motile, asporogenous rods with peritrichous flagella.

luciferase [BIOCHEM] An enzyme that catalyzes the oxidation of luciferin.

luciferin [BIOCHEM] A species-specific pigment in many luminous organisms that emits heatless light when combined with oxygen.

Luciocephalidae [VERT ZOO] A family of freshwater fishes in the suborder Anabantoidei.

Luidiidae [INV ZOO] A family of echinoderms in the suborder Paxillosina.

lumbar artery [ANAT] Any of the four or five pairs of branches of the abdominal aorta opposite the lumbar region of the spine; supplies blood to loin muscles, skin on the sides of the abdomen, and the spinal cord.

lumbar nerve [ANAT] Any of five pairs of nerves arising from lumbar segments of the spinal cord; characterized by motor, visceral sensory, somatic sensory, and sympathetic components; they innervate the skin and deep muscles of the lower back and the lumbar plexus.

lumbar vertebrae [ANAT] Those vertebrae located between the lowest ribs and the pelvic girdle in all vertebrates.

lumbodorsal fascia [ANAT] The sheath of the erector spinae muscle alone, or the sheaths of the erector spinae and the quadratus lumborum muscles.

lumbosacral plexus [ANAT] A network formed by the anterior branches of lumbar, sacral, and coccygeal nerves which for descriptive purposes are divided into the lumbar, sacral, and pudendal plexuses.

Lumbricidae [INV ZOO] A family of annelid worms in the order Oligochaeta; includes the earthworm.

Lumbriclymeninae [INV ZOO] A subfamily of mud-swallowing sedentary worms in the family Maldanidae.

Lumbriculidae [INV ZOO] A family of aquatic annelids in the order Oligochaeta.

Lumbricus [INV ZOO] A genus of earthworms recognized as the type genus of the family Lumbricidae.

Lumbrineridae [INV ZOO] A family of errantian polychaetes in the superfamily Eunicea.

lumper [SYST] A taxonomist who tends to recognize large taxa.

lunate [BIOL] Crescent-shaped

lung [ANAT] Either of the paired air-filled sacs, usually in the anterior or anteroventral part of the trunk of most tetrapods, which function as organs of respiration.

lung bud [EMBRYO] A primary outgrowth of the embryonic trachea; the anlage of a primary bronchus and all its branches.

lungfish [VERT ZOO] The common name for members of the Dipnoi; all have lungs that arise from a ventral connection with the gut.

lunule [BIOL] A crescent-shaped organ, structure, or mark.

lupine [BOT] A leguminous plant of the genus *Lupinus* with an upright stem, leaves divided into several digitate leaflets, and terminal racemes of pea-shaped blossoms.

lutein [BIOCHEM] 1. A dried, powdered preparation of corpus luteum. 2. See xanthophyll.

luteinization [PHYSIO] Acquisition of characteristics of cells of the corpus luteum by ovarian follicle cells following ovulation.

luteinizing hormone [BIOCHEM] A glycoprotein hormone secreted by the adenohypophysis of vertebrates which stimulates hormone production by interstitial cells of gonads. Also known as interstitial-cell-stimulating hormone (ICSH).

luteinizing-hormone releasing factor [BIOCHEM] A small peptide hormone released from the hypothalamus which acts on the pituitary gland to cause release of luteinizing hormone.

luteotropic hormone See prolactin.

Lutjanidae [VERT ZOO] The snappers, a family of perciform fishes in the suborder Percoidei.

lyase [BIOCHEM] An enzyme that catalyzes the nonhydrolytic cleavage of its substrate with the formation of a double bond; examples are decarboxylases.

Lycaenidae [INV ZOO] A family of heteroneuran lepidopteran insects in the superfamily Papilionoidea including blue, gossamer, hairstreak, copper, and metalmark butterflies.

Lycaeninae [INV ZOO] A subfamily of the Lycaenidae distinguished by functional prothoracic legs in the male.

lychee [BOT] A tree of the genus *Litchi* in the family Sapindaceae, especially *L. chinensis* which is cultivated for its edible fruit, a one-seeded berry distinguished by the thin, leathery, rough pericarp that is red in most varieties. Also spelled litchi.

lychnisc [INV ZOO] A hexactin in which the central part of the spicule is surrounded by a system of 12 struts.

Lychniscosa [INV ZOO] An order of sponges in the subclass Hexasterophora in which parenchymal megascleres form a rigid framework and are all or in part lychniscs.

lycopene [BIOCHEM] $C_{40}H_{56}$ A red, crystalline hydrocarbon that is the coloring matter of certain fruits, as tomatoes; it is isomeric with carotene.

lycophore larva [INV ZOO] A larva of certain cestodes characterized by cilia, large frontal glands, and 10 hooks. Also known as decanth larva.

Lycopodiales [BOT] The type order of Lycopodiopsida.

Lycopodineae [BOT] The equivalent name for Lycopodiopsida.

Lycopodiophyta [BOT] A division of the subkingdom Embryobionta characterized by a dominant independent sporophyte, dichotomously branching roots and stems, a single vascular bundle, and small, simple, spirally arranged leaves.

Lycopodiopsida [BOT] The lycopods, the type class of Lycophodiophyta.

Lycopsida [BOT] Former subphylum of the Embryophyta now designated as the division Lycopodiophyta.

Lycoriidae [INV ZOO] A family of small, darkwinged dipteran insects in the suborder Orthorrhapha.

Lycosidae [INV ZOO] A family of hunting spiders in the suborder Dipneumonomorphae that actively pursue their prey.

Lycoteuthidae [INV ZOO] A family of squids.

Lyctidae [INV ZOO] The large-winged beetles, a large cosmopolitan family of coleopteran insects in the superfamily Bostrichoidea.

Lygaeidae [INV ZOO] The lygaeid bugs, a large family of phytophagous hemipteran insects in the superfamily Lygaeoidea.

Lygaeoidea [INV ZOO] A superfamily of pentatomorphan insects having four-segmented antennae and ocelli.

Lyginopteridaceae [PALEOBOT] An extinct family of the Lyginopteridales including monostelic pteridosperms having one or two vascular traces entering the base of the petiole.

Lyginopteridales [PALEOBOT] An order of the Pteridospermae.

Lyginopteridatae [PALEOBOT] The equivalent name for Pteridospermae.

Lymantriidae [INV ZOO] The tussock moths, a family of heteroneuran lepidopteran insects in the superfamily Noctuoidea; the antennae of males is broadly pectinate and there is a tuft of hairs on the end of the female abdomen.

Lymexylonidae [INV ZOO] The ship timber beetles composing the single family of the coleopteran superfamily Lymexylonoidea.

Lymexylonoidea [INV ZOO] A monofamilial superfamily of wood-boring coleopteran insects in the suborder Polyphaga characterized by a short neck and serrate antennae.

lymph [HISTOL] The colorless fluid which circulates through the vessels of the lymphatic system.

lymphatic system [ANAT] A system of vessels and nodes conveying lymph in the vertebrate body, beginning with capillaries in tissue spaces and eventually forming the thoracic ducts which empty into the subclavian veins.

lymphatic tissue [HISTOL] Tissue consisting of networks of lymphocytes and reticular and collagenous fibers. Also known as lymphoid tissue.

lymph gland See lymph node.

lymph heart [VERT ZOO] A muscular expansion of a lymphatic vessel which contracts, driving lymph to the veins, as in amphibians.

lymph node [ANAT] An aggregation of lymphoid tissue surrounded by a fibrous capsule; found along the course of lymphatic vessels. Also known as lymph gland.

lymphoblast [HISTOL] Precursor of a lymphocyte.

lymphocyte [HISTOL] An agranular leukocyte formed primarily in lymphoid tissue; occurs as the principal cell type of lymph and composes 20–30% of the blood leukocytes.

lymphoid cell [HISTOL] A mononucleocyte that resembles a leukocyte.

lymphoid hemoblast of Pappenheim See pronormoblast.

lymphoid tissue See lymphatic tissue.

lymphopoiesis [PHYSIO] The production of lymph.

lymph sinus [ANAT] One of the tracts of diffuse lymphatic tissue between the cords and nodules, and between the septa and capsule of a lymph node.

lymph vessel [ANAT] A tubular passage for conveying lymph.

lyngbyatoxin A [BIOCHEM] An indole alkaloid toxin produced by *Lyngbya majuscula*.

lynx [VERT ZOO] Any of several wildcats of the genus *Lynx* having long legs, short tails, and usually tufted ears; differs from other felids in having 28 instead of 30 teeth.

Lyomeri [VERT ZOO] The equivalent name for Saccopharyngiformes.

Lyon hypothesis [GEN] The assumption that mammalian females are X-chromosome mosaics as a result of the inactivation of one X chromosome in some embryonic cells and the other in the rest.

Lyon phenomenon [GEN] In the normal human female, the rendering of two X chromosomes inactive, or at least largely so, at an early stage in embryogenesis.

Lyopomi [VERT ZOO] An equivalent name for Notacanthiformes.

Lysaretidae [INV ZOO] A family of errantian polychaete worms in the superfamily Eunicea.

lyse [CELL BIO] To undergo lysis.

Lysianassidae [INV ZOO] A family of pelagic amphipod crustaceans in the suborder Gammaridea.

lysigenous [BIOL] Of or pertaining to the space formed following lysis of cells.

lysine [BIOCHEM] $C_6H_{14}O_2N_2$ An essential, basic amino acid obtained from many proteins by hydrolysis.

Lysiosquillidae [INV ZOO] A family of crustaceans in the order Stomatopoda.

lysis [CELL BIO] Dissolution of a cell or tissue by the action of a lysin.

lysogeny [MICROBIO] Lysis of bacteria, with the liberation of bacteriophage particles.

lysosome [CELL BIO] A specialized cell organelle surrounded by a single membrane and containing a mixture of hydrolytic (digestive) enzymes.

lysozyme [BIOCHEM] An enzyme present in certain body secretions, principally tears, which acts to hydrolyze certain bacterial cell walls.

lyssacine [INV ZOO] An early stage of the skeletal network in hexactinellid sponges.

Lyssacinosa [INV ZOO] An order of sponges in the subclass Hexasterophora in which parenchymal megascleres are typically free and unconnected but are sometimes secondarily united.

lysyl oxidase [BIOCHEM] Any of a group of enzymes found in bone and connective tissue which oxidize terminal amino groups of lysine residues in tropocollagen molecules to aldehyde residues.

lytic infection [MICROBIO] Penetration of a host cell by lytic phage.

lytic phage [VIROL] Any phage that causes host cells to lyse.

lytic reaction [CELL BIO] A reaction that leads to lysis of a cell.

macadamia nut [BOT] The hard-shelled seed obtained from the fruit of a tropical evergreen tree, *Macadamia ternifolia*.

macaque [VERT ZOO] The common name for 12 species of Old World monkeys composing the genus *Macaca*, including the Barbary ape and the rhesus monkey.

macaw [VERT ZOO] The common name for large South and Central American parrots of the genus *Ara* and related genera; individuals are brilliantly colored with a long tail, a hooked bill, and a naked area around the eyes.

Machaeridea [INV ZOO] A class of homolozoan echinoderms in older systems of classification.

Machilidae [INV ZOO] A family of insects belonging to the Thysanura having large compound eyes and ocelli and a monocondylous mandible of the scraping type.

machozooid [INV ZOO] A defensive polyp equipped with stinging organs in certain hydroid colonies. Also known as machopolyp.

mackerel [VERT ZOO] The common name for perciform fishes composing the subfamily Scombroidei of the family Scombridae, characterized by a long slender body, pointed head, and large mouth.

mackerel shark [VERT ZOO] The common name for isurid galeoid elasmobranchs making up the family Isuridae; heavy-bodied fish with sharp-edged, awllike teeth and a nearly symmetrical tail.

macrandrous [BOT] Having both antheridia and oogonia on the same plant; used especially for certain green algae.

Macraucheniidae [PALEON] A family of extinct herbivorous mammals in the order Litopterna; members were proportioned much as camels are, and eventually lost the vertebral arterial canal of the cervical vertebrae.

Macristiidae [VERT ZOO] A family of oceanic teleostean fishes assigned by some zoologists to the order Ctenothrissiformes.

macroblast of Naegeli *See* pronormoblast.

macroconsumer [ECOL] A large consumer which ingests other organisms or particulate organic matter. Also known as biophage.

macrocyclic [MYCOL] Of a rust fungus, having binuclear spores as well as teliospores and sporidia, or having a life cycle that is long or complex.

Macrocypracea [INV ZOO] A superfamily of marine ostracods in the suborder Podocopa having all thoracic legs different from each other, greatly reduced furcae, and long, thin Zenker's organs.

macrocyte [HISTOL] An erythrocyte whose diameter or mean corpuscular volume exceed that of the mean normal by more than two standard deviations. Also known as macronormocyte.

Macrodasyoidea [INV ZOO] An order of wormlike invertebrates of the class Gastrotricha characterized by distinctive, cylindrical adhesive tubes in the cuticle which are moved by delicate muscle strands.

macroevolution [EVOL] The larger course of evolution by which the categories of animal and plant classification above the species level have been evolved from each other and have differentiated into the forms within each.

macrofauna [ECOL] 1. Widely distributed fauna. 2. Fauna of a macrohabitat. [ZOO] Animals visible to the naked eye.

macroflora [BOT] Plants which are visible to the naked eye. [ECOL] 1. Widely distributed flora. 2. Flora of a macrohabitat.

macrofossil [PALEON] A fossil large enough to be observed with the naked eye.

macrogamete [BIOL] The larger, usually female gamete produced by a heterogamous organism.

macroglia [HISTOL] That portion of the neuroglia composed of astrocytes.

macroglobulin [BIOCHEM] Any gamma globulin with a sedimentation constant of 195.

macrohabitat [ECOL] An extensive habitat presenting considerable variation of the environment, containing a variety of ecological niches, and supporting a large number and variety of complex flora and fauna.

Macrolepidoptera [INV ZOO] A former division of Lepidoptera that included the larger moths and butterflies.

macrolide antibiotic [MICROBIO] A basic antibiotic characterized by a macrocyclic ring structure.

macrolymphocyte [HISTOL] A large lymphocyte.

macromere [EMBRYO] Any of the large blastomeres composing the vegetative hemisphere of telolecithal morulas and blastulas.

Macromonas [MICROBIO] A genus of gram-negative, chemolithotrophic bacteria; large, motile, cylindrical to bean-shaped cells containing sulfur granules and calcium carbonate inclusions.

macronormocyte *See* macrocyte.

macronucleus [INV ZOO] A large, densely staining nucleus of most ciliated protozoans, believed to influence nutritional activities of the cell.

macronutrient [BIOCHEM] An element, such as potassium and nitrogen, essential in large quantities for plant growth.

macrophage [HISTOL] A large phagocyte of the reticuloendothelial system. Also known as a histiocyte.

macrophagy [BIOL] Feeding on large particulate matter.

macrophreate [INV ZOO] A comatulid with a large, deep cavity in the calyx.

macrophyllous [BOT] Having large or long leaves.

macrophyte [ECOL] A macroscopic plant, especially one in an aquatic habitat.

macropinocytosis [CYTOL] A mechanism of endocytosis in which large droplets of fluid are trapped underneath extensions (ruffles) of the cell surface.

Macropodidae [VERT ZOO] The kangaroos, a family of Australian herbivorous mammals in the order Marsupialia.

macropodous [BOT] 1. Having a large or long hypocotyl. 2. Having a long stem or stalk.

macropterous [ZOO] Having large or long wings or fins.

Macroscelidea [VERT ZOO] A monofamilial order of mammals containing the elephant shrews and their allies.

Macroscelididae [VERT ZOO] The single, African family of the mammalian order Macroscelidea.

macroseptum [INV ZOO] A primary septum in certain anthozoans.

macrosporangium [BOT] A spore case in which macrospores are produced. Also known as megasporangium.

macrospore [BOT] The larger of two spore types produced by heterosporous plants; the female gamete. Also known as megaspore. [INV ZOO] The larger gamete produced by certain radiolarians; the female gamete.

Macrostomida [INV ZOO] An order of rhabdocoels having a simple pharynx, paired protonephridia, and a single pair of longitudinal nerves.

Macrostomidae [INV ZOO] A family of rhabdocoels in the order Macrostomida; members are broad and flattened in shape and have paired sex organs.

macrostylous [BOT] 1. Having long styles. 2. Having long styles and short stamens.

Macrotermitinae [INV ZOO] A subfamily of termites in the family Termitidae.

macrothermophyte *See* megathermophyte.

Macrouridae [VERT ZOO] The grenadiers, a family of actinopterygian fishes in the order Gadiformes in which the body tapers to a point, and the dorsal, caudal, and anal fins are continuous.

Macroveliidae [INV ZOO] A family of hemipteran insects in the subdivision Amphibicorisae.

Macrura [INV ZOO] A group of decapod crustaceans in the suborder Reptantia including eryonids, spiny lobsters, and true lobsters; the abdomen is extended and bears a well-developed tail fan.

macrurous [ZOO] Having a long tail.

macula [ANAT] Any anatomical structure having the form of a spot or stain.

macula lutea [ANAT] A yellow spot on the retina; the area of maximum visual acuity, being made up almost entirely of retinal cones.

maculate [BOT] Marked with speckles or spots.

Madreporaria [INV ZOO] The equivalent name for Scleractinia.

madreporite [INV ZOO] A delicately perforated sieve plate at the distal end of the stone canal in echinoderms.

Magelonidae [INV ZOO] A monogeneric family of spioniform annelid worms belonging to Sedentaria.

magenstrasse [ANAT] Gastric canal.

maggot [INV ZOO] Larva of a dipterous insect.

magnocellular [CELL BIO] Having large cell bodies; said of various nuclei of the central nervous system.

Magnolia [BOT] A genus of trees, the type genus of the Magnoliaceae, with large, chiefly white, yellow, or pinkish flowers, and simple, entire, usually large evergreen or deciduous alternate leaves.

Magnoliaceae [BOT] A family of dicotyledonous plants of the order Magnoliales characterized by hypogynous flowers with few to numerous stamens, stipulate leaves, and uniaperturate pollen.

Magnoliales [BOT] The type order of the subclass Magnoliidae; members are woody plants distinguished by the presence of spherical ethereal oil cells and by a well-developed perianth of separate tepals.

Magnoliidae [BOT] A primitive subclass of flowering plants in the class Magnoliopsida generally having a well-developed perianth, numerous centripetal stamens, and bitegmic, crassinucellate ovules.

Magnoliophyta [BOT] The angiosperms, a division of vascular seed plants having the ovules enclosed in an ovary and well-developed vessels in the xylem.

Magnoliopsida [BOT] The dicotyledons, a class of flowering plants in the division Magnoliophyta generally characterized by having two cotyledons and net-veined leaves, with vascular bundles borne in a ring enclosing a pith.

magnum [ANAT] Large, as in foramen magnum.

maguey *See* cantala.

mahogany [BOT] Any of several tropical trees in the family Meliaceae of the Geraniales.

maidenhead *See* hymen.

Maillard reaction [BIOCHEM] A reaction in which the amino group in an amino acid tends to form condensation products with aldehydes; believed to cause the Browning reaction when an amino acid and a sugar coexist, evolving a characteristic flavor useful in food preparations.

Maindroniidae [INV ZOO] A family of wingless insects belonging to the Thysanura proper.

maize [BOT] *Zea mays*. Indian corn, a tall cereal grass characterized by large ears.

Majidae [INV ZOO] The spider, or decorator, crabs, a family of decapod crustaceans included in the Brachyura; members are slow-moving animals that often conceal themselves by attaching seaweed and sessile animals to their carapace.

Malachiidae [INV ZOO] An equivalent name for Malyridae.

Malacobothridia [INV ZOO] A subclass of worms in the class Trematoda; members typically have one or two soft, flexible suckers and are endoparasitic in vertebrates and invertebrates.

Malacocotylea [INV ZOO] The equivalent name for Digenea.

malacology [INV ZOO] The study of mollusks.

Malacopoda [INV ZOO] A subphylum of invertebrates in the phylum Oncopoda.

Malacopterygii [VERT ZOO] An equivalent name for Clupeiformes in older classifications.

Malacostraca [INV ZOO] A large, diversified subclass of Crustacea including shrimps, lobsters, crabs, sow bugs, and their allies; generally characterized by having a maximum of 19 pairs of appendages and trunk limbs which are sharply differentiated into thoracic and abdominal series.

Malapteruridae [VERT ZOO] A family of African catfishes in the suborder Siluroidei.

malar [ANAT] Of or pertaining to the cheek or to the zygomatic bone.

malar bone *See* zygomatic bone.

malar stripe [VERT ZOO] 1. The area extending from the corner of the mouth backward and down in birds. 2. Area on side of throat below the base of the lower mandible.

malate dehydrogenase *See* malic enzyme.

Malcidae [INV ZOO] A small family of Ethiopian and Oriental hemipternan insects in the superfamily Pentatomorpha.

Malcodermata [INV ZOO] The equivalent name for Cantharoidea.

Maldanidae [INV ZOO] The bamboo worms, a family of mud-swallowing annelids belonging to the Sedentaria.

Maldaninae [INV ZOO] A subfamily of the Maldanidae distinguished by cephalic and anal plaques with the anal aperture located dorsally.

male [BOT] A flower lacking pistils.

male climacteric [PHYSIO] A condition presumably due to loss of testicular function, associated with an elevated urinary excretion of gonadotropins and symptoms of loss of sexual desire and potency, hot flashes, and vasomotor instability.

male heterogamety [GEN] Having paired sex chromosomes of unequal sizes in the male.

male homogamety [GEN] Having the paired sex chromosomes of equal size in the male.

male sterility [PHYSIO] The condition in which male gametes are absent, deficient in number, or nonfunctional.

malezal swamp [ECOL] A swamp resulting from drainage of water over an extensive plain with a slight, almost imperceptible slope.

malic acid [BIOCHEM] COOH·CH₂·CHOH· COOH Hydroxysuccinic acid: a dibasic hydroxy acid existing in two optically active isomers and a racemic form; found in apples and many other fruits.

malic dehydrogenase [BIOCHEM] An enzyme in the Krebs cycle that catalyzes the conversion of L-malic acid to oxaloacetic acid.

malic enzyme [BIOCHEM] An enzyme which utilizes nicotinamide-adenine dinucleotide phosphate (NADP) to catalyze the oxidative decarboxylation of malic acid to pyruvic acid and carbon dioxide. Also known as malate dehydrogenase.

malleate trophus [INV ZOO] A type of crushing masticatory apparatus in rotifers that are incidentally predatory, such as brachionids.

mallee *See* tropical scrub.

malleolus [ANAT] A projection on the distal end of the tibia and fibula at the ankle.

malleoramate trophus [INV ZOO] An intermediate type of rotiferan masticatory apparatus having a looped manubrium and teeth on the incus (comprising the fulcrum and rami); developed for grinding.

malleus [ANAT] The outermost, hammer-shaped ossicle of the middle ear; attaches to the tympanic membrane and articulates with the incus.

Mallophaga [INV ZOO] Biting lice, a comparatively small order of wingless insects characterized by five-segmented antennae, distinctly developed mandibles, one or two terminal claws on each leg, and a prothorax developed as a distinct segment.

Malpighiaceae [BOT] A family of dicotyledonous plants in the order Polygalales distinguished by having three carpels, several fertile stamens, five petals that are commonly fringed or toothed, and indehiscent fruit.

Malpighian corpuscle [ANAT] 1. A lymph nodule of the spleen. 2. *See* renal corpuscle.

Malpighian layer [HISTOL] The germinative layer of the epidermis.

Malpighian pyramid *See* renal pyramid.

Malpighian tubule [INV ZOO] Any of the blind tubes that open into the posterior portion of the gut in most insects and certain other arthropods and excrete matter or secrete substances such as silk.

maltase [BIOCHEM] An enzyme that catalyzes the conversion of maltose to dextrose.

Malthusianism [BIOL] The theory that population increases more rapidly than the food supply unless held in check by epidemics, wars, or similar phenomena.

maltobiose *See* maltose.

maltose [BIOCHEM] C₁₂H₂₂O₁₁ A crystalline disaccharide that is a product of the enzymatic hydrolysis of starch, dextrin, and glycogen; does not appear to exist free in nature. Also known as maltobiose; malt sugar.

maltose phosphorylase [BIOCHEM] An enzyme which reacts maltose with inorganic phosphate to yield glucose and glucose-1-phosphate.

malt sugar *See* maltose.

Malvaceae [BOT] A family of herbaceous dicotyledons in the order Malvales characterized by imbricate or contorted petals, mostly unilocular anthers, and minutely spiny, multiporate pollen.

Malvales [BOT] An order of flowering plants in the subclass Dilleniidae having hypogynous flowers with valvate calyx, mostly separate petals, numerous centrifugal stamens, and a syncarpous pistil.

mamelon [BIOL] Any dome-shaped protrusion or elevation.

mamm-, mammo- [ANAT] A combining form meaning breast.

mamma [ANAT] A milk-secreting organ characterizing all mammals.

mammal [VERT ZOO] A member of Mammalia.

Mammalia [VERT ZOO] A large class of warm-blooded vertebrates containing animals characterized by mammary glands, a body covering of hair, three ossicles in the middle ear, a muscular diaphragm separating the thoracic and abdominal cavities, red blood cells without nuclei, and embryonic development in the allantois and amnion.

mammary [ANAT] Of or pertaining to the mamma, or breast.

mammary areola See areola mammae.

mammary gland [PHYSIO] A highly modified sebaceous gland that secretes milk; a unique anatomical feature of mammals.

mammary lymphatic plexus [ANAT] A network of anastomosing lymphatic vessels in the walls of the ducts and between the lobules of the mamma; also functions to drain skin, areola, and nipple.

mammary region [ANAT] The space on the anterior surface of the chest between a line drawn through the lower border of the third rib and one drawn through the upper border of the xiphoid cartilage.

mammary ridge [EMBRYO] An ectodermal thickening forming a longitudinal elevation on the chest between the limbs from which the mammary glands develop.

mammary-stimulating hormone [BIOCHEM] 1. Estrogen and progesterone considered together as the hormones which induce proliferation of the mammary ductile and acinous elements respectively. 2. See prolactin.

mammillary [ANAT] 1. Of or pertaining to the nipple. 2. Breast- or nipple-shaped.

mammillary body [ANAT] Either of two small, spherical masses of gray matter at the base of the brain in the space between the hypophysis and oculomotor nerve, which receive and relay olfactory impulses.

mammillary line [ANAT] A vertical line passing through the center of the nipple.

mammillary process [ANAT] One of the tubercles on the posterior part of the superior articular processes of the lumbar vertebrae.

mammogen See prolactin.

mammogenic hormone [BIOCHEM] 1. Any hormone that stimulates or induces development of the mammary gland. 2. See prolactin.

mammoplasia [PHYSIO] Development of breast tissue.

mammoth [PALEON] Any of various large Pleistocene elephants having long, upcurved tusks and a heavy coat of hair.

mammotropin See prolactin.

Mammutinae [PALEON] A subfamily of extinct proboscidean mammals in the family Mastodontidae.

mandarin [BOT] A large and variable group of citrus fruits in the species *Citrus reticulata* and some of its hybrids; many varieties of the trees are compact with willowy twigs and small, narrow, pointed leaves; includes tangerines, King oranges, Temple oranges, and tangelos.

mandible [ANAT] 1. The bone of the lower jaw. 2. The lower jaw. [INV ZOO] Any of various mouthparts in many invertebrates designed to hold or bite into food.

mandibular arch [EMBRYO] The first visceral arch in vertebrates.

mandibular cartilage [EMBRYO] The bar of cartilage supporting the mandibular arch.

mandibular fossa [ANAT] The depression in the temporal bone that articulates with the mandibular condyle.

mandibular gland See submandibular gland.

mandibular nerve [ANAT] A mixed nerve branch of the trigeminal nerve; innervates various structures of the lower jaw and face.

Mandibulata [INV ZOO] A subphylum of Arthropoda; members possess a pair of mandibles which characterize the group.

mandrill [VERT ZOO] *Mandrillus sphinx*. An Old World cercopithecoid monkey found in West-central Africa and characterized by large red callosities near the ischium and by blue ridges on each side of the nose in males.

mango [BOT] *Mangifera indica*. A large evergreen tree of the sumac family (Anacardiaceae), native to southeastern Asia, but now cultivated in Africa, tropical America, Florida, and California for its edible fruit, a thick-skinned, yellowish-red, fleshy drupe.

mangrove [BOT] A tropical tree or shrub of the genus *Rhizophora* characterized by an extensive, impenetrable system of prop roots which contribute to land building.

mangrove swamp [ECOL] A tropical or subtropical marine swamp distinguished by the abundance of low to tall trees, especially mangrove trees.

Manidae [VERT ZOO] The pangolins, a family of mammals comprising the order Pholidota.

manihot See cassava.

Manila hemp See abaca.

Manila maguey See cantala.

manioc See cassava.

mannan [BIOCHEM] Any of a group of polysaccharides composed chiefly or entirely of D-mannose units.

mannose [BIOCHEM] $C_6H_{12}O_6$ A fermentable monosaccharide obtained from manna.

Mantidae [INV ZOO] A family of predacious orthopteran insects characterized by a long, slender prothorax bearing a pair of large, grasping legs, and a freely moving head with large eyes.

mantis [INV ZOO] The common name for insects composing the family Mantidae.

mantle [ANAT] Collectively, the convolutions, corpus callosum, and fornix of the brain. [BIOL] An enveloping layer, as the external body wall lining the shell of many invertebrates, or the external meristematic layers in a stem apex. [VERT ZOO] The back and wing plumage of a bird if distinguished from the rest of the plumage by a uniform color.

mantle cavity [INV ZOO] The space between mantle and body proper in bivalve mollusks.

mantle lobe [INV ZOO] Either of the flaps on the dorsal and ventral sides of the mantle in bivalve mollusks.

Mantodea [INV ZOO] An order equivalent to the family Mantidae in some systems of classification.

manubrium [ANAT] 1. The triangular cephalic portion of the sternum in humans and certain other mammals. 2. The median anterior portion of the sternum in birds. 3. The process of the malleus. [BOT] A cylindrical cell that projects inward from the middle of each shield composing the antheridium in stoneworts. [INV ZOO] The elevation bearing the mouth in hydrozoan polyps.

manus [ANAT] The hand of a human or the forefoot of a quadruped. [INV ZOO] The proximal enlargement of the propodus of the chela of arthropods.

manyplies *See* omasum.

maple [BOT] Any of various broad-leaved, deciduous trees of the genus *Acer* in the order Sapindales characterized by simple, opposite, usually palmately lobed leaves and a fruit consisting of two long-winged samaras.

maquis [ECOL] A type of vegetation composed of shrubs, or scrub, usually not exceeding 3 meters in height, the majority having small, hard, leathery, often spiny or needlelike drought-resistant leaves and occurring in areas with a Mediterranean climate.

Marantaceae [BOT] A family of monocotyledonous plants in the order Zingiberales characterized by one functional stamen with a single functional pollen sac, solitary ovules in each locule, and mostly arillate seeds.

Marattiaceae [BOT] A family of ferns coextensive with the order Marattiales.

Marattiales [BOT] An ancient order of ferns having massive eusporangiate sporangia in sori on the lower side of the circinate leaves.

Marburg virus [VIROL] A large virus transmitted to humans by the grivet monkey (*Cercopithecus aethiops*).

marcescent [BOT] Withering without falling off.

Marcgraviaceae [BOT] A family of dicotyledonous shrubs or vines in the order Theales having exstipulate leaves with scanty or no endosperm, two integuments, and highly modified bracts.

Marchantiales [BOT] The thallose liverworts, an order of the class Marchantiopsida having a flat body composed of several distinct tissue layers, smooth-walled and tuberculate-walled rhizoids, and male and female sex organs borne on stalks on separate plants.

Marchantiopsida [BOT] The liverworts, a class of lower green plants; the plant body is usually a thin, prostrate thallus with rhizoids on the lower surface.

Margaritiferidae [INV ZOO] A family of gastropod mollusks with nacreous shells that provide an important source of commercial pearls.

Margarodinae [INV ZOO] A subfamily of homopteran insects in the superfamily Coccoidea in which abdominal spiracles are present in all stages of development.

marginal blight [PL PATH] A bacterial disease of lettuce caused by *Pseudomonas marginalis*, characterized by brownish marginal discoloration of the foliage.

marginal chlorosis [PL PATH] A virus disease characterized by yellowing or blanching of leaf margins; common disease of peanut plants.

marginal placentation [BOT] Arrangement of ovules near the margins of carpels.

marginal sinus [ANAT] 1. One of the small, bilateral sinuses of the dura mater which skirt the edge of the foramen magnum, usually uniting posteriorly to form the occipital sinus. 2. *See* terminal sinus. [EMBRYO] An enlarged venous sinus incompletely encircling the margin of the placenta.

marginate [BOT] Having a distinct margin or border.

maricolous [ECOL] Living in the sea.

marihuana *See* marijuana.

marijuana [BOT] The Spanish name for the dried leaves and flowering tops of the hemp plant (*Cannabis sativa*), which have narcotic ingredients and are smoked in cigarettes. Also spelled marihuana.

marine biocycle [ECOL] A major division of the biosphere composed of all biochores of the sea.

marine biology [BIOL] A branch of biology that deals with those living organisms which inhabit the sea.

marine littoral faunal region [ECOL] A geographically determined division of that portion of the zoosphere composed of marine animals.

marine marsh [ECOL] A flat, savannalike land expanse at the edge of a sea; usually covered by water during high tide.

marine microbiology [MICROBIO] The study of the microorganisms living in the sea.

marita [INV ZOO] An adult trematode.

marjoram [BOT] Any of several perennial plants of the genera *Origanum* and *Majorana* in the mint family, Labiatae; the leaves are used as a food seasoning.

marmoset [VERT ZOO] Any of 10 species of South American primates belonging to the family Callithricidae; individuals are primitive in that they have claws rather than nails and a nonprehensile tail.

marmot [VERT ZOO] Any of several species of stout-bodied, short-legged burrowing rodents of the genus *Marmota* in the squirrel family Sciuridae.

marrubium [BOT] *Marrubium vulgari*. An aromatic plant of the mint family, Labiatae; leaves have a bitter taste and are used as a tonic and anthelmintic. Also known as hoarhound; horehound.

marsh [ECOL] A transitional land-water area, covered at least part of the time by estuarine or coastal waters, and characterized by aquatic and grasslike vegetation, especially without peatlike accumulation.

Marsileales [BOT] A small monofamilial order of heterosporous, leptosporangiate ferns (Polypodiophyta); leaves arise on long stalks from the rhizome, and sporangia are enclosed in modified folded leaves or leaf segments called sporocarps.

Marsipobranchii [VERT ZOO] An equivalent name for Cyclostomata.

marsupial [VERT ZOO] 1. A member of the Marsupialia. 2. Having a marsupium. 3. Of, pertaining to, or constituting a marsupium.

marsupial anteater [VERT ZOO] *Myrmecobius fasciatus.* An anteater belonging to the Marsupialia. Also known as banded anteater.

marsupial frog [VERT ZOO] Any of various South American tree frogs which carry the eggs in a pouch on the back.

Marsupialia [VERT ZOO] The single order of the mammalian infraclass Metatheria, characterized by the presence of a marsupium in the female.

marsupial mole [VERT ZOO] *Notoryctes typhlops.* A marsupial of Australia that resembles the euterian mole.

Marsupicarnivora [VERT ZOO] An order proposed to include the polydactylous and polyprotodont carnivorous superfamilies of Marsupialia.

marsupium [VERT ZOO] A fold of skin that forms a pouch enclosing the mammary glands on the abdomen of most marsupials.

marten [VERT ZOO] Any of seven species of carnivores of the genus *Martes* in the family Mustelidae which resemble the weasel but are larger and of a semiarboreal habit.

masculine [BIOL] Having an appearance or qualities distinctive for a male.

masculine pelvis [ANAT] A female pelvis similar to the normal male pelvis in having a deeper cavity and more conical shape. Also known as android pelvis.

masculinize [PHYSIO] To cause a female or a sexually immature animal to take on male secondary sex characteristics.

masseter [ANAT] The masticatory muscle, arising from the zygomatic arch and inserted into the lower jaw.

mass extinction *See* faunal extinction.

massive [PALEON] Of corallum, composed of closely packed corallites.

mass reflex [PHYSIO] A spread of reflexes suggesting lack of control by higher cortical centers; seen in normal newborns, in persons under the influence of drugs or in severe emotional states, and in encephalopathy or high spinal cord transsections.

Mastacembeloidei [VERT ZOO] The spiny eels, a suborder of perciform fishes that are eellike in shape and have the pectoral girdle suspended from the vertebral column.

mastax [INV ZOO] The muscular pharynx in rotifers.

mast cell [HISTOL] A connective-tissue cell with numerous large, basophilic, metachromatic granules in the cytoplasm.

masticate [PHYSIO] To chew.

Mastigamoebidae [INV ZOO] A family of ameboid protozoans possessing one or two flagella, belonging to the order Rhizomastigida.

Mastigophora [INV ZOO] A superclass of the Protozoa characterized by possession of flagella.

mast-, masto- [ANAT] A combining form denoting breast; denoting mastoid.

mastodon [PALEON] A member of the Mastodontidae, especially the genus *Mammut*.

Mastodontidae [PALEON] An extinct family of elephantoid proboscideans that had low-crowned teeth with simple ridges and without cement.

mastoid [ANAT] 1. Breast-shaped. 2. The portion of the temporal bone where the mastoid process is located.

mastoid air cell *See* mastoid cell.

mastoid antrum [ANAT] An air-filled space between the upper portion of the middle ear and the mastoid cells.

mastoid canaliculus [ANAT] A small canal opening just above the stylomastoid foramen; gives passage to the auricular branch of the vagus nerve.

mastoid cell [ANAT] One of the compartments in the mastoid portion of the temporal bone, connected with the mastoid antrum and lined with a mucous membrane. Also known as mastoid air cell; mastoid sinus.

mastoid foramen [ANAT] A small opening behind the mastoid process.

mastoid fossa [ANAT] The depression behind the suprameatal spine on the lateral surface of the temporal bone.

mastoid process [ANAT] A nipple-shaped, inferior projection of the mastoid portion of the temporal bone.

mastoid sinus *See* mastoid cell.

Mastotermitidae [INV ZOO] A family of lower termites in the order Isoptera with a single living species, in Australia.

mate [BIOL] 1. To pair for breeding. 2. To copulate.

maternal [BIOL] Of, pertaining to, or related to a mother.

maternal effect [GEN] Determination of characters of the progeny by the maternal parent; mediated by the genetic constitution of the mother.

maternal inheritance [GEN] The acquisition of characters transmitted through the cytoplasm of the egg.

maternal placenta [EMBRYO] The outer placental layer, developed from the decidua basalis.

maternity [BIOL] 1. Motherhood. 2. The state of being pregnant.

mathematical biology [BIOL] A discipline that encompasses all applications of mathematics, computer technology, and quantitative theorizing to biological systems, and the underlying processes within the systems.

mathematical biophysics [BIOL] A discipline which attempts to utilize mathematics to explain biophysical processes.

matico [BOT] *Piper angustifolium.* An aromatic wild pepper found in tropical America whose leaves are rich in volatile oil, gums, and tannins; leaves were used medicinally as a stimulant and hemostatic.

mating [BIOL] The meeting of individuals for sexual reproduction.

Matricaria [BOT] A genus of weedy herbs having a strong odor and white and yellow disk flowers; chamomile oil is obtained from certain species.

matrix [HISTOL] 1. The intercellular substance of a tissue. Also known as ground substance. 2. The epithelial tissue from which a toenail or fingernail develops. [MYCOL] The substrate on or in which fungus grows.

matromycin *See* oleandomycin.

maturation [BIOL] 1. The process of coming to full development. 2. The final series of changes in the growth and formation of germ cells.

mature [BIOL] 1. Being fully grown and developed. 2. Ripe.

Mauritius hemp [BOT] A hard fiber obtained from the leaves of the cabuya, grown on the island of Mauritius; not a true hemp.

maxilla [ANAT] 1. The upper jawbone. 2. The upper jaw. [INV ZOO] Either of the first two pairs of mouthparts posterior to the mandibles in certain arthropods.

maxillary air sinus *See* maxillary sinus.

maxillary antrum *See* maxillary sinus.

maxillary artery [ANAT] A branch of the external carotid artery which supplies the deep structures of the face (internal maxillary) and the side of the face and nose (external maxillary).

maxillary hiatus [ANAT] An opening in the maxilla connecting the nasal cavity with the maxillary sinus.

maxillary nerve [ANAT] A somatic sensory branch of the trigeminal nerve; innervates the meninges, the skin of the upper portion of the face, upper teeth, and mucosa of the nose, palate, and cheeks.

maxillary process of the embryo [EMBRYO] An outgrowth of the dorsal part of the mandibular arch that forms the lateral part of the upper lip, the upper cheek region, and the upper jaw except the premaxilla.

maxillary sinus [ANAT] A paranasal air cavity in the body of the maxilla. Also known as maxillary air sinus; maxillary antrum.

maxilliped [INV ZOO] One of the three pairs of crustacean appendages immediately posterior to the maxillae.

maximal breathing capacity [PHYSIO] The greatest respiratory minute volume which an individual can produce during a given period of extremely forceful breathing.

maximum breathing capacity [PHYSIO] The greatest volume of air an individual can breathe voluntarily in 10–30 seconds; expressed as liters per minute. Abbreviated MBC.

mayfly [INV ZOO] The common name for insects composing the order Ephemeroptera.

mazaedium [BOT] The fruiting body of certain lichens, with the spores lying in a powdery mass in the capitulum. [MYCOL] A slimy layer on the hymenial surface of some ascomycetous fungi.

maz-, mazo- [EMBRYO] A combining form denoting placenta.

Mazzoni's corpuscle [ANAT] A specialized encapsulated sensory nerve end organ on a tendon in series with muscle fibers.

MBC *See* maximum breathing capacity.

McBurney's point [ANAT] A point halfway between the umbilicus and the anterior superior iliac spine; a point of extreme tenderness in appendicitis.

meadow [ECOL] A vegetation zone which is a low grassland, dense and continuous, variously interspersed with forbs but few if any shrubs. Also known as pelouse; Wiesen.

mealybug [INV ZOO] Any of various scale insects of the family Pseudococcidae which have a powdery substance covering the dorsal surface; all are serious plant pests.

Meantes [VERT ZOO] The mud eels, a small suborder of the Urodela including three species of aquatic eellike salamanders with only anterior limbs.

meatal plate [EMBRYO] A mass of ectodermal cells on the bottom of the branchial groove in a 2-month embryo.

meatus [ANAT] A natural opening or passage in the body.

mechanoreceptor [PHYSIO] A receptor that provides the organism with information about such mechanical changes in the environment as movement, tension, and pressure.

Meckel's cartilage [EMBRYO] The cartilaginous axis of the mandibular arch in the embryo and fetus.

Meckel's diverticulum [EMBRYO] The persistent blind end of the yolk stalk forming a tube connected with the lower ileum.

meconium [EMBRYO] A greenish mass of mucous, desquamated epithelial cells, lanugo, and vernix caseosa that collects in the fetal intestine, becoming the first fecal discharge of the newborn.

Mecoptera [INV ZOO] The scorpion flies, a small order of insects; adults are distinguished by the peculiar prolongation of the head into a beak, which bears chewing mouthparts.

mecystasis [PHYSIO] Increase in muscle length with maintenance of the original degree of tension.

media [HISTOL] The middle, muscular layer in the wall of a vein, artery, or lymph vessel.

mediad [ANAT] Toward the median line or plane of the body or of a part of the body.

medial [ANAT] 1. Being internal as opposed to external (lateral). 2. Toward the midline of the body.

medial lemniscus [ANAT] A lemniscus arising in the nucleus gracilis and nucleus cuneatus of the brain, crossing immediately as internal arcuate fibers, and terminating in the posterolateral ventral nucleus of the thalamus.

median infective dose *See* infective dose 50.

median lethal time [MICROBIO] The period of time required for 50% of a large group of organisms to die following a specific dose of an injurious agent, such as a drug or radiation.

median nasal process [EMBRYO] The region below the frontonasal sulcus between the olfactory sacs; forms the bridge and mobile septum of the nose and various parts of the upper jaw and lip.

mediastinum [ANAT] 1. A partition separating adjacent parts. 2. The space in the middle of the chest between the two pleurae.

Mediterranean faunal region [ECOL] A marine littoral faunal region including that offshore portion of the Atlantic Ocean from northern France to near the Equator.

medius [ANAT] The middle finger.

medulla [ANAT] 1. The central part of certain organs and structures such as the adrenal glands and hair. 2. Marrow, as of bone or the spinal cord. 3. See medulla oblongata. [BOT] 1. Pith. 2. The central spongy portion of some fungi.

medulla oblongata [ANAT] The somewhat pyramidal, caudal portion of the vertebrate brain extending from the pons to the spinal cord. Also known as medulla.

medullary cord [ANAT] Dense lymphatic tissue separated by sinuses in the medulla of a lymph node. [EMBRYO] A primary invagination of the germinal epithelium of the embryonic gonad that differentiates into rete testis and seminiferous tubules or into rete ovarii.

Medullosaceae [PALEOBOT] A family of seed ferns; these extinct plants all have large spirally arranged petioles with numerous vascular bundles.

medusa See jellyfish.

megacanthopore [INV ZOO] A large prominent tube, commonly projecting as a spine in a mature region of a bryozoan colony.

Megachilidae [INV ZOO] The leaf-cutting bees, a family of hymenopteran insects in the superfamily Apoidea.

Megachiroptera [VERT ZOO] The fruit bats, a group of Chiroptera restricted to the Old World; most species lack a tail, but when present it is free of the interfemoral membrane.

megacine [MICROBIO] The bacteriocidin produced by Bacillus megaterium.

Megadermatidae [VERT ZOO] The false vampires, a family of tailless bats with large ears and a nose leaf; found in Africa, Australia, and the Malay Archipelago.

megakaryocyte [HISTOL] A giant bone-marrow cell characterized by a large, irregularly lobulated nucleus; precursor to blood platelets.

megaloblast of Sabin See pronormoblast.

Megalodontoidea [INV ZOO] A superfamily of hymenopteran insects in the suborder Symphyta.

Megalomycteroidei [VERT ZOO] The mosaic-scaled fishes, a monofamilial suborder of the Cetomimiformes; members are rare species of small, elongate deep-sea fishes with degenerate eyes and irregularly disposed scales.

megalops larva [INV ZOO] A preimago stage of certain crabs having prominent eyes and chelae.

Megaloptera [INV ZOO] A suborder included in the order Neuroptera by some authorities.

Megalopygidae [INV ZOO] The flannel moths, a small family of lepidopteran insects in the suborder Heteroneura.

megalosphere [INV ZOO] The initial, large-chambered shell of sexual individuals of certain dimorphic species of Foraminifera.

Megamerinidae [INV ZOO] A family of myodarian cyclorrhaphous dipteran insects in the subsection Acalypteratae.

megaphyllous [BOT] Having large leaves or leaflike extensions.

Megapodiidae [VERT ZOO] The mound birds and brush turkeys, a family of birds in the order Galliformes; distinguished by their method of incubating eggs in mounds of dirt or in decomposing vegetation.

megasclere [INV ZOO] A large sclerite.

Megasphaera [MICROBIO] A genus of bacteria in the family Veillonellaceae; relatively large cells occurring in pairs arranged in chains.

megasporangium See macrosporangium.

megaspore See macrospore.

megasporophyll [BOT] A leaf bearing megasporangia.

megathermophyte [ECOL] A plant that requires great heat and abundant moisture for normal growth. Also known as macrothermophyte.

Megathymiinae [INV ZOO] The giant skippers, a subfamily of lepidopteran insects in the family Hesperiidae.

Mehlis' gland [INV ZOO] One of the large unicellular glands around the ootype of flatworms.

Meibomian gland See tarsal gland.

Meinertellidae [INV ZOO] A family of wingless insects belonging to the Microcoryphia.

Meinzer unit See permeability coefficient.

meiocyte [CELL BIO] A cell undergoing meiotic division.

meiosis [CELL BIO] A type of cell division occurring in diploid or polyploid tissues that results in a reduction in chromosome number, usually by half.

Meissner's corpuscle [ANAT] An ovoid, encapsulated cutaneous sense organ presumed to function in touch sensation in hairless portions of the skin.

Meissner's plexus See submucous plexus.

Melamphaidae [VERT ZOO] A family of bathypelagic fishes in the order Beryciformes.

Melampsoraceae [MYCOL] A family of parasitic fungi in the order Uredinales in which the teleutospores are laterally united to form crusts or columns.

Melanconiaceae [MYCOL] The single family of the order Melanconiales.

Melanconiales [MYCOL] An order of the class Fungi Imperfecti including many plant pathogens commonly causing anthracnose; characterized by densely aggregated cnidophores on an acervulus.

Melandryidae [INV ZOO] The false darkling beetles, a family of coleopteran insects in the superfamily Tenebrionoidea.

melanin [BIOCHEM] Any of a group of brown or black pigments occurring in plants and animals.

melanoblast [HISTOL] 1. Precursor cell of melanocytes and melanophores. 2. An immature pigment cell in certain vertebrates. 3. A mature cell that elaborates melanin.

melanocyte [HISTOL] A cell containing dark pigments.

melanocyte-stimulating hormone [BIOCHEM] A protein substance secreted by the intermediate lobe of the pituitary of man which causes dispersion of pigment granules in the skin; similar to intermedins in other vertebrates. Abbreviated MSH. Also known as melanophore-dilating principle; melanophore hormone.

melanogen [BIOCHEM] A colorless precursor of melanin.

melanogenesis [BIOCHEM] The formation of melanin.

melanophage [HISTOL] A phagocytic cell which engulfs and contains melanin.

melanophore [HISTOL] A type of chromatophore containing melanin.

melanophore-dilating principle See melanocyte-stimulating hormone.

melanophore hormone See melanocyte-stimulating hormone.

melanoprotein [BIOCHEM] A conjugated protein in which melanin is the associated chromagen.

melanose [PL PATH] 1. A fungus disease of grapevine caused by *Septoria ampelina*; leaves are infected and fall off. 2. A fungus disease of citrus trees and fruits caused by *Diaporthe citri*, characterized by hard, brown, usually gummy elevations on the rind, twigs, and leaves.

melanosome [CELL BIO] An organelle which contains melanin and in which tyrosinase activity is not demonstrable.

Melasidae [INV ZOO] The equivalent name for Eucnemidae.

Melastomataceae [BOT] A large family of dicotyledonous plants in the order Myrtales characterized by an inferior ovary, axile placentation, up to twice as many stamens as petals (or sepals), anthers opening by terminal pores, and leaves with prominent, subparallel longitudinal ribs.

Meleagrididae [VERT ZOO] The turkeys, a family of birds in the order Galliformes characterized by a bare head and neck.

Meliaceae [BOT] A family of dicotyledonous plants in the order Sapindales characterized by mostly exstipulate, alternate leaves, stamens mostly connate by their filaments, and syncarpous flowers.

Melinae [VERT ZOO] The badgers, a subfamily of carnivorous mammals in the family Mustelidae.

Melinninae [INV ZOO] A subfamily of sedentary annelids belonging to the Ampharetidae which have a conspicuous dorsal membrane, with or without dorsal spines.

Meliolaceae [MYCOL] The sooty molds, a family of ascomycetous fungi in the order Erysiphales, with dark mycelia and conidia.

melitose See raffinose.

melitriose See raffinose.

Melittangium [MICROBIO] A genus of bacteria in the family Cystobacteraceae; vegetative cells are tapered, and sporangia are borne singly on an unbranched stalk.

Melittidae [INV ZOO] A family of hymenopteran insects in the superfamily Apoidea.

Meloidae [INV ZOO] The blister beetles, a large cosmopolitan family of coleopteran insects in the superfamily Meloidea; characterized by soft, flexible elytra and the strongly vesicant properties of the body fluids.

Meloidea [INV ZOO] A superfamily of coleopteran insects in the suborder Polyphaga.

melon [BOT] Either of two soft-fleshed edible fruits, muskmelon or watermelon, or varieties of these.

Melusinidae [INV ZOO] A family of orthorrhaphous dipteran insects in the series Nematocera.

Melyridae [INV ZOO] The soft-winged flower beetles, a large family of cosmopolitan coleopteran insects in the superfamily Cleroidea.

Membracidae [INV ZOO] The treehoppers, a family of homopteran insects included in the series Auchenorrhyncha having a pronotum that extends backward over the abdomen, and a vertical upper portion of the head.

membrane [HISTOL] A thin layer of tissue surrounding a part of the body, separating adjacent cavities, lining cavities, or connecting adjacent structures.

membrane potential [PHYSIO] A potential difference across a living cell membrane.

membranous labyrinth [ANAT] The membranous portion of the inner ear of vertebrates.

membranous urethra [ANAT] The part of the urethra between the two facial layers of the urogenital diaphragm.

memory trace [PHYSIO] See engram.

menacme [PHYSIO] The period of a woman's life during which menstruation persists.

menarche [PHYSIO] The onset of menstruation.

Mendelian genetics [GEN] Scientific study of heredity as related to or in accordance with Mendel's laws.

Mendelian population [GEN] A group of individuals who interbreed according to a certain system of mating; the total genic content of the individuals of the group is called gene pool.

Mendelian ratio [GEN] The ratio of occurrence of various phenotypes in any cross involving Mendelian characters.

Mendelism [GEN] The basic laws of inheritance as formulated by Mendel.

Mendel's laws [GEN] Two basic principles of genetics formulated by Mendel: the law of segregation and law of independent assortment.

meninges [ANAT] The membranes that cover the brain and spinal cord; there are three in mammals and one or two in submammalian forms.

meningococcus [MICROBIO] Common name for *Neisseria meningitidis*.

meningothelium [HISTOL] Epithelium of the arachnoid which envelops the brain.

meninx [ANAT] Any one of the three membranes covering the brain and spinal cord.

meninx primitiva [VERT ZOO] The single membrane covering the brain and spinal cord of certain submammalian vertebrates.

Meniscotheriidae [PALEON] A family of extinct mammals of the order Condylarthra possessing selenodont teeth and molarized premolars.

meniscus [ANAT] A crescent-shaped body, especially an interarticular cartilage.

Menispermaceae [BOT] A family of dicotyledonous woody vines in the order Ranunculales distinguished by mostly alternate, simple leaves, unisexual flowers, and a dioecious habit.

men-, meno- [PHYSIO] A combining form denoting menses.

menopause [PHYSIO] The natural physiologic cessation of menstruation, usually occurring in the last half of the fourth decade. Also known as climacteric.

Menoponidae [INV ZOO] A family of biting lice (Mallophaga) adapted to life only upon domestic and sea birds.

menorrhea [PHYSIO] The normal flow of the menses.

menses *See* menstruation.

menstrual age [EMBRYO] The age of an embryo or fetus calculated from the first day of the mother's last normal menstruation preceding pregnancy.

menstrual cycle [PHYSIO] The periodic series of changes associated with menstruation and the intermenstrual cycle; menstrual bleeding indicates onset of the cycle.

menstrual period [PHYSIO] The time of menstruation.

menstruate [PHYSIO] To discharge the products of menstruation.

menstruation [PHYSIO] The periodic discharge of sanguineous fluid and sloughing of the uterine lining in women from puberty to the menopause. Also known as menses.

mental [ANAT] Pertaining to the chin. Also known as genial.

Menthaceae [BOT] An equivalent name for Labiatae.

mentum [ANAT] The chin.

mentum [BOT] A projection formed by union of the sepals at the base of the column in some orchids.

mentum [INV ZOO] 1. A projection between the mouth and foot in certain gastropods. 2. The median or basal portion of the labium in insects.

Menurae [VERT ZOO] A small suborder of suboscine perching birds restricted to Australia, including the lyrebirds and scrubbirds.

Menuridae [VERT ZOO] The lyrebirds, a family of birds in the suborder Menurae notable for their vocal mimicry.

meraspis [PALEON] Advanced larva of a trilobite; stage in which the pygidium begins to form.

merganser [VERT ZOO] Any of several species of diving water fowl composing a distinct subfamily of Anatidae and characterized by a serrate bill adapted for catching fish.

mericarp [BOT] An individual, one-seeded carpel of a schizocarp.

Meridosternata [INV ZOO] A suborder of echinoderms including various deep-sea forms of sea urchins.

meristem [BOT] Formative plant tissue composed of undifferentiated cells capable of dividing and giving rise to other meristematic cells

as well as to specialized cell types; found in growth areas.

meristic [BIOL] Pertaining to a change in number or in geometric relation of parts of an organism. [ZOO] Of, pertaining to, or divided into segments.

Merkel's corpuscles [ANAT] Touch receptors consisting of flattened platelets at the tips of certain cutaneous nerves.

Mermithidae [INV ZOO] A family of filiform nematodes in the superfamily Mermithoidea; only juveniles are parasitic.

Mermithoidea [INV ZOO] A superfamily of nematodes composed of two families, both of which are invertebrate parasites.

meroblastic [EMBRYO] Of or pertaining to an ovum that undergoes incomplete cleavage due to large amounts of yolk.

merocrine [PHYSIO] Pertaining to glands in which the secretory cells undergo cytological changes without loss of cytoplasm during secretion.

merogony [EMBRYO] The normal or abnormal development of a part of an egg following cutting, shaking, or centrifugation of the egg before or after fertilization.

meromyarian [INV ZOO] Having few muscle cells in each quadrant as seen in cross section; applied especially to nematodes.

meromyosin [BIOCHEM] Protein fragments of a myosin molecule, produced by limited proteolysis.

Meropidae [VERT ZOO] The bee-eaters, a family of brightly colored Old World birds in the order Coraciiformes.

meroplankton [BIOL] Plankton composed of floating developmental stages (that is, eggs and larvae) of the benthos and nekton organisms. Also known as temporary plankton.

Merostomata [INV ZOO] A class of primitive arthropods of the subphylum Chelicerata distinguished by their aquatic mode of life and the possession of abdominal appendages which bear respiratory organs; only three living species are known.

-merous [BIOL] Combining form that denotes having such parts or so many parts.

Merozoa [INV ZOO] The equivalent name for Cestoda.

merozoite [INV ZOO] An ameboid trophozoite in some sporozoans produced from a schizont by schizogony.

Merycoidodontidae [PALEON] A family of extinct tylopod ruminants in the superfamily Merycoidodontoidea.

Merycoidodontoidea [PALEON] A superfamily of extinct ruminant mammals in the infraorder Tylopoda which were exceptionally successful in North America.

Mesacanthidae [PALEON] An extinct family of primitive acanthodian fishes in the order Acanthodiformes distinguished by a pair of small intermediate spines, large scales, superficially placed fin spines, and a short branchial region.

mesappendix [ANAT] The mesentery of the vermiform appendix.

mesarch [BOT] Having metaxylem on both sides of the protoxylem in a siphonostele. [ECOL] Originating in a mesic environment.

mescal buttons [BOT] The dried tops from the cactus *Lophophora williamsii*; capable of producing inebriation and hallucinations.

mesectoderm [EMBRYO] The portion of the mesenchyme arising from ectoderm.

mesencephalon [EMBRYO] The middle portion of the embryonic vertebrate brain; gives rise to the cerebral peduncles and the tectum. Also known as midbrain.

mesenchymal cell [HISTOL] An undifferentiated cell found in mesenchyme and capable of differentiating into various specialized connective tissues.

mesenchymal epithelium [HISTOL] A layer of squamous epithelial cells lining subdural, subarachnoid, and perilymphatic spaces, and the chambers of the eyeball.

mesenchymal tissue [EMBRYO] Undifferentiated tissue composed of branching cells embedded in a coagulable fluid matrix.

mesenchyme [EMBRYO] That part of the mesoderm from which all connective tissues, blood vessels, blood, lymphatic system proper, and the heart are derived.

mesendoderm [EMBRYO] Embryonic tissue which differentiates into mesoderm and endoderm.

mesenteric [ANAT] Of or pertaining to the mesentery.

mesenteric artery [ANAT] Either of two main arterial branches arising from the abdominal aorta: the inferior, supplying the descending colon and the rectum, and the superior, supplying the small intestine, the cecum, and the ascending and transverse colon.

mesenteron [EMBRYO] See midgut. [INV ZOO] Central gastric cavity in an actinozoan.

mesentery [ANAT] A fold of the peritoneum that connects the intestine with the posterior abdominal wall.

mesentoderm [EMBRYO] 1. The entodermal portion of the mesoderm. 2. Undifferentiated tissue from which entoderm and mesoderm are derived. 3. That part of the mesoderm which gives rise to certain structures of the digestive tract.

mesethmoid [ANAT] A bone or cartilage in the center of the ethmoid region of the vertebrate skull; usually constitutes the greater portion of the nasal septum.

mesic [ECOL] 1. Of or pertaining to a habitat characterized by a moderate amount of water. 2. Of or pertaining to a mesophyte.

mesoappendix [ANAT] The mesentery of the vermiform appendix.

mesobilirubin [BIOCHEM] $C_{33}H_{40}O_6N_4$ Yellow, crystalline by-product of bilirubin reduction.

mesobilirubinogen [BIOCHEM] $C_{33}H_{44}O_6N_4$ Colorless, crystalline by-product of bilirubin reduction; may be converted to urobilin, stercobilinogen, or stercobilin.

mesobiliverdin [BIOCHEM] $C_{28}H_{38}O_6N_4$ A structural isomer of phycoerythrin and phycocyanobilin released by certain biliprotein by treatment with alkali.

mesoblast [EMBRYO] Undifferentiated mesoderm of the middle layer of the embryo.

mesoblastema See mesoderm.

mesocardium [ANAT] Epicardium covering the blood vessels which enter and leave the heart. [EMBRYO] The mesentery supporting the embryonic heart.

mesocarp [BOT] The middle layer of the pericarp.

mesocercaria [INV ZOO] The developmental stage in the second intermediate host of *Alaria*, a digenetic trematode.

mesocolon [ANAT] The part of the mesentery that is attached to the colon.

mesoderm [EMBRYO] The third germ layer, lying between the ectoderm and endoderm; gives rise to the connective tissues, muscles, urogenital system, vascular system, and the epithelial lining of the coelom. Also known as mesoblastema.

mesogaster [ANAT] The mesentery of the stomach.

Mesogastropoda [INV ZOO] The equivalent name for Pectinibranchia.

mesoglea [INV ZOO] The gelatinous layer between the ectoderm and endoderm in coelenterates and certain sponges.

Mesohippus [PALEON] An early ancestor of the modern horse; occurred during the Oligocene.

mesoinositol See myoinositol.

mesolamella [INV ZOO] A thin gelatinous membrane between the epidermis and gastrodermis in hydrozoans.

mesomere [EMBRYO] The muscle-plate region between the epimere and hypomere in vertebrates.

mesometrium [ANAT] The part of the broad ligament attached directly to the uterus.

mesonephric duct [EMBRYO] The efferent duct of the mesonephros. Also known as Wolffian duct.

mesonephric ridge [EMBRYO] A fold of the dorsal wall of the coelom lateral to the mesentery formed by development of the mesonephros. Also known as mesonephric fold.

mesonephros [EMBRYO] One of the middle of three pairs of embryonic renal structures in vertebrates; persists in adult fish and is replaced by the metanephros in higher forms.

Mesonychidae [PALEON] A family of extinct mammals of the order Condylarthra.

mesophile [BIOL] An organism, as certain bacteria, that grows at moderate temperature.

mesophily [ECOL] Physiological response of organisms living in environments with moderate temperatures and a fairly high, constant amount of moisture.

mesophyll [BOT] Parenchymatous tissue between the upper and lower epidermal layers in foliage leaves.

mesophyte [ECOL] A plant requiring moderate amounts of moisture for optimum growth.

mesopore [PALEON] A tube paralleling the autopore or chamber in fossil bryozoans.

mesopterygium [VERT ZOO] The middle one of three basal cartilages in the pectoral fin of sharks and rays.

mesoptic vision [PHYSIO] Vision in which the human eye's spectral sensitivity is changing from the photoptic state to the scotoptic state.

mesorchium [EMBRYO] The mesentery that supports the embryonic testis in vertebrates.

mesosalpinx [ANAT] The portion of the broad ligament forming the mesentery of the uterine tube.

Mesosauria [PALEON] An order of extinct aquatic reptiles which is known from a single genus, *Mesosaurus*, characterized by a long snout, numerous slender teeth, small forelimbs, and webbed hindfeet.

mesosere [ECOL] A sere originating in a mesic habitat and characterized by mesophytes.

mesosoma [INV ZOO] 1. The anterior portion of the abdomen in certain arthropods. 2. The middle of the body of some invertebrates, especially when the phylogenetic segmentation pattern cannot be determined.

mesosome [MICROBIO] An extension of the cell membrane within a bacterial cell; possibly involved in cross-wall formation, cell division, and the attachment of daughter chromosomes following deoxyribonucleic acid replication.

mesosternum [ANAT] The middle portion of the sternum in vertebrates. Also known as gladiolus. [INV ZOO] The ventral portion of the mesothorax in insects.

Mesostigmata [INV ZOO] The mites, a suborder of the Acarina characterized by a single pair of breathing pores (stigmata) located laterally in the middle of the idiosoma between the second and third, or third and fourth, legs.

Mesosuchia [PALEON] A suborder of extinct crocodiles of the Late Jurassic and Early Cretaceous.

Mesotaeniaceae [BOT] The saccoderm desmids, a family of fresh-water algae in the order Conjugales; cells are oval, cylindrical, or rectangular and have simple, undecorated walls in one piece.

Mesotardigrada [INV ZOO] An order of tardigrades which combines certain echiniscoidean features with eutardigradan characters.

mesotheca [INV ZOO] The middle lamina of bifoliate bryozoan colonies.

mesothelium [ANAT] The simple squamous-cell epithelium lining the pleural, pericardial, peritoneal, and scrotal cavities. [EMBRYO] The lining of the wall of the primitive body cavity situated between the somatopleure and splanchnopleure.

mesotherm [ECOL] A plant that grows successfully at moderate temperatures.

mesothorax [INV ZOO] The middle of three somites composing the thorax in insects.

mesovarium [ANAT] A fold of the peritoneum that connects the ovary with the broad ligament.

Mesovellidae [INV ZOO] The water treaders, a small family of hemipteran insects in the subdivision Amphibicorisae having well-developed ocelli.

mesoxalyurea See alloxan.

Mesozoa [INV ZOO] A division of the animal kingdom sometimes ranked intermediate between the Protozoa and the Metazoa; composed of two orders of small parasitic, wormlike organisms.

mesozooid [INV ZOO] A type of bryozoan heterozooid that produces slender tubes (mesozooecia or mesopores), internally subdivided by many closely spaced diaphragms, that open as tiny polygonal apertures.

mesquite [BOT] Any plant of the genus *Prosopis*, especially *P. juliflora*, a spiny tree or shrub bearing sugar-rich pods; an important livestock feed.

messenger ribonucleic acid [BIOCHEM] A linear sequence of nucleotides which is transcribed from and complementary to a single strand of deoxyribonucleic acid and which carries the information for protein synthesis to the ribosomes. Abbreviated mRNA.

metabiosis [ECOL] An ecological association in which one organism precedes and prepares a suitable environment for a second organism.

metabolic [PHYSIO] Of or pertaining to metabolism.

metabolism [PHYSIO] The physical and chemical processes by which foodstuffs are synthesized into complex elements (assimilation, anabolism), complex substances are transformed into simple ones (disassimilation, catabolism), and energy is made available for use by an organism.

metabolite [BIOCHEM] A product of intermediary metabolism.

metabolize [PHYSIO] To transform by metabolism; to subject to metabolism.

metacarpus [ANAT] The portion of a hand or forefoot between the carpus and the phalanges.

metacentric [CELL BIO] Having the centromere near the middle of the chromosome.

metacercaria [INV ZOO] Encysted cercaria of digenetic trematodes; the infective form.

metacestode [INV ZOO] Encysted larva of a tapeworm; occurs in the intermediate host.

Metachlamydeae [BOT] An artificial group of flowering plants, division Magnoliophyta, recognized in the Englerian system of classification; consists of families of dicotyledons in which petals are characteristically fused, forming a sympetalous corolla.

metachromatic granules [CELL BIO] Granules which assume a color different from that of the dye used to stain them.

metachrosis [VERT ZOO] The ability of some animals to change color by the expansion and contraction of chromatophores.

metacneme [INV ZOO] A secondary mesentery in many zoantharians.

metacone [VERT ZOO] 1. The posterior of three cusps of primitive upper molars. 2. The posteroexternal cusp of an upper molar in higher vertebrates, especially mammals.

metaconid [VERT ZOO] The posteroexternal cusp of a lower molar in mammals; corresponds with the metacone.

Metacopina [PALEON] An extinct suborder of ostracods in the order Podocopida.

metagenesis [BIOL] The phenomenon in which one generation of certain plants and animals reproduces asexually, followed by a sexually reproducing generation. Also known as alternation of generations.

metagranulocyte *See* metamyelocyte.

metakaryocyte *See* normoblast.

Metallogenium [MICROBIO] A genus of bacteria of uncertain affiliation; coccoid cells that attach to substrate; they germinate directly or form groups of elementary bodies by budding, and filaments form from these bodies.

metalloporphyrin [BIOCHEM] A compound, such as heme, consisting of a porphyrin combined with a metal such as iron, copper, silver, zinc, or magnesium.

metalloprotein [BIOCHEM] A protein enzyme containing a metallic atom as an inherent portion of its molecule.

metallothionein [BIOCHEM] A group of vertebrate and invertebrate proteins that bind heavy metals; it may be involved in zinc homeostasis and resistance to heavy-metal toxicity.

metamere [ZOO] One of the linearly arranged similar segments of the body of metameric animals. Also known as somite.

metamerism [ZOO] The condition of an animal body characterized by the repetition of similar segments (metameres), exhibited especially by arthropods, annelids, and vertebrates in early embryonic stages and in certain specialized adult structures. Also known as segmentation.

metamorphosis [BIOL] 1. A structural transformation. 2. A marked structural change in an animal during postembryonic development.

metamyelocyte [HISTOL] A granulocytic cell intermediate in development between the myelocyte and granular leukocyte; characterized by a full complement of cytoplasmic granules and a bean-shaped nucleus. Also known as juvenile cell; metagranulocyte.

metanauplius [INV ZOO] A primitive larval stage of certain decapod crustaceans characterized by seven pairs of appendages; follows the nauplius stage.

metanephridium [INV ZOO] A type of nephridium consisting of a tubular structure lined with cilia which opens into the coelomic cavity.

metanephrine [BIOCHEM] An inactive metabolite of epinephrine (3-O-methylepinephrine) that is excreted in the urine; it is recovered and measured as a test for pheochromocytoma.

metanephros [EMBRYO] One of the posterior of three pairs of vertebrate renal structures; persists as the definitive or permanent kidney in adult reptiles, birds, and mammals.

metanitricyte *See* normoblast.

metaphase [CELL BIO] 1. The phase of mitosis during which centromeres are arranged on the equator of the spindle. 2. The phase of the first meiotic division when centromeric regions of homologous chromosomes come to lie equidistant on either side of the equator.

metaphysis *See* epiphyseal plate.

Metaphyta [BIOL] A kingdom set up to include mosses, ferns, and other plants in some systems of classification.

metaplasm [CELL BIO] The ergastic substance of protoplasm.

metapodium [ANAT] 1. The metatarsus in bipeds. 2. The metatarsus and metacarpus in quadrupeds. [INV ZOO] Posterior portion of the foot of a mollusk.

metapodosoma [INV ZOO] Portion of the body bearing the third and fourth pairs of legs in Acarina.

metapterygium [VERT ZOO] The posterior one of three basal cartilages in the pectoral fin of sharks and rays.

metarubricyte *See* normoblast.

metascutellum [INV ZOO] The scutellum of the metathorax in insects.

metasicula [INV ZOO] The succeeding part of the sicula or colonial tube of graptolites.

metasoma [INV ZOO] The posterior region of the body of certain invertebrates, a term used especially when the phylogenetic segmentation pattern cannot be identified.

metasternum [INV ZOO] The ventral portion of the metathorax in insects.

metastoma [INV ZOO] Median plate posterior to the mouth in certain crustaceans and related arthropods.

Metastrongylidae [INV ZOO] A family of roundworms belonging to the Strongyloidea; species are parasitic in sheep, cattle, horses, dogs, and other domestic animals.

metatarsal [ANAT] Of or pertaining to the metatarsus.

metatarsus [ANAT] The part of a foot or hindfoot between the tarsus and the phalanges.

Metatheria [VERT ZOO] An infraclass of therian mammals including a single order, the Marsupialia; distinguished by a small braincase, a total of 50 teeth, the inflected angular process of the mandible, and a pair of marsupial bones articulating with the pelvis.

metathorax [INV ZOO] Posterior segment of the thorax in insects.

metatroch [INV ZOO] A segmented larval form following the trochophore in annelids.

metaxylem [BOT] Primary xylem differentiated after and distinguished from protoxylem by thicker tracheids and vessels with pitted or reticulated walls.

Metazoa [ZOO] The multicellular animals that make up the major portion of the animal kingdom; cells are organized in layers or groups as specialized tissues or organ systems.

metazoea [INV ZOO] The last zoea of certain decapod crustaceans; metamorphoses into a megalopa.

metencephalon [EMBRYO] The cephalic portion of the rhombencephalon; gives rise to the cerebellum and pons.

Meteoriaceae [BOT] A family of mosses in the order Isobryales in which the calyptra is frequently hairy.

metestrus [PHYSIO] The beginning of the luteal phase following estrus.

methane-oxidizing bacteria [MICROBIO] Bacteria that derive energy from oxidation of methane.

Methanobacteriaceae [MICROBIO] The single family of methane-producing bacteria; anaerobes which obtain energy via formation of methane.

Methanobacterium [MICROBIO] A genus of rod-shaped or filamentous coccoid bacteria in the family Methanobacteriaceae; they reduce carbon dioxide to methane for energy.

Methanococcus [MICROBIO] A genus of coccoid bacteria in the family Methanobacteriaceae; cells occur singly, in pairs, or in masses; obtain energy by formation of methane from hydrogen, carbon monoxide, formate, acetate, or butyrate.

methanogen [BIOL] An organism carrying out methanogenesis, requiring completely anaerobic conditions for growth; considered by some authorities to be distinct from bacteria.

methanogenesis [BIOCHEM] The biosynthesis of the hydrocarbon methane; common in certain bacteria. Also known as bacterial methanogenesis.

Methanomonadaceae [MICROBIO] Formerly a family of bacteria in the suborder Pseudomonadineae; members identified as gram-negative rods are able to use carbon monoxide (*Carboxydomonas*), methane (*Methanomonas*), and hydrogen (*Hydrogenomonas*) as their sole source of energy for growth.

Methanosarcina [MICROBIO] A genus of large coccoid bacteria in the family Methanobacteriaceae; cells generally occur in packets; obtain energy by formation of methane principally from acetate and sometimes from methanol or butyrate.

methemoglobin *See* ferrihemoglobin.

methionine [BIOCHEM] $C_5H_{11}O_2NS$ An essential amino acid; furnishes both labile methyl groups and sulfur necessary for normal metabolism.

Methylococcus [MICROBIO] A genus of bacteria in the family Methylomonadaceae; nonmotile cocci, usually found in pairs.

Methylomonadaceae [MICROBIO] A family of gram-negative, aerobic bacteria which utilize only one-carbon compounds as a source of carbon.

Methylomonas [MICROBIO] A genus of bacteria in the family Methylomonadaceae; motile, straight, curved, or branched rods that occur singly.

methyl red test [MICROBIO] A cultural test for the ability of bacteria to ferment carbohydrate to form acid; uses methyl red as the indicator.

methyl transferase [BIOCHEM] Any of a group of enzymes which catalyze the reaction of S-adenosyl methionine with a suitable acceptor to yield the methylated acceptor molecule and S-adenosyl homocysteine.

metraterm [INV ZOO] The distal portion of the uterus in trematodes.

Metridiidae [INV ZOO] A family of zoantharian coelenterates in the order Actiniaria.

Meylliidae [INV ZOO] A family of free-living nematodes in the superfamily Desmoscolecoidea.

Meziridae [INV ZOO] A family of hemipteran insects in the superfamily Aradoidea.

Miacidae [PALEON] The single, extinct family of the carnivoran superfamily Miacoidea.

Miacoidea [PALEON] A monofamilial superfamily of extinct carnivoran mammals; a stem group thought to represent the progenitors of the earliest member of modern carnivoran families.

micelle [MOL BIO] A submicroscopic structural unit of protoplasm built up from polymeric molecules.

Michaelis constant [BIOCHEM] A constant K_m such that the initial rate of reaction V, produced by an enzyme when the substrate concentration is high enough to saturate the enzyme, is related to the rate of reaction v at a lower substrate concentration c by the formula $V = v (1 + K_m/c)$.

micracanthopore [INV ZOO] Small, minute tubes projecting from the surface of bryozoan colonies.

microaerophilic [MICROBIO] Pertaining to those microorganisms requiring free oxygen but in very low concentration for optimum growth.

microanatomy [ANAT] Anatomical study of microscopic tissue structures.

Microbacterium [MICROBIO] A genus of small diphtheroid rods in the coryneform group of bacteria; gram-positive, nonmotile cells which ferment carbohydrate to produce lactic acid.

microbe [MICROBIO] A microorganism, especially a bacterium of a pathogenic nature.

microbial insecticide [MICROBIO] Species-specific bacteria which are pathogenic for and used against injurious insects.

microbiology [BIOL] The science and study of microorganisms, including protozoans, algae, fungi, bacteria, viruses, and rickettsiae.

Microbispora [MICROBIO] A genus of bacteria in the family Micromonosporaceae; spores are produced in longitudinal pairs on aerial mycelia only.

microcentrum [CELL BIO] The centrosome, or a group of centrosomes, functioning as the dynamic center of a cell.

microceratous [INV ZOO] Having short antennae.

microcercous cercaria [INV ZOO] A cercaria with a very short broad tail.

microchemistry [BIOCHEM] The chemistry of individual cells and minute organisms.

Microchiroptera [VERT ZOO] A suborder of the mammalian order Chiroptera composed of the insectivorous bats.

microcirculation [PHYSIO] The flow of blood or lymph in the vessels of the microcirculatory system.

microcirculatory system [ANAT] Those vessels of the blood and lymphatic systems which are visible only with a microscope.

microcneme [INV ZOO] Microsepta in certain anemones.

Micrococcaceae [MICROBIO] A family of gram-positive cocci; chemoorganotrophic organisms with respiratory or fermentative metabolism.

Micrococcus [MICROBIO] A genus of bacteria in the family Micrococcaceae; cells may occur singly or in pairs, but usually in irregular masses, tetrads, or cubical packets; metabolism is respiratory.

Micrococcus meningitidis See Neisseria meningitidis.

microcomposer See decomoposer.

microconsumer See decomposer.

Microcotyloidea [INV ZOO] A superfamily of ectoparasitic trematodes in the subclass Monogenea.

Microcyclus [MICROBIO] A genus of bacteria of uncertain affiliation; curved, nonmotile rods; prior to cell division, the elongated cell forms a ring.

Microcyprini [VERT ZOO] The equivalent name for Cyprinodontiformes.

microdissection [BIOL] Dissection under a microscope.

Microdomatacea [PALEON] An extinct superfamily of gastropod mollusks in the order Aspidobranchia.

Microellobosporia [MICROBIO] A genus of bacteria in the family Streptomycetaceae; hyphae form substrate and aerial mycelia; spores are produced by sporangia that are borne on short sporangiophores on aerial and substrate mycelia.

microenvironment [ECOL] The specific environmental factors in a microhabitat.

microevolution [EVOL] 1. Evolutionary processes resulting from the accumulation of minor changes over a relatively short period of time; evolutionary changes due to gene mutation. 2. Evolution of species.

microfibril [MOL BIOL] The submicroscopic unit of a microscopic cellular fiber.

microfilament [CELL BIO] One of the cytoplasmic fibrous structures, about 5 nanometers in diameter, virtually identical to actin; thought to be important in the processes of phagocytosis and pinocytosis.

microfilaria [INV ZOO] Slender, motile prelarval forms of filarial nematodes measuring 150–300 micrometers in length; adult filaria are mammalian parasites.

microflora [BOT] Microscopic plants. [ECOL] The flora of a microhabitat.

microfossil [PALEON] A small fossil which is studied and identified by means of the microscope.

microgamete [BIOL] The smaller, or male gamete produced by heterogametic species.

microgametocyte [BIOL] A cell that gives rise to microgametes.

microgamy [BIOL] Sexual reproduction by fusion of the small male and female gametes in certain protozoans and algae.

microgenesis [BIOL] Abnormally small development of a part.

microglia [HISTOL] Small neuroglia cells of the central nervous system having long processes and exhibiting ameboid and phagocytic activity under certain pathologic conditions.

microhabitat [ECOL] A small, specialized, and effectively isolated location.

Microhylidae [VERT ZOO] A family of anuran amphibians in the suborder Diplasiocoela including many heavy-bodied forms with a pointed head and tiny mouth.

microinjection [CELL BIO] Injection of cells with solutions by using a micropipet.

Microlepidoptera [INV ZOO] A former division of Lepidoptera.

Micromalthidae [INV ZOO] A family of coleopteran insects in the superfamily Cantharoidea; the single species is the telephone pole beetle.

micromanipulation [BIOL] The techniques and practice of microdissection, microvivisection, microisolation, and microinjection.

micromere [EMBRYO] A small blastomere of the upper or animal hemisphere in eggs that undergo uneven cleavage.

Micromonospora [MICROBIO] A genus of bacteria in the family Micromonosporaceae; the mycelium is well developed, branched, and septate; single spores are formed on hyphae.

Micromonosporaceae [MICROBIO] A family of bacteria in the order Actinomycetales; aerial hyphae are formed in all genera except *Micromonospora*; saprophytic soil organisms.

Micromonospora purpurea [MICROBIO] The bacterium that produces the antibiotic gentamycin.

micronekton [ECOL] Active pelagic crustaceans and other forms intermediate between thrusting nekton and feebler-swimming plankton.

micronucleus [INV ZOO] The smaller, reproductive nucleus in multinucleate protozoans.

micronutrient [BIOCHEM] Trace elements and compounds required by living systems only in minute amounts.

microorganism [MICROBIO] A microscopic organism, including bacteria, protozoans, yeast, viruses, and algae.

micropaleontology [PALEON] A branch of paleontology that deals with the study of microfossils.

Micropezidae [INV ZOO] A family of myodarian cyclorrhaphous dipteran insects in the subsection Acalypteratae.

microphage [HISTOL] A small phagocyte, especially a neutrophil.

microphagy [BIOL] Feeding on minute organisms or particles.

microphyllous [BOT] 1. Having small leaves. 2. Having leaves with a single, unbranched vein.

Microphysidae [INV ZOO] A palearctic family of hemipteran insects in the subfamily Cimicimorpha.

microphyte [ECOL] 1. A microscopic plant. 2. A dwarfed plant due to unfavorable environmental conditions.

micropinocytosis [CELL BIO] A mechanism of endocytosis in which fluid droplets are internalized by indentations (caveolae) on the surface membrane which pinch off as tiny internal vesicles (micropinosomes).

micropinosome [CELL BIO] A very tiny vesicle that is pinched off from the plasma membrane of a cell during micropinocytosis.

Micropolyspora [MICROBIO] A genus of bacteria in the family Micromonosporaceae; short chains of spores are borne on both aerial and substrate mycelia.

Micropterygidae [INV ZOO] The single family of the lepidopteran superfamily Micropterygoidea;

members are minute moths possessing toothed, functional mandibles and lacking a proboscis.

Micropterygoidea [INV ZOO] A monofamilial superfamily of lepidopteran insects in the suborder Homoneura.

Micropygidae [INV ZOO] A family of echinoderms in the order Diadematoida that includes only one genus, *Micropyga*, which has noncrenulate tubercles and umbrellalike outer tube feet.

micropyle [BOT] A minute opening in the integument at the tip of an ovule through which the pollen tube commonly enters; persists in the seed as an opening or a scar between the hilum and point of radicle.

Microsauria [PALEON] An order of Carboniferous and early Permian lepospondylous amphibians.

microsclere [INV ZOO] A minute sclerite in Porifera.

microseptum [INV ZOO] An incomplete or imperfect mesentery in zoantharians.

microsome [CELL BIO] 1. A fragment of the endoplasmic reticulum. 2. A minute granule of protoplasm.

microspecies [ECOL] A small, localized species population that is clearly differentiated from related forms. Also known as jordanon.

Microsporaceae [BOT] A monogeneric family of green algae in the suborder Ulotrichineae; the chloroplast is a parietal network.

microsporangium [BOT] A sporangium bearing microspores.

microspore [BOT] The smaller spore of heterosporous plants; gives rise to the male gametophyte.

Microsporida [INV ZOO] The single order of the class Microsporidea.

Microsporidae [INV ZOO] The equivalent name for Sphaeriidae.

Microsporidea [INV ZOO] A class of Cnidospora characterized by the production of minute spores with a single intrasporal filament or one or two intracapsular filaments and a single sporoplasm; mainly intracellular parasites of arthropods and fishes.

microsporophyll [BOT] A sporophyll bearing microsporangia.

microsurgery [BIOL] Surgery on single cells by micromanipulation.

Microtatobiotes [BIOL] An artificial taxonomic category, comprising two unrelated groups of biological entities, the rickettsiae and the viruses.

microtherm [ECOL] A plant requiring a mean annual temperature range of 0–14°C for optimum growth.

Microtinae [VERT ZOO] A subfamily of rodents in the family Muridae that includes lemmings and muskrats.

microtomy [BIOL] Cutting of thin sections of specimens with a microtome.

Microtragulidae [PALEON] A group of saltatorial caenolistoid marsupials that appeared late in the Cenozoic and paralleled the small kangaroos of Australia.

microtrichia [INV ZOO] Small hairs on the integument of various insects, especially on the wings.

microtubule [CELL BIO] One of the hollow tubelike filaments found in certain cell components, such as cilia and the mitotic spindle, and composed of repeating subunits of the protein tubulin.

microvillus [CELL BIO] One of the filiform processes that form a brush border on the surfaces of certain specialized cells, such as intestinal epithelium.

mictic [BIOL] 1. Requiring or produced by sexual reproduction. 2. Of or pertaining to eggs which without fertilization develop into males and with fertilization develop into amictic females, as occurs in rotifers.

micturition *See* urination.

midaxillary line [ANAT] A perpendicular line drawn downward from the apex of the axilla.

midbrain [ANAT] Those portions of the adult brain derived from the embryonic midbrain.

midbrain [EMBRYO] The middle portion of the embryonic vertebrate brain. Also known as mesencephalon.

midclavicular line [ANAT] A vertical line parallel to and midway between the midsternal line and a vertical line drawn downward through the outer end of the clavicle.

middle ear [ANAT] The middle portion of the ear in higher vertebrates; in mammals it contains three ossicles and is separated from the external ear by the tympanic membrane and from the inner ear by the oval and round windows.

midge [INV ZOO] Any of various dipteran insects, principally of the families Ceratopogonidae, Cecidomyiidae, and Chironomidae; many are biting forms and are vectors of parasites of man and other vertebrates.

midgut [EMBRYO] The middle portion of the digestive tube in vertebrate embryos. Also known as mesenteron. [INV ZOO] The mesodermal intermediate part of an invertebrate intestine.

midrib [BOT] The large central vein of a leaf.

migrant [ZOO] An animal that moves from one habitat to another.

migration [VERT ZOO] Periodic movement of animals to new areas or habitats.

mildew [MYCOL] 1. A whitish growth on plants, organic matter, and other materials caused by a parasitic fungus. 2. Any fungus producing such growth.

Milichiidae [INV ZOO] A family of myodarian cyclorrhaphous dipteran insects in the subsection Acalypteratae.

milieu interieur [PHYSIO] The fundamental concept that the living organism exists in an aqueous internal environment which bathes all tissues and provides a medium for the elementary exchange of nutrients and waste.

Miliolacea [INV ZOO] A superfamily of marine or brackish foraminiferans in the suborder Miliolina characterized by an imperforate test wall of tiny, disordered calcite rhombs.

Miliolidae [INV ZOO] A family of foraminiferans in the superfamily Miliolacea.

Miliolina [INV ZOO] A suborder of the Foraminiferida characterized by a porcelaneous, imperforate calcite wall.

milk [PHYSIO] 1. The whitish fluid secreted by the mammary gland for the nourishment of the young; composed of carbohydrates, proteins, fats, mineral salts, vitamins, and antibodies. 2. Any whitish fluid in nature resembling milk, as coconut milk.

milk factor [BIOCHEM] A filtrable, noncellular agent in the milk and tissues of certain strains of inbred mice; transmitted from the mother to the offspring by nursing. Also known as Bittner milk factor.

milk sugar See lactose.

milk teeth See deciduous teeth.

milkweed [BOT] Any of several latex-secreting plants of the genus Asclepias in the family Asclepiadaceae.

milky disease [INV ZOO] A bacterial disease of Japanese beetle larvae or related grubs caused by Bacillus papilliae and B. lentimorbus that penetrate the intestine and sporulate in the body cavity; blood of the grub eventually turns milky white.

Milleporina [INV ZOO] An order of the class Hydrozoa known as the stinging corals; they resemble true corals because of a calcareous exoskeleton.

millet [BOT] A common name applied to at least five related members of the grass family grown for their edible seeds.

millipede [INV ZOO] The common name for members of the arthropod class Diplopoda.

mimetic [ZOO] Pertaining to or exhibiting mimicry.

mimicry [ZOO] Assumption of color, form, or behavior patterns by one species of another species, for camouflage and protection.

Mimidae [VERT ZOO] The mockingbirds, a family of the Oscines in the order Passeriformes.

Mimosoideae [BOT] A subfamily of the legume family, Leguminosae; members are largely woody and tropical or subtropical with regular flowers and usually numerous stamens.

mineralocorticoid [BIOCHEM] A steroid hormone secreted by the adrenal cortex that regulates mineral metabolism and, secondarily, fluid balance.

mink [VERT ZOO] Any of three species of slender-bodied aquatic carnivorous mammals in the genus Mustela of the family Mustelidae.

minnow [VERT ZOO] The common name for any fresh-water fish composing the family Cyprinidae, order Cypriniformes.

minus strand [MOL BIO] A polynucleotide strand that is complementary to, and formed by transcription from, another specific polynucleotide (plus) strand, with which it produces the double-stranded (double-helix) ribonucleic acid.

Miosireninae [PALEON] A subfamily of extinct sirenian mammals in the family Dugongidae.

miosis [PHYSIO] Contraction of the pupil of the eye.

miotic [PHYSIO] Of or pertaining to miosis.

miracidium [INV ZOO] The ciliated first larva of a digenetic trematode; forms a sporocyst after penetrating intermediate host tissues.

Mirapinnatoidei [VERT ZOO] A suborder of tiny oceanic fishes in the order Cetomimiformes.

Miridae [INV ZOO] The largest family of the Hemiptera; included in the Cimicomorpha, it contains herbivorous and predacious plant bugs which lack ocelli and have a cuneus and four-segmented antennae.

Miripinnati [VERT ZOO] The equivalent name for Marapinnatoidei.

missense codon [GEN] A mutant codon that directs the incorporation of a different amino acid and results in the synthesis of a protein with a sequence in which one amino acid has been replaced by a different one; in some cases the mutant protein may be unstable or less active.

missense mutation [MOL BIO] A mutation that converts a codon coding for one amino acid to a codon coding for another amino acid.

mistletoe [BOT] 1. Viscum album. The true, Old World mistletoe having dichotomously branching stems, thick leathery leaves, and waxy-white berries. 2. Any of several species of green hemiparasitic plants of the family Loranthaceae.

mite [INV ZOO] The common name for the acarine arthropods composing the diverse suborders Onychopalpida, Mesostigmata, Trombidiformes, and Sarcoptiformes.

mitochondria [CELL BIO] Minute cytoplasmic organelles in the form of spherical granules, short rods, or long filaments found in almost all living cells; submicroscopic structure consists of an external membrane system.

mitogenesis [CELL BIO] 1. Induction of mitosis. 2. Formation as a result of mitosis.

mitogenetic [CELL BIO] Inducing or stimulating mitosis.

mitomycin [MICROBIO] A complex of three antibiotics (mitomycin A, B, and C) produced by Streptomyces caespitosus.

mitosis [CELL BIO] Nuclear division involving exact duplication and separation of the chromosome threads so that each of the two daughter nuclei carries a chromosome complement identical to that of the parent nucleus.

mitotic index [CELL BIO] The number of cells undergoing mitosis per thousand cells.

mitotic inhibitor [CELL BIO] A compound that inhibits mitosis.

mitotic poison [CELL BIO] A compound that prevents or affects the completion of mitosis.

mitral valve [ANAT] The atrioventricular valve on the left side of the heart.

mitriform [BIOL] Shaped like a miter.

mixed cryoglobulin [BIOCHEM] A cryoglobulin with a monoclonal component made of immunoglobulin belonging to two different classes, one of which is monoclonal.

mixed gland [PHYSIO] A gland that secretes more than one substance, especially a gland containing both mucous and serous components.

mixed nerve [PHYSIO] A nerve containing both sensory and motor components.

Mixodectidae [PALEON] A family of extinct insectivores assigned to the Proteutheria; a superficially rodentlike group confined to the Paleocene of North America.

mixotrophic [BIOL] Obtaining nutrition by combining autotrophic and heterotrophic mechanisms.

Mnesarchaeidae [INV ZOO] A family of lepidopteran insects in the suborder Homoneura; members are confined to New Zealand.

Mobilina [INV ZOO] A suborder of ciliophoran protozoans in the order Peritrichida.

Mobulidae [VERT ZOO] The devil rays, a family of batoids that are surface feeders and live mostly on plankton.

modifier gene [GEN] A gene that alters the phenotypic expression of a nonallelic gene.

modiolus [ANAT] The central axis of the cochlea.

Moeritheriidae [PALEON] The single family of the extinct order Moeritherioidea.

Moeritherioidea [PALEON] A suborder of extinct sirenian mammals considered as primitive proboscideans by some authorities and as a sirenian offshoot by others.

Moko disease [PL PATH] Bacterial wilt of banana caused by *Pseudomonas solanacearum*.

molar [ANAT] 1. A tooth adapted for grinding. 2. Any of the three pairs of cheek teeth behind the premolars on each side of the jaws in humans.

mold [MYCOL] Any of various woolly fungus growths. [PALEON] An impression made in rock or earth material by an inner or outer surface of a fossil shell or other organic structure; a complete mold would be the hollow space.

mole [VERT ZOO] Any of 19 species of insectivorous mammals composing the family Talpidae; the body is stout and cylindrical, with a short neck, small or vestigial eyes and ears, a long naked muzzle, and forelimbs adapted for digging.

molecular biology [BIOL] That part of biology which attempts to interpret biological events in terms of the physicochemical properties of molecules in a cell.

molecular genetics [MOL BIO] The approach which deals with the physics and chemistry of the processes of inheritance.

Molidae [VERT ZOO] A family of marine fishes, including some species of sunfishes, in the order Perciformes.

Mollicutes [MICROBIO] The mycoplasmas, a class of prokaryotic organisms lacking a true cell wall; cells are very small to submicroscopic.

Mollusca [INV ZOO] One of the divisions of phyla of the animal kingdom containing snails, slugs, octopuses, squids, clams, mussels, and oysters; characterized by a shell-secreting organ, the mantle, and a radula, a food-rasping organ located in the forward area of the mouth.

mollusk [INV ZOO] Any member of the Mollusca.

Molossidae [VERT ZOO] The free-tailed bats, a family of tropical and subtropical insectivorous mammals in the order Chiroptera.

Molpadida [INV ZOO] An order of sea cucumbers belonging to the Apodacea and characterized by a short, plump body bearing a taillike prolongation.

Molpadidae [INV ZOO] The single family of the echinoderm order Molpadida.

molt [PHYSIO] To shed an outer covering as part of a periodic process of growth.

molting hormone [BIOCHEM] Any of several hormones which activate molting in arthropods.

Momotidae [VERT ZOO] The motmots, a family of colorful New World birds in the order Coraciiformes.

monactine [INV ZOO] A single-rayed spicule in the sponges.

monadelphous [BOT] Having the filaments of the stamens united into one set.

Monadidae [INV ZOO] A family of flagellated protozoans in the order Kinetoplastida having two flagella of uneven length.

monandrous [BOT] Having one stamen.

monaxon [INV ZOO] A spicule formed by growth along a single axis.

Monera [BIOL] A kingdom that includes the bacteria and blue-green algae in some classification schemes.

monestrous [PHYSIO] Having a single estrous cycle per year.

mongoose [VERT ZOO] The common name for 39 species of carnivorous mammals which are members of the family Viveridae; they are plantigrade animals and have a long slender body, short legs, nonretractile claws, and scent glands.

Monhysterida [INV ZOO] An order of aquatic nematodes in the subclass Chromadoria.

Monhysteroidea [INV ZOO] A superfamily of free-living nematodes in the order Monhysterida characterized by single or paired outstretched ovaries, circular to cryptospiral amphids, and a stoma which is usually shallow and unarmed.

Monilia albicans *See* Candida albicans.

Moniliaceae [MYCOL] A family of fungi in the order Moniliales; sporophores are usually lacking, but when present they are aggregated into fascicles, and hyphae and spores are hyaline or brightly colored.

Moniliales [MYCOL] An order of fungi of the Fungi Imperfecti containing many plant pathogens; asexual spores are always formed free on the surface of the material on which the organism is living, and never occur in either pycnidia or acervuli.

moniliform [BIOL] Constructed with contractions and expansions at regular alternating intervals, giving the appearance of a string of beads.

monitor [VERT ZOO] Any of 27 carnivorous, voracious species of the reptilian family Varanidae characterized by a long, slender forked tongue and a dorsal covering of small, rounded scales containing pointed granules.

monkey [VERT ZOO] Any of several species of frugivorous and carnivorous primates which compose the families Cercopithecidae and Cebidae in the suborder Anthropoidea; the face is typically flattened and hairless, all species are pentadactyl, and the mammary glands are always in the pectoral region.

monkshood *See* aconite.

monoamine oxidase [BIOCHEM] An enzyme that catalyzes oxidative deamination of monoamines.

monoblast [HISTOL] A motile cell of the spleen and bone marrow from which monocytes are derived.

Monoblepharidales [MYCOL] An order of aquatic fungi in the class Phycomycetes; distinguished by a mostly hyphal thallus and zoospores with one posterior flagellum.

Monobothrida [PALEON] An extinct order of monocyclic camerate crinoids.

monocarpic [BOT] Bearing fruit once and then dying.

monocarpous [BOT] Having a single ovary.

monochlamydous [BOT] Referring to flowers having only one set of floral envelopes, that is, either a calyx or a corolla.

monoclimax [ECOL] A climax community controlled primarily by one factor, as climate.

monoclinic [BOT] Having both stamens and pistils in the same flower.

monoclonal cryoglobulin [BIOCHEM] A cryoglobulin composed of immunoglobin with only one class or subclass of heavy and light chain.

monocolpate pollen [BOT] Pollen grains having a single furrow.

monocotyledon [BOT] Any plant of the class Liliopsida; all have a single cotyledon.

Monocotyledoneae [BOT] The equivalent name for Liliopsida.

monocrepid [INV ZOO] A desma formed by secondary deposits of silica on a monaxon.

Monocyathea [PALEON] A class of extinct parazoans in the phylum Archaeocyatha containing single-walled forms.

monocyte [HISTOL] A large (about 12 micrometers), agranular leukocyte with a relatively small, eccentric, oval or kidney-shaped nucleus.

monodactylous [ZOO] Having a single digit or claw.

Monodellidae [INV ZOO] A monogeneric family of crustaceans in the order Thermosbaenacea distinguished by seven pairs of biramous pereiopods on thoracomeres 2–8, and by not having the telson united to the last pleonite.

monodelphic [VERT ZOO] 1. Having a single genital tract, in the female. 2. Having a single uterus.

monoecious [BOT] 1. Having both staminate and pistillate flowers on the same plant. 2. Having archegonia and antheridia on different branches. [ZOO] Having male and female reproductive organs in the same individual. Also known as hermaphroditic.

Monoedidae [INV ZOO] An equivalent name for Colydiidae.

Monogenea [INV ZOO] A diverse subclass of the Trematoda which are principally ectoparasites of fishes; individuals have enlarged anterior and posterior holdfasts with paired suckers anteriorly and opisthaptors posteriorly.

Monogenoidea [INV ZOO] A class of the Trematoda in some systems of classification; equivalent to the Monogenea of other systems.

Monogonota [INV ZOO] An order of the class Rotifera, characterized by the presence of a single gonad in both males and females.

monogony [BIOL] Asexual reproduction.

monogynous [BOT] Having only one pistil. [VERT ZOO] 1. Having only one female in a colony. 2. Consorting with only one female.

monohybrid [GEN] A hybrid individual heterozygous for one gene or a single character.

Monommidae [INV ZOO] A family of coleopteran insects in the superfamily Tenebrionoidea.

monomorphic [BIOL] Having or exhibiting only a single form.

mononuclear [CELL BIO] Having only one nucleus.

monophagous [ZOO] Subsisting on a single kind of food. Also known as monotrophic.

Monophisthocotylea [INV ZOO] An order of the Monogenea in which the posthaptor is without discrete multiple suckers or clamps.

Monophlebinae [INV ZOO] A subfamily of the homopteran superfamily Coccoidea distinguished by a dorsal anus.

monophyodont [VERT ZOO] Having only one set of teeth throughout life.

Monopisthocotylea [INV ZOO] An order of trematode worms in the subclass Pectobothridia.

Monoplacophora [INV ZOO] A group of shell-bearing mollusks represented by few living forms; considered to be a sixth class of mollusks.

monoploid [GEN] 1. Having only one set of chromosomes. 2. Having the haploid number of chromosomes.

monopodial [BOT] Stem branching in which there are lateral shoots on a primary axis.

monopodium [BOT] A primary axis that continues to grow while giving off successive lateral branches.

Monopylina [INV ZOO] A suborder of radiolarian protozoans in the order Oculosida in which pores lie at one pole of a single-layered capsule.

monorchid [ANAT] 1. Having one testis. 2. Having one testis descended into the scrotum.

Monorhina [VERT ZOO] The subclass of Agnatha that includes the jawless vertebrates with a single median nostril.

monorhinal [ANAT] Having only one nostril.

monosaccharide [BIOCHEM] A carbohydrate which cannot be hydrolyzed to a simpler carbohydrate; a polyhedric alcohol having reducing properties associated with an actual or potential aldehyde or ketone group; classified on the basis of the number of carbon atoms, as triose (3C), tetrose (4C), pentose (5C), and so on.

Monosigales [BOT] A botanical order equivalent to the Choanoflagellida in some systems of classification.

monosiphonous [BIOL] Having a single central tube, as in the thallus of certain filamentous algae or the hydrocaulus of some hydrozoans.

monospermous [BOT] Having or producing one seed.

monosporangium [BOT] A sporangium producing monospores.

monospore [BOT] A simple or undivided nonmotile asexual spore; produced by the diploid generation of some algae.

monostome [INV ZOO] A cercaria having only one mouth or sucker.

Monostylifera [INV ZOO] A suborder of the Hoplonemertini characterized by a single stylet.

Monotomidae [INV ZOO] The equivalent name for Rhizophagidae.

Monotremata [VERT ZOO] The single order of the mammalian subclass Prototheria containing unusual mammallike reptiles, or quasi-mammals.

monotrichous [MICROBIO] Of bacteria, having an individual flagellum at one pole.

Monotropaceae [BOT] A family of dicotyledonous herbs or half shrubs in the order Ericales distinguished by a small, scarcely differentiated embryo without cotyledons, lack of chlorophyll, leaves reduced to scales, and anthers opening by longitudinal slits.

monotrophic See monophagous.

monotype [BIOL] A single type of organism that constitutes a species or genus.

monotypic [SYST] Pertaining to a taxon that contains only one immediately subordinate taxon.

monozygotic twins [BIOL] Twins which develop from a single fertilized ovum. Also known as identical twins.

mons [ANAT] An eminence.

mons pubis [ANAT] The eminence of the lower anterior abdominal wall above the superior rami of the pubic bones.

Monstrilloida [INV ZOO] A suborder or order of microscopic crustaceans in the subclass Copepoda; adults lack a second antenna and mouthparts, and the digestive tract is vestigial.

mons veneris [ANAT] The mons pubis of the female.

montane [ECOL] Of, pertaining to, or being the biogeographic zone composed of moist, cool slopes below the timberline and having evergreen trees as the dominant life-form.

Montgomery's tubercles [ANAT] Elevations in the areola of the nipple due to apocrine sweat glands; most prominent during pregnancy and lactation.

Monticellidae [INV ZOO] A family of tapeworms in the order Proteocephaloidea, in which some or all of the organs are in the cortical mesenchyme; catfish parasites.

monticulus [ANAT] The median dorsal portion of the cerebellum.

moor See bog.

moose [VERT ZOO] An even-toed ungulate of the genus *Alces* in the family Cervidae; characterized by spatulate antlers, long legs, a short tail, and a large head with prominent overhanging snout.

Moraceae [BOT] A family of dicotyledonous woody plants in the order Urticales characterized by two styles or style branches, anthers inflexed in the bud, and secretion of a milky juice.

Morax-Axenfeld bacillus See Moraxella lacunata.

Moraxella [MICROBIO] A genus of rod-shaped, strictly aerobic bacteria in the family Neisseriaceae; cells are short and plump, sometimes almost spherical; parasites of mammalian mucous membranes.

Moraxella lacunata [MICROBIO] A short, non-motile, gram-negative, rod-shaped bacterium that causes conjunctivitis in humans. Also known as Morax-Axenfeld bacillus.

Mordellidae [INV ZOO] The tumbling flower beetles, a family of coleopteran insects in the superfamily Meloidea.

mores [ECOL] Groups of organisms preferring the same physical environment and having the same reproductive season.

moribund [BIOL] **1.** In a dying or deathlike state. **2.** In a state of suspended life functions; dormant.

Moridae [VERT ZOO] A family of actinopterygian fishes in the order Gadiformes.

Morinae [VERT ZOO] The deep-sea cods, a subfamily of the Moridae.

Mormyridae [VERT ZOO] A large family of electrogenic fishes belonging to the Osteoglossiformes; African river and lake fishes characterized by small eyes, a slim caudal peduncle, and approximately equal dorsal and anal fins in most.

Mormyriformes [VERT ZOO] Formerly an order of fishes which are now assigned to the Osteoglossiformes.

Moro reflex [PHYSIO] The startle reflex observed in normal infants from birth through the first few months, consisting in abduction and extension of all extremities, followed by flexion and abduction of the extremities.

morphallaxis [PHYSIO] Regeneration whereby one part is transformed into another by reorganization of tissue fragments rather than by cell proliferation.

Morphinae [INV ZOO] A subfamily of large tropical butterflies in the family Nymphalidae.

morphogenesis [EMBRYO] The transformation involved in the growth and differentiation of cells and tissue. Also known as topogenesis.

morphology [BIOL] A branch of biology that deals with structure and form of an organism at any stage of its life history.

morphospecies [SYST] A typological species distinguished solely on the basis of morphology.

morula [EMBRYO] A solid mass of blastomeres formed by cleavage of the eggs of many animals; precedes the blastula or gastrula, depending on the type of egg. [INV ZOO] A cluster of immature male gametes in which differentiation occurs outside the gonad; common in certain annelids.

Moruloidea [INV ZOO] The only class of the phylum Mesozoa; embryonic development in the organisms proceeds as far as the morula or stereoblastula stage.

mosaic [BIOL] An organism or part made up of tissues or cells exhibiting mosaicism. [EMBRYO] An egg in which the cytoplasm of early cleavage cells is of the type which determines its later fate.

mosaicism [GEN] The coexistence in an individual of somatic cells of genetically different types; it is caused by gene or chromosome mutations, especially nondisjunction, after fertilization, by double fertilization, or by fusion of embryos.

mosasaur [PALEON] Any reptile of the genus *Mosasaurus*; large, aquatic, fish-eating lizards from the Cretaceous which are related to the monitors but had paddle-shaped limbs.

mosquito [INV ZOO] Any member of the dipterous subfamily Culicinae; a slender fragile insect, with long legs, a long slender abdomen, and narrow wings.

moss [BOT] Any plant of the class Bryatae, occurring in nearly all damp habitats except the ocean.

moss forest See temperate rainforest.

moss land [ECOL] An area which contains abundant moss but is not wet enough to be a bog.

Motacilidae [VERT ZOO] The pipits, a family of passeriform birds in the suborder Oscines.

moth [INV ZOO] Any of various nocturnal or crepuscular insects belonging to the lepidopteran suborder Heteroneura; typically they differ from butterflies in having the antennae feathery and rarely clubbed, a stouter body, less brilliant coloration, and proportionately smaller wings.

mother-of-pearl [INV ZOO] The pearly iridescent internal layer of the shell of various pearl-bearing bivalve mollusks.

motile [BIOL] Being capable of spontaneous movement.

motoneuron See motor neuron.

motor [PHYSIO] **1.** That which causes action or movement. **2.** Pertaining to efferent nerves which innervate muscles and glands.

motor area [ANAT] The ascending frontal gyrus containing nerve centers for voluntary movement; characterized by the presence of Betz cells. Also known as Broadman's area 4; motor cortex; pyramidal area.

motor cell [BOT] See bulliform cell. [PHYSIO] An efferent nerve cell in the anterior horn of the spinal cord.

motor cortex See motor area.

motor end plate [ANAT] A specialized area beneath the sarcolemma where functional contact is made between motor nerve fibers and muscle fibers.

motor nerve [PHYSIO] A nerve composed wholly or principally of motor fibers.

motor neuron [PHYSIO] An efferent nerve cell. Also known as motoneuron.

motor speech area [ANAT] The cortical area located in the triangular and opercular portions of the inferior frontal gyrus; in right-handed people it is more developed on the left side.

motor system [PHYSIO] Any portion of the nervous system that regulates and controls the contractile activity of muscle and the secretory activity of glands.

motor unit [ANAT] The axon of an anterior horn cell, or the motor fiber of a cranial nerve, together with the striated muscle fibers innervated by its terminal branches.

mottle-leaf [PL PATH] **1.** A virus disease characterized by chlorotic mottling and wrinkling of leaves. **2.** A zinc-deficiency disease characterized by partial chlorosis of the leaves and stunting of the plant.

mountain lion See puma.

mouse [VERT ZOO] Any of various rodents which are members of the families Muridae, Hetero-myidae, Cricetidae, and Zapodidae; characterized by a pointed snout, short ears, and an elongated body with a long, slender, sparsely haired tail.

mousebane See aconite.

mouse deer See chevrotain.

mouth [ANAT] The oral or buccal cavity and its related structures.

m-RNA See messenger ribonucleic acid.

MSH See melanocyte-stimulating hormone.

Mucedinaceae [MYCOL] The equivalent name for Moniliaceae.

mucigen [BIOCHEM] A substance from which mucin is derived; contained in mucus-secreting epithelial cells.

mucin [BIOCHEM] A glycoprotein constituent of mucus and various other secretions of humans and lower animals.

muc-, muci-, muco- [ZOO] A combining form denoting pertaining to mucus, mucin, mucosa.

mucocutaneous [ANAT] Pertaining to a mucous membrane and the skin, and to the line where these join.

mucoid [BIOCHEM] Any of various glycoproteins, similar to mucins but differing in solubilities and precipitation properties and found in cartilage, in the crystalline lens, and in white of egg. **2.** Resembling mucus. [MICROBIO] Pertaining to large colonies of bacteria characterized by being moist and sticky.

mucolytic [BIOCHEM] Effecting the dissolution, liquefaction, or dispersion of mucus and mucopolysaccharides.

mucopolysaccharide [BIOCHEM] Any of a group of polysaccharides containing an amino sugar and uronic acid; a constituent of mucoproteins, glycoproteins, and blood-group substances.

mucoprotein [BIOCHEM] Any of a group of glycoproteins containing a sugar, usually chondroitinsulfuric or mucoitinsulfuric acid, combined with amino acids or polypeptides.

Mucorales [MYCOL] An order of terrestrial fungi in the class Phycomycetes, characterized by a hyphal thallus and nonmotile sporangiospores, or conidiospores.

mucosa [HISTOL] A mucous membrane.

mucous [PHYSIO] Of or pertaining to mucus; secreting mucus.

mucous cell [PHYSIO] A mucus-secreting cell.

mucous connective tissue [HISTOL] A type of loose connective tissue in which the ground substance is especially prominent and soft; occurs in the umbilical cord.

mucous epithelium [EMBRYO] The epidermis of an embryo, excluding the epitrichium. [HISTOL] The germinative layer of a stratified squamous epithelium.

mucous gland [PHYSIO] A gland that secretes mucus.

mucous membrane [HISTOL] The type of membrane lining cavities and canals which have communication with air; it is kept moist by glandular secretions. Also known as tunica mucosa.

mucro [BIOL] An abrupt, sharp terminal tip or process.

mucronate [BIOL] Terminated abruptly by a sharp terminal tip or process.

mucus [PHYSIO] A viscid fluid secreted by mucous glands, consisting of mucin, water, inorganic salts, epithelial cells, and leukocytes, held in suspension.

mudfish See bowfin.

mud puppy [VERT ZOO] Any of several American salamanders of the genera *Necturus* and *Proteus* making up the family Proteidae; distinguished by having both lungs and gills as an adult.

Mugilidae [VERT ZOO] The mullets, a family of perciform fishes in the suborder Mugiloidei.

Mugiloidei [VERT ZOO] A suborder of fishes in the order Perciformes; individuals are rather elongate, terete fishes with a short spinous dorsal fin that is well separated from the soft dorsal fin.

mulberry [BOT] Any of various trees of the genus *Morus* (family Moraceae), characterized by milky sap and simple, often lobed alternate leaves.

mule [VERT ZOO] The sterile hybrid offspring of the male ass and the mare, or female horse.

Müllerian duct See paramesonephric duct.

Müllerian mimicry [ZOO] Mimicry between two aposometic species.

Müller's larva [INV ZOO] The ciliated larva characteristic of various members of the Polycladida; resembles a modified ctenophore.

multicellular [BIOL] Consisting of many cells.

multicipital [BIOL] Having many heads or branches arising from one point.

multifid [BIOL] Divided into many lobes.

multiglandular [ANAT] Of or pertaining to several glands.

Multillidae [INV ZOO] An economically important family of Hymenoptera; includes the cow killer, a parasite of bumblebee pupae.

multilocular [BIOL] Having many small chambers or vesicles.

multiple epidermis [BOT] Epidermis that is several layers thick, occurring in many species of *Ficus, Begonia,* and *Peperomia*.

Multituberculata [PALEON] The single order of the nominally mammalian suborder Allotheria; multituberculates had enlarged incisors, the coracoid bones were fused to the scapula, and the lower jaw consisted of the dentary bone alone.

multituberculate [VERT ZOO] Of teeth, having several or many simple conical cusps.

muramic acid [BIOCHEM] An organic acid found in the mucopeptide (murein) in the cell walls of bacteria and blue-green algae.

muramidase [BIOCHEM] Lysozyme when acting as an enzyme on the hydrolysis of the muramic acid-containing mucopeptide in the cell walls of some bacteria.

Murchisoniacea [PALEON] An extinct superfamily of gastropod mollusks in the order Prosobranchia.

murein [BIOCHEM] The peptidoglycan of bacterial cell walls.

Muricacea [INV ZOO] A superfamily of gastropod mollusks in the order Prosobranchia.

muricate [ZOO] Covered with sharp, hard points.

Muricidae [INV ZOO] A family of predatory gastropod mollusks in the order Neogastropoda; contains the rock snails.

Muridae [VERT ZOO] A large diverse family of relatively small cosmopolitan rodents; distinguished from closely related forms by the absence of cheek pouches.

muriform [BIOL] 1. Resembling the arrangement of courses in a brick wall, especially having both horizontal and vertical septa. 2. Pertaining to or resembling a rat or mouse.

Murinae [VERT ZOO] A subfamily of the Muridae which contains such forms as the striped mouse, house mouse, harvest mouse, and field mouse.

Musaceae [BOT] A family of monocotyledonous plants in the order Zingiberales characterized by five functional stamens, unisexual flowers, spirally arranged leaves and bracts, and fleshy, indehiscent fruit.

Musci See Bryopsida.

Muscicapidae [VERT ZOO] A family of passeriform birds assigned to the Oscines; includes the Old World flycatchers or fantails.

Muscidae [INV ZOO] A family of myodarian cyclorrhaphous dipteran insects in the subsection Calypteratae; includes the houseflies, stable flies, and allies.

muscle [ANAT] A contractile organ composed of muscle tissue that changes in length and effects movement when stimulated. [HISTOL] A tissue composed of cells containing contractile fibers; three types are smooth, cardiac, and skeletal.

muscle fiber [HISTOL] The contractile cell or unit of which muscle is composed.

muscle hemoglobin See myoglobin.

muscularis externa [HISTOL] The layer of the digestive tube consisting of smooth muscles.

muscularis mucosae [HISTOL] Thin, deep layer of smooth muscle in some mucous membranes, as in the digestive tract.

muscular system [ANAT] The muscle cells, tissues, and organs that effect movement in all vertebrates.

muscul-, musculo- [ZOO] A combining form denoting muscle, muscular.

musculoaponeurotic [HISTOL] Composed of muscle and of fibrous connective tissue in the form of a membrane.

musculocutaneous [ANAT] Of or pertaining to muscles and skin.

musculocutaneous nerve [ANAT] A branch of the brachial plexus with both motor and somatic sensory components; innervates flexor muscles of the upper arm, and skin of the lateral aspect of the forearm.

musculoskeletal system [ANAT] The muscular and skeletal elements of vertebrates, considered as a functional unit.

mushroom [MYCOL] 1. A fungus belonging to the basidiomycetous order Agaricales. 2. The fruiting body (basidiocarp) of such a fungus.

Musidoridae [INV ZOO] A family of orthorrhaphous dipteran insects in the series Brachycera distinguished by spear-shaped wings.

musk [PHYSIO] Any of various strong-smelling substances obtained from the musk glands of musk deer or similar animals; used in the form of a tincture as a fixative for perfume.

musk bag *See* musk gland.

muskeg [ECOL] A peat bog or tussock meadow, with variably woody vegetation.

musk gland [VERT ZOO] A large preputial scent gland of the musk deer and various other animals, including skunk and musk-ox. Also known as musk bag.

muskmelon [BOT] *Cucumis melo.* The edible, fleshy, globular to long-tapered fruit of a trailing annual plant of the order Violales; surface is uniform to broadly sutured to wrinkled, and smooth to heavily netted, and flesh is pale green to orange; varieties include cantaloupe, Honey Dew, Casaba, and Persian melons.

musk-ox [VERT ZOO] *Ovibos moschatus.* An eventoed ungulate which is a member of the mammalian family Bovidae; a heavy-set animal with a shag pilage, splayed feet, and flattened horns set low on the head.

muskrat [VERT ZOO] *Ondatra zibethica.* The largest member of the rodent subfamily Microtinae; essentially a water rat with a laterally flattened, long, naked tail, a broad blunt head with short ears, and short limbs.

Musophagidae [VERT ZOO] The turacos, an African family of birds of uncertain affinities usually included in the order Cuculiformes; resemble the cuckoos anatomically but have two unique pigments, turacin and turacoverdin.

mustard [BOT] Any of several annual crucifers belonging to the genus *Brassica* of the order Capparales; leaves are lyrately lobed, flowers are yellow, and pods have linear beaks; the mustards are cultivated for their pungent seed and edible foliage, and the seeds of *B. niger* are used as a condiment, prepared as a powder, paste, or oil.

Mustilidae [VERT ZOO] A large, diverse family of low-slung, long-bodied carnivorous mammals including minks, weasels, and badgers; distinguished by having only one molar in each upper jaw, and two at the most in the lower jaw.

mutagen [GEN] An agent that raises the frequency of mutation above the spontaneous rate.

mutant [GEN] An individual bearing an allele that has undergone mutation and is expressed in the phenotype.

mutase [BIOCHEM] An enzyme able to catalyze a dismutation or a molecular rearrangement.

mutation [GEN] An abrupt change in the genotype of an organism, not resulting from recombination; genetic material may undergo qualitative or quantitative alteration, or rearrangement.

Mutillidae [INV ZOO] The velvet ants, a family of hymenopteran insects in the superfamily Scolioidea.

muton [MOL BIO] The smallest unit of genetic material capable of undergoing mutation.

mutualism [ECOL] Mutual interactions between two species that are beneficial to both species.

muzzle [VERT ZOO] The snout of an animal, as a dog or horse.

Mycelia Sterilia [MYCOL] An order of fungi of the class Fungi Imperfecti distinguished by the lack of spores; certain members are plant pathogens.

mycelium [BIOL] A mass of filaments, or hyphae, composing the vegetative body of many fungi and some bacteria.

Mycetaeidae [INV ZOO] The equivalent name for Endomychidae.

mycetocyte [INV ZOO] 1. One of the cells clustered together to form a mycetome. 2. An individual cell functioning like a mycetome.

mycetome [INV ZOO] One of the specialized structures in the body of certain insects for holding endosymbionts.

Mycetophagidae [INV ZOO] The hairy fungus beetles, a cosmopolitan family of coleopteran insects in the superfamily Cucujoidea.

Mycetozoa [BIOL] A zoological designation for organisms that exhibit both plant and animal characters during their life history (Myxomycetes); equivalent to the botanical Myxomycophyta.

Mycetozoia [INV ZOO] A subclass of the protozoan class Rhizopodea.

Mycobacteriaceae [MICROBIO] A family of bacteria in the order Actinomycetales; acid-fast, aerobic rods form a filamentous or myceliumlike growth.

Mycobacterium [MICROBIO] The single genus of the family Mycobacteriaceae; species cause tuberculosis, leprosy, and other chronic granulomas.

Mycobacterium leprae [MICROBIO] Bacterium that causes leprosy. Also known as Hansen's bacillus.

Mycobacterium tuberculosis [MICROBIO] Bacterium that causes tuberculosis; a slow-growing, drug-sensitive species. Also known as tubercle bacillus.

mycobactin [BIOCHEM] Any compound produced by some strains, and required for growth by other strains, of *Mycobacteria.*

mycology [BOT] The branch of botany that deals with the study of fungi.

mycomycin [MICROBIO] $C_{13}H_{10}O_2$ An antibiotic produced by *Nocardia acidophilus* and a species of *Actinomyces*; characterized as a highly unsaturated aliphatic acid that shows strong activity against *Mycobacterium tuberculosis.*

mycophagous [ZOO] Feeding on fungi.

Mycophiformes [VERT ZOO] An equivalent name for Salmoniformes.

Mycoplasma [MICROBIO] The single genus of the family Mycoplasmataceae.

Mycoplasma pneumoniae [MICROBIO] A bacterial agent of pneumonia; formerly it was thought to be a virus and was known as Eaton agent.

Mycoplasmataceae [MICROBIO] A family of the order Mycoplasmatales; distinguished by sterol requirement for growth.

Mycoplasmatales [MICROBIO] The single order of the class Mollicutes; organisms are gram-negative, generally nonmotile, nonsporing bacteria which lack a true cell wall.

mycorrhiza [BOT] A mutual association in which the mycelium of a fungus invades the roots of a seed plant.

Mycota [MYCOL] An equivalent name for Eumycetes.

Myctophidae [VERT ZOO] The lantern fishes, a family of deep-sea forms of the suborder Myctophoidei.

Myctophoidei [VERT ZOO] A large suborder of marine salmoniform fishes characterized by having the upper jaw bordered only by premaxillae, and lacking a mesocoracoid arch in the pectoral girdle.

Mydaidae [INV ZOO] The mydas flies, a family of orthorrhaphous dipteran insects in the series Brachycera.

myelencephalon [EMBRYO] The caudal portion of the hindbrain; gives rise to the medulla oblongata.

myelin [BIOCHEM] A soft, white fatty substance that forms a sheath around certain nerve fibers.

myelin sheath [HISTOL] An investing cover of myelin around the axis cylinder of certain nerve fibers.

myel-, myelo- [ANAT] A combining form for bone marrow, spinal cord.

myeloblast [HISTOL] The youngest precursor cell for blood granulocytes, having a nucleus with finely granular chromatin and nucleoli and intensely basophilic cytoplasm.

myeloblastic [HISTOL] Of, pertaining to, or characterized by the presence of myeloblasts.

myelocele [ANAT] The canal of the spinal cord.

myelocyte [HISTOL] A motile precursor cell of blood granulocytes found in bone marrow.

myeloid [ANAT] 1. Of or pertaining to bone marrow. 2. Of or pertaining to the spinal cord.

myeloid tissue [HISTOL] Red bone marrow attached to argyrophile fibers which form wide meshes containing scattered fat cells, erythroblasts, myelocytes, and mature myeloid elements.

myelomonocyte [HISTOL] 1. A monocyte developing in bone marrow. 2. A blood cell intermediate between monocytes and granulocytes.

myelopoiesis [PHYSIO] The process by which blood cells form in the bone marrow.

myenteric [HISTOL] Of or pertaining to the muscular coat of the intestine.

myenteric plexus [ANAT] A network of nerves between the circular and longitudinal layers of the muscular coat of the digestive tract. Also known as Auerbach's plexus.

myenteron [HISTOL] The muscular coat of the intestine.

Mygalomorphae [INV ZOO] A suborder of spiders (Araneida) including American tarantulas, trapdoor spiders, and purse-web spiders; the tarantulas may attain a leg span of 10 inches (25 centimeters).

Mylabridae [INV ZOO] The equivalent name for Bruchidae.

Myliobatidae [VERT ZOO] The eagle rays, a family of batoids which may reach a length of 15 feet (4.6 meters).

Mymaridae [INV ZOO] The fairy flies, a family of hymenopteran insects in the superfamily Chalcidoidea.

myoblast [EMBRYO] A precursor cell of a muscle fiber.

myocardium [HISTOL] The muscular tissue of the heart wall.

myocoel [EMBRYO] Portion of the coelom enclosed in a myotome.

myocomma [HISTOL] A ligamentous connection between successive myomeres. Also known as myoseptum.

myocyte [HISTOL] 1. A contractile cell. 2. A muscle cell.

Myodaria [INV ZOO] A section of the Schizophora series of cyclorrhaphous dipterans; in this group adult antennae consist of three segments, and all families except the Conopidae have the second cubitus and the second anal veins united for almost their entire length.

Myodocopa [INV ZOO] A suborder of the order Myodocopida; includes exclusively marine ostracods distinguished by possession of a heart.

Myodocopida [INV ZOO] An order of the subclass Ostracoda.

Myodopina [INV ZOO] The equivalent name for Myodocopa.

myoelastic fiber [HISTOL] An elastic fiber associated with the smooth muscles in bronchi and bronchioles.

myoelectric potential [PHYSIO] The electrical potential created by muscle action.

myofibril [CELL BIO] A contractile fibril in a muscle cell. [INV ZOO] *See* myoneme.

myofilament [CELL BIO] The structural unit of muscle proteins in a muscle cell.

myofrisk [INV ZOO] A contractile structure surrounding the spines of certain radiolarians.

myoglobin [BIOCHEM] A hemoglobinlike iron-containing protein pigment occurring in muscle fibers. Also known as muscle hemoglobin; myohemoglobin.

myohematin [BIOCHEM] A cytochrome respiratory enzyme allied to hematin.

myohemoglobin *See* myoglobin.

myoinositol [BIOCHEM] The commonest isomer of inositol. Also known as mesionositol.

myokinase [BIOCHEM] An enzyme that catalyzes the reversible transfer of phosphate groups in adenosinediphosphate; occurs in muscle and other tissues.

myomere [EMBRYO] A muscle segment differentiated from the myotome, which divides to form the epimere and hypomere.

myometrium [HISTOL] The muscular tissue of the uterus.

Myomorpha [VERT ZOO] A suborder of rodents recognized in some systems of classification.

myoneme [INV ZOO] A contractile fibril in a protozoan. Also known as myofibril.

myoneural junction [ANAT] The point of junction of a motor nerve with the muscle which it innervates. Also known as neuromuscular junction.

Myopsida [INV ZOO] A natural assemblage of cephalopod mollusks considered as a suborder in the order Teuthoida according to some systems of classification, and a group of the Decapoda according to other systems; the eye is covered by the skin of the head in all species.

myosin [BIOCHEM] A muscle protein, comprising up to 50% of the total muscle proteins; combines with actin to form actomycin.

myostatic reflex See stretch reflex.

myotasis [PHYSIO] Stretching of a muscle.

myotome [ANAT] A group of muscles innervated by a single spinal nerve.

myotome [EMBRYO] The muscle plate that differentiates into myomeres.

Myriangiales [MYCOL] An order of parasitic fungi of the class Ascomycetes which produce asci at various levels in uniascal locules within stromata.

Myriapoda [INV ZOO] Informal designation for those mandibulate arthropods having two body tagmata, one pair of antennae, and more than three pairs of adult ambulatory appendages.

Myricaceae [BOT] The single family of the plant order Myricales.

Myricales [BOT] An order of dicotyledonous plants in the subclass Hamamelidae, marked by its simple, resinous-dotted, aromatic leaves, and a unilocular ovary with two styles and a single ovule.

Myrientomata [INV ZOO] The equivalent name for the Protura.

Myriotrochidae [INV ZOO] A family of holothurian echinoderms in the order Apodida, distinguished by eight or more spokes in each wheel-shaped spicule.

Myrmecophagidae [VERT ZOO] A small family of arboreal anteaters in the order Edentata.

myrmecophagous [ZOO] Feeding on ants.

myrmecophile [ECOL] An organism, usually a beetle, that habitually inhabits the nest of ants.

myrmecophyte [ECOL] A plant that houses and benefits from the habitation of ants.

Myrmeleontidae [INV ZOO] The ant lions, a family of insects in the order Neuroptera; larvae are commonly known as doodlebugs.

Myrmicinae [INV ZOO] A large diverse subfamily of ants (Formicidae); some members are inquilines and have no worker caste.

Myrsinaceae [BOT] A family of mostly woody dicotyledonous plants in the order Primulales characterized by flowers without staminodes, a schizogenous secretory system, and gland-dotted leaves.

Myrtaceae [BOT] A family of dicotyledonous plants in the order Myrtales characterized by an inferior ovary, numerous stamens, anthers usually opening by slits, and fruit in the form of a berry, drupe, or capsule.

Myrtales [BOT] An order of dicotyledonous plants in the subclass Rosidae characterized by opposite, simple, entire leaves and perigynous to epigynous flowers with a compound pistil.

Mysida [INV ZOO] A suborder of the crustacean order Mysidacea characterized by fusion of the sixth and seventh abdominal somites in the adult, lack of gills, and other specializations.

Mysidacea [INV ZOO] An order of free-swimming Crustacea included in the division Pericarida; adult consists of 19 somites, each bearing one pair of functionally modified, biramous appendages, and the carapace envelops most of the thorax and is fused dorsally with up to four of the anterior thoracic segments.

mysis [INV ZOO] A larva of certain higher crustaceans, characterized by biramous thoracic appendages.

Mystacinidae [VERT ZOO] A monospecific family of insectivorous bats (Chiroptera) containing the New Zealand short-tailed bat; hindlegs and body are stout, and fur is thick.

Mystacocarida [INV ZOO] An order of primitive Crustacea; the body is wormlike and the cephalothorax bears first and second antennae, mandibles, and first and second maxillae.

Mysticeti [VERT ZOO] The whalebone whales, a suborder of the mammalian order Cetacea, distinguished by horny filter plates of suspended from the upper jaws.

Mytilacea [INV ZOO] A suborder of bivalve mollusks in the order Filibranchia.

Mytilidae [INV ZOO] A family of mussels in the bivalve order Anisomyaria.

myxameba [BIOL] An independent ameboid cell of the vegetative phase of Acrasiales.

Myxicolinae [INV ZOO] A subfamily of sedentary polychaete annelids in the family Sabellidae.

Myxiniformes [VERT ZOO] The equivalent name for the Myxinoidea.

Myxinoidea [VERT ZOO] The hagfishes, an order of eellike, jawless vertebrates (Agnatha) distinguished by having the nasal opening at the tip of the snout and leading to the pharynx, with barbels around the mouth and 6–15 pairs of gill pouches.

myx-, myxo- [ZOO] A combining form denoting mucus, mucous, much, mucinous.

Myxobacterales [MICROBIO] An order of gliding bacteria; unicellular, gram-negative rods embedded in a layer of slime and capable of gliding movement; form fruiting bodies containing resting cells (myxospores) under certain environmental conditions.

Myxococcaceae [MICROBIO] A family of the order Myxobacterales; vegetative cells are straight to slightly tapered, and spherical to ovoid microcysts (myxospores) are produced.

Myxococcus [MICROBIO] The single genus of the family Myxococcaceae; vegetative cells have tapered or slightly rounded ends, and myxospores are not enclosed in a sporangium.

Myxogastromycetidae [MYCOL] A large subclass of plasmodial slime molds (Myxomycetes).

Myxomycetes [BIOL] Plasmodial (acellular or true) slime molds, a class of microorganisms of the division Mycota; they are on the borderline of the plant and animal kingdoms and have a noncellular, multinucleate, jellylike, creeping, assimilative stage (the plasmodium) which alternates with a myxameba stage.

Myxomycophyta [BOT] An order of microorganisms, equivalent to the Mycetozoia of zoological classification.

Myxophaga [INV ZOO] A suborder of the Coleoptera.

Myxophyceae [BOT] An equivalent name for the Cyanophyceae.

Myxosporida [INV ZOO] An order of the protozoan class Myxosporidea characterized by the production of spores with one or more valves and polar capsules, and by possession of a single sporoplasm.

Myxosporidea [INV ZOO] A class of the protozoan subphylum Cnidospora; members are parasitic in some fish, a few amphibians, and certain invertebrates.

myxovirus [VIROL] A group of ribonucleic-acid animal viruses characterized by hemagglutination and hemadsorption; includes influenza and fowl plague viruses and the paramyxoviruses.

Myzopodidae [VERT ZOO] A monospecific order of insectivorous bats (Chiroptera) containing the Old World disk-winged bat of Madagascar; characterized by long ears and by a vestigial thumb with a monostalked sucking disk.

myzorhynchus [INV ZOO] An apical sucker on the scolex of certain tapeworms.

Myzostomaria [INV ZOO] An aberrant group of Polychaeta; most are greatly depressed, broad, and very small; true segmentation delayed or absent in adult; parasites of echinoderms.

Myzostomidae [INV ZOO] A monogeneric family of the Myzostomaria.

N

Nabidae [INV ZOO] The damsel bugs, a family of hemipteran insects in the superfamily Cimicimorpha.

Nabothian glands [ANAT] Mucous glands of the uterine cervix.

nacre [INV ZOO] An iridescent inner layer of many mollusk shells.

nail [ANAT] The horny epidermal derivative covering the dorsal aspect of the terminal phalanx of each finger and toe.

nailhead spot [PL PATH] A fungus rot of tomato caused by *Alternaria tomato* and marked by small brown to black sunken spots on the fruit.

nail-patella syndrome [GEN] A genetic disorder inherited as an autosomal dominant that is part of a linkage group with ABO blood group genes; characterized by defects in the nails and abnormalities of the elbows and other bones, skin, eyes, and kidneys.

Najadaceae [BOT] A family of monocotyledonous, submerged aquatic plants in the order Najadales distinguished by branching stems and opposite or whorled leaves.

Najadales [BOT] An order of aquatic and semiaquatic flowering plants in the subclass Alismatidae; the perianth, when present, is not differentiated into sepals and petals, and the flowers are usually not individually subtended by bracts.

naked bud [BOT] A bud covered only by rudimentary foliage leaves.

Namanereinae [INV ZOO] A subfamily of largely fresh-water errantian annelids in the family Nereidae.

Nannocystis [MICROBIO] A genus of bacteria in the family Polyangiaceae; sporangia are sessile and solitary, and vegetative cells are short rods or spheres.

nannoplankton [BIOL] Minute plankton; the smallest plankton, including algae, bacteria, and protozoans.

nano- [BIOL] A prefix meaning dwarfed.

nanophanerophyte [ECOL] A shrub not exceeding 2 meters in height.

nanozooid [INV ZOO] Dwarf zooid; bryozoan heterozooid possessing only a single tentacle.

nape [ANAT] The back of the neck.

napex [ANAT] That portion of the scalp just below the occipital protuberance.

napiform [BOT] Turnip-shaped, referring to roots.

naramycin A *See* cycloheximide.

Narcomedusae [INV ZOO] A suborder of hydrozoan coelenterates in the order Trachylina; the hydroid generation is represented by an actinula larva.

naris *See* nostril.

narrow-spectrum antibiotic [MICROBIO] An antibiotic effective against a limited number of microorganisms.

narwhal [VERT ZOO] *Monodon monoceros*. An arctic whale characterized by lack of a dorsal fin, and by possession in the male of a long, twisted, pointed tusk (or rarely, two tusks) which is a source of ivory.

nasal [ANAT] Of or pertaining to the nose.

nasal bone [ANAT] Either of two rectangular bone plates forming the bridge of the nose; they articulate with the frontal, ethmoid, and maxilla bones.

nasal cavity [ANAT] Either of a pair of cavities separated by a septum and located between the nasopharynx and anterior nares.

nasal crest [ANAT] 1. The linear prominence on the medial border of the palatal process of the maxilla. 2. The linear prominence on the medial border of the palatine bone. 3. The linear prominence on the internal border of the nasal bone and forming part of the nasal septum.

nasal process of the frontal bone [ANAT] The downward projection of the nasal part of the frontal bone which terminates as the nasal spine.

nasal process of the maxilla [ANAT] Frontal process of the maxilla.

nasal septum [ANAT] The partition separating the two nasal cavities.

Nasellina [INV ZOO] The equivalent name for Monopylina.

nasolacrimal canal [ANAT] The bony canal that lodges the nasolacrimal duct. Also known as lacrimal canal.

nasolacrimal duct [ANAT] The membranous duct lodged within the nasolacrimal canal; it gives passage to the tears from the lacrimal sac to the inferior meatus of the nose.

nasolacrimal groove [EMBRYO] The furrow, the maxillary, and the lateral nasal processes of the embryo.

nasopalatine duct [EMBRYO] A canal between the oral and nasal cavities of the embryo at the point of fusion of the maxillary and palatine processes.

nasopharynx [ANAT] The space behind the posterior nasal orifices, above a horizontal plane through the lower margin of the palate.

nastic movement [BOT] Movement of a flat plant part, oriented relative to the plant body and produced by diffuse stimuli causing disproportionate growth or increased turgor pressure in the tissues of one surface.

Nasutitermitinae [INV ZOO] A subfamily of termites in the family Termitidae, characterized by having the cephalic glands open at the tip of an elongated tube which projects anteriorly.

Natalidae [VERT ZOO] The funnel-eared bats, a monogeneric family of small, tropical American insectivorous bats (Chiroptera) with large, funnellike ears.

Natantia [INV ZOO] A suborder of decapod crustaceans comprising shrimp and related forms characterized by a long rostrum and a ventrally flexed abdomen.

Naticacea [INV ZOO] A superfamily of gastropod mollusks in the order Prosobranchia.

Naticidae [INV ZOO] A family of gastropod mollusks in the order Pectinibranchia comprising the moon-shell snails.

native [BIOL] Grown, produced or originating in a specific region or country.

naturalized [ECOL] Of a species, having become permanently established after being introduced.

natural selection [EVOL] Darwin's theory of evolution, according to which organisms tend to produce progeny far above the means of subsistence; in the struggle for existence that ensues, only those progeny with favorable variations survive; the favorable variations accumulate through subsequent generations, and descendants diverge from their ancestors.

Naucoridae [INV ZOO] A family of hemipteran insects in the superfamily Naucoroidea.

Naucoroidea [INV ZOO] The creeping water bugs, a superfamily of hemipteran insects in the subdivision Hydrocorisae; they are suboval in form, with chelate front legs.

Naumanniella [MICROBIO] A genus of bacteria in the family Siderocapsaceae; rod-shaped cells surrounded by a delicate sheath in which iron and manganese oxides are deposited.

nauplius [INV ZOO] A larval stage characteristic of many groups of Crustacea; the oval, unsegmented body has three pairs of appendages: uniramous antennules, biramous antennae, and mandibles.

Nautilidae [INV ZOO] A monogeneric family of cephalopod mollusks in the order Nautiloidea; *Nautilus pompilius* is the only well-known living species.

Nautiloidea [INV ZOO] A primitive order of tetrabranchiate cephalopods; shells are external and smooth, being straight or coiled and chambered with curved transverse septa.

Navarroan [PALEON] A North American (Gulf Coast) stage of Upper Cretaceous geologic time, above the Tayloran and below the Midwayan of the Tertiary.

navel [ANAT] The umbilicus.

navicular [ANAT] A boat-shaped bone, especially the lateral bone on the radial side of the proximal row of the carpus. [BIOL] Resembling or having the shape of a boat.

neallotype [SYST] A type specimen that, compared with the holotype, is of the opposite sex, and was collected and described later.

Neanderthal man [PALEON] A type of fossil human that is a subspecies of *Homo sapiens* and is distinguished by a low broad braincase, continuous arched browridges, projecting occipital region, short limbs, and large joints.

Nearctic fauna [ECOL] The indigenous animal communities of the Nearctic zoogeographic region.

Nearctic zoogeographic region [ECOL] The zoogeographic region that includes all of North America to the edge of the Mexican Plateau.

near point [PHYSIO] The smallest distance from the eye at which a small object can be seen without blurring.

near wilt [PL PATH] A fungus disease of peas caused by *Fusarium oxysporum pisi;* affects scattered plants and develops more slowly than true wilt.

Nebaliacea [INV ZOO] A small, marine order of Crustacea in the subclass Leptostraca distinguished by a large bivalve shell, without a definite hinge line, an anterior articulated rostrum, eight thoracic and seven abdominal somites, a pair of articulated furcal rami, and the telson.

neck [ANAT] The usually constricted communicating column between the head and trunk of the vertebrate body.

Neckeraceae [BOT] A family of mosses in the order Isobryales distinguished by undulate leaves.

neck rot [PL PATH] A fungus disease of onions caused by species of *Botrytis* and characterized by rotting of the leaves just above the bulb.

Necrolestidae [PALEON] An extinct family of insectivorous marsupials.

necrophagous [ZOO] Feeding on dead bodies.

necrotic ring spot [PL PATH] A virus leaf spot of cherries marked by small, dark water-soaked rings which may drop out, giving the leaf a tattered appearance.

nectar [BOT] A sugar-containing liquid secretion of the nectaries of many flowers.

nectarine [BOT] A smooth-skinned, fuzzless fruit originating as a spontaneous somatic mutation of the peach, *Prunus persica* and *P. persica* var. *nectarina*.

nectary [BOT] A secretory organ or surface modification of a floral organ in many flowers, occurring on the receptacle, in and around ovaries, on stamens, or on the perianth; secretes nectar.

nectocalyx [INV ZOO] A swimming bell of a siphonophore. Also known as nectophore.

Nectonematoidea [INV ZOO] A monogeneric order of worms belonging to the class Nematomorpha, characterized by dorsal and ventral epidermal chords, a pseudocoele, and dorsal and ventral rows of bristles; adults are parasites of true crabs and hermit crabs.

nectophore *See* nectocalyx.

nectosome [INV ZOO] The part of a complex siphonophore that bears swimming bells.

Nectridea [PALEON] An order of extinct lepospondylous amphibians characterized by vertebrae in which large fan-shaped hemal arches grow directly downward from the middle of each caudal centrum.

Nectrioidaceae [MYCOL] The equivalent name for Zythiaceae.

Necturus [VERT ZOO] A genus of mud puppies in the family Proteidae.

needle [BOT] A slender-pointed leaf, as of the firs and other evergreens.

neencephalon [ANAT] The neopallium and the phylogenetically new acquisitions of the cerebellum and thalamus collectively. Also spelled neoencephalon.

negative afterimage [PHYSIO] An afterimage that is seen on a bright background and is complementary in color to the initial stimulus.

negative interference [GEN] A crossover exchange between homologous chromosomes which increases the likelihood of another in the same vicinity.

negative staining [BIOL] A method in microscopy for demonstrating the form of cells, bacteria, and other small objects by staining the ground rather than the objects.

Neididae [INV ZOO] A small family of threadlegged hemipteran insects in the superfamily Lygaeoidea.

Neisseria [MICROBIO] A genus of bacteria in the family Neisseriaceae; aerobic or facultatively anaerobic cocci occurring singly or in pairs with flattened adjacent sides.

Neisseriaceae [MICROBIO] The single family of gram-negative aerobic cocci and coccobacilli; some species are human parasites and pathogens.

Neisseria flavescens [MICROBIO] A bacterial species marked by greenish-yellow chromogenesis and found within the respiratory tract and in the spinal fluid in certain cases of meningitis.

Neisseria gonorrhoeae [MICROBIO] The bacterial organism that causes gonorrhea; the type species of the genus. Also known as gonococcus.

Neisseria intracellularis *See* Neisseria meningitidis.

Neisseria meningitidis [MICROBIO] The bacterial species that causes epidemic cerebrospinal meningitis. Also known as *Micrococcus meningitidis; Neisseria intracellularis*.

nektobenthos [ECOL] Those forms of marine life that exist just above the ocean bottom and occasionally rest on it.

nekton [INV ZOO] Free-swimming aquatic animals, essentially independent of water movements.

Nelumbonaceae [BOT] A family of flowering aquatic herbs in the order Nymphaeales characterized by having roots, perfect flowers, alternate leaves, and triaperturate pollen.

Nemata [INV ZOO] A proposed equivalent name for Nematoda.

Nemataceae [BOT] A family of mosses in the order Hookeriales distinguished by having perichaetial leaves only.

Nemathelminthes [INV ZOO] A subdivision of the Amera which comprised the classes Rotatoria, Gastrotrichia, Kinorhyncha, Nematoda, Nematomorpha, and Acanthocephala.

Nematocera [INV ZOO] A series of dipteran insects in the suborder Orthorrhapha; adults have antennae that are usually longer than the head, and the flagellum consists of 10–65 similar segments.

nematocyst [INV ZOO] An intracellular effector organelle in the form of a coiled tube which may be rapidly everted in food gathering or defense by coelenterates.

Nematoda [INV ZOO] A group of unsegmented worms which have been variously recognized as an order, class, and phylum.

nematode [INV ZOO] 1. Any member of the Nematoda. 2. Of or pertaining to the Nematoda.

Nematodonteae [BOT] A group of mosses included in the subclass Eubrya in which there may be faint transverse bars on the peristome teeth.

nematogen [INV ZOO] A reproductive phase of the Dicyemida during which vermiform larvae are formed asexually from the germ cells in the axial cells.

Nematognathi [VERT ZOO] The equivalent name for Siluriformes.

Nematoidea [INV ZOO] An equivalent name for Nematoda.

nematology [INV ZOO] The study of nematodes.

Nematomorpha [INV ZOO] A group of the Aschelminthes or a separate phylum that includes the horsehair worms.

Nematophytales [PALEOBOT] A group of fossil plants from the Silurian and Devonian periods that bear some resemblance to the brown seaweeds (Phaeophyta).

Nematosporoideae [BOT] A subfamily of the Saccharomycetaceae containing parasitic yeasts; two genera have been studied in culture: *Nematospora* with asci that contain eight spindle-shaped ascospores, and *Metschnikowia* whose asci contain one or two needle-shaped ascospores.

nematozooid [INV ZOO] A zooid bearing organs of defense, in hydroids and siphonophores.

Nemertea [INV ZOO] An equivalent name for Rhynchocoela.

Nemertina [INV ZOO] An equivalent name for Rhynchocoela.

Nemertinea [INV ZOO] An equivalent name for Rhynchocoela.

Nemestrinidae [INV ZOO] The hairy flies, a family of dipteran insects in the series Brachycera of the suborder Orthorrhapha.

Nemichthyidae [VERT ZOO] A family of bathypelagic, eellike amphibians in the order Apoda.

Nemognathinae [INV ZOO] A subfamily of the coleopteran family Meloidae; members have greatly elongate maxillae that form a poorly fitted tube.

nemoral [ECOL] Pertaining to or inhabiting a grove or wooded area.

Neoanthropinae [PALEON] A subfamily of the Hominidae in some systems of classification, set up to include *Homo sapiens* and direct ancestors of *H. sapiens.*

neoblast [INV ZOO] Any of various undifferentiated cells in annelids which migrate to and proliferate at sites of repair and regeneration.

Neocathartidae [PALEON] An extinct family of vulturelike diurnal birds of prey (Falconiformes) from the Upper Eocene.

neocerebellum [ANAT] Phylogenetically, the most recent part of the cerebellum; receives cerebral cortex impulses via the corticopontocerebellar tract.

neocortex [ANAT] Phylogenetically the most recent part of the cerebral cortex; includes all but the olfactory, hippocampal, and piriform regions of the cortex.

neoencephalon *See* neencephalon.

Neogastropoda [INV ZOO] An order of gastropods which contains the most highly developed snails; respiration is by means of ctenidia, the nervous system is concentrated, an operculum is present, and the sexes are separate.

Neognathae [VERT ZOO] A superorder of the avian order Neornithes, characterized as flying birds with fully developed wings and sternum with a keel, fused caudal vertebrae, and absence of teeth.

Neogregarinida [INV ZOO] An order of sporozoan protozoans in the subclass Gregarinia which are insect parasites.

neomycin [MICROBIO] The collective name for several colorless antibiotics produced by a strain of *Streptomyces fradiae;* the commercial fraction $(C_{23}H_{46}N_6O_{13})$ has a broad spectrum of activity.

neonatal line [ANAT] A prominent incremental line formed in the neonatal period in the enamel and dentin of a deciduous tooth or of a first permanent molar.

neopallium [ANAT] Phylogenetically, the new part of the cerebral cortex; formed from the region between the pyriform lobe and the hippocampus, it comprises the nonolfactory region.

neopalynology [BOT] A field of palynology concerned with extant microorganisms and disassociated microscopic parts of megaorganisms.

Neopseustidae [INV ZOO] A family of Lepidoptera in the superfamily Eriocranioidea.

Neoptera [INV ZOO] A section of the insect subclass Pterygota; members have a muscular and articular mechanism allowing the wings to be flexed over the abdomen when at rest.

Neopterygii [VERT ZOO] An equivalent name for Actinopterygii.

Neorhabdocoela [INV ZOO] A group of the Rhabdocoela comprising fresh-water, marine, or terrestrial forms, with a bulbous pharynx, paired protonephridia, sexual reproduction, and ventral gonopores.

Neorickettsia [MICROBIO] A genus of the tribe Ehrlichieae; coccoid or pleomorphic cells; intracellular parasites in cytoplasm of reticular cells of lymphoid tissue of the Canidae.

Neornithes [VERT ZOO] A subclass of the class Aves containing all known birds except the fossil *Archaeopteryx.*

neossoptile [VERT ZOO] A downy feather on most newly hatched birds.

neotenin [BIOCHEM] A hormone secreted by cells of the corpus allatum in arthropod larvae and nymphs; inhibits the development of adult characters. Also known as juvenile hormone.

neoteny [VERT ZOO] A phenomenon peculiar to some salamanders, in which large larvae become sexually mature while still retaining gills and other larval features.

Neotropical zoogeographic region [ECOL] A zoogeographic region that includes Mexico south of the Mexican Plateau, the West Indies, Central America, and South America.

neotype [SYST] A specimen selected as type subsequent to the original description when the primary types are known to be destroyed; a nomenclatural type.

neounitarian theory of hematopoiesis [HISTOL] A theory that under certain conditions, such as in tissue culture or in pathologic states, lymphocytes or cells resembling lymphocytes can become multipotent.

Nepenthaceae [BOT] A family of dicotyledonous plants in the order Sarraceniales; includes many of the pitcher plants.

nephric tubule *See* uriniferous tubule.

nephridioblast [INV ZOO] An ecodermal precursor cell of a nephridium in certain animals.

nephridioduct [INV ZOO] The duct of a nephridium, sometimes serving as a common excretory and genital outlet.

nephridiopore [INV ZOO] The external opening of a nephridium.

nephridium [INV ZOO] Any of various paired excretory structures present in the Platyhelminthes, Rotifera, Rhynchocoela, Acanthocephala, Priapuloidea, Entoprocta, Gastrotricha, Kinorhyncha, Cephalochorda, and some Archiannelida and Polychaeta.

nephr-, nephro- [ANAT] Combining form denoting kidney.

nephroabdominal [ANAT] Of or pertaining to the kidneys and abdomen.

nephrocoel [ANAT] The cavity of a nephrotome.

nephrogenic [EMBRYO] 1. Having the potential to develop into kidney tissue. 2. Of renal origin.

nephrogenic cord [EMBRYO] The longitudinal cordlike mass of mesenchyme derived from the mesomere or nephrostomal plate of the mesoderm, from which develop the functional parts of the pronephros, mesonephros, and metanephros.

nephrogenic tissue [EMBRYO] The tissue of the nephrogenic cord derived from the nephrotome plate that forms the blastema or primordium from which the embryonic and definitive kidneys develop.

nephrolysin [BIOCHEM] A toxic substance capable of disintegrating kidney cells.

nephromixium [INV ZOO] A compound nephridium composed of flame cells and the coelomic funnel; functions as both an excretory organ and a genital duct.

nephron [ANAT] The functional unit of a kidney, consisting of the glomerulus with its capsule and attached uriniferous tubule.

Nephropidae [INV ZOO] The true lobsters, a family of decapod crustaceans in the superfamily Nephropidea.

Nephropidea [INV ZOO] A superfamily of the decapod section Macrura including the true lobsters and crayfishes, characterized by a rostrum and by chelae on the first three pairs of pereiopods, with the first pair being noticeably larger.

nephros [ANAT] The kidney.

nephrostome [INV ZOO] The funnel-shaped opening of a nephridium into the coelom.

nephrotome [EMBRYO] The narrow mass of embryonic mesoderm connecting somites and lateral mesoderm, from which the pronephros, mesonephros, metanephros, and their ducts develop.

Nephtyidae [INV ZOO] A family of errantian annelids of highly opalescent colors, distinguished by an eversible pharynx.

Nepidae [INV ZOO] The water scorpions, a family of hemipteran insects in the superfamily Nepoidea, characterized by a long breathing tube at the tip of the abdomen, chelate front legs, and a short stout beak.

Nepoidea [INV ZOO] A superfamily of hemipteran insects in the subdivision Hydrocorisae.

Nepticulidae [INV ZOO] The single family of the lepidopteran superfamily Nepticuloidea.

Nepticuloidea [INV ZOO] A monofamilial superfamily of heteroneuran Lepidoptera; members are tiny moths with wing spines, and the females have a single genital opening.

Nereidae [INV ZOO] A large family of mostly marine errantian annelids that have a well-defined head, elongated body with many segments, and large complex parapodia on most segments.

Nerillidae [INV ZOO] A family of archiannelids characterized by well-developed parapodia and setae.

Neritacea [INV ZOO] A superfamily of gastropod mollusks in the order Aspidobranchia.

Neritidae [INV ZOO] A family of primitive marine, fresh-water, and terrestrial snails in the order Archaeogastropoda.

nerve [ANAT] A bundle of nerve fibers or processes held together by connective tissue.

nerve block [PHYSIO] Interruption of impulse transmission through a nerve.

nerve cord [INV ZOO] Paired, ventral cords of nervous tissue in certain invertebrates, such as insects or the earthworm. [ZOO] Dorsal, hollow tubular cord of nervous tissue in chordates.

nerve ending [ANAT] 1. The structure on the distal end of an axon. 2. The termination of a nerve.

nerve fiber [CELL BIO] The long process of a neuron, usually the axon.

nerve impulse [PHYSIO] The transient physicochemical change in the membrane of a nerve fiber which sweeps rapidly along the fiber to its termination, where it causes excitation of other nerves, muscle, or gland cells, depending on the connections and functions of the nerve.

nerve net [INV ZOO] A network of continuous nerve cells characterized by diffuse spread of excitation, local and equipotential autonomy, spatial attenuation of conduction, and facilitation; occurs in coelenterates and certain other invertebrates.

nerve tract [ANAT] A bundle of nerve fibers having the same general origin and destination.

nervous [BIOL] 1. Of or pertaining to nerves. 2. Originating in or affected by nerves. 3. Affecting or involving nerves.

nervous system [ANAT] A coordinating and integrating system which functions in the adaptation of an organism to its environment; in vertebrates, the system consists of the brain, brainstem, spinal cord, cranial and peripheral nerves, and ganglia.

nervous tissue [HISTOL] The nerve cells and neuroglia of the nervous system.

Nesiotinidae [INV ZOO] A family of bird-infesting biting lice (Mallophaga) that are restricted to penguins.

Nesophontidae [PALEON] An extinct family of large, shrewlike lipotyphlans from the Cenozoic found in the West Indies.

nest [VERT ZOO] A bed, receptacle, or location in which the eggs of animals are laid and hatched.

net aerial production [ECOL] The biomass or biocontent which is incorporated into the aerial parts, that is, the leaf, stem, seed, and associated organs, of a plant community.

net blotch [PL PATH] A fungus disease of barley caused by *Helminthosporium teres* and marked by spotting of the foliage.

net plankton [ECOL] Plankton that can be removed from sea water by the process of filtration through a fine net.

net primary production [ECOL] Over a specified period of time, the biomass or biocontent which is incorporated into a plant community.

net production rate [ECOL] The assimilation rate (gross production rate) minus the amount of matter lost through predation, respiration, and decomposition.

nettle [BOT] A prickly or stinging plant of the family Urticaceae, especially in the genus *Urtica*.

nettle cell *See* cnidoblast.

net-veined [BIOL] Having a network of veins, as a leaf or an insect wing.

neural arc [PHYSIO] A nerve circuit consisting of effector and receptor with intercalated neurons between them.

neural arch *See* vertebral arch.

neural canal [EMBRYO] The embryonic vertebral canal.

neural crest [EMBRYO] Ectoderm composing the primordium of the cranial, spinal, and autonomic ganglia and adrenal medulla, located on either side of the neural tube.

neural ectoderm [EMBRYO] Embryonic ectoderm which will form the neural tube and neural crest.

neural fold [EMBRYO] Either of a pair of dorsal longitudinal folds of the neural plate which unite along the midline, forming the neural tube.

neural groove [EMBRYO] A longitudinal groove between the neural folds of the vertebrate embryo before the neural tube is completed.

neural plate [EMBRYO] The thickened dorsal plate of ectoderm that differentiates into the neural tube.

neural spine [ANAT] The spinous process of a vertebra.

neural tube [EMBRYO] The embryonic tube that differentiates into brain and spinal cord.

neuraminic acid [BIOCHEM] $C_9H_{17}NO_8$ An amino acid, the aldol condensation product of pyruvic acid and N-acetyl-D-mannosamine, regarded as the parent acid of a family of widely distributed acyl derivatives known as sialic acids.

neuraminidase [MICROBIO] A bacterial enzyme that acts to split sialic acid from neuraminic acid glycosides.

neurapophysis [EMBRYO] Either of two projections on each embryonic vertebra which unite to form the neural arch.

neurenteric canal [EMBRYO] A temporary duct connecting the neural tube and primitive gut in certain vertebrate and tunicate embryos.

neurexon *See* axon.

neurilemma [HISTOL] A thin tissue covering the axon directly, or covering the myelin sheath when present, of peripheral nerve fibers.

neurine [BIOCHEM] $CH_2=CHN(CH_3)_3OH$ A very poisonous, syrupy liquid with fishy aroma; soluble in water and alcohol; a product of putrefaction of choline in brain tissue and bile, and in cadavers. Also known as trimethylvinylammonium hydroxide.

neurite *See* axon.

neuroanatomy [ANAT] The study of the anatomy of the nervous system and nerve tissue.

neurobiotaxis [EVOL] Hypothetical migration of nerve cells and ganglia toward regions of maximum stimulation during phylogenetic development.

neuroblast [EMBRYO] Embryonic, undifferentiated neuron, derived from neural plate ectoderm.

neurochemistry [BIOCHEM] Chemistry of the nervous system.

neurocirculatory [ANAT] Pertaining to both the nervous and the vascular systems.

neurocoele [ANAT] The system of cavities and ventricles in the brain and spinal cord.

neurocranium [ANAT] The portion of the cranium which forms the braincase.

neurocutaneous [ANAT] 1. Concerned with both the nerves and skin. 2. Pertaining to innervation of the skin.

neurocyte [CELL BIO] The body of a nerve cell.

Neurodontiformes [PALEON] A suborder of Conodontophoridia having a lamellar internal structure.

neuroelectricity [PHYSIO] A current or voltage generated in the nervous system.

neuroendocrine [BIOL] Pertaining to both the nervous and endocrine systems, structurally and functionally.

neuroendocrinology [BIOL] The study of the structural and functional interrelationships between the nervous and endocrine systems.

neuroepidermal [BIOL] Pertaining to both the nerves and epidermis, structurally and functionally.

neurofibril [CELL BIO] A fibril of a neuron, usually extending from the processes and traversing the cell body.

neurogenesis [EMBRYO] The formation of nerves.

neurogenic [BIOL] 1. Originating in nervous tissue. 2. Innervated by nerves.

neuroglia [HISTOL] The nonnervous, supporting elements of the nervous system.

neurohemal organ [ZOO] Any of various structures in vertebrates and some invertebrates that consist of clusters of bulbous, secretion-filled axon terminals of neurosecretory cells which function as storage-and-release centers for neurohormones.

neurohormone [BIOCHEM] A hormone produced by nervous tissue.

neurohumor [BIOCHEM] A hormonal transmitter substance, such as acetylcholine, released by nerve endings in the transmission of impulses.

neurohypophysis [ANAT] The neural portion or posterior lobe of the hypophysis.

neuromast [VERT ZOO] A lateral-line sensory organ in fishes and other lower vertebrates consisting of a cluster of receptor cells connected with nerve fibers.

neuromere [EMBRYO] An embryonic segment of the central nervous system in vertebrates.

neuromuscular [BIOL] Pertaining to both nerves and muscles, functionally and structurally.

neuromuscular junction *See* myoneural junction.

neuron [HISTOL] A nerve cell, including the cell body, axon, and dendrites.

neuron doctrine [BIOL] A doctrine that the neuron is the basic structural and functional unit of the nervous system, and that it acts upon another neuron through the synapse.

neurophysiology [PHYSIO] The study of the functions of the nervous system.

neuropil [HISTOL] Nervous tissue consisting of a fibrous network of nonmyelinated nerve fibers; gray matter with few nerve cell bodies; usually a region of synapses between axons and dendrites.

neuroplasm [CELL BIO] Protoplasm of nerve cells.

neuropodium [CELL BIO] A terminal branch of an axon.

neuropore [EMBRYO] A terminal aperture of the neural tube before complete closure at the 20–25 somite stage.

Neuroptera [INV ZOO] An order of delicate insects having endopterygote development, chewing mouthparts, and soft bodies.

neurosecretion [PHYSIO] The synthesis and release of hormones by nerve cells.

neurotoxin [BIOCHEM] A poisonous substance in snake venom that acts as a nervous system depressant by blocking neuromuscular transmission by binding acetylcholine receptors on motor end plates, or on the innervated face of an electroplax.

neurotropic [BIOL] Having an affinity for nerve tissue.

neurovascular [BIOL] Pertaining structurally and functionally to both the nervous and vascular structures.

neurulation [EMBRYO] Differentiation of nerve tissue and formation of the neural tube.

neuston [BIOL] Minute organisms that float or swim on surface water or on a surface film of water.

neutralism [ECOL] A neutral interaction between two species, that is, one having no evident effect on either species.

neutrophil [HISTOL] A large granular leukocyte with a highly variable nucleus, consisting of three to five lobes, and cytoplasmic granules which stain with neutral dyes and eosin.

neutrophilia [BIOL] Affinity for neutral dyes.

neutrophilous [BIOL] Preferring an environment free of excess acid or base.

Nevskia [MICROBIO] A genus of appendaged bacteria; rod-shaped cells produce slime-forming hyaline stalks; reproduce by binary fission.

Newcastle virus [VIROL] A ribonucleic acid hemagglutinating myxovirus responsible for Newcastle disease.

newt [VERT ZOO] Any of the small, semiaquatic salamanders of the genus *Triturus* in the family Salamandridae; all have an aquatic larval stage.

niacin *See* nicotinic acid.

niacinamide *See* nicotinamide.

niche [ECOL] The unique role or way of life of a plant or animal species.

Nicoletiidae [INV ZOO] A family of the insect order Thysanura proper.

Nicomachinae [INV ZOO] A subfamily of the limnivorous sedentary annelids in the family Maldanidae.

nicotinamide [BIOCHEM] $C_6H_6ON_2$ Crystalline basic amide of the vitamin B complex that is interconvertible with nicotinic acid in the living organism; the amide of nicotinic acid. Also known as niacinamide.

nicotinamide adenine dinucleotide *See* diphosphopyridine nucleotide.

nicotinic acid [BIOCHEM] $C_6H_5NO_2$ A component of the vitamin B complex; a white, water-soluble powder stable to heat, acid, and alkali; used for the treatment of pellagra. Also known as niacin.

nictitating membrane [VERT ZOO] A membrane of the inner angle of the eye or below the eyelid in many vertebrates, and capable of extending over the eyeball.

nidamental gland [ZOO] Any of various structures that secrete covering material for eggs or egg masses.

nidicolous [ZOO] 1. Spending a short time in the nest after hatching. 2. Sharing the nest of another species.

nidus [ZOO] A nest or breeding place.

night ape *See* bushbaby.

nigrescent [BIOL] Blackish.

Nilionidae [INV ZOO] The false ladybird beetles, a family of coleopteran insects in the superfamily Tenebrionoidea.

nipple [ANAT] The conical projection in the center of the mamma, containing the outlets of the milk ducts.

Nippotaeniidea [INV ZOO] An order of tapeworms of the subclass Cestoda including some internal parasites of certain fresh-water fishes; the head bears a single terminal sucker.

Nissl bodies [CELL BIO] Chromophil granules of nerve cells which ultrastructurally are composed of large ribosomes.

Nitelleae [BOT] A tribe of stoneworts, order Charales, characterized by 10 cells in two tiers of five each composing the apical crown.

Nitidulidae [INV ZOO] The sap-feeding beetles, a large family of coleopteran insects in the superfamily Cucujoidea; individuals have five-jointed tarsi and antennae with a terminal three-jointed clavate expansion.

nitrification [MICROBIO] Formation of nitrous and nitric acids or salts by oxidation of the nitrogen in ammonia; specifically, oxidation of ammonium salts to nitrites and oxidation of nitrites to nitrates by certain bacteria.

nitrifying bacteria [MICROBIO] Members of the family Nitrobacteraceae.

Nitrobacter [MICROBIO] A genus of short, rod-shaped (often wedge- or pear-shaped) bacteria in the family Nitrobacteraceae; cells oxidize nitrites to nitrates.

Nitrobacteraceae [MICROBIO] The nitrifying bacteria, a family of gram-negative, chemolithotrophic bacteria; autotrophs which derive energy from nitrification of ammonia or nitrite, and obtain carbon for growth by fixation of carbon dioxide.

Nitrococcus [MICROBIO] A genus of bacteria in the family Nitrobacteraceae; spherical cells which oxidize nitrite to nitrate.

nitrogenase [BIOCHEM] An enzyme that catalyzes a six-electron reduction of N_2 in the process of nitrogen fixation.

nitrogen balance [PHYSIO] The difference between nitrogen intake (as protein) and total nitrogen excretion for an individual.

nitrogen fixation [MICROBIO] Assimilation of atmospheric nitrogen by heterotrophic bacteria. Also known as dinitrogen fixation.

nitrophyte [BOT] A plant that requires nitrogen-rich soil for growth.

Nitrosococcus [MICROBIO] A genus of bacteria in the family Nitrobacteraceae; spherical cells which oxidize ammonia to nitrite.

Nitrosolobus [MICROBIO] A genus of bacteria in the family Nitrobacteraceae; cells are lobate and partially compartmentalized by plasma membranes; organisms oxidize ammonia to nitrite.

Nitrosomonas [MICROBIO] A genus of bacteria in the family Nitrobacteraceae; straight, rod-shaped cells which oxidize ammonia to nitrite.

Nitrospina [MICROBIO] A genus of bacteria in the family Nitrobacteraceae; rod-shaped cells are long and slender; nitrite is oxidized to nitrate.

Nitrospira [MICROBIO] A genus of bacteria in the family Nitrobacteraceae; spiral cells which oxidize ammonia to nitrite.

nival [ECOL] 1. Characterized by or living in or under the snow. 2. Of or pertaining to a snowy environment.

niveous See niveus.

niveus [BIOL] Snow-white in color. Also spelled niveous.

Nocardia [MICROBIO] A genus of bacteria in the family Nocardiaceae; mycelium production is sparse to abundant; reproduction is by mycelial fragments.

Nocardiaceae [MICROBIO] A family of aerobic bacteria in the order Actinomycetales; mycelium and spore production is variable.

Noctilionidae [VERT ZOO] The fish-eating bats, a tropical American monogeneric family of the Chiroptera having small eyes and long, narrow wings.

Noctuidae [INV ZOO] A large family of dull-colored, medium-sized moths in the superfamily Noctuoidea; larva are mostly exposed foliage feeders, representing an important group of agricultural pests.

Noctuoidea [INV ZOO] A large superfamily of lepidopteran insects in the suborder Heteroneura; most are moderately large moths with reduced maxillary palpi.

nocturnal emission [PHYSIO] Normal, involuntary seminal discharge occurring during sleep in males after puberty.

nodal rhythm [PHYSIO] A cardiac rhythm characterized by pacemaker function originating in the atrioventricular node, with a heart rate of 40–70 per minute.

nodal tissue [HISTOL] 1. Tissue from the sinoatrial node, and the atrioventricular node and bundle and its branches, composed of a dense network of Purkinje fibers. 2. Tissue from a lymph node.

node [ANAT] 1. A knob or protuberance. 2. A small, rounded mass of tissue, such as a lymph node. 3. A point of constriction along a nerve.

node of Ranvier [ANAT] The region of a local constriction in a myelinated nerve; formed at the junction of two Schwann cells.

Nodosariacea [INV ZOO] A superfamily of Foraminiferida in the suborder Rotaliina characterized by a radial calcite test wall with monolamellar septa, and a test that is coiled, uncoiled, or spiral about the long axis.

nodose [BIOL] Having many or noticeable protuberances; knobby.

nodule [ANAT] 1. A small node. 2. A small aggregation of cells.

nodules of the semilunar valves [ANAT] Small nodes in the midregion of the pulmonary and aortic semilunar valves.

nodulose [BIOL] Having minute nodules or fine knobs.

Noeggerathiales [PALEOBOT] A poorly defined group of fossil plants whose geologic range extends from Upper Carboniferous to Triassic.

nogalamycin [MICROBIO] $C_{39}H_{45}NO_{16}$ An antineoplastic antibiotic produced by Streptomyces nogalaster.

nomen dubium [SYST] A proposed taxonomic name invalid because it is not accompanied by a definition or description of the taxon to which it applies.

nomen nudum [SYST] A proposed taxonomic name invalid because the accompanying definition or description of the taxon cannot be interpreted satisfactorily.

noncompetitive inhibition [BIOCHEM] Enzyme inhibition in which the inhibitor can combine with either the free enzyme or the enzyme-substrate complex so that the inhibitor does not compete with the substrate for the enzyme.

nondisjunction mosaic [GEN] A population of cells with different chromosome numbers produced when one chromosome is lost during mitosis or when both members of a pair of chromosomes are included in the same daughter nucleus; can occur during embryogenesis or adulthood.

nonessential amino acid [BIOCHEM] An amino acid which can be synthesized by an organism and thus need not be supplied in the diet.

nongranular leukocyte [HISTOL] A white blood cell, such as a lymphocyte or monocyte, with clear homogeneous cytoplasm.

Nonionacea [INV ZOO] A superfamily of Foraminiferida in the suborder Orbitoidacea, characterized by a granular calcite test wall with monolamellar septa, and a planispiral to trochospiral test.

nonprotein nitrogen [BIOCHEM] The nitrogen fraction in the body tissues, excretions, and secretions, not precipitated by protein precipitants.

nonsaccharine sorghum See grain sorghum.

nonsense mutation [MOL BIO] A mutation that changes a codon that codes for one amino acid into a codon that does not specify any amino acid (a nonsense codon).

nonspecific hepatitis See interstitial hepatitis.

Noon pollen unit [BIOL] The quantity of pollen extract which contains 0.00001 milligram of total nitrogen.

norepinephrine [BIOCHEM] $C_8H_{11}O_3N$ A hormone produced by chromaffin cells of the adrenal medulla; acts as a vasoconstrictor and mediates transmission of sympathetic nerve impulses. Also known as noradrenaline.

normal saline [PHYSIO] U.S. Pharmacopoeia title for a sterile solution of sodium chloride in purified water, containing 0.9 gram of sodium chloride in 100 milliliters; isotonic with body fluids. Also known as isotonic sodium chloride solution; normal salt solution; physiological saline; physiological salt solution; physiological sodium chloride solution; sodium chloride solution.

normal salt solution See normal saline.

normoblast [HISTOL] The smallest of the nucleated precursors of the erythrocyte; slightly larger than a mature adult erythrocyte. Also known as acidophilic erythroblast; arthochromatic erythroblast; eosinophilic erythroblast; karyocyte; metakaryocyte; metanitricyte; metarubricyte.

normochromatic [CELL BIO] Pertaining to cells of the erythrocytic series which have a normal staining color; attributed to the presence of a full complement of hemoglobin.

normochromic [CELL BIO] Pertaining to erythrocytes which have a mean corpuscular hemoglobin (MCH), or color, index and a mean corpuscular hemoglobin concentration (MCHC), or saturation, index within two standard deviations above or below the mean normal.

normocyte [HISTOL] An erythrocyte having both a diameter and a mean corpuscular volume (MCV) within two standard deviations above or below the mean normal.

normothermia [PHYSIO] A state of normal body temperature.

northern anthracnose [PL PATH] A fungus disease of red and crimson clovers in North America, Asia, and Europe caused by *Kabatulla caulivora*; depressed, linear brown lesions form on the stems and petioles.

nose [ANAT] The nasal cavities and the structures surrounding and associated with them in all vertebrates.

nose leaf [VERT ZOO] A leaflike expansion of skin on the nose of certain bats; believed to have a tactile function.

Nosodendridae [INV ZOO] The wounded-tree beetles, a small family of coleopteran insects in the superfamily Dermestoidea.

nostril [ANAT] One of the external orifices of the nose. Also known as naris.

Notacanthidae [VERT ZOO] A family of benthic, deep-sea teleosts in the order Notacanthiformes, including the spiny eel.

Notacanthiformes [VERT ZOO] An order of actinopterygian fishes whose body is elongated, tapers posteriorly, and has no caudal fin.

notch graft [BOT] A plant graft in which the scion is inserted in a narrow slit in the stock.

Noteridae [INV ZOO] The burrowing water beetles, a small family of coleopteran insects in the suborder Adephaga.

Nothosauria [PALEON] A suborder of chiefly marine Triassic reptiles in the order Sauropterygia.

Notidanoidea [VERT ZOO] A suborder of rare sharks in the order Selachii; all retain the primitive jaw suspension of the order.

Notiomastodontinae [PALEON] A subfamily of extinct elephantoid proboscidean mammals in the family Gomphotheriidae.

Notioprogonia [PALEON] A suborder of extinct mammals comprising a diversified archaic stock of Notoungulata.

notochord [VERT ZOO] An elongated dorsal cord of cells which is the primitive axial skeleton in all chordates; persists in adults in the lowest forms (*Branchiostoma* and lampreys) and as the nuclei pulposi of the intervertebral disks in adult vertebrates.

notochordal canal [EMBRYO] A canal formed by a continuation of the primary pit into the head process of mammalian embryos; provides a temporary connection between the yolk sac and amnion.

notochordal plate [EMBRYO] A plate of cells representing the root of the head process of the embryo after the embryo becomes vesiculated.

Notodelphyidiformes [INV ZOO] A tribe of the Gnathostoma in some systems of classification.

Notodelphyoida [INV ZOO] A small group of crustaceans bearing a superficial resemblance to many insect larvae as a result of uniform segmentation, comparatively small trunk appendages, and crowding of inconspicuous oral appendages into the anterior portion of the head.

Notodontidae [INV ZOO] The puss moths, a family of lepidopteran insects in the superfamily Noctuoidea, distinguished by the apparently three-branched cubitus.

Notogaean [ECOL] Pertaining to or being a biogeographic region including Australia, New Zealand, and the southwestern Pacific islands.

Notommatidae [INV ZOO] A family of rotifers in the order Monogonota including forms with a cylindrical body covered by a nonchitinous cuticle and with a slender posterior foot.

Notomyotina [INV ZOO] A suborder of echinoderms in the order Phanerozonida in which the upper marginals alternate in position with the lower marginals, and each tube foot has a terminal sucking disk.

Notonectidae [INV ZOO] The backswimmers, a family of aquatic, carnivorous hemipteran insects in the superfamily Notonectoidea; individuals swim ventral side up, aided in breathing by an air bubble.

Notonectoidea [INV ZOO] A superfamily of Hemiptera in the subdivision Hydrocorisae.

notopodium [INV ZOO] The dorsal branch of a parapodium in certain annelids.

Notopteridae [VERT ZOO] The featherbacks, a family of actinopterygian fishes in the order Osteoglossiformes; bodies are tapered and compressed, with long anal fins that are continuous with the caudal fin.

Notoryctidae [PALEON] An extinct family of Australian insectivorous mammals in the order Marsupialia.

Notostigmata [INV ZOO] The single suborder of the Opilioacriformes, an order of mites.

Notostigmophora [INV ZOO] A subclass or suborder of the Chilopoda, including those centipedes embodying primitive as well as highly advanced characters, distinguished by dorsal respiratory openings.

Notostraca [INV ZOO] The tadpole shrimps, an order of crustaceans generally referred to the Branchiopoda, having a cylindrical trunk that consists of 25–44 segments, a dorsoventrally flattened dorsal shield, and two narrow, cylindrical cercopods on the telson.

Nototheniidae [VERT ZOO] A family of perciform fishes in the suborder Blennioidei, including most of the fishes of the permanently frigid waters surrounding Antarctica.

Notoungulata [PALEON] An extinct order of hoofed herbivorous mammals, characterized by a skull with an expanded temporal region, primitive dentition, and primitive feet with five toes, the weight borne mainly by the third digit.

novobiocin [MICROBIO] $C_{30}H_{36}O_{11}N_2$ A moderately broad-spectrum antibiotic produced by strains of *Streptomyces niveus* and *S. spheroides*; it is a dibasic acid and is converted either to the monosodium salt or to the calcium acid salt for pharmaceutical use.

nucellus [BOT] The oval central mass of tissue in the ovule; contains the embryo sac.

nucha [ANAT] The nape of the neck.

nuchal ligament [ANAT] An elastic ligament extending from the external occipital protuberance and middle nuchal line to the spinous process of the seventh cervical vertebra. Also known as ligamentum nuchae.

nuchal organ [INV ZOO] Any of various sense organs on the prostomium of many annelids, which are sensitive to changes in the immediate environment of the individual.

nuchal tentacle [INV ZOO] Any of various filiform or thick, fleshy tactoreceptors on anterior segments of many annelids.

nuclear membrane [CELL BIO] The envelope surrounding the cell nucleus, separating the nucleoplasm from the cytoplasm; composed of two membranes and contains numerous pores.

nuclease [BIOCHEM] An enzyme that catalyzes the splitting of nucleic acids to nucleotides, nucleosides, or the components of the latter.

nucleic acid [BIOCHEM] A large, acidic, chainlike molecule containing phosphoric acid, sugar, and purine and pyrimidine bases; two types are ribonucleic acid and deoxyribonucleic acid.

nuclein [BIOCHEM] Any of a poorly defined group of nucleic acid protein complexes occurring in cell nuclei.

nucleocytoplasmic ratio [CELL BIO] The ratio between the measured cross-sectional area or estimated volume of the nucleus of a cell to the volume of its cytoplasm. Also known as karyoplasmic ratio.

nucleolar [CELL BIO] Of or pertaining to the nucleolus.

nucleolus [CELL BIO] A small, spherical body composed principally of protein and located in the metabolic nucleus. Also known as plasmosome.

nucleoplasm [CELL BIO] The protoplasm of a nucleus. Also known as karyoplasm.

nucleoprotein [BIOCHEM] Any member of a class of conjugated proteins in which molecules of nucleic acid are closely associated with molecules of protein.

nucleoreticulum [CELL BIO] Any type of network found within a nucleus.

nucleosidase [BIOCHEM] An enzyme that catalyzes the hydrolysis of a nucleoside to its component pentose and its purine or pyrimidine base.

nucleoside [BIOCHEM] The glycoside resulting from removal of the phosphate group from a nucleotide; consists of a pentose sugar linked to a purine or pyrimidine base.

nucleosome [CELL BIO] A morphologically repeating unit of DNA containing 190 base pairs of DNA folded together with eight histone molecules. Also known as v-body.

nucleospindle [CELL BIO] A mitotic spindle derived from nuclear material.

nucleotidase [BIOCHEM] Any of a group of enzymes which split phosphoric acid from nucleotides, leaving nucleosides.

nucleotide [BIOCHEM] An ester of a nucleoside and phosphoric acid; the structural unit of a nucleic acid.

nucleus [CELL BIO] A small mass of differentiated protoplasm rich in nucleoproteins and surrounded by a membrane; found in most animal and plant cells, contains chromosomes, and functions in metabolism, growth, and reproduction.

nucleus [HISTOL] A mass of nerve cells in the central nervous system.

Nuda [INV ZOO] A class of the phylum Ctenophora distinguished by the lack of tentacles.

Nudechiniscidae [INV ZOO] A family of heterotardigrades in the suborder Echiniscoidea characterized by a uniform cuticle.

Nudibranchia [INV ZOO] A suborder of the Opisthobranchia containing the sea slugs; these mollusks lack a shell and a mantle cavity, and the gills are variable in size and shape.

numerical taxonomy [SYST] The numerical evaluation of the affinity or similarity between taxonomic units and the ordering of these units into taxa on the basis of their affinities.

Numididae [VERT ZOO] A family of birds in the order Galliformes commonly known as guinea fowl; there are few if any feathers on the neck or head, but there may be a crest of feathers and various fleshy appendages.

nurse cell [HISTOL] A cell type of the ovary of many animals which nourishes the developing egg cell.

nurse graft [BOT] A plant graft in which the scion remains united with the stock only until roots develop on the scion.

nut [BOT] **1.** A fruit which has at maturity a hard, dry shell enclosing a kernel consisting of an embryo and nutritive tissue. **2.** An indehiscent, one-celled, one-seeded, hard fruit derived from a single, simple, or compound ovary.

nutation [BOT] The rhythmic change in the position of growing plant organs caused by variation in the growth rates on different sides of the growing apex.

nutgall [PL PATH] A nutlike gall.

nutmeg [BOT] *Myristica fragrans*. A dark-leafed evergreen tree of the family Myristicaceae cultivated for the golden-yellow fruits which resemble apricots; a delicately flavored spice is obtained from the kernels inside the seeds.

nutrient [BIOL] Providing nourishment.

nutrient foramen [ANAT] The opening into the canal which gives passage to the blood vessels of the medullary cavity of a bone.

nutrition [BIOL] The science of nourishment, including the study of nutrients that each organism must obtain from its environment in order to maintain life and reproduce.

Nuttalliellidae [INV ZOO] A family of ticks (Ixodides) containing one rare African species, *Nuttalliella namaqua*, morphologically intermediate between the families Argasidae and Ixodidae.

nux vomica [BOT] The seed of *Strychnos nuxvomica*, an Indian tree of the family Loganiaceae; contains the alkaloid strychnine, and was formerly used in medicine.

Nyctaginaceae [BOT] A family of dicotyledonous plants in the order Caryophyllales characterized by an apocarpous, monocarpous, or syncarpous gynoecium, sepals joined to a tube, a single carpel, and a cymose inflorescence.

Nycterldae [VERT ZOO] The slit-faced bats, a monogeneric family of insectivorous chiropterans having a simple, well-developed nose leaf, and large ears joined together across the forehead.

Nyctiblidae [VERT ZOO] A family of birds in the order Caprimulgiformes including the neotropical potoos.

nyctinasty [BOT] A nastic movement in higher plants associated with diurnal light and temperature changes.

Nyctribildae [INV ZOO] The bat tick flies, a family of myodarian cyclorrhaphous dipteran insects in the subsection Acalyptratae.

nymph [INV ZOO] Any immature larval stage of various hemimetabolic insects.

Nymphaeaceae [BOT] A family of dicotyledonous plants in the order Nymphaeales distinguished by the presence of roots, perfect flowers, alternate leaves, and uniaperturate pollen.

Nymphaeales [BOT] An order of flowering aquatic herbs in the subclass Magnoliidae; all lack cambium and vessels and have laminar placentation.

Nymphalidae [INV ZOO] The four-footed butterflies, a family of lepidopteran insects in the superfamily Papilionoidea; prothoracic legs are atrophied, and the well-developed patagia are heavily sclerotized.

Nymphalinae [INV ZOO] A subfamily of the lepidopteran family Nymphalidae.

Nymphonidae [INV ZOO] A family of marine arthropods in the subphylum Pycnogonida; members have chelifores, five-jointed palpi, and ten-jointed ovigers.

Nymphulinae [INV ZOO] A subfamily of the lepidopteran family Pyralididae which is notable because some species are aquatic.

Nysmyth's membrane [ANAT] The primary enamel cuticle which is the transitory remnants of the enamel organ and oral epithelium covering the enamel of a tooth after eruption.

Nyssaceae [BOT] A family of dicotyledonous plants in the order Cornales characterized by perfect or unisexual flowers with imbricate petals, a solitary ovule in each locule, a unilocular ovary, and more stamens than petals.

nystatin [MICROBIO] $C_{46}H_{77}NO_{19}$ An antifungal antibiotic produced by *Streptomyces noursei*; used for the treatment of infections caused by *Candida (Monilia) albicans*.

O

oak [BOT] Any tree of the genus *Quercus* in the order Fagales, characterized by simple, usually lobed leaves, scaly winter buds, a star-shaped pith, and its fruit, the acorn, which is a nut; the wood is tough, hard, and durable, generally having a distinct pattern.

oak wilt [PL PATH] A fungus disease of oak trees caused by *Chalara quercina*, characterized by wilting and yellow and red discoloration of the leaves progressing from the top downward and inward.

O antigen [MICROBIO] A somatic antigen of certain flagellated microorganisms.

oat [BOT] Any plant of the genus *Avena* in the family Graminae, cultivated as an agricultural crop for its seed, a cereal grain, and for straw.

obclavate [BIOL] Inversely clavate.

obcordate [BOT] Referring to a leaf, heart-shaped with the notch apical.

obdiplastemonous [BOT] Having the stamens arranged in two whorls, with members of the outer whorl positioned opposite the petals.

obese [ANAT] Extremely fat.

obligate [BIOL] Restricted to a specified condition of life, as an obligate parasite.

oblique [ANAT] Referring to a muscle, positioned obliquely and having one end that is not attached to bone. [BOT] Referring to a leaf, having the two sides of a blade unequal.

Obolellida [PALEON] A small order of Early and Middle Cambrian inarticulate brachiopods, distinguished by a shell of calcium carbonate.

obovate [BIOL] Inversely ovate.

obsolete [BIOL] A part of an organism that is imperfect or indistinct, compared with a corresponding part of similar organisms.

obturator [ANAT] 1. Pertaining to that which closes or stops up, as an obturator membrane. 2. Either of two muscles, originating at the pubis and ischium, which rotate the femur laterally.

obturator artery [ANAT] A branch of the internal iliac; it branches into the pubic and acetabular arteries.

obturator foramen [ANAT] A large opening in the pelvis, between the ischium and the pubis, that gives passage to vessels and nerves; it is partly closed by a fibrous obturator membrane.

obturator membrane [ANAT] 1. A fibrous membrane closing the obturator foramen of the pel-

vis. 2. A thin membrane between the crura and foot plates of the stapes.

obturator nerve [ANAT] A mixed nerve arising in the lumbar plexus; innervates the adductor, gracilis, and obturator externus muscles, and the skin of the medial aspect of the thigh, hip, and knee joints.

obtuse [BOT] Of a leaf, having a blunt or rounded free end.

obvallate [BIOL] Surrounded by or as if by a wall.

obvolute [BIOL] Overlapping.

occipital arch [INV ZOO] A part of an insect cranium lying between the occipital suture and postoccipital suture.

occipital artery [ANAT] A branch of the external carotid which branches into the mastoid, auricular, sternocleidomastoid, and meningeal arteries.

occipital bone [ANAT] The bone which forms the posterior portion of the skull, surrounding the foramen magnum.

occipital condyle [ANAT] An articular surface on the occipital bone which articulates with the atlas. [INV ZOO] A projection on the posterior border of an insect head which articulates with the lateral neck plates.

occipital crest [ANAT] Either of two transverse ridges connecting the occipital protuberances with the foramen magnum.

occipital ganglion [INV ZOO] One of a pair of ganglia located just posterior to the brain in insects.

occipital lobe [ANAT] The posterior lobe of the cerebrum having the form of a three-sided pyramid.

occipital pole [ANAT] The tip of the occipital lobe of the brain.

occipital protuberance [ANAT] A prominence on the surface of the occipital bone to which the ligamentum nuchae is attached.

occipitofrontalis [ANAT] A muscle in two parts, the frontal (inserting in the skin of the forehead) and the occipital (inserting in the galea sponeurotica).

occiput [ZOO] The back of the head of an insert or vertebrate.

occlusion [ANAT] The relationship of the masticatory surfaces of the maxillary teeth to the masticatory surfaces of the mandibular teeth when the jaws are closed. [PHYSIO] The deficit in muscular tension when two afferent nerves that share certain motor neurons in the central nervous system are stimulated simultaneously, as compared to the sum of tensions when the two nerves are stimulated separately.

occult virus [VIROL] A virus whose presence is assumed but which cannot be recovered.

Oceanian [ECOL] Of or pertaining to the zoogeographic region that includes the archipelagos and islands of the central and south Pacific.

oceanodromous [VERT ZOO] Of a fish, migratory in salt water.

ocellus [INV ZOO] A small, simple invertebrate eye composed of photoreceptor cells and pigment cells.

ocelot [VERT ZOO] *Felis pardalis.* A small arboreal wild cat, of the family Felidae, characterized by a golden head and back, silvery flanks, and rows of somewhat metallic spots on the body.

Ochnaceae [BOT] A family of dicotyledonous plants in the order Theales, characterized by simple, stipulate leaves, a mostly gynobasic style, and anthers that generally open by terminal pores.

Ochotonidae [VERT ZOO] A family of the mammalian order Lagomorpha; members are relatively small, and all four legs are about equally long.

ochratoxin A [BIOCHEM] $C_{20}H_{18}ClNO_6$ A toxic metabolite from *Aspergillus ochraceus*; a crystalline compound which exhibits green fluorescence; melting point is 169°C; inhibits phosphorylase and mitochondrial respiration in rat liver.

ochre mutation [GEN] Alteration of a codon to UGA, a codon that results in premature termination of the polypeptide chain in bacteria.

Ochrobium [MICROBIO] A genus of bacteria in the family Siderocapsaceae; cells are ellipsoidal to rod-shaped and are surrounded by a delicate sheath, resembling a horseshoe, that is heavily embedded with iron oxides.

ochroleucous [BIOL] Pale ocher or buff colored.

Ochteridae [INV ZOO] The velvety shorebugs, the single family of the hemipteran superfamily Ochteroidea.

Ochteroidea [INV ZOO] A monofamilial tropical and subtropical superfamily of hemipteran insects in the subdivision Hydrocorisae; individuals are black with a silky sheen, and the antennae are visible from above.

ocrea [BOT] A tubular stipule or pair of coherent stipules.

9,12-octadecadienoic acid *See* linoleic acid.

9,12,15-octadecatrienoic acid *See* linolenic acid.

Octocorallia [INV ZOO] The equivalent name for Alcyonaria.

Octopoda [INV ZOO] An order of the dibranchiate cephalopods, characterized by having eight arms equipped with one to three rows of suckers.

Octopodidae [INV ZOO] The octopuses, in family of cephalopod mollusks in the order Octopoda.

octopus [INV ZOO] Any member of the genus *Octopus* in the family Octopodidae; the body is round with a large head and eight partially webbed arms, each bearing two rows of suckers, and there is no shell.

ocular [BIOL] Of or pertaining to the eye.

ocular skeleton [VERT ZOO] A rigid structure in most submammalian vertebrates consisting of a cup of hyaline cartilage enclosing the posterior part of the eye, and a thin-walled ring of intramembranous bones in the edge of the sclera at its junction with the cornea.

oculomotor [PHYSIO] 1. Pertaining to eye movement. 2. Pertaining to the oculomotor nerve.

oculomotor nerve [ANAT] The third cranial nerve; a paired somatic motor nerve arising in the floor of the midbrain, which innervates all extrinsic eye muscles except the lateral rectus and superior oblique, and furnishes autonomic fibers to the ciliary and pupillary sphincter muscles within the eye.

oculomotor nucleus [ANAT] A nucleus in the floor of the midbrain that gives rise to motor fibers of the oculomotor nerve.

Oculosida [INV ZOO] An order of the protozoan subclass Radiolaria; pores are restricted to certain areas in the central capsule, and an olive-colored material is always present near the astropyle.

odd-pinnate [BOT] Of a compound leaf, having a single leaflet at the tip of the petiole with leaflets on both sides of the petiole. Also known as imparipinnate.

Odiniidae [INV ZOO] A family of cyclorrhaphous myodarian dipteran insects in the subsection Acalyptratae.

Odobenidae [VERT ZOO] A family of carnivorous mammals in the suborder Pinnipedia; contains a single species, the walrus (*Odobenus rosmarus*).

Odonata [INV ZOO] The dragonflies, an order of the class Insecta, characterized by a head with large compound eyes, and wings with clear or transparent membranes traversed by networks of veins.

odontoblast [HISTOL] One of the elongated, dentin-forming cells covering the dental papilla.

Odontoceti [VERT ZOO] The toothed whales, a suborder of cetacean mammals distinguished by a single blowhole.

odontoclast [HISTOL] A multinuclear cell concerned with resorption of the roots of milk teeth.

odont-, odonto- [VERT ZOO] A combining form meaning tooth.

odontogenesis [EMBRYO] Formation of teeth.

odontogenic [HISTOL] 1. Pertaining to the origin and development of teeth. 2. Originating in tissues associated with teeth.

Odontognathae [PALEON] An extinct superorder of the avian subclass Neornithes, including all large, flightless aquatic forms and other members of the single order Hesperornithiformes.

odontoid [BIOL] Toothlike.

odontoid process [ANAT] A toothlike projection on the anterior surface of the axis vertebra with which the atlas articulates.

odontology [VERT ZOO] A branch of science that deals with the formation, development, and abnormalities of teeth.

Odontostomatida [INV ZOO] An order of the protozoan subclass Spirotrichia; individuals are compressed laterally and possess very little ciliature.

Oecophoridae [INV ZOO] A family of small to moderately small moths in the lepidopteran superfamily Tineoidea, characterized by a comb of bristles, the pecten, on the scape of the antennae.

Oedemeridae [INV ZOO] The false blister beetles, a large family of coleopteran insects in the superfamily Tenebrionoidea.

Oedogoniales [BOT] An order of fresh-water algae in the division Chlorophyta; characterized as branched or unbranched microscopic filaments with a basal holdfast cell.

Oegophiurida [INV ZOO] An order of echinoderms in the subclass Ophiuroidea, represented by a single living genus; members have few external skeletal plates and lack genital bursae, dorsal and ventral arm plates, and certain jaw plates.

Oegopsida [INV ZOO] A suborder of cephalopod mollusks in the order Decapoda of one classification system, and in the order Teuthoidea of another system.

Oepikellacea [PALEON] A dimorphic superfamily of extinct ostracods in the order Paleocopa, distinguished by convex valves and the absence of any trace of a major sulcus in the external configuration.

Oestridae [INV ZOO] A family of cyclorrhaphous myodarian dipteran insects in the subsection Calypteratae.

oidiophore [MYCOL] A hypha that produces oidia.

oidium [MYCOL] One of the small, thin-walled spores with flat ends produced by autofragmentation of the vegetative hyphae in certain Eumycetes.

Oikomonadidae [INV ZOO] A family of protozoans in the order Kinetoplastida containing organisms that have a single flagellum.

oil gland *See* uropygial gland.

okapi [VERT ZOO] *Okapia johnstoni*. An artiodactylous mammal in the family Giraffidae; has a hazel coat with striped hindquarters, and the head shape, lips, and tongue are the same as those of the giraffe, but the neck is not elongate.

okra [BOT] *Hibiscus esculentus*. A tall annual plant grown for its edible immature pods. Also known as gumbo.

Olacaceae [BOT] A family of dicotyledonous plants in the order Santalales characterized by dry or fleshy indehiscent fruit, the presence of petals, stamens, and chlorophyll, and a 2–5-celled ovary.

Oldhaminidina [PALEON] A suborder of extinct articulate brachiopods in the order Strophomenida distinguished by a highly lobate brachial valve seated within an irregular convex pedicle valve.

Oleaceae [BOT] A family of dicotyledonous plants in the order Scrophulariales characterized generally by perfect flowers, two stamens, axile to parietal or apical placentation, a four-lobed corolla, and two ovules in each locule.

oleandomycin [MICROBIO] $C_{35}H_{61}O_{12}N$ A macrolide antibotic produced by *Streptomyces antibioticus*; active mainly against gram-positive microorganisms. Also known as matromycin.

olecranon [ANAT] The large process at the distal end of the ulna that forms the bony prominence of the elbow and receives the insertion of the triceps muscle.

Olenellidae [PALEON] A family of extinct arthropods in the class Trilobita.

Olethreutidae [INV ZOO] A family of moths in the superfamily Tortricoidea whose hindwings usually have a fringe of long hairs along the basal part of the cubitus.

olfaction [PHYSIO] 1. The function of smelling. 2. The sense of smell.

olfactoreceptor [PHYSIO] A structure which is a receptor for the sense of smell.

olfactory bulb [VERT ZOO] The bulbous distal end of the olfactory tract located beneath each anterior lobe of the cerebrum; well developed in lower vertebrates.

olfactory cell [PHYSIO] One of the sensory nerve cells in the olfactory epithelium.

olfactory foramen [ANAT] Any of the openings in the cribriform plate of the ethmoid bone through which pass the fila olfactoria of the olfactory nerves.

olfactory gland [PHYSIO] A type of serous gland in the nasal mucous membrane.

olfactory lobe [VERT ZOO] A lobe projecting forward from the inferior surface of the frontal lobe of each cerebral hemisphere, including the olfactory bulb, tracts, and trigone; well developed in most vertebrates, but reduced in man.

olfactory nerve [ANAT] The first cranial nerve; a paired sensory nerve with its origin in the olfactory lobe and formed by processes of the olfactory cells which lie in the nasal mucosa; greatly reduced in man.

olfactory organ [PHYSIO] Any of the small chemoreceptors in the mucous membrane lining the upper part of the nasal gravity which receive stimuli interpreted as odors.

olfactory pit [EMBRYO] A depression near the olfactory placode in the embryo that develops into part of the nasal cavity. Also known as nasal pit.

olfactory region [ANAT] The area on and above the superior conchae and on the adjoining nasal septum where the mucous membrane has olfactory epithelium and olfactory glands.

olfactory stalk [ANAT] The structure that connects the olfactory bulb to the cerebrum of the vertebrate brain.

olfactory tract [ANAT] A narrow tract of white nerve fibers originating in the olfactory bulb and extending posteriorly to the anterior perforated substance, where it enlarges to form a lateral root (olfactory trigone).

Oligobrachiidae [INV ZOO] A monotypic family of the order Athecanephria.

Oligochaeta [INV ZOO] A class of the phylum Annelida including worms that exhibit both external and internal segmentation, and setae which are not borne on parapodia.

oligodendroglia [HISTOL] Small neuroglial cells with spheroidal or ovoid nuclei and fine cytoplasmic processes with secondary divisions.

oligodynamic action [MICROBIO] The inhibiting or killing of microorganisms by use of very small amounts of a chemical substance.

Oligomera [INV ZOO] A subphylum of the phylum Vermes comprising groups with two or three coelomic divisions.

oligomeric protein [BIOCHEM] A protein composed of two or more polypeptide chains.

oligomerous [BOT] Having one or more whorls with fewer members than other whorls of the flower.

oligomycin [MICROBIO] $C_{25}H_{40}CFNPIFw_{42}O_7$ An antifungal antibiotic produced by an actinomycete resembling *Streptomyces diastachromogenes*; the colorless, hexagonal crystals are soluble in many organic solvents.

oligonucleotide [BIOCHEM] A polynucleotide of low molecular weight, consisting of less than 20 nucleotide polymers.

oligophagous [ZOO] Eating only a limited variety of foods.

Oligopygidae [PALEON] An extinct family of exocyclic Euechinoidia in the order Holectypoida which were small ovoid forms of the Early Tertiary.

oligosaccharide [BIOCHEM] A sugar composed of two to eight monosaccharide units joined by glycosidic bonds. Also known as compound sugar.

Oligotrichida [INV ZOO] A minor order of the Spirotrichia; the body is round in cross section, and the adoral zone of membranelles is often highly developed at the oral end of the organism.

olivaceous [BIOL] 1. Resembling an olive. 2. Olive colored.

olivary nucleus [ANAT] A prominent, convoluted gray band that opens medially and occupies the upper two-thirds of the medulla oblongata.

olive [BOT] Any plant of the genus *Olea* in the order Schrophulariales, especially the evergreen olive tree (*O. europeae*) cultivated for its drupaceous fruit, which is eaten ripe (black olives) and unripe (green), and is of high oil content.

olive knot [PL PATH] A bacterial disease of the olive caused by *Pseudomonas sevastonoi* and characterized by excrescences on the foliage and branches, and sometimes on the trunk. Also known as olive tubercle.

Olividae [INV ZOO] A family of snails in the gastropod order Neogastropoda.

omasum [VERT ZOO] The third chamber of the ruminant stomach where the contents are mixed to a more or less homogeneous state. Also known as manyplies; psalterium.

ombrophilous [ECOL] Able to thrive in areas of abundant rainfall.

ombrophobous [ECOL] Unable to live in the presence of long, continuous rain.

omentum [ANAT] A fold of the peritoneum connecting or supporting abdominal viscera.

ommatidium [INV ZOO] The structural unit of a compound eye, composed of a cornea, a crystalline cone, and a receptor element connected to the optic nerve.

ommatophore [INV ZOO] A movable peduncle that bears an eye, as in snails.

omnivore [ZOO] An organism that eats both animal and vegetable matter.

omohyoid [ANAT] 1. Pertaining conjointly to the scapula and the hyoid bone. 2. A muscle attached to the scapula and the hyoid bone.

Omophronidae [INV ZOO] The savage beetles, a small family of coleopteran insects in the suborder Adephaga.

omphalomesenteric artery See vitelline artery.

omphalomesenteric duct See vitelline duct.

omphalomesenteric vein See vitelline vein.

Omphralidae [INV ZOO] A family of orthorrhaphous dipteran insects in the series Nematocera.

Onagraceae [BOT] A family of dicotyledonous plants in the order Myrtales characterized generally by an inferior ovary, axile placentation, twice as many stamens as petals, a four-nucleate embryo sac, and many ovules.

Onchidiidae [INV ZOO] An intertidal family of sluglike pulmonate mollusks of the order Systellommatophora in which the body is oval or lengthened, with the convex dorsal integument lacking a mantle cavity or shell.

onchosphere [INV ZOO] The hexacanth embryo identified as the earliest differentiated stage of cyclophyllidean tapeworms.

oncocyte [HISTOL] A columnar-shaped cell with finely granular eosinophilic cytoplasm, found in salivary and certain endocrine glands, nasal mucosa, and other locations.

oncogene [GEN] A gene that causes cancer in an animal; the gene specifies the structure of an enzyme that catalyzes events that can induce cancerous growth.

Oncopoda [INV ZOO] A phylum of the superphylum Articulata.

oncotic pressure [PHYSIO] Also known as colloidal osmotic pressure. 1. The osmotic pressure exerted by colloids in a solution. 2. The pressure exerted by plasma proteins.

onion [BOT] 1. *Allium cepa*. A biennial plant in the order Liliales cultivated for its edible bulb. 2. Any plant of the genus *Allium*.

onion smudge [PL PATH] A fungus disease of the onion caused by *Colletotrichum circinans* and characterized by black concentric integral rings or smutty spots on the bulb scales. Also known as onion scab.

onion smut [PL PATH] A fungus disease of onion, especially seedlings, caused by *Urocystis cepulae* and characterized by elongate black blisters on the scales and foliage.

Oniscoidea [INV ZOO] A terrestrial suborder of the Isopoda; the body is either dorsoventrally flattened or highly vaulted, and the head, thorax, and abdomen are broadly joined.

ontogeny [EMBRYO] The origin and development of an organism from conception to adulthood.

Onuphidae [INV ZOO] A family of tubicolous, herbivorous, scavenging errantian annelids in the superfamily Eunicea.

Onychodontidae [PALEON] A family of Lower Devonian lobefin fishes in the order Osteolepiformes.

onych-, onycho- [ZOO] A combining form denoting claw or nail.

Onychopalpida [INV ZOO] A suborder of mites in the order Acarina.

Onychophora [INV ZOO] A phylum of wormlike animals that combine features of both the annelids and the arthropods.

Onygenaceae [MYCOL] A family of ascomycetous fungi in the order Eurotiales comprising forms that inhabit various animal substrata, such as horns and hoofs.

oocyst [INV ZOO] The encysted zygote of some Sporozoa.

oocyte [HISTOL] An egg before the completion of maturation.

oogamete [BIOL] A large, nonmotile female gamete containing reserve materials.

oogamous [BIOL] Of sexual reproduction, characterized by fusion of a motile sperm with an oogamete.

oogenesis [PHYSIO] Processes involved in the growth and maturation of the ovum in preparation for fertilization.

oogonium [BOT] The unisexual female sex organ in oogamous algae and fungi. [HISTOL] A descendant of a primary germ cell which develops into an oocyte.

ookinete [INV ZOO] The elongated, mobile zygote of certain Sporozoa, as that of the malaria parasite.

oolemma See zona pellucida.

oology [VERT ZOO] A branch of zoology concerned with the study of eggs, especially bird eggs.

Oomycetes [MYCOL] A class of the Phycomycetes comprising the biflagellate water molds and downy mildews.

oophagous [ZOO] Feeding or living on eggs.

ooplasm [CELL BIO] Cytoplasm of an egg.

oospore [BOT] A spore which is produced by heterogamous fertilization and from which the sporophytic generation develops.

oostegite [INV ZOO] In many crustaceans, a platelike expansion of the basal segment of a thoracic appendage that aids in forming an egg receptacle.

ootype [INV ZOO] In trematodes and tapeworms, a thickening of the oviduct near the ovaries.

Opalinata [INV ZOO] A superclass of the subphylum Sarcomastigophora containing highly specialized forms which resemble ciliates.

Opegraphaceae [BOT] A family of the Hysteriales characterized by elongated ascocarps; members are crustose on bark and rocks.

open-circle deoxyribonucleic acid See relaxed circular deoxyribonucleic acid.

open community [ECOL] A community which other organisms readily colonize because some niches are unoccupied.

open water [ECOL] Lake water that is free from emergent vegetation, artificial obstructions, or tangled masses of underwater vegetation at very shallow depths.

operator [GEN] A sequence at one end of an operon on which a repressor acts, thus regulating the transcription of the operon.

operculum [ANAT] 1. The soft tissue partially covering the crown of an erupting tooth. 2. That part of the cerebrum which borders the lateral fissure.

operculum [BIOL] 1. A lid, flap, or valve. 2. A lidlike body process.

operon [GEN] A functional unit composed of a number of adjacent cistrons on the chromosome; its transcription is regulated by a receptor sequence, the operator, and a repressor.

Ophelilidae [INV ZOO] A family of limivorous worms belonging to the annelid group Sedentaria.

Ophiacodonta [VERT ZOO] A suborder of extinct reptiles in the order Pelycosauria, including primitive, partially aquatic carnivores.

Ophidiidae [VERT ZOO] A family of small actinopterygian fishes in the order Gadiformes, comprising the cusk eels and brotulas.

Ophiocanopidae [INV ZOO] A family of asterozoan echinoderms in the subclass Ophiuroidea.

Ophiocistioidea [PALEON] A small class of extinct Echinozoa in which the domed aboral surface of the test was roofed by a polygonal plates and carried an anal pyramid.

Ophioglossales [BOT] An order of ferns in the subclass Ophioglossidae.

Ophioglossidae [BOT] The adder's-tongue ferns, a small subclass of the class Polypodiopsida; the plants are homosporous and eusporangiate and are distinguished by the arrangement of the sporogenous tissue in the characteristic fertile spike of the sporophyte.

Ophiomyxidae [INV ZOO] The single family of the echinoderm suborder Ophiomyxina distinguished by a soft, unprotected integument.

Ophiomyxina [INV ZOO] A monofamilial suborder of ophiuroid echinoderms in the order Phrynophiurida.

ophiopluteus [INV ZOO] The pluteus larva of brittle stars.

Ophiurida [INV ZOO] An order of echinoderms in the subclass Ophiuroidea in which the vertebrae articulate by means of ball-and-socket joints, and the arms, which do not branch, move mainly from side to side.

Ophiuroidea [INV ZOO] The brittle stars, a subclass of the Asterozoa in which the arms are usually clearly demarcated from the central disk and perform whiplike locomotor movements.

ophthalmic [ANAT] Of or pertaining to the eye.

ophthalmic nerve [ANAT] A sensory branch of the trigeminal nerve which supplies the lacrimal glands, upper eyelids, skin of the forehead, and anterior portion of the scalp, meninges, nasal mucosa, and frontal, ethmoid, and sphenoid air sinuses.

Opilioacaridae [INV ZOO] The single family of moderately large mites of the suborder Notostigmata which comprises the Opiliocariformes.

Opilioacariformes [INV ZOO] A small monofamilial order of the Acari comprising large mites characterized by long legs and by the possession of a pretarsus on the pedipalp, with prominent claws.

opine [BIOCHEM] A type of amino acid usually not found in nature, such as that secreted by a crown gall.

opisthaptor [INV ZOO] A posterior adhesive organ in monogenetic trematodes.

Opisthobranchia [INV ZOO] A subclass of the class Gastropoda containing the sea hares, sea butterflies, and sea slugs; generally characterized by having gills, a small external or internal shell, and two pairs of tentacles.

Opisthocoela [VERT ZOO] A suborder of the order Anura; members have opisthocoelous trunk vertebrae, and the adults typically have free ribs.

opisthocoelous [ANAT] Of, related to, or being a vertebra with the centrum convex anteriorly and concave posteriorly.

Opisthocomidae [VERT ZOO] A family of birds in the order Galliformes, including the hoatzins.

opisthognathous [INV ZOO] Having the mouthparts ventral and posterior to the cranium. [VERT ZOO] Having retreating jaws.

opisthonephros [VERT ZOO] The fundamental adult kidney in amphibians and fishes.

Opisthopora [INV ZOO] An order of the class Oligochaeta distinguished by meganephridiostomal, male pores opening posteriorly to the last testicular segment.

opisthotic [ANAT] Of, relating to, or being the posterior and inferior portions of the bony elements in the inner ear capsule.

Opomyzidae [INV ZOO] A family of cyclorrhaphous myodarian dipteran insects in the subsection Acalypteratae.

opossum [VERT ZOO] Any member of the family Didelphidae in the order Marsupialia; these mammals are arboreal and mainly omnivorous, and have many incisors, with all teeth pointed and sharp.

opportunistic microorganism [MICROBIO] A normally harmless endogenous microorganism that produces disease due to fortuitous events that affect the host.

opposite [BOT] 1. Located side by side. 2. Of leaves, being in pairs on an axis with each member separated from the other of the pair by half the circumference of the axis.

optic [BIOL] Pertaining to the eye.

optical axis [ANAT] An imaginary straight line passing through the midpoint of the cornea (anterior pole) and the midpoint of the retina (posterior pole).

optical-righting reflex See visual-righting reflex.

optic canal [ANAT] The channel at the apex of the orbit, the anterior termination of the optic groove, just beneath the lesser wing of the sphenoid bone; it gives passage to the optic nerve and ophthalmic artery.

optic capsule [VERT ZOO] A cartilaginous capsule that develops around the eye in elasmobranchs and higher vertebrate embryos.

optic chiasma [ANAT] The partial decussation of the optic nerves on the undersurface of the hypothalamus.

optic cup [EMBRYO] A two-layered depression formed by invagination of the optic vesicle from which the pigmented and sensory layers of the retina will develop.

optic disk [ANAT] The circular area in the retina that is the site of the convergence of fibers from the ganglion cells of the retina to form the optic nerve.

optic gland [INV ZOO] Either of a pair of endocrine glands in the octopus and squid which are found near the brain and produce a substance which causes gonadal maturation.

optic lobe [ANAT] One of the anterior pair of colliculi of the mammalian corpora quadrigemina.

optic lobe [INV ZOO] A lateral lobe of the forebrain in certain arthropods.

optic lobe [VERT ZOO] Either of the corpora bigemina of lower vertebrates.

optic nerve [ANAT] The second cranial nerve; a paired sensory nerve technically consisting of three layers of special nerve cells in the retina of the eye; fibers converge to form the optic tracts.

optic stalk [EMBRYO] The constriction of the optic vesicle which connects the embryonic eye and forebrain in vertebrates.

optic tectum [VERT ZOO] The roof of the mesencephalon constituting a major visual center and association area of the brain of premature vertebrates.

optic tract [ANAT] The band of optic nerve fibers running from the optic chiasma to the lateral geniculate body and midbrain.

optic vesicle [EMBRYO] An evagination of the lateral wall of the forebrain in vertebrate embryos which precedes formation of the optic cup.

oral [ANAT] Of or pertaining to the mouth.

oral arm [INV ZOO] In a jellyfish, any of the prolongations of the distal end of the manubrium.

oral cavity [ANAT] The cavity of the mouth.

oral disc [INV ZOO] The flattened upper or free end of the body of a polyp that has the mouth in the center and tentacles around the margin.

oral groove [INV ZOO] A depressed, groovelike peristome.

orange [BOT] Any of various evergreen trees of the genus *Citrus*, cultivated for the edible fruit, a berry with an aromatic, leathery rind containing numerous oil glands.

orangeophile [HISTOL] A type of acidophile cell of the anterior lobe of the adenohypophysis, presumed to elaborate growth hormone.

orangutan [VERT ZOO] *Pongo pygmaeus.* The largest of the great apes, a long-armed primate distinguished by long sparse reddish-brown hair, naked face and hands and feet, and a large laryngeal cavity which appears as a pouch below the chin.

Orbiniidae [INV ZOO] A family of polychaete annelids belonging to the Sedentaria; the prostomium is exposed, and the thorax and abdomen are weakly separated.

Orbiniinae [INV ZOO] A subfamily of sedentary polychaete annelids in the family Orbiniidae.

orbit [ANAT] The bony cavity in the lateral front of the skull beneath the frontal bone which contains the eyeball. Also known as eye socket.

orbital fossa [INV ZOO] A depression from which the eyestalk arises on the front of the carapace of crustaceans.

Orbitoidacea [INV ZOO] A superfamily of foraminiferan protozoans in the suborder Rotaliina characterized by a low trochospire or a planispiral, uncoiled or branching test composed of radial calcite with bilamellar septa.

orchid [BOT] Any member of the family Orchidaceae; plants have complex, specialized irregular flowers usually with only one or two stamens.

Orchidaceae [BOT] A family of monocotyledonous plants in the order Orchidales characterized by irregular flowers with only one or two stamens which are adnate to the style, and pollen grains which cohere in large masses called pollinia.

Orchidales [BOT] An order of monocotyledonous plants in the subclass Liliidae; plants are mycotropic and sometimes nongreen with numerous tiny seeds that have an undifferentiated embryo and little or no endosperm.

orch-, orchi-, orchid-, orchido-, orchio- [ZOO] A combining form denoting testis.

order [SYST] A taxonomic category ranked below the class and above the family, made up either of families, subfamilies, or suborders.

Orectolobidae [VERT ZOO] An ancient isurid family of galeoid sharks, including the carpet and nurse sharks, which are primarily bottom feeders with small teeth and a blunt rostrum with barbels near the mouth.

oreodont [PALEON] Any member of the family Merycoidodontidae.

organ [ANAT] A differentiated structure of an organism composed of various cells or tissues and adapted for a specific function.

organelle [CELL BIO] A specialized subcellular structure, such as a mitochondrion, having a special function; a condensed system showing a high degree of internal order and definite limits of size and shape.

organic evolution [EVOL] The processes of change in organisms by which descendants come to differ from their ancestors, and a history of the sequence of such changes.

organicism See holism.

organism [BIOL] An individual constituted to carry out all life functions.

organized ferment See intracellular enzyme.

organizer [EMBRYO] Any part of the embryo which exerts a morphogenetic stimulus on an adjacent part or parts, as in the induction of the medullary plate by the dorsal lip of the blastopore.

organ of Corti [ANAT] A specialized structure located on the basilar membrane of the mammalian cochlea, which contains rods of Corti and hair cells connected to ganglia of the cochlear nerve. Also known as spiral organ.

organ of Leydig [VERT ZOO] Two large accumulations of lymphoid tissues which run longitudinally the length of the esophagus in selachian fishes.

organogenesis [EMBRYO] The formation of an organ.

organoleptic [PHYSIO] Having an effect or making an impression on sense organs; usually used in connection with subjective testing of food and drug products.

organotropic [MICROBIO] Of microorganisms, localizing in or entering the body by way of the viscera or, occasionally, somatic tissue.

organs of Zuckerkandl See aortic paraganglion.

orgasm [PHYSIO] The intense, diffuse, and subjectively pleasurable sensation experienced during sexual intercourse or genital manipulation, culminating in the male with seminal ejaculation, and in the female with uterine contractions, warm suffusion, and pelvic throbbing sensations.

Oribatei [INV ZOO] A heavily sclerotized group of free-living mites in the suborder Sarcoptiformes which serve as intermediate hosts of tapeworms.

Oribatulidae [INV ZOO] A family of oribatid mites in the suborder Sarcoptiformes.

Oriental zoogeographic region [ECOL] A zoogeographic region which encompasses tropical Asia from the Iranian Peninsula eastward through the East Indies to, and including, Borneo and the Philippines.

ormer See abalone.

Ormyridae [INV ZOO] A small family of hemipteran insects in the superfamily Chalcidoidea.

Orneodidae [INV ZOO] A small family of lepidopteran insects in the superfamily Tineoidea; adults have each wing divided into six featherlike plumes.

ornithine [BIOCHEM] $C_5H_{12}O_2N_2$ An amino acid occurring in the urine of some birds, but not found in native proteins.

Ornithischia [PALEON] An order of extinct terrestrial reptiles, popularly known as dinosaurs; distinguished by a four-pronged pelvis, and a median, toothless predentary bone at the front of the lower jaw.

ornithology [VERT ZOO] The study of birds.

Ornithopoda [PALEON] A suborder of extinct reptiles in the order Ornithischia including all bipedal forms in the order.

Ornithorhynchidae [VERT ZOO] A monospecific order of monotremes containing the semiaquatic platypus; characterized by a duck-billed snout, horny plates instead of teeth in the adult, and a flattened, well-developed tail.

Oromericidae [VERT ZOO] An extinct family of camellike tylopod ruminants in the superfamily Cameloidea.

oropharynx [ANAT] The oral pharynx, located between the lower border of the soft palate and the larynx.

orophyte [ECOL] Any plant that grows in the subalpine region.

orotic acid [BIOCHEM] $C_4H_4O_4N_2$ A crystalline acid which is a growth factor for certain bacteria and is also a pyrimidine precursor.

Orthacea [PALEON] An extinct group of articulate brachiopods in the suborder Orthidina in which the delthyrium is open.

Ortheziinae [INV ZOO] A subfamily of homopteran insects in the superfamily Coccoidea having abdominal spiracles present in all stages and a flat anal ring bearing pores and setae in immature forms and adult females.

Orthida [PALEON] An order of extinct articulate brachiopods which includes the oldest known representatives of the class.

Orthidina [PALEON] The principal suborder of the extinct Orthida, including those articulate brachiopods characterized by biconvex, finely ribbed shells with a straight hinge line and well-developed interareas on both valves.

orthoceratite [INV ZOO] Any nautiloid belonging to the genus *Orthoceras*, characterized by the presence of three longitudinal furrows on the body chamber.

orthochromatic [BIOL] Having normal staining characteristics.

orthokinesis [BIOL] Random movement of a motile cell or organism in response to a stimulus.

Orthonectida [INV ZOO] An order of Mesozoa; orthonectids parasitize various marine invertebrates as multinucleate plasmodia, and sexually mature forms are ciliated organisms.

Orthoperidae [INV ZOO] The minute fungus beetles, a family of coleopteran insects in the superfamily Cucujoidea.

Orthopsida [INV ZOO] An order of echinoderms in the subclass Euechinoidea.

Orthopsidae [PALEON] A family of extinct echinoderms in the order Hemicidaroida distinguished by a camarodont lantern.

Orthoptera [INV ZOO] A heterogeneous order of generalized insects with gradual metamorphosis, chewing mouthparts, and four wings.

Orthorrhapha [INV ZOO] A suborder of the Diptera; in this group of flies, the adult escapes from the puparium through a T-shaped opening.

orthotropism [BOT] The tendency of a plant to grow with the longer axis oriented vertically.

orthotropous [BOT] Having a straight ovule with the micropyle at the end opposite the stalk.

Orussidae [INV ZOO] A small family of hymenopteran insects in the superfamily Siricoidea.

oryctocoenosis [PALEON] The part of a thanatocoenosis that has been preserved as a fossil.

osage orange [BOT] *Maclura pomifera*. A tree in the mulberry family of the Urticales characterized by yellowish bark, milky sap, simple entire leaves, strong axillary thorns, and aggregate green fruit about the size and shape of an orange.

osazone [BIOCHEM] Any of the compounds that contain two phenylhydrazine residues and are produced by a reaction between a reducing sugar and phenylhydrazine.

Oscillatoriales [BOT] An order of blue-green algae (Cyanophyceae) which are filamentous and truly multicellular.

Oscillospira [MICROBIO] A genus of endospore-forming, motile rods or filaments of uncertain affiliation; have not been grown in pure culture.

Oscillospiraceae [MICROBIO] Formerly a family of large, gram-negative, motile bacteria of the order Caryophanales which lose motility on exposure to oxygen.

Oscines [VERT ZOO] The songbirds, a suborder of the order Passeriformes.

osculum [INV ZOO] An excurrent orifice in Porifera.

osmophile [MICROBIO] A microorganism adapted to media with high osmotic pressure.

osmoreceptor [PHYSIO] One of a group of structures in the hypothalamus which respond to changes in osmotic pressure of the blood by regulating the secretion of the neurohypophyseal antidiuretic hormone.

osmoregulatory mechanism [PHYSIO] Any physiological mechanism for the maintenance of an optimal and constant level of osmotic activity of the fluid in and around the cells.

osmotic fragility [PHYSIO] Susceptibility of red blood cells to lyses when placed in dilute (hypotonic) salt solutions.

osmotic shock [PHYSIO] The bursting of cells suspended in a dilute salt solution.

osseous [ANAT] Bony; composed of or resembling bone.

osseous system [ANAT] The skeletal system of the body.

osseous tissue [HISTOL] Bone tissue.

ossicle [ANAT] Any of certain small bones, as those of the middle ear.

ossicle [INV ZOO] Any of various calcareous bodies.

ossify [PHYSIO] To form or turn into bone.

Ostariophysi [VERT ZOO] A superorder of actinopterygian fishes distinguished by the structure of the anterior four or five vertebrae which are modified as an encasement for the bony ossicles connecting the inner ear and swim bladder.

Osteichthyes [VERT ZOO] The bony fishes, a class of fishlike vertebrates distinguished by having a bony skeleton, a swim bladder, a true gill cover, and mesodermal ganoid, cycloid, or ctenoid scales.

osteoblast [HISTOL] A bone-forming cell of mesenchymal origin.

osteoclasis [PHYSIO] 1. Destruction of bony tissue. 2. Bone resorption.

osteoclast [HISTOL] A large multinuclear cell associated with bone resorption.

osteocyte [HISTOL] A bone cell.

osteogenesis [PHYSIO] Formation or histogenesis of bone.

Osteoglossidae [VERT ZOO] The bony tongues, a family of actinopterygian fishes in the order Osteoglossiformes.

Osteoglossiformes [VERT ZOO] An order of softrayed, actinopterygian fishes distinguished by paired, usually bony rods at the base of the second gill arch, a single dorsal fin, no adipose fin, and a usually abdominal pelvic fin.

osteoid [HISTOL] The young hyaline matrix of true bone in which the calcium salts are deposited.

Osteolepidae [PALEON] A family of extinct fishes in the order Osteolepiformes.

Osteolepiformes [PALEON] A primitive order of fusiform lobefin fishes, subclass Crossopterygii, generally characterized by rhombic bony scales, two dorsal fins placed well back on the body, and a well-ossified head covered with large dermal plating bones.

osteolith [PALEON] A fossil bone.

osteology [ANAT] The study of anatomy and structure of bone.

osteolysis [PHYSIO] Resorption of bone.

osteometry [ANAT] The study of the size and proportions of the osseous system.

osteon [HISTOL] A microscopic unit of mature bone composed of layers of osteocytes and bone surrounding a central canal. Also known as Haversian system.

osteophony [PHYSIO] Conduction of sound by bone.

Osteostraci [PALEON] An order of extinct jawless vertebrates; they were mostly small, with the head and part of the body encased in a solid armor of bone, and the posterior part of the body and the tail covered with thick scales.

ostiole [BIOL] A small orifice or pore.

ostium [BIOL] A mouth, entrance, or aperture.

Ostomidae [INV ZOO] The bark-gnawing beetles, a family of coleopteran insects in the superfamily Cleroidea.

ost-, oste-, osteo- [ANAT] A combining form meaning bone.

Ostracoda [INV ZOO] A subclass of the class Crustacea containing small, bivalved aquatic forms; the body is unsegmented and there is no true abdominal region.

ostracoderm [PALEON] Any of various extinct jawless vertebrates covered with an external skeleton of bone which together with the Cyclostomata make up the class Agnatha.

Ostreidae [INV ZOO] A family of bivalve mollusks in the order Anisomyaria containing the oysters.

ostrich [VERT ZOO] *Struthio camelus.* A large running bird with soft plumage, naked head, neck and legs, small wings, and thick powerful legs with two toes on each leg; the only living species of the Struthioniformes.

Otariidae [VERT ZOO] The sea lions, a family of carnivorous mammals in the superfamily Canoidea.

Othniidae [INV ZOO] The false tiger beetles, a small family of coleopteran insects in the superfamily Tenebrionoidea.

otic [ANAT] Of or pertaining to the ear or a part thereof.

otic capsule [EMBRYO] A cartilaginous capsule surrounding the auditory vesicle during development, later fusing with the spheroid and occipital cartilages.

otic ganglion [ANAT] The nerve ganglion located immediately below the foramen ovale of the sphenoid bone.

Otitidae [INV ZOO] A family of cyclorrhaphous myodarian dipteran insects in the subsection Acalyptratae.

otocyst [EMBRYO] The auditory vesicle of vertebrate embryos. [INV ZOO] An auditory vesicle, otocell, or otidium in some invertebrates.

otolith [ANAT] A calcareous concretion on the end of a sensory hair cell in the vertebrate ear and in some invertebrates.

Otopheidomenidae [INV ZOO] A family of parasitic mites in the suborder Mesostigmata.

ot-, oto- [ANAT] A combining form meaning ear.

otter [VERT ZOO] Any of various members of the family Mustelidae, having a long thin body, short legs, a somewhat flattened head, webbed toes, and a broad flattened tail; all are adapted to aquatic life.

ovalbumin [BIOCHEM] The major, conjugated protein of eggwhite.

oval window [ANAT] The membrane-covered opening into the inner ear of tetrapods, to which the ossicles of the middle ear are connected.

ovarian [ANAT] Of or pertaining to the ovaries.

ovarian follicle [HISTOL] An ovum and its surrounding follicular cells, found in the ovarian cortex.

ovariole [INV ZOO] The tubular structural unit of an insect ovary.

ovary [ANAT] A glandular organ that produces hormones and gives rise to ova in female vertebrates. [BOT] The enlarged basal portion of a pistil that bears the ovules in angiosperms.

overdominance [GEN] Monohybrid heterosis, that is, the phenomenon of the phenotype being more pronounced in the heterozygote than in either homozygote with respect to a single specified pair of alleles.

ovicell [INV ZOO] A broad chamber in certain bryozoans.

ovicyst [INV ZOO] The pouch of a tunicate in which the eggs develop.

oviduct [ANAT] A tube that serves to conduct ova from the ovary to the exterior or to an intermediate organ such as the uterus. Also known in mammals as Fallopian tube; uterine tube.

oviger [INV ZOO] A modified leg used for carrying eggs in some pycnogonids.

oviparous [VERT ZOO] Producing eggs that develop and hatch externally.

ovipositor [INV ZOO] A specialized structure in many insects for depositing eggs. [VERT ZOO] A tubular extension of the genital orifice in most fishes.

ovoviviparous [VERT ZOO] Producing eggs that develop internally and hatch before or soon after extrusion.

ovulation [PHYSIO] Discharge of an ovum or ovule from the ovary.

ovule [BOT] A structure in the ovary of a seed plant that develops into a seed following fertilization.

ovum [CELL BIO] A female gamete. Also known as egg.

Oweniidae [INV ZOO] A family of limivorous polychaete annelids of the Sedentaria.

owl [VERT ZOO] Any of a number of diurnal and nocturnal birds of prey composing the order Strigiformes; characterized by a large head, more or less forward-directed large eyes, a short hooked bill, and strong talons.

Oxalidaceae [BOT] A family of dicotyledonous plants in the order Geraniales, generally characterized by regular flowers, two or three times as many stamens as sepals or petals, a style which is not gynobasic, and the fruit which is a beakless, loculicidal capsule.

Oxford unit [MICROBIO] The minimum quantity of penicillin which, when dissolved in 50 milliliters of a meat broth, is sufficient to inhibit completely the growth of a test strain of *Micrococcus aureus*; equivalent to the specific activity of 0.6 microgram of the master standard penicillin.

oxidase [BIOCHEM] An enzyme that catalyzes oxidation reactions by the utilization of molecular oxygen as an electron acceptor.

oxidative phosphorylation [BIOCHEM] Conversion of inorganic phosphate to the energy-rich phosphate of adenosinetriphosphatase by reactions associated with the electron transfer system.

oxidoreductase [BIOCHEM] An enzyme catalyzing a reaction in which two molecules of a compound interact so that one molecule is oxidized and the other reduced, with a molecule of water entering the reaction.

oximetry [PHYSIO] Measurement of the degree of oxygen saturation of the blood.

Oxyaenidae [PALEON] An extinct family of mammals in the order Deltatheridea; members were short-faced carnivores with powerful jaws.

oxygenase [BIOCHEM] An oxidoreductase that catalyzes the direct incorporation of oxygen into its substrate.

oxygen debt [PHYSIO] **1.** A bodily condition in which oxygen demand is greater than oxygen supply. **2.** The amount of oxygen needed to restore the body to a steady state after a muscular exertion.

oxygen toxicity [PHYSIO] Harmful effects of breathing oxygen at pressures greater than atmospheric.

oxyhemoglobin [BIOCHEM] The red crystalline pigment formed in blood by the combination of oxygen and hemoglobin, without the oxidation of iron.

oxylophyte [ECOL] A plant that thrives in or is restricted to acid soil.

Oxymonadida [INV ZOO] An order of xylophagous protozoans in the class Zoomastigophorea; colorless flagellate symbionts in the digestive tract of the roach *Cryptocercus* and of certain termites.

oxyntic cell *See* parietal cell.

oxypetalous [BOT] Having sharp-pointed petals.

oxyphytia [ECOL] Discordant habitat control due to an excessively acidic substratum.

Oxystomata [INV ZOO] A subsection of the Brachyura, including those true crabs in which the first pair of pereiopods is chelate, and the mouth frame is triangular and forward.

Oxystomatidae [INV ZOO] A family of free-living marine nematodes in the superfamily Enoploidea, distinguished by amphids that are elongated longitudinally.

oxytetracycline [MICROBIO] $C_{22}H_{24}O_9N_2$ A crystalline, amphoteric, broad-spectrum antibiotic produced by *Streptomyces rimosus*; produced commercially by fermentation.

oxytocin [BIOCHEM] $C_{43}H_{66}O_{12}N_{12}S_2$ A polypeptide hormone secreted by the neurohypophysis that stimulates contraction of the uterine muscles.

Oxyurata [INV ZOO] The equivalent name for Oxyurina.

Oxyuridae [INV ZOO] A family of the nematode superfamily Oxyuroidea.

Oxyurina [INV ZOO] A suborder of nematodes in the order Ascaridida.

Oxyuroidea [INV ZOO] A superfamily of the class Nematoda.

oyster [INV ZOO] Any of various bivalve mollusks of the family Ostreidae; the irregular shell is closed by a single adductor muscle, the foot is small or absent, and there is no siphon.

Ozawainellidae [PALEON] A family of extinct protozoans in the superfamily Fusulinacea.

P

P₁ [GEN] The parental generation; parents of the F_1 generation.

PABA *See para-*aminobenzoic acid.

paca [VERT ZOO] Any of several rodents of the genus *Cuniculus,* especially *C. paca,* with a white-spotted brown coat, found in South and Central America.

Pacchionian bodies *See* arachnoidal granulations.

pachycephalosaur [PALEON] A bone-headed dinosaur, composing the family Pachycephalosauridae.

Pachycephalosauridae [PALEON] A family of ornithischian dinosaurs characterized by a skull with a solid rounded mass of bone 10 centimeters thick above the minute brain cavity.

pachyderm [VERT ZOO] Any of various nonruminant hooved mammals characterized by thick skin, including the elephants, hippopotamuses, rhinoceroses, and others.

pachyglossal [VERT ZOO] Of lizards, having a thick tongue.

pachynema *See* pachytene.

pachytene [CELL BIO] The third stage of meiotic prophase during which paired chromosomes thicken, each chromosome splits into chromatids, and breakage and crossing over between nonsister chromatids occur. Also known as pachynema.

Pacific faunal region [ECOL] A marine littoral faunal region including offshore waters west of Central America, running from the coast of South America at about 5° south latitude to the southern tip of California.

Pacific temperate faunal region [ECOL] A marine littoral faunal region including a narrow zone in the North Pacific Ocean, from Indochina to Alaska and along the west coast of the United States to about 40° north latitude.

Pacinian corpuscle [ANAT] An encapsulated lamellar sensory nerve ending that functions as a kinesthetic receptor.

packet [BIOL] A cluster of organisms in the form of a cube resulting from cell division in three planes.

packet gland [INV ZOO] A cluster of gland cells opening through the epidermis of nemertines.

pactamycin [MICROBIO] An antitumor and antibacterial antibiotic produced by *Streptomyces pactum* var. *pactum.*

pad [ANAT] A small circumscribed mass of fatty tissue, as in terminal phalanges of the fingers or the underside of the toes of an animal, such as a dog.

paedogamy [INV ZOO] A type of autogamy in certain protozoans whereby there is mutual fertilization of gametes derived from a single cell.

paedomorphosis [EVOL] Phylogenetic change in which adults retain juvenile characters, accompanied by an increased capacity for further change; indicates potential for further evolution.

Paenungulata [VERT ZOO] A superorder of mammals, including proboscideans, xenungulates, and others.

Paeoniaceae [BOT] A monogeneric family of dicotyledonous plants in the order Dilleniales; members are mesophyllic shrubs characterized by cleft leaves, flowers with an intrastaminal disk, and seeds having copious endosperm.

Paguridae [INV ZOO] The hermit crabs, a family of decapod crustaceans belonging to the Paguridea.

Paguridea [INV ZOO] A group of anomuran decapod crustaceans in which the abdomen is nearly always asymmetrical, being either soft and twisted or bent under the thorax.

pain [PHYSIO] Patterns of somesthetic sensation, generally unpleasant, or causing suffering or distress.

pain spot [PHYSIO] Any of the small areas of skin overlying the endings of either very small myelinated (delta) or unmyelinated (C) nerve fibers whose stimulation, depending on the intensity and duration, results in the sensation of either pain or itching.

pain threshold [PHYSIO] The lowest limit for the perception of pain sensations.

Palaeacanthaspidoidei [PALEON] A suborder of extinct, placoderm fishes in the order Rhenanida; members were primitive, arthrodire-like species.

Palaeacanthocephala [INV ZOO] An order of the Acanthocephala including parasitic worms characterized by fragmented nuclei in the hypodermis, lateral placement of the chief lacunar vessels, and proboscis hooks arranged in long rows.

Palaeechinoida [PALEON] An extinct order of echinoderms in the subclass Perischoechinoidea with a rigid test in which the ambulacra bevel over the adjoining interambulacra.

Palaemonidae [INV ZOO] A family of decapod crustaceans in the group Caridea.

Palaeocaridacea [INV ZOO] An order of crustaceans in the superorder Syncarida.

Palaeocaridae [INV ZOO] A family of the crustacean order Palaeocaridacea.

Palaeoconcha [PALEON] An extinct order of simple, smooth-hinged bivalve mollusks.

Palaeocopida [PALEON] An extinct order of crustaceans in the subclass Ostracoda characterized by a straight hinge and by the anterior location for greatest height of the valve.

Palaeodonta [VERT ZOO] A suborder of artiodactylous mammals including piglike forms such as the extinct "giant pigs" and the hippopotami.

Palaeognathae [VERT ZOO] The ratites, making up a superorder of birds in the subclass Neornithes; merged with the Neognathae in some systems of classification.

Palaeoisopus [PALEON] A singular, monospecific, extinct arthropod genus related to the pycnogonida, but distinguished by flattened anterior appendages.

Palaeomastodontinae [PALEON] An extinct subfamily of elaphantoid proboscidean mammals in the family Mastodontidae.

Palaeomerycidae [PALEON] An extinct family of pecoran ruminants in the superfamily Cervoidea.

Palaeonemertini [INV ZOO] A family of the class Anopla distinguished by the two- or three-layered nature of the body-wall musculature.

Palaeonisciformes [PALEON] A large extinct order of chondrostean fishes including the earliest known and most primitive ray-finned forms.

Palaeoniscoidei [PALEON] A suborder of extinct fusiform fishes in the order Palaeonisciformes with a heavily ossified exoskeleton and thick rhombic scales on the body surface.

Palaeopantopoda [PALEON] A monogeneric order of extinct marine arthropods in the subphylum Pycnogonida.

Palaeopneustidae [INV ZOO] A family of deepsea echinoderms in the order Spatangoida characterized by an oval test, long spines, and weakly developed fascioles and petals.

Palaeopterygii [VERT ZOO] An equivalent name for the Actinopterygii.

Palaeoryctidae [PALEON] A family of extinct insectivorous mammals in the order Deltatheridia.

Palaeospondyloidea [PALEON] An ordinal name assigned to the single, tiny fish *Palaeospondylus*, known only from Middle Devonian shales in Carthness, Scotland.

Palaeotheriidae [PALEON] An extinct family of perissodactylous mammals in the superfamily Equoidea.

palaeotheriodont [VERT ZOO] Being or having lophodont teeth with longitudinal external tubercles that are connected with inner tubercles by transverse oblique crests.

palaeotropical *See* paleotropical.

palama [VERT ZOO] The membranous web on the feet of aquatic birds.

palate [ANAT] The roof of the mouth.

palatine bone [ANAT] Either of a pair of irregularly L-shaped bones forming portions of the hard palate, orbits, and nasal cavities.

palatine canal [ANAT] One of the canals in the palatine bone, giving passage to branches of the descending palatine nerve and artery.

palatine gland [ANAT] Any of numerous small oral glands on the palate of mammals.

palatine process [ANAT] A thick process that projects horizontally mediad from the medial aspect of the maxilla. [EMBRYO] An outgrowth on the ventromedial aspect of the maxillary process that develops into the definite palate.

palatine suture [ANAT] The median suture joining the bones of the palate.

palatine tonsil [ANAT] Either of a pair of almond-shaped aggregations of lymphoid tissue embedded between folds of tissue connecting the pharynx and posterior part of the tongue with the soft palate. Also known as faucial tonsil; tonsil.

palatomaxillary arch [ANAT] An arch formed by the palatine, maxillary, and premaxillary bones. Also known as maxillary arch.

palatoquadrate [VERT ZOO] A series of bones or a cartilaginous rod constituting part of the roof of the mouth or upper jaw of most nonmammalian vertebrates.

palea [BOT] 1. The upper, enclosing bract of a grass flower. 2. A chaffy scale found on the receptacle of the disk flowers of some composite plants. [INV ZOO] One of the enlarged flattened setae forming the operculum of the tube of certain polychaete worms.

Palearctic [ECOL] Pertaining to a biogeographic region including Europe, northern Asia and Arabia, and Africa north of the Sahara.

paleate [BOT] Having a covering of chaffy scales, as some rhizomes.

paleoagrostology [PALEOBOT] The study of fossil grasses.

paleoalgology [PALEOBOT] The study of fossil algae. Also known as paleophycology.

paleobiochemistry [PALEON] The study of chemical processes used by organisms that lived in the geologic past.

paleobioclimatology [PALEON] The study of climatological events affecting living organisms for millennia or longer.

paleobiocoenosis [PALEON] An assemblage of organisms that lived together in the geologic past as an interrelated community. Also known as paleocoenosis.

paleobotany [PALEON] The branch of paleontology concerned with the study of ancient and fossil plants and vegetation of the geologic past.

Paleocharaceae [PALEOBOT] An extinct group of fossil plants belonging to the Charophyta distinguished by sinistrally spiraled gyrogonites.

paleocoenosis *See* paleobiocoenosis.

Paleocopa [PALEON] An order of extinct ostracods distinguished by a long, straight hinge.

paleodepth [PALEON] The water level at which an ancient organism or group of organisms flourished.

paleoecology [PALEON] The ecology of the geologic past.

paleoherpetology [PALEON] The study of fossil reptiles.

paleoichnology [PALEON] The study of trace fossils in the fossil state. Also spelled palichnology.

paleomorphology [PALEON] The study of the form and structure of fossil remains in order to describe the original anatomy of an organism.

paleomycology [PALEOBOT] The study of fossil fungi.

Paleonthropinae [PALEON] A former subfamily of fossil man in the family Hominidae; set up to include the Neanderthalers together with Rhodesian man.

paleontology [BIOL] The study of life of the past as recorded by fossil remains.

paleopalynology [PALEON] A field of palynology concerned with fossils of microorganisms and of dissociated microscopic parts of megaorganisms.

Paleoparadoxidae [PALEON] A family of extinct hippopotamuslike animals in the order Desmostylia.

paleophycology See paleoalgology.

Paleophytic [PALEOBOT] A paleobotanic division of geologic time, signifying that period during which the pteridophytes flourished, sometime between the evolution of the algae and the appearance of the first gymnosperms. Also known as Pteridophytic.

Paleoptera [INV ZOO] A section of the insect subclass Pterygota including primitive forms that are unable to flex their wings over the abdomen when at rest.

paleosere [ECOL] A series of ecologic communities that have led to a climax community.

paleotropical [ECOL] Of or pertaining to a biogeographic region that includes the Oriental and Ethiopian regions. Also spelled palaeotropical.

paleozoology [PALEON] The branch of paleontology concerned with the study of ancient animals as recorded by fossil remains.

palindrome [GEN] A nucleic acid sequence that is self-complementary.

palingenesis [EMBRYO] Unaltered recapitulation of ancestral features by the developing stages of an organism.

Palinuridae [INV ZOO] The spiny lobsters or langoustes, a family of macruran decapod crustaceans belonging to the Scyllaridea.

palisade cell [BOT] One of the columnar cells of the palisade mesophyll which contain numerous chloroplasts.

palisade mesophyll [BOT] A tissue system of the chlorenchyma in well-differentiated broad leaves composed of closely spaced palisade cells oriented parallel to one another, but with their long axes perpendicular to the surface of the blade.

pallet [INV ZOO] One of a pair of plates on the siphon tubes of certain Bivalvia.

pallial artery [INV ZOO] The artery that supplies blood to the mantle of a mollusk.

pallial chamber [INV ZOO] The mantle cavity in mollusks.

pallial line [INV ZOO] A mark on the inner surface of a bivalve shell caused by attachment of the mantle.

pallial nerve [INV ZOO] One of the pair of dorsal nerves that innervate the mantle in mollusks.

pallial sinus [INV ZOO] An inward bend in the posterior portion of the pallial line in bivalve mollusks.

pallium [ANAT] The cerebral cortex. [INV ZOO] The mantle of a mollusk or brachiopod.

Pallopteridae [INV ZOO] A family of myodarian cyclorrhaphous dipteran insects in the subsection Acalypteratae.

palm [ANAT] The flexor or volar surface of the hand. [BOT] Any member of the monocotyledonous family Arecaceae; most are trees with a slender, unbranched trunk and a terminal crown of large leaves that are folded between the veins.

Palmales [BOT] An equivalent name for Arecales.

palmar [ANAT] Of or pertaining to the palm of the hand.

palmar aponeurosis [ANAT] Bundles of fibrous connective tissue which radiate from the tendons of the deep fascia of the forearm toward the proximal ends of the fingers.

palmar arch See deep palmar arch; superficial palmar arch.

palmar reflex [PHYSIO] Flexion of the fingers when the palm of the hand is irritated.

palmate [BOT] Having lobes, such as on leaves, that radiate from a common point. [VERT ZOO] Having webbed toes. [ZOO] Having the distal portion broad and lobed, resembling a hand with the fingers spread.

palmetto fiber [BOT] Brush or broom fiber obtained from young leafstalks of the cabbage palm tree (Sabal palmetto).

palm nut [BOT] The edible seed of the African oil palm (Elaeis guineensis).

Palmyridae [INV ZOO] A mongeneric family of errantian polychaete annelids.

palp [INV ZOO] Any of various sensory, usually fleshy appendages near the oral aperture of certain invertebrates.

palpal organ [INV ZOO] An organ on the terminal joint of each pedipalp of a male spider which functions to convey sperm to the female genital orifice.

Palpatores [INV ZOO] A suborder of long-legged arachnids in the order Phalangida.

palpebra [ANAT] The eyelid.

palpebral disk [VERT ZOO] A scale, often transparent, covering the eyelid of certain lizards.

palpebral fissure [ANAT] The opening between the eyelids.

palpebral fold [ANAT] A fold formed by the reflection of the conjunctiva from the eyelid onto the eye.

Palpicornia [INV ZOO] The equivalent name for Hydrophiloidea.

palpiger [INV ZOO] The palpi-bearing portion of an insect labium.

Palpigradida [INV ZOO] An order of rare tropical and warm-temperate arachnids; all are minute, whitish, eyeless animals with an elongate body that terminates in a slender, multisegmented flagellum set with setae.

palpocil [INV ZOO] A fine, filamentous tactile hair.

palpus [INV ZOO] 1. A process on a mouthpart of an arthropod that has a tactile or gustatory function. 2. Any similar process on other invertebrates.

paludal [ECOL] Relating to swamps or marshes and to material that is deposited in a swamp environment.

paludification [ECOL] Bog expansion resulting from the gradual rising of the water table as accumulation of peat impedes water drainage.

palustrine [ECOL] Being, living, or thriving in a marsh.

palynofacies [PALEON] An assemblage of palynomorphs in a portion of a sediment, representing local environmental conditions, but not representing the regional palynoflora.

palynology [PALEON] The study of spores, pollen, microorganisms, and microscopic fragments of megaorganisms that occur in sediments.

palynomorph [PALEON] A microscopic feature such as a spore or pollen that is of interest in palynological studies.

palynostratigraphy [PALEON] The stratigraphic application of palynologic methods.

palytoxin [BIOCHEM] A water-soluble toxin produced by several species of *Palythoa;* considered to be one of the most poisonous substances known.

pampa [ECOL] An extensive plain in South America, usually covered with grass.

Pamphiliidae [INV ZOO] The web-spinning sawflies, a family of hymenopteran insects in the superfamily Megalodontoidea.

pampiniform [ANAT] Of the network of veins in the spermatic cord and in the broad ligament, having the form of a tendril.

pampiniform plexus [ANAT] A venous network in the spermatic cord in the male, and in the broad ligament in the female.

pamprodactylous [VERT ZOO] Having the toes turned forward, as of certain birds.

Panama disease [PL PATH] A fungus disease of banana caused by invasion of the vascular system by *Fusarium oxysporum cubense*, resulting in yellowing and wilting of the foliage and ultimate death of the shoots.

Pancarida [INV ZOO] A superorder of the subclass Malacostraca; the cylindrical, cruciform body lacks an external division between the thorax and pleon and has the cephalon united with the first thoracomere.

panclimax [ECOL] Two or more related climax communities or formations having similar climate, life forms, and genera or dominants. Also known as panformation.

pancreas [ANAT] A composite gland in most vertebrates that produces and secretes digestive enzymes, as well as at least two hormones, insulin and glucagon.

pancreatic diverticulum [EMBRYO] One of two diverticula (dorsal and ventral) from the embryonic duodenum or hepatic diverticulum that form the pancreas or its ducts.

pancreatic duct [ANAT] The main duct of the pancreas formed from the dorsal and ventral pancreatic ducts of the embryo.

pancreatic juice [PHYSIO] The thick, transparent, colorless secretion of the pancreas.

pancreatic lipase See steapsin.

pancreatin [BIOCHEM] A cream-colored, amorphous powder obtained from the fresh pancreas of a hog; contains amylopsin, trypsin, steapsin, and other enzymes.

pancreozymin [BIOCHEM] A crude extract of the intestinal mucosa that stimulates secretion of pancreatic juice.

panda [VERT ZOO] Either of two Asian species of carnivores in the family Procyonidae; the red panda (*Ailurus fulgens*) has long, thick, red fur, with black legs; the giant panda (*Ailuropoda melanoleuca*) is white, with black legs and black patches around the eyes.

Pandanaceae [BOT] The single, pantropical family of the plant order Pandanales.

Pandanales [BOT] A monofamilial order of monocotyledonous plants; members are more or less arborescent and sparingly branched, with numerous long, firm, narrow, parallel-veined leaves that usually have spiny margins.

Pandaridae [INV ZOO] A family of dimorphic crustaceans in the suborder Caligoida; members are external parasites of sharks.

Pandionidae [VERT ZOO] A monospecific family of birds in the order Falconiformes; includes the osprey (*Pandion haliaetus*), characterized by a reversible hindtoe, well-developed claws, and spicules on the scales of the feet.

pandurate [BOT] Of a leaf, having the outline of a fiddle.

Paneth cells See cells of Paneth.

panformation See panclimax.

pangene [CELL BIO] A hypothetical heredity-controlling protoplasmic particle proposed by Darwin.

pangenesis [BIOL] Darwin's comprehensive theory of heredity and development, according to which all parts of the body give off gemmules which aggregate in the germ cells; during development, they are sorted out from one another and give rise to parts similar to those of their origin.

pangolin [VERT ZOO] Any of seven species composing the mammalian family Manidae; the entire dorsal surface of the body is covered with broad, horny scales, the small head is elongate, and the mouth is terminal in the snout.

panicle [BOT] A branched or compound raceme in which the secondary branches are often racemose as well.

panmixis [BIOL] Random mating within a breeding population; in a closed population this results in a high degree of uniformity.

Panmycin [MICROBIO] A trade name for tetracycline.

panniculus [ANAT] A membrane or layer.

pannose [BIOL] Having a felty or woolly texture.

panspermia [BIOL] A 19th-century theory in opposition to the theory of spontaneous generation and proposing that all reproductive bodies are universal, developing wherever there is a favorable environment.

pansporoblast [INV ZOO] A sporont of cnidosporan protozoans that contains two sporoblasts.

Pantodonta [PALEON] An extinct order of mammals which included the first large land animals of the Tertiary.

Pantodontidae [VERT ZOO] A family of fishes in the order Osteoglossiformes; the single, small species is known as African butterflyfish because of its expansive pectoral fins.

Pantolambdidae [PALEON] A family of middle to late Paleocene mammals of North America in the superfamily Pantolambdoidea.

Pantolambdodontidae [PALEON] A family of late Eocene mammals of Asia in the superfamily Pantolambdoidea.

Pantolambdoidea [PALEON] A superfamily of extinct mammals in the order Pantodonta.

Pantolestidae [PALEON] An extinct family of large aquatic insectivores referred to the Proteutheria.

pantophagous [ZOO] Feeding on a variety of foods.

Pantophthalmidae [INV ZOO] The wood-boring flies, a family of orthorrhaphous dipteran insects in the series Brachycera.

Pantopoda [INV ZOO] The equivalent name for Pycnogonida.

pantothenate [BIOCHEM] A salt or ester of pantothenic acid.

pantothenic acid [BIOCHEM] $C_9H_{17}O_5N$ A member of the vitamin B complex that is essential for nutrition of some animal species. Also known as vitamin B_3.

Pantotheria [PALEON] An infraclass of carnivorous and insectivorous Jurassic mammals; early members retained many reptilian features of the jaws.

papain [BIOCHEM] An enzyme preparation obtained from the juice of the fruit and leaves of the papaya (*Carica papaya*); contains proteolytic enzymes.

Papaveraceae [BOT] A family of dicotyledonous plants in the order Papaverales, with regular flowers, numerous stamens, and a well-developed latex system.

Papaverales [BOT] An order of dicotyledonous plants in the subclass Magnoliidae, marked by a syncarpous gynoecium, parietal placentation, and only two sepals.

Papilionidae [INV ZOO] A family of lepidopteran insects in the superfamily Papilionoidea; members are the only butterflies with fully developed forelegs bearing an epiphysis.

Papilionoidea [INV ZOO] A superfamily of diurnal butterflies (Lepidoptera) with clubbed antennae, which are rounded at the tip, and forewings that always have two or more veins.

Papilionoideae [BOT] A subfamily of the family Leguminosae with characteristic irregular flowers that have a banner, two wing petals, and two lower petals united to form a boat-shaped keel.

papilla [BIOL] A small, nipplelike eminence.

papilla of Vater *See* ampulla of Vater.

papillary muscle [ANAT] Any of the muscular eminences in the ventricles of the heart from which the chordae tendineae arise.

papillate [BIOL] 1. Having or covered with papillae. 2. Resembling a papilla.

papovavirus [VIROL] A deoxyribonucleic acid–containing group of animal viruses, including papilloma and vacuolating viruses.

Pappotheriidae [PALEON] A family of primitive, tenreclike Cretaceous insectivores assigned to the Proteutheria.

pappus [BOT] An appendage or group of appendages consisting of a modified perianth on the ovary or fruit of various seed plants; adapted to dispersal by wind and other means.

paprika [BOT] *Capsicum annuum*. A type of pepper with nonpungent flesh, grown for its long red fruit from which a dried, ground condiment is prepared.

papula [BIOL] A small papilla.

paraaortic body [ANAT] One of the small masses of chromaffin tissue lying along the abdominal aorta. Also known as glomus aorticum.

parabasal body *See* kinetoplast.

parabiosis [BIOL] Experimental joining of two individuals to study the effects of one partner upon the other.

Paracanthopterygii [VERT ZOO] A superorder of teleost fishes, including the codfishes and allied groups.

paracentric inversion [GEN] A type of chromosomal alteration that occurs within one arm of a chromosome and does not span the centromere.

Paracoccus [MICROBIO] A genus of gram-negative, aerobic, coccoid, or nearly spherical bacteria of uncertain affiliation.

paracolon bacteria [MICROBIO] A group of bacteria intermediate between the *Escherichia-Aerobacter* genera and the *Salmonella-Shigella* group.

paracondyloid [VERT ZOO] A process on the outer side of each condyle of the occipital bone in the skull of certain mammals.

paracone [VERT ZOO] 1. The anterior cusp of a primitive tricuspid upper molar. 2. The principal anterior, external cusp of an upper molar in higher forms.

paraconid [VERT ZOO] 1. The cusp of a primitive lower molar corresponding to the paracone. 2. The anterior, internal cusp of a lower molar in higher forms.

Paracrinoidea [PALEON] A class of extinct Crinozoa characterized by the numerous, irregularly arranged plates, uniserial armlike appendages, and no clear distinction between adoral and aboral surfaces.

Paracucumidae [INV ZOO] A family of holothurian echinoderms in the order Dendrochirotida; the body is invested with plates and has a simplified calcareous ring.

paradidymis [ANAT] Atrophic remains of the paragenital tubules of the mesonephros, occurring near the convolutions of the epididymal duct.

paraganglion [ANAT] Any of various isolated chromaffin bodies associated with structures such

as the abdominal aorta, heart, kidney, and gonads. Also known as chromaffin body.

paragastric [ANAT] Located near the stomach.
[INV ZOO] A cavity in Porifera into which radial
canals open, and which opens to the outside
through the cloaca.

paragnath [INV ZOO] 1. One of the paired leaflike
lobes of the metastoma situated behind the mandibles in most crustaceans. 2. One of the paired
lobes of the hypopharynx in certain insects. 3.
One of the small, sharp and hard jaws of certain
annelids.

parainfluenza [MICROBIO] An organism exhibiting growth characteristics of *Hemophilus influenzae*.

parakeet [VERT ZOO] Any of various small, slender species of parrots with long tails in the family
Psittacidae.

parallel evolution [EVOL] Evolution of similar
characteristics in different groups of organisms.

parallel muscle [ANAT] Any muscle having the
long fibers arranged parallel to each other.

parallel-veined [BOT] Of a leaf, having the veins
parallel, or nearly parallel, to each other.

paralutein cells [HISTOL] Epithelioid cells of the
corpus luteum.

paralytic secretion [PHYSIO] Glandular secretion
occurring in a denervated gland.

Parameciidae [INV ZOO] A family of ciliated protozoans in the order Holotrichia; the body has
differentiated anterior and posterior ends and is
bounded by a hard but elastic pellicle.

paramecium [INV ZOO] A single-celled protozoan
belonging to the family Parameciidae.

Paramecium [INV ZOO] The genus of protozoans
composing the family Parameciidae.

Paramelina [VERT ZOO] An order of marsupials
that includes the bandicoots in some systems of
classification.

paramere [BIOL] One half of a bilaterally symmetrical animal or somite. [INV ZOO] Any of
several paired structures of an insect, especially
those on the ninth abdominal segment.

paramesonephric duct [EMBRYO] An embryonic
genital duct; in the female, it is the anlage of
the oviducts, uterus, and vagina; in the male, it
degenerates, leaving the appendix testes. Also
known as Müllerian duct.

paramo [ECOL] A biological community, essentially a grassland, covering extensive high areas
in equatorial mountains of the Western Hemisphere.

paramutation [GEN] A mutation in which one
member of a heterozygous pair of alleles permanently changes its partner allele.

paramylum [BIOCHEM] A reserve, starchlike carbohydrate of various protozoans and algae.

paramyosin [BIOCHEM] A type of fibrous protein
found in the adductor muscles of bivalves and
thought to form the core of a filament with myosin
molecules at the surface.

paramyxovirus [VIROL] A subgroup of myxoviruses, including the viruses of mumps, measles,
parainfluenza, and Newcastle disease; all are ribonucleic acid–containing viruses and possess an
ether-sensitive lipoprotein envelope.

Paranaplasma [MICROBIO] A genus of the family
Anaplasmataceae; organisms form inclusions with
appendages in red blood cells of cattle.

paranasal sinus [ANAT] Any of the paired sinus
cavities of the human face; includes the frontal,
ethmoid, and sphenoid sinuses.

paranthropophytia [ECOL] Discrepant control of
regions or areas due to immediate and continuous or periodic interference, as by certain cultivation practices.

Paranyrocidae [PALEON] An extinct family of
birds in the order Anseriformes, restricted to
the Miocene of South Dakota.

Paraonidae [INV ZOO] A family of small, slender
polychaete annelids belonging to the Seden-
teria.

Paraparchitacea [PALEON] A superfamily of extinct ostracods in the suborder Kloedenellocopina including nonsulcate, nondimorphic forms.

parapatric [ECOL] Referring to populations or
species that occupy nonoverlapping but adjacent
geographical areas without interbreeding.

paraphysis [BOT] A sterile filament borne among
the sporogenous or gametogenous organs in many
cryptogams. [VERT ZOO] A median evagination
of the roof of the telencephalon of some lower
vertebrates.

parapodium [INV ZOO] 1. One of the short, paired
processes on the sides of the body segments in
certain annelids. 2. A lateral expansion of the
foot in gastropod mollusks.

parapolar cell [INV ZOO] Either of the first two
trunk cells in the development of certain Mesozoa.

Parasalenidae [INV ZOO] A family of echinacean
echinoderms in the order Echinoida composed
of oblong forms with trigeminate ambulacral
plates.

Paraselloidea [INV ZOO] A group of the Asellota
that contains forms in which the first pleopods
of the male are coupled along the midline, and
are lacking in the female.

Paraseminotidae [PALEON] A family of Lower
Triassic fishes in the order Palaeonisciformes.

parasexual cycle [GEN] A series of events leading to genetic recombination in vegetative or somatic cells; it was first described in filamentous
fungi; there are three essential steps: heterokaryosis; fusion of unlike haploid nuclei in the heterokaryon to yield heterozygous diploid nuclei;
and recombination and segregation at mitosis by
two independent processes, mitotic crossing-over
and loss of chromosomes.

parasite [BIOL] An organism that lives in or on
another organism of different species from which
it derives nutrients and shelter.

Parasitica [INV ZOO] A group of hymenopteran
insects that includes four superfamilies of the
Apocrita: Ichneumonoidea, Chalcidoidea, Cynipoidea, and Proctotrupoidea; some are phytophagous, while others are parasites of other
insects.

parasitic castration [BIOL] Destruction of the
reproductive organs by parasites.

parasitism [ECOL] A symbiotic relationship in
which the host is harmed, but not killed im-

mediately, and the species feeding on it is benefited.

parasitoidism [BIOL] Systematic feeding by an insect larva on living host tissues so that the host will live until completion of larval development.

parasitology [BIOL] A branch of biology which deals with those organisms, plant or animal, which have become dependent on other living creatures.

parasphenoid [VERT ZOO] A bone in the base of the skull of many vertebrates.

parastacidae [INV ZOO] A family of crayfishes assigned to the Nephropoidea.

parastyle [VERT ZOO] A small cusp anterior to the paracone of an upper molar.

Parasuchia [PALEON] The equivalent name for Phytosauria.

parasympathetic [ANAT] Of or pertaining to the craniosacral division of the autonomic nervous system.

parasympathetic nervous system [ANAT] The craniosacral portion of the autonomic nervous system, consisting of preganglionic nerve fibers in certain sacral and cranial nerves, outlying ganglia, and postganglionic fibers.

parathormone [BIOCHEM] A polypeptide hormone that functions in regulating calcium and phosphate metabolism. Also known as parathyroid hormone.

Parathuramminacea [PALEON] An extinct superfamily of foraminiferans in the suborder Fusulinina, with a test having a globular or tubular chamber and a simple, undifferentiated wall.

parathyroid gland [ANAT] A paired endocrine organ located within, on, or near the thyroid gland in the neck region of all vertebrates except fishes.

paratroch [INV ZOO] The ciliated band encircling the anus in certain trichophore larvae.

paratype [SYST] A specimen other than the holotype which is before the author at the time of original description and which is designated as such or is clearly indicated as being one of the specimens upon which the original description was based.

parauterine organ [INV ZOO] In certain tapeworms, a pouchlike sac which receives and retains the embryos.

paraxonic [VERT ZOO] Pertaining to a state or condition wherein the axis of the foot lies between the third and fourth digits.

Parazoa [INV ZOO] A name proposed for a subkingdom of animals which includes the sponges (Porifera).

Parelasauridae [PALEON] A family of large, heavy-boned terrestrial reptiles of the late Permian, assigned to the order Cotylosauria.

parenchyma [BOT] A tissue of higher plants consisting of living cells with thin walls that are agents of photosynthesis and storage; abundant in leaves, roots, and the pulp of fruit, and found also in leaves and stems. [HISTOL] The specialized epithelial portion of an organ, as contrasted with the supporting connective tissue and nutritive framework.

parenchymella See diploblastula.

parenchymula [INV ZOO] The flagellate larva of calcinean sponges in which there is a cavity filled with gelatinous connective tissue.

Pareulepidae [INV ZOO] A monogeneric family of errantian polychaete annelids.

parietal [ANAT] Of or situated on the wall of an organ or other body structure. [BOT] Of a plant part, having a peripheral location or orientation; in particular, attached to the main wall of an ovary.

parietal bone [ANAT] The bone that forms the side and roof of the cranium.

parietal cell [HISTOL] One of the peripheral, hydrochloric acid–secreting cells in the gastric fundic glands. Also known as acid cell; delomorphous cell; oxyntic cell.

Parietales [BOT] An order of plants in the Englerian system; families are placed in the order Violales in other systems.

parietal lobe [ANAT] The cerebral lobe of the brain above the lateral cerebral sulcus and behind the central sulcus.

parietal peritoneum [ANAT] The portion of the peritoneum lining the interior of the body wall.

parietal pleura [ANAT] The pleura lining the inner surface of the thoracic cavity.

Parkinje effect See Purkinje effect.

parkland See temperate woodland; tropical woodland.

Parmeliaceae [BOT] The foliose shield lichens, a family of the order Lecanorales.

Parnidae [INV ZOO] The equivalent name for Dryopidae.

paromomycin [MICROBIO] A broad-spectrum antibiotic produced by *Streptomyces rimosus forma paromomycinus;* it is effective in the treatment of intestinal amebiasis in humans.

paronychium See perionychium.

parotid duct [ANAT] The duct of the parotid gland. Also known as Stensen's duct.

parotid gland [ANAT] The salivary gland in front of and below the external ear; the largest salivary gland in humans; a compound racemose serous gland that communicates with the mouth by Steno's duct.

parovarium See epoophoron.

parrot [VERT ZOO] Any member of the avian family Psittacidae, distinguished by the short, stout, strongly hooked beak.

pars anterior [ANAT] The major secretory portion of the anterior lobe of the adenohypophysis. Also known as pars distalis.

pars distalis See pars anterior.

pars intermedia [ANAT] The intermediate lobe of the adenohypophysis.

parsley [BOT] *Petroselinum crispum.* A biennial herb of European origin belonging to the order Umbellales; grown for its edible foliage.

pars nervosa [ANAT] The inferior subdivision of the neurohypophysis. Also known as pars neuralis.

pars neuralis See pars nervosa.

parsnip [BOT] *Pastinaca sativa.* A biennial herb of Mediterranean origin belonging to the order Umbellales; grown for its edible thickened taproot.

pars tuberalis [ANAT] A pair of processes that grow forward or upward along the stalk of the adenohypophysis.

parthenita [INV ZOO] A stage, such as the sporocyst, redia, or cercaria, in the development of a fluke which reproduces parthenogenetically.

parthenocarpy [BOT] Production of fruit without fertilization.

parthenogenesis [INV ZOO] A special type of sexual reproduction in which an egg develops without entrance of a sperm; common among rotifers, aphids, thrips, ants, bees, and wasps.

parthenomerogony [EMBRYO] Development of a nucleated fragment of an unfertilized egg following parthenogenetic stimulation.

partial cleavage [EMBRYO] Cleavage in which only part of the egg divides into blastomeres.

partridge [VERT ZOO] Any of the game birds comprising the genera *Alectoris* and *Perdix* in the family Phasianidae.

parvovirus [VIROL] The equivalent name for picodnavirus.

pasmo [PL PATH] A destructive fungus disease of flax caused by *Mycosphaerella linorum*.

Passalidae [INV ZOO] The peg beetles, a family of tropical coleopteran insects in the superfamily Scarabaeoidea.

Passeres [VERT ZOO] The equivalent name for Oscines.

Passeriformes [VERT ZOO] A large order of perching birds comprising two major divisions: Suboscines and Oscines.

Passifloraceae [BOT] A family of dicotyledonous, often climbing plants in the order Violales; flowers are polypetalous and hypogynous with a corona, and seeds are arillate with an oily endosperm.

Pasteur-Chamberland filter [MICROBIO] A porcelain filter with small pores used in filtration sterilization.

Pasteur effect [MICROBIO] Inhibition of fermentation by supplying an abundance of oxygen to replace anerobic conditions.

Pasteurella [MICROBIO] A genus of gram-negative, ovoid or rod-shaped bacteria of uncertain affiliation; distinguished by bipolar straining; parasites on mammals, including humans, and birds.

Pasteuria [MICROBIO] A genus of budding bacteria; cells are spherical to pear-shaped; reproduce by budding at the rounded end.

Pasteuriaceae [MICROBIO] Formerly a family of stalked bacteria in the order Hyphomicrobiales.

patagium [VERT ZOO] 1. A membrane or fold of skin extending between the forelimbs and hindlimbs of flying squirrels, flying lizards, and other arboreal animals. 2. A membrane or fold of skin on a bird's wing anterior to the humeral and radioulnar bones.

patch budding [BOT] Budding in which a small rectangular patch of bark bearing the scion (a bud) is fitted into a corresponding opening in the bark of the stock.

patella [ANAT] A sesamoid bone in front of the knee, developed in the tendon of the quadriceps femoris muscle. Also known as kneecap.

Patellacea [PALEON] An extinct superfamily of gastropod mollusks in the order Aspidobranchia which developed a cap-shaped shell and were specialized for clinging to rock.

Patellidae [INV ZOO] The true limpets, a family of gastropod mollusks in the order Archeogastropoda.

Paterinida [PALEON] A small extinct order of inarticulated brachiopods, characterized by a thin shell of calcium phosphate and convex valves.

pathotoxin [PL PATH] A chemical of biological origin, other than an enzyme, that plays an important causal role in a plant disease.

paua *See* abalone.

Paucituberculata [VERT ZOO] An order of marsupial mammals in some systems of classification, including the opossum, rats, and polydolopids.

paunch [ANAT] In colloquial usage, the cavity of the abdomen and its contents. [VERT ZOO] *See* rumen.

paurometabolous metamorphosis [INV ZOO] A simple, gradual, direct metamorphosis in which immature forms resemble the adult except in size and are referred to as nymphs.

Pauropoda [INV ZOO] A class of the Myriapoda distinguished by bifurcate antennae, 12 trunk segments with 9 pairs of functional legs, and the lack of eyes, spiracles, tracheae, and a circulatory system.

Paussidae [INV ZOO] The flat-horned beetles, a family of coleopteran insects in the suborder Adephaga.

Pavlov's pouch [PHYSIO] A small portion of stomach, completely separated from the main stomach, but retaining its vagal nerve branches, which communicates with the exterior; used in the long-term investigation of gastric secretion, and particularly in the study of conditioned reflexes.

paw [VERT ZOO] The foot of an animal, especially a quadruped having claws.

paxilla [INV ZOO] A pillarlike spine in certain starfishes that sometimes has a flattened summit covered with spinules.

Paxillosida [INV ZOO] An order of the Asteroidea in some systems of classification, equivalent to the Paxillosina.

Paxillosina [INV ZOO] A suborder of the Phanerozonida with pointed tube feet which lack suckers, and with paxillae covering the upper body surface.

PBI test *See* protein-bound iodine test.

PC *See* phosphocreatine.

pea [BOT] 1. *Pisum sativum.* The garden pea, an annual leafy leguminous vine cultivated for its smooth or wrinkled, round edible seeds which are borne in dehiscent pods. 2. Any of several related or similar cultivated plants.

peach [BOT] *Prunus persica.* A low, spreading, freely branching tree of the order Rosales, cultivated in less rigorous parts of the temperate zone for its edible fruit, a juicy drupe with a single large seed, a pulpy yellow or white mesocarp, and a thin firm epicarp.

peak zone [PALEON] An informal biostratigraphic zone consisting of a body of strata characterized by the exceptional abundance of some taxon (or taxa) or representing the maximum development of some taxon.

peanut [BOT] *Arachis hypogaea*. A low, branching, self-pollinated annual legume cultivated for its edible seed, which is a one-loculed legume formed beneath the soil in a pod.

pear [BOT] Any of several tree species of the genus *Pyrus* in the order Rosales, cultivated for their fruit, a pome that is wider at the apical end and has stone cells throughout the flesh.

peat ball [ECOL] A lake ball containing an abundance of peaty fragments.

peat flow [ECOL] A mudflow of peat produced in a peat bog by a bog burst.

peat moss [ECOL] Moss, especially sphagnum moss, from which peat has been produced.

pébrine [INV ZOO] A contagious protozoan disease of silkworms and other caterpillars caused by *Nosema bombycis*.

pecan [BOT] *Carya illinoensis*. A large deciduous hickory tree in the order Fagales which produces an edible, oblong, thin-shelled nut.

peccary [VERT ZOO] Either of two species of small piglike mammals in the genus *Tayassu*, composing the family Tayassuidae.

pecking order [VERT ZOO] A hierarchy of social dominance within a flock of poultry where each bird is allowed to peck another lower in the scale and must submit to pecking by one of higher rank.

Pecora [VERT ZOO] An infraorder of the Artiodactyla; includes those ruminants with a reduced ulna and usually with antlers, horns, or deciduous horns.

pecten [ZOO] Any of various comblike structures possessed by animals.

Pectenidae [INV ZOO] A family of bivalve mollusks in the order Anisomyaria; contains the scallops.

pectic acid [BIOCHEM] A complex acid, partially demethylated, obtained from the pectin of fruits.

pectin [BIOCHEM] A purified carbohydrate obtained from the inner portion of the rind of citrus fruits, or from apple pomace; consists chiefly of partially methoxylated polygalacturonic acids.

Pectinariidae [INV ZOO] The cone worms, a family of polychaete annelids belonging to the Sedentaria.

pectinase [BIOCHEM] An enzyme that catalyzes the transformation of pectin into sugars and galacturonic acid.

pectinesterase [BIOCHEM] An enzyme that catalyzes the hydrolytic breakdown of pectins to pectic acids.

pectineus [ANAT] A muscle arising from the pubis and inserted on the femur.

Pectinibranchia [INV ZOO] An order of gastropod mollusks which contains many families of snails; respiration is by means of ctenidia, the nervous system is not concentrated, and sexes are separate.

Pectobothridia [INV ZOO] A subclass of parasitic worms in the class Trematoda, characterized by caudal hooks or hard posterior suckers or both.

pectoral fin [VERT ZOO] One of the pair of fins of fishes corresponding to forelimbs of a quadruped.

pectoral girdle [ANAT] The system of bones supporting the upper or anterior limbs in vertebrates. Also known as shoulder girdle.

pectoralis major [ANAT] The large muscle connecting the anterior aspect of the chest with the shoulder and upper arm.

pectoralis minor [ANAT] The small, deep muscle connecting the third to fifth ribs with the scapula.

pedal [BIOL] Of or pertaining to the foot.

pedal disk [INV ZOO] The broad, flat base of many sea anemones, used for attachment to a substrate.

pedal ganglion [INV ZOO] One of the paired ganglia supplying nerves to the foot muscles in most mollusks.

pedal gland *See* foot gland.

pedate [BIOL] 1. Having toelike parts. 2. Having a foot. 3. Having tube feet.

pedicel [BOT] 1. The stem of a fruiting or spore-bearing organ. 2. The stem of a single flower. [ZOO] A short stalk in an animal body.

pedicellaria [INV ZOO] In echinoids and starfishes, any of various small grasping organs in the form of a beak carried on a stalk.

pedicellate [BIOL] Having a pedicel.

Pedicellinea [INV ZOO] The single order of the class Calyssozoa, including all entoproct bryozoans.

pedicle [ANAT] A slender process acting as a foot or stalk (as the base of a tumor), or the basal portion of an organ that is continuous with other structures.

pedigree [GEN] The ancestral line of an individual.

Pedilidae [INV ZOO] The false ant-loving flower beetles, a family of coleopteran insects in the superfamily Tenebrionoidea.

Pedinidae [INV ZOO] The single family of the order Pedinoida.

Pedinoida [INV ZOO] An order of Diadematacea making up those forms of echinoderms which possess solid spines and a rigid test.

Pediococcus [MICROBIO] A genus of bacteria in the family Streptococcaceae; cells occur in pairs or tetrads; ferment glucose with production of inactive lactic acid (homofermentative).

Pedionomidae [VERT ZOO] A family of quaillike birds in the order Gruiformes.

Pedipalpida [INV ZOO] Former order of the Arachnida; these animals are now placed in the orders Uropygi and Amblypygi.

pedipalpus [INV ZOO] One of the second pair of appendages of an arachnid.

Pedomicrobium [MICROBIO] A genus of prosthecate bacteria; cells are pear-, bean-, or rod-shaped or oval; reproduction is by budding at hyphal tips or directly on mother cells; iron or manganese oxides are deposited on mother cells or hyphae.

peduncle [ANAT] A band of white fibers joining different portions of the brain. [BOT] 1. A flower-bearing stalk. 2. A stalk supporting the fruiting body of certain thallophytes. [INV ZOO] The stalk supporting the whole or a large part of the body of certain crinoids, brachiopods, and barnacles.

pedunculate [BIOL] 1. Having or growing on a peduncle. 2. Being attached to a peduncle.

Pegasidae [VERT ZOO] The single family of the order Pegasiformes.

Pegasiformes [VERT ZOO] The sea moths or sea dragons, a small order of actinopterygian fishes; the anterior of the body is encased in bone, and the nasal bones are enlarged to form a rostrum that projects well forward of the mouth.

peg graft [BOT] A graft made by driving a scion of leafless dormant wood with wedge-shaped base into an opening in the stock and sealing with wax or other material.

Peisidicidae [INV ZOO] A monogeneric family of polychaete annelids belonging to the Errantia.

Peking man [PALEON] *Sinanthropus pekinensis*. An extinct human type; the braincase was thick, with a massive basal and occipital torus structure and heavy browridges.

pelargonidin [BIOCHEM] An anthocyanidin pigment obtained by hydrolysis of pelargonin in the form of its red-brown crystalline chloride, $C_{15}H_{11}ClO_5$.

pelargonin [BIOCHEM] An anthocyanin obtained from the dried petals of red pelargoniums or blue cornflowers in the form of its red crystalline chloride, $C_{27}H_{31}ClO_{15}$.

Pelecanidae [VERT ZOO] The pelicans, a family of aquatic birds in the order Pelecaniformes.

Pelecaniformes [VERT ZOO] An order of aquatic, fish-eating birds characterized by having all four toes joined by webs.

Pelecanoididae [VERT ZOO] The diving petrels, a family of oceanic birds in the order Procellariiformes.

Pelecinidae [INV ZOO] The pelecinid wasps, a monospecific family of hymenopteran insects in the superfamily Proctotrupoidea.

Pelecypoda [INV ZOO] The equivalent name for Bivalvia.

pelican [VERT ZOO] Any of several species of birds composing the family Pelecanidae, distinguished by the extremely large bill which has a distensible pouch under the lower mandible.

pellet [VERT ZOO] A mass of undigestible material regurgitated by a carnivorous bird.

pellicle [CELL BIO] A plasma membrane. [INV ZOO] A thin protective membrane, as on certain protozoans.

pellicularia disease [PL PATH] A fungus disease of coffee and other tropical plants caused by *Pellicularia koleroga* and characterized by leaf spots.

Pelmatozoa [INV ZOO] A division of the Echinodermata made up of those forms which are anchored to the substrate during at least part of their life history.

Pelobatidae [VERT ZOO] A family of frogs in the suborder Anomocoela, including the spadefoot toads.

Pelodictyon [MICROBIO] A genus of bacteria in the family Chlorobiaceae; cells are rod-shaped to ovoid and arranged in netlike aggregates, are nonmotile, contain gas vacuoles, and are free-living.

Pelodytidae [VERT ZOO] A family of frogs in the suborder Anomocoela.

Pelogonidae [INV ZOO] The equivalent name for Ochteridae.

Pelomedusidae [VERT ZOO] The side-necked or hidden-necked turtles, a family of the order Chelonia.

Pelonema [MICROBIO] A genus of bacteria in the family Pelonemataceae; cells have a smooth, delicate wall and usually contain gas vacuoles.

Pelonemataceae [MICROBIO] A family of gliding bacteria of uncertain affiliation; straight, flexuous, or spiral, unbranched filaments containing colorless, cylindrical cells.

Pelopidae [INV ZOO] A family of oribatid mites, order Sarcoptiformes.

Peloploca [MICROBIO] A genus of bacteria in the family Pelonemataceae; filaments are uniform, are bound together to form bundles, and are with or without a sheath; cells have delicate walls; gas vacuoles may be present.

Peloplocaceae [MICROBIO] Formerly a family in the order Chlamydobacteriales; long, unbranched trichomes in a delicate sheath.

Peloridiidae [INV ZOO] The single family of the homopteran series Coleorrhyncha.

Pelosigma [MICROBIO] A genus of bacteria of uncertain affiliation; cells are slender, S-shaped filaments with a slight spiral twist; usually arranged in flat groups of four or multiples thereof.

pelouse *See* meadow.

peltate [BOT] Of leaves, having the petiole attached to the lower surface instead of the base.

pelvic cavity *See* pelvis.

pelvic fin [VERT ZOO] One of the pair of fins of fishes corresponding to the hindlimbs of a quadruped.

pelvic girdle [ANAT] The system of bones supporting the lower limbs, or the hindlimbs, of vertebrates.

pelvic index [ANAT] The ratio of the anteroposterior diameter to the transverse diameter of the pelvis.

pelvis [ANAT] 1. The main, basin-shaped cavity of the kidney into which urine is discharged by nephrons. 2. The basin-shaped structure formed by the hipbones together with the sacrum and coccyx, or caudal vertebrae. 3. The cavity of the bony pelvis. Also known as pelvic cavity.

Pelycosauria [PALEON] An extinct order of primitive, mammallike reptiles of the subclass Synapsida, characterized by a temporal fossa that lies low on the side of the skull.

Penaeidea [INV ZOO] A primitive section of the Decapoda in the suborder Natantia; in these forms, the pleurae of the first abdominal somite overlap those of the second, the third legs are chelate, and the gills are dendrobranchiate.

penesaline [ECOL] Referring to an environment intermediate between normal marine and saline, characterized by evaporitic carbonates often interbedded with gypsum or anhydrite, and by a salinity high enough to be toxic to normal marine organisms.

penetrance [GEN] The proportion of individuals carrying a dominant gene in the heterozygous condition or a recessive gene in the homozygous condition in which the specific phenotypic effect is apparent. Also known as gene penetrance.

penetrant [INV ZOO] A large barbed nematocyst that pierces the body of the prey and injects a paralyzing agent.

penetration gland [INV ZOO] A gland at the anterior end of certain cercariae that secretes a histolytic substance.

penguin [VERT ZOO] Any member of the avian order Sphenisciformes; structurally modified wings do not fold and they function like flippers, the tail is short, feet are short and webbed, and the legs are set far back on the body.

penicillate [BIOL] Having a tuft of fine hairs.

penicillin [MICROBIO] 1. The collective name for salts of a series of antibiotic organic acids produced by a number of *Penicillium* and *Aspergillus* species; active against most gram-positive bacteria and some gram-negative cocci. 2. *See* benzyl penicillin sodium.

penicillinase [BIOCHEM] A bacterial enzyme that hydrolyzes and inactivates penicillin.

penicillin G₁ potassium *See* benzyl penicillin potassium.

Penicillium [MYCOL] A genus of fungi in the family Moniliaceae characterized by erect branching conidiophores having terminal tufts of club-shaped cells from which conidia are formed.

Penicillium chrysogenum [MYCOL] A penicillin-producing fungus.

Penicillium griseofulvum [MYCOL] The fungus that produces griseofulvin.

Penicillium notatum [MYCOL] A penicillin-producing fungus.

Peniculina [INV ZOO] A suborder of the Hymenostomatida.

penis [ANAT] The male organ of copulation in humans and certain other vertebrates. Also known as phallus.

Pennales [BOT] An order of diatoms (Bacillariophyceae) in which the form is often circular, and the markings on the valves are radial.

pennate [BIOL] 1. Wing-shaped. 2. Having wings. 3. Having feathers.

Pennatulacea [INV ZOO] The sea pens, an order of the subclass Alcyonaria; individuals lack stolons and live with their bases embedded in the soft substratum of the sea.

Pennellidae [INV ZOO] A family of copepod crustaceans in the suborder Caligoida; skin-penetrating external parasites of various marine fishes and whales.

penniculus [ANAT] A tuft of arterioles in the spleen. [BIOL] A brush-shaped structure.

pentacrinoid [INV ZOO] The larva of a feather star.

pentactinal [ZOO] Having five rays or branches.

pentacula [INV ZOO] The five-tentacled stage in the life history of echinoderms.

pentadactyl [VERT ZOO] Having five digits on the hand or foot.

pentadelphous [BOT] Having the stamens in five sets with the filaments more or less united within each set.

pentahydroxyhexoic acid *See* galactonic acid.

Pentamerida [PALEON] An extinct order of articulate brachiopods.

Pentameridina [PALEON] A suborder of extinct brachiopods in the order Pentamerida; dental plates associated with the brachiophores were well developed, and their bases enclosed the dorsal adductor muscle field.

pentamerous [BOT] Having each whorl of the flower consisting of five members, or a multiple of five.

pentandrous [BOT] Having five stamens.

Pentastomida [INV ZOO] A class of bloodsucking parasitic arthropods; the adult is vermiform, and there are two pairs of hooklike, retractile claws on the cephalothorax.

Pentatomidae [INV ZOO] The true stink bugs, a family of hemipteran insects in the superfamily Pentatomoidea.

Pentatomoidea [INV ZOO] A subfamily of the hemipteran group Pentatomorpha distinguished by marginal trichobothria and by antennae which are usually five-segmented.

Pentatomorpha [INV ZOO] A large group of hemipteran insects in the subdivision Geocorisae in which the eggs are nonoperculate, a median spermatheca is present, accessory salivary glands are tubular, and the abdomen has trichobothria.

pentosan [BIOCHEM] A hemicellulose present in cereal, straws, brans, and other woody plant tissues; yields five-carbon-atom sugars.

pentose [BIOCHEM] Any one of a class of carbohydrates containing five atoms of carbon.

pentose phosphate pathway [BIOCHEM] A pathway by which glucose is metabolized or transformed in plants and microorganisms; glucose-6-phosphate is oxidized to 6-phosphogluconic acid, which then undergoes oxidative decarboxylation to form ribulose-5-phosphate, which is ultimately transformed to fructose-6-phosphate.

pepo [BOT] A fleshy indehiscent berry with many seeds and a hard rind; characteristic of the Cucurbitaceae.

pepper [BOT] Any of several warm-season perennials of the genus *Capsicum* in the order Polemoniales, especially *C. annum* which is cultivated for its fruit, a many-seeded berry with a thickened integument.

peppermint [BOT] Any of various aromatic herbs of the genus *Mentha* in the family Labiatae, especially *M. piperita*.

pepsin [BIOCHEM] A proteolytic enzyme found in the gastric juice of mammals, birds, reptiles, and fishes.

pepsinogen [BIOCHEM] The precursor of pepsin, found in the stomach mucosa.

peptic [PHYSIO] 1. Of or pertaining to pepsin. 2. Of or pertaining to digestion.

peptidase [BIOCHEM] An enzyme that catalyzes the hydrolysis of peptides to amino acids.

peptide [BIOCHEM] A compound of two or more amino acids joined by peptide bonds.

peptide synthetase [BIOCHEM] A ribosomal synthetase that catalyzes the formation of peptide bonds during protein synthesis.

Peptococcaceae [MICROBIO] A family of grampositive cocci; organisms can use either amino acids or carbohydrates for growth and energy.

Peptococcus [MICROBIO] A genus of bacteria in the family Peptococcaceae; cells occur singly, in pairs, in tetrads, or in irregular clusters; can use amino acids as the sole source of energy.

peptone [BIOCHEM] A water-soluble mixture of proteoses and amino acids derived from albumin, meat, or milk; used as a nutrient and to prepare nutrient media for bacteriology.

Peptostreptococcus [MICROBIO] A genus of bacteria in the family Peptococcaceae; spherical to ovoid cells occur in pairs or chains; ferment carbohydrates and often pyruvate.

Peracarida [INV ZOO] A superorder of the Eumalacostraca; these crustaceans have the first thoracic segment united with the head, the cephalothorax usually larger than the abdomen, and some thoracic segments free from the carapace.

Peramelidae [VERT ZOO] The bandicoots, a family of insectivorous mammals in the order Marsupialia.

perception [PHYSIO] Recognition in response to sensory stimuli; the act or process by which the memory of certain qualities of an object is associated with other qualities impressing the senses, thereby making possible recognition of the object.

perch [VERT ZOO] 1. Any member of the family Percidae. 2. The common name for a number of unrelated species of fish belonging to the Centrarchidae, Anabantoidei, and Percopsiformes.

Percidae [VERT ZOO] A family of fresh-water actinopterygian fishes in the suborder Percoidei; comprises the true perches.

Perciformes [VERT ZOO] The typical spiny-rayed fishes, comprising the largest order of vertebrates; characterized by fin spines, a swim bladder without a duct, usually ctenoid scales, and 17 or fewer caudal fin rays.

Percoidei [VERT ZOO] A large, typical suborder of the order Perciformes; includes over 50% of the species in this order.

Percomorphi [VERT ZOO] An equivalent, ordinal name for the Perciformes.

Percopsidae [VERT ZOO] A family of fishes in the order Percopsiformes.

Percopsiformes [VERT ZOO] A small order of actinopterygian fishes characterized by single, ray-supported dorsal and anal fins and a subabdominal pelvic fin with three to eight soft rays.

perennial [BOT] A plant that lives for an indefinite period, dying back seasonally and producing new growth from a perennating part.

perfect flower [BOT] A flower having both stamens and pistils.

perfoliate [BOT] Pertaining to the form of a leaf having its base united around the stem. [INV ZOO] Pertaining to the form of certain insect antennae having the terminal joints expanded and flattened to form plates which encircle the stalk.

perforatorium See acrosome.

perfusion [PHYSIO] The pumping of a fluid through a tissue or organ by way of an artery.

Pergidae [INV ZOO] A small family of hymenopteran insects in the superfamily Tenthredinoidea.

perianal [ANAT] Situated or occurring around the anus.

perianth [BOT] The calyx and corolla considered together.

periblast [EMBRYO] The nucleated layer of cytoplasm that surrounds the blastodisk of an egg undergoing discoidal cleavage.

periblastula [EMBRYO] The blastula of a centrolecithal egg, formed by superficial segmentation.

periblem [BOT] A layer of primary meristem which produces the cortical cells.

pericardial [ANAT] 1. Of or pertaining to the pericardium. 2. Located around the heart.

pericardial cavity [ANAT] A potential space between the inner layer of the pericardium and the epicardium of the heart.

pericardial fluid [PHYSIO] The fluid in the pericardial cavity.

pericardial organ [INV ZOO] One of the neurohemal organs associated with the pericardial cavity in crustaceans.

pericardium [ANAT] The membranous sac that envelops the heart; it contains 5–20 grams of clear serous fluid.

pericarp [BOT] The wall of a fruit, developed by ripening and modification of the ovarian wall.

pericentric inversion [GEN] A type of chromosome aberration in which chromosome material involving both arms of the chromosome is inverted, thus spanning the centromere.

perichondrium [ANAT] The fibrous connective tissue covering cartilage, except at joints.

periclinal chimera [GEN] A plant carrying a mixture of cells of two distinct species.

pericranium [ANAT] The periosteum on the outer surface of the cranial bones.

pericycle [BOT] The outer boundary of the stele of plants; may not be present as a distinct layer of cells.

pericystium [ANAT] The tissues surrounding a bladder.

pericyte [HISTOL] A mesenchymal cell found around a capillary; it may or may not be contractile.

periderm [BOT] A group of secondary tissues forming a protective layer which replaces the epidermis of many plant stems, roots, and other parts; composed of cork cambium, phelloderm, and cork. [EMBRYO] The superficial transient layer of epithelial cells of the embryonic epidermis.

peridium [BOT] The outer investment of the sporophore of many fungi.

perifollicular [HISTOL] Surrounding a follicle.

perigonium [BOT] The perianth of a liverwort. [INV ZOO] The sac containing the generative bodies in the gonophore of a hydroid.

perigynium [BOT] A fleshy cup- or tubelike structure surrounding the archegonium of various bryophytes.

perigynous [BOT] Bearing the floral organs on the rim of an expanded saucer- or cup-shaped receptacle or hypanthium.

perikaryon [CELL BIO] 1. The body of a nerve cell, containing the nucleus. 2. A cytoplasmic mass surrounding a nucleus.

Perilampidae [INV ZOO] A family of hymenopteran insects in the superfamily Chalcidoidea.

perilymph [PHYSIO] The fluid separating the membranous from the osseous labyrinth of the internal ear.

perimetrium [ANAT] The serous covering of the uterus.

perimysium [ANAT] The connective tissue sheath enveloping a muscle or a bundle of muscle fibers.

perineum [ANAT] 1. The portion of the body included in the outlet of the pelvis, bounded in front by the pubic arch, behind by the coccyx and sacrotuberous ligaments, and at the sides by the tuberosities of the ischium. 2. The region between the anus and the scrotum in the male, between the anus and the posterior commissure of the vulva in the female.

perineural [ANAT] Situated around nervous tissue or a nerve.

periocular [ANAT] Surrounding the eye.

periodontal [ANAT] 1. Surrounding a tooth. 2. Of or pertaining to the periodontium.

periodontium [ANAT] The tissues surrounding a tooth.

perionychium [ANAT] The border of epidermis surrounding an entire nail. Also known as paronychium.

periosteum [ANAT] The fibrous membrane enveloping bones, except at joints and the points of tendonous and ligamentous attachment.

periostracum [INV ZOO] A protective layer of chitin covering the outer portion of the shell in many mollusks, especially fresh-water forms.

periotic [ANAT] 1. Situated about the ear. 2. Of or pertaining to the parts immediately about the internal ear.

peripheral [ANAT] Pertaining to or located at or near the surface of a body or an organ.

peripheral nervous system [ANAT] The autonomic nervous system, the cranial nerves, and the spinal nerves including their associated sensory receptors.

peripheral vision [PHYSIO] The act of seeing images that fall upon parts of the retina outside the macula lutea. Also known as indirect vision.

periphyton [ECOL] Sessile biotal components of a fresh-water ecosystem.

periplast [CELL BIO] 1. A cell membrane. 2. A pellicle covering ectoplasm. [HISTOL] The stroma of an animal organ. [INV ZOO] The ectoplasm of a flagellate.

periproct [INV ZOO] The area surrounding the anus of echinoids.

Periptychidae [PALEON] A family of extinct herbivorous mammals in the order Condylarthra distinguished by specialized, fluted teeth.

Peripylina [INV ZOO] An equivalent name for Porulosida.

perisarc [INV ZOO] The outer integument of a hydroid.

Periscelidae [INV ZOO] A family of myodarian cyclorrhaphous dipteran insects in the subsection Acalypteratae.

Perischoechinoidea [INV ZOO] A subclass of principally extinct echinoderms belonging to the Echinoidea and lacking stability in the number of columns of plates that make up the ambulacra and interambulacra.

perisperm [BOT] In a seed, the nutritive tissue that is derived from the nucellus and deposited on the outside of the embryo sac.

Perissodactyla [VERT ZOO] An order of exclusively herbivorous mammals distinguished by an odd number of toes and mesaxonic feet, that is, with the axis going through the third toe.

peristalsis [PHYSIO] The rhythmic progressive wave of muscular contraction in tubes, such as the intestine, provided with both longitudinal and transverse muscular fibers.

peristome [BOT] The fringe around the opening of a moss capsule. [INV ZOO] The area surrounding the mouth of various invertebrates.

perithecium [MYCOL] A spherical, cylindrical, or oval ascocarp which usually opens by a terminal slit or pore.

peritoneal cavity [ANAT] The potential space between the visceral and parietal layers of the peritoneum.

peritoneum [ANAT] The serous membrane enveloping the abdominal viscera and lining the abdominal cavity.

Peritrichia [INV ZOO] A specialized subclass of the class Ciliatea comprising both sessile and mobile forms.

Peritrichida [INV ZOO] The single order of the protozoan subclass Peritrichia.

peritrichous [INV ZOO] Of certain protozoans, having spirally arranged cilia around the oral disk.

peritrichous [MICROBIO] Of bacteria, having a uniform distribution of flagella on the body surface.

perivitelline space [CELL BIO] In mammalian ova, the space formed between the ovum and the zona pellucida at the time of maturation, into which the polar bodies are given off.

permanent teeth [ANAT] The second set of teeth of a mammal, following the milk teeth; in humans, the set of 32 teeth consists of 8 incisors, 4 canines, 8 premolars, and 12 molars.

permease [BIOCHEM] Any of a group of enzymes which mediate the phenomenon of active transport.

permissive cell [MOL BIO] A cell in which viral genome replication can occur after integration of the genome into one or more chromosomes of the cell.

Perognathinae [VERT ZOO] A subfamily of the rodent family Heteromyidae, including the pocket and kangaroo mice.

Peronosporales [MYCOL] An order of aquatic and terrestrial phycomycetous fungi with a hyphal thallus and zoospores with two flagella.

Perothopidae [INV ZOO] A small family of coleopteran insects in the superfamily Elateroidea found only in the United States.

peroxidase [BIOCHEM] An enzyme that catalyzes reactions in which hydrogen peroxide is an electron acceptor.

Persian melon [BOT] A variety of muskmelon (*Cucumis melo*) in the order Violales; the fruit is globular and without sutures, and has dark-green skin, thin abundant netting, and firm, thick, orange flesh.

persistence of vision [PHYSIO] The ability of the eye to retain the impression of an image for a short time after the image has disappeared.

persistent [BOT] Of a leaf, withering but remaining attached to the plant during the winter.

perspiration See sweat.

pessulus [VERT ZOO] A bar composed of cartilage or bone that crosses the windpipe of a bird at its division into bronchi.

petal [BOT] One of the sterile, leaf-shaped flower parts that make up the corolla.

Petalichthyida [PALEON] A small order of extinct dorsoventrally flattened fishes belonging to the class Placodermi; the external armor is in two shields of large plates.

Petalodontidae [PALEON] A family of extinct cartilaginous fishes in the order Bradyodonti distinguished by teeth with deep roots and flattened diamond-shaped crowns.

Petaluridae [INV ZOO] A family of dragonflies in the suborder Anisoptera.

petasma [INV ZOO] A modified endopodite of the first abdominal appendage in a male decapod crustacean.

petiole [BOT] The stem which supports the blade of a leaf.

petrel [VERT ZOO] A sea bird of the families Procellariidae and Hydrobatidae, generally small to medium-sized with long wings and dark plumage with white areas near the rump.

petri dish [MICROBIO] A shallow glass or plastic dish with a loosely fitting overlapping cover used for bacterial plate cultures and plant and animal tissue cultures.

Petriidae [INV ZOO] A small family of coleopteran insects in the superfamily Tenebrionoidea.

petroleum microbiology [MICROBIO] Those aspects of microbiological science and engineering of interest to the petroleum industry, including the role of microbes in petroleum formation, and the exploration, production, manufacturing, storage, and food synthesis from petroleum.

Petromyzonida [VERT ZOO] The lampreys, an order of eellike, jawless vertebrates (Agnatha) distinguished by a single, dorsal nasal opening, and the mouth surrounded by an oral disk and provided with a rasping tongue.

Petromyzontiformes [VERT ZOO] The equivalent name for Petromyzonida.

petrosal nerve [ANAT] Any of several small nerves passing through the petrous part of the temporal bone and usually attached to the geniculate ganglion.

petrosal process [ANAT] A sharp process of the sphenoid bone located below the notch for the passage of the abducens nerve, which articulates with the apex of the petrous portion of the temporal bone and forms the medial boundary of the foramen lacerum.

Petrosaviaceae [BOT] A small family of monocotyledonous plants in the order Triuridales characterized by perfect flowers, three carpels, and numerous seeds.

Peyer's patches [HISTOL] Aggregates of lymph nodules beneath the epithelium of the ileum.

phacella See gastric filament.

Phaenocephalidae [INV ZOO] A monospecific family of coleopteran insects in the superfamily Cucujoidea, found only in Japan.

Phaenothontidae [VERT ZOO] The tropic birds, a family of fish-eating aquatic forms in the order Pelecaniformes.

Phaeocoleosporae [MYCOL] A spore group of the Fungi Imperfecti with dark filiform spores.

Phaeodictyosporae [MYCOL] A spore group of the Fungi Imperfecti with dark muriform spores.

Phaeodidymae [MYCOL] A spore group of the Fungi Imperfecti with dark two-celled spores.

Phaeodorina [INV ZOO] The equivalent name for Tripylina.

Phaeohelicosporae [MYCOL] A spore group of the Fungi Imperfecti with dark, spirally coiled, septate spores.

Phaeophragmiae [MYCOL] A spore group of the Fungi Imperfecti with dark three- to many-celled spores.

Phaeophyta [BOT] The brown algae, constituting a division of plants; the plant body is multicellular, varying from a simple filamentous form to a complex, sometimes branched body having a basal attachment.

Phaeosporae [MYCOL] A spore group of Fungi Imperfecti characterized by dark one-celled, nonfiliform spores.

Phaeostaurosporae [MYCOL] A spore group of the Fungi Imperfecti with dark star-shaped or forked spores.

phage See bacteriophage.

phage cross [VIROL] Multiple infection of a single bacterium by phages that differ at one or more genetic sites, leading to the production of recombinant progeny phage.

phagocyte [CELL BIO] An ameboid cell that engulfs foreign material.

phagocytic vacuole See food vacuole.

phagocytin [BIOCHEM] A type of bactericidal agent present within phagocytic cells.

phagocytosis [CELL BIO] A specialized form of macropinocytosis in which cells engulf large solid objects such as bacteria and deliver the internalized objects to special digesting vacuoles; exists in certain cell types, such as macrophages and neutrophils.

phagolysosome [CELL BIO] An intracellular vesicle formed by fusion of a lysosome with a phagosome.

phagosome [CELL BIO] A closed intracellular vesicle containing material captured by phagocytosis.

phagotroph [INV ZOO] An organism that ingests nutrients by phagocytosis.

Phalacridae [INV ZOO] The shining flower beetles, a family of coleopteran insects in the superfamily Cucujoidea.

Phalacrocoracidae [VERT ZOO] The cormorants, a family of aquatic birds in the order Pelecaniformes.

Phalaenidae [INV ZOO] The equivalent name for Noctuidae.

Phalangeridae [VERT ZOO] A family of marsupial mammals in which the marsupium is well developed and opens anteriorly, the hindfeet are syndactylous, and the hallux is opposable and lacks a claw.

Phalangida [INV ZOO] An order of the class Arachnida characterized by an unsegmented cephalothorax broadly joined to a segmented abdomen, paired chelate chelicerae, and paired palpi.

phalanx [ANAT] One of the bones of the fingers or toes.

Phalaropodidae [VERT ZOO] The phalaropes, a family of migratory shore birds characterized by lobate toes and by reversal of the sex roles with respect to dimorphism and care of the young.

Phallostethidae [VERT ZOO] A family of actinopterygian fishes in the order Atheriniformes.

Phallostethiformes [VERT ZOO] An equivalent name for Atheriniformes.

phallotoxin [BIOCHEM] One of a group of toxic peptides produced by the mushroom *Amanita phalloides*.

phallus [ANAT] *See* penis. [EMBRYO] An undifferentiated embryonic structure derived from the genital tubercle that differentiates into the penis in males and the clitoris in females.

phanerophyte [ECOL] A perennial tree or shrub with dormant buds borne on aerial shoots.

Phanerorhynchidae [PALEON] A family of extinct chondrostean fishes in the order Palaeonisciformes having vertical jaw suspension.

Phanerozonida [INV ZOO] An order of the Asteroidea in which the body margins are defined by two conspicuous series of plates and in which pentamerous symmetry is generally constant.

Phanodermatidae [INV ZOO] A family of free-living nematodes in the superfamily Enoploidea.

Pharetronida [INV ZOO] An order of calcareous sponges in the subclass Calcinea characterized by a leuconoid structure.

pharmacogenetics [GEN] The science of genetically determined variations in drug responses.

pharyngeal aponeurosis [ANAT] The fibrous submucous layer of the pharynx.

pharyngeal bursa [EMBRYO] A small pit caudal to the pharyngeal tonsil, resulting from the ingrowth of epithelium along the course of the degenerating tip of the notochord of the vertebrate embryo.

pharyngeal cleft [EMBRYO] One of the paired open clefts on the sides of the embryonic pharynx between successive visceral arches in vertebrates.

pharyngeal plexus [ANAT] 1. A nerve plexus innervating the pharynx. 2. A plexus of veins situated at the side of the pharynx.

pharyngeal pouch [EMBRYO] One of the five paired sacculations in the lateral aspect of the pharynx in vertebrate embryos. Also known as visceral pouch.

pharyngeal tonsil *See* adenoid.

pharyngeal tooth [VERT ZOO] A tooth developed on the pharyngeal bone in many fishes.

Pharyngobdellae [INV ZOO] A family of leeches in the order Arhynchobdellae distinguished by the lack of jaws.

pharynx [ANAT] A chamber at the oral end of the vertebrate alimentary canal, leading to the esophagus.

phase-shift mutation *See* frameshift mutation.

Phasianidae [VERT ZOO] A family of game birds in the order Galliformes; typically, members are ground feeders, have bare tarsi and copious plumage, and lack feathers around the nostrils.

phasmid [INV ZOO] One of a pair of lateral caudal pores which function as chemoreceptors in certain nematodes.

Phasmidae [INV ZOO] A family of the insect order Orthoptera including the walking sticks and leaf insects.

Phasmidea [INV ZOO] An equivalent name for Secernentea.

Phasmidia [INV ZOO] An equivalent name for Secernentea.

pheasant [VERT ZOO] Any of various large sedentary game birds with long tails in the family Phasianidae; sexual dimorphism is typical of the group.

phellem [BOT] Cork; the outer tissue layer of the periderm.

phelloderm [BOT] Layers of parenchymatous cells formed as inward derivatives of the phellogen.

phellogen [BOT] The meristematic portion of the periderm, consisting of one layer of cells that initiate formation of the cork and secondary cortex tissue.

Phenacodontidae [PALEON] An extinct family of large herbivorous mammals in the order Condylartha.

Phengodidae [INV ZOO] The fire beetles, a New World family of coleopteran insects in the superfamily Cantharoidea.

phenocopy [GEN] The nonhereditary alteration of a phenotype to a form imitating a mutant trait; caused by external conditions during development.

phenogenetics [GEN] The study of the phenotypic effects of the genetic material. Also known as physiological genetics.

phenotype [GEN] The observable characters of an organism.

phenotypic lag [GEN] Delay in the expression of a newly acquired character.

β-phenylalanine *See* phenylalanine.

phenylalanine [BIOCHEM] $C_9H_{11}O_2N$ An essential amino acid, obtained in the levo form by hydrolysis of proteins (as lactalbumin); converted to tyrosine in the normal body. Also known as α-aminohydrocinnamic acid; α-amino-β-phenylpropionic acid; β-phenylalanine.

phenylpyruvic acid [BIOCHEM] $C_6H_5CH_2\cdot CO\cdot COOH$ A keto acid, occurring as a metabolic product of phenylalanine.

pheochromoblast [HISTOL] A precursor of a pheochromocyte.

pheromone [PHYSIO] Any substance secreted by an animal which influences the behavior of other individuals of the same species.

phialospore [MYCOL] One of a chain of spores produced successively on phialides.

Philomycidae [INV ZOO] A family of pulmonate gastropods composed of slugs.

Philopteridae [INV ZOO] A family of biting lice (Mallophaga) that are parasitic on most land birds and water birds.

phlebotaxis [BIOL] Movement of a simple motile organism in response to the presence of blood.

phlegm [PHYSIO] A viscid, stringy mucus, secreted by the mucosa of the air passages.

phleomycin [MICROBIO] An antibacterial antibiotic produced by *Streptomyces verticillatus;* antitumor activity has also been demonstrated.

Phloeidae [INV ZOO] The bark bugs, a small neotropical family of hemipteran insects in the superfamily Pentatomoidea.

phloem [BOT] A complex, food-conducting vascular tissue in higher plants; principal conducting cells are sieve elements. Also known as bast; sieve tissue.

phloem necrosis [PL PATH] A pathological state in a plant in which the phloem undergoes brown discoloration and disintegration.

Phocaenidae [VERT ZOO] The porpoises, a family of marine mammals in the order Cetacea.

Phocidae [VERT ZOO] The seals, a pinniped family of carnivoran mammals in the superfamily Canoidea.

Phodilidae [VERT ZOO] A family of birds in the order Strigiformes; the bay owl (*Pholidus bodius*) is the single species.

Phoenicopteridae [VERT ZOO] The flamingos, a family of long-legged, long-necked birds in the order Ciconiiformes.

Phoenicopteriformes [VERT ZOO] An order comprising the flamingos in some systems of classification.

Phoeniculidae [VERT ZOO] The African wood hoopoes, a family of birds in the order Coraciiformes.

Pholadidae [INV ZOO] A family of bivalve mollusks in the subclass Eulamellibranchia; individuals may have one or more dorsal accessory plates, and the visceral mass is attached to the valves in the dorsal portion of the body.

Pholidophoridae [PALEON] A generalized family of extinct fishes belonging to the Pholidophoriformes.

Pholidophoriformes [PALEON] An extinct actinopterygian group composed of mostly small fusiform marine and fresh-water fishes of an advanced holostean level.

Pholidota [VERT ZOO] An order of mammals comprising the living pangolins and their fossil predecessors; characterized by an elongate tubular skull with no teeth, a long protrusive tongue, strong legs, and five-toed feet with large claws.

Phomaceae [MYCOL] The equivalent name for Sphaerioidaceae.

Phomales [MYCOL] The equivalent name for Sphaeropsidales.

phonation [PHYSIO] Production of speech sounds.

phonoreception [PHYSIO] The perception of sound through specialized sense organs.

phony disease [PL PATH] A virus disease of the peach characterized by dwarfing, abnormal darkening of leaves, and a light crop of small, highly colored fruit; tree stops bearing fruit after a few years.

phoresy [ECOL] A type of commensalism which involves the transporation of one organism (the guest) by a larger organism (the host) of a different species.

Phoridae [INV ZOO] The hump-backed flies, a family of cyclorrhaphous dipteran insects in the series Aschiza.

Phoronida [INV ZOO] A small, homogeneous group, or phylum, of animals having an elongate body, a crown of tentacles surrounding the mouth, and the anus occurring at the level of the mouth.

phosphatase [BIOCHEM] An enzyme that catalyzes the hydrolysis and synthesis of phosphoric acid esters and the transfer of phosphate groups from phosphoric acid to other compounds.

phosphatide *See* phospholipid.

phosphocreatine [BIOCHEM] $C_4H_{10}N_3O_5P$ Creatine phosphate, a phosphoric acid derivative of creatine which contains an energy-rich phosphate bond; it is present in muscle and other tissues, and during the anaerobic phase of muscular contraction it hydrolyzes to creatine and phosphate and makes energy available. Abbreviated PC.

phosphoenolpyruvic acid [BIOCHEM] $CH_2{=}O(OPO_3H_2)COOH$ A high-energy phosphate formed by dehydration of 2-phosphoglyceric acid; it reacts with adenosinediphosphate to form adenosinetriphosphate and enolpyruvic acid.

phosphoglucoisomerase [BIOCHEM] An enzyme that catalyzes the conversion of galactose-1-phosphate to glucose-1-phosphate.

phosphoglucomutase [BIOCHEM] An enzyme that catalyzes the conversion of glucose-1-phosphate to glucose-6-phosphate.

phospholipase [BIOCHEM] An enzyme that catalyzes a hydrolysis of a phospholipid, especially a lecithinase that acts in this manner on a lecithin.

phospholipid [BIOCHEM] Any of a class of esters of phosphoric acid containing one or two molecules of fatty acid, an alcohol, and a nitrogenous base. Also known as phosphatide.

phosphomonoesterase [BIOCHEM] An enzyme catalyzing hydrolysis of phosphoric acid esters containing one ester linkage.

phosphorolysis [BIOCHEM] A reaction by which elements of phosphoric acid are incorporated into the molecule of a compound.

phosphorylase [BIOCHEM] An enzyme that catalyzes the formation of glucose-1-phosphate (Cori ester) from glycogen and inorganic phosphate; it is widely distributed in animals, plants, and microorganisms.

phosphotransacetylase [BIOCHEM] An enzyme that catalyzes the reversible transfer of an acetyl group from acetyl coenzyme A to a phosphate, with formation of acetyl phosphate.

photic zone [ECOL] The uppermost layer of a body of water (approximately the upper 100 meters) that receives enough sunlight to permit the occurrence of photosynthesis.

Photidae [INV ZOO] A family of amphipod crustaceans in the suborder Gammaridea.

photoautotrophic [BIOL] Pertaining to organisms which derive energy from light and manufacture their own food.

Photobacterium [MICROBIO] A genus of bacteria in the family Vibrionaceae; luminescent, motile, asporogenous coccobacilli, occasionally rods, occurring singly and sometimes in pairs.

photomorphogenesis [BOT] The control exerted by light over growth, development, and differentiation of plants that is independent of photosynthesis.

photoperiodism [PHYSIO] The physiological responses of an organism to the length of night or day or both.

photophilic [BIOL] Thriving in full light.

photophobic [BIOL] 1. Avoiding light. 2. Exhibiting negative phototropism.

photophore gland [VERT ZOO] A highly modified integumentary gland which develops into a luminous organ composed of a lens and a light-emitting gland; occurs in deep-sea teleosts and elasmobranchs.

photophosphorylase [BIOCHEM] An enzyme that is associated with the surface of a thylakoid membrane and is involved in the final stages of adenosinetriphosphate production by photosynthetic phosphorylation.

photophosphorylation [BIOCHEM] Phosphorylation induced by light energy in photosynthesis.

photophygous [BIOL] Thriving in shade.

photopic vision *See* foveal vision.

photopigment [BIOCHEM] A pigment that is unstable in the presence of light of appropriate wavelengths, such as the chromophore pigment which combines with opsins to form rhodopsin in the rods and cones of the vertebrate eye.

photoreactive chlorophyll [BIOCHEM] Chlorophyll molecules which receive light quanta from antenna chlorophyll and constitute a photoreaction center where light energy conversion occurs.

photoreception [PHYSIO] The process of absorption of light energy by plants and animals and its utilization for biological functions, such as photosynthesis and vision.

photoreceptor [PHYSIO] A highly specialized, light-sensitive cell or group of cells containing photopigments.

photorespiration [BIOCHEM] Respiratory activity taking place in plants during the light period; CO_2 is released and O_2 is taken up, but no useful form of energy, such as adenosinetriphosphate, is derived.

photosynthesis [BIOCHEM] Synthesis of chemical compounds in light, especially the manufacture of organic compounds (primarily carbohydrates) from carbon dioxide and a hydrogen source (such as water), with simultaneous liberation of oxygen, by chlorophyll-containing plant cells.

photosystem I [BIOCHEM] One of two reaction sequences of the light phase of photosynthesis in green plants that involves a pigment system which is excited by wavelengths shorter than 700 nanometers and which transfers this energy to energy carriers such as NADPH that are subsequently utilized in carbon dioxide fixation.

photosystem II [BIOCHEM] One of two reaction sequences of the light phase of photosynthesis in green plants which involves a pigment system excited by wavelengths shorter than 685 nanometers and which is directly involved in the splitting or photolysis of water.

phototaxis [BIOL] Movement of a motile organism or free plant part in response to light stimulation.

phototroph [BIOL] An organism that utilizes light as a source of metabolic energy.

phototrophic bacteria [MICROBIO] Primarily aquatic bacteria comprising two principal groups: purple bacteria and green sulfur bacteria; all contain bacteriochlorophylls.

phototropism [BOT] A growth-mediated response of a plant to stimulation by visible light.

Phoxichilidiidae [INV ZOO] A family of marine arthropods in the subphylum Pycnogonida; typically, chelifores are present, palpi are lacking, and ovigers have five to nine joints in males only.

Phoxocephalidae [INV ZOO] A family of amphipod crustaceans in the suborder Gammaridea.

Phractolaemidae [VERT ZOO] A family of tropical African fresh-water fishes in the order Gonorynchiformes.

Phragmidiothrix [MICROBIO] A genus of sheathed bacteria; cells are nonmotile, and sheaths are attached and not encrusted with iron or manganese oxides.

Phragmobasidiomycetes [MYCOL] An equivalent name for Heterobasidiomycetidae.

phragmoid [BOT] Having septae perpendicular to the long axis, as the conidia of certain fungi.

phragmoplast [CELL BIO] A thin barrier which is formed across the spindle equator in late cytokinesis in plant cells and within which the cell wall is laid down.

phragmosome [CELL BIO] A differentiated cytoplasmic partition in which the phragmoplast and cell plate develop during cell division in plant cells.

Phragmosporae [MYCOL] A spore group of the Fungi Imperfecti with three- to many-celled spores.

Phreatoicidae [INV ZOO] A family of isopod crustaceans in the suborder Phreatoicoidea in which only the left mandible retains a lacinia mobilis.

Phreatoicoidea [INV ZOO] A suborder of the Isopoda having a subcylindrical body that appears laterally compressed, antennules shorter than the antennae, and the first thoracic segment fused with the head.

phreatophyte [ECOL] A plant with a deep root system which obtains water from the groundwater or the capillary fringe above the water table.

phrenic nerve [ANAT] A nerve, arising from the third, fourth, and fifth cervical (cervical plexus) segments of the spinal cord; innervates the diaphragm.

Phrynophiurida [INV ZOO] An order of the Ophiuroidea in which the vertebrae usually articulate by means of hourglass-shaped surfaces, and the arms are able to coil upward or downward in the vertical plane.

Phycitinae [INV ZOO] A large subfamily of moths in the family Pyralididae in which the frenulum of the female is a simple spine rather than a bundle of bristles.

phycobilin [BIOCHEM] Any of various protein-bound pigments which are open-chain tetrapyrroles and occur in some groups of algae.

phycocyanin [BIOCHEM] A blue phycobilin.

phycocyanobilin [BIOCHEM] $C_{31}H_{38}O_2N_4$ Phycobilin with an ethylidene side chain $(=CH—CH_3)$ and only one asymmetric carbon atom (C_1).

phycoerythrin [BIOCHEM] A red phycobilin.

phycoerythrobilin [BIOCHEM] $C_{31}H_{38}O_2N_4$ Phycobilin with seven conjugated double bonds, an ethylidene side chain $(=CH—CH_3)$, and two asymmetric carbon atoms $(C_1$ and $C_7)$.

Phycomycetes [MYCOL] A primitive class of true fungi belonging to the Eumycetes; they lack regularly spaced septa in the actively growing portions of the plant body, and have the sporangiospore, produced in the sporangium by cleavage, as the fundamental, asexual reproductive unit.

Phycosecidae [INV ZOO] A small family of coleopteran insects of the superfamily Cucujoidea, including five species found in New Zealand, Australia, and Egypt.

Phylactolaemata [INV ZOO] A class of fresh-water ectoproct bryozoans; individuals have lophophores which are U-shaped in basal outline, and relatively short, wide zooecia.

phyletic evolution [EVOL] The gradual evolution of population without separation into isolated parts.

phyllary [BOT] A bract of the involucre of a composite plant.

Phyllobothrioidea [INV ZOO] The equivalent name for Tetraphyllidea.

phyllobranchiate gill [INV ZOO] A type of decapod crustacean gill with flattened branches, or lamellae usually arranged in two opposite series.

phylloclade [BOT] A flattened stem that fulfills the same functions as a leaf.

phyllode [BOT] A broad, flat petiole that replaces the blade of a foliage leaf.

phyllode [INV ZOO] A petal-shaped group of ambulacra near the mouth of certain echinoderms.

Phyllodocidae [INV ZOO] A leaf-bearing family of errantian annelids in which the species are often brilliantly iridescent and are highly motile.

Phyllogoniaceae [BOT] A family of mosses in the order Isobryales in which the leaves are equitant.

Phyllolepida [PALEON] A monogeneric order of placoderms from the late Upper Devonian in which the armor is broad and low with a characteristic ornament of concentric and transverse ridges on the component plates.

Phyllophoridae [INV ZOO] A family of dendrochirotacean holothurians in the order Dendrochirotida having a rather naked skin and a complex calcareous ring.

phyllosoma [INV ZOO] A flat, transparent, long-legged larval stage of various spiny lobsters.

phyllospondylous [VERT ZOO] Of vertebrae, having a hypocentrum but no pleurocentra; the neural arch extends ventrad to enclose the notochord and form transverse processes which articulate with the ribs.

Phyllosticales [MYCOL] An equivalent name for Sphaeropsidales.

Phyllostomatidae [VERT ZOO] The New World leaf-nosed bats (Chiroptera), a large tropical and subtropical family of insect- and fruit-eating forms with narrow, pointed ears.

phyllotaxy [BOT] The arrangement of leaves on a stem.

Phylloxerinae [INV ZOO] A subfamily of homopteran insects in the family Chermidae in which the sexual forms lack mouthparts, and the parthenogenetic females have a beak but the digestive system is closed, and no honeydew is produced.

phylogeny [EVOL] The evolutionary or ancestral history of organisms.

phylum [SYST] A major taxonomic category in classifying animals (and plants in some systems), composed of groups of related classes.

Phymatidae [INV ZOO] A family of carnivorous hemipteran insects characterized by strong, thick forelegs.

Phymosomatidae [INV ZOO] A family of echinacean echinoderms in the order Phymosomatoida with imperforate crenulate tubercles; one surviving genus is known.

Phymosomatoida [INV ZOO] An order of Echinacea with a stirodont lantern and diademoid ambulacral plates.

physa [INV ZOO] The rounded basal portion of the body of certain sea anemones.

Physalopteridae [INV ZOO] A family of parasitic nematodes in the superfamily Spiruroidea.

Physaraceae [MYCOL] A family of slime molds in the order Physarales.

Physarales [MYCOL] An order of Myxomycetes in the subclass Myxogastromycetidae.

physiological biophysics [BIOPHYS] An area of biophysics concerned with the use of physical mechanisms to explain the behavior and the functioning of living organisms or parts thereof, and with the response of living organisms to physical forces.

physiological dead space *See* dead space.

physiological ecology [ECOL] The study of biological processes and growth under natural or simulated environments.

physiological saline *See* normal saline.

physiological salt solution *See* normal saline.

physiological sodium chloride solution *See* normal saline.

physiological diplopia [PHYSIO] A normal phenomenon in which there is formation of images in noncorresponding retinal points, giving a perception of depth. Also known as introspective diplopia.

physiologic tremor [PHYSIO] A tremor in normal individuals, caused by fatigue, apprehension, or overexposure to cold.

physiology [BIOL] The study of the basic activities that occur in cells and tissues of living organisms by using physical and chemical methods.

Physopoda [INV ZOO] The equivalent name for Thysanoptera.

Physosomata [INV ZOO] A superfamily of amphipod crustaceans in the suborder Hyperiidea; the eyes are small or rarely absent, and the inner plates of the maxillipeds are free at the apex.

Phytalmiidae [INV ZOO] A family of myodarian cyclorrhaphous dipteran insects in the subsection Acalypteratae.

phytal zone [ECOL] The part of a lake bottom covered by water shallow enough to permit the growth of rooted plants.

Phytamastigophorea [INV ZOO] A class of the subphylum Sarcomastigophora, including green and colorless phytoflagellates.

phytase [BIOCHEM] An enzyme occurring in plants, especially cereals, which catalyzes hydrolysis of phytic acid to inositol and phosphoric acid.

phytochrome [BIOCHEM] A protein plant pigment which serves to direct the course of plant growth and development in response variously to the presence or absence of light, to photoperiod, and to light quality.

phytocoenosis [ECOL] The entire plant population of a particular habitat.

phytogenic dam [ECOL] A natural dam consisting of plants and plant remains.

phytogenic dune [ECOL] Any dune in which the growth of vegetation influences the form of the dune, for example, by arresting the drifting of sand.

phytohemagglutinin *See* phytolectin.

phytohormone *See* plant hormone.

phytolectin [BIOCHEM] A lectin found in plants. Also known as phytohemagglutinin.

phytolith [PALEON] A fossilized part of a living plant that secreted mineral matter.

Phytomastigina [INV ZOO] The equivalent name for Phytamastigophorea.

Phytomonadida [INV ZOO] The equivalent name for Volvocida.

phytopathogen [ECOL] An organism that causes a disease in a plant.

phytophagous [ZOO] Feeding on plants.

phytoplankton [ECOL] Planktonic plant life.

Phytosauria [PALEON] A suborder of Late Triassic long-snouted aquatic thecodonts resembling crocodiles but with posteriorly located external nostrils, absence of a secondary palate, and a different structure of the pelvic and pectoral girdles.

Phytoseiidae [INV ZOO] A family of the suborder Mesostigmata.

phytosociology [ECOL] A broad study of plants that includes the study of all phenomena affecting their lives as social units.

phytosterol [BIOCHEM] Any of various sterols obtained from plants, including ergosterol and stigmasterol.

phytotoxin [BIOCHEM] 1. A substance toxic to plants. 2. A toxin produced by plants.

pia arachnoid [VERT ZOO] The outer meninx of certain submammalian forms having two membranes covering the brain and spinal cord.

pia mater [ANAT] The vascular membrane covering the surface of the brain and spinal cord.

Picidae [VERT ZOO] The woodpeckers, a large family of birds in the order Piciformes; adaptive modifications include a long tongue and hyoid mechanism, and stiffened tail feathers.

Piciformes [VERT ZOO] An order of birds characterized by the peculiar arrangement of the tendons of the toes.

Picinae [VERT ZOO] The true woodpeckers, a subfamily of the Picidae.

picodnavirus [VIROL] A group of deoxyribonucleic acid–containing animal viruses including the adeno-satellite viruses.

picornavirus [VIROL] A viral group made up of small (18–30 nanometers), ether-sensitive viruses that lack an envelope and have a ribonucleic acid genome; among subgroups included are enteroviruses and rhinoviruses, both of human origin.

Picrodendraceae [BOT] A small family of dicotyledonous plants in the order Juglandales characterized by unisexual flowers borne in catkins, four apical ovules in a superior ovary, and trifoliate leaves.

picrotoxin [BIOCHEM] $C_{30}H_{34}O_{13}$ A poisonous, crystalline plant alkaloid found primarily in *Cocculus indicus*; used as a stimulant and convulsant drug. Also known as cocculin.

Picumninae [VERT ZOO] The piculets, a subfamily of the avian family Picidae.

piece-root grafting [BOT] Grafting in which each piece of a cut seedling root is used as a stock.

Pierce's disease [PL PATH] A virus disease of grapes in which there is mottling between the veins of leaves, early defoliation, and early ripening and withering of the fruit.

Pieridae [INV ZOO] A family of lepidopteran insects in the superfamily Papilionoidea including white, sulfur, and orange-tip butterflies; characterized by the lack of a prespiracular bar at the base of the abdomen.

Plesmatidae [INV ZOO] The ash-gray leaf bugs, a family of hemipteran insects belonging to the Pentatomorpha.

Piesmidae [INV ZOO] A small family of hemipteran insects in the superfamily Lygaeoidea.

pig [VERT ZOO] Any wild or domestic mammal of the superfamily Suoidea in the order Artiodactyla; toes terminate in nails which are modified into hooves, the tail is short, and the body is covered sparsely with hair which is frequently bristlelike.

pigeon [VERT ZOO] Any of various stout-bodied birds in the family Columbidae having short legs, a bill with a horny tip, and a soft cere.

pigeon milk [PHYSIO] A milky glandular secretion of the crop of pigeons that is regurgitated to feed newly hatched young.

pigment [BIOCHEM] Any coloring matter in plant or animal cells.

pigmentation [PHYSIO] The normal color of the body and its organs, resulting from a summation of the natural color of the tissue, the pigments deposited therein, and the pigments carried through the blood bathing the tissue.

pigment cell [CELL BIO] Any cell containing deposits of pigment.

pika [VERT ZOO] Any member of the family Ochotonidae, which includes 14 species of lagomorphs resembling rabbits but having a vestigial tail and short, rounded ears.

pike [VERT ZOO] Any of about five species of predatory fish which compose the family Esocidae in the order Clupeiformes; the body is cylindrical and compressed, with cycloid scales that have deeply scalloped edges.

Pilacraceae [MYCOL] A family of Basidiomycetes.

Pilargidae [INV ZOO] A family of small, short, depressed errantian polychaete annelids.

pileum [VERT ZOO] The top of a bird's head, from the nape to the bill.

pileus [BIOL] The umbrella-shaped upper cap of mushrooms and other basidiomycetous fungi.

Pilidae [INV ZOO] A family of fresh-water snails in the order Pectinibranchia.

Pilifera [VERT ZOO] Collective designation for animals with hair, that is, mammals.

Pilimelia [MICROBIO] A genus of bacteria in the family Actinoplanaceae; sporangia are cylindrical; rod-shaped spores are arranged in parallel chains and are motile by means of one polar flagellum or several lateral flagella; grow on hair or other keratin substrate.

pilomotor nerve [ANAT] A nerve causing contraction of one of the arrectoris pilorum muscles.

pilomotor reflex [PHYSIO] Erection of the hairs of the skin (gooseflesh) in response to chilling or irritation of the skin or to an emotional stimulus.

pilosebaceous [ANAT] Pertaining to the hair follicles and sebaceous glands, as the pilosebaceous apparatus, comprising the hair follicle and its attached gland.

Piltdown man [PALEON] An alleged fossil man based on fragments of a skull and mandible that were eventually discovered to constitute a skillful hoax.

pilus [ANAT] A hair. [BIOL] A fine, slender, hairlike body. [MICROBIO] Any filamentous appendage other than flagella on certain gramnegative bacteria. Also known as fimbria.

pimento [BOT] *Capsicum annuum.* A type of pepper in the order Polemoniales grown for its thick, sweet-fleshed red fruit.

piña [BOT] A fiber obtained from the large leaves of the pineapple plant. Also known as pineapple fiber.

pinacocyte [INV ZOO] A flattened polygonal cell occurring in the dermal epithelium of sponges, and lining the exhalant canals.

Pinales [BOT] An order of gymnospermous woody trees and shrubs in the class Pinopsida, including pine, spruce, fir, cypress, yew, and redwood; the largest plants are the conifers.

pincer [INV ZOO] A grasping apparatus, as on the anterior legs of a lobster, consisting of two hinged jaws.

pine [BOT] Any of the cone-bearing trees composing the genus *Pinus;* characterized by evergreen leaves (needles), usually in tight clusters of two to five.

pineal body [ANAT] An unpaired, elongated, club-shaped, knoblike or threadlike organ attached by a stalk to the roof of the vertebrate forebrain. Also known as conarium; epiphysis.

pineapple [BOT] *Ananas sativus.* A perennial plant of the order Bromeliales with long, swordlike, usually rough-edged leaves and a dense head of small abortive flowers; the fruit is a sorosis that develops from the fleshy inflorescence and ripens into a solid mass, covered by the persistent bracts and crowned by a tuft of leaves.

pineapple fiber See piña.

pine nut [BOT] The edible seed borne in the cone of various species of pine (*Pinus*), such as stone pine (*P. pinea*) and piñon pine (*P. cembroides* var. *edulis*).

pinfeather [VERT ZOO] A young, underdeveloped feather, especially one still enclosed in a cylindrical horny sheath which is afterward cast off.

pinguecula [ANAT] A small patch of yellowish-white connective tissue located on the conjunctiva, between the cornea and the canthus of the eye.

Pinicae [BOT] A large subdivision of the Pinophyta, comprising woody plants with a simple trunk and excurrent branches, simple, usually alternative, needlelike or scalelike leaves, and wood that lacks vessels and usually has resin canals.

pinion [VERT ZOO] The distal portion of a bird's wing.

pink disease [PL PATH] A fungus disease of the bark of rubber, cacao, citrus, coffee, and other trees caused by *Corticium salmonicolor* and characterized by a pink covering of hyphae on the stems and branches.

pink root [PL PATH] A fungus disease of onion and garlic caused by various organisms, especially species of *Phoma* and *Fusarium;* marked by red discoloration of the roots.

pink rot [PL PATH] 1. A fungus disease of potato tubers caused by *Phytophtora erythroseptica* and characterized by wet rot and pink color of the cut surfaces of the tuber upon exposure to air. 2. A rot disease of apples caused by the fungus *Tricothecium roseum.* 3. A watery soft rot of celery caused by the fungus *Sclerotinia sclerotiorum.*

pinna [ANAT] The cartilaginous, projecting flap of the external ear of vertebrates. Also known as auricle.

pinnate [BOT] Having parts arranged like a feather, branching from a central axis.

pinnate muscle [ANAT] A muscle having a central tendon onto which many short, diagonal muscle fibers attach at rather acute angles.

Pinnipedia [VERT ZOO] A suborder of aquatic mammals in the order Carnivora, including walruses and seals.

Pinnotheridae [INV ZOO] The pea crabs, a family of decapod crustaceans belonging to the Brachygnatha.

pinnulate [BIOL] Having pinnules.

pinnule [BIOL] The secondary branch of a plumelike or pinnate organ.

pinocytosis [CELL BIO] Deprecated term formerly used to describe the process of uptake or internalization of particles, macromolecules, and fluid droplets by living cells; the process is now termed endocytosis.

Pinophyta [BOT] The gymnosperms, a division of seed plants characterized as vascular plants with roots, stems, and leaves, and with seeds that are not enclosed in an ovary but are borne on cone scales or exposed at the end of a stalk.

Pinopsida [BOT] A class of gymnospermous plants in the subdivision Pinicae characterized by entire-margined or slightly toothed, narrow leaves.

pinosome [CELL BIO] A closed intracellular vesicle containing material captured by pinocytosis.

pinulus [INV ZOO] A sponge spicule, usually with five rays, one of which develops numerous small spines.

Pinus [BOT] The type genus of the family Pinaceae; the true pines, coniferous trees of north temperate regions having early deciduous primary leaves, needlelike secondary leaves, and cones with woody scales.

pinworm [INV ZOO] *Enterobius vermicularis*. A phasmid nematode of the superfamily Oxyuroidea; causes enterobiasis. Also known as human threadworm; seatworm.

pioneer [ECOL] An organism that is able to establish itself in a barren area and begin an ecological cycle.

Plophilidae [INV ZOO] The skipper flies, a family of myodarian cyclorrhaphous dipteran insects in the subsection Acalypteratae.

Piperaceae [BOT] A family of dicotyledonous plants in the order Piperales characterized by alternate leaves, a solitary ovule, copious perisperm, and scanty endosperm.

Piperales [BOT] An order of dicotyledonous herbaceous plants marked by ethereal oil cells, uniaperturate pollen, and reduced crowded flowers with orthotropous ovules.

Pipidea [VERT ZOO] A family of frogs sometimes included in the suborder Opisthocoela, but more commonly placed in its own suborder, Aglossa; a definitive tongue is lacking, and free ribs are present in the tadpole but they fuse to the vertebrae in the adult.

Pipridae [VERT ZOO] The manakins, a family of colorful, neotropical suboscine birds in the order Passeriformes.

piptoblast [INV ZOO] A statoblast that is free but has no float.

piriformis [ANAT] A muscle arising from the front of the sacrum and inserted into the greater trochanter of the femur.

Piroplasmea [INV ZOO] A class of parasitic protozoans in the superclass Sarcodina; includes the single genus *Babesia*.

Pisces [VERT ZOO] The fish and fishlike vertebrates, including the classes Agnatha, Placodermi, Chondrichthyes, and Osteichthyes.

piscivorous [ZOO] Feeding on fishes.

Pisionidae [INV ZOO] A small family of errantian polychaete annelids; allies of the scale bearers.

pistachio [BOT] *Pistacia vera*. A small, spreading dioecious evergreen tree with leaves that have three to five broad leaflets, and with large drupaceous fruit; the edible seed consists of a single green kernel covered by a brown coat and enclosed in a tough shell.

pistil [BOT] The ovule-bearing organ of angiosperms; consists of an ovary, a style, and a stigma.

pistillate [BOT] 1. Having a pistil. 2. Having pistils but no stamens.

pit [BOT] 1. A cavity in the secondary wall of a plant cell, formed where secondary deposition has failed to occur, and the primary wall remains uncovered; two main types are simple pits and bordered pits. 2. The stone of a drupaceous fruit.

pitch [MOL BIO] The distance between two adjacent turns of double-stranded deoxyribonucleic acid.

pitcher plant [BOT] Any of various insectivorous plants of the families Sarraceniaceae and Nepenthaceae; the leaves form deep pitchers in which water collects and insects are drowned and digested.

pith [BOT] A central zone of parenchymatous tissue that occurs in most vascular plants and is surrounded by vascular tissue.

Pittidae [VERT ZOO] The pittas, a homogeneous family of brightly colored suboscine birds with an erectile crown of feathers, in the suborder Tyranni.

pituicyte [HISTOL] The characteristic cell of the neurohypophysis; these cells are pigmented and fusiform and are probably derived from neuroglial cells.

pituitary [ANAT] Of or pertaining to the hypophysis. [PHYSIO] Secreting phlegm or mucus (archaic usage).

pituitary gland *See* hypophysis.

Pityaceae [PALEOBOT] A family of fossil plants in the order Cordaitales known only as petrifactions of branches and wood.

pivot joint [ANAT] A diarthrosis that permits a rotation of one bone around another; an example is the articulation of the atlas with the axis. Also known as trochoid.

placenta [BOT] A plant surface bearing a sporangium. [EMBRYO] A vascular organ that unites the fetus to the wall of the uterus in all mammals except marsupials and monotremes.

placental barrier [EMBRYO] The tissues intervening between the maternal and the fetal blood of the placenta, which prevent or hinder certain substances or organisms from passing from mother to fetus.

placentation [BOT] The arrangement of ovules and placenta in the ovary of a plant. [EMBRYO] The formation and fusion of the placenta to the uterine wall.

placode [EMBRYO] A platelike epithelial thickening, frequently marking, in the embryo, the anlage of an organ or part.

Placodermi [PALEON] A large and varied class of Paleozoic fishes characterized by a complex bony armor covering the head and the front portion of the trunk.

Placodontia [PALEON] A small order of Triassic marine reptiles of the subclass Euryapsida characterized by flat-crowned teeth in both the upper and lower jaws and on the palate.

Placothuriidae [INV ZOO] A family of holothurian echinoderms in the order Dendrochirotida; individuals are invested in plates and have a complex calcareous ring mechanism.

Plagiaulacida [PALEON] A primitive, monofamilial suborder of multituberculate mammals distinguished by their dentition (dental formula I 3/0 C 0/0 Pm 5/4 M 2/2), having cutting premolars and two rows of cusps on the upper molars.

Plagiaulacidae [PALEON] The single family of the extinct mammalian suborder Plagiaulacida.

plagioclimax [ECOL] A plant community which is in equilibrium under present conditions, but which has not reached its natural climax, or has regressed from it, due to biotic factors such as human intervention.

plagiodont [VERT ZOO] Of a snake, having obliquely set, or two converging series of, palatal teeth.

Plagiosauria [PALEON] An aberrant Triassic group of labyrinthodont amphibians.

plagiosere [ECOL] A plant succession deflected from its normal course by biotic factors.

planaria [INV ZOO] Any flatworm of the turbellarian order Tricladida; the body is broad and dorsoventrally flattened, with anterior lateral projections, the auricles, and a pair of eyespots on the anterior dorsal surface.

Planctomyces [MICROBIO] A genus of appendaged bacteria; spherical, oblong, or pear-shaped cells with long, slender stalks; reproduce by budding.

planidium [INV ZOO] A first-stage legless larva of various insects in the orders Diptera and Hymenoptera.

Planipennia [INV ZOO] A suborder of insects in the order Neuroptera in which the larval mandibles are modified for piercing and for sucking.

plankton [ECOL] Passively floating or weakly motile aquatic plants and animals.

Planobispora [MICROBIO] A genus of bacteria in the family Actinoplanaceae; linear or fingerlike sporangia, each containing a pair of motile, rod-shaped spores.

planoblast [INV ZOO] The medusa form of a hydrozoan.

Planococcus [MICROBIO] A genus of bacteria in the family Micrococcaceae; motile cells occur singly, in pairs, in threes, or in tetrads; metabolism is respiratory.

Planomonospora [MICROBIO] A genus of bacteria in the family Actinoplanaceae; club-shaped or fingerlike sporangia, each containing a single, large, motile spore.

planomycin *See* fervenulin.

planospiral [INV ZOO] Having the shell coiled in one plane, used particularly of foraminiferans and mollusks.

plant [BOT] Any organism belonging to the kingdom Plantae, generally distinguished by the presence of chlorophyll, a rigid cell wall, and abundant, persistent, active embryonic tissue, and by the absence of the power of locomotion.

Plantae [BOT] The plant kingdom.

Plantaginaceae [BOT] The single family of the plant order Plantaginales.

Plantaginales [BOT] An order of dicotyledonous herbaceous plants in the subclass Asteridae, marked by small hypogynous flowers with a persistent regular corolla and four petals.

plantar [ANAT] Of or relating to the sole of the foot.

plantaris [ANAT] A small muscle of the calf of the leg; origin is the lateral condyle of the femur, and insertion is the calcaneus; flexes the knee joint.

plantar reflex [PHYSIO] Flexion of the toes in response to stroking of the outer surface of the sole, from heel to little toe.

plant fermentation [BIOCHEM] A form of plant metabolism in which carbohydrates are partially degraded without the consumption of molecular oxygen.

plant geography [BOT] A major division of botany, concerned with all aspects of the spatial distribution of plants. Also known as geographical botany; phytochorology; phytogeography.

plant hormone [BIOCHEM] An organic compound that is synthesized in minute quantities by one part of a plant and translocated to another part, where it influences physiological processes. Also known as phytohormone.

plantigrade [VERT ZOO] Pertaining to walking with the whole sole of the foot touching the ground.

plant key [BOT] An analytical guide to the identification of plants, based on the use of contrasting characters to subdivide a group under study into branches.

plant kingdom [BOT] The worldwide array of plant life constituting a major division of living organisms.

plant pathology [BOT] The branch of botany concerned with diseases of plants.

plant physiology [BOT] The branch of botany concerned with the processes which occur in plants.

plant societies [ECOL] Assemblages of plants which constitute structural parts of plant communities.

plantula [INV ZOO] A small, cushionlike structure on the ventral surface of the segments of insect tarsi.

plant virus [VIROL] A virus that replicates only within plant cells.

planula [INV ZOO] The ciliated, free-swimming larva of coelenterates.

Planuloidea [INV ZOO] The equivalent name for Moruloidea.

plaque [VIROL] A clear area representing a colony of viruses on a plate culture formed by lysis of the host cell.

plasma [HISTOL] The fluid portion of blood or lymph.

plasmacyte [HISTOL] A fairly large, generally ovoid cell with a small, eccentrically placed nucleus; the chromatin material is adherent to the nuclear membrane and the cytoplasm is agranular and deeply basophilic everywhere except for a clear area adjacent to the nucleus in the area of the cytocentrum. Also known as plasma cell.

plasmagel [CELL BIO] The outer, gelated zone of protoplasm in a pseudopodium.

plasmagene [CELL BIO] A cytoplasmic particle or substance, which may be present in bodies such as plastids or mitochondria, and which can reproduce and pass on inherited qualities to daughter cells.

plasmalemma See cell membrane.

plasma membrane See cell membrane.

plasmasol [CELL BIO] The inner, solated zone of protoplasm in a pseudopodium.

plasma thromboplastin antecedent See factor XI.

plasma thromboplastin component See Christmas factor.

plasmid [GEN] An extrachromosomal genetic element found among various strains of Escherichia coli and other bacteria.

plasmin [BIOCHEM] A proteolytic enzyme in plasma which can digest many proteins through the process of hydrolysis. Also known as fibrinolysin.

plasminogen [BIOCHEM] The inert precursor, or zymogen, of plasmin. Also known as profibrinolysin.

plasmodesma [CELL BIO] An intercellular bridge, thought to be strands of cytoplasm connecting two cells.

Plasmodiidae [INV ZOO] A family of parasitic protozoans in the suborder Haemosporina inhabiting the erythrocytes of the vertebrate host.

Plasmodiophorida [INV ZOO] An order of the protozoan subclass Mycetozoia occurring as endoparasites of plants.

Plasmodiophoromycetes [MYCOL] A class of the Fungi.

plasmoditrophoblast See syncytiotrophoblast.

Plasmodium [INV ZOO] A genus of protozoans in the family Plasmodiidae in which all the true malarial parasites are placed.

plasmodium [MICROBIO] The noncellular, multinucleate, jellylike, ameboid, assimilative stage of the Myxomycetes.

Plasmodroma [INV ZOO] A subphylum of the Protozoa, including Mastigophora, Sarcodina, and Sporozoa, in some taxonomic systems.

plasmogamy [INV ZOO] Fusion of protoplasts, without nuclear fusion, to form a multinucleate mass; occurs in certain protozoans.

plasmolysis [PHYSIO] Shrinking of the cytoplasm away from the cell wall due to exosmosis by immersion of a plant cell in a solution of higher osmotic activity.

plasmotomy [INV ZOO] Subdivision of a plasmodium into two or more parts.

plastid [CELL BIO] One of the specialized cell organelles containing pigments or protein materials, often serving as centers of special metabolic activities; examples are chloroplasts and leukoplasts.

plastogene [CELL BIO] A cytoplasmic factor, controlled by or interacting with the nucleus, which determines differentiation of a plastid.

plastron [INV ZOO] The ventral plate of the cephalothorax of spiders. [VERT ZOO] The ventral portion of the shell of tortoises and turtles.

Platanaceae [BOT] A small family of monoecious dicotyledonous plants in which flowers have several carpels which are separate, three or four stamens, and more or less orthotropous ovules, and leaves are stipulate.

Plataspidae [INV ZOO] A family of shining, oval hemipteran insects in the superfamily Pentatomoidea.

plate budding [BOT] Plant budding by inserting a rectangular scion with a bud under a flap of bark on the stock in such a manner that the exposed wood on the stock is covered.

platelet [HISTOL] See thrombocyte.

Platyasterida [INV ZOO] An order of Asteroidea in which traces of metapinnules persist, the ossicles of the arm skeleton being arranged in two growth gradient systems.

Platybelondoninae [PALEON] A subfamily of extinct elephantoid mammals in the family Gomphotheriidae consisting of species with digging specializations of the lower tusks.

platycelous [VERT ZOO] Of a vertebra, having a flat or concave ventral surface and a convex dorsal surface.

Platycephalidae [VERT ZOO] The flatheads, a family of perciform fishes in the suborder Cottoidei.

Platyceratacea [PALEON] A specialized superfamily of extinct gastropod mollusks which adapted to a coprophagous life on crinoid calices.

Platycopa [INV ZOO] A suborder of ostracod crustaceans in the order Podocopida including marine forms with two pairs of thoracic legs.

Platycopina [INV ZOO] The equivalent name for Platycopa.

Platyctenea [INV ZOO] An order of the ctenophores whose members are sedentary or parasitic; adults often lack ribs and are flattened due to shortening of the main axis.

Platygasteridae [INV ZOO] A family of hymenopteran insects in the superfamily Proctotrupoidea.

Platyhelminthes [INV ZOO] A phylum of invertebrates composed of bilaterally symmetrical, nonsegmented, dorsoventrally flattened worms characterized by lack of coelom, anus, circulatory and respiratory systems, and skeleton.

platymyarian [INV ZOO] In nematodes, pertaining to flat muscle cells with the fibrillar region limited to a basal zone.

Platypodidae [INV ZOO] The ambrosia beetles, a family of coleopteran insects in the superfamily Curculionoidea.

Platypsyllidae [INV ZOO] The equivalent name for Leptinidae.

platypus [VERT ZOO] *Ornithorhynchus anatinus*. A monotreme, making up the family Ornithorhynchidae, which lays and incubates eggs in a manner similar to birds, and retains some reptilian characters; the female lacks a marsupium. Also known as duckbill platypus.

platysma [ANAT] A subcutaneous muscle of the neck, extending from the face to the clavicle; muscle of facial expression.

Platysomidae [PALEON] A family of extinct palaeonisciform fishes in the suborder Platysomoidei; typically, the body is laterally compressed and rhombic-shaped, with long dorsal and anal fins.

Platysomoidei [PALEON] A suborder of extinct deep-bodied marine and fresh-water fishes in the order Palaeonisciformes.

Platysternidae [VERT ZOO] The big-headed turtles, a family of Asiatic fresh-water Chelonia with a single species (*Platysternon megacephalum*), characterized by a large head, hooked mandibles, and a long tail.

Plecoptera [INV ZOO] The stoneflies, an order of primitive insects in which adults differ only slightly from immature stages, except for wings and tracheal gills.

plectane [INV ZOO] A cuticular plate supporting papillae in some nematodes.

Plectascales [MYCOL] An equivalent name for Eurotiales.

Plectognathi [VERT ZOO] The equivalent name for Tetraodontiformes.

Plectoidea [INV ZOO] A superfamily of small, free-living nematodes characterized by simple spiral amphids or variants thereof, elongate cylindroconoid stoma, and reflexed ovaries.

plectostele [BOT] A protostele that has the xylem divided into plates.

Pleidae [INV ZOO] A family of hemipteran insects in the superfamily Pleoidea.

pleiotropy [GEN] The quality of a gene having more than one phenotypic effect.

pleodont [VERT ZOO] Having solid teeth.

Pleoidea [INV ZOO] A superfamily of suboval hemipteran insects belonging to the subdivision Hydrocoriseae.

pleomorphism [BIOL] The occurrence of more than one distinct form of an organism in a single life cycle.

pleopod [INV ZOO] An abdominal appendage in certain crustaceans that is modified for swimming.

Pleosporales [BOT] The equivalent name for the lichenized Pseudophaeriales.

plerocercoid [INV ZOO] The infective metacestode of certain cyclophyllidean tapeworms; distinguished by a solid body.

plerome [BOT] Central core of primary meristem which gives rise to all cells of the stele from the pericycle inward.

plesioaster [INV ZOO] A type of poriferan microscleric monaxonic spicule.

Plesiocidaroida [PALEON] An extinct order of echinoderms assigned to the Euechinoidea.

Plesiomonas [MICROBIO] A genus of bacteria in the family Vibrionaceae; straight, motile rods with rounded ends, occurring singly, in pairs, or in short chains with polar flagella.

plesiomorph [EVOL] The original character of a branching phyletic lineage, found in the ancestral forms.

Plesiosauria [PALEON] A group of extinct reptiles in the order Sauropterygia constituting a highly specialized offshoot of the nothosaurs.

plesiotype [SYST] A specimen or specimens on which subsequent descriptions are based.

Plethodontidae [VERT ZOO] A large family of salamanders in the suborder Salamandroidea characterized by the absence of lungs and the presence of a fine groove from nostril to upper lip.

pleura [ANAT] The serous membrane covering the lung and lining the thoracic cavity.

Pleuracanthodii [PALEON] An order of Paleozoic sharklike fishes distinguished by two-pronged teeth, a long spine projecting from the posterior braincase, and direct backward extension of the tail.

pleural cavity [ANAT] The potential space included between the parietal and visceral layers of the pleura.

pleural rib *See* ventral rib.

pleurapophysis [ANAT] One of the lateral processes of a vertebra, corresponding morphologically to a rib.

pleurobranchia [INV ZOO] A gill that arises from the lateral wall of the thorax in certain arthropods.

pleurocarpous [BOT] Having the sporophyte in leaf axils along the side of the stem or on lateral branches; refers specifically to mosses.

Pleuroceridae [INV ZOO] A family of fresh-water snails in the order Pectinibranchia.

Pleurocoelea [INV ZOO] An extinct superfamily of gastropod mollusks of the order Opisthobranchia in which the shell, mantle cavity, and gills were present.

Pleurodira [VERT ZOO] A suborder of turtles (Chelonia) distinguished by spines on the posterior cervical vertebrae so that the head is retractile laterally.

pleurodontia [VERT ZOO] Attachment of the teeth to the inner surface of the jawbone.

pleurolophocercous cercaria [INV ZOO] A larval digenetic trematode distinguished by a long, powerful tail with a pair of fin folds, a protrusible oral sucker, and pigmented dorsal eyespots.

Pleuromeiaceae [PALEOBOT] A family of plants in the order Pleuromiales, but often included in the Isoetales due to a phylogenetic link.

Pleuromeiales [PALEOBOT] An order of Early Triassic lycopods consisting of the genus *Pleuromeia*; the upright branched stem had grasslike leaves and a single terminal strobilus.

pleuron [INV ZOO] The lateral portion of a single thoracic segment in arthropods.

Pleuronectiformes [VERT ZOO] The flatfishes, an order of actinopterygian fishes distinguished by the loss of bilateral symmetry.

Pleuronematina [INV ZOO] A suborder of the Hymenostomatida.

pleuroperitoneal cavity [VERT ZOO] The body cavity containing both the lungs and the abdominal viscera in all pulmonate vertebrates except mammals.

pleuropneumonialike organism [MICROBIO] Any of a poorly defined group of microorganisms classified in the order Mycoplasmatales, including the smallest organisms capable of independent life, and comparable in size to the large filterable viruses. Abbreviated PPLO.

Pleurostigmophora [INV ZOO] A subclass of the centipedes, in some taxonomic systems, distinguished by lateral spiracles.

Pleurotomariacea [PALEON] An extinct superfamily of gastropod mollusks in the order Aspidobranchia.

plexus [ANAT] A network of interlacing nerves or anastomosing vessels.

plica [BIOL] A fold, as of skin or a leaf.

Pliohyracinae [PALEON] An extinct subfamily of ungulate mammals in the family Procaviidae.

ploidy [GEN] Number of complete chromosome sets in a nucleus.

Ploiophilidae [INV ZOO] A small family of predacious hemipteran insects in the superfamily Cimicoidea; individuals live in the webs of spiders and embiids.

Plotosidae [VERT ZOO] A family of Indo-Pacific salt-water catfishes (Siluriformes).

plum [BOT] Any of various shrubs or small trees of the genus *Prunus* that bear smooth-skinned, globular to oval, drupaceous stone fruit.

plumage [VERT ZOO] The entire covering of feathers of a bird.

Plumatellina [INV ZOO] The single order of the ectoproct bryozoan class Phylactolaemata.

Plumbaginaceae [BOT] The leadworts, the single family of the order Plumbaginales.

Plumbaginales [BOT] An order of dicotyledonous plants in the subclass Caryophyllidae; flowers are pentamerous with fused petals, trinucleate pollen, and a compound ovary containing a single basal ovule.

plum blotch [PL PATH] A fungus disease of plums caused by *Phyllosticta congesta* and characterized by minute brown or gray angular leaf spots and brown or gray blotches on the fruit.

plumicome [BIOL] A spicule with plumelike tufts.

plumose [VERT ZOO] Having feathers or plumes.

plum pocket [PL PATH] A mild fungus disease of plums, caused either by *Taphrina pruni* or *T.*

communia, in which the stone of the fruit is aborted.

plumule [BOT] The primary bud of a plant embryo. [VERT ZOO] A down feather.

plus strand [MOL BIO] A parental ribonucleic acid strand in RNA bacteriophages that is used as a template for a complementary RNA strand (minus strand) produced with the formation of a double-stranded (double-helix) RNA.

pluteus [INV ZOO] The free-swimming, bilaterally symmetrical, easel-shaped larva of ophiuroids and echinoids.

pluvilignosa [ECOL] A tropical rain forest.

pneumatocodon [INV ZOO] Exumbrellar surface of the float or pneumatophore of siphonophorans.

pneumatophore [BOT] 1. An air bladder in marsh plants. 2. A submerged or exposed erect root that functions in the respiration of certain marsh plants. [INV ZOO] The air sac of a siphonophore.

pneumatosaccus [INV ZOO] Subumbrellar surface of the float or pneumatophore of siphonophorans.

pneumobacillus *See* Klebsiella pneumoniae.

pneumostome [INV ZOO] The respiratory aperture of gastropod mollusks.

Poaceae [BOT] The equivalent name for Gramineae.

Poales [BOT] The equivalent name for Cyperales.

pocket gopher *See* gopher.

pod [BOT] A dry dehiscent fruit; a legume.

Podargidae [VERT ZOO] The heavy-billed frogmouths, a family of Asian and Australian birds in the order Caprimulgiformes.

pod blight [PL PATH] A fungus disease of legumes caused by *Diaporthe* species.

Podicipedidae [VERT ZOO] The single family of the avian order Podicipediformes.

Podicipediformes [VERT ZOO] The grebes, an order of swimming and diving birds distinguished by dense, silky plumage, a rudimentary tail, and toes that are individually broadened and lobed.

Podicipitiformes [VERT ZOO] The equivalent name for Podicipediformes.

podite [INV ZOO] A segment of a limb of an arthropod.

podium [INV ZOO] The terminal portion of a body wall appendage in certain echinoderms.

podobranch [INV ZOO] A gill of a crustacean attached to the basal segment of a thoracic limb.

Podocopa [INV ZOO] A suborder of fresh-water ostracod crustaceans in the order Podocopida in which the inner lamella has a calcified rim joining the outer lamella along a chitinous zone of concrescence, and the two valves fit together firmly.

Podocopida [INV ZOO] An order of the Ostracoda; contains all fresh-water ostracods and is divided into the suborders Podocopa, Metacopina, and Platycopina.

Podocopina [INV ZOO] The equivalent name for Podocopa.

podocyst [INV ZOO] A sinus in the foot of certain gastropod mollusks.

Podogona [INV ZOO] The equivalent name for Ricinuleida.

Podostemaceae [BOT] The single family of the order Podostemales.

Podostemales [BOT] An order of dicotyledonous plants in the subclass Rosidae; plants are submerged aquatics with modified, branching shoots and small, perfect flowers having a superior ovary and united carpels.

pod rot [PL PATH] A fungus disease of cacao caused by *Monilia roreri* and characterized by lesions on the pods.

Poeciliidae [VERT ZOO] A family of fishes in the order Atheriniformes including the live-bearers, such as guppies, swordtails, and mollies.

Poecilosclerida [INV ZOO] An order of sponges of the class Demospongiae in which the skeleton includes two or more types of megascleres.

Poeobiidae [INV ZOO] A monotypic family of spioniform worms (*Poeobius meseres*) belonging to the Sedentaria and found in the North Pacific Ocean.

pogonochore [BOT] A type of plant that produces plumed disseminules.

Pogonophora [INV ZOO] The single class of the phylum Brachiata; the elongate body consists of three segments, each with a separate coelom; there is no mouth, anus, or digestive canal, and sexes are separate.

poikilotherm [ZOO] An animal, such as reptiles, fishes, and invertebrates, whose body temperature varies with and is usually higher than the temperature of the environment; a cold-blooded animal.

point mutation [GEN] Mutation of a single gene due to addition, loss, replacement, or change of sequence in one or more base pairs of the deoxyribonucleic acid of that gene.

poison gland [VERT ZOO] Any of various specialized glands in certain fishes and amphibians which secrete poisonous mucuslike substances.

poison hemlock [BOT] *Conium maculatum*. A branching biennial poisonous herb that contains a volatile alkaloid, coniine, in its fruits and leaves.

poison ivy [BOT] Any of several climbing, shrubby, or arborescent plants of the genus *Rhus* in the sumac family (Anacardiaceae); characterized by ternate leaves, greenish flowers, and white berries that produce an irritating oil.

poison oak [BOT] Any of several bushy poison ivy plants or shrubby poison sumacs.

poisonous plant [BOT] Any of about 400 species of vascular plants containing principles which initiate pathological conditions in man and animals.

poison sumac [BOT] *Rhus vernix*. A tall bush of the sumac family (Anacardiaceae) bearing pinnately compound leaves with 7–13 entire leaflets, and drooping, axillary clusters of white fruits that produce an irritating oil.

polar bear [VERT ZOO] *Thalarctos maritimus*. A large aquatic carnivore found in the polar regions of the Northern Hemisphere.

polar body [CELL BIO] One of the small bodies cast off by the oocyte during maturation.

polarity [MOL BIO] The orientation of a strand of polynucleotide with respect to its partner, expressed in terms of nucleotide linkages.

polar mutations [GEN] A class of mutations in the genes of an operon that affect the expression not only of the gene in which the mutation resides, but also of the genes located to one side of the mutated gene.

polar nucleus [BOT] One of the two nuclei in the center of the embryo sac of a seed plant which fuse to form the endosperm nucleus.

pole blight [PL PATH] A destructive disease of white pines characterized by shortening of the needle-bearing stems, yellowing and shortening of needles, and copious flow of resin.

Polemoniaceae [BOT] A family of autotrophic dicotyledonous plants in the order Polemoniales distinguished by lack of internal phloem, corolla lobes that are convolute in the bud, three carpels, and axile placentation.

Polemoniales [BOT] An order of dicotyledonous plants in the subclass Asteridae, characterized by sympetalous flowers, a regular, usually five-lobed corolla, and stamens equal in number and alternate with the petals.

polian vesicle [INV ZOO] Interradial reservoirs connecting with the ring vessel in most asteroids and holothuroids.

pollen [BOT] The small male reproductive bodies produced in pollen sacs of the seed plants.

pollen count [BOT] The number of grains of pollen that collect on a specified area (often taken as 1 square centimeter) in a specified time.

pollen tube [BOT] The tube produced by the wall of a pollen grain which enters the embryo sac and provides a passage through which the male nuclei reach the female nuclei.

pollination [BOT] The transfer of pollen from a stamen to a pistil; fertilization in flowering plants.

pollution [ECOL] Destruction or impairment of the purity of the environment. [PHYSIO] Emission of semen at times other than during coitus.

Polyangiaceae [MICROBIO] A family of bacteria in the order Myxobacterales; vegetative cells and myxospores are cylindrical with blunt, rounded ends; the slime capsule is lacking; sporangia are sessile or stalked.

Polyangium [MICROBIO] A genus of bacteria in the family Polyangiaceae; sporangia are sessile, and vegetative cells and myxospores are rod-shaped.

polyaxon [INV ZOO] A spicule that is laid down along several axes.

Polybrachiidae [INV ZOO] A family of sedentary marine animals in the order Thecanephria.

Polychaeta [INV ZOO] The largest class of the phylum Annelida, distinguished by paired, lateral, fleshy appendages (parapodia) provided with setae, on most segments.

Polycirrinae [INV ZOO] A subfamily of polychaete annelids in the family Terebellidae.

polycistronic messenger [BIOCHEM] In ribonucleic acid viruses, messenger ribonucleic acid that contains the amino acid sequence for several proteins.

Polycladida [INV ZOO] A class of marine Turbellaria whose leaflike bodies have a central intestine with radiating branches, many eyes, and tentacles in most species.

polyclimax [ECOL] A climax community under the controlling influence of many environmental factors, including soils, topography, fire, and animal interactions.

polyclonal mixed cryoglobulin [BIOCHEM] A cryoglobulin made of heterogeneous immunoglobin molecules belonging to two or more different classes, and sometimes additional serum proteins.

Polycopidae [INV ZOO] The single family of the suborder Cladocopa.

Polyctenidae [INV ZOO] A family of hemipteran insects in the superfamily Cimicoidea; the individuals are bat ectoparasites which resemble bedbugs but lack eyes and have ctenidia and strong claws.

Polydolopidae [PALEON] A Cenozoic family of rodentlike marsupial mammals.

polyembryony [ZOO] A form of sexual reproduction in which two or more offspring are derived from a single egg.

polyestrous [PHYSIO] Having several periods of estrus in a year.

Polygalaceae [BOT] A family of dicotyledonous plants in the order Polygalales distinguished by having a bicarpellate pistil and monadelphous stamens.

polygalacturonase [BIOCHEM] An enzyme that catalyzes the hydrolysis of glycosidic linkage of polymerized galacturonic acids.

Polygalales [BOT] An order of dicotyledonous plants in the subclass Rosidae characterized by its simple leaves and usually irregular, hypogynous flowers.

polygamous [BOT] Having both perfect and imperfect flowers on the same plant. [VERT ZOO] Having more than one mate at one time.

polygene [GEN] One of a group of nonallelic genes that collectively control a quantitative character.

Polygnathidae [PALEON] A family of Middle Silurian to Cretaceous conodonts in the suborder Conodontiformes, having platforms with small pitlike attachment scars.

Polygonaceae [BOT] The single family of the order Polygonales.

Polygonales [BOT] An order of dicotyledonous plants in the subclass Caryophyllidae characterized by well-developed endosperm, a unilocular ovary, and often trimerous flowers.

polyhedral disease See polyhedrosis.

polyhedrosis [INV ZOO] Any of several virus diseases of insect larvae characterized by the breakdown of tissues and presence of polyhedral granules. Also known as polyhedral disease.

Polymera [INV ZOO] Formerly a subphylum of the Vermes; equivalent to the phylum Annelida.

polymerase [BIOCHEM] An enzyme that links nucleotides together to form polynucleotide chains.

polymorph [BIOL] An organism that exhibits polymorphism. [HISTOL] See granulocyte.

polymorphism [BIOL] 1. Occurrence of different forms of individual in a single species. 2. Occurrence of different structural forms in a single individual at different periods in the life cycle. [GEN] The coexistence of genetically determined distinct forms in the same population, even the rarest of them being too common to be maintained solely by mutation; human blood groups are an example.

polymorphonuclear leukocyte See granulocyte.

polymyarian [INV ZOO] Referring to the cross-sectional appearance of muscle cells in a nematode, having many cells in each quadrant.

polymyxin [MICROBIO] Any of the basic polypeptide antibiotics produced by certain strains of *Bacillus polymyxa*.

Polynemidae [VERT ZOO] A family of perciform shore fishes in the suborder Mugiloidei.

Polynoidae [INV ZOO] The largest family of polychaetes, included in the Errantia and having a body of varying size and shape that is covered with elytra.

polynucleotide [BIOCHEM] A linear sequence of nucleotides.

Polyodontidae [INV ZOO] A family of tubicolous, often large-bodied errantian polychaetes with characteristic cephalic and parapodial structures.

polyoma virus [VIROL] A small deoxyribonucleic acid virus normally causing inapparent infection in mice, but experimentally capable of producing parotid tumors and a wide variety of other tumors.

Polyopisthocotylea [INV ZOO] An order of the trematode subclass Monogenea having a solid posterior holdfast bearing suckers or clamps.

polyp [INV ZOO] A sessile coelenterate individual having a hollow, somewhat cylindrical body, attached at one end, with a mouth surrounded by tentacles at the free end; may be solitary (hydra) or colonial (coral).

polypeptide [BIOCHEM] A chain of amino acids linked together by peptide bonds but with a lower molecular weight than a protein; obtained by synthesis, or by partial hydrolysis of protein.

polypetalous [BOT] Having distinct petals, in reference to a flower or a corolla. Also known as choripetalous.

Polyphaga [INV ZOO] A suborder of the order Coleoptera; members are distinguished by not having the hind coxae fused to the metasternum and by lacking notopleural sutures.

polyphagous [ZOO] Feeding on many different kinds of plants or animals.

polyphenol oxidase [BIOCHEM] A copper-containing enzyme that catalyzes the oxidation of phenol derivatives to quinones.

polyphyodont [VERT ZOO] Having teeth which may be constantly replaced.

polypide [INV ZOO] The internal contents of an ectoproct bryozoan zooid.

Polyplacophora [INV ZOO] The chitons, an order of mollusks in the class Amphineura distinguished by an elliptical body with a dorsal shell that comprises eight calcareous plates overlapping posteriorly.

polyploidy [GEN] The occurrence of related forms possessing chromosome numbers which are three or more times the haploid number.

Polypodiales [BOT] The true ferns; the largest order of modern ferns, distinguished by being leptosporangiate and by having small sporangia with a definite number of spores.

Polypodiophyta [BOT] The ferns, a division of the plant kingdom having well-developed roots, stems, and leaves that contain xylem and phloem and show well-developed alternation of generations.

Polypodiopsida [BOT] A class of the division Polypodiophyta; stems of these ferns bear several large, spirally arranged, compound leaves with sporangia grouped in sori on their undermargins.

Polypteridae [VERT ZOO] The single family of the order Polypteriformes.

Polypteriformes [VERT ZOO] An ancient order of actinopterygian fishes distinguished by thick, rhombic, ganoid scales with an enamellike covering, a slitlike spiracle behind the eye, a symmetrical caudal fin, and a dorsal series of free, spinelike finlets.

polyribosome *See* polysome.

polysaccharide [BIOCHEM] A carbohydrate composed of many monosaccharides.

polysaprobic [ECOL] Referring to a body of water in which organic matter is decomposing rapidly and free oxygen either is exhausted or is present in very low concentrations.

polysepalous [BOT] Having separate sepals. Also known as chorisepalous.

polysome [CELL BIO] A complex of ribosomes bound together by a single messenger ribonucleic acid molecule. Also known as polyribosome.

polysomy [GEN] The occurrence in a nucleus of one or more individual chromosomes in a number higher than that of the remainder.

polyspermy [PHYSIO] Penetration of the egg by more than one sperm.

polystele [BOT] A stele consisting of vascular units in the parenchyma.

Polystomatoidea [INV ZOO] A superfamily of monogeneid trematodes characterized by strong suckers and hooks on the posterior end.

Polystylifera [INV ZOO] A suborder of the Hoplonemertini distinguished by many stylets.

polytene chromosome [GEN] A giant, multistranded, cablelike chromosome composed of many identical chromosomes having their chromomeres in register and produced by polyteny.

Polytrichales [BOT] An order of ascocarpous perennial mosses; rigid, simple stems are highly developed and arise from a prostrate subterranean rhizome.

polytypic [SYST] A taxon that contains two or more taxa in the immediately subordinate category.

Polyzoa [INV ZOO] The equivalent name for Bryozoa.

Pomacentridae [VERT ZOO] The damselfishes, a family of perciform fishes in the suborder Percoidei.

Pomadasyidae [VERT ZOO] The grunts and sweetlips, a family of perciform fishes in the suborder Percoidei.

Pomatiasidae [INV ZOO] A family of land snails in the order Pectinibranchia.

Pomatomidae [VERT ZOO] A monotypic family of the Perciformes containing the bluefish (*Pomatomus saltatrix*).

pomegranate [BOT] *Punica granatum*. A small, deciduous ornamental tree of the order Myrtales cultivated for its fruit, which is a reddish, pomelike berry containing numerous seeds embedded in crimson pulp.

Pompilidae [INV ZOO] The spider wasps, the single family of the superfamily Pompiloidea.

Pompiloidea [INV ZOO] A monofamilial superfamily of hymenopteran insects in the suborder Apocrita with oval abdomen and strong spinose legs.

ponderosa pine [BOT] *Pinus ponderosa*. A hard pine tree of western North America; attains a height of 150–225 feet (46–69 meters) and has long, dark-green leaves in bundles of two to five and tawny, yellowish bark.

Ponerinae [INV ZOO] A subfamily of tropical carnivorous ants (Formicidae) in which pupae characteristically form in cocoons.

Pongidae [VERT ZOO] A family of anthropoid primates in the superfamily Hominoidea; includes the chimpanzee, gorilla, and orangutan.

pons [ANAT] **1.** A process or bridge of tissue connecting two parts of an organ. **2.** A convex white eminence located at the base of the brain; consists of fibers receiving impulses from the cerebral cortex and sending fibers to the contralateral side of the cerebellum.

pontine flexure [EMBRYO] A flexure in the embryonic brain concave dorsally, occurring in the region of the myelencephalon.

Pontodoridae [INV ZOO] A monotypic family of pelagic polychaetes assigned to the Errantia.

poplar [BOT] Any tree of the genus *Populus*, family Salicaceae, marked by simple, alternate leaves, scaly buds, bitter bark, and flowers and fruits in catkins.

popliteal artery [ANAT] A continuation of the femoral artery in the posterior portion of the thigh above the popliteal space and below the buttock.

popliteal nerve [ANAT] Either of two branches of the sciatic nerve in the lower part of the thigh; the larger branch continues as the tibial nerve, and the smaller branch continues as the peroneal nerve.

popliteal space [ANAT] A diamond-shaped area behind the knee joint.

popliteal vein [ANAT] A vein passing through the popliteal space, formed by merging of the tibial veins and continuing to become the femoral vein.

popliteus [ANAT] **1.** The ham or hinder part of the knee joint. **2.** A muscle on the back of the knee joint.

poppy [BOT] Any of various ornamental herbs of the genus *Papaver*, family Papaveraceae, with large, showy flowers; opium is obtained from the fruits of the opium poppy (*P. somniferum*).

population [BIOL] A group of organisms occupying a specific geographic area or biome.

population density [ECOL] The size of the population within a particular unit of space.

population dispersal [BIOL] The process by which groups of living organisms expand the space or range within which they live.

population dispersion [BIOL] The spatial distribution at any particular moment of the individuals of a species of plant or animal.

population dynamics [BIOL] The aggregate of processes that determine the size and composition of any population.

population genetics [GEN] The study of both experimental and theoretical consequences of Mendelian heredity on the population level; includes studies of gene frequencies, genotypes, phenotypes, and mating systems.

Porcellanasteridae [INV ZOO] A family of essentially deep-water forms in the suborder Paxillosina.

Porcellanidae [INV ZOO] The rock sliders, a family of decapod crustaceans of the group Anomura which resemble true crabs but are distinguished by the reduced, chelate fifth pereiopods and the well-developed tail fan.

porcupine [VERT ZOO] Any of about 26 species of rodents in two families (Hystricidae and Erethizontidae) which have spines or quills in addition to regular hair.

pore [BIOL] Any minute opening by which matter passes through a wall or membrane.

pore fungus [MYCOL] The common name for members of the families Boletaceae and Polyporaceae in the group Hymenomycetes; spore-bearing surfaces are characteristically within tubes or pores.

Porifera [INV ZOO] The sponges, a phylum of the animal kingdom characterized by the presence of canal systems and chambers through which water is drawn in and released; tissues and organs are absent.

porocyte [INV ZOO] One of the perforated, tubular cells which constitute the wall of the incurrent canals in certain Porifera.

porogamy [BOT] Passage of the pollen tube through the micropyle of an ovule in a seed plant.

Poroxylaceae [PALEOBOT] A monogeneric family of extinct plants included in the Cordaitales.

porphin [BIOCHEM] A heterocyclic ring consisting of four pyrrole rings linked by methine (—CH=) bridges; the basic structure of chlorophyll, hemoglobin, the cytochromes, and certain other related substances.

porphobilinogen [BIOCHEM] $C_{10}H_{14}O_4N_2$ Dicarboxylic acid derived from pyrrole; a product of hemoglobin breakdown that gives the urine a Burgundy-red color.

porphyrin [BIOCHEM] A class of red-pigmented compounds with a cyclic tetrapyrrolic structure in which the four pyrrole rings are joined through their α-carbon atoms by four methene bridges (=C—); the porphyrins form the active nucleus of chlorophylls and hemoglobin.

porpoise [VERT ZOO] Any of several species of marine mammals of the family Phocaenidae which have small flippers, a highly developed sonar system, and smooth, thick, hairless skin.

porta hepatis [ANAT] The transverse fissure of the liver through which the portal vein and hepatic artery enter the liver and the hepatic ducts leave.

portal [ANAT] 1. Of or pertaining to the porta hepatis. 2. Pertaining to the portal vein or system.

portal circulation [PHYSIO] The passage of venous blood through a portal system.

portal system [ANAT] A system of veins that break into a capillary network before returning the blood to the heart.

portal vein [ANAT] Any vein that terminates in a network of capillaries.

Portuguese man-of-war [INV ZOO] Any of several brilliantly colored tropical siphonophores in the genus *Physalia* which possess a large float and extremely long tentacles.

Portulacaceae [BOT] A family of dicotyledonous plants in the order Caryophyllales distinguished by a syncarpous gynoecium, few, cyclic tepals and stamens, two sepals, and two to many ovules.

Portunidae [INV ZOO] The swimming crabs, a family of the Brachyura having the last pereiopods modified as swimming paddles.

Porulosida [INV ZOO] An order of the protozoan subclass Radiolaria in which the central capsule shows many pores.

position effect [GEN] 1. Change in expressivity of a gene associated with chromosome aberrations. 2. Inherent gene expression as influenced by neighboring genes.

positive afterimage [PHYSIO] An afterimage persisting after the eyes are closed or turned toward a dark background, and of the same color as the stimulating light.

positive interference [GEN] The reduction, by one crossover exchange, of the likelihood of another crossover in its vicinity.

postcentral gyrus [ANAT] The cerebral convolution that lies immediately posterior to the central sulcus and extends from the longitudinal fissure above the posterior ramus of the lateral sulcus.

postcentral sulcus [ANAT] The first sulcus of the parietal lobe of the cerebrum, lying behind and roughly parallel to the central sulcus.

posterior [ZOO] 1. The hind end of an organism. 2. Toward the back, or hinder end, of the body.

posterior chamber [ANAT] The space in the eye between the posterior surface of the iris and the ciliary body, and the lens.

Potamogalinae [VERT ZOO] An aberrant subfamily of West African tenrecs (Tenrecidae).

Potamogetonaceae [BOT] A large family of monocotyledonous plants in the order Najadales characterized by a solitary, apical or lateral ovule, usually two or more carpels, flowers in spikes or racemes, and four each of tepals and stamens.

Potamogetonales [BOT] The equivalent name for Najadales.

Potamonidae [INV ZOO] A family of fresh-water crabs included in the Brachyura.

potamoplankton [BIOL] Plankton found in rivers.

potassium benzyl penicillinate See benzyl penicillin potassium.

potato [BOT] *Solanum tuberosum.* An erect herbaceous annual that has a round or angular aerial stem, underground lateral stems, pinnately compound leaves, and white, pink, yellow, or purple flowers occurring in cymose inflorescences; produces an edible tuber which is a shortened, thickened underground stem having nodes (eyes) and internodes. Also known as Irish potato; white potato.

Pottiales [BOT] An order of mosses distinguished by erect stems, lanceolate to broadly ovate or obovate leaves, a strong, mostly percurrent or excurrent costa, and a cucullate calyptra.

pour-plate culture [MICROBIO] A technique for pure-culture isolation of bacteria; liquid, cooled agar in a test tube is inoculated with one loopful of bacterial suspension and mixed by rolling the tube between the hands; subsequent transfers are made from this to a second test tube, and from the second to a third; contents of each tube are poured into separate petri dishes; pure cultures can be isolated from isolated colonies appearing on the plates after incubation.

Pourtalesiidae [INV ZOO] A family of exocyclic Euechinoidea in the order Holasteroida, including those forms with a bottle-shaped test.

powdery mildew [MYCOL] A fungus characterized by production of abundant powdery conidia on the host; a member of the family Erysiphaceae or the genus *Oidium.* [PL PATH] A plant disease caused by a powdery mildew fungus.

powdery scab [PL PATH] A fungus disease of potato tubers caused by *Spongospora subterranea* and characterized by nodular discolored lesions, which burst and expose masses of powdery fungus spores.

poxvirus [VIROL] A deoxyribonucleic acid–containing animal virus group including the viruses of smallpox, molluscum contagiosum, and various animal pox and fibromas.

PPLO See pleuropneumonialike organism.

prairie dog [VERT ZOO] The common name for three species of stout, fossorial rodents belonging to the genus *Cynomys* in the family Sciuridae; all have a short, flat tail, small ears, and short limbs terminating in long claws.

Prasinovolvocales [BOT] An order of green algae in which there are lateral appendages in the flagellum.

pratincolous [ECOL] 1. Living in meadows. 2. Living in low grass.

preadaptation [EVOL] Possession by an organism or group of organisms, specialized to one mode of life, of characters which favor easy adaptation to a new environment.

precentral gyrus [ANAT] The cerebral convolution that lies between the precentral sulcus and the central sulcus and extends from the supermedial border of the hemisphere to the posterior ramus of the lateral sulcus.

precollagenous fiber See reticular fiber.

predation [BIOL] The killing and eating of an individual of one species by an individual of another species.

predator [ZOO] An animal that preys on other animals as a source of food.

prednisolone [BIOCHEM] $C_{21}H_{28}O_5$ A glucocorticoid that is a dehydrogenated analog of hydrocortisone.

preen gland See uropygial gland.

prefoliation See vernation.

prefrontal [ANAT] Situated in the anterior part of the frontal lobe of the brain. [VERT ZOO] 1. Of or pertaining to a bone of some vertebrate skulls, located anterior and lateral to the frontal bone. 2. Of, pertaining to, or being a scale or plate in front of the frontal scale on the head of some reptiles and fishes.

pregnanediol [BIOCHEM] $C_{21}H_{36}O_2$ A metabolite of progesterone, present in urine during the progestational phase of the menstrual cycle and also during pregnancy.

pregnenolone [BIOCHEM] $C_{21}H_{32}O_2$ A steroid ketone that is formed as an oxidation product of cholesterol, stigmasterol, and certain other steroids.

prehensile [VERT ZOO] Adapted for seizing, grasping, or plucking, especially by wrapping around some object.

premaxilla [ANAT] Either of two bones of the upper jaw of vertebrates located in front of and between the maxillae.

premolar [ANAT] In each quadrant of the permanent human dentition, one of the two teeth between the canine and the first molar; a bicuspid.

prepuce [ANAT] 1. The foreskin of the penis, a fold of skin covering the glans penis. 2. A similar fold over the glans clitoridis.

prescutum [INV ZOO] The anterior part of the tergum of a segment of the thorax in insects.

presoma [INV ZOO] The anterior portion of an invertebrate that lacks a definitive head structure.

pressure point [PHYSIO] A point of marked sensibility to pressure or weight, arranged like the temperature spots, and showing a specific end apparatus arranged in a punctate manner and connected with the pressure sense.

Priapulida [INV ZOO] A minor phylum of wormlike marine animals; the body is made up of three distinct portions (proboscis, trunk, and caudal appendage) and is often covered with spines and tubercles, and the mouth is surrounded by concentric rows of teeth.

Priapuloidea [INV ZOO] An equivalent name for Priapulida.

primary [VERT ZOO] Of or pertaining to quills on the distal joint of a bird wing.

primary constriction See centromere.

primary meristem [BOT] Meristem which is derived directly from embryonic tissue and which gives rise to epidermis, vascular tissue, and the cortex.

primary phloem [BOT] Phloem derived from apical meristem.

primary production [ECOL] The total amount of new organic matter produced by photosynthesis.

primary root [BOT] The first plant root to develop; derived from the radicle.

primary succession *See* prisere.

primary tissue [BOT] Plant tissue formed during primary growth. [HISTOL] Any of the four fundamental tissues composing the vertebrate body.

primary xylem [BOT] Xylem derived from apical meristem.

Primates [VERT ZOO] The order of mammals to which man belongs; characterized in terms of evolutionary trends by retention of a generalized limb structure and dentition, increasing digital mobility, replacement of claws by flat nails, development of stereoscopic vision, and progressive development of the cerebral cortex.

primibrach [INV ZOO] In crinoids, the brachials of the unbranched arm.

Primitiopsacea [PALEON] A small dimorphic superfamily of extinct ostracods in the suborder Beyrichicopina; the velum of the male was narrow and uniform, but that of the female was greatly expanded posteriorly.

primitive gut [EMBRYO] The tubular structure in embryos which differentiates into the alimentary canal.

primitive streak [EMBRYO] A dense, opaque band of ectoderm in the bilaminar blastoderm associated with the morphogenetic movements and proliferation of the mesoderm and notochord; indicates the first trace of the vertebrate embryo.

primordial gut *See* archenteron.

primordium *See* anlage.

Primulaceae [BOT] A family of dicotyledonous plants in the order Primulales characterized by a herbaceous habit and capsular fruit with two to many seeds.

Primulales [BOT] An order of dicotyledonous plants in the subclass Dilleniidae distinguished by sympetalous flowers, stamens located opposite the corolla lobes, and a compound ovary with a single style.

Prioniodidae [PALEON] A family of conodonts in the suborder Conodontiformes having denticulated bars with a large denticle at one end.

Prioniodinidae [PALEON] A family of conodonts in the suborder Conodontiformes characterized by denticulated bars or blades with a large denticle in the middle third of the specimen.

prionodont [VERT ZOO] Having many simple, similar teeth set in a row like sawteeth.

prisere [ECOL] The ecological succession of vegetation that occurs in passing from barren earth or water to a climax community. Also known as primary succession.

Pristidae [VERT ZOO] The sawfishes, a family of modern sharks belonging to the batoid group.

Pristiophoridae [VERT ZOO] The saw sharks, a family of modern sharks often grouped with the squaloids which have a greatly extended rostrum with enlarged denticles along the margins.

proaccelerin [BIOCHEM] A labile procoagulant in normal plasma but deficient in the blood of patients with parahemophilia; essential for rapid conversion of prothrombin to thrombin. Also known as factor V; labile factor.

proamnion [EMBRYO] The part of the embryonic area at the sides and in front of the head of the developing amniote embryo, which remains without mesoderm for a considerable period.

Proanura [PALEON] Triassic forerunners of the Anura.

probend [GEN] The clinically affected individual who is being studied with respect to a pedigree of interest to human genetics.

Proboscidea [VERT ZOO] An order of herbivorous placental mammals characterized by having a proboscis, incisors enlarged to become tusks, and pillarlike legs with five toes bound together on a broad pad.

proboscis [INV ZOO] A tubular organ of varying form and function on a large number of invertebrates, such as insects, annelids, and tapeworms. [VERT ZOO] The flexible, elongated snout of certain mammals.

Procampodeidae [INV ZOO] A family of the insect order Diplura.

Procaviidae [VERT ZOO] A family of mammals in the order Hyracoidea including the hyraxes.

Procaviinae [VERT ZOO] A subfamily of ungulate mammals in the family Procaviidae.

Procellariidae [VERT ZOO] A family of birds in the order Procellariiformes comprising the petrels, fulmars, and shearwaters.

Procellariiformes [VERT ZOO] An order of oceanic birds characterized by tubelike nostril openings, webbed feet, dense plumage, compound horny sheath of the bill, and, often, a peculiar musky odor.

procephalon [INV ZOO] The part of an insect's head that lies anteriorly to the segment in which the mandibles are located.

procercoid [INV ZOO] The solid parasitic larva of certain eucestodes, such as pseudophyllideans, that develops in the body of the intermediate host.

procoagulant [BIOCHEM] Any of blood clotting factors V to VIII; accelerates the conversion of prothrombin to thrombin in the presence of thromboplastin and calcium.

Procoela [VERT ZOO] A suborder of the Anura characterized by a procoelous vertebral column and a free coccyx articulating with a double condyle.

procoelous [VERT ZOO] The form of a vertebra that is concave anteriorly and convex posteriorly.

procollagen [BIOCHEM] A high-molecular-weight form of collagen that is found in intracellular spaces and is believed to be the precursor of collagen.

Procolophonia [PALEON] A subclass of extinct cotylosaurian reptiles.

proctiger [INV ZOO] The cone-shaped, reduced terminal segment of the abdomen of an insect which contains the anus.

Proctotrupidae [INV ZOO] A family of hymenopteran insects in the superfamily Proctotrupoidea.

Proctotrupoidea [INV ZOO] A superfamily of parasitic Hymenoptera in the suborder Apocrita.

procumbent [BOT] Having stems that lie flat on the ground but do not root at the nodes.

Procyonidae [VERT ZOO] A family of carnivoran mammals in the superfamily Canoidea, including raccoons and their allies.

Prodinoceratinae [PALEON] A subfamily of extinct herbivorous mammals in the family Untatheriidae; animals possessed a carnivorelike body of moderate size.

producer [ECOL] An autotrophic organism of the ecosystem; any of the green plants.

Productinida [PALEON] A suborder of extinct articulate brachiopods in the order Strophomenida characterized by the development of spines.

proenzyme *See* zymogen.

proerythroblast of Ferrata *See* pronormoblast.

proestrus [PHYSIO] The beginning of the follicular phase of estrus.

profibrinolysin *See* plasminogen.

profunda [ANAT] Deep-seated; applied to certain arteries.

profundal zone [ECOL] The region occurring below the limnetic zone and extending to the bottom in lakes deep enough to develop temperature stratification.

Proganosauria [PALEON] The equivalent name for Mesosauria.

progeny [BIOL] Offspring; descendants.

progestational hormone [BIOCHEM] 1. The natural hormone progesterone, which induces progestational changes of the uterine mucosa. 2. Any derivative or modification or progesterone having similar actions.

progesterone [BIOCHEM] $C_{21}H_{30}O_2$ A steroid hormone produced in the corpus luteum, placenta, testes, and adrenals; plays an important physiological role in the luteal phase of the menstrual cycle and in the maintenance of pregnancy; it is an intermediate in the biosynthesis of androgens, estrogens, and the corticoids.

proglottid [INV ZOO] One of the segments of a tapeworm.

Progymnospermopsida [PALEON] A class of plants intermediate between ferns and gymnosperms; comprises the Denovian genus *Archaeopteris*.

prohaptor [INV ZOO] The anterior attachment organ of a typical monogenetic trematode.

Projapygidae [INV ZOO] A family of wingless insects in the order Diplura.

projection area [ANAT] An area of the cortex connected with lower centers of the brain by projection fibers.

projection fibers [ANAT] Fibers joining the cerebral cortex to lower centers of the brain, and vice versa.

prokaryote [CELL BIO] 1. A primitive nucleus, where the deoxyribonucleic acid–containing region lacks a limiting membrane. 2. Any cell containing such a nucleus, such as the bacteria and the blue-green algae.

Prolacertiformes [PALEON] A suborder of extinct terrestrial reptiles in the order Eosuchia distinguished by reduction of the lower temporal arcade.

prolactin [BIOCHEM] A protein hormone produced by the adenohypophysis; stimulates lactation and promotes functional activity of the corpus luteum. Also known as lactogenic hormone; luteotropic hormone; mammary-stimulating hormone; mammogen; mammogenic hormone; mammotropin.

prolamin [BIOCHEM] Any of the simple proteins, such as zein, found in plants; soluble in strong alcohol, insoluble in absolute alcohol and water.

proline [BIOCHEM] $C_5H_9O_2$ A heterocyclic amino acid occurring in essentially all proteins, and as a major constituent in collagen proteins.

prometaphase [CELL BIO] A stage between prophase and metaphase in mitosis in which the nuclear membrane disappears and the spindle forms.

promoter [GEN] The site on deoxyribonucleic acid to which ribonucleic acid polymerase binds preparatory to initiating transcription of an operon.

promyelocyte [HISTOL] The earliest myelocyte stage derived from the myeloblast.

pronate [ANAT] 1. To turn the forearm so that the palm of the hand is down or toward the back. 2. To turn the sole of the foot outward with the lateral margin of the foot elevated; to evert.

pronator [PHYSIO] A muscle which pronates, as the muscles of the forearm attached to the ulna and radius.

pronephros [EMBRYO] One of the anterior pair of renal organs in higher vertebrate embryos; the pair initiates formation of the archinephric duct.

pronghorn [VERT ZOO] *Antilocapra americana*. An antelopelike artiodactyl composing the family Antilocapridae; the only hollow-horned ungulate with branched horns present in both sexes.

pronormoblast [HISTOL] A nucleated erythrocyte precursor with scanty basophilic cytoplasm without hemoglobin. Also known as lymphoid hemoblast of Pappenheim; macroblast of Naegeli; megaloblast of Sabin; proerythroblast of Ferrata; prorubricyte; rubriblast; rubricyte.

pronucleus [CELL BIO] One of the two nuclear bodies of a newly fertilized ovum, the male pronucleus and the female pronucleus, the fusion of which results in the formation of the germinal (cleavage) nucleus.

propagule [BOT] 1. A reproductive structure of brown algae. 2. A propagable shoot.

Propalticidae [INV ZOO] A family of coleopteran insects of the superfamily Cucujoidea found in Old World tropics and Pacific islands.

prophage [VIROL] Integrated unit formed by union of the provirus into the bacterial genome.

prophase [CELL BIO] The initial stage of mitotic or meiotic cell division in which chromosomes are condensed from the nuclear material and split logitudinally to form pairs.

Propionibacteriaceae [MICROBIO] A family of bacteria related to the actinomycetes; grampositive, anaerobic to aerotolerant rods or filaments; ferment carbohydrates, with propionic acid as the principal product.

Propionibacterium [MICROBIO] The type genus of bacteria in the family Propionibacteriaceae; all species ferment glucose; principal fermentation products are propionic and acetic acids.

proplastid [BOT] Precursor body of a cell plastid.

propleuron [INV ZOO] A pleuron of the prothorax in insects.

propodite [INV ZOO] The sixth leg joint of certain crustaceans. Also known as propodus.

propodus See propodite.

proprioception [PHYSIO] The reception of internal stimuli.

proprioceptor [PHYSIO] A sense receptor that signals spatial position and movements of the body and its members, as well as muscular tension.

prop root [BOT] A root that serves to support or brace the plant. Also known as brace root.

propterygium [VERT ZOO] The anterior of the three principal basal cartilages forming a support of one of the paired fins of sharks, rays, and certain other fishes.

Prorastominae [PALEON] A subfamily of extinct dugongs (Dugongidae) which occur in the Eocene of Jamaica.

prorennin See renninogen.

Prorhynchidae [INV ZOO] A family of turbellarians in the order Alloeocoela.

prorubricyte See pronormoblast.

Prosauropoda [PALEON] A division of the extinct reptilian suborder Sauropodomorpha; they possessed blunt teeth, long forelimbs, and extremely large claws on the first finger of the forefoot.

Prosobranchia [INV ZOO] The largest subclass of the Gastropoda; generally, respiration is by means of ctenidia, an operculum is present, there is one pair of tentacles, and the sexes are separate.

prosodus [INV ZOO] A canal leading from an incurrent canal to a flagellated chamber in Porifera.

prosoma [INV ZOO] The anterior part of the body of mollusks and other invertebrates; primitive segmentation is not apparent.

Prosopora [INV ZOO] An order of the class Oligochaeta comprising mesonephridiostomal forms in which there are male pores in the segment of the posterior testes.

prosopyle [INV ZOO] The opening into a flagellated chamber from an inhalant canal in sponges.

prostaglandin [BIOCHEM] Any of various physiologically active compounds containing 20 carbon atoms and formed from essential fatty acids; found in highest concentrations in normal human semen; activities affect the nervous system, circulation, female reproductive organs, and metabolism.

prostate [ANAT] A glandular organ that surrounds the urethra at the neck of the urinary bladder in the male.

prosthecae [MICROBIO] Appendages that are part of the wall in bacteria in the genus *Caulobacter*.

prosthecate bacteria [MICROBIO] Single-celled microorganisms that differ from typical unicellular bacteria in having one or more appendages which extend from the cell surface; the best-known genus is *Caulobacter*.

Prosthecochloris [MICROBIO] A genus of bacteria in the family Chlorobiaceae; cells are irregular-spherical, form prosthecae, are nonmotile, do not have gas vacuoles, contain bacteriochlorophyll *c* or *e*, and are free-living.

Prosthecomicrobium [MICROBIO] A genus of prosthecate bacteria; motile or nonmotile, unicellular forms with many prosthecae on each cell; reproduction is by binary fission of cells.

prosthetic group [BIOCHEM] A characteristic nonamino acid substance that is strongly bound to a protein and necessary for the protein portion of an enzyme to function; often used to describe the function, as in hemeprotein for hemoglobin.

Prostigmata [INV ZOO] The equivalent name for Trombidiformes.

prostomium [INV ZOO] The portion of the head that is anterior to the mouth in annelids and mollusks.

protamine [BIOCHEM] Any of the simple proteins that are combined with nucleic acid in the sperm of certain fish, and that upon hydrolysis yield basic amino acids; used in medicine to control hemorrhage, and in the preparation of an insulin form to control diabetes.

protandry [PHYSIO] That condition in which an animal is first a male and then becomes a female.

Proteaceae [BOT] A large family of dicotyledonous plants in the order Proteales, notable for often having a large cluster of small or reduced flowers.

Proteales [BOT] An order of dicotyledonous plants in the subclass Rosidae marked by its strongly perigynous flowers, a four-lobed, often corolla-like calyx, and reduced or absent true petals.

protease [BIOCHEM] An enzyme that digests proteins.

protective coloration [ZOO] A color pattern that blends with the environment and increases the animal's probability of survival.

Proteeae [MICROBIO] Formerly a tribe of the Enterobacteriaceae comprising the genus *Proteus*; included organisms which were characteristically motile, fermented dextrose with gas production, and produced urease.

Q

quadrant [ANAT] One of the four regions into which the abdomen may be divided for purposes of physical diagnosis. [PHYSIO] A sector of one-fourth of the field of vision of one or both eyes.

quadrate bone [VERT ZOO] A small element forming part of the upper jaw joint on each side of the head in vertebrates below mammals.

quadratojugal [VERT ZOO] A small bone connecting the quadrate and jugal bones on each side of the skull in many lower vertebrates.

quadriceps [ANAT] Four-headed, as a muscle.

quadriceps femoris [ANAT] The large extensor muscle of the thigh, combining the rectus femoris and vastus muscles.

Quadrijugatoridae [PALEON] A monomorphic family of extinct ostracods in the superfamily Hollinacea.

quadruped [VERT ZOO] An animal that has four legs.

quagmire *See* bog.

quail [VERT ZOO] Any of several migratory game birds in the family Phasianidae.

quantasome [CELL BIO] One of the highly ordered array of units that has a "cobblestone" appearance in electron micrographs of the lamella of chloroplasts, and thought to be the most probable site of the light reaction in photosynthesis.

quantitative genetics [GEN] The study of continuously varying traits, such as those of the intellect and personality, which cannot be categorized as dichotomies.

quantitative inheritance [GEN] The acquisition of characteristics, such as height, weight, and intelligence, which show a quantitative and continuous type of variation.

quantum evolution [EVOL] A special but extreme case of phyletic evolution; the rapid evolution that takes place when relatively sudden and drastic change occurs in the environment or when organisms spread into new habitats where conditions differ from those to which they are adapted; the organisms must then adapt quickly to the new conditions if they are to survive.

quebracho [BOT] Any of a number of South American trees in different genera in the order Sapindales, but all being a valuable source of wood, bark, and tannin.

quebracho bark [BOT] Bark of the white quebracho tree *Aspidosperma quebracho* of Chile and Argentina; main components are aspidospermine, tannin, and quebrachine; used in medicine and tanning.

queen [INV ZOO] A mature, fertile female in a colony of ants, bees, or termites, whose function is to lay eggs.

quellung reaction [MICROBIO] Swelling of the capsule of a bacterial cell, caused by contact with serum containing antibodies capable of reacting with polysaccharide material in the capsule; applicable to *Pneumococcus*, *Klebsiella*, and *Hemophilus*.

quercetin [BIOCHEM] $C_{15}H_5O_2(OH)_5$ A yellow, crystalline flavonol obtained from oak bark and Douglas fir bark; used as an antioxidant and absorber of ultraviolet rays, and in rubber, plastics, and vegetable oils.

quill [VERT ZOO] The hollow, horny shaft of a large stiff wing or tail feather.

quillwort [BOT] The common name for plants of the genus *Isoetes*.

quince [BOT] *Cydonia oblonga*. A deciduous tree of the order Rosales characterized by crooked branching, leaves that are densely hairy on the underside and solitary white or pale-pink flowers; fruit is an edible pear- or apple-shaped tomentose pome.

quinoa [BOT] *Chenopodium quinoa*. An annual herb of the family Chenopodiaceae grown at high altitudes in South America for the highly nutritious seeds.

quinolinic acid *See* 2,3-pyradine dicarboxylic acid.

quinquefoliate [BOT] Of a leaf, having five leaflets.

quintuplet [BIOL] One of five children who have been born at one birth.

R

rabbit [VERT ZOO] Any of a large number of burrowing mammals in the family Leporidae.

raccoon [VERT ZOO] Any of 16 species of carnivorous nocturnal mammals belonging to the family Procyonidae; all are arboreal or semiarboreal and have a bushy, long ringed tail.

race [BIOL] 1. An infraspecific taxonomic group of organisms, such as subspecies or microspecies. 2. A fixed variety or breed.

racemase [BIOCHEM] Any of a group of enzymes that catalyze racemization reactions.

raceme [BOT] An inflorescence on which flowers are borne on stalks of equal length on an unbranched main stalk that continues to grow during flowering.

racemose [ANAT] Of a gland, compound and shaped like a bunch of grapes, with freely branching ducts that terminate in acini. [BOT] Bearing, or occurring in the form of, a raceme.

rachiglossate radula [INV ZOO] A radula of certain gastropod mollusks which has one or three longitudinal series of teeth, each of which may bear many cusps.

rachilla [BOT] The axis of a grass spikelet.

rachis [ANAT] The vertebral column. [BIOL] An axial structure such as the axis of an inflorescence, the central petiole of a compound leaf, or the central cord of an ovary in Nematoda.

radial artery [ANAT] A branch of the brachial artery in the forearm; principal branches are the radial recurrent and the main artery of the thumb.

radial canal [INV ZOO] 1. One of the numerous canals that radiate from the spongocoel in certain Porifera. 2. Any of the canals extending from the coelenteron to the circular canal in the margin of the umbrella in jellyfishes. 3. A canal radiating from the circumoral canal along each ambulacral area in many echinoderms.

radial cleavage [EMBRYO] A cleavage pattern characterized by formation of a mass of cells that show radial symmetry.

radial nerve [ANAT] A large nerve that arises in the brachial plexus and branches to enervate the extensor muscles and skin of the posterior aspect of the arm forearm, and hand.

Radiata [INV ZOO] Members of the Eumetazoa which have a primary radial symmetry; includes the Coelenterata and Ctenophora.

radiation biochemistry [BIOCHEM] The study of the response of the constituents of living matter to radiation.

radiation biology See radiobiology.

radiation biophysics [BIOPHYS] The study of the response of organisms to ionizing radiations and to ultraviolet light.

radiation cytology [CELL BIO] An aspect of biology that deals with the effects of radiations on living cells.

radiation effects [BIOL] The harmful effects of ionizing radiation on humans and other animals, such as production of cancers, cataracts, and radiation ulcers, loss of hair, reddening of skin, sterilization, nausea, vomiting, mucous or bloody diarrhea, purpura, epilation, and agranulocytic infections.

radiation genetics [GEN] The study of the genetic effects of radiation. Also known as radiogenetics.

radiation microbiology [MICROBIO] A field of basic and applied radiobiology concerned chiefly with the damaging effects of radiation on microorganisms.

radical [BOT] 1. Of, pertaining to, or proceeding from the root. 2. Arising from the base of a stem or from an underground stem.

radicle [BOT] The embryonic root of a flowering plant.

radiobiology [BIOL] Study of the scientific principles, mechanisms, and effects of the interaction of ionizing radiation with living matter. Also known as radiation biology.

radioecology [ECOL] The interdisciplinary study of organisms, radionuclides, ionizing radiation, and the environment.

radiogenetics See radiation genetics.

Radiolaria [INV ZOO] A subclass of the protozoan class Actinopodea whose members are noted for their siliceous skeletons and characterized by a membranous capsule which separates the outer from the inner cytoplasm.

radiole [INV ZOO] A spine on a sea urchin.

radiomimetic activity [BIOL] The radiationlike effects of certain chemicals, such as nitrogen mustard, urethane, and fluorinated pyrimidines.

radiomutation [GEN] A mutation which is the result of exposure of living-tissue chromosomes to ionizing radiation.

radioresistance [BIOL] The resistance of organisms or tissues to the harmful effects of various radiations.

radish [BOT] *Raphanus sativus*. 1. An annual or biennial crucifer belonging to the order Capparales. 2. The edible, thickened hypocotyl of the plant.

radius [ANAT] The outer of the two bones of the human forearm or of the corresponding part in vertebrates other than fish.

radula [INV ZOO] A filelike ribbon studded with horny or chitinous toothlike structures, found in the mouth of all classes of mollusks except Bivalvia.

raffinase [BIOCHEM] An enzyme that hydrolyzes raffinose, yielding fructose in the reaction.

raffinose [BIOCHEM] $C_{18}H_{32}O_{16} \cdot 5H_2O$ A white, crystalline trisaccharide found in sugarbeets, cottonseed meal, and molasses; yields glucose, fructose, and galactose on complete hydrolysis. Also known as gossypose; melitose; melitriose.

Rafflesiales [BOT] A small order of dicotyledonous plants; members are highly specialized, non-green, rootless parasites which grow from the roots of the host.

Raillietiellidae [INV ZOO] A small family of parasitic arthropods in the order Cephalobaenida.

rain desert [ECOL] A desert in which rainfall is sufficient to maintain a sparse general vegetation.

Rainey's corpuscle [INV ZOO] The sickle-shaped spore of an encysted sarcosporidian.

rainforest [ECOL] A forest of broad-leaved, mainly evergreen, trees found in continually moist climates in the tropics, subtropics, and some parts of the temperate zones.

raised bog [ECOL] An area of acid, peaty soil, especially that developed from moss, in which the center is relatively higher than the margins.

Rajidae [VERT ZOO] The skates, a family of elasmobranchs included in the batoid group.

Rajiformes [VERT ZOO] The equivalent name for Batoidea.

Rallidae [VERT ZOO] A large family of birds in the order Gruiformes comprising rails, gallinules, and coots.

ram [VERT ZOO] A male sheep or goat.

Ramapithecinae [PALEON] A subfamily of Hominidae including the protohominids of the Miocene and Pliocene.

Ramapithecus [PALEON] The genus name given to a fossilized upper jaw fragment found in the Siwalik hills, India; closely related to the family of man.

ramate [BIOL] Having branches.

ramentum [BOT] A thin brownish scale consisting of a single layer of cells and occurring on the leaves and young shoots of many ferns.

ramicolous [BOT] Living on twigs.

ramie [BOT] *Boehmeria nivea*. A shrub or half-shrub of the nettle family (Urticaceae) cultivated as a source of a tough, strong, durable, lustrous natural woody fiber resembling flax, obtained from the phloem of the plant; used for high-quality papers and fabrics. Also known as China grass; rhea.

ramose [BIOL] Having lateral divisions or branches.

Ramphastidae [VERT ZOO] The toucans, a family of birds with large, often colorful bills in the order Piciformes.

ramus [ANAT] A slender bone process branching from a large bone. [VERT ZOO] The barb of a feather. [ZOO] The branch of a structure such as a blood vessel, nerve, arthropod appendage, and so on.

range of motion [BIOPHYS] The degree of movement that can occur in a joint.

Ranidae [VERT ZOO] A family of frogs in the suborder Diplasiocoela including the large, widespread genus *Rana*.

Ranunculaceae [BOT] A family of dicotyledonous herbs in the order Ranunculales distinguished by alternate leaves with net venation, two or more distinct carpels, and numerous stamens.

Ranunculales [BOT] An order of dicotyledons in the subclass Magnoliidae characterized by its mostly separate carpels, triaperturate pollen, herbaceous or only secondarily woody habit, and frequently numerous stamens.

rape [BOT] *Brassica napus*. A plant of the cabbage family in the order Capparales; the plant does not form a compact head, the leaves are bluish-green, deeply lobed, and curled, and the small flowers produce black seeds; grown for forage.

raphe [ANAT] A broad seamlike junction between two lateral halves of an organ or other body part. [BOT] 1. The part of the funiculus attached along its full length to the integument of an anatropous ovule, between the chalaza and the attachment to the placenta. 2. The longitudinal median line or slit on a diatom valve.

Raphidae [VERT ZOO] A family of birds in the order Columbiformes that included the dodo (*Raphus calcullatus*); completely extirpated during the 17th and early 18th centuries.

raphide [BOT] One of the long, needle-shaped crystals, usually consisting of calcium oxalate, occurring as a metabolic by-product in certain plant cells.

raptorial [ZOO] 1. Living on prey. 2. Adapted for snatching or seizing prey, as birds of prey.

rasorial [ZOO] Adapted for scratching for food; applied to birds.

raspberry [BOT] Any of several species of upright shrubs of the genus *Rubus*, with perennial roots and prickly biennial stems, in the order Rosales; the edible black or red juicy berries are aggregate fruits, and when ripe they are easily separated from the fleshy receptacle.

rat [VERT ZOO] The name applied to over 650 species of mammals in several families of the order Rodentia; they differ from mice in being larger and in having teeth modified for gnawing.

rataria larva [INV ZOO] The second, hourglass-shaped, free-swimming larva of the siphonophore *Velella*.

ratfish [VERT ZOO] The common name for members of the chondrichthyan order Chimaeriformes.

Rathke's pouch *See* craniobuccal pouch.

ratites [VERT ZOO] A group of flightless, mostly large, running birds comprising several orders and including the emus, cassowaries, kiwis, and ostriches.

rattan [BOT] Any of several long-stemmed, climbing palms, especially of the genera *Calamus* and *Daemonothops*; stem material is used to make walking sticks, wickerwork, and cordage.

rattlesnake [VERT ZOO] Any of a number of species of the genera *Sistrurus* or *Crotalus* distinguished by the characteristic rattle on the end of the tail.

Raunklaer system [BOT] A classification system for plant life-forms based on the position of perennating buds in relation to the soil surface.

Rauwolfia [BOT] A genus of mostly poisonous, tropical trees and shrubs of the dogbane family (Apocynaceae); certain species yield substances used as emetics and cathartics, while *R. serpentina* is a source of alkaloids used as tranquilizers.

ray [VERT ZOO] Any of about 350 species of the elasmobranch order Batoidea having flattened bodies with large pectoral fins attached to the side of the head, ventral gill slits, and long, spikelike tails.

rayfin fish [VERT ZOO] The common name for members of the Actinopterygii.

ray flower [BOT] One of the small flowers with a strap-shaped corolla radiating from the margin of the head of a capitulum.

ray initial [BOT] One of the cells of the cambium which divide to produce new phloem and xylem ray cells.

ray shake [BOT] A radial crack in wood caused by wounds in a tree along the barrier zone.

reaction time [PHYSIO] The interval between application of a stimulus and the beginning of the response.

reaction wood [BOT] An abnormal development of a tree and therefore its wood as the result of unusual forces acting on it, such as an atypical gravitational pull.

reading [MOL BIO] A linear process by which amino acid sequences are recognized by the protein-synthesizing system of a cell from messenger ribonucleic codes.

readthrough [GEN] Transcription beyond a termination sequence due to failure of ribonucleic acid polymerase to recognize the termination codon.

recapitulation theory [BIOL] The biological theory that an organism passes through developmental stages resembling various stages in the phylogeny of its group; ontogeny recapitulates phylogeny. Also known as biogenetic law; Haeckel's law.

recent [EVOL] Referring to taxa which still exist; the antonym of fossil.

receptor [BIOCHEM] A site or structure in a cell which combines with a drug or other biological to produce a specific alteration of cell function. [PHYSIO] A sense organ.

recessive [GEN] **1.** An allele that is not expressed phenotypically when present in the heterozygous condition. **2.** An organism homozygous for a recessive gene.

reciprocal inhibition [PHYSIO] In muscular movement, the simultaneous relaxation of one muscle and the contraction of its antagonist.

reciprocal translocation [CELL BIO] The special case of translocation in which two segments exchange positions.

recombination [GEN] **1.** The occurrence of gene combinations in the progeny that differ from those of the parents as a result of independent assortment, linkage, and crossing-over. **2.** The production of genetic information in which there are elements of one line of descent replaced by those of another line, or additional elements.

recombination mosaic [GEN] A mosaic produced as the result of somatic crossing-over.

recon [GEN] The smallest deoxyribonucleic acid unit capable of recombination.

recruitment [PHYSIO] A serial discharge from neurons innervating groups of muscle fibers.

Recticornia [INV ZOO] A family of amphipod crustaceans in the superfamily Genuina containing forms in which the first antennae are straight, arise from the anterior margin of the head, and have few flagellar segments.

rectrix [VERT ZOO] One of the stiff tail feathers used by birds to control direction of flight.

rectum [ANAT] The portion of the large intestine between the sigmoid flexure and the anus.

rectus [ANAT] Having a straight course, as certain muscles.

rectus abdominis [ANAT] The long flat muscle of the anterior abdominal wall which, as vertical fibers, arises from the pubic crest and symphysis, and is inserted into the cartilages of the fifth, sixth, and seventh ribs.

rectus femoris [ANAT] A division of the quadriceps femoris inserting in the patella and ultimately into the tubercle of the tibia.

rectus oculi [ANAT] Any of four muscles (superior, inferior, lateral, and medial) of the eyeball, running forward from the optic foramen and inserted into the sclerotic coat.

recumbent [BOT] Of or pertaining to a plant or plant part that tends to rest on the surface of the soil.

red algae [BOT] The common name for members of the phylum Rhodophyta.

red blood cell *See* erythrocyte.

red fir *See* Douglas fir.

redia [INV ZOO] A larva produced within the miracidial sporocyst of certain digenetic trematodes which may give rise to daughter rediae or to cercariae.

redifferentiation [PHYSIO] The return to a position of greater specialization in actual and potential functions, or the developing of new characteristics.

red leaf [PL PATH] Any of various nonparasitic plant diseases marked by red discoloration of the foliage.

red nucleus [HISTOL] A mass of reticular fibers in the gray matter of the tegmentum of the mesencephalon of higher vertebrates; it receives fibers from the cerebellum of the opposite side and gives rise to rubrospinal tract fibers of the opposite side.

red ring [PL PATH] A nematode disease of the coconut palm caused by *Aphelenchoides cocophilus* and marked by the appearance of red rings in the stem cross section.

red rot [PL PATH] Any of several fungus diseases of plants characterized by red patches on stems or leaves; common in sugarcane, sisal, and various evergreen and deciduous trees.

red rust [PL PATH] An algal disease of certain subtropical plants, such as tea and citrus, caused by the green alga *Cephaleuros virescens* and characterized by a rusty appearance of the leaves or twigs.

red stele [PL PATH] A fatal fungus disease of strawberries caused by *Phytophthora fragariae* invading the roots, producing redness and rotting with consequent dwarfing and wilting of the plant.

red stripe [PL PATH] 1. A fungus decay of timber caused by *Polyporus vaporarius* and characterized by reddish streaks. 2. A bacterial disease of sugarcane caused by *Xanthomonas rubrilineans* and characterized by red streaks in the young leaves, followed by invasion of the vascular system.

red thread [PL PATH] A fungus disease of turf grasses caused by *Cortecium fuciforme* and characterized by the appearance of red stromata on the pinkish hyphal threads.

red tide [BIOL] A reddish discoloration of coastal surface waters due to concentrations of certain toxin-producing dinoflagellates. Also known as red water.

redtop grass [BOT] One of the bent grasses, *Agrostis alba* and its relatives, which grow on a wide variety of soils; it is a perennial, spreads slowly by rootstocks, and has top growth 2–3 feet (60–90 centimeters) tall.

reducer [BIOL] *See* decomposer.

redundancy [GEN] 1. Repetition of a specified deoxyribonucleic acid sequence in a nucleus. 2. Multiplicity of codons for individual amino acids.

Reduvildae [INV ZOO] The single family of the hemipteran group Reduvioidea; nearly all have a stridulatory furrow on the prosternum, ocelli are generally present, and the beak is three-segmented.

Reduvioidea [INV ZOO] The assassin bugs or conenose bugs, a monofamilial group of hemipteran insects in the subdivision Geocorisae.

red water [BIOL] *See* red tide.

redwood [BOT] *Sequoia sempervirens*. An evergreen tree of the pine family; it is the tallest tree in the Americas, attaining 350 feet (107 meters); its soft heartwood is a valuable building material.

reed [BOT] Any tall grass characterized by a slender jointed stem.

reflex [PHYSIO] An automatic response mediated by the nervous system.

reflex arc [ANAT] A chain of neurons composing the anatomical substrate or pathway of the unconditioned reflex.

reflexed [BOT] Turned abruptly backward.

reflex time [PHYSIO] The time required for the nerve impulse to travel in a reflex action.

refugium [ECOL] An area which has escaped the great changes which occurred in the region as a whole, often providing conditions in which relic colonies can survive; for example, a driftless area which has escaped the effects of glaciation because it projected above the ice.

regeneration [BIOL] The replacement by an organism of tissues or organs which have been lost or severely injured.

regional anatomy [ANAT] The detailed study of the anatomy of a part or region of the body of an animal.

regular [BOT] Having radial symmetry, referring to a flower.

regular connective tissue [HISTOL] Connective tissue in which the fibers are arranged in definite patterns.

Regularia [INV ZOO] An assemblage of echinoids in which the anus and periproct lie within the apical system; not considered a valid taxon.

regulative egg [EMBRYO] An egg in which unfertilized fragments develop as complete, normal individuals.

regulator gene [GEN] A gene that controls the rate of transcription of one or more other genes.

regulon [GEN] In bacteria, a system of genes, formed by one or more operons, which regulate enzyme induction and whose activity is controlled by a single repressor substance.

regurgitation [PHYSIO] Bringing back into the mouth undigested food from the stomach.

Reichert's cartilage [EMBRYO] The cartilage of the hyoid arch in a human embryo.

Reighardiidae [INV ZOO] A monotypic family of arthropods in the order Cephalobaenida; the posterior end of the organism is rounded, without lobes, and the cuticula is covered with minute spines.

reindeer [VERT ZOO] *Rangifer tarandus*. A migratory ruminant of the deer family (Cervidae) which inhabits the Arctic region and has a circumpolar distribution; characteristically, both sexes have antlers and are brown with yellow-white areas on the neck and chest.

Reissner's membrane [ANAT] The anterior wall of the cochlear duct, which separates the cochlear duct from the scala vestibuli. Also known as vestibular membrane of Reissner.

relaxed circular deoxyribonucleic acid [BIOCHEM] A form of circular deoxyribonucleic acid in which the circle of one strand is broken. Also known as open-circle deoxyribonucleic acid.

relaxin [BIOCHEM] A hormone found in the serum of humans and certain other animals during pregnancy; probably acting with progesterone and estrogen, it causes relaxation of pelvic ligaments in the guinea pig.

releaser stimulus [ZOO] A stimulus which affects an animal by initiating an instinctual behavior pattern.

relict [BIOL] A persistent, isolated remnant of a once-abundant species.

Remak's ganglion [ANAT] A ganglion near the junction of the coronary sinus and the right atrium.

renal artery [ANAT] A branch of the abdominal or ventral aorta supplying the kidneys in vertebrates.

renal corpuscle [ANAT] The glomerulus together with its Bowman's capsule in the renal cortex. Also known as Malpighian corpuscle.

renal papilla [ANAT] A fingerlike projection into the renal pelvis through which the collecting tubules discharge.

renal pyramid [ANAT] Any of the conical masses composing the medullary substance of the kidney. Also known as Malpighian pyramid.

renal threshold [PHYSIO] A concentration of a substance within the blood which, when reached, causes the substance to appear in the urine.

renal tubule [ANAT] One of the glandular tubules which elaborate urine in the kidneys.

renal vein [ANAT] A vein which returns blood from the kidney to the vena cava.

renaturation [BIOCHEM] The process of restoring denatured proteins to their original condition.

renette [INV ZOO] An excretory cell found in certain nematodes.

renin [BIOCHEM] A proteolytic enzyme produced in the afferent glomerular arteriole which reacts with the plasma component hypertensinogen to produce angiotensin II.

rennet [VERT ZOO] The lining of the stomach of certain animals, especially the fourth stomach in ruminants.

rennin [BIOCHEM] An enzyme found in the gastric juice of the fourth stomach of calfs; used for coagulating milk casein in cheesemaking. Also known as chymosin.

renninogen [BIOCHEM] The zymogen of rennin. Also known as prorennin.

reovirus [VIROL] A group of ribonucleic acid–containing animal viruses, including agents of encephalitis and phlebotomus fever.

repair synthesis [MOL BIO] Enzymatic excision and replacement of regions of damaged deoxyribonucleic acid, as in repair of thymine dimers by ultraviolet irradiation.

repand [BOT] Having a margin that undulates slightly, referring to a leaf.

repent [BOT] Of a stem, creeping along the ground and rooting at the nodes.

replacement [PALEON] Substitution of inorganic matter for the original organic constituents of an organism during fossilization.

replica plating [MICROBIO] A method for the isolation of nutritional mutants in microorganisms; colonies are grown from a microorganism suspension previously exposed to a mutagenic agent, on a complete medium in a petri dish; a velour surface is used to transfer the impression of all these colonies to a petri dish containing a minimal medium; colonies that do not grow on the minimal medium are the mutants.

replicating fork [MOL BIO] The Y-shaped region of a chromosome that is a growing point in the replication of deoxyribonucleic acid.

replication [MOL BIO] Duplication, as of a nucleic acid, by copying from a molecular template. [VIROL] Multiplication of phage in a bacterial cell.

replicon [GEN] A genetic element characterized by possession of the structural gene that controls a specific initiator and receptor locus (replicator) for its action.

replum [BOT] A thin wall separating the two valves or chambers of certain fruits.

repressor [BIOCHEM] An end product of metabolism which represses the synthesis of enzymes in the metabolic pathway. [GEN] The product of a regulator gene that acts to repress the transcription of another gene.

reproduction [BIOL] The mechanisms by which organisms give rise to other organisms of the same kind.

reproductive behavior [ZOO] The behavior patterns in different types of animals by means of which the sperm is brought to the egg and the parental care of the resulting young insured.

reproductive distribution [ECOL] The range of areas where conditions are favorable to maturation, spawning, and early development of marine animals.

reproductive system [ANAT] The structures concerned with the production of sex cells and perpetuation of the species.

Reptantia [INV ZOO] A suborder of the crustacean order Decapoda including all decapods other than shrimp.

reptile [VERT ZOO] Any member of the class Reptilia.

Reptilia [VERT ZOO] A class of terrestrial vertebrates composed of turtles, tuatara, lizards, snakes, and crocodileans; characteristically they lack hair, feathers, and mammary glands, the skin is covered with scales, they have a three-chambered heart, and the pleural and peritoneal cavities are continuous.

RES See reticuloendothelial system.

Resedaceae [BOT] A family of dicotyledonous herbs in the order Capparales having irregular, hypogynous flowers.

reserve cell [HISTOL] 1. One of the small, undifferentiated epithelial cells at the base of the stratified columnar lining of the bronchial tree. 2. A chromophobe cell.

residual air See residual volume.

residual volume [PHYSIO] Air remaining in the lungs after the most complete expiration possible; it is elevated in diffuse obstructive emphysema and during an attack of asthma. Also known as residual air.

resin duct [BOT] A canal (intercellular space) lined with secretory cells that release resins into the canal; common in gymnosperms.

resistance factor See R factor.

resistance transfer factor [GEN] A carrier of genetic information in bacteria which is considered to control the ability of self-replication and conjugal transfer of R factors. Abbreviated RTF.

respiration [PHYSIO] 1. The processes by which tissues and organisms exchange gases with their environment. **2.** The act of breathing with the lungs, consisting of inspiration and expiration.

respiratory center [PHYSIO] A large area of the brain involved in regulation of respiration.

respiratory dead space [PHYSIO] That part of the respiratory system which has no alveoli and in which little or no exchange of gas between air and blood takes place.

respiratory epithelium [HISTOL] The ciliated pseudostratified epithelium lining the respiratory tract.

respiratory minute volume [PHYSIO] The total amount of air which moves in and out of the lungs in a minute.

respiratory pigment [BIOCHEM] Any of various conjugated proteins that function in living organisms to transfer oxygen in cellular respiration.

respiratory quotient [PHYSIO] The ratio of volumes of carbon dioxide evolved and oxygen consumed during a given period of respiration. Abbreviated RQ.

respiratory system [ANAT] The structures and passages involved with the intake, expulsion, and exchange of oxygen and carbon dioxide in the vertebrate body.

respiratory tree [ANAT] The trachea, bronchi, and bronchioles. [INV ZOO] Either of a pair of branched tubular appendages of the cloaca in certain holothurians that is thought to have a respiratory function.

restiform body *See* inferior cerebellar peduncle.

resting cell [CELL BIO] An interphase cell.

resting potential [PHYSIO] The potential difference between the interior cytoplasm and the external aqueous medium of the living cell.

resting spore [BIOL] A spore that remains dormant for long periods before germination, withstanding adverse conditions; usually invested in a thickened cell wall.

Restionaceae [BOT] A large family of monocotyledonous plants in the order Restionales characterized by unisexual flowers, wholly cauline leaves, unilocular anthers, and a more or less open inflorescence.

Restionales [BOT] An order of monocotyledonous plants in the subclass Commelinidae having reduced flowers and a single, pendulous, orthotropous ovule in each of the one to three locules of the ovary.

restoration [ECOL] A conservation measure involving the correction of past abuses that have impaired the productivity of the resources base.

resupinate [BOT] Inverted, usually through 180°, so as to appear upside down or reversed.

rete cord [EMBRYO] One of the deep, anastomosing strands of cells of the medullary cords of the vertebrate embryo, that form the rete testis or the rete ovarii.

rete mirabile [VERT ZOO] A network of small blood vessels that are formed by the branching of a large vessel and that usually reunite into a single trunk; believed to have an oxygen-storing function in certain aquatic fauna.

rete ovarii [ANAT] Vestigial tubules or cords of cells near the hilus of the ovary, corresponding

with the rete testis, but not connected with the mesonephric duct.

rete testis [ANAT] The network of anastomosing tubules in the mediastinum testis.

reticular cell *See* reticulocyte.

reticular fiber [HISTOL] Any of the delicate, branching argentophile fibers conspicuous in the connective tissue of lymphatic tissue, myeloid tissue, the red pulp of the spleen, and most basement membranes. Also known as argentaffin fiber; argyrophil lattice fiber; precollagenous fiber.

reticular formation [ANAT] The portion of the central nervous system which consists of small islands of gray matter separated by fine bundles of nerve fibers running in every direction.

Reticulariaceae [MYCOL] A family of plasmodial slime molds in the order Liceales.

reticular system *See* reticuloendothelial system.

reticular tissue [HISTOL] Connective tissue having reticular fibers as the principal element.

reticulate [BIOL] Having or resembling a network of fibers, veins, or lines. [GEN] Of or relating to evolutionary change resulting from genetic recombination between strains in an interbreeding population.

reticulin [BIOCHEM] A protein isolated from reticular fibers.

reticulocyte [HISTOL] Also known as reticular cell. **1.** A large, immature red blood cell, having a reticular appearance when stained due to retention of portions of the nucleus. **2.** A cell of reticular tissue.

reticuloendothelial system [ANAT] The macrophage system, including all phagocytic cells such as histiocytes, macrophages, reticular cells, monocytes, and microglia, except the granular white blood cells. Abbreviated RES. Also known as reticular system; hematopoietic system.

reticulopodia [INV ZOO] Pseudopodia in the form of a branching network.

Reticulosa [PALEON] An order of Paleozoic hexactinellid sponges with a branching form in the subclass Hexasterophora.

reticulospinal tract [ANAT] Nerve fibers descending from large cells of the reticular formation of the pons and medulla into the spinal cord.

reticulum [BIOL] A fine network. [VERT ZOO] The second stomach in ruminants.

retina [ANAT] The photoreceptive layer and terminal expansion of the optic nerve in the dorsal aspect of the vertebrate eye.

retinaculum [INV ZOO] **1.** A clasp on the forewing of certain moths for retaining the frenulum of the hindwing. **2.** An appendage on the third abdominal somite of springtails that articulates with the furcula.

retinal [BIOCHEM] A carotenoid, produced as an intermediate in the bleaching of rhodopsin and decomposition to vitamin A. Also known as vitamin A aldehyde.

retinal pigment *See* rhodopsin.

retinene [BIOCHEM] A pigment extracted from the retina, which turns yellow by the action of light; the chief carotenoid of the retina.

retinoid [BIOCHEM] The set of molecules composing vitamin A and its synthetic analogs, such as retinal or retinyl acetate.

retinol *See* vitamin A.

retinula [INV ZOO] The receptor element at the inner end of the ommatidium in a compound eye.

Retortamonadida [INV ZOO] An order of parasitic flagellate protozoans belonging to the class Zoomastigophorea, having two or four flagella and a complex blepharoplast-centrosome-axostyle apparatus.

retractor [ANAT] A muscle that draws a limb or other body part toward the body.

retrocerebral gland [INV ZOO] Any of various endocrine glands located behind the brain in insects which function in postembryonic development and metamorphosis.

retroflexion [ANAT] The state of being bent backward.

retrorse [BIOL] Bent downward or backward.

retrostalsis [PHYSIO] Reverse peristalsis.

retroversion [ANAT] A turning back.

retuse [BOT] Having a rounded apex with a slight, central notch.

reverse graft [BOT] A plant graft made by inserting the scion in an inverted position.

reverse mutation [GEN] A mutation in a mutant allele which makes it capable of producing the nonmutant phenotype; may actually restore the original deoxyribonucleic-acid sequence of the gene or produce a new one which has a similar effect. Also known as back mutation.

reverse pinocytosis *See* emiocytosis.

revolute [BOT] Rolled backward and downward.

R factor [GEN] A self-replicating, infectionlike agent that carries genetic information and transmits drug resistance from bacterium to bacterium by conjugation of cell. Also known as resistance factor.

Rhabdiasoidea [INV ZOO] An order or superfamily of parasitic nematodes.

rhabdion [INV ZOO] One of the sclerotized segments lining the buccal cavity of nematodes.

rhabdite [INV ZOO] A small rodlike or fusiform body secreted by epidermal or parenchymal cells of certain turbellarians and trematodes.

Rhabditia [INV ZOO] A subclass of nematodes in the class Secernentea.

Rhabditida [INV ZOO] An order of nematodes in the subclass Rhabditia including parasites of humans and domestic animals.

Rhabditoidea [INV ZOO] A superfamily of small to moderate-sized nematodes in the order Rhabditidia with small, porelike, anteriorly located amphids, and esophagus with corpus, isthmus, and valvulated basal bulb.

Rhabdocoela [INV ZOO] Formerly an order of the Turbellaria, and now divided into three orders, Catenulida, Macrostomida, and Neorhabdocoela.

rhabdoglyph [PALEON] A trace fossil consisting of a presumable worm trail appearing on the undersurface of flysch beds (sandstones) as a nearly straight bulge with little or no branching.

rhabdolith [BOT] A minute coccolith having a shield surmounted by a long stem and found at all depths in the ocean, from the surface to the bottom.

rhabdome [INV ZOO] The central translucent cylinder in the retinula of a compound eye.

Rhabdophorina [INV ZOO] A suborder of ciliates in the order Gymnostomatida.

rhabdosome [INV ZOO] A colonial graptolite that develops from a single individual.

rhabdovirus [VIROL] A group of ribonucleic acid–containing animal viruses, including rabies virus and certain infective agents of fish and insects.

rhabdus [INV ZOO] A uniaxial sponge spicule.

Rhachitomi [PALEON] A group of extinct amphibians in the order Temnospondyli in which pleurocentra were retained.

rhachitomous [VERT ZOO] Being, having, or pertaining to vertebrae with centra whose parts do not fuse.

Rhacophoridae [VERT ZOO] A family of arboreal frogs in the suborder Diplasiocoela.

Rhacopilaceae [BOT] A family of mosses in the order Isobryales generally having dimorphous leaves with smaller dorsal leaves and a capsule that is plicate when dry.

Rhagionidae [INV ZOO] The snipe flies, a family of predatory orthorrhaphous dipteran insects in the series Brachycera that are brownish or gray with spotted wings.

rhagon [INV ZOO] A pyramid-shaped, colonial sponge having an osculum at the apex and flagellated chambers in the upper wall only.

Rhamnaceae [BOT] A family of dicotyledonous plants in the order Rhamnales characterized by a solitary ovule in each locule, free stamens, simple leaves, and flowers that are hypogynous to perigynous or epigynous.

Rhamnales [BOT] An order of dicotyledonous plants in the subclass Rosidae having a single set of stamens, opposite the petals, usually a well-developed intrastamenal disk, and two or more locules in the ovary.

rhamnose [BIOCHEM] $C_6H_{12}O_5$ A deoxysugar occurring free in poison sumac, and in glycoside combination in many plants. Also known as isodulcitol.

rhamphoid [BIOL] Beak-shaped.

Rhamphorhynchoidea [PALEON] A Jurassic suborder of the Pterosauria characterized by long, slender tails with an expanded tip.

rhampotheca [VERT ZOO] The horny sheath covering a bird's beak.

rhea [BOT] *See* ramie. [VERT ZOO] The common name for members of the avian order Rheiformes.

Rheidae [VERT ZOO] The single family of the avian order Rheiformes.

Rheiformes [VERT ZOO] The rheas, an order of South American running birds; called American ostriches, they differ from the true ostrich in their smaller size, feathered head and neck, three-toed feet, and other features.

Rhenanida [PALEON] An order of extinct marine fishes in the class Placodermi distinguished by mosaics of small bones between the large plates in the head shield.

rheobase [PHYSIO] The intensity of the steady current just sufficient to excite a tissue when suddenly applied.

rheophile [ECOL] Living or thriving in running water.

rheophilous bog [ECOL] A bog which draws its source of water from drainage.

rheoplankton [ECOL] Plankton found in flowing water.

rheotaxis [BIOL] Movement of a motile cell or organism in response to the direction of water currents.

rheotropism [BIOL] Orientation response of an organism to the stimulus of a flowing fluid, as water.

rhesus monkey [VERT ZOO] *Macaque mulatta*. An agile, gregarious primate found in southern Asia and having a short tail, short limbs of almost equal length, and a stocky build. Also known as rhesus macaque.

Rhigonematidae [INV ZOO] A family of nematodes in the superfamily Oxyuroidea.

Rhincodontidae [VERT ZOO] The whale sharks, a family of essentially tropical galeoid elasmobranchs in the isurid line.

rhinencephalon [ANAT] The anterior olfactory portion of the vertebrate brain.

Rhinobatidae [VERT ZOO] The guitarfishes, a family of elasmobranchs in the batoid group.

Rhinoceratidae [VERT ZOO] A family of perissodactyl mammals in the superfamily Rhinoceratoidea, comprising the living rhinoceroses.

Rhinoceratoidea [VERT ZOO] A superfamily of perissodactyl mammals in the suborder Ceratomorpha including living and extinct rhinoceroses.

rhinoceros [VERT ZOO] The common name for the odd-toed ungulates composing the family Rhinoceratidae, characterized by massive, thick-skinned limbs and bodies, and one or two horns which are composed of a solid mass of hairs attached to the bony prominence of the skull.

Rhinochimaeridae [VERT ZOO] A family of ratfishes, order Chimaeriformes, distinguished by an extremely elongate rostrum.

Rhinocryptidae [VERT ZOO] The tapaculos, a family of ground-inhabiting suboscine birds in the suborder Tyranni characterized by a large, movable flap which covers the nostrils.

Rhinolophidae [VERT ZOO] The horseshoe bats, a family of insect-eating chiropterans widely distributed in the Eastern Hemisphere and distinguished by extremely complex, horseshoe-shaped nose leaves.

rhinophore [INV ZOO] An olfactoreceptor of certain land mollusks, usually borne on a tentacle.

Rhinopomatidae [VERT ZOO] The mouse-tailed bats, a small family of insectivorous chiropterans found chiefly in arid regions of northern Africa and southern Asia and characterized by long, wirelike tails and rudimentary nose leaves.

Rhinopteridae [VERT ZOO] The cow-nosed rays, a family of batoid sharks having a fleshy pad at the front end of the head and a well-developed poison spine.

Rhinotermitidae [INV ZOO] A family of lower termites of the order Isoptera.

rhinotheca [VERT ZOO] The horny sheath on the upper part of a bird's bill.

rhinovirus [VIROL] A subgroup of the picornavirus group including small, ribonucleic acid–containing forms which are not inactivated by ether.

Rhipiceridae [INV ZOO] The cedar beetles, a family of coleopteran insects in the superfamily Elateroidea.

Rhipidistia [VERT ZOO] The equivalent name for Osteolepiformes.

rhipidium [BOT] A fan-shaped inflorescence with cymose branching in which branches lie in the same plane and are suppressed alternately on each side.

Rhipiphoridae [INV ZOO] The wedge-shaped beetles, a family of coleopteran insects in the superfamily Meloidea.

rhizanthous [BOT] Producing flowers directly from the root.

rhizautoicous [BOT] Of mosses, having the antheridial branch and the archegonial branch connected by rhizoids.

rhizine [BOT] The rhizoid of a lichen.

Rhizobiaceae [MICROBIO] A family of gram-negative, motile, aerobic rods; utilize carbohydrates and produce slime on carbohydrate media.

Rhizobium [MICROBIO] The type genus of the family Rhizobiaceae; cells stimulate the production of nodules on legume roots which fix molecular nitrogen.

rhizocarpous [BOT] Pertaining to perennial herbs having perennating underground parts from which stems and foliage arise annually.

Rhizocephala [INV ZOO] An order of crustaceans which parasitize other crustaceans; adults have a thin-walled sac enclosing the visceral mass and show no trace of segmentation, appendages, or sense organs.

Rhizochloridina [INV ZOO] A suborder of flagellate protozoans in the order Heterochlorida.

Rhizodontidae [PALEON] An extinct family of lobefin fishes in the order Osteolepiformes.

rhizoid [BOT] A rootlike structure which helps to hold the plant to a substrate; found on fungi, liverworts, lichens, mosses, and ferns.

Rhizomastigina [INV ZOO] An order of the protozoan class Zoomastigophorea; all species are microscopic and ameboid, and have one or two flagella.

Rhizomastigina [INV ZOO] The equivalent name for Rhizomastigida.

rhizome [BOT] An underground horizontal stem, often thickened and tuber-shaped, and possessing buds, nodes, and scalelike leaves.

rhizomorph [BOT] A rootlike structure, characteristic of many basidiomycetes, consisting of a mass of densely packed and intertwined hyphae.

Rhizophagidae [INV ZOO] The root-eating beetles, a family of minute coleopteran insects in the superfamily Cucujoidea.

Rhizophoraceae [BOT] A family of dicotyledonous plants in the order Cornales distinguished by opposite, stipulate leaves, two ovules per locule, folded or convolute bud petals, and a berry fruit.

rhizophore [BOT] A leafless, downward-growing dichotomous *Selaginella* shoot that has tufts of adventitious roots at the apex.

rhizoplast [CELL BIO] A delicate fiber or thread running between the nucleus and the blepharoplast in cells bearing flagella.

rhizopod [INV ZOO] An anastomosing rootlike pseudopodium.

Rhizopodea [INV ZOO] A class of the protozoan superclass Sarcodina in which pseudopodia may be filopodia, lobopodia, or reticulopodia, or may be absent.

Rhizostomeae [INV ZOO] An order of the class Scyphozoa having the umbrella generally higher than it is wide with the margin divided into many lappets but not provided with tentacles.

L-rhodeose See L-fucose.

Rhodesian man [PALEON] A type of fossil man inhabiting southern and central Africa during the late Pleistocene; the skull was large and low, marked by massive browridges, with a cranial capacity of 1300 cubic centimeters or less.

Rhodininae [INV ZOO] A subfamily of limivorous worms in the family Maldanidae.

Rhodobacterlineae [MICROBIO] Formerly a suborder of the order Pseudomonadales comprising all of the photosynthetic, or phototrophic, bacteria except those of the genus *Rhodomicrobium*.

Rhodomicroblum [MICROBIO] A genus of bacteria in the family Rhodospirillaceae; cells are ovoid, have peritrichous flagella, and contain bacteriochlorophyll *a*; reproduce by budding at hyphal tips.

Rhodophyceae [BOT] A class of algae belonging to the division or subphylum Rhodophyta.

Rhodophyta [BOT] The red algae, a large diverse phylum or division of plants distinguished by having an abundance of the pigment phycoerythrin.

rhodoplast [BOT] A reddish chromatophore occurring in red algae.

Rhodopseudomonas [MICROBIO] A genus of bacteria in the family Rhodospirillaceae; cells are spherical, rod-shaped, or ovoid with polar flagella and contain bacteriochlorophyll *a* or *b*.

rhodopsin [BIOCHEM] A deep-red photosensitive pigment contained in the rods of the retina of marine fishes and most higher vertebrates. Also known as retinal pigment; visual purple.

Rhodospirillaceae [MICROBIO] A family of bacteria in the suborder Rhodospirillineae; cells are motile by flagella, multiplication is by budding or binary fission, and photosynthetic membranes are continuous with the cytoplasmic membrane.

Rhodospirillales [MICROBIO] The single order of the phototrophic bacteria; cells are spherical, rod-shaped, spiral, or vibrio-shaped, and all contain bacteriochlorophylls and carotenoid pigments.

Rhodospirillineae [MICROBIO] The purple bacteria, a suborder of the order Rhodospirillales; contain bacteriochlorophyll *a* or *b*, located on internal membranes.

Rhodospirillum [MICROBIO] A genus of bacteria in the family Rhodospirillaceae; cells are spiral-shaped with polar flagella and contain bacteriochlorophyll *a*.

rhodoxanthin [BIOCHEM] $C_{40}H_{50}O_2$ A xanthophyll carotenoid pigment.

rhohelos [ECOL] A stream-crossed, nonalluvial marsh typical of filled lake areas.

Rholpteleaceae [BOT] A monotypic family of dicotyledonous plants in the order Juglandales having pinnately compound leaves, and flowers in triplets with four sepals and six stamens, and the lateral flowers female but sterile.

rhombencephalon [EMBRYO] The most caudal of the primary brain vesicles in the vertebrate embryo. Also known as hindbrain.

Rhombifera [PALEON] An extinct order of Cystoidea in which the thecal canals crossed the sutures at the edges of the plates, so that one-half of any canal lay in one plate and the other half on an adjoining plate.

rhombogen [INV ZOO] A form of reproductive individual of the mesozoan order Dicyemida found in the sexually mature host which arises from nematogens and gives rise to free-swimming infusorigens.

rhomboporold cryptostome [PALEON] Any of a group of extinct bryozoans in the order Cryptostomata that built twiglike colonies with zooecia opening out in all directions from the central axis of each branch.

Rhopalidae [INV ZOO] A family of pentatomorphan hemipteran insects in the superfamily Coreoidea.

rhopalium [INV ZOO] A sense organ found on the margin of a discomedusan.

Rhopalocera [INV ZOO] Formerly a suborder of Lepidoptera comprising those forms with clubbed antennae.

rhopalocercous cercaria [INV ZOO] A free-swimming digenetic trematode larva distinguished by a very wide tail.

Rhopalodinidae [INV ZOO] A family of holothurian echinoderms in the order Dactylochirotida in which the body is flask-shaped, the mouth and anus lying together.

Rhopalosomatidae [INV ZOO] A family of hymenopteran insects in the superfamily Scolioidea.

rhubarb [BOT] *Rheum rhaponticum*. A herbaceous perennial of the order Polygoniales grown for its thick, edible petioles.

Rhynchobdellae [INV ZOO] An order of the class Hirudinea comprising leeches that possess an eversible proboscis and lack hemoglobin in the blood.

Rhynchocephalia [VERT ZOO] An order of lepidosaurian reptiles represented by a single living species, *Sphenodon punctatus*, and characterized by a diapsid skull, teeth fused to the edges of the jaws, and an overhanging beak formed by the upper jaw.

rhynchocoel [INV ZOO] A cavity that holds the inverted proboscis in nemertinean worms.

Rhynchocoela [INV ZOO] A phylum of bilaterally symmetrical, unsegmented, ribbonlike worms having an eversible proboscis and a complete digestive tract with an anus.

rhynchodaeum [INV ZOO] The part of the proboscis lying anterior to the brain in nemertinean worms.

Rhynchodina [INV ZOO] A suborder of ciliate protozoans in the order Thigmotrichida.

Rhynchonellida [INV ZOO] An order of articulate brachiopods; typical forms are dorsibiconvex, the posterior margin is curved, the dorsal interarea is absent, and the ventral one greatly reduced.

rhynchophorous [ZOO] Having a beak.

Rhynchosauridae [PALEON] An extinct family of generally large, stout, herbivorous lepidosaurian reptiles in the order Rhynchocephalea.

Rhynchotherinae [PALEON] A subfamily of extinct elaphantoid mammals in the family Gomphotheriidae comprising the beak-jawed mastodonts.

Rhyniophyta [PALEOBOT] A subkingdom of the Embryobionta including the relatively simple, uppermost Silurian-Devonian vascular plants.

Rhyniopsida [PALEOBOT] A class of extinct plants in the subkingdom Rhyniophyta characterized by leafless, usually dichotomously branched stems that bore terminal sporangia.

Rhynochetidae [VERT ZOO] A monotypic family of gruiform birds containing only the kagu of New Caledonia.

Rhysodidae [INV ZOO] The wrinkled bark beetles, a family of coleopteran insects in the suborder Adephaga.

rib [ANAT] One of the long curved bones forming the wall of the thorax in vertebrates. [BOT] A primary vein in a leaf.

ribitol See adonitol.

riboflavin [BIOCHEM] $C_{17}H_{20}N_4O_6$ A water-soluble, yellow-orange fluorescent pigment that is essential to human nutrition as a component of the coenzymes flavin mononucleotide and flavin adenine dinucleotide. Also known as lactoflavin; vitamin B_2; vitamin G.

riboflavin 5′-phosphate [BIOCHEM] $C_{17}H_{21}N_4O_9P$ The phosphoric acid ester of riboflavin. Also known as flavin phosphate; flavin mononucleotide; FMN; isoalloxazine mononucleotide; vitamin B_2 phosphate.

D-riboketose See ribulose.

ribonuclease [BIOCHEM] $C_{587}H_{909}N_{171}O_{197}S_{12}$ An enzyme that catalyzes the depolymerization of ribonucleic acid.

ribonucleic acid [BIOCHEM] A long-chain, usually single-stranded nucleic acid consisting of repeating nucleotide units containing four kinds of heterocyclic, organic bases: adenine, cytosine, quanine, and uracil; they are conjugated to the pentose sugar ribose and held in sequence by phosphodiester bonds; involved intracellularly in protein synthesis. Abbreviated RNA.

ribonucleoprotein [BIOCHEM] Any of a large group of conjugated proteins in which molecules of ribonucleic acid are closely associated with molecules of protein.

ribose [BIOCHEM] $C_5H_{10}O_5$ A pentose sugar occurring as a component of various nucleotides, including ribonucleic acid.

riboside [BIOCHEM] Any glycoside containing ribose as the sugar component.

ribosomal ribonucleic acid [BIOCHEM] Any of three large types of ribonucleic acid found in ribosomes: 5S RNA, with molecular weight 40,000; 14–16S RNA, with molecular weight 600,000; and 18–22S RNA with molecular weight 1,200,000. Abbreviated rRNA.

ribosome [CELL BIO] One of the small, complex particles composed of various proteins and three molecules of ribonucleic acid which synthesize proteins within the living cell.

ribulose [BIOCHEM] $C_5H_{10}O_5$ A pentose sugar that exists only as a syrup; synthesized from arabinose by isomerization with pyridine; important in carbohydrate metabolism. Also known as D-erythropentose; D-riboketose.

ribulose diphosphate [BIOCHEM] $C_5H_{12}O_{11}P_2$ The phosphate ester of ribulose.

rice [BOT] *Oryza sativa*. An annual cereal grass plant of the order Cyperales, cultivated as a source of human food for its carbohydrate-rich grain.

Ricinidae [INV ZOO] A family of bird lice, order Mallophaga, which occur on numerous land and water birds.

Ricinuleida [INV ZOO] An order of rare, ticklike arachnids in which the two anterior pairs of appendages are chelate, and the terminal segments of the third legs of the male are modified as copulatory structures.

Rickettsia [MICROBIO] A genus of the tribe Rickettsieae; short rods which grow in cytoplasm and sometimes in nuclei of vertebrate and arthropod cells.

Rickettsiaceae [MICROBIO] A family of the order Rickettsiales; small, rod-shaped, coccoid, or diplococcoid cells often found in arthropods; includes human and animal parasites and pathogens.

Rickettsiales [MICROBIO] An order of prokaryotic microorganisms; gram-negative, obligate, intracellular animal parasites (may be grown in tissue cultures); many cause disease in humans and animals.

Rickettsieae [MICROBIO] A tribe of the family Rickettsiaceae; cells are occasionally filamentous; infect arthropods and some vertebrates and are pathogenic for humans, most frequently an incidental host.

Rickettsiella [MICROBIO] A genus of the tribe Wolbachieae; small rods, pathogenic for insect larva and certain other invertebrates.

rictus [VERT ZOO] The mouth aperture in birds.

RIF See resistance transfer factor.

rifampicin [MICROBIO] An antibacterial and antiviral antibiotic; action depends upon its preferential inhibition of bacterial ribonucleic acid polymerase over animal-cell RNA polymerase.

rim blight [PL PATH] A fungus disease of tea caused by members of the genus *Cladosporium* and characterized by yellow discoloration of the leaf margins followed by browning.

rind [BOT] 1. The bark of a tree. 2. The thick outer covering of certain fruits.

ring canal [INV ZOO] In echinoderms, the circular tube of the water-vascular system that surrounds the esophagus.

ring deoxyribonucleic acid *See* circular deoxyribonucleic acid.

ringent [BOT] Having widely separated, gaping lips. [ZOO] Gaping irregularly.

ring rot [PL PATH] 1. A fungus disease of the sweet potato root caused by *Rhizopus stolonifer* and marked by rings of dry rot. 2. A bacterial disease of potatoes caused by *Corynebacterium sepedonicum* and characterized by brown discoloration of the annular vascular tissue.

ring spot [PL PATH] Any of various virus and fungus diseases of plants characterized by the appearance of a discolored, annular lesion.

ringtail *See* cacomistle.

ring vessel [INV ZOO] A part of the water-vascular system in echinoderms; it is the circular canal around the mouth into which the stone canal empties, and from which a radial water vessel traverses to each of five radii.

Riodininae [INV ZOO] A subfamily of the lepidopteran family Lycaenidae in which prothoracic legs are nonfunctional in the male.

riparian [BIOL] Living or located on a riverbank.

ripe [BOT] Of fruit, fully developed, having mature seed and so usable as food.

Rissoacea [PALEON] An extinct superfamily of gastropod mollusks.

ristocetin [MICROBIO] The generic name for an antibiotic produced by *Nocardia lurida* that is effective in test-tube experiments against such microorganisms as *Diplococcus pneumoniae*, *Streptococcus hemolyticus*, and *Clostridium tetani*.

river-delta marsh [EVOL] A brackish or freshwater marsh bordering the mouth of a distributary stream.

rivulose [BOT] Marked by irregular, narrow lines.

RNA *See* ribonucleic acid.

roach [INV ZOO] An insect of the family Blattidae; the body is wide and flat, the anterior part of the thorax projects over the head, and antennae are long and filiform, with many segments. Also known as cockroach.

Robertinacea [INV ZOO] A superfamily of marine, benthic foraminiferans in the suborder Rotaliina characterized by a trochospiral or modified test with a wall of radial aragonite, and having bilamellar septa.

Robisonester *See* glucose-6-phosphate.

Roccilaceae [BOT] A family of fruticose species of Hysterales that grow profusely on trees and rocks along the coastlines of Portugal, California, and western South America.

Rochalimaea [MICROBIO] A genus of the tribe Rickettsieae; short rods usually found as extracellular parasites in arthropods.

rock shell [INV ZOO] The common name for a large number of gastropod mollusks composing

the family Muridae and characterized by having conical shells with various sculpturing.

rod [HISTOL] One of the rod-shaped sensory bodies in the retina which are sensitive to dim light.

rodent [VERT ZOO] The common name for members of the order Rodentia.

Rodentia [VERT ZOO] An order of mammals characterized by a single pair of ever-growing upper and lower incisors, a maximum of five upper and four lower cheek teeth on each side, and free movement of the lower jaw in an anteroposterior direction.

roll-tube technique [MICROBIO] A pure-culture technique, employed chiefly in tissue culture, in which, during incubation, the test tubes are held in a wheellike instrument at an angle of about 15° from the horizontal and the wheel is rotated vertically about once every 2 minutes.

rookery [ZOO] A location used by birds for breeding and nesting.

rooster [VERT ZOO] An adult male of certain birds and fowl, such as pheasants and ptarmigans.

root [BOT] The absorbing and anchoring organ of a vascular plant; it bears neither leaves nor flowers and is usually subterranean.

root canal [ANAT] The cavity within the root of a tooth, occupied by pulp, nerves, and vessels.

root cap [BOT] A thick, protective mass of parenchymal cells covering the meristematic tip of the root.

root hair [BOT] One of the hairlike outgrowths of the root epidermis that function in absorption.

root knot [PL PATH] Any of various plant diseases caused by root-knot nematodes which produce gall-like enlargements on the roots.

root nodule [PL PATH] An abnormal nodular growth on a plant root system caused by the establishment of symbiotic nitrogen-fixing bacteria in the host tissue.

root rot [PL PATH] Any of various plant diseases characterized by decay of the roots.

rootstock [BOT] A root or part of a root used as the stock for grafting.

rootworm [INV ZOO] 1. An insect larva that feeds on plant roots. 2. A nematode that infests the roots of plants.

Roproniidae [INV ZOO] A small family of hymenopteran insects in the superfamily Proctotrupoidea.

Rosaceae [BOT] A family of dicotyledonous plants in the order Rosales typically having stipulate leaves and hypogynous, slightly perigynous, or epigynous flowers, numerous stamens, and several or many separate carpels.

Rosales [BOT] A morphologically diffuse order of dicotyledonous plants in the subclass Rosidae.

rose [BOT] A member of the genus *Rosa* in the rose family (Rosaceae); plants are erect, climbing, or trailing shrubs, generally prickly stemmed, and bear alternate, odd-pinnate single leaves.

rose hip [BOT] The ripened false fruit of a rose plant.

rosemary [BOT] *Rosmarinus officinalis*. A fragrant evergreen of the mint family from France, Spain, and Portugal; leaves have a pungent bitter taste and are used as an herb and in perfumes.

Rosenmueller's organ *See* epoophoron.

rosette [BIOL] Any structure or marking resembling a rose. [PL PATH] Any of various plant diseases in which the leaves become clustered in the form of a rosette.

Rosidae [BOT] A large subclass of the class Magnoliatae; most have a well-developed corolla with petals separate from each other, binucleate pollen, and ovules usually with two integuments.

rostellum [BIOL] The anterior, flattened region of the scolex of armed tapeworms.

Rostratulidae [VERT ZOO] A small family of birds in the order Charadriiformes containing the painted snipe; females are more brightly colored than males.

rostrum [BIOL] A beak or beaklike process.

rot [PL PATH] Any plant disease characterized by breakdown and decay of plant tissue.

Rotaliacea [INV ZOO] A superfamily of foraminiferans in the suborder Rotaliina characterized by a planispiral or trochospiral test having apertural pores and composed of radial calcite, with secondarily bilamellar septa.

rotate [BOT] Of a sympetalous corolla, having a short tube and petals radiating like the spokes of a wheel.

Rotatoria [INV ZOO] The equivalent name for Rotifera.

Rothia [MICROBIO] A genus of bacteria in the family Actinomycetaceae; coccoid, diphtheroid, or branched filamentous cells which are aerobic; carbohydrates are fermented.

Rotifera [INV ZOO] A class of the phylum Aschelminthes distinguished by the corona, a retractile trochal disk provided with several groups of cilia and located on the head.

rough bark [PL PATH] 1. Any of various virus diseases of woody plants characterized by roughening and often splitting of the bark. 2. A fungus disease of apples caused by *Phomopsis mali* and characterized by rough cankers on the bark.

rough colony [MICROBIO] A flattened, irregular, and wrinkled colony of bacteria indicative of decreased capsule formation and virulence.

round ligament [ANAT] 1. A flattened band extending from the fovea on the head of the femur to attach on either side of the acetabular notch between which it blends with the transverse ligament. 2. A fibrous cord running from the umbilicus to the notch in the anterior border of the liver; represents the remains of the obliterated umbilical vein.

round window [ANAT] A membrane-covered opening between the middle and inner ears in amphibians and mammals through which energy is dissipated after traveling in the membranous labyrinth.

roundworm [INV ZOO] The name applied to nematodes.

Rovamycin [MICROBIO] A trade name for spiramycin.

RQ *See* respiratory quotient.

rRNA *See* ribosomal ribonucleic acid.

rubber tree [BOT] *Hevea brasiliensis.* A tall tree of the spurge family (Euphorbiaceae) from which latex is collected and coagulated to produce rubber.

Rubiaceae [BOT] The single family of the plant order Rubiales.

Rubiales [BOT] An order of dicotyledonous plants marked by their inferior ovary, regular or nearly regular corolla, and opposite leaves with interpetiolar stipules or whorled leaves without stipules.

rubriblast *See* pronormoblast.

rubricyte *See* pronormoblast.

ruddy turnstone [VERT ZOO] *Arenaria interpes.* A member of the avian order Charadriiformes that perform transpacific flights during their migration.

ruderal [ECOL] 1. Growing on rubbish, or waste or disturbed places. 2. A plant that thrives in such a habitat.

rudistids [PALEON] Fossil sessile bivalves that formed reefs during the Cretaceous in the southern Mediterranean or the Tethyan belt.

Ruffini cylinder [ANAT] A cutaneous nerve ending suspected as the mediator of warmth.

rufous [BOT] Having a reddish-brown color.

Rugosa [PALEON] An order of extinct corals having either simple or compound skeletons with internal skeletal structures consisting mainly of three elements, the septa, tabulae, and dissepiments.

rugose [BIOL] Having a wrinkled surface.

rugose mosaic [PL PATH] A virus disease of potatoes marked by dwarfed, wrinkled, and mottled leaves and resulting in premature death.

rumen [VERT ZOO] The first chamber of the ruminant stomach. Also known as paunch.

ruminant [PHYSIO] Characterized by the act of regurgitation and rechewing of food. [VERT ZOO] A mammal belonging to the Ruminantia.

Ruminantia [VERT ZOO] A suborder of the Artiodactyla including sheep, goats, camels, and other forms which have a complex stomach and ruminate their food.

rumination [PHYSIO] Regurgitation and remastication of food in preparation for true digestion in ruminants.

Ruminococcus [MICROBIO] A genus of bacteria in the family Peptococcaceae; cells are spherical to elongated and occur singly, in pairs, or in chains of three or four cells; ferment cellobiose and digest cellulose.

runcinate [BOT] Pinnately cut with downward-pointing lobes.

runner [BOT] A horizontally growing, sympodial stem system; adventitious roots form near the apex, and a new runner emerges from the axil of a reduced leaf. Also known as stolon.

running bird [VERT ZOO] Any of the large, flightless, heavy birds usually categorized as ratites.

runoff desert [ECOL] An arid region in which local rain is insufficient to support any perennial vegetation except in drainage or runoff channels.

rupicolous [ECOL] Living among or growing on rocks.

Russell's viper *See* tic polonga.

rust [PL PATH] Any plant disease caused by rust fungi (Uredinales) and characterized by reddish-brown lesions on the plant parts.

rusty blotch [PL PATH] A fungus disease of barley caused by *Helminthosporium californicum* and characterized by brown blotches on the foliage.

rusty mottle [PL PATH] A virus disease of cherry characterized by retarded development of blossoms and leaves in the spring, followed by necrotic spotting and shot-holing of the foliage with considerable defoliation.

rut [PHYSIO] The period during which the male animal has a heightened mating drive.

rutabaga [BOT] *Brassica napobrassica.* A biennial crucifer of the order Capparales probably resulting from the natural crossing of cabbage and turnip and characterized by a large, edible, yellowish fleshy root.

Rutaceae [BOT] A family of dicotyledonous plants in the order Sapindales distinguished by mostly free stamens and glandular-punctate leaves.

rye [BOT] *Secale cereale.* A cereal plant of the order Cyperales cultivated for its grain, which contains the most desirable gluten, next to wheat.

rye buckwheat *See* tartary buckwheat.

Rynchopidae [VERT ZOO] The skimmers, a family of birds in the order Charadriiformes distinguished by a knifelike lower beak that is longer and narrower than the upper one.

Rytiodinae [VERT ZOO] A subfamily of trichechiform sirenians in the family Dugongidae.

S

saba [BOT] A plant (*Musa sapientum* var. *compressa*) that is common in the Philippines; the fruit is a cooking banana.

Sabellariidae [INV ZOO] The sand-cementing worms, a family of polychaete annelids belonging to the Sedentaria and characterized by a compact operculum formed of setae of the first several segments.

Sabellidae [INV ZOO] A family of sedentary polychaete annelids often occurring in intertidal depths but descending to great abyssal depths; one of two families that make up the feather-duster worms.

Sabellinae [INV ZOO] A subfamily of the Sabellidae including the most numerous and largest members.

sable [VERT ZOO] *Martes zibellina*. A carnivore of the family Mustelidae; a valuable fur-bearing animal, quite similar to the American marten.

Sabouraud's agar [MICROBIO] A peptone-maltose agar used as a culture medium for pathogenic fungi, especially the dermatophytes.

sac [BIOL] A soft-walled cavity within a plant or animal, often containing a special fluid and usually having a narrow opening or none at all.

saccate [BOT] Having a saclike or pouchlike form.

saccharase [BIOCHEM] An enzyme that catalyzes the hydrolysis of disaccharide to monosaccharides, specifically of sucrose to dextrose and levulose. Also known as invertase; invertin; sucrase.

Saccharomyces [MYCOL] A genus of unicellular yeasts in the subfamily Saccharomycetoideae which have simple, budding cells, a pseudomycelium, or both, and one to four round to oval spores per ascus.

Saccharomycetaceae [MYCOL] The single family of the order Saccharomycetales.

Saccharomycetales [MYCOL] An order of the subclass Hemiascomycetidae comprising typical yeasts, characterized by the presence of naked asci in which spores are formed by free cells.

Saccharomycetoideae [MYCOL] A subfamily of Saccharomycetacae in which spores may be hat-, sickle-, or kidney-shaped, or round or oval.

Saccoglossa [INV ZOO] An order of gastropod mollusks belonging to the Opisthobranchia.

Saccopharyngiformes [VERT ZOO] Formerly an order of actinopterygian fishes, the gulpers, now included in the Anguilliformes.

Saccopharyngoidei [VERT ZOO] The gulpers, a suborder of actinopterygian fishes in the order Anguilliformes having degenerate adaptations, including loss of swim bladder, opercle, branchiostegal ray, caudal fin, scales, and ribs.

sacculus [ANAT] The smaller, lower saclike chamber of the membranous labyrinth of the vertebrate ear.

sac fungus [MYCOL] The common name for members of the class Ascomycetes.

sacral nerve [ANAT] Any of five pairs of spinal nerves in the sacral region which innervate muscles and skin of the lower back, lower extremities, and perineum, and branches to the hypogastric and pelvic plexuses.

sacral vertebrae [ANAT] Three to five fused vertebrae that form the sacrum in most mammals; amphibians have one sacral vertebra, reptiles usually have two, and birds have 10–23 fused in the synsacrum.

sacrococcygeus [ANAT] One of two inconstant thin muscles extending from the lower sacral vertebrae to the coccyx.

sacroiliac [ANAT] Pertaining to the sacrum and the ilium.

sacrospinous [ANAT] Pertaining to the sacrum and the spine of the ischium.

sacrum [ANAT] A triangular bone, consisting in man of five fused vertebrae, located below the last lumbar vertebra, above the coccyx, and between the hipbones.

Saefftigen's pouch [INV ZOO] An elongated pouch inside the genital sheath in many acanthocephalans.

safflower [BOT] *Carthamnus tinctorius*. An annual thistlelike herb belonging to the composite family (Compositae); the leaves are edible, flowers yield dye, and seeds yield a cooking oil.

saffron [BOT] *Crocus sativus*. A crocus of the iris family (Iridaceae); the source of a yellow dye used for coloring food and medicine.

Sagartiidae [INV ZOO] A family of zoantharians in the order Actiniaria.

sage [BOT] *Salvia officinalis*. A half-shrub of the mint family (Labiatae); the leaves are used as a spice.

sagebrush [BOT] Any of various hoary undershrubs of the genus *Artemisia* found on the alkaline plains of the western United States.

Sagenocrinida [PALEON] A large order of extinct, flexible crinoids that occurred from the Silurian to the Permian.

Saghathiinae [PALEON] An extinct subfamily of hyracoids in the family Procaviidae.

sagitta [VERT ZOO] The larger of two otoliths in the ear of most fishes.

sagittal [ZOO] In the median longitudinal plane of the body, or parallel to it.

Sagittariidae [VERT ZOO] A family of birds in the order Falconiformes comprising a single species, the secretary bird, noted for its nuchal plumes resembling quill pens stuck behind an ear.

sagittate [BOT] Shaped like an arrowhead, especially referring to leaves.

sagittocyst [INV ZOO] A cyst in the epidermis of certain turbellarians containing a single spindle-shaped needle.

sailfish [VERT ZOO] Any of several large fishes of the genus *Istiophorus* characterized by a very large dorsal fin that is highest behind its middle.

salamander [VERT ZOO] The common name for members of the order Urodela.

Salamandridae [VERT ZOO] A family of urodele amphibians in the suborder Salamandroidea characterized by a long row of prevomerine teeth.

Salamandroidea [VERT ZOO] The largest suborder of the Urodela characterized by teeth on the roof of the mouth posterior to the openings of the nostrils.

Salangidae [VERT ZOO] A family of soft-rayed fishes, in the suborder Galaxioidei, which live in estuaries of eastern Asia.

Saldidae [INV ZOO] The shore bugs, a family of predacious hemipteran insects in the superfamily Saldoidea.

Saldoidea [INV ZOO] A superfamily of the hemipteran group Leptopodoidea.

Saleniidae [INV ZOO] A family of echinoderms in the order Salenioida distinguished by imperforate tubercles.

Salenioida [INV ZOO] An order of the Echinacea in which the apical system includes one or several large angular plates covering the periproct.

Salicaceae [BOT] The single family of the order Salicales.

Salicales [BOT] A monofamilial order of dicotyledonous plants in the subclass Dilleniidae; members are dioecious, woody plants, with alternate, simple, stipulate leaves and plumose-hairy mature seeds.

Salientia [VERT ZOO] The equivalent name for Anura.

saliva [PHYSIO] The opalescent, tasteless secretions of the oral glands.

salivary amylase *See* ptyalin.

salivary diastase *See* ptyalin.

salivary gland [PHYSIO] A gland that secretes saliva, such as the sublingual or parotid.

salivary gland chromosomes [CELL BIO] Polytene chromosomes found in the interphase nuclei of salivary glands in the larvae of Diptera; chromosomes in the larva undergo complete somatic pairing to form two homologous polytene chromosomes fused side by side.

salivation [PHYSIO] Excessive secretion of saliva.

salmon [VERT ZOO] The common name for a number of fish in the family Salmonidae which live in coastal waters of the North Atlantic and North Pacific and breed in rivers tributary to the oceans.

Salmonella [MICROBIO] A genus of pathogenic bacteria in the family Enterobacteriaceae; usually motile rods that lack proteolytic enzymes and can utilize citrate as a carbon source.

Salmonella aertrycke *See* Salmonella typhimurium.

Salmonella choleraesuis [MICROBIO] The organism that is a secondary invader of pigs in hog cholera; may cause localized lesions, enteric fever, or gastroenteritis in humans. Also known as *Salmonella suipestifer*.

Salmonella enteritidis [MICROBIO] An organism causing gastroenteritis in humans. Also known as *Bacterium enteritidis*.

Salmonella hirschfeldii [MICROBIO] An organism causing enteric fever in humans. Also known as *Bacterium paratyphosum* C; *Salmonella paratyphi* C.

Salmonella oranienburg [MICROBIO] An organism isolated from feces of normal carriers and of persons with food poisoning.

Salmonella paratyphi A [MICROBIO] An organism that causes gastroenteritis and enteric fever in humans. Also known as *Salmonella paratyphosa*.

Salmonella paratyphi B *See* Salmonella schottmülleri.

Salmonella paratyphi C *See* Salmonella hirschfeldii.

Salmonella paratyphosa *See* Salmonella paratyphi A.

Salmonella pullorum [MICROBIO] An organism causing pullorum disease or bacillary white diarrhea of chicks.

Salmonella schottmülleri [MICROBIO] An organism causing enteric fever in humans. Also known as *Bacterium paratyphosum* B; *Salmonella paratyphi* B.

Salmonella suipestifer *See* Salmonella choleraesuis.

Salmonella typhi *See* Salmonella typhosa.

Salmonella typhimurium [MICROBIO] An organism causing diarrhea in mice, rats, and birds, and gastroenteritis in humans. Also known as *Salmonella aertrycke*.

Salmonella typhosa [MICROBIO] The organism that causes typhoid fever in humans. Also known as *Bacterium typhosum*; *Eberthella typhosa*; *Salmonella typhi*.

Salmonelleae [MICROBIO] Formerly a tribe of the Enterobacteriaceae comprising the pathogenic genera *Salmonella* and *Shigella*.

Salmonidae [VERT ZOO] A family of soft-rayed fishes in the suborder Salmonoidei including the trouts, salmons, whitefishes, and graylings.

Salmoniformes [VERT ZOO] An order of soft-rayed fishes comprising salmon and their allies; the stem group from which most higher teleostean fishes evolved.

Salmonoidei [VERT ZOO] A suborder of the Salmoniformes comprising forms having an adipose fin.

Salmopercae [VERT ZOO] An equivalent name for Percopsiformes.

Salpida [INV ZOO] An order of tunicates in the class Thaliacea including transparent forms ringed by muscular bands.

Salpingidae [INV ZOO] The narrow-waisted bark beetles, a family of coleopteran insects in the superfamily Tenebrionoidea.

saltatorial [ZOO] Adapted for leaping.

salt gland [VERT ZOO] A compound tubular gland, located around the eyes and nasal passages in certain marine turtles, snakes, and birds, which copiously secretes a watery fluid containing a high percentage of salt.

Salticidea [INV ZOO] The jumping spiders, a family of predacious arachnids in the suborder Dipneumonomorphae having keen vision and rapid movements.

saltmarsh [ECOL] A maritime habitat found in temperate regions, but typically associated with tropical and subtropical mangrove swamps, in which excess sodium chloride is the predominant environmental feature.

saltmarsh plain [ECOL] A salt marsh that has been raised above the level of the highest tide and has become dry land.

salt-spray climax [ECOL] A climax community along exposed Atlantic and Gulf seacoasts composed of plants able to tolerate the harmful effects of salt picked up and carried by onshore winds from seawater.

Salviniales [BOT] A small order of heterosporous, leptosporangiate ferns (division Polypodiophyta) which float on the surface of the water.

samara [BOT] A dry, indehiscent, winged fruit usually containing a single seed, such as sugar maple (*Acer saccharum*).

Sambonidae [INV ZOO] A family of pentastomid arthropods in the suborder Porocephaloidea of the order Porocephalida.

Samythinae [INV ZOO] A subfamily of sedentary polychaete annelids in the family Ampharetidae having a conspicuous dorsal membrane.

Sandalidae [INV ZOO] The equivalent name for Rhipiceridae.

sandalwood [BOT] 1. Any species of the genus *Santalum* of the sandalwood family (Santalaceae) characterized by a fragrant wood. 2. *S. album*. A parasitic tree with hard, close-grained, aromatic heartwood used in ornamental carving and cabinetwork.

sandblow [ECOL] A patch of coarse, sandy soil denuded of vegetation by wind action.

sand dollar [INV ZOO] The common name for the flat, disk-shaped echinoderms belonging to the order Clypeasteroida.

sandfly [INV ZOO] Any of various small biting Diptera, especially of the genus *Phlebotomus*, which are vectors for phlebotomus (sandfly) fever.

sand hopper [INV ZOO] The common name for gammaridean crustaceans found on beaches.

sandpiper [VERT ZOO] Any of various small birds that are related to plovers and that frequent sandy and muddy shores in temperate latitudes; bill is moderately long with a soft, sensitive tip, legs and neck are moderately long, and plumage is streaked brown, gray, or black above and is white below.

sand shark [VERT ZOO] Any of various shallow-water predatory elasmobranchs of the family Carchariidae. Also known as tiger shark.

sanguivorous [ZOO] Feeding on blood.

sanidaster [INV ZOO] A rod-shaped spicule having spines at intervals along its length.

SA node *See* sinoauricular node.

Santalaceae [BOT] A family of parasitic dicotyledonous plants in the order Santalales characterized by dry or fleshy indehiscent fruit, plants with chlorophyll, petals absent, and ovules without integument.

Santalales [BOT] An order of dicotyledonous plants in the subclass Rosidae characterized by progressive adaptation to parasitism, accompanied by progressive simplification of the ovules.

sap [BOT] The fluid part of a plant which circulates through the vascular system and is composed of water, gases, salts, and organic products of metabolism.

saphenous nerve [ANAT] A somatic sensory nerve arising from the femoral nerve and innervating the skin of the medial aspect of the leg, foot, and knee joint.

Sapindaceae [BOT] A family of dicotyledonous plants in the order Sapindales distinguished by mostly alternate leaves, usually one and less often two ovules per locule, and seeds lacking endosperm.

Sapindales [BOT] An order of mostly woody dicotyledonous plants in the subclass Rosidae with compound or lobed leaves and polypetalous, hypogynous to perigynous flowers with one or two sets of stamens.

sapling [BOT] A young tree with a trunk less than 4 inches (10 centimeters) in diameter at a point approximately 4 feet (1.2 meters) above the ground.

Sapotaceae [BOT] A family of dicotyledonous plants in the order Ebenales characterized by a well-developed latex system.

saprobic [BOT] Living on decaying organic matter; applied to plants and microorganisms.

saprogen [BIOL] An organism that lives on nonliving organic matter.

Saprolegniales [MYCOL] An order of aquatic fungi belonging to the class Phycomycetes, having a mostly hyphal thallus and zoospores with two flagella.

saprophage [BIOL] An organism that lives on decaying organic matter.

saprophyte [BOT] A plant that lives on decaying organic matter.

Saprospira [MICROBIO] A genus of bacteria in the family Cytophagaceae; cells are motile, unsheathed, unbranched, helical filaments; microcysts are not known.

saprovore [ZOO] A detritus-eating animal.

saprozoic [ZOO] Feeding on decaying organic matter; applied to animals.

sapwood [BOT] The younger, softer, outer layers of a woody stem, between the cambium and heartwood. Also known as alburnum.

Sapygidae [INV ZOO] A family of hymenopteran insects in the superfamily Scolioidea.

Sarcina [MICROBIO] A genus of strictly anaerobic bacteria in the family Peptococcaceae; spherical cells occur in packets; ferment carbohydrates.

sarcochore [BOT] A plant dispersing minute, light disseminules.

Sarcodina [INV ZOO] A superclass of Protozoa in the subphylum Sarcomastigophora in which movement involves protoplasmic flow, often with recognizable pseudopodia.

sarcoglia [CELL BIO] The protoplasm occurring at a myoneural junction.

sarcolemma [HISTOL] The thin connective tissue sheath enveloping a muscle fiber.

Sarcomastigophora [INV ZOO] A subphylum of Protozoa comprising forms that possess flagella or pseudopodia or both.

sarcomere [HISTOL] One of the segments defined by Z disks in a skeletal muscle fibril.

Sarcophagidae [INV ZOO] A family of the myodarian orthorrhaphous dipteran insects in the subsection Calyptratae comprising flesh flies, blowflies, and scavenger flies.

sarcoplasm [HISTOL] Hyaline, semifluid interfibrillar substance of striated muscle tissue.

sarcoplasmic reticulum [CELL BIO] Collectively, the cysternae of a single muscle fiber.

Sarcopterygii [VERT ZOO] A subclass of Osteichthyes, including Crossopterygii and Dipnoi in some systems of classification.

Sarcoptiformes [INV ZOO] A suborder of the Acarina including minute globular mites without stigmata.

sarcosoma [INV ZOO] The fleshy portion of an anthozoan.

Sarcosporida [INV ZOO] An order of Protozoa of the class Haplosporea which comprises parasites in skeletal and cardiac muscle of vertebrates.

sarcostyle [INV ZOO] A fibril or column of muscular tissue.

sarcotubule [CELL BIO] A tubular invagination of a muscle fiber.

sardine [VERT ZOO] 1. *Sardina pilchardus*. The young of the pilchard, a herringlike fish in the family Clupeidae found in the Atlantic along the European coasts. 2. The young of any of various similar and related forms which are processed and eaten as sardines.

Sargassum [BOT] A genus of brown algae characterized by branching thalli with lateral outgrowths; they develop along tropical shores, then break away to drift in the ocean.

sarkomycin [MICROBIO] $C_7H_8O_3$ An antibiotic produced by an actinomycete which acts as a carcinolytic agent.

sarmentocymarin [BIOCHEM] A cardioactive, steroid glycoside from the seeds of *Strophanthus sarmentosus*; on hydrolysis it yields sarmentogenin and sarmentose.

sarmentogenin [BIOCHEM] $C_{23}H_{34}O_5$ The steroid aglycon of sarmentocymarin; isometric with digitoxigenin, and characterized by a hydroxyl group at carbon number 11.

sarmentose [BOT] Producing slender, prostrate stems or runners.

Sarothriidae [INV ZOO] The equivalent name for Jacobsoniidae.

Sarraceniaceae [BOT] A small family of dicotyledonous plants in the order Sarraceniales in which leaves are modified to form pitchers, placentation is axile, and flowers are perfect with distinct filaments.

Sarraceniales [BOT] An order of dicotyledonous herbs or shrubs in the subclass Dilleniidae; plants characteristically have alternate, simple leaves that are modified for catching insects, and grow in waterlogged soils.

sarsaparilla [BOT] Any of various tropical American vines of the genus *Smilax* (family Liliaceae) found in dense, moist jungles; a flavoring material used in medicine and soft drinks is obtained from the dried roots of at least four species.

sartorius [ANAT] A large muscle originating in the anterior superior iliac spine and inserting in the tibia; flexes the hip and knee joints, and rotates the femur laterally.

sassafras [BOT] *Sassafras albidum*. A medium-sized tree of the order Magnoliales recognized by the bright-green color and aromatic odor of the leaves and twigs.

satellite band [MOL BIO] A fraction of the deoxyribonucleic acid (DNA) of an organism which has a different density from the rest and is therefore separable as a band in density gradient centrifugation; these bands are usually made up of highly repetitive sequences of DNA.

satellite cell [HISTOL] One of the neurilemmal cells surrounding nerve cells in the peripheral nervous system.

saturation diving [PHYSIO] Diving in which the tissues exposed to high pressure at great ocean depths for 24 hours become saturated with gases, especially inert gases, thereby reaching a new equilibrium state.

Saturniidae [INV ZOO] A family of medium- to large-sized moths in the superfamily Saturnioidea including the giant silkworms, characterized by reduced, often vestigial, mouthparts and strongly bipectinate antennae.

Saturnioidea [INV ZOO] A superfamily of medium- to very-large-sized moths in the suborder Heteroneura having the frenulum reduced or absent, reduced mouthparts, no tympanum, and pectinate antennae.

Satyrinae [INV ZOO] A large, cosmopolitan subfamily of lepidopterans in the family Nymphalidae, containing the wood nymphs, meadow browns, graylings, and arctics, characterized by bladderlike swellings at the bases of the forewing veins.

Sauria [VERT ZOO] The lizards, a suborder of the Squamata, characterized generally by two or four limbs but sometimes none, movable eyelids, external ear openings, and a pectoral girdle.

Saurichthyidae [PALEON] A family of extinct chondrostean fishes bearing a superficial resemblance to the Aspidorhynchiformes.

Saurischia [PALEON] The lizard-hipped dinosaurs, an order of extinct reptiles in the subclass Archosauria characterized by an unspecialized, three-pronged pelvis.

Sauropoda [PALEON] A group of fully quadrupedal, seemingly herbivorous dinosaurs from the Jurassic and Cretaceous periods in the suborder Sauropodomorpha; members had small heads, spoon-shaped teeth, long necks and tails, and columnar legs.

Sauropodomorpha [PALEON] A suborder of extinct reptiles in the order Saurischia, including large, solid-limbed forms.

Sauropterygia [PALEON] An order of Mesozoic marine reptiles in the subclass Euryapsida.

Saururaceae [BOT] A family of dicotyledonous plants in the order Piperales distinguished by mostly alternate leaves, two to ten ovules per carpel, and carpels distinct or united into a compound ovary.

savane armée *See* thornbush.

savane épineuse *See* thornbush.

savanna [ECOL] Any of a variety of physiognomically or environmentally similar vegetation types in tropical and extratropical regions; all contain grasses and one or more species of trees of the families Leguminosae, Bombacaceae, Bignoniaceae, or Dilleniaceae.

savanna-woodland *See* tropical woodland.

sawfish [VERT ZOO] Any of several elongate viviparous fishes of the family Pristidae distinguished by a dorsoventrally flattened elongated snout with stout toothlike projections along each edge.

saxicolous [ECOL] Living or growing among rocks.

Saxifragaceae [BOT] A family of dicotyledonous plants in the order Rosales which are scarcely or not at all succulent and have two to five carpels usually more or less united, and leaves not modified into pitchers.

saxitoxin [BIOCHEM] A nonprotein toxin produced by the dinoflagellate *Gonyaulax catenella*.

scabrous [BIOL] Having a rough surface covered with stiff hairs or scales.

scala media [ANAT] The middle channel of the cochlea, filled with endolymph and bounded above by Reissner's membrane and below by the basilar membrane. Also known as cochlear duct.

scalariform [BIOL] Resembling a ladder; having transverse markings or bars.

scala tympani [ANAT] The lowest channel in the cochlea of the ear; filled with perilymph.

scala vestibuli [ANAT] The uppermost channel of the cochlea; filled with perilymph.

scale [BOT] The bract of a catkin. [VERT ZOO] A flat calcified or cornified platelike structure on the skin of most fishes and of some tetrapods.

scale insect [INV ZOO] Any of various small, structurally degenerate homopteran insects in the superfamily Coccoidea which resemble scales on the surface of a host plant.

scalenus [ANAT] One of three muscles in the neck, arising from the transverse processes of the cervical vertebrae, and inserted on the first two ribs.

scale scar [BOT] A mark left on a stem after bud scales have fallen off.

Scalibregmidae [INV ZOO] A family of mud-swallowing worms belonging to the Sedentaria and found chiefly in sublittoral and great depths.

scaling [BIOL] The removing of scales from fishes.

scallion *See* shallot.

scallop [INV ZOO] Any of various bivalve mollusks in the family Pectinidae distinguished by radially ribbed valves with undulated margins.

Scalpellidae [INV ZOO] A primitive family of barnacles in the suborder Lepadomorpha having more than five plates.

scandent [BOT] Climbing by stem-roots or tendrils.

scansorial [BOT] Adapted for climbing.

Scapanorhychidae [VERT ZOO] The goblin sharks, a family of deep-sea galeoids in the isurid line having long, sharp teeth and a long, pointed rostrum.

scapha [ANAT] The furrow of the auricle between the helix and the antihelix.

Scaphidiidae [INV ZOO] The shining fungus beetles, a family of coleopteran insects in the superfamily Staphylinoidea.

scaphoid [ANAT] A boat-shaped bone of the carpus or of the tarsus.

Scaphopoda [INV ZOO] A class of the phylum Mollusca in which the soft body fits the external, curved and tapering, nonchambered, aragonitic shell which is open at both ends.

scapula [ANAT] The large, flat, triangular bone forming the back of the shoulder. Also known as shoulder blade.

scapulet [INV ZOO] In some medusae, fringed outgrowths on the outer surfaces of the arms near the bell.

scapulus [INV ZOO] A modified submarginal region in some sea anemones.

scapus [BIOL] The stem, shaft, or column of a structure.

Scarabaeidae [INV ZOO] The lamellicorn beetles, a large cosmopolitan family of coleopteran insects in the superfamily Scarabaeoidea including the Japanese beetle and other agricultural pests.

Scarabaeoidea [INV ZOO] A superfamily of Coleoptera belonging to the suborder Polyphaga.

Scaridae [VERT ZOO] The parrotfishes, a family of perciform fishes in the suborder Percoidei which have the teeth of the jaw generally coalescent.

scarious [BOT] Having a thin, membranous texture.

Scarpa's fascia [ANAT] The deep, membranous layer of the superficial fascia of the lower abdomen.

Scatopsidae [INV ZOO] The minute black scavenger flies, a family of orthorrhaphous dipteran insects in the series Nematocera.

scavenger [ECOL] An organism that feeds on carrion, refuse, and similar matter.

Scelionidae [INV ZOO] A family of small, shining wasps in the superfamily Proctotrupoidea, characterized by elbowed, 11- or 12-segmented antennae.

scent gland [VERT ZOO] A specialized skin gland of the tubuloalveolar or acinous variety which produces substances having peculiar odors; found in many mammals.

Schardinger dextrin [BIOCHEM] Any of several water-soluble, nonreducing, dextrorotatory polysaccharides that have a low molecular weight and that are obtained by the action of *Bacillus macerans* on a starch solution.

schemochrome [ZOO] A feather color that originates within the feather structures, through refraction of light independent of pigments.

Schindleriidae [VERT ZOO] The single family of the order Schindlerioidei.

Schindlerioidei [VERT ZOO] A suborder of fishes in the order Perciformes composed of one monogeneric family comprising two tiny oceanic species that are transparent and neotenic.

schindylesis [ANAT] A synarthrosis in which a plate of one bone is fixed in a fissure of another.

Schistosoma [INV ZOO] A genus of blood flukes infecting man.

Schistostegiales [BOT] A monospecific order of mosses; the small, slender, glaucous plants are distinguished by the luminous protonema.

schizaxon [ANAT] An axon that divides, in its course, into equal or nearly equal branches.

schizocarp [BOT] A dry fruit that separates at maturity into single-seeded indehiscent carpels.

Schizocoela [INV ZOO] A group of animal phyla, including Bryozoa, Brachiopoda, Phoronida, Sipunculoidea, Echiuroidea, Priapuloidea, Mollusca, Annelida, and Arthropoda, all characterized by the appearance of the coelom as a space in the embryonic mesoderm.

schizodont [INV ZOO] A multinucleate trophozoite that segments into merozoites.

schizogamy [BIOL] A form of reproduction involving division of an organism into a sexual and an asexual individual.

schizogenesis [BIOL] Reproduction by fission.

schizognathous [VERT ZOO] Descriptive of birds having a palate in which the vomer is small and pointed, the maxillopalatines are not united with each other or with the vomer, and the palatines articulate posteriorly with the rostrum.

Schizogoniales [BOT] A small order of the Chlorophyta containing algae that are either submicroscopic filaments or macroscopic ribbons or sheets a few centimeters wide and attached by rhizoids to rocks.

schizogony [INV ZOO] Asexual reproduction by multiple fission of a trophozoite; a characteristic of certain Sporozoa.

Schizomeridaceae [BOT] A family of green algae in the order Ulvales.

Schizomycetes [MICROBIO] Formerly a class of the division Protophyta which included the bacteria.

Schizomycophyta [BOT] The designation for bacteria in those taxonomic systems that consider bacteria as plants.

schizont [INV ZOO] A multinucleate cell in certain members of the Sporozoa that is produced from a trophozoite in a cell of the host, and that segments into merozoites.

Schizopathidae [INV ZOO] A family of dimorphic zoantharians in the order Antipatharia.

schizopelmous [VERT ZOO] Having the two flexor tendons of the toes separate, as in certain birds.

Schizophora [INV ZOO] A series of the dipteran suborder Cyclorrhapha in which adults possess a frontal suture through which a distensible sac, or ptilinum, is pushed to help the organism escape from its pupal case.

Schizophyceae [MICROBIO] The blue-green algae, a class of the division Protophyta.

Schizophyta [BOT] The prokaryotes, a division of the plant subkingdom Thallobionta; includes the bacteria and blue-green algae.

schizopod [INV ZOO] 1. Having the limbs split so that each has an endopodite and an exopodite, as in certain crustaceans. 2. A biramous appendage.

Schizopteridae [INV ZOO] A family of minute ground-inhabiting hemipterans in the group Dipsocoeoidea; individuals characteristically live in leaf mold.

schizorhinal [VERT ZOO] Having a deep cleft on the posterior margin of the osseous external nares, as in certain birds.

schizothecal [VERT ZOO] Having the horny envelope of the tarsus divided into scalelike plates; refers to most birds.

schizothoracic [INV ZOO] Having a prothorax that is large and loosely articulated with the thorax.

Schlemm's canal [ANAT] A space or series of spaces at the junction of the sclera and cornea in the eye; drains aqueous humor from the anterior chamber.

Schmitz bacillus [MICROBIO] The common name for the dysentery bacillus *Shigella ambigua*.

Schneiderian membrane [ANAT] The mucosa lining the nasal cavities and paranasal sinuses.

Schoenobiinae [INV ZOO] A subfamily of moths in the family Pyralididae, including the genus *Acentropus*, the most completely aquatic Lepidoptera.

Schubertellidae [PALEON] An extinct family of marine protozoans in the superfamily Fusulinacea.

Schwagerinidae [PALEON] A family of fusulinacean protozoans that flourished during the Early and Middle Pennsylvanian and became extinct during the Late Permian.

Schwann cell [HISTOL] One of the cells that surround peripheral axons forming sheaths of the neurilemma.

Sciaenidae [VERT ZOO] A family of perciform fishes in the suborder Percoidei, which includes the drums.

sciatic nerve [ANAT] Either of a pair of long nerves that originate in the lower spinal cord and send fibers to the upper thigh muscles and the joints, skin, and muscles of the leg.

Scincidae [VERT ZOO] The skinks, a family of the reptilian suborder Sauria which have reduced limbs and snakelike bodies.

Scinidae [INV ZOO] A family of bathypelagic, amphipod crustaceans in the suborder Hyperiidea.

Sciomyzidae [INV ZOO] A family of myodarian cyclorrhaphous dipteran insects in the subsection Acalypteratae.

scion [BOT] A section of a plant, usually a stem or bud, which is attached to the stock in grafting.

sciophilous [ECOL] Capable of thriving in shade.

sciophyte [BOT] A plant that thrives at lowered light intensity.

Scitaminales [BOT] An equivalent name for Zingiberales.

Scitamineae [BOT] An equivalent name for Zingiberales.

Sciuridae [VERT ZOO] A family of rodents including squirrels, chipmunks, marmots, and related forms.

Sciuromorpha [VERT ZOO] A suborder of Rodentia according to the classical arrangement of the order.

sclera [ANAT] The hard outer coat of the eye, continuous with the cornea in front and with the sheath of the optic nerve behind.

Scleractinia [INV ZOO] An order of the subclass Zoantharia which comprises the true, or stony, corals; these are solitary or colonial anthozoans which attach to a firm substrate.

Scleraxonia [INV ZOO] A suborder of coelenterates in the order Gorgonacea in which the axial skeleton has calcareous spicules.

sclereid [BOT] A thick-walled, lignified plant cell typically found in sclerenchyma.

sclerenchyma [BOT] A supporting plant tissue composed principally of sclereids whose walls are often mineralized.

sclerite [INV ZOO] One of the sclerotized plates of the integument of an arthropod.

scleroblast [INV ZOO] A spicule-secreting cell in Porifera.

scleroblastema [EMBRYO] Embryonic tissue from which bones are formed.

sclerocaulous [BOT] Having a hard, dry stem because of exceptional development of sclerenchyma.

sclerochore [BOT] A plant that disperses disseminules without apparent morphological adaptations.

Sclerodactylidae [INV ZOO] A family of echinoderms in the order Dendrochirotida having a complex calcareous ring.

sclerodermatous [INV ZOO] Having a skeleton that is composed of scleroderm, as certain corals. [VERT ZOO] Having a hard outer covering, for example, hard plate or horny scale.

Sclerogibbidae [INV ZOO] A monospecific family of the hymenopteran superfamily Bethyloidea.

sclerophyllous [BOT] Characterized by thick, hard foliage due to well-developed sclerenchymatous tissue.

scleroprotein [BIOCHEM] Any one of a class of proteins, such as keratin, fibroin, and the collagens, which occur in hard parts of the animal body and serve to support or protect. Also known as albuminoid.

scleroseptum [INV ZOO] A calcareous radial septum in certain corals.

sclerotic [ANAT] Pertaining to the sclera.

sclerotium [MICROBIO] The hardened, resting or encysted condition of the plasmodium of Myxomycetes. [MYCOL] A hardened, resting mass of hyphae, usually black on the outside, from which fructifications may develop.

sclerotome [EMBRYO] The part of a mesodermal somite which enters into the formation of the vertebrae. [VERT ZOO] The fibrous tissue separating successive myotomes in certain lower vertebrates.

scobiform [BOT] Resembling sawdust.

scolecodont [PALEON] Any of the paired, pincerlike jaws occurring as fossils of annelid worms.

Scolecosporae [MYCOL] A spore group of Fungi Imperfecti characterized by filiform spores.

scolex [INV ZOO] The head of certain tapeworms, typically having a muscular pad with hooks, and two pairs of lateral suckers.

Scoliidae [INV ZOO] A family of the Hymenoptera in the superfamily Scolioidea.

Scolioidea [INV ZOO] A superfamily of hymenopteran insects in the suborder Apocrita.

scolop [INV ZOO] The thickened, distal tip of a vibration-sensitive organ in insects.

Scolopacidea [VERT ZOO] A large, cosmopolitan family of birds of the order Charadriiformes including snipes, sandpipers, curlews, and godwits.

Scolopendridae [INV ZOO] A family of centipedes in the order Scolopendromorpha which characteristically possess eyes.

Scolopendromorpha [INV ZOO] An order of the chilopod subclass Pleurostigmophora containing the dominant tropical forms, and also the largest of the centipedes.

scolophore See scolopophore.

scolopophore [INV ZOO] A spindle-shaped, bipolar nerve ending in the integument of insects, believed to be auditory in function. Also known as scolophore.

Scolytidae [INV ZOO] The bark beetles, a large family of coleopteran insects in the superfamily Curculionoidea characterized by a short beak and clubbed antennae.

Scombridae [VERT ZOO] A family of perciform fishes in the suborder Scombroidei including the mackerels and tunas.

Scombroidei [VERT ZOO] A suborder of fishes in the order Perciformes; all are moderate- to large-sized shore and oceanic fishes having fixed premaxillae.

scopa [INV ZOO] A brushlike arrangement of short stiff hairs on the body surface of certain insects.

Scopeumatidae [INV ZOO] The dung flies, a family of myodarian cyclorrhaphous dipteran insects in the subsection Calyptratae.

Scopidae [VERT ZOO] A family of birds in the order Ciconiiformes containing a single species, the hammerhead (*Scopus umbretta*) of tropical Africa.

scopula [ZOO] A tuft of hair, as on the feet and chelicerae of certain spiders.

scorching [PL PATH] Browning of plant tissues caused by heat or parasites; may also be symptomatic of disease.

Scorpaenidae [VERT ZOO] The scorpion fishes, a family of Perciformes in the suborder Cottoidei, including many tropical shorefishes, some of which are venomous.

Scorpaeniformes [VERT ZOO] An order of fishes coextensive with the perciform suborder Cottoidei in some systems of classification.

scorpioid cyme [BOT] A cyme with a curved axis and flowers arising two-ranked on alternate sides of the axis.

scorpion [INV ZOO] The common name for arachnids constituting the order Scorpionida.

Scorpionida [VERT ZOO] The scorpions, an order of arachnids characterized by a shieldlike carapace covering the cephalothorax and by large pedipalps armed with chelae.

Scotch pine [BOT] *Pinus sylvestris*. A hard pine of North America having two short, bluish needles in a cluster.

scotochromogen [MICROBIO] 1. Any microorganism which produces pigment when grown without light as well as with light. 2. A member of group II of the atypical mycobacteria.

scotopic vision [PHYSIO] Vision that is due to the activity of the rods of the retina only; it is the type of vision that occurs at very low levels of illumination, and it can detect differences of brightness but not of hue.

Scraptiidae [INV ZOO] An equivalent name for Melandryidae.

scrod [VERT ZOO] A young fish, especially cod.

Scrophulariaceae [BOT] A large family of dicotyledonous plants in the order Scrophulariales, characterized by a usually herbaceous habit, irregular flowers, axile placentation, and dry, dehiscent fruit.

Scrophulariales [BOT] An order of flowering plants in the subclass Asteridae distinguished by a usually superior ovary and, generally, either by an irregular corolla or by fewer stamens than corolla lobes, or commonly both.

scrotum [ANAT] The pouch containing the testes.

scrub [ECOL] A tract of land covered with a generally thick growth of dwarf or stunted trees and shrubs and a poor soil.

sculpin [VERT ZOO] Any of several species of small fishes in the family Cottidae characterized by a large head that sometimes has spines, spiny fins, broad mouth, and smooth, scaleless skin.

scute [INV ZOO] A cornified, epithelial, scalelike structure in lizards and snakes.

Scutechiniscidae [INV ZOO] A family of heterotardigrades in the suborder Echiniscoidea, with segmental and intersegmental thickenings of cuticle.

Scutelleridae [INV ZOO] The shield bugs, a family of Hemiptera in the superfamily Pentatomoidea.

scutellum [BOT] 1. A rounded apothecium with an elevated rim found in certain lichens. 2. The flattened cotyledon of a monocotyledonous plant embryo, such as a grass. [INV ZOO] The third of four pieces forming the upper part of the thoracic segment in certain insects. [VERT ZOO] One of the scales on the tarsi and toes of birds.

Scutigeromorpha [INV ZOO] The single order of notostigmophorous centipedes; members are distinguished by a dorsal respiratory opening, compound-type eyes, long flagellate multisegmental antennae, and long thin legs with multisegmental tarsi.

scutum [INV ZOO] 1. A bony, horny, or chitinous plate. 2. The second of four pieces forming the upper part of the thoracic segment in certain insects. 3. One or two lower opercular valves in certain barnacles.

Scydmaenidae [INV ZOO] The antlike stone beetles, a large cosmopolitan family of the Coleoptera in the superfamily Staphylinoidea.

Scyllaridae [INV ZOO] The Spanish, or shovelnosed, lobsters, a family of the Scyllaridea.

Scyllaridea [INV ZOO] A superfamily of decapod crustaceans in the section Macrura including the heavily armored spiny lobsters and the Spanish lobsters, distinguished by the absence of a rostrum and chelae.

Scylliorhinidae [VERT ZOO] The catsharks, a family of the cacharinid group of galeoids; members exhibit the most exotic color patterns of all sharks.

scyphistoma [INV ZOO] A sessile, polyploid larva of many Scyphozoa which may produce either more scyphistomae or free-swimming medusae.

scyphomedusa [INV ZOO] A medusa of the scyphozoans.

Scyphomedusae [INV ZOO] A subclass of the class Scyphozoa characterized by reduced marginal tentacles, tetramerous medusae, and medusalike polyploids.

scyphopolyp [INV ZOO] A polyp of the scyphozoans.

Scyphozoa [INV ZOO] A class of the phylum Coelenterata; all members are marine and are characterized by large, well-developed medusae and by small, fairly well-organized polyps.

sea anemone [INV ZOO] Any of the 1000 marine coelenterates that constitute the order Actiniaria; the adult is a cylindrical polyp or hydroid stage with the free end bearing tentacles that surround the mouth.

sea cucumber [INV ZOO] The common name for the echinoderms that make up the class Holothuroidea.

sea fan [INV ZOO] A form of horny coral that branches like a fan.

sea grass [BOT] Marine plants which are found in shallow brackish or marine waters, are more highly organized than algae, are seed-bearing, and attain lengths of up to 8 feet (2.4 meters).

sea horse [INV ZOO] Any of about 50 species of tropical and subtropical marine fishes constituting the genus *Hippocampus* in the family Syngnathidae; the body is compressed, the head is bent ventrally and has a tubiform snout, and the tail is tapering and prehensile.

seal [VERT ZOO] Any of various carnivorous mammals of the suborder Pinnipedia, especially the families Phoridae, containing true seals, and Otariidae, containing the eared and fur seals.

sea lily [INV ZOO] The common name for those crinoids in which the body is flower-shaped and is carried at the tip of an anchored stem.

sea lion [VERT ZOO] Any of several large, eared seals of the Pacific Ocean; related to fur seals but lack a valuable coat.

sea marsh [ECOL] A salt marsh periodically overflowed or flooded by the sea. Also known as sea meadow.

sea meadow [ECOL] *See* sea marsh.

sea otter [VERT ZOO] *Enhydra lutris.* A large marine otter found close to the shoreline in the North Pacific; these animals are diurnally active and live in herds.

sea pen [INV ZOO] The common name for coelenterates constituting the order Pennatulacea.

sea-run [VERT ZOO] Having the habit of ascending a river from the sea, especially to spawn, as salmon and brook trout.

seashell [INV ZOO] The shell of a marine invertebrate, especially a mollusk.

sea slug [INV ZOO] The common name for the naked gastropods composing the suborder Nudibranchia.

sea spider [INV ZOO] The common name for arthropods in the subphylum Pycnogonida.

sea squirt [INV ZOO] A sessile, marine tunicate of the class Ascidiacea; it squirts water from two openings in the unattached end when touched or disturbed.

sea turtle [VERT ZOO] Any of various marine turtles, principally of the families Cheloniidae and Dermochelidae, having paddle-shaped feet.

seatworm *See* pinworm.

sea urchin [INV ZOO] A marine echinoderm of the class Echinoidea; the soft internal organs are enclosed in and protected by a test or shell consisting of a number of close-fitting plates beneath the skin.

seaweed [BOT] A marine plant, especially algae.

sebaceous gland [PHYSIO] A gland, arising in association with a hair follicle, which produces and liberates sebum.

Sebekidae [INV ZOO] A family of pentastomid arthropods in the suborder Porocephaloidea.

sebum [PHYSIO] The secretion of sebaceous glands, composed of fat, cellular debris, and keratin.

secalose [BIOCHEM] A polysaccharide consisting of fructose units; occurs in green rye and oats, and in rye flour.

Secernentea [INV ZOO] A class of the phylum Nematoda in which the primary excretory system consists of intracellular tubular canals joined anteriorly and ventrally in an excretory sinus, into which two ventral excretory gland cells may also open.

secodont [VERT ZOO] Having teeth adapted for cutting.

secondary cambium [BOT] One of the tissue layers formed after the initial cambial layers in certain plant roots, and that produce a ring of tissue.

secondary periderm [BOT] Any layer of the periderm except the first and outermost layer.

secondary phloem [BOT] Phloem produced by the cambium, consisting of two interpenetrating systems, the vertical or axial and the horizontal or ray.

secondary structure [PALEON] A coarse structure usually between the thin sheets in the protective wall of a tintinnid.

secondary tympanic membrane [ANAT] The membrane closing the fenestra cochleae.

secondary wall [BOT] The portion of a plant cell wall produced internal to and following deposition of the primary wall; usually consists of several anisotropic layers, and often has prominent internal rings, spirals, bars, or reticulations.

secondary xylem [BOT] Xylem produced by cambium, composed of two interpenetrating systems, the horizontal (ray) and vertical (axial).

second generation *See* F_2.

secretin [BIOCHEM] A basic polypeptide hormone produced by the duodenum in response to the presence of acid; acts to excite the pancreas to activity.

secretion [PHYSIO] 1. The act or process of producing a substance which is specialized to perform a certain function within the organism or is excreted from the body. 2. The material produced by such a process.

secretor gene [GEN] A dominant autosomal gene in man which controls secretion of A and B antigenic material in saliva, urine, plasma, and other body fluids; it is not linked to the ABO genes.

secretory granules [CELL BIO] Accumulations of material produced within a cell for secretion outside the cell.

secretory structure [BOT] Plant cells or organizations of plant cells which produce a variety of secretions.

secund [BOT] Having lateral members arranged on one side only.

Sedentaria [INV ZOO] A group of families of polychaete annelids in which the anterior, or cephalic, region is more or less completely concealed by overhanging peristomial structures, or the body is divided into an anterior thoracic and a posterior abdominal region.

sedoheptulose [BIOCHEM] A seven-carbon ketose sugar widely distributed in plants of the Crassulaceae family; a significant intermediary compound in the cyclic regeneration of D-ribulose.

seed [BOT] A fertilized ovule containing an embryo which forms a new plant upon germination.

seed coat [BOT] The envelope which encloses the seed except for a tiny pore, the micropyle.

seed fern [PALEOBOT] The common name for the extinct plants classified as Pteridospermae, characterized by naked seeds borne on large, fernlike fronds.

seedling [BOT] 1. A plant grown from seed. 2. A tree younger and smaller than a sapling. 3. A tree grown from a seed.

segmental reflex [PHYSIO] A reflex arc having afferent inputs by way of the spinal dorsal roots, and efferent outputs over spinal ventral roots of the same or adjacent segments.

segmentation cavity *See* blastocoele.

segregation [GEN] The separation of alleles and homologous chromosomes during meiosis in the formation of gametes.

segregation distorter [GEN] An abnormality of meiosis which produces a distortion of the 1:1 segregation ratio in a heterozygote.

Seisonacea [INV ZOO] A monofamiliar order of the class Rotifera characterized by an elongated jointed body with a small head, a long slender neck region, a thick fusiform trunk, and an elongated foot terminating in a perforated disk.

Seisonidea [INV ZOO] The equivalent name for Seisonacea.

Seitz filter [MICROBIO] A bacterial filter made of asbestos and used to sterilize solutions without the use of heat.

Selachii [VERT ZOO] An order of elasmobranchs including all fossil sharks, except Cladoselachii and Pleuracanthodii.

Selaginellales [BOT] The plant order of small club mosses, containing one living genus, *Selaginella*; distinguished from other lycopods in being heterosporous and in having a ligule borne on the upper base of the leaf.

selection [GEN] Any natural or artificial process which favors the survival and propagation of individuals of a given genotype in a population.

selection coefficient [GEN] A measure of the rate of transmission through successive generations of a given allele compared to the rate of transmission of another (usually the wild-type) allele.

selection pressure [EVOL] Those factors that influence the direction of natural selection.

selective breeding [BIOL] Breeding of animals or plants having desirable characters.

selective medium [MICROBIO] A bacterial culture medium containing an individual organic compound as the sole source of carbon, nitrogen, or sulfur for growth of an organism.

selenodont [VERT ZOO] 1. Being or pertaining to molars having crescentic ridges on the crown. 2. A mammal with selenodont dentition.

Selenomonas [MICROBIO] A genus of gram-negative, strictly anaerobic bacteria of uncertain affiliation; short, crescent-shaped, motile cells with a tuft of up to 16 flagella; ferment carbohydrates and some amino acids.

self-differentiation [PHYSIO] The differentiation of a tissue, even when isolated, solely as a result of intrinsic factors after determination.

self-pollination [BOT] Transfer of pollen from the anther to the stigma of the same flower or of another flower on the same plant.

Seliberia [MICROBIO] A genus of budding bacteria; spirally twisted, rod-shaped cells form rosettes; reproduce by transverse fission and by budding.

sella turcica [ANAT] A depression in the upper surface of the sphenoid bone in which the pituitary gland rests in vertebrates.

selva *See* tropical rainforest.

Semaeostomeae [INV ZOO] An order of the class Scyphozoa including most of the common medusae, characterized by a flat, domelike umbrella whose margin is divided into many lappets.

sematic *See* aposematic.

semen [PHYSIO] The fluid that carries the male germ cells.

semicircular canal [ANAT] Any of three loop-shaped tubular structures of the vertebrate labyrinth; they are arranged in three different spatial planes at right angles to each other, and function in the maintenance of body equilibrium.

semiconservative replication [MOL BIO] Replication of deoxyribonucleic acid by longitudinal separation of the two complementary strands of the molecule, each being conserved and acting as a template for synthesis of a new complementary strand.

semidesert [ECOL] An area intermediate in character and often located between a desert and a grassland or woodland.

semidormancy [BOT] Decrease in plant growth rate; may be seasonal or associated with unfavorable environmental conditions.

semidouble [BOT] Pertaining to a flower that has more than the usual number of petals or disk florets while it retains some pollen-bearing stamens or some perfect disk florets.

semilate [BOT] Pertaining to a plant whose growing season is intermediate between midseason forms and late forms.

semilethal gene [GEN] A mutant causing the death of some of the individuals of the relevant genotype, but never 100%. Also known as sublethal gene.

semilunar cartilage [ANAT] One of the two interarticular knee cartilages.

semilunar valve [ANAT] Either of two tricuspid valves in the heart, one at the orifice of the pulmonary artery and the other at the orifice of the aorta.

semimembranosus [ANAT] One of the hamstring muscles, arising from the ischial tuber, and inserted into the tibia.

seminal bursa [INV ZOO] A sac which retains sperm for a period of time in turbellarians.

seminal groove [ZOO] A passage in many animals providing a pathway for sperm.

seminal receptacle *See* spermatheca.

seminal vesicle [ANAT] A saclike, glandular diverticulum on each ductus deferens in male vertebrates; it is united with the excretory duct and serves for temporary storage of semen.

seminiferous tubule [ANAT] Any of the tubercles of the testes which produce spermatozoa.

seminivorous [ZOO] Feeding on seeds.

semiochemical [PHYSIO] Any of a class of substances produced by organisms, especially insects, that participate in regulation of their behavior in such activities as aggregation of both sexes, sexual stimulation, and trail following.

Semionotiformes [VERT ZOO] An order of actinopterygian fishes represented by the single living genus *Lepisosteus*, the gars; the body is characteristically encased in a heavy armor of interlocking ganoid scales.

semipalmate [VERT ZOO] Having a web halfway down the toes.

semiparasite *See* hemiparasite.

semispecies [SYST] 1. The species that compose a superspecies. 2. Populations that have acquired some attributes of species rank. 3. Organisms that are borderline between species and subspecies.

semispinalis [ANAT] One of the deep longitudinal muscles of the back, attached to the vertebrae.

semitendinosus [ANAT] One of the hamstring muscles, arising from the ischium and inserted into the tibia.

Semper's larva [INV ZOO] A cylindrical larva in the life history of certain zoanthid corals, characterized by a hole at each end and an annular or longitudinal band of long cilia.

senescence [BIOL] The study of the biological changes related to aging, with special emphasis on plant, animal, and clinical observations which may apply to man.

sensation [PHYSIO] The subjective experience that results from the stimulation of a sense organ.

sense organ [PHYSIO] A structure which is a receptor for external or internal stimulation.

sense strand [MOL BIO] The strand of a double-stranded deoxyribonucleic acid molecule that is complementary to the ribonucleic acid formed by transcription.

sensillum [ZOO] A simple, epithelial sense organ composed of one cell or of a few cells.

sensitivity [PHYSIO] The capacity for receiving sensory impressions from the environment.

sensorium [PHYSIO] **1.** A center, especially in the brain, for receiving and integrating sensations. **2.** The entire sensory apparatus of an individual.

sensory area [PHYSIO] Any area of the cerebral cortex associated with the perception of sensations.

sensory cell [PHYSIO] **1.** A neuron having its terminal processes connected with sensory nerve endings. **2.** A modified epithelial or connective tissue cell adapted for the reception and transmission of sensations.

sensory nerve [PHYSIO] A nerve that conducts afferent impulses from the periphery to the central nervous system.

sepal [BOT] One of the leaves composing the calyx.

separation disk [BOT] A layer of gelatinous material between two adjacent negative cells in some blue-green algae; associated with hormogonium formation.

separation layer [BOT] A structurally distinct layer of the abscission zone of a plant containing abundant starch and dense cytoplasm.

Sepioidea [INV ZOO] An order of the molluscan subclass Coleoidea having a well-developed eye, an internal shell, fins separated posteriorly, and chromatophores in the dermis.

Sepsidae [INV ZOO] The spiny-legged flies, a family of myodarian cyclorrhaphous dipteran insects in the subsection Acalypteratae; development takes place in decaying organic matter.

septal filament [INV ZOO] In anthozoans, the free edges of the septum containing gland cells and nematocysts.

septal ostium [INV ZOO] Any of the openings in septa of anthozoans.

septate [BIOL] Having a septum.

Septibranchia [INV ZOO] A small order of bivalve mollusks in which the anterior and posterior abductor muscles are about equal in size, the foot is long and slender, and the gills have been transformed into a muscular septum.

septulum [ANAT] A small septum.

septum [BIOL] A partition or dividing wall between two cavities.

septum pellucidum [ANAT] A thin translucent septum forming the internal boundary of the lateral ventricles of the brain and enclosing between its two laminas the so-called fifth ventricle.

septum primum [EMBRYO] The first incomplete interatrial septum of the embryo.

septum secundum [EMBRYO] The second incomplete interatrial septum of the embryo, containing the foramen ovale; it develops to the right of the septum primum and fuses with it to form the adult interatrial septum.

Sequoia [BOT] A genus of conifers having overlapping, scalelike evergreen leaves and vertical grooves in the trunk; the giant sequoia (*Sequoia gigantea*) is the largest and oldest of all living things.

sere [ECOL] A temporary community which occurs during a successional sequence on a given site.

Sergestidae [INV ZOO] A family of decapod crustaceans including several species of prawns.

serial homology [ZOO] The similarity between the members of a single series of structures, such as vertebrae, in an organism.

sericeous [BOT] Of, pertaining to, or consisting of silk.

serine [BIOCHEM] $C_3H_7O_3N$ An amino acid obtained by hydrolysis of many proteins; a biosynthetic precursor of several metabolites, including cysteine, glycine, and choline.

seritinous [ECOL] Of, pertaining to, or occurring during the latter, drier half of the summer.

serofibrinous [PHYSIO] Composed of serum and fibrin.

Serolidae [INV ZOO] A family of isopod crustaceans which contains greatly flattened forms that live partially buried on sandy bottoms.

serology [BIOL] The branch of science dealing with the properties and reactions of blood sera.

Seromycin [MICROBIO] A trade name for cycloserine.

serosa [ANAT] The serous membrane lining the pleural, peritoneal, and pericardial cavities. [EMBRYO] The chorion of reptile and bird embryos.

serotinous [BOT] Plants which flower or develop late in a season.

serotonin [BIOCHEM] $C_{10}H_{12}ON_2$ A compound derived from tryptophan which functions as a local vasoconstrictor, plays a role in neurotransmission, and has pharmacologic properties. Also known as 5-hydroxytryptamine.

serotype [MICROBIO] A serological type of intimately related microorganisms, distinguished on the basis of antigenic composition.

serous gland [PHYSIO] A structure that secretes a watery, albuminous fluid.

serous membrane [HISTOL] A delicate membrane covered with flat, mesothelial cells lining closed cavities of the body.

Serpentes [VERT ZOO] The snakes, a suborder of the Squamata characterized by the lack of limbs and pectoral girdle and external ear openings, immovable eyelids, and a braincase that is completely bony anteriorly.

serpentine locomotion [VERT ZOO] The wavelike or undulating movements characteristic of snakes.

Serpulidae [INV ZOO] A family of polychaete annelids belonging to the Sedentaria including many of the feather-duster worms which construct calcareous tubes in the earth, sometimes in such abundance as to clog drains and waterways.

Serranidae [VERT ZOO] A family of perciform fishes in the suborder Percoidei including the sea basses and groupers.

serrate [BIOL] Possessing a notched or toothed edge.

Serratia [MICROBIO] A genus of bacteria in the family Enterobacteriaceae; motile rods; many strains produce prodigiosin, a bright orange to deep red pigment.

Serratieae [MICROBIO] Formerly a tribe of the Enterobacteriaceae containing the genus *Serratia*, with soil and water forms characterized by the production of a bright-orange to deep-red pigment, prodigiosin.

Serridentinae [PALEON] An extinct subfamily of elephantoids in the family Gomphotheriidae.

Serritermitidae [INV ZOO] A family of the Isoptera which contains the single monotypic genus *Serritermes*.

Serropalpidae [INV ZOO] An equivalent name for Melandryidae.

serrulate [BIOL] Finely serrate.

Sertoli cell [HISTOL] One of the sustentacular cells of the seminiferous tubules.

serum [PHYSIO] The liquid portion that remains when blood clots spontaneously and the formed and clotting elements are removed by centrifugation; it differs from plasma by the absence of fibrinogen.

serum albumin [BIOCHEM] The principal protein fraction of blood serum and serous fluids.

serum globulin [BIOCHEM] The globulin fraction of blood serum.

sessile [BOT] Attached directly to a branch or stem without an intervening stalk. [ZOO] Permanently attached to the substrate.

Sessilina [INV ZOO] A suborder of ciliates in the order Peritrichida.

sessoblast [INV ZOO] A statoblast that attaches to zooecial tubes or to the substratum.

seta [BIOL] A slender, usually rigid bristle or hair. Also known as chaeta.

sex [BIOL] The state of condition of an organism which comes to expression in the production of germ cells.

sex chromosome [GEN] Either member of a pair of chromosomes responsible for sex determination of an organism.

sex cords [EMBRYO] Cordlike masses of epithelial tissue that invaginate from germinal epithelium of the gonad and give rise to seminiferous tubules and rete testes in the male, and primary ovarian follicles and rete ovarii in the female.

sex determination [GEN] The mechanisms by which sex is determined in a species.

sex factor *See* fertility factor.

sex hormone [BIOCHEM] Any hormone secreted by a gonad, but also found in other tissues.

sex-influenced inheritance [GEN] That part of the inheritance pattern on which sex differences operate to promote character differences.

sex-limited inheritance [GEN] Expression of a phenotype in only one sex; may be due to either a sex-linked or autosomal gene.

sex-linked inheritance [GEN] The transmission to successive generations of differences that are due to genes located in the sex chromosomes.

sex organs [ANAT] The organs pertaining entirely to the sex of an individual, both physiologically and anatomically.

sex ratio [BIOL] The relative proportion of males and females in a population.

sexual cycle [PHYSIO] A cycle of physiological and structural changes associated with sex; examples are the estrous cycle and the menstrual cycle.

sexual dimorphism [BIOL] Diagnostic morphological differences between the sexes.

sexuality [BIOL] 1. The sum of a person's sexual attributes, behavior, and tendencies. 2. The psychological and physiological sexual impulses whose satisfaction affords pleasure.

sexual reproduction [BIOL] Reproduction involving the paired union of special cells (gametes) from two individuals.

sexual spore [BIOL] A spore resulting from conjugation of gametes or nuclei of opposite sex.

Seymouriamorpha [PALEON] An extinct group of labyrinthodont Amphibia of the Upper Carboniferous and Permian in which the intercentra were reduced.

shadscale [BOT] *Atriplex confertifolia*. A small shiny shrub found in the Great Basin Desert.

shake culture [MICROBIO] 1. A method for isolating anaerobic bacteria by shaking a deep liquid culture of an agar or gelatin to distribute the inoculum before solidification of the medium. 2. A liquid medium in a flask that has been inoculated with an aerobic microorganism and placed on a shaking machine; action of the machine continually aerates the culture.

shallot [BOT] *Allium ascalonicum*. A bulbous onionlike herb. Also known as scallion.

shark [VERT ZOO] Any of about 225 species of carnivorous elasmobranchs which occur principally in tropical and subtropical oceans; the body is fusiform with a heterocercal tail and a tough, usually gray, skin roughened by tubercles, and the snout extends beyond the mouth.

shearwater [VERT ZOO] Any of various species of oceanic birds of the genus *Puffinus* having tubular nostrils and long wings.

sheathed bacteria [MICROBIO] Chains of bacterial cells, usually rod-shaped, enclosed in a hyaline envelope or sheath.

sheep [VERT ZOO] Any of various mammals of the genus *Ovis* in the family Bovidae characterized by a stocky build and horns, when present, which tend to curl in a spiral.

shell [ZOO] 1. A hard, usually calcareous, outer covering on an animal body, as of bivalves and turtles. 2. The hard covering of an egg. 3. Chitinous exoskeleton of certain arthropods.

shellfish [INV ZOO] An aquatic invertebrate, such as a mollusk or crustacean, that has a shell or exoskeleton.

shell gland [INV ZOO] An organ that secretes the embryonic shell in many mollusks. [VERT ZOO] A specialized structure attached to the oviduct in certain animals that secretes the eggshell material.

shell membrane [CELL BIO] Either of a pair of membranes lining the inner surface of an egg shell; they allow free entry of oxygen but prevent rapid evaporation of moisture.

shelterbelt [ECOL] A natural or planned barrier of trees or shrubs to reduce erosion and provide shelter from wind and storm activity.

Shetland sheep [VERT ZOO] A breed of sheep raised in the Shetland Isles of Scotland.

Shiga's bacillus [MICROBIO] Type A1 of *Shigella dysenteriae*.

Shigella [MICROBIO] The dysentery bacilli, a genus of the family Enterobacteriaceae; nonmotile rods that ferment glucose and other carbohydrates, with acid production.

Shigella dysenteriae [MICROBIO] The organism that causes dysentery in humans and monkeys; found only in the feces of the sick.

shikimic acid [BIOCHEM] $C_7H_{10}O_5$ A crystalline acid that is a plant constituent, and an intermediate in the biochemical pathway from phosphoenolpyruvic acid to tyrosine.

shipworm [INV ZOO] Any of several bivalve mollusk species belonging to the family Teredinidae and which superficially resemble earthworms because the two valves are reduced to a pair of plates at the anterior of the animal or are used for boring into wood.

shoot [BOT] 1. The aerial portion of a plant, including stem, branches, and leaves. 2. A new, immature growth on a plant.

shore bird [VERT ZOO] A general term applied to a large number of birds in 12 families of the suborder Charadrii which are always found near water, although the habitat and morphology is varied. Also known as wader.

shoulder [ANAT] 1. The area of union between the upper limb and the trunk in humans. 2. The corresponding region in other vertebrates.

shoulder blade See scapula.

shoulder girdle See pectoral girdle.

shrew [VERT ZOO] Any of more than 250 species of insectivorous mammals of the family Soricidae; individuals are small with a moderately long tail, minute eyes, a sharp-pointed snout, and small ears.

shrimp [INV ZOO] The common name for a number of crustaceans, principally in the decapod suborder Natantia, characterized by having well-developed pleopods and by having the abdomen

sharply bent in most species, producing a humped appearance.

shrub [BOT] A low woody plant with several stems.

sialic acid [BIOCHEM] Any of a family of amino sugars, containing nine or more carbon atoms, that are nitrogen- and oxygen-substituted acyl derivatives of neuraminic acid; as components of lipids, polysaccharides, and mucoproteins, they are widely distributed in bacteria and in animal tissues.

sialomucin [BIOCHEM] An acid mucopolysaccharide containing sialic acid as the acid component.

Siboglinidae [INV ZOO] A family of pogonophores in the order Athecanephria.

sicula [INV ZOO] The cone-shaped chitinous skeleton of the first zooid of a graptolite colony.

Siderocapsa [MICROBIO] A genus of bacteria in the family Siderocapsaceae; cells are spherical to ovoid, and one to many are embedded in a common capsule; deposit oxides of iron or magnesium on or in the capsule.

Siderocapsaceae [MICROBIO] A family of gram-negative, chemolithotrophic bacteria; characterized by the ability to deposit iron or manganese compounds on or around the cells.

Siderococcus [MICROBIO] A genus of bacteria in the family Siderocapsaceae; coccoid cells deposit iron but not manganese oxides.

siderocyte [CELL BIO] An erythrocyte which contains granules staining blue with the Prussian blue reaction.

Sierolomorphidae [INV ZOO] A small family of hymenopteran insects in the superfamily Scolioidea.

sieve area [BOT] An area in the wall of a sieve-tube element, sieve cell, or parenchyma cell characterized by clusters of pores through which strands of cytoplasm pass to adjoining cells.

sieve cell [BOT] A long, tapering cell that is characteristic of phloem in gymnosperms and lower vascular plants, in which all the sieve areas are of equal specialization.

sieve tissue See phloem.

sieve tube [BOT] A phloem element consisting of a series of thin-walled cells arranged end to end, in which some sieve areas are more specialized than others.

Sigalionidae [INV ZOO] A family of scale-bearing polychaete annelids belonging to the Errantia.

Siganidae [VERT ZOO] A small family of herbivorous perciform fishes in the suborder Acanthuroidei having minute concealed scales embedded in the skin and strong, sharp fin spines.

Sigatoka [PL PATH] Leaf-spot disease of banana caused by the fungus *Mycosphaerella musicola*.

sight [PHYSIO] See vision.

sigma [INV ZOO] A C-shaped spicule.

sigmaspire [INV ZOO] An S-shaped sponge spicule.

sigmoid [BIOL] S-shaped.

sigmoid colon [ANAT] The S-shaped portion of the colon between the descending colon and the rectum.

signet-ring cell [HISTOL] A cell with a large fat- or carbohydrate-filled vacuole that pushes the nucleus against the cell membrane.

silent mutation [GEN] A mutation that does not result in amino acid sequence change.

silicle [BOT] A many-seeded capsule formed from two united carpels, usually of equal length and width, and divided on the inside by a replum.

silicoblast [INV ZOO] Poriferan amebocytes involved in formation of siliceous spicules.

Silicoflagellata [BOT] A class of unicellular flagellates of the plant division Chrysophyta represented by a single living genus, *Dictyocha*.

Silicoflagellida [INV ZOO] An order of marine flagellates in the class Phytamastigophorea which have an internal, siliceous, tubular skeleton, numerous yellow chromatophores, and a single flagellum.

silique [BOT] A silicle-like capsule, but usually at least four times as long as it is wide, which opens by sutures at either margin and has parietal placentation.

silk [INV ZOO] A continuous protein fiber consisting principally of fibroin and secreted by various insects and arachnids, especially the silkworm, for use in spinning cocoons, webs, egg cases, and other structures.

silk cotton *See* kapok.

silk cotton tree *See* kapok tree.

silk gland [INV ZOO] A gland in certain insects which secretes a viscous fluid in the form of filaments known as silk; it is a salivary gland in insects and an abdominal gland in spiders.

silkworm [INV ZOO] The larva of various moths, especially *Bombyx mori*, that produces a large amount of silk for building its cocoon.

Silphidae [INV ZOO] The carrion beetles, a family of coleopteran insects in the superfamily Staphylinoidea.

Siluridae [VERT ZOO] A family of European catfish in the suborder Siluroidei in which the adipose dorsal fin is rudimentary or lacking.

Siluriformes [VERT ZOO] The catfishes, a distinctive order of actinopterygian fishes in the superorder Ostariophysi, distinguished by a complex Weberian apparatus that involves the fifth vertebrae and one to four pair of barbels.

Siluroidei [VERT ZOO] A suborder of the Siluriformes.

Silvanidae [INV ZOO] An equivalent name for Cucujidae.

silverfish [INV ZOO] Any of over 350 species of insects of the order Thysanura; they are small, wingless forms with biting mouthparts.

silverline system [INV ZOO] A series of superficial argentophilic lines in many protozoans, especially ciliates.

similarity coefficient [SYST] In numerical taxonomy, a factor S used to calculate the similarity between organisms, according to the formula $S = n_s/(n_s + n_d)$, where n_s represents the number of positive features shared by two strains, and n_d represents the number of features positive for one strain and negative for the other.

Simonsiella [MICROBIO] A genus of bacteria in the family Simonsiellaceae; cells are closely apposed, with free faces of terminal cells rounded.

Simonsiellaceae [MICROBIO] A family of bacteria in the order Cytophagales; cells are arranged to form flat filaments capable of gliding motility when the flat surface is in contact with the substrate.

simple [BIOL] 1. Made up of one piece. 2. Unbranched. 3. Consisting of identical units, as a simple tissue.

simple branched tubular gland [ANAT] A structure consisting of two or more unbranched, tubular secreting units joining a common outlet duct.

simple gland [ANAT] A gland having a single duct.

simple leaf [BOT] A leaf having one blade, or a lobed leaf in which the separate parts do not reach down to the midrib.

simple protein [BIOCHEM] One of a group of proteins which, upon hydrolysis, yield exclusively amino acids; included are globulins, glutelins, histones, prolamines, and protamines.

simple stomach [ANAT] A stomach consisting of a single dilation of the alimentary canal, as found in man, the dog, and many higher and lower vertebrates.

simple tubular gland [ANAT] A gland consisting of a single, tubular secreting unit.

simplex uterus [ANAT] A uterus consisting of a single cavity, representing the greatest degree of fusion of the Müllerian ducts; found in man and apes.

Simuliidae [INV ZOO] The black flies, a family of orthorrhaphous dipteran insects in the series Nematocera.

single-blind technique [BIOL] A method in which the subjects of a drug experiment do not know whether or not they have received the drug.

sinistrorse [BIOL] Twisting or coiling counterclockwise.

sinoatrial node [ANAT] A bundle of Purkinje fibers located near the junction of the superior vena cava with the right atrium which acts as a pacemaker for cardiac excitation. Abbreviated SA node. Also known as sinoauricular node.

sinoauricular node *See* sinoatrial node.

sinuate [BOT] Having a wavy margin with strong indentations.

sinus [BIOL] A cavity, recess, or depression in an organ, tissue, or other part of an animal body.

sinus gland [INV ZOO] An endocrine gland in higher crustaceans, lying in the eyestalk in most stalk-eyed species, which is the site of storage and release of a molt-inhibiting hormone.

sinus hairs *See* vibrissae.

sinus of Morgagni [ANAT] The space between the upper border of the levator veli palatini muscle and the base of the skull.

sinusoid [ANAT] Any of the relatively large spaces comprising part of the venous circulation in certain organs, such as the liver.

sinus venosus [EMBRYO] The vessel in the transverse septum of the embryonic mammalian heart into which open the vitelline, allantoic, and common cardinal veins. [VERT ZOO] The chamber of the lower vertebrate heart to which the veins return blood from the body.

Siphinodentallidae [INV ZOO] A family of mollusks in the class Scaphopoda characterized by a subterminal epipodial ridge which is not slit dorsally and which terminates with a crenulated disk.

siphon [BOT] A tubular element in various algae. [INV ZOO] 1. A tubular structure for intake or output of water in bivalves and other mollusks. 2. The sucking-type of proboscis in many arthropods.

Siphonales [BOT] A large order of green algae (Chlorophyta) which are coenocytic, nonseptate, and mostly marine.

Siphonaptera [INV ZOO] The fleas, an order of insects characterized by a small, laterally compressed, oval body armed with spines and setae, three pairs of legs modified for jumping, and sucking mouthparts.

Siphonocladaceae [BOT] A family of green algae in the order Siphonocladales.

Siphonocladales [BOT] An order of green algae in the division Chlorophyta including marine, mostly tropical forms.

siphonogamous [BOT] In plants, especially seed plants, the accomplishment of fertilization by means of a pollen tube.

siphonoglyph [INV ZOO] A ciliated groove leading from the mouth to the gullet in certain anthozoans.

Siphonolaimidae [INV ZOO] A family of nematodes in the superfamily Monhysteroidea in which the stoma is modified into a narrow, elongate, hollow, spearlike apparatus.

Siphonophora [INV ZOO] An order of the coelenterate class Hydrozoa characterized by the complex organization of components which may be connected by a stemlike region or may be more closely united into a compact organism.

siphonosome [INV ZOO] The lower part of a siphonophore colony, bearing the nutritive and reproductive zooids.

siphonostele [BOT] A type of stele consisting of pith surrounded by xylem and phloem.

Siphonotretacea [PALEON] A superfamily of extinct, inarticulate brachiopods in the suborder Acrotretidina of the order Acrotretida having an enlarged, tear-shaped, apical pedicle valve.

siphonozooid [INV ZOO] A zooid of certain alcyonarians that lacks tentacles and gonads.

siphuncle [INV ZOO] 1. A honeydew-secreting tube (cornicle) in aphids. 2. A tubular extension of the mantle extending through all the chambers to the apex of a shelled cephalopod.

Siphunculata [INV ZOO] The equivalent name for Anoplura.

Sipunculida [INV ZOO] A phylum of marine worms which dwell in burrows, secreted tubes, or adopted shells; the mouth and anus occur close together at one end of the elongated body, and the jawless mouth, surrounded by tentacles, is situated in an eversible proboscis.

Sipunculoidea [INV ZOO] An equivalent name for Sipunculida.

Sirenia [VERT ZOO] An order of aquatic placental mammals which include the living manatees and dugongs; these are nearly hairless, thick-skinned mammals without hindlimbs and with paddlelike forelimbs.

Siricidae [INV ZOO] The horntails, a family of the Hymenoptera in the superfamily Siricoidea; females use a stout, hornlike ovipositor to deposit eggs in wood.

Siricoidea [INV ZOO] A superfamily of wasps of the suborder Symphala in the order Hymenoptera.

sisal [BOT] *Agave sisalina*. An agave of the family Amaryllidaceae indigenous to Mexico and Central America; a coarse, stiff yellow fiber produced from the leaves is used for making twine and brush bristles.

sister chromatids [CELL BIO] The two daughter strands of a chromosome after it has duplicated.

skate [VERT ZOO] Any of various batoid elasmobranchs in the family Rajidae which have flat bodies with winglike pectoral fins and a slender tail with two small dorsal fins.

skeletal muscle [ANAT] A striated, voluntary muscle attached to a bone and concerned with body movements.

skeletal system [ANAT] Structures composed of bone or cartilage or a combination of both which provide a framework for the vertebrate body and serve as attachment for muscles.

skimmer [VERT ZOO] Any of various ternlike birds, members of the Rhynchopidae, that inhabit tropical waters around the world and are unique in having the knifelike lower mandible substantially longer than the wider upper mandible.

skin [ANAT] The external covering of the vertebrate body, consisting of two layers, the outer epidermis and the inner dermis.

skink [VERT ZOO] Any of numerous small- to medium-sized lizards comprising the family Scincidae with a cylindrical body; short, sometimes vestigial, legs; cores of bone in the body scales; and pleurodont dentition.

skipjack *See* bluefish.

skull [ANAT] The bones and cartilages of the vertebrate head which form the cranium and the face.

skunk [VERT ZOO] Any one of a group of carnivores in the family Mustelidae characterized by a glossy black and white coat and two musk glands at the base of the tail.

slant culture [MICROBIO] A method for maintaining bacteria in which the inoculum is streaked on the surface of agar that has solidified in inclined glass tubes.

slavery [INV ZOO] An interspecific association among ants in which members of one species bring pupae of another species to their nest, which, when adult, become slave workers in the colony.

sleep [PHYSIO] A state of rest in which consciousness and activity are diminished.

slime bacteria [MICROBIO] The common name for bacteria in the order Myxobacterales, so named for the layer of slime deposited behind cells as they glide on a surface.

slime disease [PL PATH] Any of several diseases of plants characterized by slimy rot of the parts.

slime flux [PL PATH] The fluid or viscous outflow from the bark or wood of a deciduous tree that is indicative of injury or disease.

slime fungus See slime mold.

slime gland [ZOO] A glandular structure in many animals producing a mucous material.

slime mold [MYCOL] The common name for members of the Myxomycetes. Also known as slime fungus.

slop culture [BOT] A method of growing plants in which surplus nutrient fluid is allowed to run through the sand or other medium in which the plants are growing.

sloth [VERT ZOO] Any of several edentate mammals in the family Bradypodidae found exclusively in Central and South America; all are slow-moving, arboreal species that cling to branches upside down by means of long, curved claws.

slow virus [VIROL] Any member of a group of animal viruses characterized by prolonged periods of incubation and an extended clinical course lasting months or years.

slug [INV ZOO] Any of a number of pulmonate gastropods which have a rudimentary shell and the body elevated toward the middle and front end where the mantle covers the lung region.

small intestine [ANAT] The anterior portion of the intestine in man and other mammals; it is divided into three parts, the duodenum, the jejunum, and the ileum.

smear [BIOL] A preparation for microscopic examination made by spreading a drop of fluid, such as blood, across a slide and using the edge of another slide to leave a uniform film.

smegma [PHYSIO] The sebaceous secretion that accumulates around the glans penis and the clitoris.

smell [PHYSIO] To perceive by olfaction.

Smilacaceae [BOT] A family of monocotyledonous plants in the order Liliales; members are usually climbing, leafy-stemmed plants with tendrils, trimerous flowers, and a superior ovary.

Sminthuridae [INV ZOO] A family of insects in the order Collembola which have simple tracheal systems.

smooth muscle [ANAT] The involuntary muscle tissue found in the walls of viscera and blood vessels, consisting of smooth muscle fibers.

smooth muscle fiber [HISTOL] Any of the elongated, nucleated, spindle-shaped cells comprising smooth muscles. Also known as involuntary fiber; nonstriated fiber; unstriated fiber.

smudge [PL PATH] Any of several fungus diseases of cereals and other plants characterized by dark, sooty discolorations.

smut [PL PATH] Any of various destructive fungus diseases of cereals and other plants characterized by large dusty masses of dark spores on the plant organs.

smut fungus [MYCOL] The common name for members of the Ustilaginales.

snail [INV ZOO] Any of a large number of gastropod mollusks distinguished by a spiral shell that encloses the body, a head, a foot, and a mantle.

snake [VERT ZOO] Any of about 3000 species of reptiles which belong to the 13 living families composing the suborder Serpentes in the order Squamata.

sneeze [PHYSIO] A sudden, noisy, spasmodic expiration through the mouth and nose.

snout [VERT ZOO] The elongated nose of various mammals.

sobole [BOT] An underground creeping stem.

social animal [ZOO] An animal that exhibits social behavior.

social behavior [ZOO] Any behavior on the part of an organism stimulated by, or acting upon, another member of the same species.

social hierarchy [VERT ZOO] The establishment of a dominance-subordination relationship among higher animal societies.

social parasitism [VERT ZOO] An aberrant type of parasitism occurring in some birds, in which the female of one species lays her eggs in the nests of other species and permits the foster parents to raise the young.

social releaser [ZOO] A releaser stimulus which an animal receives from a member of its species.

society [ECOL] A secondary or minor plant community forming part of a community.

sodium chloride solution See normal saline.

sodium penicillin G₁ See benzyl penicillin sodium.

soft coral [INV ZOO] The common name for coelenterates composing the order Alcyonacea; the colony is supple and leathery.

soft palate [ANAT] The posterior part of the palate which consists of an aggregation of muscles, the tensor veli palatini, levator veli palatini, azygos uvulae, palatoglossus, and palatopharyngeus, and their covering mucous membrane.

soft rot [PL PATH] A mushy, watery, or slimy disintegration of plant parts caused by either fungi or bacteria.

soft-shell disease [INV ZOO] A disease of lobsters caused by a chitinous bacterium which extracts chitin from the exoskeleton.

soil conservation [ECOL] Management of soil to prevent or reduce soil erosion and depletion by wind and water.

soil microbiology [MICROBIO] A study of the microorganisms in soil, their functions, and the effect of their activities on the character of the soil and the growth and health of plant life.

soil rot [PL PATH] Plant rot caused by soil microorganisms.

Solanaceae [BOT] A family of dicotyledonous plants in the order Polemoniales having internal phloem, mostly numerous ovules and seeds on axile placentae, and mostly cellular endosperm.

solar propagation [BOT] A method of rooting plant cuttings involving the use of a modified hotbed; bottom heat is provided by radiation of stored solar heat from bricks or stones in the bottom of the hotbed frame.

Solasteridae [INV ZOO] The sun stars, a family of asteroid echinoderms in the order Spinulosida.

Solemyidae [INV ZOO] A family of bivalve mollusks in the order Protobranchia.

Solenichthyes [VERT ZOO] An equivalent name for Gasterosteiformes.

solenium [INV ZOO] A diverticulum of the enteron in certain hydroids.

solenocyte [INV ZOO] Any of various hollow, flagellated cells in the nephridia of the larvae of certain annelids, mollusks, rotifers, and lancelets.

solenodon [VERT ZOO] Either of two species of insectivorous mammals comprising the family Solenodontidae; the almique (*Atopogale cubana*) is found only in Cuba, while the white agouta (*Solenodon paradoxus*) is confined to Haiti.

Solenodontidae [VERT ZOO] The solenodons, a family of insectivores belonging to the group Lipotyphla.

Solenogastres [INV ZOO] The equivalent name for Aplacophora.

Solenopora [PALEOBOT] A genus of extinct calcareous red algae in the family Solenoporaceae that appeared in the Late Cambrian and lasted until the Early Tertiary.

Solenoporaceae [PALEOBOT] A family of extinct red algae having compact tissue and the ability to deposit calcium carbonate within and between the cell walls.

soleus [ANAT] A flat muscle of the calf; origin is the fibula, popliteal fascia, and tibia, and insertion is the calcaneus; plantar-flexes the foot.

Solo man [PALEON] A relative but primitive form of fossil man from Java; this form had a small brain, heavy horizontal browridges, and a massive cranial base.

Solpugida [INV ZOO] The sun spiders, an order of nonvenomous, spiderlike, predatory arachnids having large chelicerae for holding and crushing prey.

soma [BIOL] The whole of the body of an individual, excluding the germ tract.

Somasteroidea [INV ZOO] A subclass of Asterozoa comprising sea stars of generalized structure, the jaws often only partly developed, and the skeletal elements of the arm arranged in a double series of transverse rows termed metapinnules.

somatic aneuploidy [CELL BIO] An irregular variation in number of one or more individual chromosomes in the cells of a tissue.

somatic cell [BIOL] Any cell of the body of an organism except the germ cells.

somatic copulation [MYCOL] A form of reproduction in ascomycetes and basidiomycetes involving sexual fusion of undifferentiated vegetative cells.

somatic crossing-over [CELL BIO] Crossing-over during mitosis in somatic or vegetative cells.

somatic death [BIOL] The cessation of characteristic life functions.

somatic mesoderm [EMBRYO] The external layer of the lateral mesoderm associated with the ectoderm after formation of the coelom.

somatic nervous system [PHYSIO] The portion of the nervous system concerned with the control of voluntary muscle and relating the organism with its environment.

somatic pairing [CELL BIO] The pairing of homologous chromosomes at mitosis in somatic cells; occurs in Diptera.

somatic reflex system [PHYSIO] An involuntary control system characterized by a control loop which includes skeletal muscles.

somatoblast [INV ZOO] 1. An undifferentiated cleavage cell that gives rise to somatic cells in annelids. 2. The outer cell layer of the nematogen in Dicyemida.

somatochrome [CELL BIO] A nerve cell possessing a well-defined body completely surrounding the nucleus on all sides, the cytoplasm having a distinct contour, and readily taking a stain.

somatocyst [INV ZOO] A cavity filled with air in the float of certain Siphonophora.

somatometry [ANAT] Measurement of the human body with the soft parts intact.

somatophyte [BOT] A plant composed of distinct somatic cells that develop especially into mature or adult tissue.

somatopleure [EMBRYO] A complex layer of tissue consisting of the somatic layer of the mesoblast together with the epiblast, forming the body wall in craniate vertebrates and the amnion and chorion in amniotes.

somatotropin [BIOCHEM] The growth hormone of the pituitary gland.

somesthesis [PHYSIO] The general name for all systems of sensitivity present in the skin, muscles and their attachments, visceral organs, and nonauditory labyrinth of the ear.

somnambulism [PHYSIO] 1. Sleepwalking. 2. The performance of any fairly complex act while in a sleeplike state or trance.

Sonne's bacillus [MICROBIO] The bacterium *Shigella sonnei*.

sooty mold [MYCOL] Ascomycetous fungi of the family Capnodiaceae, with dark mycelium and conidia.

sooty mold [PL PATH] A plant disease, common on *Citrus* species, characterized by a dense velvety layer of a sooty mold on exposed parts of the plant.

sorbin *See* sorbose.

sorbose [BIOCHEM] $C_6H_{12}O_6$ A carbohydrate prepared by fermentation; produced as water-soluble crystals that melt at 165°C; used in the production of vitamin C. Also known as sorbin; L-sorbose.

soredium [BOT] A structure comprising algal cells wrapped in the hyphal tissue of lichens, as in certain Lecanorales; when separated from the thallus, it grows into a new thallus.

sore shin [PL PATH] A fungus disease of cowpea, cotton, tobacco, and other plants, beyond the seedling stage, marked by annular growth of the pathogen on the stem at the groundline.

sorghum [BOT] Any of a variety of widely cultivated grasses, especially *Sorghum bicolor* in the United States, grown for grain and herbage; growth habit and stem form are similar to Indian corn, but leaf margins are serrate and spikelets occur in pairs on a hairy rachis.

Soricidae [VERT ZOO] The shrews, a family of insectivorous mammals belonging to the Lipotyphla.

sorrel tree *See* sourwood.

sorus [BOT] 1. A cluster of sporangia on the lower surface of a fertile fern leaf. 2. A clump of reproductive bodies or spores in lower plants.

sourwood [BOT] *Oxydendrum arboreum.* A deciduous tree of the heath family (Ericaceae) indigenous along the Alleghenies and having long, simple, finely toothed, long-pointed leaves that have an acid taste, and white, urn-shaped flowers. Also known as sorrel tree.

South Australian faunal region [ECOL] A marine littoral region along the southwestern coast of Australia.

sow [VERT ZOO] An adult female swine.

soybean [BOT] *Glycine max.* An erect annual legume native to China and Manchuria and widely cultivated for forage and for its seed.

space biology [BIOL] A term for the various biological sciences and disciplines that are concerned with the study of living things in the space environment.

space perception [PHYSIO] The awareness of the spatial properties and relations of an object, or of one's own body, in space; especially, the sensory appreciation of position, size, form, distance, and direction of an object, or of the observer himself, in space.

spadix [BOT] A fleshy spike that is enclosed in a leaflike spathe and is the characteristic inflorescence of palms and arums.

spadix [INV ZOO] A cone-shaped structure in male Nautiloidea formed of four modified tentacles, and believed to be homologous with the hectocotylus in male squids.

Sparganiaceae [BOT] A family of monocotyledonous plants in the order Typhales distinguished by the inflorescence of globose heads, a vestigial perianth, and achenes that are sessile or nearly sessile.

sparganum [INV ZOO] The plerocercoid larva of a tapeworm.

Sparidae [VERT ZOO] A family of perciform fishes in the suborder Percoidei, including the porgies.

Spatangoida [INV ZOO] An order of exocyclic Euechinoidea in which the posterior ambulacral plates form a shield-shaped area behind the mouth.

spathe [BOT] A large, usually colored bract or pair of bracts enclosing an inflorescence, especially a spadix, on the same axis.

spatulate [BIOL] Shaped like a spoon.

spawn [ZOO] 1. The collection of eggs deposited by aquatic animals, such as fish. 2. To produce or deposit eggs or discharge sperm; applied to aquatic animals.

spearmint [BOT] *Mentha spicata.* An aromatic plant of the mint family, Labiatae; the leaves are used as a flavoring in foods.

speciation [EVOL] The evolution of species.

species [SYST] A taxonomic category ranking immediately below a genus and including closely related, morphologically similar individuals which actually or potentially interbreed.

species concept [EVOL] The idea that the diversity of nature is divisible into a finite number of definable species.

species population [ECOL] A group of similar organisms residing in a defined space at a certain time.

specific locus test [GEN] A technique used to detect recessive induced mutations in diploid organisms; a strain which carries several known recessive mutants in a homozygous condition is crossed with a nonmutant strain treated to induce mutations in its germ cells; induced recessive mutations allelic with those of the test strain will be expressed in the progeny.

speck [PL PATH] A fungus or bacterial disease of rice characterized by speckled grains.

spectacle [ZOO] A colored marking in the form of rings around the eyes, as in certain birds, reptiles, and mammals (as the raccoon).

speech [PHYSIO] A set of audible sounds produced by disturbing the air through the integrated movements of certain groups of anatomical structures.

Spelaeogriphacea [INV ZOO] A peracaridan order of the Malacostraca comprised of the single species *Spelaeogriphus lepidops*, a small, blind, transparent, shrimplike crustacean with a short carapace that coalesces dorsally with the first thoracic somite.

sperm *See* spermatozoon.

spermatheca [ZOO] A sac in the female for receiving and storing sperm until fertilization; found in many invertebrates and certain vertebrates. Also known as seminal receptacle.

spermatic cord [ANAT] The cord consisting of the ductus deferens, epididymal and testicular nerves and blood vessels, and connective tissue that extends from the testis to the deep inguinal ring.

spermatid [HISTOL] A male germ cell immediately before assuming its final typical form.

spermatin [BIOCHEM] An albuminoid material occurring in semen.

spermatocyte [HISTOL] A cell of the last or next to the last generation of male germ cells which differentiates to form spermatozoa.

spermatogenesis [PHYSIO] The process by which spermatogonia undergo meiosis and transform into spermatozoa.

spermatogonium [HISTOL] A primitive male germ cell, the last generation of which gives rise to spermatocytes.

spermatophore [ZOO] A bundle or packet of sperm produced by certain animals, such as annelids, arthropods, and some vertebrates.

spermatozoon [HISTOL] A mature male germ cell. Also known as sperm.

spermidine [BIOCHEM] $H_2N(CH_2)_3NH(CH_2)_4NH_2$ The triamine found in semen and other animal tissues.

spermine [BIOCHEM] $C_{10}H_{26}N_4$ A tetramine found in semen, blood serum, and other body tissues.

spermiogenesis [CELL BIO] Nuclear and cytoplasmic transformation of spermatids into spermatozoa.

sperm nucleus [BOT] One of the two nuclei in a pollen grain that function in double fertilization in seed plants.

sperm whale [VERT ZOO] *Physeter catadon*. An aggressive toothed whale belonging to the group Odontoceti of the order Cetacea; it produces ambergris and contains a mixture of spermaceti and oil in a cavity of the nasal passage.

Sphaeractinoidea [PALEON] An extinct group of fossil marine hydrozoans distinguished in part by the relative prominence of either vertical or horizontal trabeculae and by the presence of long, tabulate tubes called autotubes.

Sphaeriales [MYCOL] An order of fungi in the subclass Euascomycetes characterized by hard, dark perithecia with definite ostioles.

Sphaeriidae [INV ZOO] The minute bog beetles, a small family of coleopteran insects in the suborder Myxophaga.

Sphaeroidaceae [MYCOL] A family of fungi of the order Sphaeropsidales in which the pycnidia are black or dark-colored and are flask-, cone-, or lens-shaped with thin walls and a round, relatively small pore.

Sphaeroceridae [INV ZOO] A family of myodarian cyclorrhaphous dipteran insects in the subsection Acalypteratae.

Sphaerodoridae [INV ZOO] A family of polychaete annelids belonging to the Errantia in which species are characterized by small bodies, and are usually papillated.

Sphaerolaimidae [INV ZOO] A family of free-living nematodes in the superfamily Monhysteroidea characterized by a spacious and deep stoma.

Sphaeromatidae [INV ZOO] A family of isopod crustaceans in the suborder Flabellifera in which the body is broad and oval and the inner branch of the uropod is immovable.

Sphaerophoraceae [BOT] A family of the Ascolichenes in the order Caliciales which are fruticose with a solid thallus.

Sphaeropleineae [BOT] A suborder of green algae in the order Ulotrichales distinguished by long, coenocytic cells, numerous bandlike chloroplasts, and heterogametes produced in undifferentiated vegetative cells.

Sphaeropsidaceae [MYCOL] An equivalent name for Sphaerioidaceae.

Sphaeropsidales [MYCOL] An order of fungi of the class Fungi Imperfecti in which asexual spores are formed in pycnidia, which may be separate or joined to vegetative hyphae, conidiophores are short or absent, and conidia are always slime spores.

Sphaerotilus [MICROBIO] A genus of sheathed bacteria; single cells are motile by means of polar or subpolar flagella, and sheaths are not encrusted with iron or manganese oxides.

Sphagnaceae [BOT] The single monogeneric family of the order Sphagnales.

Sphagnales [BOT] The single order of mosses in the subclass Sphagnobrya containing the single family Sphagnaceae.

Sphagnobrya [BOT] A subclass of the Bryopsida; plants are grayish-green with numerous, spirally arranged branches and grow in deep tufts or mats, commonly in bogs and in other wet habitats.

sphagnum bog [ECOL] A bog composed principally of mosses of the genus *Sphagnum* (Sphagnales) but also of other plants, especially acid-tolerant species, which tend to form peat.

Sphecidae [INV ZOO] A large family of hymenopteran insects in the superfamily Sphecoidea.

Sphecoidea [INV ZOO] A superfamily of wasps belonging to the suborder Apocrita.

Sphenacodontia [PALEON] A suborder of extinct reptiles in the order Pelycosauria which were advanced, active carnivores.

sphenethmoid [VERT ZOO] A bone that surrounds the anterior portion of the brain in many amphibians.

Spheniscidae [VERT ZOO] The single family of the avian order Sphenisciformes.

Sphenisciformes [VERT ZOO] The penguins, an order of aquatic birds found only in the Southern Hemisphere and characterized by paddlelike wings, erect posture, and scalelike feathers.

Sphenodontidae [VERT ZOO] A family of lepidosaurian reptiles in the order Rhynchocephalia represented by a single living species, *Sphenodon punctatus*, a lizardlike form distinguished by lack of a penis.

sphenoid bone [ANAT] The butterfly-shaped bone forming the anterior part of the base of the skull and portions of the cranial, orbital, and nasal cavities.

sphenoid sinus [ANAT] Either of a pair of paranasal sinuses located centrally between and behind the eyes, below the ethymoid sinus.

sphenopalatine [ANAT] Of or pertaining to the region of or surrounding the sphenoid and palatine bones.

sphenopalatine foramen [ANAT] The space between the sphenoid and orbital processes of the palatine bone; it opens into the nasal cavity and gives passage to branches from the pterygopalatine ganglion and the sphenopalatine branch of the maxillary artery.

Sphenopsida [BOT] A group of vascular cryptogams characterized by whorled, often very small leaves and by the absence of true leaf gaps in the stele; essentially equivalent to the division Equisetophyta.

Sphenyllopsida [PALEOBOT] An extinct class of embryophytes in the division Equisetophyta.

spheroplast [CELL BIO] A plant cell which possesses only a partial or modified cell wall. [MICROBIO] A bacterial cell that assumes a spherical shape due to partial or complete absence of the wall.

sphincter [ANAT] A muscle that surrounds and functions to close an orifice.

sphincter of Oddi [ANAT] Sphincter of the hepatopancreatic ampulla.

Sphinctozoa [PALEON] A group of fossil sponges in the class Calcarea which have a skeleton of massive calcium carbonate organized in the form of hollow chambers.

Sphindidae [INV ZOO] The dry fungus beetles, a family of coleopteran insects in the superfamily Cucujoidea.

Sphingidae [INV ZOO] The single family of the lepidopteran superfamily Sphingoidea.

Sphingoidea [INV ZOO] A superfamily of Lepidoptera in the suborder Heteroneura consisting of the sphinx, hawk, or hummingbird moths; these are heavy-bodied forms with antennae that are thickened with a pointed apex, a well-developed proboscis, and narrow wings.

sphingolipid [BIOCHEM] Any lipid, such as a sphingomyelin, that yields sphingosine or one of its derivatives as a product of hydrolysis.

sphingomyelin [BIOCHEM] A phospholipid consisting of choline, sphingosine, phosphoric acid, and a fatty acid.

sphingosine [BIOCHEM] $C_{18}H_{37}O_2N$ A moiety of sphingomyelin, cerebrosides, and certain other phosphatides.

Sphyraenidae [VERT ZOO] A family of shore fishes in the suborder Mugiloidei of the order Perciformes comprising the barracudas.

Sphyriidae [INV ZOO] A family of ectoparasitic Crustacea belonging to the group Lernaeopodoida; the parasite embeds its head and part of its thorax into the host.

spicule [BOT] An empty diatom shell. [INV ZOO] A calcareous or siliceous, usually spikelike supporting structure in many invertebrates, particularly in sponges and alcyonarians.

spiculin [BIOCHEM] An organic material making up a portion of a spicule.

spiculum [INV ZOO] A bristlelike copulatory organ in certain nematodes. Also known as copulatory spicule.

spider [INV ZOO] The common name for arachnids comprising the order Araneida.

spike [BOT] An indeterminate inflorescence with sessile flowers.

spikelet [BOT] The compound inflorescence of a grass consisting of one or several bracteate spikes.

spinacene See squalene.

spinach [BOT] Spinacia oleracea. An annual potherb of Asiatic origin belonging to the order Caryophyllales and grown for its edible foliage.

spinal column See spine.

spinal cord [ANAT] The cordlike posterior portion of the central nervous system contained within the spinal canal of the vertebral column of all vertebrates.

spinal foramen [ANAT] Central canal of the spinal cord.

spinal ganglion [ANAT] Any one of the sensory ganglions, each associated with the dorsal root of a spinal nerve.

spinal nerve [ANAT] Any of the paired nerves arising from the spinal cord.

spinal reflex [PHYSIO] A reflex mediated through the spinal cord without the participation of the more cephalad structures of the brain or spinal cord.

spindle [CELL BIO] A structure formed of fiberlike elements just before metaphase that extends between the poles of the achromatic figure and

is attached to the centromeric regions of the chromatid pairs.

spindle fiber [CELL BIO] One of the fiberlike elements of the spindle; an aggregation of microtubules resulting from the polymerization of a series of small protein fibrils by primary —S—S— linkages.

spindle tuber [PL PATH] A virus disease of the potato characterized by spindliness of the tops and tubers.

spine [ANAT] An articulated series of vertebrae forming the axial skeleton of the trunk and tail, and being a characteristic structure of vertebrates. Also known as backbone; spinal column; vertebral column. [BOT] A rigid sharp-pointed process in plants; many are modified leaves. [INV ZOO] One of the processes covering the surface of a sea urchin. [VERT ZOO] 1. One of the spiny rays supporting the fins of most fishes. 2. A sharp-pointed modified hair on certain mammals, such as the porcupine.

spinneret [INV ZOO] An organ that spins fiber from the secretion of silk glands.

spinney [ECOL] A small grove of trees or a thicket with undergrowth.

spinoblast [INV ZOO] A statoblast having a float of air cells and barbs or hooks on the surface.

spinochrome [BIOCHEM] A type of echinochrome; an organic pigment that is known only from sea urchins and certain homopteran insects.

spinous process [ANAT] Any slender, sharp-pointed projection on a bone.

Spintheridae [INV ZOO] An amphinomorphan family of small polychaete annelids included in the Errantia.

Spinulosida [INV ZOO] An order of Asteroidea in which pedicellariae rarely occur, marginal plates bounding the arms and disk are small and inconspicuous, and spines occur in groups on the upper surface.

spiny-rayed fish [VERT ZOO] The common designation for actinopterygian fishes, so named for the presence of stiff, unbranched, pointed fin rays, known as spiny rays.

Spionidae [INV ZOO] A family of spioniform annelid worms belonging to the Sedentaria.

spioniform worm [INV ZOO] A polychaete annelid characterized by the presence of a pair of short to long, grooved palpi near the mouth.

spiracle [INV ZOO] An external breathing orifice of the tracheal system in insects and certain arachnids. [VERT ZOO] 1. The external respiratory orifice in cetaceous and amphibian larvae. 2. The first visceral cleft in fishes.

spiral cleavage [EMBRYO] A cleavage pattern characterized by formation of a cell mass showing spiral symmetry; occurs in mollusks.

spiral ganglion [ANAT] The ganglion of the cochlear part of the vestibulocochlear nerve embedded in the spiral canal of the modiolus.

spiral ligament [ANAT] The reticular connective tissue connecting the basilar membrane to the outer cochlear wall in the ear of mammals.

spiral valve [VERT ZOO] A spiral fold of mucous membrane in the small intestine of elasmobranchs and some primitive fishes which increases the surface area for absorption.

spiramycin [MICROBIO] A complex of related antibiotics, which resemble erythromycin structurally and in antibacterial spectrum, produced by *Streptomyces ambofaciens*.

spiraster [INV ZOO] A spiral spicule bearing rays in Porifera.

spire [BOT] A narrow, tapering blade or stalk.

spiricle [BOT] Any of the coiled threads in certain seed coats which uncoil when moistened.

Spiriferida [PALEON] An order of fossil articulate brachiopods distinguished by the spiralium, a pair of spirally coiled ribbons of calcite supported by the crura.

Spiriferidina [PALEON] A suborder of the extinct brachiopod order Spiriferida including mainly ribbed forms having laterally or ventrally directed spires, well-developed interareas, and a straight hinge line.

Spirillaceae [MICROBIO] A family of bacteria; motile, helically curved rods that move with a characteristic corkscrewlike motion.

Spirillinacea [INV ZOO] A superfamily of foraminiferan protozoans in the suborder Rotaliina characterized by a planispiral or low conical test with a wall composed of radial calcite.

Spirillospora [MICROBIO] A genus of bacteria in the family Actinoplanaceae; sporangia are spherical to subspherical; spores are rod-shaped, curved, or spiral, and motile by means of subpolar flagella.

Spirillum [MICROBIO] A genus of bacteria in the family Spirillaceae; motile by means of a tuft of 5–20 polar flagella, usually at both poles; have polyhydroxybutyrate granules in the cytoplasm.

Spirobrachiidae [INV ZOO] A family of the Brachiata in the order Thecanephria.

Spirochaeta [MICROBIO] A genus of bacteria in the family Spirochaetaceae; helical cells have axial fibrils and are free-living in hydrogen sulfide-containing water, mud, and sewage.

Spirochaetaceae [MICROBIO] The single family of the order Spirochaetales.

Spirochaetales [MICROBIO] An order of bacteria characterized by slender, helically coiled cells sometimes occurring in chains.

spirochete [MICROBIO] The common name for any member of the order Spirochaetales.

spirocyst [INV ZOO] A thin-walled capsule that contains a long, unarmed, evertable, spirally coiled thread of uniform diameter; found in coelenterates.

spirometry [PHYSIO] The measurement, by a form of gas meter (spirometer), of volumes of air that can be moved in or out of the lungs.

Spiroplasma [MICROBIO] A genus of the class Mollicutes; pleomorphic cells varying from spherical to helical with branched nonhelical filaments.

Spirotrichia [INV ZOO] A subclass of the protozoan class Ciliatea which contains those ciliates characterized by conspicuous, compound ciliary structures, known as cirri, and buccal organelles.

Spirulidae [INV ZOO] A family of cephalopod mollusks containing several species of squids.

Spiruria [INV ZOO] A subclass of nematodes in the class Secernentea.

Spirurida [INV ZOO] An order of phasmid nematodes in the subclass Spiruria.

Spiruroidea [INV ZOO] A superfamily of spirurid nematodes which are parasitic in the respiratory and digestive systems of vertebrates.

splanchnic mesoderm [EMBRYO] The internal layer of the lateral mesoderm that is associated with the entoderm after the formation of the coelom.

splanchnic nerve [ANAT] A nerve carrying nerve fibers from the lower thoracic paravertebral ganglions to the collateral ganglions.

splanchnocranium [ANAT] Portions of the skull derived from the primitive skeleton of the gill apparatus.

splanchnopleure [EMBRYO] The inner layer of the mesoblast from which part of the wall of the alimentary canal and portions of the visceral organs are derived in coelomates.

spleen [ANAT] A blood-forming lymphoid organ of the circulatory system, present in most vertebrates.

splenic flexure [ANAT] An abrupt turn of the colon beneath the lower end of the spleen, connecting the descending with the transverse colon.

splenium [ANAT] The rounded posterior extremity of the corpus callosum.

split gene [GEN] A gene that is not continuous. Also known as interrupted gene.

splitter [SYST] A taxonomist who divides taxa very finely.

sponge [INV ZOO] The common name for members of the phylum Porifera.

Spongiidae [INV ZOO] A family of sponges of the order Dictyoceratida; members are encrusting, massive, or branching in form and have small spherical flagellated chambers which characteristically join the exhalant canals by way of narrow channels.

Spongillidae [INV ZOO] A family of fresh- and brackish water sponges in the order Haplosclerida which are chiefly gray, brown, or white in color, and encrusting, massive, or branching in form.

spongin [BIOCHEM] A scleroprotein, occurring as the principal component of skeletal fibers in many sponges.

spongioblast [EMBRYO] A primordial cell arising from the ectoderm of the embryonic neural tube which differentiates to form the neuroglia, the ependymal cells, the neurolemma sheath cells, the satellite cells of ganglions, and Müller's fibers of the retina.

spongiocyte [HISTOL] 1. A neuroglia cell. 2. A cell of the adrenal cortex which has a spongy appearance due to the solution of lipids during tissue preparation for microscopical examination.

Spongiomorphida [PALEON] A small, extinct Mesozoic order of fossil colonial Hydrozoa in which the skeleton is a reticulum composed of perforate lamellae parallel to the upper surface and of regularly spaced vertical elements in the form of pillars.

Spongiomorphidae [PALEON] The single family of extinct hydrozoans comprising the order Spongiomorphida.

spongocoel [INV ZOO] The branching, internal cavity of a sponge, connected to the outside by way of the osculum.

spongy mesophyll [BOT] A system of loosely and irregularly arranged parenchymal cells with numerous intercellular spaces found near the lower surface in well-differentiated broad leaves. Also known as spongy parenchyma.

spongy parenchyma See spongy mesophyll.

spontaneous mutation [GEN] A mutation that occurs naturally.

sporangiophore [BOT] A stalk or filament on which sporangia are borne.

sporangiospore [BOT] A spore that forms in a sporangium.

sporangium [BOT] A case in which asexual spores are formed and borne.

spore [BIOL] A uni- or multicellular, asexual, reproductive or resting body that is resistant to unfavorable environmental conditions and produces a new vegetative individual when the environment is favorable.

spore mother cell [BOT] One of the cells of the archespore of a sporebearing plant from which a spore, but usually a tetrad of spores, is produced.

Sporichthya [MICROBIO] A genus of bacteria in the family Streptomycetaceae; aerial hyphae form only aerial mycelia; motile spores are produced on aerial hyphae.

sporidium [MYCOL] A small spore, especially one formed on a promycelium.

sporoblast [INV ZOO] A sporozoan cell from which sporozoites arise.

Sporobolomycetaceae [MYCOL] The single family of the order Sporobolomycetales.

Sporobolomycetales [MYCOL] An order of yeastlike and moldlike fungi assigned to the class Basidiomycetes characterized by the formation of sterigmata, upon which the asexual ballistospores are formed.

sporocarp [BOT] Any multicellular structure in or on which spores are formed.

sporocyst [BOT] A unicellular resting body from which asexual spores arise. [INV ZOO] 1. A resistant envelope containing an encysted sporozoan. 2. An encysted sporozoan. 3. The first reproductive form of a digenetic trematode in which rediae develop.

Sporocytophaga [MICROBIO] A genus of bacteria in the family Cytophagaceae; cells are motile rods with rounded ends; microcysts are formed.

sporogenesis [BIOL] 1. Reproduction by means of spores. 2. Formation of spores.

sporogony [BIOL] Reproduction by means of spores. [INV ZOO] Propagative reproduction involving formation, by sexual processes, and subsequent division of a zygote.

Sporolactobacillus [MICROBIO] A genus of bacteria in the family Bacillaceae; rod-shaped cells

occurring singly or in pairs; microaerophilic and do not produce catalase.

sporont [INV ZOO] A stage in the life history of sporozoans which gives rise to spores.

sporophore [MYCOL] A structure on the thallus of fungi which produces spores.

sporophyll [BOT] A modified leaf that develops sporangia.

sporophyte [BOT] 1. An individual of the spore-bearing generation in plants exhibiting alternation of generation. 2. The spore-producing generation. 3. The diplophase in a plant life cycle.

sporopollenin [BIOCHEM] A substance related to suberin and cutin but more resistant to decay that is found in the exine of pollen grains.

sporosac [INV ZOO] A degenerate gonophore in certain hydroid coelenterates.

Sporosarcina [MICROBIO] A genus of bacteria in the family Bacillaceae; spherical cells occur in packets and form endospores.

Sporozoa [INV ZOO] A subphylum of parasitic Protozoa, typically producing spores during the asexual stages of the life cycle.

sporozoite [INV ZOO] A motile, infective stage of certain sporozoans, which is the result of sexual reproduction and which gives rise to an asexual cycle in the new host.

sporulation [BIOL] The act and process of spore formation.

spot blotch [PL PATH] A fungus disease of barley caused by *Helminthosporium sativum* and characterized by the appearance of dark, elongated spots on the foliage.

spotted wilt [PL PATH] A virus disease of various crop and wild plants, especially tomato, characterized by bronzing and downward curling of the leaves.

spout hole [VERT ZOO] 1. A blowhole of a cetacean mammal. 2. A nostril of a walrus or seal.

spreading factor See hyaluronidase.

Sprigginidae [INV ZOO] An extinct family of annelid worms distinguished by a horseshoe-shaped head.

springwood [BOT] The portion of an annual ring that is formed principally during the growing season; it is softer, more porous, and lighter than summerwood because of its higher proportion of large, thin-walled cells.

spruce [BOT] An evergreen tree belonging to the genus *Picea* characterized by single, four-sided needles borne on small peglike projections, pendulous cones, and resinous wood.

Spumellina [INV ZOO] The equivalent name for Peripylina.

spur [BOT] 1. A hollow process at the base of a petal or sepal. 2. A short fruit-bearing tree branch. 3. A short projecting root. [ZOO] A stiff, sharp outgrowth, as on the legs of certain birds and insects.

spur blight [PL PATH] A fungus disease of raspberries and blackberries caused by *Didymella applanata* which kills the fruit spurs and causes dark spotting of the cane.

sputum [PHYSIO] Material discharged from the surface of the respiratory passages, mouth, or throat; may contain saliva, mucus, pus, microorganisms, blood, or inhaled particulate matter in any combination.

squalene [BIOCHEM] $C_{30}H_{50}$ A liquid triterpene which is found in large quantities in shark liver oil, and which appears to play a role in the biosynthesis of sterols and polycyclic terpenes; used as a bactericide and as an intermediate in the synthesis of pharmaceuticals. Also known as spinacene.

Squalidae [VERT ZOO] The spiny dogfishes, a family of squaloid elasmobranchs recognized by their well-developed fin spines.

Squamata [VERT ZOO] An order of reptiles, composed of the lizards and snakes, distinguished by a highly modified skull that has only a single temporal opening, or none, by the lack of shells or secondary palates, and by possession of paired penes on the males.

squamodisk [INV ZOO] In monogenetic trematodes, a disk bearing concentric circles of spines, scales, or ridges, and located on the opisthaptor.

squamosal bone [ANAT] The part of the temporal bone in man corresponding with the squamosal bone in lower vertebrates.

squamosal bone [VERT ZOO] A membrane bone lying external and dorsal to the auditory capsule of many vertebrate skulls.

squamous [BIOL] Covered with or composed of scales.

squamous epithelium [HISTOL] A single-layered epithelium consisting of thin, flat cells.

squamulose [BIOL] Covered with or composed of minute scales.

squarrose [BOT] Having stiff divergent bracts, or other processes.

squarrulose [BOT] Mildly squarrose.

squash [BOT] Either of two plants of the genus *Cucurbita*, order Violales, cultivated for its fruit; some types are known as pumpkins.

Squatinidae [VERT ZOO] A group of squaloid elasmobranchs of uncertain affinity characterized by a greatly extended rostrum with enlarged denticles along the margins; maximum length is under 4 feet (1.2 meters).

squid [INV ZOO] Any of a number of marine cephalopod mollusks characterized by a reduced internal shell, ten tentacles, an ink sac, and chromatophores.

Squillidae [INV ZOO] The single family of the eumalacostracan order Stomatopoda, the mantis shrimp.

squirrel [VERT ZOO] Any of over 200 species of arboreal rodents of the families Sciuridae and Anomaluridae having a bushy tail and long, strong hind limbs.

stab culture [MICROBIO] A culture of anaerobic bacteria made by piercing a solid agar medium in a test tube with an inoculating needle covered with the bacterial inoculum.

stable factor *See* factor VII.

Staffellidae [PALEON] An extinct family of marine protozoans (superfamily Fusulinacea) that persisted during the Pennsylvanian and Early Permian.

stage theory [PHYSIO] A theory of color vision which proposes that there are three or more types

of cone receptors whose responses are conducted to higher visual centers, and that interactions occur at some stage along the conducting paths so that strong activity in one type of response inhibits that of other response paths. Also known as zone theory.

staghead *See* witches'-broom disease.

stalked barnacle [INV ZOO] The common name for crustaceans composing the suborder Lepadomorpha.

stallion [VERT ZOO] 1. A mature male equine mammal. 2. A male horse not castrated.

stamen [BOT] The male reproductive structure of a flower, consisting of an anther and a filament.

staminode [BOT] A stamen with no functional anther.

stand [ECOL] A group of plants, distinguishable from adjacent vegetation, which is generally uniform in species composition, age, and condition.

standing crop [ECOL] The number of individuals or total biomass present in a community at one particular time.

stapedius muscle [ANAT] The muscle which attaches to and controls the stapes in the inner ear.

stapes [ANAT] The stirrup-shaped middle-ear ossicle, articulating with the incus and the oval window. Also known as columella.

Staphylinidae [INV ZOO] The rove beetles, a very large family of coleopteran insects in the superfamily Staphylinoidea.

Staphylinoidea [INV ZOO] A superfamily of Coleoptera in the suborder Polyphaga.

Staphylococcus [MICROBIO] A genus of bacteria in the family Micrococcaceae; cells may occur singly or in pairs, but usually in irregular masses; metabolism is respiratory and fermentative; many strains are potential pathogens.

Staphylococcus aureus [MICROBIO] A common human pathogen that causes furunculosis, pyemia, osteomyelitis, suppuration of wounds, and food poisoning. Also known as *Micrococcus pyogenes*.

staphylomycin [MICROBIO] An antibiotic composed of three active components produced by a strain of *Actinomyces* that inhibits growth of gram-positive microorganisms and acid-fast bacilli.

staphylotoxin [BIOCHEM] Any of the various toxins elaborated by strains of *Staphylococcus aureus*, including hemolysins, enterotoxins, and leukocidin.

starch [BIOCHEM] Any one of a group of carbohydrates or polysaccharides, of the general composition $(C_6H_{10}O_5)_n$, occurring as organized or structural granules of varying size and markings in many plant cells; it hydrolyzes to several forms of dextrin and glucose; its chemical structure is not completely known, but the granules consist of concentric shells containing at least two fractions: an inner portion called amylose, and an outer portion called amylopectin.

starfish [INV ZOO] The common name for echinoderms belonging to the subclass Asteroidea.

Starling's law of the heart [PHYSIO] The energy associated with cardiac contraction is proportional to the length of the myocardial fibers in diastole.

starter [MICROBIO] A culture of microorganisms, either pure or mixed, used to commence a process, for example, cheese manufacture.

startle response [PHYSIO] The complex, involuntary, usually spasmodic psychophysiological response movement of an organism to a sudden unexpected stimulus.

static contraction See isometric contraction.

static reflex [PHYSIO] Any one of a series of reflexes which are involved in the establishment of muscular tone for postural purpose.

stationary phase [MICROBIO] The period following termination of exponential growth in a bacterial culture when the number of viable microorganisms remains relatively constant for a time.

stationary population [ECOL] A population containing a basically even distribution of age groups.

statoblast [INV ZOO] A chitin-encapsulated body which serves as a special means of asexual reproduction in the Phylactolaemata.

statocone [INV ZOO] One of the minute calcareous granules found in the statocyst of certain animals.

statocyst [BOT] A cell containing statoliths in a fluid medium. Also known as statocyte. [INV ZOO] A sensory vesicle containing statoliths and which functions in the perception of the position of the body in space.

statocyte See statocyst.

statokinetic [PHYSIO] Pertaining to the balance and posture of the body or its parts during movement, as in walking.

statolith [BOT] A sand grain or other solid inclusion which moves readily in the fluid contents of a statocyst, comes to rest on the lower surface of the cell, and is believed to function in gravity perception. [INV ZOO] A secreted calcareous body, a sand grain, or other solid inclusion contained in a statocyst.

statoreceptor [PHYSIO] A sense organ concerned primarily with equilibrium.

stauractine [INV ZOO] A sponge spicule in which the four rays lie in one plane.

Stauromedusae [INV ZOO] An order of the class Scyphozoa in which the medusa is composed of a cuplike bell called a calyx and a stem that terminates in a pedal disk.

Staurosporae [MYCOL] A spore group of the Fungi Imperfecti characterized by star-shaped or forked spores.

steapsin [BIOCHEM] An enzyme in pancreatic juice that catalyzes the hydrolysis of fats. Also known as pancreatic lipase.

Steatornithidae [VERT ZOO] A family of birds in the order Caprimulgiformes which contains a single, South American species, the oilbird or guacharo (*Steatornis caripensis*).

Steganopodes [VERT ZOO] Formerly, an order of birds that included the totipalmate swimming birds.

Stegodontinae [PALEON] An extinct subfamily of elephantoid proboscideans in the family Elephantidae.

Stegosauria [PALEON] A suborder of extinct reptiles of the order Ornithischia comprising the plated dinosaurs of the Jurassic which had tiny heads, great triangular plates arranged on the back in two alternating rows, and long spikes near the end of the tail.

Steinheim man [PALEON] A prehistoric human represented by a skull, without mandible, found near Stuttgart, Germany; the browridges are massive, the face is relatively small, and the braincase is similar in shape to that of *Homo sapiens*.

stele [BOT] The part of a plant stem including all tissues and regions of plants from the cortex inward, including the pericycle, phloem, cambium, xylem, and pith.

Stelenchopidae [INV ZOO] A family of polychaete annelids belonging to the Myzostomaria, represented by a single species from Crozet Island in the Antarctic Ocean.

stellate ganglion [ANAT] The ganglion formed by the fusion of the inferior cervical and the first thoracic sympathetic ganglions.

stellate reticulum [HISTOL] The part of the epithelial dental organ of a developing tooth which lies between the inner and the outer dental epithelium; composed of stellate cells with long, anastomosing processes in a mucoid fluid in the interstitial spaces.

Stelleroidea [INV ZOO] The single class of echinoderms in the subphylum Asterozoa; characters coincide with those of the subphylum.

stem [BOT] The organ of vascular plants that usually develops branches and bears leaves and flowers.

stem blight [PL PATH] Any of various fungus blights that affect the plant stem.

stem break See browning.

stem canker [PL PATH] Any canker disease affecting the stem.

stem cell [EMBRYO] A formative cell. [HISTOL] See hemocytoblast.

Stemonitaceae [MYCOL] The single family of the order Stemonitales.

Stemonitales [MYCOL] An order of fungi in the subclass Myxogastromycetidae of the class Myxomycetes.

stem rust [PL PATH] Any of several fungus diseases, especially of grasses, affecting the stem and marked by black or reddish-brown lesions.

Stenetrioidea [INV ZOO] A group of isopod crustaceans in the suborder Asellota consisting mostly of tropical marine forms in which the first pleopods are fused.

Stenocephalidae [INV ZOO] A family of Old World, neotropical Hemiptera included in the Pentatomorpha.

Stenoglossa [INV ZOO] The equivalent name for Neogastropoda.

stenohaline [ECOL] In marine organisms, indicating the ability to tolerate only a narrow range of salinities.

Stenolaemata [INV ZOO] A class of marine ecto-proct bryozoans having lophophores which are circular in basal outline and zooecia which are long, slender, tubular or prismatic, and gradually tapering to their proximal ends.

Stenomasteridae [PALEON] An extinct family of Euchinoidea in the order Holasteroida comprising oval and heart-shaped forms with fully developed pore pairs.

stenoplastic [BIOL] An organism which exhibits a limited capacity for modification or adaptation to a new environment.

Stenopodidea [INV ZOO] A section of decapod crustaceans in the suborder Natantia which includes shrimps having the third pereiopods chelate and much longer and stouter than the first pair.

Stenostomata [INV ZOO] The equivalent name for Cyclostomata.

stenotherm [BIOL] An organism able to tolerate only a small variation of temperature in the environment.

stenothermic [BIOL] Indicating the ability to tolerate only a limited range of temperatures.

Stenothoidae [INV ZOO] A family of amphipod crustaceans in the suborder Gammaridea containing semiparasitic and commensal species.

stenotopic [ECOL] Referring to an organism with a restricted distribution.

Stensen's duct See parotid duct.

Stensioellidae [PALEON] A family of Lower Devonian placoderms of the order Petalichthyida having large pectoral fins and a broad subterminal mouth.

Stenurida [PALEON] An order of Ophiuroidea, comprising the most primitive brittlestars, known only from Paleozoic sediments.

Stephanidae [INV ZOO] A small family of the Hymenoptera in the superfamily Ichneumonoidea characterized by many-segmented filamentous antennae.

stepping reflex [PHYSIO] A reflex response of the newborn and young infant, characterized by alternating stepping movements with the legs, as in walking, elicited when the infant is held upright so that both soles touch a flat surface while the infant is moved forward to accompany any step taken.

stercobilin [BIOCHEM] Urobilin as a component of the brown fecal pigment.

stercobilinogen [BIOCHEM] A colorless reduction product of stercobilin found in feces.

Stercorariidae [VERT ZOO] A family of predatory birds of the order Charadriiformes including the skuas and jaegers.

Sterculiaceae [BOT] A family of dicotyledonous trees and shrubs of the order Malvales distinguished by imbricate or contorted petals, bilocular anthers, and ten to numerous stamens arranged in two or more whorls.

stereoblastula [EMBRYO] A blastula that lacks a cavity, making it unable to gastrulate.

stereocilia [CELL BIO] 1. Nonmotile tufts of secretory microvilli on the free surface of cells of the male reproductive tract. 2. Homogeneous cilia within simple membrane coverings; found on the free-surface hair cells.

stereogastrula [EMBRYO] A gastrula that lacks a cavity.

stereopsis See stereoscopy.

stereoscopic radius [PHYSIO] The greatest distance at which there is a sensation of depth in vision due to the fact that the two eyes do not perceive exactly the same view.

stereoscopic vision See stereoscopy.

stereoscopy [PHYSIO] The phenomenon of simultaneous vision with two eyes in which there is a vivid perception of the distances of objects from the viewer; it is present because the two eyes view objects in space from two points, so that the retinal image patterns of the same object are slightly different in the two eyes. Also known as stereopsis; stereoscopic vision.

Stereospondyli [PALEON] A group of labyrinthodont amphibians from the Triassic characterized by a flat body without pleurocentra and with highly developed intercentra.

stereotaxis [BIOL] An orientation movement in response to stimulation by contact with a solid body. Also known as thigmotaxis.

stereotropism [BIOL] Growth or orientation of a sessile organism or part of an organism in response to the stimulus of a solid body. Also known as thigmotropism.

sterigma [BOT] A peg-shaped structure to which needles are attached in certain conifers. [MYCOL] A slender stalk arising from the basidium of some fungi, from the top of which basidiospores are formed by abstriction.

sterile distribution [ECOL] A range of areas in which marine animals may live and spawn, but in which eggs do not hatch and larvae do not survive.

sterility [PHYSIO] The inability to reproduce because of congenital or acquired reproductive system disorders involving lack of gamete production or production of abnormal gametes.

sterilization [MICROBIO] An act or process of destroying all forms of microbial life on and in an object.

Sternaspidae [INV ZOO] A monogeneric family of polychaete annelids belonging to the Sedentaria.

sternebra [VERT ZOO] A segment of the sternum in vertebrates.

Sterninae [VERT ZOO] A subfamily of birds in the family Laridae, including the Arctic tern.

sternite [INV ZOO] 1. The ventral part of an arthropod somite. 2. The chitinous plate on the ventral surface of an abdominal segment of an insect.

sternocleidomastoid [ANAT] A muscle of the neck that flexes the head; origin is the manubrium of the sternum and clavicle, and insertion is the mastoid process.

sternocostal [ANAT] Pertaining to the sternum and the ribs.

sternohyoid [ANAT] A muscle arising from the manubrium of the sternum and inserted into the hyoid bone.

Sternorrhyncha [INV ZOO] A series of the insect order Homoptera in which the beak appears to arise either between or behind the fore coxae, and the antennae are long and filamentous with no well-differentiated terminal setae.

sternothyroid [ANAT] Pertaining to the sternum and thyroid cartilage.

Sternoxia [INV ZOO] The equivalent name for Elateroidea.

sternum [ANAT] The bone, cartilage, or series of bony or cartilaginous segments in the median line of the anteroventral part of the body of vertebrates above fishes, connecting with the ribs or pectoral girdle.

steroid [BIOCHEM] A member of a group of compounds, occurring in plants and animals, that are considered to be derivatives of a fused, reduced ring system, cyclopenta[α]phenanthrene, which consists of three fused cyclohexane rings in a nonlinear or phenanthrene arrangement.

sterol [BIOCHEM] Any of the natural products derived from the steroid nucleus; all are waxy, colorless solids soluble in most organic solvents but not in water, and contain one alcohol functional group.

sterone [BIOCHEM] A ketone derived from a steroid.

Sthenurinae [PALEON] An extinct subfamily of marsupials of the family Diprotodontidae, including the giant kangaroos.

Stichaeidae [VERT ZOO] The pricklebacks, a family of perciform fishes in the suborder Blennioidei.

Stichocotylidae [INV ZOO] A family of trematodes in the subclass Aspidogastrea in which adults are elongate and have a single row of alveoli.

Stichopodidae [INV ZOO] A family of the echinoderm order Aspidochirotida characterized by tentacle ampullae and by left and right gonads.

Stickland reaction [BIOCHEM] An amino acid fermentation involving the coupled decomposition of two or more substrates.

stickleback [VERT ZOO] Any fish which is a member of the family Gasterosteidae, so named for the variable number of free spines in front of the dorsal fin.

stigma [BOT] The rough or sticky apical surface of the pistil for reception of the pollen. [INV ZOO] **1.** The eyespot of certain protozoans, such as *Euglena*. **2.** The spiracle of an insect or arthropod. **3.** A colored spot on many lepidopteran wings.

Stigmatella [MICROBIO] A genus of bacteria in the family Cystobacteraceae; vegetative cells are tapered, and sporangia are borne in clusters on branched or unbranched stalks.

stigmatism [PHYSIO] A condition of the refractive media of the eye in which rays of light from a point are accurately brought to a focus on the retina.

Stilbaceae [MYCOL] The equivalent name for Stilbellaceae.

Stilbellaceae [MYCOL] A family of fungi of the order Moniliales in which conidiophores are aggregated in long bundles or fascicles, forming synnemata or coremia, generally having the conidia in a head at the top.

stilbesterol *See* diethylstilbesterol.

stilt root [BOT] A prop root of a mangrove tree.

stimulus [PHYSIO] An agent that produces a temporary change in physiological activity in an organism or in any of its parts.

stinger [ZOO] A sharp piercing organ, as of a bee, stingray, or wasp, usually connected with a poison gland.

stinging cell *See* cnidoblast.

stingray [VERT ZOO] Any of various rays having a whiplike tail armed with a long serrated spine, at the base of which is a poison gland.

stipe [BOT] **1.** The petiole of a fern frond. **2.** The stemlike portion of the thallus in certain algae. [MYCOL] The short stalk or stem of the fruit body of a fungus, such as a mushroom.

stippen *See* fitten pit.

start codon *See* initiation codon.

stipule [BOT] Either of a pair of appendages that are often present at the base of the petiole of a leaf.

Stirodonta [INV ZOO] Formerly, an order of Euechinoidea that included forms with stirodont dentition.

stirodont dentition [INV ZOO] In Echinoidea, the condition in which the teeth are keeled within and the foramen magnum is open.

stolon [BOT] *See* runner. [INV ZOO] An elongated projection of the body wall from which buds are formed giving rise to new zooids in Anthozoa, Hydrozoa, Bryozoa, and Ascidiacea. [MYCOL] A hypha produced above the surface and connecting a group of conidiophores.

Stolonifera [INV ZOO] An order of the Alcyonaria, lacking a coenenchyme; they form either simple (*Clavularia*) or rather complex colonies (*Tubipora*).

stoma [BIOL] A small opening or pore in a surface. [BOT] One of the minute openings in the epidermis of higher plants which are regulated by guard cells and through which gases and water vapor are exchanged between internal spaces and the external atmosphere.

stomach [ANAT] The tubular or saccular organ of the vertebrate digestive system located between the esophagus and the intestine and adapted for temporary food storage and for the preliminary stages of food breakdown.

stomatoblastula [INV ZOO] A blastula stage in some sponges capable of engulfing maternal amebocytes for nutrition.

Stomatopoda [INV ZOO] The single order of the Eumalacostraca in the superorder Hoplocarida distinguished by raptorial arms, especially the second pair of maxillipeds.

Stomiatoidei [VERT ZOO] A suborder of fishes of the order Salmoniformes including the lightfishes and allies, which are of small size and often grotesque form and are equipped with photophores.

stomocnidae nematocyst [INV ZOO] A nematocyst which has an open-ended thread.

stomodaeum [EMBRYO] The anterior part of the embryonic alimentary tract formed as an invagination of the ectoderm.

stone canal [INV ZOO] A canal in many echinoderms that has a more or less calcified wall and that leads from the madreporite to the ring vessel.

stone cell See brachysclereid.

stone fruit See drupe.

stonewort [BOT] The common name for algae comprising the class Charophyceae, so named because most species are lime-encrusted.

stony coral [INV ZOO] Any coral characterized by a calcareous skeleton.

stork [VERT ZOO] Any of several species of long-legged wading birds in the family Ciconiidae.

straight sinus [ANAT] A sinus of the dura mater running from the inferior sagittal sinus along the junction of the falx cerebri and tentorium to the transverse sinus.

stratified squamous epithelium [HISTOL] A multiple-layered epithelium composed of thin, flat superficial cells and cuboidal and columnar deeper cells.

Stratiomyidae [INV ZOO] The soldier flies, a family of orthorrhaphous dipteran insects in the series Brachycera.

stratum corneum [HISTOL] The outer layer of flattened keratinized cells of the epidermis.

stratum disjunctum [HISTOL] The outermost layer of desquamating keratinized cells of the stratum corneum.

stratum germinativum [HISTOL] The innermost germinative layer of the epidermis.

stratum granulosum [HISTOL] A layer of granular cells interposed between the stratum corneum and the stratum germinativum in the thick skin of the palms and soles.

stratum lucidum [HISTOL] A layer of irregular transparent epidermal cells with traces of nuclei interposed between the stratum corneum and stratum germinativum in the thick skin of the palms and soles.

straw [BOT] A stem of grain, such as wheat or oats.

strawberry [BOT] A low-growing perennial of the genus *Fragaria*, order Rosales, that spreads by stolons; the juicy, usually red, edible fruit consists of a fleshy receptacle with numerous seeds in pits or nearly superficial on the receptacle.

streak plate [MICROBIO] A method of culturing aerobic bacteria by streaking the surface of a solid medium in a petri dish with an inoculating wire or glass rod in a continuous movement so that most of the surface is covered; used to isolate majority members of a mixed population.

Streblidae [INV ZOO] The bat flies, a family of cyclorrhaphous dipteran insects in the section Pupipara; adults are ectoparasites on bats.

Strelitziaceae [BOT] A family of monocotyledonous plants in the order Zingiberales distinguished by perfect flowers with five functional stamens and without an evident hypanthium, penniveined leaves, and symmetrical guard cells.

strepaster [INV ZOO] A short, spiny microscleric, monaxonic spicule.

strepogenin [BIOCHEM] A factor, possibly a peptide derivative of glutamic acid, reported to exist in certain proteins, acting as a growth stimulant in bacteria and mice in the presence of completely hydrolyzed protein. Also known as streptogenin.

Strepsiptera [INV ZOO] An order of the Coleoptera that is coextensive with the family Stylopidae.

Streptobacillus [MICROBIO] A genus of gram-negative, facultatively anaerobic rods of uncertain affiliation; rod-shaped cells frequently occur in chains and filaments; parasites and pathogens of certain mammals.

streptobiosamine [BIOCHEM] $C_{13}H_{23}NO_9$ A nitrogen-containing disaccharide, obtained when streptomycin undergoes acid hydrolysis; in the streptomycin molecule it is glycosidally linked to streptidine.

Streptococcaceae [MICROBIO] A family of gram-positive cocci; chemoorganotrophs with fermentative metabolism.

Streptococceae [MICROBIO] Formerly a tribe of the family Lactobacillaceae including cocci that occur in pairs, short chains, or tetrads and which generally obtain energy by fermentation of carbohydrates or related compounds.

Streptococcus [MICROBIO] A genus of bacteria in the family Streptococcaceae; coccoid to ovoid cells occurring in pairs of chains; ferment glucose, with production of dextrorotatory lactic acid (homofermentative).

streptogenin See strepogenin.

streptokinase [BIOCHEM] An enzyme occurring as a component of fibrinolysin in cultures of certain hemolytic streptococci.

streptolysin [BIOCHEM] Any of a group of hemolysins elaborated by *Streptococcus pyogenes*.

Streptomyces [MICROBIO] A genus of bacteria in the family Streptomycetaceae; hyphae are slender and coenocytic; chains of nonmotile spores form on aerial hyphae; many strains produce antibiotics.

Streptomycetaceae [MICROBIO] A family of soil-inhabiting bacteria in the order Actinomycetales; branched mycelia are produced by vegetative hyphae; spores are produced on aerial hyphae.

streptomycin [MICROBIO] $C_{21}H_{39}O_{12}N_7$ Water-soluble antibiotic obtained from *Streptomyces griseus* that is used principally in the treatment of tuberculosis.

Streptosporangium [MICROBIO] A genus of bacteria in the family Actinoplanaceae; sporangia are spherical to subspherical; spores are nonmotile and spherical and are arranged in a coil in the sporangium.

streptothricin [MICROBIO] $C_{19}H_{34}O_7N_8$ An antibiotic produced by *Streptomyces lavendulae*; active against various gram-negative and gram-positive microorganisms.

Streptothrix [MICROBIO] A genus of sheathed bacteria; cells are nonmotile, and sheaths are attached and are not encrusted with iron or manganese oxides.

Streptoverticillium [MICROBIO] A genus of bacteria in the family Streptomycetaceae; a branched aerial mycelium is produced in a whorl; chains of nonmotile spores form on secondary branches.

stress [BIOL] A stimulus or succession of stimuli of such magnitude as to tend to disrupt the homeostasis of the organism.

stretch reflex [PHYSIO] Contraction of a muscle in response to a sudden, brisk, longitudinal stretching of the same muscle. Also known as myostatic reflex.

stria [BIOL] A minute line, band, groove, or channel.

striated muscle [HISTOL] Muscle tissue consisting of muscle fibers having cross striations.

stridulation [INV ZOO] Creaking and other audible sounds made by certain insects, produced by rubbing various parts of the body together.

Strigidae [VERT ZOO] A family of birds of the order Strigiformes containing the true owls.

Strigiformes [VERT ZOO] The order of birds containing the owls.

strigose [BIOL] Covered with stiff, pointed, hairlike scales or bristles.

Strigulaceae [BOT] A family of Ascolichenes in the order Pyrenulales comprising crustose species confined to tropical evergreens, and which form extensive crusts on or under the cuticle of leaves.

stripe canker *See* flack thread

strobilation [INV ZOO] Asexual reproduction by segmentation of the body into zooids, proglottids, or separate individuals.

strobilocercus [INV ZOO] A larval tapeworm that has undergone strobilation.

strobilus [BOT] 1. A conelike structure made up of sporophylls, or spore-bearing leaves, as in Equisetales. 2. The cone of members of the Pinophyta.

stroke volume [PHYSIO] The amount of blood pumped during each cardiac contraction; quantitatively, the diastolic volume of the left ventricle minus the volume of blood in the ventricle at the end of systole.

stroma [ANAT] The supporting tissues of an organ, including connective and nervous tissues and blood vessels.

Stromateidae [INV ZOO] A family of perciform fishes in the suborder Stromateoidei containing the butterfishes.

Stromateoidei [VERT ZOO] A suborder of fishes of the order Perciformes in which most species have teeth in pockets behind the pharyngeal bone.

Stromatoporoidea [PALEON] An extinct order of fossil colonial organisms thought to belong to the class Hydrozoa; the skeleton is a coenosteum.

Strombacea [PALEON] An extinct superfamily of gastropod mollusks in the order Prosobranchia.

Strombidae [INV ZOO] A family of gastopod mollusks comprising tropical conchs.

strongyle [INV ZOO] A monaxonic spicule rounded at each end.

Strongyloidea [INV ZOO] The hookworms, an order or superfamily of roundworms which, as

adults, are endoparasites of most vertebrates, including man.

strongylote [INV ZOO] Rounded at one end, referring to sponge spicules.

Strophanthus [BOT] A genus of woody climbers of the dogbane family (Apocynaceae), natives of tropical Asia and Africa; the source of arrow poisons and of strophanthin.

strophiole [BOT] A crestlike excrescence around the hilum in certain seeds.

Strophomenida [PALEON] A large diverse order of articulate brachiopods which first appeared in Lower Ordovician times and became extinct in the Late Triassic.

Strophomenidina [PALEON] A suborder of extinct, articulate brachiopods in the order Strophomenida characterized by a concavo-convex shell, the pseudodeltidium and socket plates disposed subparallel to the hinge.

Struthionidae [VERT ZOO] The single family of the avian order Struthioniformes.

Struthioniformes [VERT ZOO] A monofamilial order of ratite birds containing the single living species of ostrich (*Struthio camelus*).

Stuart factor [BIOCHEM] A procoagulant in normal plasma but deficient in the blood of patients with a hereditary bleeding disorder; may be closely related to prothrombin since both are formed in the liver by action of vitamin K. Also known as factor X; Stuart-Power factor.

Stuart-Power factor *See* Stuart factor.

stubborn disease [PL PATH] A virus disease of citrus trees characterized by short internodes resulting in stiff brushy growth and chlorotic leaves.

stunt [PL PATH] Any of several plant diseases marked by reduction in size of the plant.

sturgeon [VERT ZOO] Any of 10 species of large bottom-living fish which comprise the family Acipenseridae; the body has five rows of bony plates, and the snout is elongate with four barbels on its lower surface.

Styginae [INV ZOO] A subfamily of butterflies in the family Lycaenidae in which the prothoracic legs in the male are nonfunctional.

Stygocaridacea [INV ZOO] An order of crustaceans in the superorder Syncarida characterized by having a furca.

Stylasterina [INV ZOO] An order of the class Hydrozoa, including several brightly colored branching or encrusting coral-like coelenterates of warm seas.

style [BOT] The portion of a pistil connecting the stigma and ovary. [ZOO] A slender elongated process on an animal.

stylet [INV ZOO] A slender, rigid, elongated appendage.

styloglossus [ANAT] A muscle arising from the styloid process of the temporal bone, and inserted into the tongue.

stylohyoid [ANAT] Pertaining to the styloid process of the temporal bone and the hyoid bone.

styloid [ZOO] Resembling a style.

stylomastoid [ANAT] Relating to the styloid and the mastoid processes of the temporal bone.

Stylommatophora [INV ZOO] A large order of the molluscan subclass Pulmonata characterized by having two pairs of retractile tentacles with eyes located on the tips of the large tentacles.

stylopodium [BOT] A conical or disk-shaped enlargement at the base of the style in plants of the family Umbelliferae.

Stypocapitellidae [INV ZOO] A family of polychaete annelids belonging to the Sedentaria and consisting of a monotypic genus found in western Germany.

subalpine See alpestrine.

subarachnoid space [ANAT] The space between the pia mater and the arachnoid of the brain.

subboreal [ECOL] A biogeographic zone whose climatic condition approaches that of the boreal.

subcardinal vein [VERT ZOO] Either of a pair of longitudinal veins of the mammalian embryo or the adult of some lower vertebrates which partly replace the postcardinals in the abdominal region, ventromedial to the mesonephros.

subclavian artery [ANAT] The proximal part of the principal artery in the arm or forelimb.

subclavian vein [ANAT] The proximal part of the principal vein in the arm or forelimb.

subclavius [ANAT] A small muscle attached to the clavicle and the first rib.

subclimax [ECOL] A community immediately preceding a climax in an ecological succession.

subcollateral [ANAT] Ventrad of the collateral sulcus of the brain.

subcutaneous connective tissue [HISTOL] The layer of loose connective tissue beneath the dermis.

subdominant [ECOL] A species which may appear more abundant at particular times of the year than the true dominant in a climax; for example, in a savannah trees and shrubs are more conspicuous than the grasses, which are the true dominants.

subendothelial layer [HISTOL] The middle layer of the tunica intima of veins and of medium and larger arteries, consisting of collagenous and elastic fibers and a few fibroblasts.

suberin [BIOCHEM] A fatty substance found in many plant cell walls, especially cork.

suberization [BOT] Infiltration of plant cell walls by suberin resulting in the formation of corky tissue that is impervious to water.

suberose [BOT] Having a texture like cork due to or resembling that due to suberization.

sublethal gene See semilethal gene.

subliminal [PHYSIO] Below the threshold of responsiveness, consciousness, or sensation to a stimulus.

sublingual gland [ANAT] A complex of salivary glands located in the sublingual fold on each side of the floor of the mouth.

submandibular duct [ANAT] The duct of the submandibular gland which empties into the mouth on the side of the frenulum of the tongue.

submandibular gland [ANAT] A large seromucous or mixed salivary gland located below the mandible on each side of the jaw. Also known as mandibular gland; submaxillary gland.

submaxillary gland See submandibular gland.

submerged culture [MICROBIO] A method for growing pure cultures of aerobic bacteria in which

microorganisms are incubated in a liquid medium subjected to continuous, vigorous agitation.

submerged fermentation [MICROBIO] Industrial production of antibiotics, enzymes, and other substances by growing the microorganisms that produce the product in a submerged culture.

submucosa [HISTOL] The layer of fibrous connective tissue that attaches a mucous membrane to its subadjacent parts.

submucous plexus [ANAT] A visceral nerve network lying in the submucosa of the digestive tube. Also known as Meissner's plexus.

Suboscines [VERT ZOO] A major division of the order Passeriformes, usually divided into the suborders Eurylaimi, Tyranni, and Memirae.

subscapularis [ANAT] A muscle arising from the costal surface of the scapula and inserted on the lesser tubercle of the humerus.

subsere [ECOL] A secondary community that succeeds an interrupted climax.

subspecies [SYST] A geographically defined grouping of local populations which differs taxonomically from similar subdivisions of species.

substance P [BIOCHEM] An undecapeptide widely distributed in the central nervous system and found in highest concentrations in superficial layers of the dorsal horn of the spinal cord, in the trigeminal nerve nucleus, and in the substantia nigra; acts as a neurotransmitter.

substrate [BIOCHEM] The substance with which an enzyme reacts.

subtend [BOT] To lie adjacent to and below another structure, often enclosing it.

subtilin [MICROBIO] An antibiotic substance obtained from *Bacillus subtilis*, active against grampositive bacteria.

Subtriquetridae [INV ZOO] A family of arthropods in the suborder Porocephaloidea.

subtropical forest See temperate rainforest.

subulate [BOT] Linear, delicate, and tapering to a sharp point.

Subulitacea [PALEON] An extinct superfamily of gastropod mollusks in the order Prosobranchia which possessed a basal fold but lacked an apertural sinus.

Subuluridae [INV ZOO] The equivalent name for Heterakidae.

subumbrella [INV ZOO] The concave undersurface of the body of a jellyfish.

subunit See protomer.

succession [ECOL] A gradual process brought about by the change in the number of individuals of each species of a community and by the establishment of new species populations which may gradually replace the original inhabitants.

succinamide [BIOCHEM] $H_2NCOCH_2CONH_2$ The amide of succinic acid.

succinic acid dehydrogenase [BIOCHEM] An enzyme that catalyzes the dehydrogenation of succinic acid to fumaric acid in the presence of a hydrogen acceptor. Also known as succinic dehydrogenase.

succinic dehydrogenase See succinic acid dehydrogenase.

Succinimonas [MICROBIO] A genus of gram-negative, strictly anaerobic bacteria of uncertain affiliation; motile, straight, short rods or cocci; ferment carbohydrates to form large amounts of succinate.

Succinivibrio [MICROBIO] A genus of gram-negative, strictly anaerobic bacteria of uncertain affiliation; straight or slightly curved to helical rods with pointed ends; ferment carbohydrates and form succinate acetate, and formate.

succinoxidase [BIOCHEM] A complex enzyme system containing succinic dehydrogenase and cytochromes that catalyzes the conversion of succinate ion and molecular oxygen to fumarate ion.

succulent [BOT] Describing a plant having juicy, fleshy tissue.

succus entericus [PHYSIO] The intestinal juice secreted by the glands of the intestinal mucous membrane; it is thin, opalescent, alkaline, and has a specific gravity of 1.011.

sucker [BOT] A shoot that develops rapidly from the lower portion of a plant, and usually at the expense of the plant. [ZOO] A disk-shaped organ in various animals for adhering to or holding onto an individual, usually of another species.

sucking louse [INV ZOO] The common name for insects of the order Anoplura, so named for the slender, tubular mouthparts.

sucrase *See* saccharase.

Suctoria [INV ZOO] A small subclass of the protozoan class Ciliatea, distinguished by having tentacles which serve as mouths.

Suctorida [INV ZOO] The single order of the protozoan subclass Suctoria.

sudomotor [PHYSIO] Pertaining to the efferent nerves that control the activity of sweat glands.

suffrutescent [BOT] Of or pertaining to a stem intermediate between herbaceous and shrubby, becoming partly woody and perennial at the base.

suffruticose [BOT] Low stems which are woody, grading into herbaceous at the top.

sugar [BIOCHEM] A generic term for a class of carbohydrates usually crystalline, sweet, and water soluble; examples are glucose and fructose.

sugarbeet [BOT] *Beta vulgaris.* A beet characterized by a white root and cultivated for the high sugar content of the roots.

sugarcane [BOT] *Saccharum officinarum.* A stout, perennial grass plant characterized by two-ranked leaves, and a many-jointed stalk with a terminal inflorescence in the form of a silky panicle; the source of more than 50% of the world's annual sugar production.

sugar maple [BOT] *Acer saccharum.* A commercially important species of maple tree recognized by its gray furrowed bark, sharp-pointed scaly winter buds, and symmetrical oval outline of the crown.

Suidae [VERT ZOO] A family of paleodont artiodactyls in the superfamily Suoidea including wild and domestic pigs.

sulcate [ZOO] Having furrows or grooves on the surface.

sulculus [ZOO] A small sulcus.

sulcus [ZOO] A furrow or groove, especially one on the surface of the cerebrum.

sulfatase [BIOCHEM] Any of a group of esterases that catalyze the hydrolysis of sulfuric esters.

sulfhemoglobin [BIOCHEM] A greenish substance derived from hemoglobin by the action of hydrogen sulfide; it may appear in the blood following the ingestion of sulfanilamide and other substances.

Sulfolobus [MICROBIO] A genus of gram-negative, chemolithotrophic bacteria; spherical cells with lobes; obtain energy by metabolizing elemental sulfur.

sulfur bacteria [MICROBIO] Any of various bacteria having the ability to oxidize sulfur compounds.

Sulidae [VERT ZOO] A family of aquatic birds in the order Pelecaniformes including the gannets and boobies.

summation wave [PHYSIO] A sustained contraction of muscles, caused by the rapid firing of nerve impulses.

summerwood [BOT] The less porous, usually harder portion of an annual ring that forms in the latter part of the growing season.

sundew [BOT] Any plant of the genus *Drosera* of the family Droseraceae; the genus comprises small, herbaceous, insectivorous plants that grow on all continents, especially Australia.

sunfish [VERT ZOO] Any of several species of marine and freshwater fishes in the families Centrarchidae and Molidae characterized by brilliant metallic skin coloration.

sunflower [BOT] *Helianthus annuus.* An annual plant native to the United States characterized by broad, ovate leaves growing from a single, usually long (3–20 feet or 1–6 meters) stem, and large, composite flowers with yellow petals.

sunscald [PL PATH] An injury to woody plants which results in local death of the plant tissues; in summer it is caused by excessive action of the sun's rays, in winter, by the great variation of temperature on the side of trees that is exposed to the sun in cold weather.

Suoidea [VERT ZOO] A superfamily of artiodactyls of the suborder Paleodonta which comprises the pigs and peccaries.

supercilium [ANAT] The eyebrow.

superfecundation [PHYSIO] Multiple, simultaneous fertilization by a number of sperm of many eggs released at ovulation.

superfemale [GEN] A female with three X chromosomes and two sets of autosomes resulting in sterility and generally early death.

superficial cleavage [EMBRYO] Meroblastic cleavage restricted to the peripheral cytoplasm, as in the centrolecithal insect ovum.

superficial palmar arch [ANAT] The arterial anastomosis formed by the ulnar artery in the palm with a branch from the radial artery. Also known as palmar arch.

superhelix [BIOCHEM] A macromolecular structure consisting of a number of alpha-helical polypeptide strands which are twisted together.

superinfection [VIROL] An attack on a bacterial cell by several phages due to the introduction of large numbers of viruses into the bacterial culture.

superior [BOT] 1. Positioned above another organ or structure. 2. Referring to a calyx that is attached to the ovary. 3. Referring to an ovary that is above the insertion of the floral parts.

superior alveolar canals [ANAT] The alveolar canals of the maxilla.

superior ganglion [ANAT] 1. The upper sensory ganglion of the glossopharyngeal nerve, located in the upper part of the jugular foramen; it is inconstant. 2. The upper sensory ganglion of the vagus nerve, located in the jugular foramen.

superior mesenteric artery [ANAT] A major branch of the abdominal aorta with branches to the pancreas and intestine.

superior vena cava [ANAT] The principal vein collecting blood from the head, chest wall, and upper extremities and draining into the right atrium.

supermale [GEN] A male with one X chromosome and three or more sets of autosomes, resulting in sterility and generally early death.

supernumerary bud See accessory bud.

supernumerary chromosome [CELL BIO] A chromosome present in addition to the normal chromosome complement. Also known as accessory chromosome.

superposed [BOT] 1. Growing vertically over another part. 2. Of or pertaining to floral parts that are opposite each other.

superposition eye [INV ZOO] A compound eye in which a given rhabdome receives light from a number of facets; visual acuity is reduced in this type of eye.

supination [ANAT] 1. Turning the palm upward. 2. Inversion of the foot.

suppressor gene [GEN] A gene that reverses the effect of a mutation in another gene.

suppressor mutation [GEN] A mutation that restores functional loss of a primary mutation and is located at a different genetic site from the primary mutation.

supracardinal veins [VERT ZOO] Paired longitudinal veins in the mammalian embryo and various adult lower vertebrates in the thoracic and abdominal regions, dorsolateral to and on the sides of the descending aorta; they replace the postcardinal and subcardinal veins.

suprahyoid muscles [ANAT] The muscles attached to the upper margin of the hyoid bone.

supraliminal [PHYSIO] Above, or in excess of, a threshold.

supranuclear [ANAT] In the nervous system, central to a nucleus.

supraoccipital [ANAT] Situated above the occipital bone.

supraoptic [ANAT] Situated above the optic tract.

suprarenal gland See adrenal gland.

suprascapula [ANAT] An anomalous bone sometimes found between the superior border of the scapula and the spines of the lower cervical or first thoracic vertebrae.

suprasegmental reflex [PHYSIO] A reflex employing complex multineuronal channels to integrate the body and limb musculature with fixed positions or movements of the head.

suprasternal notch [ANAT] Jugular notch of the sternum.

suprasternal space [ANAT] The triangular space above the manubrium, enclosed by the layers of the deep cervical fascia which are attached to the front and back of this bone.

supravital [BIOL] Pertaining to the staining of living cells after removal from a living animal or of still living cells from a recently killed animal.

survival ratio [BIOL] The number of organisms surviving irradiation by ionizing radiation divided by the number of organisms before irradiation.

suscept [PL PATH] A plant that is susceptible to disease caused by either parasitic or nonparasitic plant pathogens.

suspension feeder [ZOO] An animal that feeds on small particles suspended in water; particles may be minute living plants or animals, or products of excretion or decay from these or larger organisms.

suspensor [BOT] A mass of cells in higher plants that pushes the embryo down into the embryo sac and into contact with the nutritive tissue. [MYCOL] A hypha which bears an apical gametangium in fungi of the Mucorales.

sustained yield [BIOL] In a biological resource such as timber or grain, the replacement of a harvest yield by growth or reproduction before another harvest occurs.

sustentacular cell [HISTOL] One of the supporting cells of an epithelium as contrasted with other cells with special function, as the nonnervous cells of the olfactory epithelium or the Sertoli cells of the seminiferous tubules.

suture [BIOL] A distinguishable line of union between two closely united parts.

swamp [ECOL] A waterlogged land supporting a natural vegetation predominantly of shrubs and trees.

swan [VERT ZOO] Any of several species of large waterfowl comprising the subfamily Anatinae; they are herbivorous stout-bodied forms with long necks and spatulate bills.

Swanscombe man [PALEON] A partial skull recovered in Swanscombe, Kent, England, which represents an early stage of *Homo sapiens* but differing in having a vertical temporal region and a rounded occipital profile.

swarmer cell [MICROBIO] The daughter cell which separates from the stalked mother cell in bacteria in the genus *Caulobacter*.

sweat [PHYSIO] The secretion of the sweat glands. Also known as perspiration.

sweat gland [PHYSIO] A coiled tubular gland of the skin which secretes sweat.

sweepstakes route [ECOL] A means that allows chance migration across a sea on natural rafts, so that oceanic islands can be colonized.

sweetgum [BOT] *Liquidambar styraciflua*. A deciduous tree of the order Hamamelidales found in the southeastern United States, and distinguished by its five-lobed, or star-shaped, leaves, and by the corky ridges developed on the twigs.

sweet potato [BOT] *Ipomoea batatas.* A tropical vine having variously shaped leaves, purplish flowers, and a sweet, fleshy, edible tuberous root.

swim bladder [VERT ZOO] A gas-filled cavity found in the body cavities of most bony fishes; has various functions in different fishes, acting as a float, a lung, a hearing aid, and a sound-producing organ.

swimmeret [INV ZOO] Any of a series of paired biramous appendages under the abdomen of many crustaceans, used for swimming and egg carrying.

swimming bird [VERT ZOO] Any bird belonging to the orders Charadriiformes and Pelicaniformes.

swine [VERT ZOO] Any of various species comprising the Suidae.

sycamore [BOT] 1. Any of several species of deciduous trees of the genus *Platanus*, especially *P. occidentalis* of eastern and central North America, distinguished by simple, large, three- to five-lobed leaves and spherical fruit heads. 2. The Eurasian maple (*Acer pseudoplatanus*).

Sycettida [INV ZOO] An order of calcareous sponges of the subclass Calcaronea in which choanocytes occur in flagellated chambers, and the spongocoel is not lined with these cells.

Sycettidae [INV ZOO] A family of sponges in the order Sycettida.

Sycidales [PALEON] A group of fossil aquatic plants assigned to the Charophyta, characterized by vertically ribbed gyrogonites.

sycon [INV ZOO] A canal system in sponges in which the flagellated layer is confined to outpocketings of the paragaster that are indirectly connected to the incurrent canals.

syconium [BOT] A fleshy fruit, as a fig, with an enlarged pulpy receptacle internally lined with minute flowers.

Syllidae [INV ZOO] A large family of polychaete annelids belonging to the Errantia; identified by their long, linear, translucent bodies with articulated cirri; size ranges from minute *Exogone* to *Trypanosyllis*, which may be 100 millimeters long.

Syllinae [INV ZOO] A subfamily of polychaete annelids of the family Syllidae.

Sylonidae [INV ZOO] A family of parasitic crustaceans in the order Rhizocephala.

Sylopidae [INV ZOO] A family of coleopteran insects in the superfamily Meloidea in which the elytra in males are reduced to small leathery flaps while the hindwings are large and fan-shaped.

Sylvicolidae [INV ZOO] A family of orthorrhaphous dipteran insects in the series Nematocera.

symbiont [ECOL] A member of a symbiotic pair.

symbiosis [ECOL] 1. An interrelationship between two different species. 2. An interrelationship between two different organisms in which the effects of that relationship is expressed as being harmful or beneficial. Also known as consortism.

Symbiotes [MICROBIO] A genus of the tribe Wolbachieae; pleomorphic organisms; intracellular

symbionts, generally found in special paired organs (mycetomes) in bedbugs.

Symmetrodonta [PALEON] An order of the extinct mammalian infraclass Pantotheria distinguished by the central high cusp, flanked by two smaller cusps and several low minor cusps, on the upper and lower molars.

symmetry [BIOL] The disposition of organs and other constituent parts of the body of living organisms with respect to imaginary axes.

sympathetic nervous system [ANAT] The portion of the autonomic nervous system, innervating smooth muscle and glands of the body, which upon stimulation produces a functional state of preparation for flight or combat.

sympathicotropic cell [HISTOL] Any of various cells possessing special affinity for the sympathetic nervous system.

sympathochromaffin cell [HISTOL] One of the precursors of sympathetic and medullary cells in the adrenal medulla.

sympatric [ECOL] Of a species, occupying the same range as another species but maintaining identity by not interbreeding.

sympetalous *See* gamopetalous.

symphile [ECOL] An organism, usually a beetle, living as a guest in the nest of a social insect, such as an ant, where it is reared and bred in exchange for its exudates.

Symphyla [INV ZOO] A class of the Myriapoda comprising tiny, pale, centipedelike creatures which inhabit humus or soil.

symphysis [ANAT] An immovable articulation of bones connected by fibrocartilaginous pads.

symphysis pubis *See* pubic symphysis.

Symphyta [INV ZOO] A suborder of the Hymenoptera including the sawflies and horntails characterized by a broad base attaching the abdomen to the thorax.

sympodium [BOT] A branching system in trees in which the main axis is composed of successive secondary branches, each representing the dominant fork of a dichotomy.

Synallactidae [INV ZOO] A family of echinoderms of the order Aspidochirotida comprising mainly deep-sea forms which lack tentacle ampullae.

synandrous [BOT] Having several united stamens.

synangium [BOT] A compound sorus made up of united sporangia. [VERT ZOO] In lower vertebrates, a peripheral arterial trunk from which branches arise.

Synanthae [BOT] An equivalent name for Cyclanthales.

Synanthales [BOT] An equivalent name for Cyclanthales.

synapse [ANAT] A site where the axon of one neuron comes into contact with and influences the dendrites of another neuron or a cell body.

synapsis [CELL BIO] Pairing of homologous chromosomes during the zygotene stage of meiosis.

synaptic transmission [PHYSIO] The mechanisms by which a presynaptic neuron influences the activity of an anatomically adjacent postsynaptic neuron.

synapticulum [INV ZOO] A conical or cylindrical supporting process, as those extending between septa in some corals, or connecting gill bars in *Branchiostoma*.

Synaptidae [INV ZOO] A family of large sea cucumbers of the order Apodida lacking a respiratory tree and having a reduced water-vascular system.

synaptinemal complex [CELL BIO] Ribbonlike structures that extend the length of synapsing chromosomes and are believed to function in exchange pairing.

synarthrosis [ANAT] An articulation in which the connecting material (fibrous connective tissue) is continuous, immovably binding the bones.

Synbranchiformes [VERT ZOO] An order of eel-like actinopterygian fishes that, unlike true eels, have the premaxillae present as distinct bones.

Synbranchii [VERT ZOO] The equivalent name for Synbranchiformes.

Syncarida [INV ZOO] A superorder of crustaceans of the subclass Melacostraca lacking a carapace and oostegites and having exopodites on all thoracic limbs.

syncarp [BOT] A compound fleshy fruit.

syncarpous [BOT] Descriptive of a gynoecium having the carpels united in a compound ovary.

synchondrosis [ANAT] A type of synarthrosis in which the bone surfaces are connected by cartilage.

synchorology [ECOL] A study which involves the distribution ranges of plant communities, phytosociological zones, vegetation and geographical complexes, dissemination spectra, and current plant migration patterns.

synchronous growth [MICROBIO] A population of bacteria in which all cells divide at approximately the same time.

syncytial trophoblast *See* syncytiotrophoblast.

syncytiotrophoblast [CELL BIO] An irregular sheet or net of deeply staining cytoplasm in which nuclei are irregularly scattered. Also known as plasmoditrophoblast; syncytial trophoblast.

syncytium [CELL BIO] A mass of multinucleated cytoplasm without division into separate cells.

syndactyly [ANAT] The condition characterized by union of two or more digits, as in certain birds and mammals; it is a familial anomaly in man.

syndesmosis [ANAT] An articulation in which the bones are joined by collagen fibers.

syndynamics [ECOL] The study of the causes of and trends in successional changes within a plant community.

synecology [ECOL] The study of environmental relations of groups of organisms, such as communities.

Synentognathi [VERT ZOO] The equivalent name for Beloniformes.

synergid [BOT] Either of two small cells lying in the embryo sac in seed plants adjacent to the egg cell toward the micropylar end.

synergism [ECOL] An ecological association in which the physiological processes or behavior of an individual are enhanced by the nearby presence of another organism.

Syngamidae [INV ZOO] A family of roundworms belonging to the Strongyloidea and including parasites of birds and mammals.

syngamy [BIOL] Sexual reproduction involving union of gametes.

syngeneic *See* isogeneic.

Syngnathidae [VERT ZOO] A family of fishes in the order Gasterosteiformes including the seahorses and pipefishes.

synkinesia [PHYSIO] Involuntary movement coincident with purposeful movements carried out by a distant part of the body, such as swinging the arms while walking. Also known as accessory movement; associated automatic movement.

synonym [SYST] A taxonomic name that is rejected as being incorrectly applied, or incorrect in form, or not representative of a natural genetic grouping.

synopsis [SYST] In taxonomy, a brief summary of current knowledge about a taxon.

synostosis [ANAT] A type of synarthrosis in which the bones are continuous.

synovia *See* synovial fluid.

synovial fluid [PHYSIO] A transparent viscid fluid secreted by synovial membranes. Also known as synovia.

synovial membrane [HISTOL] A layer of connective tissue which lines sheaths of tendons at freely moving articulations, ligamentous surfaces of articular capsules, and bursae.

synpelmous [VERT ZOO] Having the two main flexor tendons of the toes united beyond the branches that go to each digit, as in certain birds.

synphylogeny [ECOL] The study of the trends and changes in plant communities through historical and evolutionary perspectives.

synphysiology [ECOL] The study of the metabolic processes of plant communities or species which constantly compete with each other, by investigating water needs, transpiration, assimilation and production or organic matter, physiological effects of light, temperature, root exudates, and various other ecological factors.

synsepalous *See* gamosepalous.

Syntelidae [INV ZOO] The sap-flow beetles, a small family of coleopteran insects in the superfamily Histeroidea.

syntenic group [GEN] The loci on the same chromosome pair, irrespective of whether or not they are known to show linkage in heredity.

Syntexidae [INV ZOO] A family of the Hymenoptera in the superfamily Siricoidea.

synthetase *See* ligase.

Syntrophiidina [PALEON] A suborder of extinct articulate brachiopods of the order Pentamerida characterized by a strong dorsal median fold.

syntrophism [BIOL] Mutual dependence of cells for nutritional needs, especially between strains of bacteria.

syntrophoblast [EMBRYO] The outer synctial layer of the trophoblast that forms the outermost fetal element of the placenta.

syntype [SYST] Any specimen of a series when no specimen is designated as the holotype. Also known as cotype.

synusia [ECOL] A structural unit of a community characterized by uniformity of life-form or of height.

Synxiphosura [PALEON] An extinct heteorgeneous order of arthropods in the subclass Merostomata possibly representing an explosive proliferation of aberrant, terminal, and apparently blind forms.

Syringophyllidae [PALEON] A family of extinct corals in the order Tabulata.

syrinx [PALEON] A tube surrounding the pedicle in certain fossil brachiopods. [VERT ZOO] The vocal organ in birds.

Syrphidae [INV ZOO] The flower flies, a family of cyclorrhaphous dipteran insects in the series Aschiza.

Systellomatophora [INV ZOO] An order of the subclass Pulmonata in which the eyes are contractile but stalks are not retractile, the body is sluglike, oval, or lengthened, and the lung is posterior.

systematics [BIOL] The science of animal and plant classification.

systemic circulation [PHYSIO] The general circulation, as distinct from the pulmonary circulation.

systems ecology [ECOL] The combined approaches of systems analysis and the ecology of whole ecosystems and subsystems.

systole [PHYSIO] The contraction phase of the heart cycle.

syzygy [INV ZOO] End-to-end union of the sporonts of certain gregarine protozoans.

T

Tabanidae [INV ZOO] The deer and horse flies, a family of orthorrhaphous dipteran insects in the series Brachycera.

tabled whelk [INV ZOO] *Neptunea tabulata.* A marine gastropod mollusk about 5 inches (13 centimeters) in length and 2 inches (5 centimeters) in diameter, found at depths of 150–200 feet (45–60 meters), off the west coast of Canada and the United States.

tabula [PALEON] A transverse septum that closes off the lower part of the polyp cavity in certain extinct corals and hydroids.

Tabulata [PALEON] An extinct Paleozoic order of corals of the subclass Zoantharia characterized by an exclusively colonial mode of growth and by secretion of a calcareous exoskeleton of slender tubes.

Tachinidae [INV ZOO] The tachina flies, a family of bristly, grayish or black Diptera whose larvae are parasitic in caterpillars and other insects.

Tachyglossidae [VERT ZOO] A family of monotreme mammals having relatively large brains with convoluted cerebral hemispheres; comprises the echidnas or spiny anteaters.

Tachyniscidae [INV ZOO] A family of myodarian cyclorrhaphous dipteran insects in the subsection Acalypteratae.

tachysterol [BIOCHEM] The precursor of calciferol in the irradiation of ergosterol; an isomer of ergosterol.

tachytely [EVOL] Evolution at a rapid rate resulting in differential selection and fixation of new types.

tactile [PHYSIO] Pertaining to the sense of touch.

tactile hairs *See* vibrissae.

tactoid [BIOCHEM] A particle that appears as a spindle-shaped body under the polarizing microscope and occurs in mosaic virus, fibrin, and myosin.

tactoreceptor [PHYSIO] A sense organ that responds to touch. Also known as tactile receptor.

tadpole [VERT ZOO] The larva of a frog or toad; at hatching it has a rounded body with a long fin-bordered tail, and the gills are external but shortly become internal.

tadpole shrimp [INV ZOO] Any of the phyllopod crustaceans that are members of the genus *Lepidurus*.

taenia [ANAT] A ribbon-shaped band of nerve fibers or muscle.

Taenia [INV ZOO] A genus of tapeworms which occur in humans and other mammals.

Taeniodidea [INV ZOO] An equivalent name for Cyclophyllidea.

Taeniodonta [PALEON] An order of extinct quadrupedal land mammals, known from early Cenozoic deposits in North America.

Taenioidea [INV ZOO] An equivalent name for Cyclophyllidea.

Taeniolabidoidea [PALEON] An advanced suborder of the extinct mammalian order Multituberculata having incisors that were self-sharpening in a limited way.

taenoglossate radula [INV ZOO] A long, narrow radula with seven teeth in each transverse row, found in certain pectinibranch bivalves.

tagua palm [BOT] *Phytelephas macrocarpa.* A palm tree of tropical America; the endosperm of the seed is used as an ivory substitute.

taiga [ECOL] A zone of forest vegetation encircling the Northern Hemisphere between the arctic-subarctic tundras in the north and the steppes, hardwood forests, and prairies in the south.

tail [VERT ZOO] **1.** The usually slender appendage that arises immediately above the anus in many vertebrates and contains the caudal vertebrae. **2.** The uropygium, and its feathers, of a bird. **3.** The caudal fin of a fish or aquatic mammal.

Talitridae [INV ZOO] A family of terrestrial amphipod crustaceans in the suborder Gammaridea.

talon [VERT ZOO] A sharply hooked claw on the foot of a bird of prey.

Talpidae [VERT ZOO] The moles, a family of insectivoran mammals; distinguished by the forelimbs which are adapted for digging, having powerful muscles and a spadelike bony structure.

talus *See* astragalus.

tamarack [BOT] *Larix laricina.* A larch and a member of the pine family; it has an erect narrowly pyramidal habit, and grows in wet and moist soils in the northeastern United States, west to the Lake States and across Canada to Alaska; used for railroad ties, posts, sills, and boats. Also known as hackmarack.

Tanaidacea [INV ZOO] An order of eumalacostracans of the crustacean superorder Peracarida; the body is linear, more or less cylindrical or dorsoventrally depressed, and the first and second thoracic segments are fused with the head, forming a carapace.

Tanaostigmatidae [INV ZOO] A small family of hymenopteran insects in the superfamily Chalcidoidea.

tandem duplication [CELL BIO] The occurrence of two identical sequences, one following the other, in a chromosome segment.

tangelo [BOT] A tree that is hybrid between a tangerine or other mandarin and a grapefruit or shaddock; produces an edible fruit.

tangerine [BOT] Any of several trees of the species *Citrus reticulata*; the fruit is a loose-skinned mandarin with a deep-orange or scarlet rind.

tangoreceptor [PHYSIO] A sense organ in the skin that responds to touch and pressure.

tannase [BIOCHEM] An enzyme that catalyzes the hydrolysis of tannic acid to gallic acid; found in cultures of *Aspergillus* and *Penicillium*.

tan rot [PL PATH] A fungus disease of strawberries caused by *Pezizella lythri* and characterized by the appearance of tan depressions on the fruit.

Tanyderidae [INV ZOO] The primitive crane flies, a family of orthorrhaphous dipteran insects in the series Nematocera.

Tanypezidae [INV ZOO] A family of myodarian cyclorrhaphous dipteran insects in the subsection Acalyptratae.

tape grass [BOT] *Vallisnerida spiralis*. An aquatic flowering plant belonging to the family Hydrocharitaceae. Also known as eel grass.

tapetum [ANAT] 1. A reflecting layer in the choroid coat behind the neural retina, chiefly in the eyes of nocturnal mammals. 2. A tract of nerve fibers forming part of the roof of each lateral ventricle in the vertebrate brain. [BOT] A layer of nutritive cells surrounding the spore mother cells in the sporangium in higher plants; it is broken down to provide nourishment for developing spores.

tapeworm [INV ZOO] Any member of the class Cestoidea; all are vertebrate endoparasites, characterized by a ribbonlike body divided into proglottids, and the anterior end modified into a holdfast organ.

taphocoenosis See thanatocoenosis.

taphonomy [PALEON] The study of fossil preservation, including all events during the transition of organisms from the biosphere to the lithosphere.

tapir [VERT ZOO] Any of several large odd-toed ungulates of the family Tapiridae that have a heavy, sparsely hairy body, stout legs, a prehensile muzzle, a short tail, and small eyes.

Tapiridae [VERT ZOO] The tapirs, a family of perissodactyl mammals in the superfamily Tapiroidea.

Tapiroidea [VERT ZOO] A superfamily of the mammalian order Perissodactyla in the suborder Ceratomorpha.

taproot [BOT] A root system in which the primary root forms a dominant central axis that penetrates vertically and rather deeply into the soil; it is generally larger in diameter than its branches.

tarantula [INV ZOO] 1. Any of various large hairy spiders of the araneid suborder Mygalomorphae. 2. Any of the wolf spiders comprising the family Lycosidae.

Tardigrada [INV ZOO] A class of microscopic, bilaterally symmetrical invertebrates in the subphylum Malacopoda; the body consists of an anterior prostomium and five segments surrounded by a soft, nonchitinous cuticle, with four pairs of ventrolateral legs.

target spot [PL PATH] Any plant disease characterized by lesions in the form of concentric markings.

targusic acid See lapachol.

tarpon [VERT ZOO] *Megalops atlantica*. A herringlike fish of the family Elopidae weighing up to 300 pounds (136 kilograms) and reaching a length of 8 feet (2.4 meters); it has a single soft, rayed dorsal fin, strong jaws, a bony plate under the mouth, numerous small teeth, and coarse, bony flesh covered with large scales.

tarsal gland [ANAT] Any of the sebaceous glands in the tarsal plates of the eyelids. Also known as Meibomian gland.

tarsier [VERT ZOO] Any of several species of primates comprising the genus *Tarsius* of the family Tarsiidae characterized by a round skull, a flattened face, and large eyes that are separated from the temporal fossae in the orbital depression, and by adhesive pads on the expanded ends of the fingers and toes.

Tarsiidae [VERT ZOO] The tarsiers, a family of prosimian primates distinguished by incomplete postorbital closure and a greatly elongated ankle region.

Tarsonemidae [INV ZOO] A small family of phytophagous mites in the suborder Trombidiformes.

tarsus [ANAT] 1. The instep of the foot consisting of the calcaneus, talus, cuboid, navicular, medial, intermediate, and lateral cuneiform bones. 2. The dense connective tissues supporting an eyelid.

tartary buckwheat [BOT] One of three buckwheat species grown commercially; the leaves are narrower than the other two species and arrow-shaped, and the flowers are smaller with inconspicuous greenish-white sepals. Also known as duck wheat; hulless buckwheat; rye buckwheat.

tassel [BOT] The male inflorescence of corn and certain other plants.

taste [PHYSIO] A chemical sense by which flavors are perceived depending on taste, tactile, and warm and cold receptors in the mouth, as well as smell receptors in the nose.

taste bud [ANAT] An end organ consisting of goblet-shaped clusters of elongate cells with microvilli on the distal end to mediate the sense of taste.

taurocholic acid [BIOCHEM] $C_{26}H_{45}NO_7S$ A common bile acid with a five-carbon chain; it is the product of the conjugation of taurine with cholic acid; crystallizes from an alcohol ether solution, and decomposes at about 125°C. Also known as cholaic acid; cholytaurine.

taurodont [ANAT] Of teeth, having a large pulp cavity and reduced roots.

Taxales [BOT] A small order of gymnosperms in the class Pinatae; members are trees or shrubs with evergreen, often needlelike leaves, with a well-developed fleshy covering surrounding the individual seeds, which are terminal or subterminal on short shoots.

taxis [PHYSIO] A mechanism of orientation by means of which an animal moves in a direction related to a source of stimulation.

Taxocrinida [PALEON] An order of flexible crinoids distributed from Ordovician to Mississippian.

Taxodonta [INV ZOO] A subclass of pelecypod mollusks in which the hinge is of the taxodontal type, that is, the dentition is a series of similar alternating teeth and sockets along the hinge margin.

taxon [SYST] A taxonomic group or entity.

taxonomic category [SYST] One of a hierarchy of levels in the biological classification of organisms; the seven major categories are kingdom, phylum, class, order, family, genus, species.

taxonomy [SYST] A study aimed at producing a hierarchical system of classification of organisms which best reflects the totality of similarities and differences.

Tayassuidae [VERT ZOO] The peccaries, a family of artiodactyl mammals in the superfamily Suoidae.

tea [BOT] *Thea sinensis.* A small tree of the family Theaceae having lanceolate leaves and fragrant white flowers; a caffeine beverage is made from the leaves of the plant.

technosphere [ECOL] The part of the physical environment affected through building or modification by humans.

Tectibranchia [INV ZOO] An order of mollusks in the subclass Opisthobranchia containing the sea hares and the bubble shells; the shell may be present, rudimentary, or absent.

tectorial membrane [ANAT] 1. A jellylike membrane covering the organ of Corti in the ear. 2. A strong sheet of connective tissue running from the basilar part of the occipital bone to the dorsal surface of the bodies of the axis and third cervical vertebra.

tectum [ANAT] A rooflike structure of the body, especially the roof of the midbrain including the corpora quadrigemina.

tegmen [BIOL] An integument or covering. [BOT] The inner layer of a seed coat. [INV ZOO] A thickened forewing of Orthoptera, Coleoptera, and certain other insects.

tegmentum [ANAT] A mass of white fibers with gray matter in the cerebral peduncles of higher vertebrates. [BOT] The outer layer, or scales, of a leaf bud. [INV ZOO] The upper layer of a shell plate in Amphineura.

teichoic acid [BIOCHEM] A polymer of ribitol or glycerol phosphate with additional compounds such as glucose linked to the backbone of the polymer; found in the cell walls of some bacteria.

Teiidae [VERT ZOO] The tegus lizards, a diverse family of the suborder Sauria that is especially abundant and widespread in South America.

T-E index *See* temperature-efficiency index.

telamon [INV ZOO] A curved chitinous outgrowth of the cloacal wall in various male nematodes.

teleceptor [PHYSIO] A sense receptor which transmits information about portions of the external environment which are not necessarily in direct contact with the organism, such as the receptors of the ear, eye, and nose.

Telegeusidae [INV ZOO] The long-lipped beetles, a small family of colepteran insects in the superfamily Cantharoidea confined to the western United States.

telencephalon [EMBRYO] The anterior subdivision of the forebrain in a vertebrate embryo; gives rise to the olfactory lobes, cerebral cortex, and corpora striata.

Teleosauridae [PALEON] A family of Jurassic reptiles in the order Crocodilia characterized by a long snout and heavy armor.

Teleostei [VERT ZOO] An infraclass of the subclass Actinopterygii, or rayfin fishes; distinguished by paired bracing bones in the supporting skeleton of the caudal fin, a homocercal caudal fin, thin cycloid scales, and a swim bladder with a hydrostatic function.

telephone theory *See* frequency theory.

Telestacea [INV ZOO] An order of the subclass Alcyonaria comprised of individuals which form erect branching colonies by lateral budding from the body wall of an elongated axial polyp.

teliospore [MYCOL] A thick-walled spore of the terminal stage of Uredinales and Ustilaginales which is a probosidium or a group of probosidia. Also known as teleutospore.

teloblast [INV ZOO] A large cell that produces many smaller cells at the growing end of many embryos, especially in annelids and mollusks.

telocentric [CELL BIO] Pertaining to a chromosome with a terminal centromere.

telocoel [EMBRYO] A cavity of the telencephalon.

telodendrion [ANAT] The terminal branching of an axon. Also known as telodendron.

telodendron *See* telodendrion.

telogen [PHYSIO] A quiescent phase in the cycle of hair growth when the hair is retained in the hair follicle as a dead or "club" hair.

telolecithal [CELL BIO] Of an ovum, having a large, evenly dispersed volume of yolk and a small amount of cytoplasm concentrated at one pole.

telomere [CELL BIO] A centromere in the terminal position on a chromosome.

telophase [CELL BIO] The phase of meiosis or mitosis at which the chromosomes, having reached the poles, reorganize into interphase nuclei with the disappearance of the spindle and the reappearance of the nuclear membrane; in many organisms telophase does not occur at the end of the first meiotic division.

Telosporea [INV ZOO] A class of the protozoan subphylum Sporozoa in which the spores lack a polar capsule and develop from an oocyst.

telotaxis [BIOL] Tactic movement of an organism by the orientation of one or the other of two bilaterally symmetrical receptors toward the stimulus source.

telotroch [INV ZOO] A preanal tuft of cilia in a trochophore larva.

telson [INV ZOO] The postabdominal segment in lobsters, amphipods, and certain other invertebrates.

Temnocephalida [INV ZOO] A group of rhabdocoeles sometimes considered a distinct order but usually classified under the Neorhabdocoela; members are characterized by the possession of tentacles and adhesive organs.

Temnochilidae [INV ZOO] The equivalent name for Ostomidae.

Temnopleuridae [INV ZOO] A family of echinoderms in the order Temnopleuroida whose tubercles are imperforate, though usually crenulate.

Temnopleuroida [INV ZOO] An order of echinoderms in the superorder Echinacea with a camarodont lantern, smooth or sculptured test, imperforate or perforate tubercles, and bronchial slits which are usually shallow.

Temnospondyli [PALEON] An order of extinct amphibians in the subclass Labyrinthodontia having vertebrae with reduced pleurocentra and large intercentra.

temperate and cold savannah [ECOL] A regional vegetation zone, very extensively represented in North America and in Eurasia at high altitudes; consists of scattered or clumped trees (very often conifers and mostly needle-leaved evergreens) and a shrub layer of varying coverage; mosses and, even more abundantly, lichens form an almost continuous carpet.

temperate and cold scrub [ECOL] Regional vegetation zone whose density and periodicity vary a good deal; requires a considerable amount of moisture in the soil, whether from mist, seasonal downpour, or snowmelt; shrubs may be evergreen or deciduous; and undergrowth of ferns and other large-leaved herbs are quite frequent, especially at subalpine level; wind shearing and very cold winters prevent tree growth. Also known as bosque; fourré; heath.

temperate mixed forest [ECOL] A forest of the North Temperate Zone containing a high proportion of conifers with a few broad-leafed species.

temperate phage [VIROL] A deoxyribonucleic acid phage, the genome (DNA) of which can under certain circumstances become integrated with the genome of the host.

temperate rainforest [ECOL] A vegetation class in temperate areas of high and evenly distributed rainfall characterized by comparatively few species with large populations of each species; evergreens are somewhat short with small leaves, and there is an abundance of large tree ferns. Also known as cloud forest; laurel forest; laurisilva; moss forest; subtropical forest.

temperate woodland [ECOL] A vegetation class similar to tropical woodland in spacing, height, and stratification, but it can be either deciduous or evergreen, broad-leaved or needle-leaved. Also known as parkland; woodland.

temperature-efficiency index [ECOL] For a given location, a measure of the long-range effectiveness of temperature (thermal efficiency) in promoting plant growth. Abbreviated T-E index. Also known as thermal-efficiency index.

temperature-efficiency ratio [ECOL] For a given location and month, a measure of thermal efficiency; it is equal to the departure, in degrees Fahrenheit, of the normal monthly temperature above 32°F (0°C) divided by 4: $(T - 32)/4$. Abbreviated T-E ratio. Also known as thermal-efficiency ratio.

temperature-sensitive mutant [GEN] A mutant gene that is functional at high (low) temperature but is inactivated by lowering (elevating) the temperature.

template [MOL BIO] The macromolecular model for the synthesis of another macromolecule.

temporal bone [ANAT] The bone forming a portion of the lateral aspect of the skull and part of the base of the cranium in vertebrates.

temporary plankton See meroplankton.

Tendipedidae [INV ZOO] The midges, a family of orthorrhaphous dipteran insects in the series Nematocera whose larvae occupy intertidal waveswept rocks on the seacoasts.

tendon [ANAT] A white, glistening, fibrous cord which joins a muscle to some movable structure such as a bone or cartilage; tendons permit concentration of muscle force into a small area and allow the muscle to act at a distance.

tendon sheath [ANAT] The synovial membrane surrounding a tendon.

tendril [BOT] A stem modification in the form of a slender coiling structure capable of twining about a support to which the plant is then attached.

Tenebrionidae [INV ZOO] The darkling beetles, a large cosmopolitan family of coleopteran insects in the superfamily Tenebrionoidea; members are common pests of grains, dried fruits, beans, and other food products.

Tenebrionoidea [INV ZOO] A superfamily of the Coleoptera in the suborder Polyphaga.

teniae coli [HISTOL] The three bands comprising the longitudinal layer of the tunica muscularis of the colon: the tenia libera, tenia mesocolica, and tenia omentalis.

tenrec [VERT ZOO] Any of about 30 species of unspecialized, insectivorous mammals indigenous to Madagascar, and which have poor vision and clawed digits.

Tenrecidae [VERT ZOO] The tenrecs, a family of insectivores in the group Lipotyphla.

tensor muscle [PHYSIO] A muscle that stretches a part or makes it tense.

tentacle [INV ZOO] Any of various elongate, flexible processes with tactile, prehensile, and sometimes other functions, and which are borne on the head or about the mouth of many animals.

Tentaculata [INV ZOO] A class of the phylum Ctenophora whose members are characterized by having variously modified tentacles.

tentaculocyst [INV ZOO] A sense organ located at the margin of the umbrella in some coelenterate medusoids, consisting of a modified tentacle with a cavity that often contains lithites.

tentaculozoid [INV ZOO] A slender tentacular individual of a hydrozoan colony.

tented arch [ANAT] A fingerprint pattern which possesses either an angle, an upthrust, or two of the three basic characteristics of a loop.

Tenthredinidae [INV ZOO] A family of hymenopteran insects in the superfamily Tenthredinoidea including economically important species whose larvae are plant pests.

Tenthredinoidea [INV ZOO] A superfamily of Hymenoptera in the suborder Symphyla.

tentilium [INV ZOO] A contractile branch of a tentacle containing many nematocysts in certain siphonophores.

Tenulpalpidae [INV ZOO] A small family of mites in the suborder Trombidiformes.

tepary bean [BOT] *Phaseolus acutifolius* var. *latifolius*. One of the four species of beans of greatest economic importance in the United States.

Tephritidae [INV ZOO] The fruit flies, a family of myodarian cyclorrhaphous dipteran insects in the subsection Acalyptratae.

T-E ratio *See* temperature-efficiency ratio.

Teratornithidae [PALEON] An extinct family of vulturelike birds of the Pleistocene of western North America included in the order Falconiformes.

Terebellidae [INV ZOO] A family of polychaete annelids belonging to the Sedentaria which are chiefly large, thick-bodied, tubicolous forms with the anterior end covered by a matted mass of tentacular cirri.

Terebratellidina [PALEON] An extinct suborder of articulate brachiopods in the order Terebratulida in which the loop is long and offers substantial support to the side arms of the lophophore.

Terebratulida [INV ZOO] An order of articulate brachiopods that has a punctate shell structure and is characterized by the possession of a loop extending anteriorly from the crural bases, providing some degree of support for the lophophore.

Terebratulidina [INV ZOO] A suborder of articulate brachiopods in the order Terebratulida distinguished by a short V- or W-shaped loop.

Teredinidae [INV ZOO] The pileworms or shipworms, a family of bivalve mollusks in the subclass Eulamellibranchia distinguished by having the two valves reduced to a pair of small plates at the anterior end of the animal.

terete [BOT] Of a stem, cylindrical in section, but tapering at both ends.

tergite [INV ZOO] The dorsal plate covering a somite in arthropods and certain other articulate animals.

tergum [INV ZOO] A dorsal plate of the operculum in barnacles.

terminal bar [CELL BIO] One of the structures formed in certain epithelial cells by the combination of local modifications of contiguous surfaces and intervening intercellular substances; they become visible with the light microscope

after suitable staining and appear to close the spaces between the epithelial cells of the intestine at their free surfaces.

terminal bud [BOT] A bud that develops at the apex of a stem. Also known as apical bud.

terminal hair [ANAT] One of three types of hair in man based on hair size, time of appearance, and structural variations; the larger, coarser hair in the adult that replaces the vellus hair.

terminal nerve [ANAT] Either of a pair of small cranial nerves that run from the nasal area to the forebrain, present in most vertebrates; the function is not known.

terminal sinus [EMBRYO] The vascular sinus bounding the area vasculosa of the blastoderm of a meroblastic ovum. Also known as marginal sinus.

terminator codon [GEN] A codon that acts as a stopping point in the code sequence for protein synthesis.

Termitaphididae [INV ZOO] The termite bugs, a small family of Hemiptera in the superfamily Aradoidea.

termitarium [INV ZOO] A termites' nest.

termite [INV ZOO] A soft-bodied insect of the order Isoptera; individuals feed on cellulose and live in colonies with a caste system comprising three types of functional individuals: sterile workers and soldiers, and the reproductives. Also known as white ant.

termiticole [ECOL] An organism that lives in a termites' nest.

Termitidae [INV ZOO] A large family of the order Isoptera which contains the higher termites, representing 80% of the species.

termitophile [ECOL] An organism that lives in a termites' nest in a symbiotic association with the termites.

Termopsidae [INV ZOO] A family of insects in the order Isoptera composed of damp wood-dwelling forms.

ternate [BOT] Composed of three subdivisions, as a leaf with three leaflets.

Ternifine man [PALEON] The name for a fossil human type, represented by three lower jaws and a parietal bone discovered in France and thought to be from the upper part of the middle Pleistocene.

Terramycin [MICROBIO] Trade name for the antibiotic oxytetracycline.

terrapin [VERT ZOO] Any of several North American tortoises in the family Testudinidae, especially the diamondback terrapin.

territoriality [ZOO] A pattern of behavior in which one or more animals occupy and defend a definite area or territory.

tertiary structure [BIOCHEM] The characteristic three-dimensional folding of the polypeptide chains in a protein molecule.

Tessaratomidae [INV ZOO] A family of large tropical Hemiptera in the superfamily Pentatomoidea.

tessellate [BOT] Marked by a pattern of small squares resembling a tiled pavement.

test [INV ZOO] A hard external covering or shell that is calcareous, siliceous, chitinous, fibrous, or membranous.

testa [BOT] A seed coat. Also known as episperm.

Testacellidae [INV ZOO] A family of pulmonate gastropods that includes some species of slugs.

testicular hormone [BIOCHEM] Any of various hormones secreted by the testes.

testis [ANAT] One of a pair of male reproductive glands in vertebrates; after sexual maturity, the source of sperm and hormones.

testosterone [BIOCHEM] $C_{19}H_{28}O_2$ The principal androgenic hormone released by the human testis; may be synthesized from cholesterol and certain other sterols.

Testudinata [VERT ZOO] The equivalent name for Chelonia.

Testudinellidae [INV ZOO] A family of free-swimming rotifers in the suborder Flosculariacea.

Testudinidae [VERT ZOO] A family of tortoises in the suborder Cryptodira; there are about 30 species found on all continents except Australia.

tetanolysin [BIOCHEM] A hemolysin produced by *Clostridium tetani*.

tetanospasmin [BIOCHEM] A neurotoxin elaborated by the bacterium *Clostridium tetani* and which is responsible for the manifestations of tetanus.

Tethinidae [INV ZOO] A family of myodarian cyclorrhaphous dipteran insects in the subsection Acalyptratae.

Tetrabranchia [INV ZOO] A subclass of primitive mollusks of the class Cephalopoda; *Nautilus* is the only living form and is characterized by having four gills.

Tetracentraceae [BOT] A family of dicotyledonous trees in the order Trochodendrales distinguished by possession of a perianth, four stamens, palmately veined leaves, and secretory idioblasts.

Tetracorallia [PALEON] The equivalent name for Rugosa.

Tetractinomorpha [INV ZOO] A heterogeneous subclass of Porifera in the class Demospongiae.

tetracycline [MICROBIO] 1. Any of a group of broad-spectrum antibiotics produced biosynthetically by fermentation with a strain of *Streptomyces aureofaciens* and certain other species or chemically by hydrogenolysis of chlortetracycline. 2. ($C_{22}H_{24}O_8N_2$) A broad-spectrum antibiotic belonging to the tetracycline group of antibiotics; useful because of broad antimicrobial action, with low toxicity, in the therapy of infections caused by gram-positive and gram-negative bacteria as well as rickettsiae and large viruses such as psittacosis-lymphogranuloma viruses.

tetrad [CELL BIO] A group of four chromatids lying parallel to each other as a result of the longitudinal division of each of a pair of homologous chromosomes during the pachytene and later stages of the prophase of meiosis.

tetradactylous [VERT ZOO] Having four digits on a limb.

tetrad analysis [GEN] A method of genetic analysis possible in fungi, algae, bryophytes, and orchids in which the four products of an individual cell which has gone through meiosis are recovered as a group; it provides more direct and complete information regarding segregation and recombination mechanisms than is possible to obtain from meiotic products collected at random.

4,6,3′,4′-tetrahydroxyaurone *See* aureusidin.

Tetrahymenina [INV ZOO] A suborder of ciliated protozoans in the order Hymenostomatida.

Tetralophodontinae [PALEON] An extinct subfamily of proboscidean mammals in the family Gomphotheridae.

tetramerous [BIOL] Characterized by or having four parts.

Tetranychidae [INV ZOO] The spider mites, a family of phytophagous trombidiform mites.

Tetraodontiformes [VERT ZOO] An order of specialized teleost fishes that includes the triggerfishes, puffers, trunkfishes, and ocean sunfishes.

Tetraonidae [VERT ZOO] The ptarmigans and grouse, a family of upland game birds in the order Galliformes characterized by rounded tails and wings and feathered nostrils.

Tetraphidaceae [BOT] The single family of the plant order Tetraphidales.

Tetraphidales [BOT] A monofamilial order of mosses distinguished by scalelike protonema and the peristomes of four rigid, nonsegmented teeth.

Tetraphyllidea [INV ZOO] An order of small tapeworms of the subclass Cestoda characterized by the variation in the structure of the scolex; all species are intestinal parasites of elasmobranch fishes.

tetraploidy [CELL BIO] The occurrence of related forms possessing in the somatic cells chromosome numbers four times the haploid number.

tetrapod [VERT ZOO] A four-footed animal.

Tetrapoda [VERT ZOO] The superclass of the subphylum Vertebrata whose members typically possess four limbs; includes all forms above fishes.

Tetrarhyncholdea [INV ZOO] The equivalent name for Trypanorhyncha.

Tetrasporales [BOT] A heterogeneous and artificial assemblage of colonial fresh-water and marine algae in the division Chlorophyta.

tetraspore [BOT] One of the haploid asexual spores of the red algae formed in groups of four.

tetraxon [INV ZOO] A type of sponge spicule with four axes.

Tetrigidae [INV ZOO] The grouse locusts or pygmy grasshoppers in the order Orthoptera in which the front wings are reduced to small scalelike structures.

tetrodotoxin [BIOCHEM] $C_{11}H_{17}N_3O_8$ A toxin that blocks the action potential in the nerve impulse.

tetrose [BIOCHEM] Any of a group of monosaccharides that have a four-carbon chain; an example is erythrose, $CH_2OH \cdot (CHOH)_2 \cdot CHO$.

Tettigoniidae [INV ZOO] A family of insects in the order Orthoptera which have long antennae, hindlegs fitted for jumping, and an elongate, vertically flattened ovipositor; consists of the longhorn or green grasshopper.

Teuthidae [VERT ZOO] The rabbitfishes, a family of perciform fishes in the suborder Acanthuroidei.

Teuthoidea [INV ZOO] An order of the molluscan subclass Coleoidea in which the rostrum is not developed, the proostracum is represented by the elongated pen or gladus, and ten arms are present.

textile microbiology [MICROBIO] That branch of microbiology concerned with textile materials; deals with microorganisms that are harmful either to the fibers or to the consumer, and microorganisms that are useful, as in the retting process.

Textulariina [INV ZOO] A suborder of foraminiferan protozoans characterized by an agglutinated wall.

thalamus [ANAT] Either one of two masses of gray matter located on the sides of the third ventricle and forming part of the lateral wall of that cavity.

Thalassinidea [INV ZOO] The mud shrimps, a group of thin-shelled, burrowing decapod crustaceans belonging to the Macrura; individuals have large chelate or subchelate first pereiopods, and no chelae on the third pereiopods.

Thalattosauria [PALEON] A suborder of extinct reptiles in the order Eosuchia from the Middle Triassic.

Thaliacea [INV ZOO] A small class of pelagic Tunicata in which oral and atrial apertures occur at opposite ends of the body.

Thalloblonta [BOT] One of the two subkingdoms of plants, characterized by the absence of specialized tissues or organs and multicellular sex organs.

Thallophyta [BOT] The equivalent name for Thalloblonta.

thallospore [BOT] A spore that develops by budding of hyphal cells.

thallus [BOT] A plant body that is not differentiated into special tissue systems or organs and may vary from a single cell to a complex, branching multicellular structure.

thanatocoenosis [PALEON] The assemblage of dead organisms or fossils that occurred together in a given area at a given moment of geologic time. Also known as death assemblage; taphocoenosis.

Thaumaleidae [INV ZOO] A family of orthorrhaphous dipteran insects in the series Nematocera.

Thaumastellidae [INV ZOO] A monospecific family of the Hemiptera assigned to the Pentatomorpha found only in Ethiopia.

Thaumastocoridae [INV ZOO] The single family of the hemipteran superfamily Thaumastocoroidea.

Thaumastocoroidea [INV ZOO] A monofamilial superfamily of the Hemiptera in the subdivision Geocorisae which occurs in Australia and the New World tropics.

Thaumatoxenidae [INV ZOO] A family of cyclorrhaphous dipteran insects in the series Aschiza.

Theaceae [BOT] A family of dicotyledonous erect trees or shrubs in the order Theales characterized by alternate, exstipulate leaves, usually five petals, and mostly numerous stamens.

Theales [BOT] An order of dicotyledonous mostly woody plants in the subclass Dilleniidae with simple or occasionally compound leaves, petals usually separate, numerous stamens, and the calyx arranged in a tight spiral.

theca [ANAT] The sheath of dura mater which covers the spinal cord. [BOT] 1. A moss capsule. 2. A pollen sac. [HISTOL] The layer of stroma surrounding a Graafian follicle. [INV ZOO] The test of a testate protozoan or a rotifer.

theca folliculi [HISTOL] The capsule surrounding a developing or mature Graafian follicle; consists of two layers, theca interna and theca externa.

Thecanephria [INV ZOO] An order of the phylum Brachiata containing a group of elongate, tube-dwelling tentaculate, deep-sea animals of bizarre structure.

thecate [BIOL] Having a theca.

Thecideidina [PALEON] An extinct suborder of articulate brachiopods doubtfully included in the order Terebratulida.

Thecodontia [PALEON] An order of archosaurian reptiles, confined to the Triassic and distinguished by the absence of a supratemporal bone, parietal foramen, and palatal teeth, and by the presence of an antorbital fenestra.

Thelastomidae [INV ZOO] A family of nematode worms in the superfamily Oxyuroidea.

thenar [ANAT] The ball of the thumb.

Theophrastaceae [BOT] A family of tropical and subtropical dicotyledonous woody plants in the order Primulales characterized by flowers having staminodes alternate with the corolla lobes.

Therapsida [PALEON] An order of mammallike reptiles of the subclass Synapsida which first appeared in mid-Permian times and persisted until the end of the Triassic.

Therevidae [INV ZOO] The stiletto flies, a family of orthorrhaphous dipteran insects in the series Brachycera.

Theria [VERT ZOO] A subclass of the class Mammalia including all living mammals except the monotremes.

Theridiidae [INV ZOO] The comb-footed spiders, a family of the suborder Dipneumonomorphae.

thermal belt [ECOL] Any one of several possible horizontal belts of a vegetation type found in mountainous terrain, resulting primarily from vertical temperature variation. Also known as thermal zone.

thermal-efficiency index *See* temperature-efficiency index.

thermal-efficiency ratio *See* temperature-efficiency ratio.

Thermoactinomyces [MICROBIO] A genus of bacteria in the family Micromonosporaceae; single spores form on aerial and substrate mycelia; optimum growth is at temperatures between 45 and 60°C.

thermoduric bacteria [MICROBIO] Bacteria which survive pasteurization, but do not grow at temperatures used in a pasteurizing process.

thermometer bird [VERT ZOO] The name applied to the brush turkey, native to Australia, because it lays its eggs in holes in mounds of earth and vegetation, with the heat from the decaying vegetation serving to incubate the eggs.

Thermomonospora [MICROBIO] A genus of bacteria in the family Micromonosporaceae; aerial and substrate mycelia are formed; single spores are produced on aerial mycelia; thermophilic organisms, with optimum growth temperature between 45 and 55°C.

thermoperiodicity [BOT] The totality of responses of a plant to appropriately fluctuating temperatures.

thermophile [BIOL] An organism that thrives at high temperatures.

Thermoplasma [MICROBIO] A genus of uncertain affiliation in the order Mycoplasmatales; pleomorphic cells grow at about 59°C.

thermoreception [PHYSIO] The process by which environmental temperature affects specialized sense organs (thermoreceptors).

thermoreceptor [PHYSIO] A sense receptor that responds to stimulation by heat and cold.

thermoregulation [PHYSIO] A mechanism by which mammals and birds attempt to balance heat gain and heat loss in order to maintain a constant body temperature when exposed to variations in cooling power of the external medium.

Thermosbaenacea [INV ZOO] An order of small crustaceans in the superorder Pancarida.

Thermosbaenidae [INV ZOO] A family of the crustacean order Thermosbaenacea.

thermotaxis [BIOL] Orientation movement of a motile organism in response to the stimulus of a temperature gradient.

Thermus [MICROBIO] A genus of gram-negative, aerobic bacteria of uncertain affiliation; nonmotile rods and filaments that thrive at 70–72°C.

therophyte [ECOL] An annual plant whose seed is the only overwintering structure.

Theropoda [PALEON] A suborder of carnivorous bipedal saurischian reptiles which first appeared in the Upper Triassic and culminated in the uppermost Cretaceous.

Theropsida [PALEON] An order of extinct mammallike reptiles in the subclass Synapsida.

Thesium [BOT] The hymenium of the apothecium in lichens.

thesocyte [INV ZOO] An amebocyte in Porifera containing ergastic cytoplasmic inclusions.

thiamine [BIOCHEM] $C_{12}H_{17}ClN_4OS$ A member of the vitamin B complex that occurs in many natural sources, frequently in the form of cocarboxylase. Also known as aneurine; vitamin B_1.

thiamine pyrophosphate [BIOCHEM] The coenzyme or prosthetic component of carboxylase; catalyzes decarboxylation of various α-keto acids. Also known as cocarboxylase.

Thiaridae [INV ZOO] A family of freshwater gastropod mollusks in the order Pectinibranchia.

thicket See tropical scrub.

thick-tailed bushbaby [VERT ZOO] *Galago crassicaudatus*. A primate animal in the family Lorisidae; one of the six species of bushbaby; the thick-tailed bushbaby is more aggressive and solitary than the other species, and grows to over

1 foot (30 centimeters) in length with an equally long tail. Also known as great galago.

thigh [ANAT] The upper part of the leg, from the pelvis to the knee.

thigmotaxis See stereotaxis.

Thigmotrichida [INV ZOO] An order of ciliated protozoans in the subclass Holotrichia.

Thinocoridae [VERT ZOO] The seed snipes, family of South American birds in the order Charadriiformes.

Thiobacillus [MICROBIO] A genus of gram-negative, chemolithotrophic bacteria; motile, rod-shaped cells obtain energy by metabolizing sulfur compounds, including elemental sulfur, sulfides, thiosulfate, polythionates, and sometimes thiocyanate; carbon dioxide is the sole carbon source.

Thiobacteriaceae [MICROBIO] Formerly a family of nonfilamentous, gram-negative bacteria of the suborder Pseudomonadineae characterized by the ability to oxidize hydrogen sulfide, free sulfur, and inorganic sulfur compounds to sulfuric acid.

Thiobacterium [MICROBIO] A genus of gram-negative, chemolithotrophic bacteria; rod-shaped cells containing sulfur granules and embedded in a gelatinous mass.

Thiocapsa [MICROBIO] A genus of bacteria in the family Chromatiaceae; cells are spherical, are nonmotile, do not have gas vacuoles, and contain bacteriochlorophyll *a* or *b* on vesicular or tabular photosynthetic membranes.

Thiocystis [MICROBIO] A genus of bacteria in the family Chromatiaceae; cells are spherical, are motile, do not have gas vacuoles, and contain bacteriochlorophyll *a* on vesicular internal membranes.

Thiodendron [MICROBIO] A genus of prosthecate bacteria; spirally twisted, vibrioid cells with thin "stalks" at one or both poles.

Thiodictyon [MICROBIO] A genus of bacteria in the family Chromatiaceae; cells are rod-shaped, are nonmotile, have gas vacuoles, and contain bacteriochlorophyll *a* on vesicular photosynthetic membranes.

Thiopedia [MICROBIO] A genus of bacteria in the family Chromatiaceae; cells are spherical to ovoid, are characteristically arranged in flat sheets composed of tetrads, are nonmotile, have gas vacuoles, and contain bacteriochlorophyll *a* on vesicular or stack-lamellar photosynthetic membranes.

Thioploca [MICROBIO] A genus of bacteria in the family Beggiatoaceae; filaments are composed of segments, and there are one to many filaments in a single sheath; cells usually contain sulfur granules.

Thiorhodaceae [MICROBIO] Formerly a family of bacteria in the suborder Rhodobacteriineae composed of the purple, red, orange, and brown sulfur bacteria; characterized as strict anaerobes which oxidize hydrogen sulfide and store sulfur globules internally.

Thiosarcina [MICROBIO] A genus of bacteria in the family Chromatiaceae; cells are spherical to ovoid, forming cubical sarcina packets of 8–64 cells, are motile, do not have gas vacuoles, and contain bacteriochlorophyll *a*.

Thiospira [MICROBIO] A genus of gram-negative, chemolithotrophic bacteria; motile, spiral cells that have pointed ends and contain sulfur granules.

Thiospirillum [MICROBIO] A genus of bacteria in the family Chromatiaceae; cells are spiral-shaped, are motile, do not have gas vacuoles, and contain bacteriochlorophyll *a* on vesicular photosynthetic membranes.

thiostreptone [MICROBIO] A polypeptide antibiotic produced by a species of *Streptomyces* that crystallizes from a chloroform methanol solution; used in veterinary medicine.

Thiothrix [MICROBIO] A genus of bacteria in the family Leucotrichaceae; morphological features are as for the family; sulfur granules are deposited within the cells.

Thiovulum [MICROBIO] A genus of gram-negative, chemolithotrophic bacteria; motile, round to ovoid cells containing sulfur granules.

thirst [PHYSIO] A sensation, as of dryness in the mouth and throat, resulting from water deprivation.

thistle [BOT] Any of the various prickly plants comprising the family Compositae.

Thlipsuridae [PALEON] A Paleozoic family of ostracod crustaceans in the suborder Platycopa.

Thoracica [INV ZOO] An order of the subclass Cirripedia; individuals are permanently attached in the adult stage, the mantle is usually protected by calcareous plates, and six pairs of biramous thoracic appendages are present.

thoracic cavity *See* thorax.

thoracic duct [ANAT] The common lymph trunk beginning in the crura of the diaphragm at the level of the last thoracic vertebra, passing upward, and emptying into the left subclavian vein at its junction with the left internal jugular vein.

thoracic vertebrae [ANAT] The vertebrae associated with the chest and ribs in vertebrates; there are 12 in humans.

thoracoabdominal breathing [PHYSIO] The process of air breathing in reptiles, birds, and mammals that depends upon aspiration or sucking inspiration, and involves trunk musculature to supply pulmonary ventilation.

Thoracostomopsidae [INV ZOO] A family of marine nematodes in the superfamily Enoploidea, which have the stomatal armature modified to form a hollow tube.

thorax [ANAT] The chest; the cavity of the mammalian body between the neck and the diaphragm, containing the heart, lungs, and mediastinal structures. Also known as thoracic cavity. [INV ZOO] The middle of three principal divisions of the body of certain classes of arthropods.

Thorictidae [INV ZOO] The ant blood beetles, a family of coleopteran insects in the superfamily Dermestoidea.

thorn [BOT] A short, sharp, rigid, leafless branch on a plant. [ZOO] Any of various sharp spinose structures on an animal.

thornback [VERT ZOO] *Raja clavata*. A ray found in European waters and characterized by spines on its back.

thornbush [ECOL] A vegetation class that is dominated by tall succulents and profusely branching smooth-barked deciduous hardwoods which vary in density from mesquite bush in the Caribbean to the open spurge thicket in Central Africa; the climate is that of a warm desert, except for a rather short intense rainy season. Also known as Dorngeholz; Dorngestrauch; dornveld; savane armée; savane épineuse; thorn scrub.

thorn forest [ECOL] A type of forest formation, mostly tropical and subtropical, intermediate between desert and steppe; dominated by small trees and shrubs, many armed with thorns and spines; leaves are absent, succulent, or deciduous during long dry periods, which may also be cool; an example is the caatinga of northeastern Brazil.

thorn scrub *See* thornbush.

thread blight [PL PATH] A fungus disease of a number of tropical and semitropical woody plants, including cocoa and tea, caused by species of *Pellicularia* and *Marasmius* which form filamentous mycelia on the surface of twigs and leaves.

threadfin [VERT ZOO] Common name for any of the fishes in the family Polynemidae.

threonine [BIOCHEM] $CH_3CHOHCH(NH_2)$-COOH A crystalline α-amino acid considered essential for normal growth of animals; it is biosynthesized from aspartic acid and is a precursor of isoleucine in microorganisms.

thresher shark [VERT ZOO] Common name for fishes in the family Alopiidae; pelagic predacious sharks of generally wide distribution that have an extremely long, whiplike tail with which they thrash the water, destroying schools of small fishes.

threshold [PHYSIO] The minimum level of a stimulus that will evoke a response in an irritable tissue.

threshold of audibility [PHYSIO] The minimum effective sound pressure of a specified signal that is capable of evoking an auditory sensation in a specified fraction of the trials; the threshold may be expressed in decibels relative to 0.0002 microbar (2×10^{-5} pascal) or 1 microbar (0.1 pascal). Also known as threshold of detectability; threshold of hearing.

threshold of detectability *See* threshold of audibility.

threshold of feelings [PHYSIO] The minimum effective sound pressure of a specified signal that, in a specified fraction of trials, will stimulate the ear to a point at which there is a sensation of feeling, discomfort, tickle, or pain; normally expressed in decibels relative to 0.0002 microbar (2×10^{-5} pascal) or 1 microbar (0.1 pascal).

threshold of hearing *See* threshold of audibility.

Threskiornithidae [VERT ZOO] The ibises, a family of long-legged birds in the order Ciconiiformes.

thrip [INV ZOO] A small, slender-bodied phytophagous insect of the order Thysanoptera with suctorial mouthparts, a stout proboscis, a vestigial right mandible, and a fully developed left mandible, while wings may be present or absent.

Thripidae [INV ZOO] A large family of thrips, order Thysanoptera, which includes the most common species.

throat [ANAT] The region of the vertebrate body that includes the pharynx, the larynx, and related structures. [BOT] The upper, spreading part of the tube of a gamopetalous calyx or corolla.

thrombin [BIOCHEM] An enzyme elaborated from prothrombin in shed blood which induces clotting by converting fibrinogen to fibrin.

thrombocyte [HISTOL] One of the minute protoplasmic disks found in vertebrate blood; thought to be fragments of megakaryocytes. Also known as blood platelet; platelet.

thrombokinase [BIOCHEM] A proteolytic enzyme in blood plasma that, together with thromboplastin, calcium, and factor V, converts prothrombin to thrombin.

thromboplastin [BIOCHEM] Any of a group of lipid and protein complexes in blood that accelerate the conversion of prothrombin to thrombin. Also known as factor III; plasma thromboplastin component (PTC).

thromboplastinogen *See* antihemophilic factor.

Throscidae [INV ZOO] The false metallic wood-boring beetles, a cosmopolitan family of the Coleoptera in the superfamily Elateroidea.

Thunburg technique [BIOCHEM] A technique used to study oxidation of a substrate occurring by dehydrogenation reactions; methylene blue, a reversibly oxidizable indicator, substitutes for molecular oxygen as the ultimate hydrogen acceptor (oxidant), becoming reduced to the colorless leuco form.

Thunnidae [VERT ZOO] The tunas, a family of perciform fishes; there are no scales on the posterior part of the body, and those on the anterior are fused to form an armored covering, the body is streamlined, and the tail is crescent-shaped.

Thurniaceae [BOT] A small family of monocotyledonous plants in the order Juncales distinguished by an inflorescence of one or more dense heads, vascular bundles of the leaf in vertical pairs, and silica bodies in the leaf epidermis.

Thylacinidae [VERT ZOO] A family of Australian carnivorous marsupials in the superfamily Dasyuroidea.

Thylacoleonidae [PALEON] An extinct family of carnivorous marsupials in the superfamily Phalangeroidea.

thylakoid [CELL BIO] An internal membrane system which occupies the main body of a plastid; particularly well developed in chloroplasts.

thyme [BOT] A perennial mint plant of the genus *Thymus*; pungent aromatic herb is made from the leaves.

Thymelaeaceae [BOT] A family of dicotyledonous woody plants in the order Myrtales characterized by a superior ovary with a solitary ovule, and petals, if present, are scalelike.

thymic corpuscle [HISTOL] A characteristic, rounded, acidophil body in the medulla of the thymus; composed of hyalinized cells concentrically arranged about a core which is occasionally calcified. Also known as Hassal's body.

thymidine [BIOCHEM] $C_{10}H_{14}N_2O_5$ A nucleoside derived from deoxyribonucleic acid; essential growth factor for certain microorganisms in mediums lacking vitamin B_12 and folic acid.

thymidylic acid [BIOCHEM] $C_{10}H_{15}N_2O_8P$ A mononucleotide component of deoxyribonucleic acid which yields thymine, D-ribose, and phosphoric acid on complete hydrolysis.

thymine [BIOCHEM] $C_5H_6N_2O_2$ A pyrimidine component of nucleic acid, first isolated from the thymus.

thymocyte [HISTOL] A lymphocyte formed in the thymus.

thymopharyngeal duct [EMBRYO] The third pharyngobranchial duct; it may elongate between the pharynx and thymus.

thymus gland [ANAT] A lymphoid organ in the neck or upper thorax of all vertebrates; it is most prominent in early life and is essential for normal development of the circulating pool of lymphocytes.

Thyrididae [INV ZOO] The window-winged moths, a small tropical family of lepidopteran insects in the suborder Heteroneura.

thyrocalcitonin *See* calcitonin.

thyroglobulin [BIOCHEM] An iodinated protein found as the storage form of the iodinated hormones in the thyroid follicular lumen and epithelial cells.

thyroglossal duct [EMBRYO] A narrow temporary channel connecting the anlage of the thyroid with the surface of the tongue.

thyroid cartilage [ANAT] The largest of the laryngeal cartilages in humans and most other mammals, located anterior to the cricoid; in man, forms the Adam's apple.

thyroid gland [ANAT] An endocrine gland found in all vertebrates that produces, stores, and secretes the thyroid hormones.

thyroid hormone [BIOCHEM] Commonly, thyroxine or triiodothyronine, or both; a metabolically active compound formed and stored in the thyroid gland which functions to regulate the rate of metabolism.

thyroprotein [BIOCHEM] A protein secreted in the thyroid gland, such as thyroxine.

Thyropteridae [VERT ZOO] The New-World disk-winged bats, a family of the Chiroptera found in Central and South America, characterized by a stalked sucking disk and a well-developed claw on the thumb.

thyrotropic hormone [BIOCHEM] A hormone produced by the adenohypophysis which regulates thyroid gland function. Also known as thyroid-stimulating hormone (TSH).

thyrotropin [BIOCHEM] A thyroid-stimulating hormone produced by the adenohypophysis.

thyroxine [BIOCHEM] $C_{15}H_{11}I_4NO_4$ The active physiologic principle of the thyroid gland; used in the form of the sodium salt for replacement therapy in states of hypothyroidism or absent thyroid function.

thyrse [BOT] An inflorescence with a racemose primary axis and cymose secondary and later axes.

Thysanidae [INV ZOO] A family of hymenopteran insects in the superfamily Chalcidoidea.

Thysanoptera [INV ZOO] The thrips, an order of small, slender insects having exopterygote development, sucking mouthparts, and exceptionally narrow wings with few or no veins and bordered by long hairs.

Thysanura [INV ZOO] The silverfish, machilids, and allies, an order of primarily wingless insects with soft, fusiform bodies.

tibia [ANAT] The larger of the two leg bones, articulating with the femur, fibula, and talus.

tibialis [ANAT] 1. A muscle of the leg arising from the proximal end of the tibia and inserted into the first cuneiform and first metatarsal bones. 2. A deep muscle of the leg arising proximally from the tibia and fibula and inserted into the navicular and first cuneiform bones.

tick [INV ZOO] Any arachnid comprising Ixodoidea; a bloodsucking parasite and important vector of various infectious diseases of humans and lower animals.

tickle [PHYSIO] A tingling sensation of the skin or a mucous membrane following light, tactile stimulation.

tic polonga [VERT ZOO] *Vipera russellii*. A member of the Viperidae; one of the most deadly and most common snakes in India; it may reach a length of 5 feet (1.5 meters), is nocturnal in its habits, and pursues rodents into houses. Also known as Russell's viper.

tidal air [PHYSIO] That air which is inspired and expired during normal breathing.

tidal volume [PHYSIO] The volume of air moved in and out of the lungs during a single normal respiratory cycle.

Tiedemann's body [INV ZOO] One of the small glands opening into the ring vessel in many echinoderms in which amebocytes are produced.

tiger [VERT ZOO] *Felis tigris*. An Asiatic carnivorous mammal in the family Felidae characterized by a tawny coat with transverse black stripes and white underparts.

tiger beetle [INV ZOO] The common name for any of the bright-colored beetles in the family Cicindelidae; there are about 1300 species distributed all over the world.

tiger salamander [VERT ZOO] *Ambystoma tigrinum*. A salamander in the family Ambystomatidae, found in a variety of subspecific forms from Canada to Mexico and over most of the United States; lives in arid and humid regions, and is the only salamander in much of the Great Plains and Rocky Mountains.

tiger shark *See* sand shark.

Tilletiaceae [MYCOL] A family of fungi in the order Ustilaginales in which basidiospores form at the tip of the apibasidium.

Tillodontia [PALEON] An order of extinct quadrupedal land mammals known from early Cenozoic deposits in the Northern Hemisphere and distinguished by large, rodentlike incisors, bluntcuspid cheek teeth, and five clawed toes.

timberline [ECOL] The elevation or latitudinal limits for arboreal growth. Also known as tree line.

time-interval radiosonde *See* pulse-time-modulated radiosonde.

timothy [BOT] *Phleum pratense*. A perennial hay grass of the order Cyperales characterized by moderately leafy stems and a dense cylindrical inflorescence.

Tinamidae [VERT ZOO] The single family of the avian order Tinamiformes.

Tinamiformes [VERT ZOO] The tinamous, an order of South and Central American birds which are superficially fowllike but have fully developed wings and are weak fliers.

Tineidae [INV ZOO] A family of small moths in the superfamily Tineoidea distinguished by an erect, bristling vestiture on the head.

Tineoidea [INV ZOO] A superfamily of heteroneuran Lepidoptera which includes small moths that usually have well-developed maxillary palpi.

Tingidae [INV ZOO] The lace bugs, the single family of the hemipteran superfamily Tingoidea.

Tingoidea [INV ZOO] A superfamily of the Hemiptera in the subdivision Geocorisae characterized by the wings with many lacelike areolae.

Tintinnida [INV ZOO] An order of ciliated protozoans in the subclass Spirotrichia whose members are conical or trumpet-shaped pelagic forms bearing shells.

tipburn [PL PATH] A disease of certain cultivated plants, such as potato and lettuce, characterized by browning of the leaf margins due to excessive loss of water.

Tiphiidae [INV ZOO] A family of the Hymenoptera in the superfamily Scolioidea.

Tipulidae [INV ZOO] The crane flies, a family of orthorrhaphous dipteran insects in the series Nematocera.

tissue [HISTOL] An aggregation of cells more or less similar morphologically and functionally.

tissue culture [CELL BIO] Growth of tissue cells in artificial media.

Titanoideidae [PALEON] A family of extinct land mammals in the order Pantodonta.

titanothere [PALEON] Any member of the family Brontotheriidae.

T method [BOT] A budding method in which a T-shaped cut is made through the bark at the internode of the stock, the bark of the scion is separated from the xylem along the cambium and removed, and the scion is forced into the incision on the stock.

toad [VERT ZOO] Any of several species of the amphibian order Anura, especially in the family Bufonidae; glandular structures in the skin secrete acrid, irritating substances of varying toxicity.

toadstool [MYCOL] Any of various fleshy, poisonous or inedible fungi with a large umbrella-shaped fruiting body.

tobacco [BOT] 1. Any plant of the genus *Nicotinia* cultivated for its leaves, which contain 1–3% of the alkaloid nicotine. 2. The dried leaves of the plant.

tobacco mosaic [PL PATH] Any of a complex of virus diseases of tobacco and other solanaceous plants in which the leaves are mottled with light- and dark-green patches, sometimes interspersed with yellow.

Todidae [VERT ZOO] The todies, a family of birds in the order Coraciiformes found in the West Indies.

toe [ANAT] One of the digits on the foot of man and other vertebrates.

tomato [BOT] A plant of the genus *Lycopersicon*, especially *L. esculentum*, in the family Solanaceae cultivated for its fleshy edible fruit, which is red, pink, orange, yellow, white, or green, with fleshy placentas containing many small, oval seeds with short hairs and covered with a gelatinous matrix.

tomentose [BOT] Covered with densely matted hairs.

tomentum [ANAT] The deep layer of the pia mater composed principally of minute blood vessels. [BIOL] Pubescence consisting of densely matted wooly hairs.

tomium [VERT ZOO] The cutting edge of a bird's beak.

Tomopteridae [INV ZOO] The glass worms, a family of pelagic polychaete annelids belonging to the group Errantia.

tongue [ANAT] A muscular organ located on the floor of the mouth in man and most vertebrates which may serve various functions, such as taking and swallowing food or tasting or as a tactile organ or sometimes a prehensile organ.

tongue worm See acorn worm.

tonic labyrinthine reflexes [PHYSIO] Rotation or deviation of the head causes extension of the limbs on the same side as the chin, and flexion of the opposite extremities: dorsiflexion of the head produces increased extensor tonus of the upper extremities and relaxation of the lower limbs, while ventroflexion of the head produces the reverse; seen in the young infant and patients with a lesion at the midbrain level or above.

tonic neck reflexes [PHYSIO] Reflexes in which rotation or deviation of the head causes extension of the limbs on the same side as the chin, and flexion of the opposite extremities; dorsiflexion of the head produces increased extension tonus of the upper extremities and relaxation of the lower limbs, and ventroflexion of the head, the reverse; seen normally in incomplete forms in the very young infant, and thereafter in patients with a lesion at the midbrain level or above.

tonofibril [CELL BIO] Any of the fibrils converging on desmosomes in epithelial cells.

tonoplast [BOT] The membrane surrounding a plant-cell vacuole.

tonsil [ANAT] 1. Localized aggregation of diffuse and nodular lymphoid tissue found in the throat where the nasal and oral cavities open into the pharynx. 2. See palatine tonsil.

tonus [PHYSIO] The degree of muscular contraction when not undergoing shortening.

tooth [ANAT] One of the hard bony structures supported by the jaws in mammals and by other bones of the mouth and pharynx in lower vertebrates serving principally for prehension and mastication.

tooth shell [INV ZOO] A mollusk of the class Scaphopoda characterized by the elongate, tube-shaped, or cylindrical shell which is open at both ends and slightly curved.

top grafting [BOT] Grafting a scion of one variety of tree onto the main branch of another.

topocline [ECOL] A graded series of characters exhibited by a species or other closely related organisms along a geographical axis.

topogenesis See morphogenesis.

topographic anatomy [ANAT] The use of bony and soft tissue landmarks on the surface of the body to indicate the known location of deeper structures.

topographic climax [ECOL] A climax plant community under a uniform macroclimate over which minor topographic features such as hills, rivers, valleys, or undrained depressions exert a controlling influence.

topotype [SYST] A specimen of a species not of the original type series collected at the type locality.

top shell [INV ZOO] Any of the marine snails of the family Trochidae characterized by a spiral conical shell with a flat base.

topwork [BOT] A procedure employed to propagate seedless varieties of fruit and hybrids, to change the variety of fruit, and to correct pollination problems, using any of three methods: root grafting, crown grafting, and top grafting.

tornaria [INV ZOO] The larva of some acorn worms (Enteropneusta) which is large and marked by complex bands of cilia.

tornote [INV ZOO] A monaxon spicule in certain Porifera having both ends terminating abruptly in points.

torose [INV ZOO] 1. Having knobby prominences on the surface. 2. Cylindrical with alternate swellings and contractions.

Torpedinidae [VERT ZOO] The electric rays or torpedoes, a family of batoid sharks.

torpor [PHYSIO] The condition in hibernating poikilotherms during winter when body temperature drops in a parallel relation to ambient environmental temperatures.

Torridincolidae [INV ZOO] A small family of coleopteran insects in the suborder Myxophaga found only in Africa and Brazil.

tortoise [VERT ZOO] Any of various large terrestrial reptiles in the order Chelonia, especially the family Testudinidae.

Tortricidae [INV ZOO] A family of phytophagous moths in the superfamily Tortricoidea which have a stout body, lightly fringed wings, and thread-like antennae.

Tortricoidea [INV ZOO] A superfamily of small widewinged moths in the suborder Heteroneura.

Torulopsidales [MYCOL] The equivalent name for Cryptococcales.

torus [ANAT] A rounded protruberance occurring on a body part. [BOT] The thickened membrane closing a bordered pit.

Torymidae [INV ZOO] A family of hymenopteran insects in the superfamily Chalcidoidea.

total lung capacity [PHYSIO] The volume of gas contained within the lungs at the end of a maximum inspiration.

totipalmate [VERT ZOO] Having all four toes connected by webs, as in the Pelecaniformes.

totipotence [EMBRYO] Capacity of a blastomere to develop into a fully formed embryo.

toucan [VERT ZOO] Any of numerous fruit-eating birds, of the family Ramphastidae, noted for their large and colorful bills.

touch [PHYSIO] The array of sensations arising from pressure sensitivity of the skin.

toxa [INV ZOO] A curved sponge spicule.

Toxasteridae [PALEON] A family of Cretaceous echinoderms in the order Spatangoida which lacked fascioles and petals.

toxicyst [INV ZOO] A type of trichocyst in Protozoa which may, upon contact, induce paralysis or lysis of the prey.

toxigenicity [MICROBIO] A microorganism's capability for producing toxic substances.

toxin [BIOCHEM] Any of various poisonous substances produced by certain plant and animal cells, including bacterial toxins, phytotoxins, and zootoxins.

Toxodontia [PALEON] An extinct suborder of mammals representing a central stock of the order Notoungulata.

Toxoglossa [INV ZOO] A group of carnivorous marine gastropod mollusks distinguished by a highly modified radula (toxoglossate).

toxoglossate radula [INV ZOO] A radula in certain carnivorous gastropods having elongated, spearlike teeth often perforated by the ducts of large poison glands.

Toxoplasmea [INV ZOO] A class of the protozoan subphylum Sporozoa composed of small, crescent-shaped organisms that move by body flexion or gliding and are characterized by a two-layered pellicle with underlying microtubules, micropyle, paired organelles, and micronemes.

Toxoplasmida [INV ZOO] An order of the class Toxoplasmea; members are parasites of vertebrates.

toxoplasmin [BIOCHEM] The *Toxoplasma* antigen; used in a skin test to demonstrate delayed hypersensitivity to toxoplasmosis.

Toxopneustidae [INV ZOO] A family of Tertiary and extant echinoderms of the order Temnopleuroida where the branchial slits are deep and the test tends to be absent.

Toxothrix [MICROBIO] A genus of gliding bacteria of uncertain affiliation; long, often U-shaped filaments contain colorless, cylindrical cells; move slowly with ends of filament trailing.

Toxotidae [VERT ZOO] The archerfishes, a family of small fresh-water forms in the order Perciformes.

T phage [VIROL] Any of a series (T1–T7) of deoxyribonucleic acid phages which lyse strains of the gram-negative bacterium *Escherichia coli* and its relatives.

TPN *See* triphosphopyridine nucleotide.

trabecula [ANAT] A band of fibrous or muscular tissue extending from the capsule or wall into the interior of an organ.

trachea [ANAT] The cartilaginous and membranous tube by which air passes to and from the lungs in humans and many vertebrates. [BOT] A xylem vessel resembling the trachea of vertebrates. [INV ZOO] One of the anastomosing air-conveying tubules composing the respiratory system in most insects.

tracheid [BOT] An elongate, spindle-shaped xylem cell, lacking protoplasm at maturity, and having secondary walls laid in various thicknesses and patterns over the primary wall.

Tracheophyta [BOT] A large group of plants characterized by the presence of specialized conducting tissues (xylem and phloem) in the roots, stems, and leaves.

Trachylina [INV ZOO] An order of moderate-sized jellyfish of the class Hydrozoa distinguished by having balancing organs and either a small polyp stage or none.

Trachymedusae [INV ZOO] A group of marine jellyfish, recognized as a separate order or as belonging to the order Trachylina whose tentacles have a solid core consisting of a single row of endodermal cells.

Trachypsammiacea [INV ZOO] An order of colonial anthozoan coelenterates characterized by a dendroid skeleton.

Trachystomata [VERT ZOO] The name given to the Meantes when the group is considered to be an order.

Tragulidae [VERT ZOO] The chevrotains, a family of pecoran ruminants in the superfamily Traguloidea.

Traguloidea [VERT ZOO] A superfamily of pecoran ruminants, composed of the most primitive forms with large canines; the chevrotain is the only extant member.

tragus [ANAT] 1. The prominence in front of the opening of the external ear. 2. One of the hairs in the external ear canal.

trama [MYCOL] The loosely woven hyphal tissue between adjacent hymenia in basidiomycetes.

transaminase [BIOCHEM] One of a group of enzymes that catalyze the transfer of the amino group of an amino acid to a keto acid to form another amino acid. Also known as aminotransferase.

transcapsidation [VIROL] Change in the capsid of PARA (particle aiding replication of adenovirus) from one type of adenovirus to another.

transcription [MOL BIO] The process by which ribonucleic acid is formed from deoxyribonucleic acid.

transduction [MICROBIO] Transfer of genetic material between bacterial cells by bacteriophages.

transfection [GEN] Infection of a cell with viral deoxyribonucleic acid or ribonucleic acid.

transferase [BIOCHEM] Any of various enzymes that catalyze the transfer of a chemical group from one molecule to another.

transfer ribonucleic acid [MOL BIO] The smallest ribonucleic acid molecule found in cells; its structure is complementary to messenger ribonucleic acid and it functions by transferring amino acids from the free state to the polymeric form of growing polypeptide chains. Abbreviated tRNA.

transferrin [BIOCHEM] Any of various beta globulins in blood serum which bind and transport iron to the bone marrow and storage areas.

transforming principle [MICROBIO] Deoxyribonucleic acid which effects transformation in bacterial cells.

transition [MOL BIO] A mutation resulting from the substitution in deoxyribonucleic acid or ribonucleic acid of one purine or pyrimidine for another.

transitional epithelium [HISTOL] A form of stratified epithelium found in the urinary bladder; cells vary between squamous, when the tissue is stretched, and columnar, when not stretched.

transketolase [BIOCHEM] An enzyme that cleaves a substrate at the position of the carbonyl carbon and transports a two-carbon fragment to an acceptor compound to form a new compound.

translation [MOL BIO] The process by which the linear sequence of nucleotides in a molecule of messenger ribonucleic acid directs the specific linear sequence of amino acids, as during protein synthesis.

translocation [BOT] Movement of water, mineral salts, and organic substances from one part of a plant to another. [CYTOL] The transfer of a chromosome segment from its usual position to a new position in the same or in a different chromosome.

transmethylase [BIOCHEM] A transferase enzyme involved in catalyzing chemical reactions in which methyl groups are transferred from a substrate to a new compound.

transmethylation [BIOCHEM] A metabolic reaction in which a methyl group is transferred from one compound to another; methionine and choline are important donors of methyl groups.

transpiration [BIOL] The passage of a gas or liquid (in the form of vapor) through the skin, a membrane, or other tissue.

transplantation [BIOL] 1. The artificial removal of part of an organism and its replacement in the body of the same or of a different individual. 2. To remove a plant from one location and replant it in another place.

transversion [MOL BIO] A mutation resulting from the substitution in deoxyribonucleic acid or ribonucleic acid of a purine for a pyrimidine or a pyrimidine for a purine.

trapeziform [BIOL] Having the form of a trapezium.

traumatotropism [BIOL] Orientation response of an organ of a sessile organism in response to a wound.

Trebidae [INV ZOO] A family of copepod crustaceans of the order Caligoida which are external parasites on selachians.

tree [BOT] A perennial woody plant at least 20 feet (6 meters) in height at maturity, having an erect stem or trunk and a well-developed crown or leaf canopy.

tree fern [BOT] The common name for plants belonging to the families Cyatheaceae and Dicksoniaceae; all are ferns that exhibit an arborescent habit.

tree frog [VERT ZOO] Any of the arboreal frogs comprising the family Hylidae characterized by expanded digital adhesive disks.

tree line See timberline.

Trematoda [INV ZOO] A loose grouping of acoelomate, parasitic flatworms of the phylum Platyhelminthes; they exhibit cephalization, bilateral symmetry, and well-developed holdfast structures.

Trematosauria [PALEON] A group of Triassic amphibians in the order Temnospondyli.

Tremellales [MYCOL] An order of basidiomycetous fungi in the subclass Heterobasidiomycetidae in which basidia have longitudinal walls.

Trentepohliaceae [BOT] A family of green algae belonging to the Ulotrichales having thick walls, bandlike or reticulate chloroplasts, and zoospores or isogametes produced in enlarged, specialized cells.

Treponema [MICROBIO] A genus of bacteria in the family Spirochaetaceae; cells are helical rods with tight spirals and have axial fibrils at both ends of the protoplasmic cylinder; some species are pathogens.

Treponema pallidum [MICROBIO] The spirochetal bacterium which causes syphilis.

Treponemataceae [MICROBIO] Formerly a family of the bacterial order Spirochaetales including the spirochetes less than 20 micrometers long and less than 5 micrometers in diameter; most species are parasitic.

Trepostomata [PALEON] An extinct order of ectoproct bryozoans in the class Stenolaemata characterized by delicate to massive colonies composed of tightly packed zooecia with solid calcareous zooecial walls.

Treroninae [VERT ZOO] The fruit pigeons, a subfamily of the avian family Columbidae distinguished by the gaudy coloration of the feathers.

Tretothoracidae [INV ZOO] A family of the Coleoptera in the superfamily Tenebrionoidea which contains a single species found in Queensland, Australia.

triacetyloleandomycin [MICROBIO] An antibiotic produced by *Streptomyces antibioticus* and used clinically in the treatment of pneumonia, osteomyelitis, furuncles, and carbuncles.

triaene [INV ZOO] An elongated spicule in certain Porifera with three rays diverging from one end.

Triakidae [VERT ZOO] A family of galeoid sharks in the carcharinid line.

triandrous [BOT] Possessing three stamens.

triangular ligament See urogenital diaphragm.

Triatominae [INV ZOO] The kissing bugs, a subfamily of hemipteran insects in the family Reduviidae, distinguished by a long, slender rostrum.

triaxon [INV ZOO] A spicule in Porifera having three axes which cross each other at right angles.

tricarboxylic acid cycle See Krebs cycle.

Trichechidae [VERT ZOO] The manatees, a family of nocturnal, solitary sirenian mammals in the suborder Trichechiformes.

Trichechiformes [VERT ZOO] A suborder of mammals in the order Sirenia which contains the manatees and dugongids.

trichesthesia [PHYSIO] A form of tactile sensibility in hair-covered regions of the body.

Trichiaceae [MYCOL] A family of slime molds in the order Trichiales.

Trichiales [MYCOL] An order of Myxomycetes in the subclass Myxogastromycetidae.

Trichiuridae [VERT ZOO] The cutlass-fishes, a family of the suborder Scombroidei.

trichobothrium [INV ZOO] An erect, bristlelike sensory hair found on certain arthropods, insects, and other invertebrates.

trichobranchiate gill [INV ZOO] A gill with filamentous branches arranged in several series around the axis; found in some decapod crustaceans.

Trichobranchidae [INV ZOO] A family of polychaete annelids belonging to the Sedentaria; most members are rare and live at great ocean depths.

trichocercous cercaria [INV ZOO] A trematode larva distinguished by a spiny tail.

Trichocomaceae [MYCOL] A small tropical family of ascomycetous fungi in the order Eurotiales with ascocarps from which a tuft of capillitial threads extrudes, releasing the ascospores after dissolution of the asci.

trichocyst [INV ZOO] A minute structure in the cortex of certain protozoans that releases filamentous or fibrillar threads when discharged.

Trichodactylidae [INV ZOO] A family of freshwater crabs in the section Brachyura, found mainly in tropical regions.

Trichogrammatidae [INV ZOO] A family of the Hymenoptera in the superfamily Chalcidoidea whose larvae are parasitic in the eggs of other insects.

trichogyne [BOT] A terminal portion of a procarp or archicarp which receives a spermatium.

trichome [BOT] An appendage derived from the protoderm in plants, including hairs and scales. [INV ZOO] A brightly colored tuft of hairs on the body of a myrmecophile that releases an aromatic substance attractive to ants.

Trichomonadida [INV ZOO] An order of the protozoan class Zoomastigophorea which contains four families of uninucleate species.

Trichomonadidae [INV ZOO] A family of flagellate protozoans in the order Trichomonadida.

Trichomonas [INV ZOO] A genus of flagellate, parasitic protozoans, belonging to the Mastigophora, characterized by three to five flagella and an undulating membrane.

Trichomonas vaginalis [INV ZOO] A species of Protozoa that causes vaginitis.

Trichomycetes [MYCOL] A class of true fungi, division Fungi.

trichomycin [MICROBIO] An antibiotic produced by *Streptomyces hachijoensis* and *S. abikoensis*; a water-soluble yellow powder that inhibits yeasts and fungi.

Trichoniscidae [INV ZOO] A primitive family of isopod crustaceans in the suborder Oniscoidea found in damp littoral, halophilic, or riparian habitats.

Trichophilopteridae [INV ZOO] A family of lice in the order Mallophaga adapted to life upon the lemurs of Madagascar.

Trichoptera [INV ZOO] The caddis flies, an aquatic order of the class Insecta; larvae are wormlike and adults have two pairs of well-veined hairy wings, long antennae, and mouthparts capable of lapping only liquids.

Trichopterygidae [INV ZOO] The equivalent name for Ptiliidae.

Trichostomatida [INV ZOO] An order of ciliated protozoans in the subclass Holotrichia in which no true buccal ciliature is present but there is a vestibulum.

Trichostrongylidae [INV ZOO] A family of parasitic roundworms belonging to the Strongyloidea; hosts are cattle, sheep, goats, swine, and cats.

Trichuroidea [INV ZOO] A group of nematodes parasitic in various vertebrates and characterized by a slender body sometimes having a thickened posterior portion.

Tricladida [INV ZOO] The planarians, an order of the Turbellaria distinguished by diverticulated intestines with a single anterior branch and two posterior branches separated by the pharynx.

triconodont [VERT ZOO] **1.** A tooth with three main conical cusps. **2.** Having such teeth.

Triconodonta [PALEON] An extinct mammalian order of small flesh-eating creatures of the Mesozoic era having no angle or a pseudoangle on the lower jaw and triconodont molars.

Trictenotomidae [INV ZOO] A small family of Indian and Malaysian beetles in the superfamily Tenebrionoidea.

tricuspid [ANAT] Having three cusps or points, as a tooth.

tricuspid valve [ANAT] A valve consisting of three flaps located between the right atrium and right ventricle of the heart.

Tridacnidae [INV ZOO] A family of bivalve mollusks in the subclass Eulamellibranchia which contains the giant clams of the tropical Pacific.

Tridactylidae [INV ZOO] The pygmy mole crickets, a family of insects in the order Orthoptera, highly specialized for fossorial existence.

trifid [BIOL] Divided into three lobes separated by narrow sinuses partway to the base.

trifoliate [BOT] Having three leaves or leaflets.

trigeminal nerve [ANAT] The fifth cranial nerve in vertebrates; either of a pair of composite nerves rising from the side of the medulla, and with three great branches: the ophthalmic, maxillary, and mandibular nerves.

Triglidae [VERT ZOO] The searobins, a family of perciform fishes in the suborder Cottoidei.

Trigonalidae [INV ZOO] A small family of hymenopteran insects in the superfamily Proctotrupoidea.

trigone [ANAT] A triangular area inside the bladder limited by the openings of the ureters and urethra. [BOT] A thickening of plant cell walls formed when three or more cells adjoin.

Trigonostylopoidea [PALEON] A suborder of Paleocene-Eocene ungulate mammals in the order Astrapotheria.

trigonous [BIOL] 1. Having three corners. 2. Having a triangular cross section.

Trilobita [PALEON] The trilobites, a class of extinct Cambrian-Permian arthropods characterized by an exoskeleton covering the dorsal surface, delicate biramous appendages, body segments divided by furrows on the dorsal surface, and a pygidium composed of fused segments.

Trilobitoidea [PALEON] A class of Cambrian arthropods that are closely related to the Trilobita.

Trilobitomorpha [INV ZOO] A subphylum of the Arthropoda including Trilobita.

trilocular [BIOL] Having three cavities or cells.

Trimenoponidae [INV ZOO] A family of lice in the order Mallophaga occurring as parasites on South American rodents.

Trimerellacea [PALEON] A superfamily of extinct inarticulate brachiopods in the order Lingulida; they have valves, usually consisting of calcium carbonate.

Trimerophytopsida [PALEOBOT] A group of extinct land vascular plants with leafless, dichotomously branched stems that bear terminal sporangia.

trimerous [BOT] Having parts in sets of three. [INV ZOO] In insects, having the tarsus divided or apparently divided into three segments.

trimethylvinylammonium hydroxide *See* neurine.

trimorphous [BIOL] Characterized by occurring in three distinct forms, as an organ or whole organism.

trinomial [SYST] A nomenclatural designation for an organism composed of three terms: genus, species, and subspecies or variety.

trinominal nomenclature [SYST] The designation of subspecies by a three-word name.

Trionychidae [VERT ZOO] The soft-shelled turtles, a family of reptiles in the order Chelonia.

triose [BIOCHEM] A group of monsaccharide compounds that have a three-carbon chain length.

triphosphopyridine dinucleotide *See* triphosphopyridine nucleotide.

triphosphopyridine nucleotide [BIOCHEM] $C_{12}H_{28}N_7O_{17}P_3$ A grayish-white powder, soluble in methanol and in water; a coenzyme and an important component of enzymatic systems concerned with biological oxidation-reduction systems. Abbreviated TPN. Also known as codehydrogenase II; coenzyme II; triphosphopyridine dinucleotide.

tripinnate [BIOL] Being bipinnate and having each division pinnate.

triple response [PHYSIO] The three stages of vasomotor reaction consisting of reddening, flushing of adjacent skin, and development of wheals, when a pointed instrument is drawn heavily across the skin.

Triploblastica [ZOO] Animals that develop from three germ layers.

triploidy [CELL BIO] The occurrence of related forms possessing chromosome numbers three times the haploid number.

Tripylina [INV ZOO] A subdivision of the protozoan order Oculosida in which the major opening (astropyle) usually contains a perforated plate.

trisaccate pollen [BOT] A three-pored pollen grain, often having a triangular outline in cross section.

trisaccharide [BIOCHEM] A carbohydrate which, on hydrolysis, yields three molecules of monosaccharides.

trisomy [CELL BIO] The presence in triplicate of one of the chromosomes of the complement.

tritonymph [INV ZOO] The third stage of development in certain acarids.

Triuridaceae [BOT] A family of monocotyledonous plants in the order Triuridales distinguished by unisexual flowers and several carpels with one seed per carpel.

Triuridales [BOT] A small order of terrestrial, mycotrophic monocots in the subclass Alismatidae without chlorophyll, and with separate carpels, trinucleate pollen, and a well-developed endosperm.

trivium [INV ZOO] The three rays opposite the madreporite in starfish.

tRNA *See* transfer ribonucleic acid.

Trochacea [PALEON] A recent subfamily of primitive gastropod mollusks in the order Aspidobranchia.

trochal disk [INV ZOO] A flat or funnel-shaped ciliated disk at the anterior end of a rotifer that functions in locomotion and food ingestion.

trochanter [ANAT] A process on the proximal end of the femur in many vertebrates, which serves for muscle attachment and, in birds, for articulation with the ilium. [INV ZOO] The second segment of an insect leg, counting from the base.

Trochidae [INV ZOO] A family of gastropod mollusks in the order Aspidobranchia, including many of the top shells.

Trochili [VERT ZOO] A suborder of the avian order Apodiformes.

Trochilidae [VERT ZOO] The hummingbirds, a tropical New World family of the suborder Trochili with tubular tongues modified for nectar feeding; slender bills and the ability to hover are further feeding adaptations.

Trochiliscales [PALEOBOT] A group of extinct plants belonging to the Charophyta in which the gyrogonites are dextrally spiraled.

trochlea [ANAT] A pulleylike anatomical structure.

trochlear nerve [ANAT] The fourth cranial nerve; either of a pair of somatic motor nerves which innervate the superior oblique muscle of the eyeball.

trochoblast [INV ZOO] A cell bearing cilia on a trochophore.

Trochodendraceae [BOT] A family of dicotyledonous trees in the order Trochodendrales distinguished by the absence of a perianth and stipules, numerous stamens, and pinnately veined leaves.

Trochodendrales [BOT] An order of dicotyledonous trees in the subclass Hamamelidae characterized by primitively vesselless wood and unique, elongate, often branched idioblasts in the leaves.

trochoid *See* pivot joint.

trochophore [INV ZOO] A generalized but distinct free-swimming larva found in several invertebrate groups, having a pear-shaped form with an external circlet of cilia, apical ciliary tufts, a complete functional digestive tract, and paired nephridia with excretory tubules. Also known as trochosphere.

trochosphere *See* trochophore.

trochus [INV ZOO] The inner band of cilia on a trochal disk.

Troglodytidae [VERT ZOO] The wrens, a family of songbirds in the order Passeriformes.

Trogonidae [VERT ZOO] The trogons, the single, pantropical family of the avian order Trogoniformes.

Trogoniformes [VERT ZOO] An order of brightly colored, slow-moving birds characterized by a unique foot structure with the first and second toes directed backward.

Troland and Fletcher theories [PHYSIO] Theories of hearing according to which the time nature of a sound stimulation affects the sensation of pitch.

Trombiculidae [INV ZOO] The chiggers, or red bugs, a family of mites in the suborder Trombidiformes whose larvae are parasites of vertebrates.

Trombidiformes [INV ZOO] The trombidiform mites, a suborder of the Acarina distinguished by the presence of a respiratory system opening at or near the base of the chelicerae.

Tropaeolaceae [BOT] A family of dicotyledonous plants in the order Geraniales characterized by strongly irregular flowers, simple peltate leaves, eight stamens, and schizocarpous fruit.

trophallaxis [ECOL] Exchange of food between organisms, not only of the same species but between different species, especially among social insects.

trophic [BIOL] Pertaining to or functioning in nutrition.

trophic level [ECOL] Any of the feeding levels through which the passage of energy through an ecosystem proceeds; examples are photosynthetic plants, herbivorous animals, and microorganisms of decay.

trophobiosis [ECOL] A nutritional relationship associated only with certain species of ants in which alien insects supply food to the ants and are milked by the ants for their secretions.

trophoblast [EMBRYO] A layer of ectodermal epithelium covering the outer surface of the chorion and chorionic villi of many mammals.

trophocyte [INV ZOO] A nutritive cell of the ovary or testis of an insect.

trophogenic [ECOL] Originating from nutritional differences rather than resulting from genetic determinants, such as various castes of social insects.

tropholytic [ECOL] Pertaining to the deep zone in a lake where dissimilation of organic matter predominates.

trophosome [INV ZOO] The nutritional zooids of a hydroid colony.

trophotaeniae [VERT ZOO] Vascular rectal processes which establish placental relationships with the ovarian tissue in live-bearing fishes.

trophozoite [INV ZOO] A vegetative protozoan; used especially of a parasite.

trophus [INV ZOO] Masticatory apparatus in Rotifera.

tropical life zone [ECOL] A subdivision of the eastern division of Merriam's life zones; an example is southern Florida, where the vegetation is the broadleaf evergreen forest; typical and important plants are palms and mangroves; typical and important animals are the armadillo and alligator; typical and important crops are citrus fruits, avocado, and banana.

tropical rainforest [ECOL] A vegetation class consisting of tall, close-growing trees, their columnar trunks more or less unbranched in the lower two-thirds, and forming a spreading and frequently flat crown; occurs in areas of high temperature and high rainfall. Also known as hylaea; selva.

tropical savanna *See* tropical woodland.

tropical scrub [ECOL] A class of vegetation composed of low woody plants (shrubs), sometimes growing quite close together, but more often separated by large patches of bare ground, with clumps of herbs scattered throughout; an example is the Ghanaian evergreen coastal thicket. Also known as brush; bush; fourré; mallee; thicket.

tropical woodland [ECOL] A vegetation class similar to a forest but with wider spacing between trees and sparse lower strata characterized by evergreen shrubs and seasonal graminoids; the climate is warm and moist. Also known as parkland; savanna-woodland; tropical savanna.

Tropiometridae [INV ZOO] A family of feather stars in the class Crinoidea which are bottom crawlers.

tropism [BIOL] Orientation movement of a sessile organism in response to a stimulus. Also known as topotaxis.

tropocollagen [BIOCHEM] The fundamental units of collagen fibrils.

tropomyosin [BIOCHEM] A muscle protein similar to myosin and implicated as being part of the structure of the Z bands separating sarcomeres from each other.

troponin [BIOCHEM] A protein species located at specific stations every 36.5 nanometers on the actin helix in muscle sarcomere.

tropophytia [BOT] Plants that thrive in a climate that undergoes marked periodic changes.

trout [VERT ZOO] Any of various edible freshwater fishes in the order Salmoniformes that are generally much smaller than the salmon.

Trucherognathidae [PALEON] A family of conodonts in the order Conodontophorida in which the attachment scar permits the conodont to rest on the jaw ramus.

truffle [BOT] The edible underground fruiting body of various European fungi in the family Tuberaceae, especially the genus *Tuber*.

trumpeter [VERT ZOO] A bird belonging to the Psophiidae, a family with three South American species; the common trumpeter (*Psophia crepitans*) is the size of a pheasant and resembles a long-legged guinea fowl.

truncate [BIOL] Abbreviated at an end, as if cut off.

truncus arteriosis [EMBRYO] The embryonic arterial trunk between the bulbous arteriosis and the ventral aorta in anamniotes and early stages of amniotes.

trunk [ANAT] The main mass of the human body, exclusive of the head, neck, and extremities; it is divided into thorax, abdomen, and pelvis. [BOT] The main stem of a tree.

Tryblidiidae [PALEON] An extinct family of Paleozoic mollusks.

Trypanorhyncha [INV ZOO] An order of tapeworms of the subclass Cestoda; all are parasites in the intestine of elasmobranch fishes.

Trypanosoma [INV ZOO] A genus of slender, polymorphic, elongate protozoans belonging to the Mastigophora, characterized by a central nucleus, posterior blepharoplast, and an undulating membrane; responsible for such infections as trypanosomiasis and Chagas' disease in man.

Trypanosomatidae [INV ZOO] A family of Protozoa, order Kinetoplastida, containing flagellated parasites which exhibit polymorphism during their life cycle.

trypanosome [INV ZOO] A flagellated protozoan of the genus *Trypanosoma*.

trypsin [BIOCHEM] A proteolytic enzyme which catalyzes the hydrolysis of peptide linkages in proteins and partially hydrolyzed proteins; derived from trypsinogen by the action of enterokinase in intestinal juice.

trypsinogen [BIOCHEM] The zymogen of trypsin, secreted in the pancreatic juice. Also known as protrypsin.

tryptophan [BIOCHEM] $C_{11}H_{12}O_2N_2$ An amino acid obtained from casein, fibrin, and certain other proteins; it is a precursor of indoleacetic acid, serotonin, and nicotinic acid.

tsetse fly [INV ZOO] Any of various South African muscoid flies of the genus *Glossina*; medically important as vectors of sleeping sickness or trypanosomiasis.

tubal bladder [VERT ZOO] A urine reservoir organ that is an enlargement of the mesonephric ducts in most fish; there are four types: duplex, bilobed, simplex with ureters tied, and simplex with separate ureters.

tube [BIOL] A narrow channel within the body of an animal or plant.

tube foot [INV ZOO] One of the tentaclelike outpushings of the radial vessels of the water-vascular system in echinoderms; may be suctorial, or serve as stiltlike limbs or tentacles.

tuber [BOT] The enlarged end of a rhizome in which food accumulates, as in the potato.

tuber cinereum [ANAT] An area of gray matter extending from the optic chiasma to the mammillary bodies and forming part of the floor of the third ventricle.

tubercle [BIOL] A small knoblike prominence.

tubercle bacillus See Mycobacterium tuberculosis.

Tuberculariaceae [MYCOL] A family of fungi of the order Moniliales having short conidia that form cushion-shaped, often waxy or gelatinous aggregates (sporodochia).

tuberculate [BIOL] Having or characterized by knoblike processes.

tuberosity [ANAT] A large or obtuse prominence, especially as on bone for muscle attachment.

tuberous organ [PHYSIO] An electroreceptor most sensitive to high-frequency electric signals, distributed over the body surface of electric fish.

Tubicola [INV ZOO] An order of sedentary polychaete annelids that surround themselves with a calcareous tube or one which is composed of agglutinated foreign particles.

Tubulanidae [INV ZOO] A family of the order Palaeonemertini.

tubular gland [ANAT] A secreting structure whose secretory endpieces are tubelike or cylindrical in shape.

tubule [ANAT] A slender, elongated microscopic tube in an anatomical structure.

Tubulidentata [VERT ZOO] An order of mammals which contains a single living genus, the aardvark (*Orycteropus*) of Africa.

tubulin [BIOCHEM] A globular protein containing two subunits; 10–14 molecules are arranged to form a microtubule.

tubuloalveolar gland [ANAT] A secreting structure having both tubular and alveolar secretory endpieces. Also known as acinotubular gland; tubuloacinous gland.

tulip [BOT] Any of various plants with showy flowers constituting the genus *Tulipa* in the family Liliaceae; characterized by coated bulbs, lanceolate leaves, and a single flower with six equal perianth segments and six stamens.

tulip poplar See tulip tree.

tulip tree [BOT] *Liriodendron tulipifera*. A tree belonging to the magnolia family (Magnoliaceae) distinguished by leaves which are squarish at the tip, large terminal buds, cone-shaped fruit, and large greenish-yellow and orange-colored flowers. Also known as tulip poplar.

tumbleweed [BOT] Any of various plants that break loose from their roots in autumn and are driven by the wind in rolling masses over the ground.

tumid [BIOL] Marked by swelling or inflation.

tuna [VERT ZOO] Any of the large, pelagic, cosmopolitan marine fishes which form the family Thunnidae including species that rank among the most valuable of food and game fish.

tundra [ECOL] An area supporting some vegetation between the northern upper limit of trees and the lower limit of perennial snow on mountains, and on the fringes of the Antarctic continent and its neighboring islands.

tung nut [BOT] The seed of the tung tree (*Aleurites fordii*), which is the source of tung oil.

tung tree [BOT] *Aleurites fordii*. A plant of the spurge family in the order Euphorbiales, native to central and western China and grown in the southern United States.

tunica [BIOL] A membrane or layer of tissue that covers or envelops an organ or other anatomical structure.

tunica adventitia *See* adventitia.

tunica intima *See* intima.

tunica mucosa *See* mucous membrane.

Tunicata [INV ZOO] A subphylum of the Chordata characterized by restriction of the notochord to the tail and posterior body of the larva, absence of mesodermal segmentation, and secretion of an outer covering or tunic about the body.

Tupaiidae [VERT ZOO] The tree shrews, a family of mammals in the order Insectivora.

tupelo [BOT] Any of various trees belonging to the genus *Nyssa* of the sour gum family, Nyssaceae, distinguished by small, obovate, shiny leaves, a small blue-black drupaceous fruit, and branches growing at a wide angle from the axis.

Turbellaria [INV ZOO] A class of the phylum Platyhelminthes having bodies that are elongate and flat to oval or circular in cross section.

turbidostat [MICROBIO] A device in which a bacterial culture is maintained at a constant volume and cell density (turbidity) by adjusting the flow rate of fresh medium into the growth tube by means of a photocell and appropriate electrical connections.

turbinate [BOT] Shaped like an inverted cone. [INV ZOO] Spiral with rapidly decreasing whorls from base to apex.

Turbinidae [INV ZOO] A family of gastropod mollusks including species of top shells.

Turdidae [VERT ZOO] The thrushes, a family of passeriform birds in the suborder Oscines.

turgor [BOT] Distension of a plant cell wall and membrane by the fluid contents.

turgor movement [BOT] A reversible change in the position of plant parts due to a change in turgor pressure in certain specialized cells; movement of *Mimosa* leaves when touched is an example.

turgor pressure [BOT] The actual pressure developed by the fluid content of a turgid plant cell.

turion [BOT] A scaly shoot, such as asparagus, developed from an underground bud.

turkey [VERT ZOO] Either of two species of wild birds, and any of various derived domestic breeds, in the family Meleagrididae characterized by a bare head and neck, and in the male a large pendant wattle which hangs on one side from the base of the bill.

turmeric [BOT] *Curcuma longa*. An East Indian perennial of the ginger family (Zingiberaceae) with a short stem, tufted leaves, and short thick rhizomes; a spice with a pungent, bitter taste and a musky odor is derived from the rhizome.

Turnicidae [VERT ZOO] The button quails, a family of Old World birds in the order Gruiformes.

turnip [BOT] *Brassica rapa* or *B. campestris* var. *rapa*. An annual crucifer of Asiatic origin belonging to the family Brassiaceae in the order Capparales and grown for its foliage and edible root.

turnover [MOL BIO] The number of substrate molecules transformed by a single molecule of enzyme per minute, when the enzyme is operating at maximum rate.

turnover number [BIOCHEM] The number of molecules of a substrate acted upon in a period of 1 minute by a single enzyme molecule, with the enzyme working at a maximum rate.

turtle [VERT ZOO] Any of about 240 species of reptiles which constitute the order Chelonia distinguished by the two bony shells enclosing the body.

tussock [ECOL] A small hummock of generally solid ground in a bog or marsh, usually covered with and bound together by the roots of low vegetation such as grasses, sedges, or ericaceous shrubs.

twin [BIOL] One of two individuals born at the same time.

twiner [BOT] A climbing stem that winds about its support, as pole beans or many tropical lianas.

Tylenchida [INV ZOO] An order of soil-dwelling or phytoparasitic nematodes in the subclass Rhabdita.

Tylenchoidea [INV ZOO] A superfamily of mainly soil and insect-associated nematodes in the order Tylenchida with a stylet for piercing live cells and sucking the juices.

Tylopoda [VERT ZOO] An infraorder of artiodactyls in the suborder Ruminantia that contains the camels and extinct related forms.

tylostyle [INV ZOO] A uniradiate spicule in Porifera with a point at one end and a knob at the other end.

tylote [INV ZOO] A slender sponge spicule with a knob at each end.

tympanic cavity [ANAT] The irregular, air-containing, mucous-membrane-lined space of the middle ear; contains the three auditory ossicles and communicates with the nasopharynx through the auditory tube.

tympanic membrane [ANAT] The membrane separating the external from the middle ear. Also known as eardrum; tympanum.

tympanum [ANAT] *See* tympanic membrane. [INV ZOO] A thin membrane covering an organ of hearing in insects.

type [SYST] A specimen on which a species or subspecies is based.

Typhaceae [BOT] A family of monocotyledonous plants in the order Typhales characterized by an inflorescence of dense, cylindrical spikes and absence of a perianth.

Typhales [BOT] An order of marsh or aquatic monocotyledons in the subclass Commelinidae with emergent or floating stems and leaves and reduced, unisexual flowers having a single ovule in an ovary composed of a single carpel.

Typhlopidae [VERT ZOO] A family of small, burrowing circumtropical snakes, suborder Serpentes, with vestigial eyes and toothless jaws.

Typhloscolecidae [INV ZOO] A family of pelagic polychaete annelids belonging to the Errantia.

typhlosole [INV ZOO] A dorsal longitudinal invagination of the intestinal wall in certain invertebrates serving to increase the absorptive surface.

Typotheria [PALEON] A suborder of extinct rodentlike herbivores in the order Notoungulata.

Tyranni [VERT ZOO] A suborder of suboscine Passeriformes containing birds with limited song power and having the tendon of the hind toe separate and the intrinsic muscles of the syrinx reduced to one pair.

Tyrannidae [VERT ZOO] The tyrant flycatchers, a family of passeriform birds in the suborder Tyranni confined to the Americas.

Tyrannoidea [VERT ZOO] The flycatchers, a superfamily of suboscine birds in the suborder Tyranni.

tyrocidine [MICROBIO] A peptide antibiotic produced by *Bacillus brevis*; used to control fungi, bacteria, and protozoa.

tyrosinase [BIOCHEM] An enzyme found in plants, molds, crustaceans, mollusks, and some bacteria which, in the presence of oxygen, catalyzes the oxidation of monophenols and polyphenols with the introduction of —OH groups and the formation of quinones.

tyrosine [BIOCHEM] $C_9H_{11}NO_3$ A phenolic alpha amino acid found in many proteins; a precursor of the hormones epinephrine, norepinephrine, thyroxine, and triiodothyronine, and of the black pigment melanin.

tyrothricin [MICROBIO] A polypeptide mixture produced by *Bacillus brevis* and consisting of the antibiotic substances gramicidin and tyrocidine; effective as an antibacterial applied locally in infections due to germ-positive organisms.

Tyson's gland [ANAT] A small scent gland in the human male which secretes the smegma. Also known as preputial gland.

Tytonidae [VERT ZOO] The barn owls, a family of birds in the order Strigiformes distinguished by an unnotched sternum which is fused to large clavicles.

tyvelose [BIOCHEM] A dideoxy sugar found in bacterial lipopolysaccharides.

U

udder [VERT ZOO] A pendulous organ consisting of several mammary glands enclosed in a single envelope; each gland has its own nipple; found in some mammals, such as the cow and goat.

UDP *See* uridine diphosphate.

UDPG *See* uridine diphosphoglucose.

Uintatheriidae [PALEON] The single family of the extinct mammalian order Dinocerata.

Uintatheriinae [PALEON] A subfamily of extinct herbivores in the family Uintatheriidae including all horned forms.

Ulmaceae [BOT] A family of dicotyledonous trees in the order Urticales distinguished by alternate stipulate leaves, two styles, a pendulous ovule, and lack of a latex system.

ulna [ANAT] The larger of the two bones of the forearm or forelimb in vertebrates; articulates proximally with the humerus and radius and distally with the radius.

Ulotrichaceae [BOT] A family of green algae in the suborder Ulotrichineae; contains both attached and floating filamentous species with cells having parietal, platelike or bandlike chloroplasts.

Ulotrichales [BOT] A large, artificial order of the Chlorophyta composed mostly of fresh-water, branched or unbranched filamentous species with mostly cylindrical, uninucleate cells having cellulose, but often mucilaginous walls.

Ulotrichineae [BOT] A suborder of the Ulotrichales characterized by short cylindrical cells.

ultimobranchial body [EMBRYO] One of the small, endocrine structures which originate as terminal outpocketings from each side of the embryonic vertebrate pharynx; can produce the hormone calcitonin.

ultrastructure [MOL BIO] The ultimate physiochemical organization of protoplasm.

Ulvaceae [BOT] A large family of green algae in the order Ulvales.

Ulvales [BOT] An order of algae in the division Chlorophyta in which the thalli are macroscopic, attached tubes or sheets.

umbel [BOT] An indeterminate inflorescence with the pedicels all arising at the top of the peduncle and radiating like umbrella ribs; there are two types, simple and compound.

Umbellales [BOT] An order of dicotyledonous herbs or woody plants in the subclass Rosidae with mostly compound or conspicuously lobed or dissected leaves, well-developed schizogenous secretory canals, separate petals, and an inferior ovary.

Umbelliferae [BOT] A large family of aromatic dicotyledonous herbs in the order Umbellales; flowers have an ovary of two carpels, ripening to form a dry fruit that splits into two halves, each containing a single seed.

umbilical artery [EMBRYO] Either of a pair of arteries passing through the umbilical cord to carry impure blood from the mammalian fetus to the placenta.

umbilical cord [EMBRYO] The long, cylindrical structure containing the umbilical arteries and vein, and connecting the fetus with the placenta.

umbilical duct *See* vitelline duct.

umbilical vein [EMBRYO] A vein passing through the umbilical cord and conveying purified, nutrient-rich blood from placenta to fetus.

Umbilicariaceae [BOT] The rock tripes, a family of Ascolichenes in the order Lecanorales having a large, circular, umbilicate thallus.

umbilicus [ANAT] The navel; the round, depressed cicatrix in the median line of the abdomen, marking the site of the aperture through which passed the fetal umbilical vessels.

umbo [ANAT] A rounded elevation of the surface of the tympanic membrane. [INV ZOO] A prominence above the hinge of a bivalve mollusk shell.

umbonate [BIOL] Having or forming an umbo.

uncinate trophus [INV ZOO] A trophus in rotifers characterized by a hooked or curved uncus.

uncompetitive enzyme inhibition [BIOCHEM] The prevention of an enzymic process as a result of the interaction of an inhibitor with the enzyme-substrate complex or a subsequent intermediate form of the enzyme, but not with the free enzyme.

underground stem [BOT] Any of the stems that grow underground and are often mistaken for roots; principal kinds are rhizomes, tubers, corms, bulbs, and rhizomorphic droppers.

underwing [INV ZOO] Either of a pair of posterior wings on certain insects, as the moth.

ungula [VERT ZOO] A nail, hoof, or claw.

ungulate [VERT ZOO] Referring to an animal that has hoofs.

unguiculate [VERT ZOO] Having claws or nails.

unguligrade [VERT ZOO] Walking on hoofs.

unicellular [BIOL] Composed of a single cell.

unicellular gland [ANAT] A gland consisting of a single cell.

unicuspid [ANAT] Having one cusp, as certain teeth.

unilateral hermaphroditism [ZOO] A type of hermaphroditism in which there is a combination of ovatestis on one side of the body with an ovary or testis on the other side.

unilocular [BIOL] Having a single cavity.

Unionidae [INV ZOO] The fresh-water mussels, a family of bivalve mollusks in the subclass Eulamellibranchia; the larvae, known as glochidia, are parasitic on fish.

Unipolarina [INV ZOO] A suborder of the protozoan order Myxosporida characterized by spores with one to six (never five) polar capsules located at the anterior end.

unitegmic [BOT] Referring to an ovule having a single integument.

unmyelinated [HISTOL] Lacking myelin, either as a normal condition or as the result of a disease.

unstriated fiber *See* smooth muscle fiber.

Upupidae [VERT ZOO] The Old World hoopoes, a family of birds in the order Coraciiformes whose young are hatched with sparse down.

urachus [EMBRYO] A cord or tube of epithelium connecting the apex of the urinary bladder with the allantois; its connective tissue forms the median umbilical ligament.

uracil [BIOCHEM] $C_4H_4N_2O_2$ A pyrimidine base important as a component of ribonucleic acid.

Uraniidae [INV ZOO] A tropical family of moths in the superfamily Geometroidea including some slender-bodied, brilliantly colored diurnal insects which lack a frenulum and are often mistaken for butterflies.

urceolate [BIOL] Shaped like an urn.

urease [BIOCHEM] An enzyme that catalyzes the degradation of urea to ammonia and carbon dioxide; obtained from the seed of jack bean.

Urechinidae [INV ZOO] A family of echinoderms in the order Holasteroida which have an ovoid test lacking a marginal fasciole.

Uredinales [MYCOL] An order of parasitic fungi of the subclass Heterobasidiomycetidae characterized by the teleutospore, a spore with one or more cells, each of which is a modified hypobasidium; members cause plant diseases known as rusts.

uredinium [MYCOL] The aggregation of spore-bearing hyphae and urediospores of a rust fungus that forms beneath the cuticle or epidermis of a host plant.

urediospore [MYCOL] A thin-walled spore produced by rust fungi; gives rise to a vegetative mycelium which may produce more urediospores.

ureotelic [BIOL] Referring to animals that produce urea as their main nitrogenous excretion.

ureter [ANAT] A long tube conveying urine from the renal pelvis to the urinary bladder or cloaca in vertebrates.

urethra [ANAT] The canal in most mammals through which urine is discharged from the urinary bladder to the outside.

urethral gland [ANAT] One of the small, branched tubular mucous glands in the mucosa lining the urethra.

uric acid [BIOCHEM] $C_5H_4N_4O_3$ A white, crystalline compound, the excretory end product in amino acid metabolism by uricotelic species. Also known as 8-hydroxyxanthine.

uricase [BIOCHEM] An enzyme present in the liver, spleen, and kidney of most mammals except humans; converts uric acid to allantoin in the presence of gaseous oxygen.

uricotelism [PHYSIO] An adaptation of terrestrial reptiles and birds which effectively provides for detoxification of ammonia and also for efficient conservation of water due to a relatively low rate of glomerular filtration and active secretion of uric acid by the tubules to form a urine practically saturated with urate.

uridine [BIOCHEM] $C_9H_{12}N_2O_6$ A crystalline nucleoside composed of one molecule of uracil and one molecule of D-ribose; a component of ribonucleic acid.

uridine diphosphate [BIOCHEM] The chief transferring coenzyme in carbohydrate metabolism. Abbreviated UDP.

uridine diphosphoglucose [BIOCHEM] A compound in which α-glucopyranose is esterified, at carbon atom 1, with the terminal phosphate group of uridine-5′-pyrophosphate (that is, uridine diphosphate); occurs in animal, plant, and microbial cells; functions as a key in the transformation of glucose to other sugars. Abbreviated UDPG.

uridine monophosphate *See* uridylic acid.

uridine phosphoric acid *See* uridylic acid.

uridylic acid [BIOCHEM] $C_9H_{13}N_2O_9P$ Water- and alcohol-soluble crystals, melting at 202°C; used in biochemical research. Also known as uridine monophosphate (UMP); uridine phosphoric acid.

urinary bladder [ANAT] A hollow organ which serves as a reservoir for urine.

urinary system [ANAT] The system which functions in the elaboration and excretion of urine in vertebrates; in humans and most mammals, consists of the kidneys, ureters, urinary bladder, and urethra.

urination [PHYSIO] The discharge of urine from the bladder. Also known as micturition.

urine [PHYSIO] The fluid excreted by the kidneys.

uriniferous tubule [ANAT] One of the numerous winding tubules of the kidney. Also known as nephric tubule.

urn [BOT] The theca of a moss.

urobilin [BIOCHEM] A bile pigment produced by reduction of bilirubin by intestinal bacteria and excreted by the kidneys or removed by the liver.

urobilinogen [BIOCHEM] A chromogen, formed in feces and present in urine, from which urobilin is formed by oxidation.

urocanic acid [BIOCHEM] $C_6H_6N_2O_2$ A crystalline compound formed as an intermediate in the degradative pathway of histidine.

Urochordata [INV ZOO] The equivalent name for Tunicata.

urochrome [BIOCHEM] $C_{43}H_{51}O_{26}N$ Yellow pigment found in normal urine.

Urodela [VERT ZOO] The tailed amphibians or salamanders, an order of the class Amphibia distinguished superficially from frogs and toads by the possession of a tail, and from caecilians by the possession of limbs.

urogenital diaphragm [ANAT] The sheet of tissue stretching across the pubic arch, formed by the deep transverse perineal and the sphincter urethrae muscles. Also known as triangular ligament.

urogenital system [ANAT] The combined urinary and genital system in vertebrates, which are intimately related embryologically and anatomically. Also known as genitourinary system.

urokinase [BIOCHEM] An enzyme, present in human urine, that catalyzes the conversion of plasminogen to plasmin.

uropepsin [BIOCHEM] The end product of the secretion of pepsinogen into the blood by gastric cells; occurs in urine.

uropod [INV ZOO] One of the flattened abdominal appendages of various crustaceans that with the telson forms the tail fan.

uroporphyrin [BIOCHEM] Any of several isomeric, metal-free porphyrins, occurring in small quantities in normal urine and feces; molecule has four acetic acid ($—CH_2COOH$) and four propionic acid ($—CH_2CH_2COOH$) groups.

Uropygi [INV ZOO] The tailed whip scorpions, an order of arachnids characterized by an elongate, flattened body which bears in front a pair of thickened, raptorial pedipalps set with sharp spines and used to hold and crush insect prey.

uropygial gland [VERT ZOO] A relatively large, compact, bilobed, secretory organ located at the base of the tail (uropygium) of most birds having a keeled sternum. Also known as oil gland; preen gland.

urostyle [VERT ZOO] An unsegmented bone representing several fused vertebrae and forming the posterior part of the vertebral column in Anura.

Urostylidae [INV ZOO] A family of hemipteran insects in the superfamily Pentatomoidea.

Ursidae [VERT ZOO] A family of mammals in the order Carnivora including the bears and their allies.

ursolic acid [BIOCHEM] $C_{30}H_{48}O_3$ A pentacyclic terpene that crystallizes from absolute alcohol solution, found in leaves and berries of plants; used in pharmaceutical and food industries as an emulsifying agent.

Urticaceae [BOT] A family of dicotyledonous herbs in the order Urticales characterized by a single unbranched style, a straight embryo, and the lack of milky juice (latex).

Urticales [BOT] An order of dicotyledons in the subclass Hamamelidae; woody plants or herbs with simple, usually stipulate leaves, and reduced clustered flowers that usually have a vestigial perianth.

use-dilution test [MICROBIO] A bioassay method for testing disinfectants for use on surfaces where a substantial reduction of bacterial contamination is not achieved by prior cleaning; the test organisms *Salmonella choleraesuis* and *Staphylococcus aureus* are deposited in stainless steel cylinders which are then exposed to the action of the test disinfectant.

Usneaceae [BOT] The beard lichens, a family of Ascolichenes in the order Lecanorales distinguished by their conspicuous fruticose growth form.

usnic acid [BIOCHEM] $C_{18}H_{16}O_7$ Yellow crystals, insoluble in water, slightly soluble in alcohol and ether, melts about 198°C; found in lichens; used as an antibiotic. Also known as usninic acid.

usninic acid *See* usnic acid.

Ustilaginaceae [MYCOL] A family of fungi in the order Ustilaginales in which basidiospores bud from the sides of the septate epibasidium.

Ustilaginales [MYCOL] An order of the subclass Heterobasidiomycetidae comprising the smut fungi which parasitize plants and cause diseases known as smut or bunt.

uterine tube *See* oviduct.

uterus [ANAT] The organ of gestation in mammals which receives and retains the fertilized ovum, holds the fetus during development, and becomes the principal agent of its expulsion at term.

uterus bicornis [ANAT] A uterus divided into two horns or compartments; an abnormal condition in humans but normal in many mammals, such as carnivores.

utriculus [ANAT] **1.** That part of the membranous labyrinth of the ear into which the semicircular canals open. **2.** A small, blind pouch extending from the urethra into the prostate. Also known as utricle.

uvea [ANAT] The pigmented, vascular layer of the eye: the iris, ciliary body, and choroid.

uvula [ANAT] **1.** A fingerlike projection in the midline of the posterior border of the soft palate. **2.** A lobe of the vermiform process of the lower surface of the cerebellum.

V

vacuole [CELL BIO] A membrane-bound cavity within a cell; may function in digestion, storage, secretion, or excretion.

vagility [ECOL] The ability of organisms to disseminate.

vagina [ANAT] The canal from the vulvar opening to the cervix uteri.

vagina fibrosa tendinis [ANAT] A fibrous sheath surrounding the tendon of a muscle and usually confining the tendon in a bony groove.

vaginate [BIOL] Invested in a sheath.

vagotonine [BIOCHEM] An endocrine substance which is thought to be elaborated by cells of the pancreas and which regulates autonomic tonus.

vagus [ANAT] The tenth cranial nerve; either of a pair of sensory and motor nerves forming an important part of the parasympathetic system in vertebrates.

valence [BIOCHEM] The relative ability of a biological substance to react or combine.

valid [SYST] Describing a taxon classified on the basis of distinctive characters of accepted importance.

valine [BIOCHEM] $C_5H_{11}NO_2$ An amino acid considered essential for normal growth of animals, and biosynthesized from pyruvic acid. Also known as 2-aminoisovaleric acid; α-aminoisovaleric acid; 2-amino-3-methylbutyric acid.

vallate papilla [ANAT] One of the large, flat papillae, each surrounded by a trench, in a group anterior to the sulcus terminalis of the tongue. Also known as circumvallate papilla.

Valoniaceae [BOT] A family of green algae in the order Siphonocladales consisting of plants that are essentially unicellular, coenocytic vesicles, spherical or clavate, and up to 6 centimeters in diameter.

Valvatacea [PALEON] A superfamily of extinct gastropod mollusks in the order Prosobranchia.

valvate [BOT] Having valvelike parts, as those which meet edge to edge or which open as if by valves.

Valvatida [INV ZOO] An order of echinoderms in the subclass Asteroidea.

Valvatina [INV ZOO] A suborder of echinoderms in the order Phanerozonida in which the upper marginals lie directly over, and not alternate with, the corresponding lower marginals.

valve [ANAT] A flat of tissue, as in the veins or between the chambers in the heart, which permits movement of fluid in one direction only. [BOT] 1. A segment of a dehiscing capsule or legume. 2. The lidlike portion of certain anthers. [INV ZOO] 1. One of the distinct, articulated pieces composing the shell of certain animals, such as barnacles and brachiopods. 2. One of two shells encasing the body of a bivalve mollusk or a diatom.

Valvifera [INV ZOO] A suborder of isopod crustaceans distinguished by having a pair of flat, valvelike uropods which hinge laterally and fold inward beneath the rear part of the body.

valvula [BIOL] A small valve. [INV ZOO] One of the small processes forming a sheath for the ovipositor in certain insects.

valvulate [BIOL] Having valvules.

vampire [VERT ZOO] The common name for bats making up the family Desmodontidae which have teeth specialized for cutting and which subsist on a blood diet.

Vampyrellidae [INV ZOO] A family of protozoans in the order Proteomyxida including species which invade filamentous algae and sometimes higher plants.

Vampyromorpha [INV ZOO] An order of dibranchiate cephalopod mollusks represented by *Vampyroteuthis infernalis,* an inhabitant of the deeper waters of tropical and temperate seas.

vancomycin [MICROBIO] A complex antibiotic substance produced by *Streptomyces orientalis;* useful for treatment of severe staphylococcic infections.

Vaneyellidae [INV ZOO] A family of holothurian echinoderms in the order Dactylochirotida.

Vanhornidae [INV ZOO] A monospecific family of the Hymenoptera in the superfamily Proctotrupoidea.

Varanidae [VERT ZOO] The monitors, a family of reptiles in the suborder Sauria found in the hot regions of Africa, Asia, Australia, and Malaya.

varicose vein [ANAT] An enlarged tortuous blood vessel that occurs chiefly in the superficial veins and their tributaries in the lower extremities. Also known as varicosity.

variegate [BIOL] Having irregular patches of diverse colors.

variegated position effect [GEN] A phenomenon observed in some cases when a chromosome aberration causes a wild-type gene from the euchromatin to be relocated adjacent to heterochromatin; the phenotypic expression of the wild-type allele will be unstable, producing patches of phenotypically mutant tissue that differ from the surrounding wild-type tissue.

variety [SYST] A taxonomic group or category inferior in rank to a subspecies.

varix [INV ZOO] A conspicuous ridge across each whorl of certain univalves marking the ancestral position of the outer lip of the aperture.

varnish tree [BOT] *Rhus vernicifera*. A member of the sumac family (Anacardiaceae) cultivated in Japan; the cut bark exudes a juicy milk which darkens and thickens on exposure and is applied as a thin film to become a varnish of extreme hardness. Also known as lacquer tree.

vasa vasorum [ANAT] The blood vessels supplying the walls of arteries and veins.

vascular bundle [BOT] A strandlike part of the plant vascular system containing xylem and phloem.

vascular cambium [BOT] The lateral meristem which produces secondary xylem and phloem.

vascular ray [BOT] A ray derived from cambium and found in the stele of some vascular plants, often separating vascular bundles.

vascular tissue [BOT] The conducting tissue found in higher plants, consisting principally of xylem and phloem.

vas deferens [ANAT] The portion of the excretory duct system of the testis which runs from the epididymal duct to the ejaculatory duct. Also known as ductus deferens.

vasoconstrictor [PHYSIO] A nerve or an agent that causes blood vessel constriction.

vasodilator [PHYSIO] A nerve or an agent that causes blood vessel dilation.

vasomotor center [PHYSIO] A large, diffuse area in the reticular formation of the lower brainstem; stimulation of different portions of this center causes either a rise in blood pressure and tachycardia (pressor area) or a fall in blood pressure and bradycardia (depressor area).

vasopressin [BIOCHEM] A peptide hormone which is elaborated by the posterior pituitary and which has a pressor effect; used medicinally as an antidiuretic. Also known as antidiuretic hormone (ADH).

vasotocin [BIOCHEM] A hormone from the neurosecretory cells of the posterior pituitary of lower vertebrates; increases permeability to water in amphibian skin and in bladder.

vault [BIOL] An anatomical structure that is arched or dome-shaped.

vectorcardiogram [PHYSIO] The part of the pathway of instantaneous vectors during one cardiac cycle. Also known as monocardiogram.

vectorcardiography [PHYSIO] A method of recording the magnitude and direction of the instantaneous cardiac vectors.

vegetable [BOT] Resembling or relating to plants.

vegetation [BOT] The total mass of plant life that occupies a given area.

vegetational plant geography [ECOL] A field of study concerned with the mapping of vegetation regions and the interpretation of these in terms of environmental or ecological influences.

vegetation and ecosystem mapping [BOT] An art and a science concerned with the drawing of maps which locate different kinds of plant cover in a geographic area.

vegetation management [ECOL] The art and practice of manipulating vegetation such as timber, forage, crops, or wild life, so as to produce a desired part or aspect of that material in higher quantity or quality.

vegetation zone [ECOL] **1.** An extensive, even transcontinental, band of physiognomically similar vegetation on the earth's surface. **2.** Plant communities assembled into regional patterns by the area's physiography, geological parent material, and history.

vegetative [BIOL] Having nutritive or growth functions, as opposed to reproductive.

vegetative propagation [BOT] Production of a new plant from a portion of another plant, such as a stem or branch.

Veillonella [MICROBIO] The type genus of the family Veillonellaceae; small cells occurring in pairs, chains, and clusters.

Veillonellaceae [MICROBIO] The single family of gram-negative, anaerobic cocci; characteristically occur in pairs with adjacent sides flattened; parasites of homotherms, including humans, rodents, and pigs.

vein [ANAT] A relatively thin-walled blood vessel that carries blood from capillaries to the heart in vertebrates. [BOT] One of the vascular bundles in a leaf. [INV ZOO] **1.** One of the thick, stiff ribs providing support for the wing of an insect. **2.** A venous sinus in invertebrates.

velamen [BOT] The corky epidermis covering the aerial roots of an epiphytic orchid.

velarium [INV ZOO] The velum of certain scyphozoans and cubomedusans distinguished by the presence of canals lined with endoderm.

veldt [ECOL] Grasslands of eastern and southern Africa that are usually level and mixed with trees and shrubs. Also spelled veld.

veliger [INV ZOO] A mollusk larval stage following the trochophore, distinguished by an enlarged girdle of ciliated cells (velum).

Veliidae [INV ZOO] A family of the Hemiptera in the subdivision Amphibicorisae composed of small water striders which have short legs and a longitudinal groove between the eyes.

vellus [ANAT] Fine body hair that is present until puberty.

Velocipedidae [INV ZOO] A tropical family of hemipteran insects in the superfamily Cimicoidea.

velum [BIOL] A veil- or curtainlike membrane. [INV ZOO] A swimming organ on the larva of certain marine gastropod mollusks that develops as a contractile ciliated collar-shaped ridge.

vena cava [ANAT] One of two large veins which in air-breathing vertebrates conveys blood from the systemic circulation to the right atrium.

venation [BOT] The system or pattern of veins in the tissues of a leaf. [INV ZOO] The arrangement of veins in an insect wing.

venom [PHYSIO] Any of various poisonous materials secreted by certain animals, such as snakes or bees.

venous pressure [PHYSIO] Tension of the blood within the veins.

vent [ZOO] The external opening of the cloaca or rectum, especially in fish, birds, and amphibians.

venter [ANAT] The abdomen, or other body cavity containing organs. [BOT] The thickened basal portion of an archegonium. [INV ZOO] 1. The undersurface of an arthropod's abdomen. 2. The outer, convex part of a curved or coiled gastropod or cephalopod shell.

ventral [BOT] On the lower surface of a dorsiventral plant structure, such as a leaf. [ZOO] On or belonging to the lower or anterior surface of an animal, that is, on the side opposite the back.

ventral aorta [VERT ZOO] The arterial trunk or trunks between the heart and the first aortic arch in embryos or lower vertebrates.

ventral light reflex [INV ZOO] A basic means of orientation in aquatic invertebrates, such as shrimp, which swim belly up toward the light.

ventral rib [VERT ZOO] Any of the ribs which lie in the septa dividing the trunk musculature into segments in fish. Also known as pleural rib.

ventricle [ANAT] 1. A chamber, or one of two chambers, in the vertebrate heart which receives blood from the atrium and forces it into the arteries by contraction of the muscular wall. 2. One of the interconnecting, fluid-filled chambers of the vertebrate brain that are continuous with the canal of the spinal cord. [ZOO] A cavity in a body part or organ.

ventricose [BIOL] Swollen or distended, especially on one side.

ventriculus [ZOO] A ventricle that performs digestive functions, such as a stomach or a gizzard.

ventromedial nucleus [ANAT] A central nervous system nucleus in the hypothalamus that appears to be the satiation center; bilateral surgical damage to this nucleus results in overeating.

venule [ANAT] A small vein.

Venus' flytrap [BOT] *Dionaea muscipula*. An insectivorous plant (order Sarraceniales) of North and South Carolina; the two halves of a leaf blade can swing upward and inward as though hinged, thus trapping insects between the closing halves of the leaf blade.

Verbeekinidae [PALEON] A family of extinct marine protozoans in the superfamily Fusulinacea.

Verbenaceae [BOT] A family of variously woody or herbaceous dicotyledons in the order Lamiales characterized by opposite or whorled leaves and regular or irregular flowers, usually with four or two functional stamens.

Vermes [INV ZOO] An artificial taxon considered to be a phylum in some systems of classification, but variously defined as including all invertebrates except arthropods, or including all vermiform invertebrates.

vermiform [BIOL] Wormlike; resembling a worm.

vermiform appendix [ANAT] A small, blind sac projecting from the cecum. Also known as appendix.

Vermilingua [VERT ZOO] An infraorder of the mammalian order Edentata distinguished by lack of teeth and in having a vermiform tongue; includes the South American true anteaters.

vermis [ANAT] The median lobe of the cerebellum.

vernalization [BOT] The induction in plants of the competence or ripeness to flower by the influence of cold, that is, at temperatures below the optimal temperature for growth.

vernation [BOT] The characteristic arrangement of young leaves within the bud. Also known as prefoliation.

vernix caseosa [EMBRYO] A cheesy deposit on the surface of the fetus derived from the stratum corneum, sebaceous secretion, and remnants of the epitrichium.

verruca [BIOL] A wartlike elevation on the surface of a plant or animal.

Verrucariaceae [BOT] A family of crustose lichens in the order Pyrenulales typically found on rocks, especially in intertidal or salt-spray zones along rocky coastlines.

Verrucomorpha [INV ZOO] A suborder of the crustacean order Thoracica composed of sessile, asymmetrical barnacles.

verrucose [BIOL] Having the surface covered with wartlike protuberances.

versatile anther [BOT] An anther whose attachment is near its middle, thus enabling it to swing freely.

vertebra [ANAT] One of the bones that make up the spine in vertebrates.

vertebral arch [ANAT] An arch formed by the paired pedicles and laminas of a vertebra; the posterior part of a vertebra which together with the anterior part, the body, encloses the vertebral foramen in which the spinal cord is lodged in vertebrates. Also known as neural arch.

Vertebrata [VERT ZOO] The major subphylum of the phylum Chordata including all animals with backbones, from fish to man.

vertebrate zoology [ZOO] That branch of zoology concerned with the study of members of the Vertebrata.

verticillate [BOT] Whorled, in an arrangement resembling the spokes of a wheel.

vesicle [BIOL] A small, thin-walled bladderlike cavity, usually filled with fluid.

Vespertilionidae [VERT ZOO] The common bats, a large cosmopolitan family of the Chiroptera characterized by a long tail, extending to the edge of the uropatagium; almost all members are insect-eating.

vespertine [VERT ZOO] Active in the evening.

Vespidae [INV ZOO] A widely distributed family of Hymenoptera in the superfamily Vespoidea including hornets, yellow jackets, and potter wasps.

Vespoidea [INV ZOO] A superfamily of wasps in the suborder Apocrita.

vestibular apparatus [ANAT] The anatomical structures concerned with the vestibular portion of the eighth cranial nerve; includes the saccule, utricle, semicircular canals, vestibular nerve, and vestibular nuclei of the ear.

vestibular nerve [ANAT] A somatic sensory branch of the auditory nerve, which is distributed about the ampullae of the semicircular canals, macula sacculi, and macula utriculi.

vestibular reflexes [PHYSIO] The responses of the vestibular apparatus to strong stimulation; responses include pallor, nausea, vomiting, and postural changes.

vestibule [ANAT] 1. The central cavity of the bony labyrinth of the ear. 2. The parts of the membranous labyrinth within the cavity of the bony labyrinth. 3. The space between the labia minora. 4. *See* buccal cavity.

vestibulocerebellar [ANAT] Pertaining to the vestibular fibers and the cerebellum.

vestibulospinal tract [ANAT] A tract of nerve fibers that originates principally from the lateral vestibular nucleus and descends in the anterior funiculus of the spinal cord.

vestige [BIOL] A degenerate anatomical structure or organ that remains from one more fully developed and functional in an earlier phylogenetic form of the individual.

vestigial [BIOL] Of, being, or resembling a vestige.

vetch [BOT] Any of a group of mostly annual legumes, especially of the genus *Vicia*, with weak viny stems terminating in tendrils and having compound leaves; some varieties are grown for their edible seed.

V factor [MICROBIO] Phosphopyridine nucleotide, a growth factor required by the parasitic bacteria of the genus *Haemophilus*.

Vianaidae [INV ZOO] A small family of South American Hemiptera in the superfamily Tingordea.

vibraculum [INV ZOO] A specially modified bryozoan zooid with a bristlelike seta that sweeps debris from the surface of the colony.

Vibrio [MICROBIO] A genus of bacteria in the family Vibrionaceae; short, motile, asporogenous rods, occasionally united into S-shaped groups; some species are human pathogens.

Vibrionaceae [MICROBIO] A family of gram-negative, facultatively anaerobic rods; cells are straight or curved and usually motile by polar flagella; generally found in water.

vibrissae [VERT ZOO] Hairs with specialized erectile tissue; found on all mammals except man. Also known as sinus hairs; tactile hairs; whiskers.

vicariants [ECOL] Two or more closely related taxa, presumably derived from one another or from a common immediate ancestor, that inhabit geographically distinct areas.

vicuna [VERT ZOO] *Lama vicugna*. A rare, wild ruminant found in the Andes mountains; the fiber of the vicuna is strong, resilient, and elastic but is the softest and most delicate of animal fibers.

villus [ANAT] A fingerlike projection from the surface of a membrane.

vine [BOT] A plant having a stem that is too flexible or weak to support itself.

vinegar eel [INV ZOO] *Turbatrix aceti*. A very small nematode often found in large numbers in vinegar fermentation. Also known as vinegar worm.

Viocin [MICROBIO] A trademark for viomycin.

Violaceae [BOT] A family of dicolyledonous plants in the order Violales characterized by polypetalous, mostly perfect, hypogynous flowers with a single style and five stamens.

Violales [BOT] A heterogeneous order of dicotyledons in the subclass Dilleniidae distinguished by a unilocular, compound ovary and mostly parietal placentation.

viomycin [MICROBIO] A polypeptide antibiotic or mixture of antibiotic substances produced by strains of *Streptomyces griseus* var. *purpureus* (*Streptomyces puniceus*); the sulfate salt is administered intramuscularly for treatment of tuberculosis resistant to other therapy.

viper [VERT ZOO] The common name for reptiles of the family Viperidae; thick-bodied poisonous snakes having a pair of long fangs, present on the anterior part of the upper jaw, which fold against the roof of the mouth when the jaws are closed.

Viperidae [VERT ZOO] A family of reptiles in the suborder Serpentes found in Eurasia and Africa; all species are proglyphodont.

Vireonidae [VERT ZOO] The vireos, a family of New World passeriform birds in the suborder Oscines.

virgate [BOT] Banded.

virgate trophus [INV ZOO] A piercing type of trophus in rotifers that is thin and slightly toothed.

virgo-forcipate trophus [INV ZOO] A type of muscular chamber in rotifers containing jaws of a cuticular material intermediate between a piercing and grasping type of structure.

viridans streptococci [MICROBIO] A group of pathogenic and saprophytic streptococci including strains not causing beta hemolysis, although many cause alpha hemolysis, and none which elaborate a C substance.

virion [VIROL] The complete, mature virus particle.

viroid [MICROBIO] The smallest known agents of infectious disease, characterized by the absence of encapsidated proteins.

virology [MICROBIO] The study of submicroscopic organisms known as viruses.

virotoxin [BIOCHEM] One of a group of toxins present in the mushroom *Amanita virosa*.

virulence [MICROBIO] The disease-producing power of a microorganism; infectiousness.

virus [VIROL] A large group of infectious agents ranging from 10 to 250 nanometers in diameter, composed of a protein sheath surrounding a nucleic acid core and capable of infecting all animals, plants, and bacteria; characterized by total dependence on living cells for reproduction and by lack of independent metabolism.

virus interference [MICROBIO] A phenomenon which may be defined as protection of host cells against one virus, conferred as a result of prior infection with a different virus.

viscera [ANAT] The organs within the cavities of the body of an organism.

visceral arch [ANAT] One of the series of mesodermal ridges covered by epithelium bounding the lateral wall of the oral and pharyngeal regions of vertebrates; embryonic in higher forms, they contribute to formation of the face and neck. [VERT ZOO] One of the first two arches of the series in gill-bearing forms.

visceral peritoneum [ANAT] That portion of the peritoneum covering the organs of the abdominal cavity.

viscid [BOT] Having a sticky surface, as certain leaves.

viscus [ANAT] Singular of viscera.

vision [PHYSIO] The sense which perceives the form, color, size, movement, and distance of objects. Also known as sight.

visual acuity [PHYSIO] The ability to see fine details of an object; specifically, the ability to see an object whose angle subtended at the eye is 1 minute of arc.

visual pigment [BIOCHEM] Any of various photosensitive pigments of vertebrate and invertebrate photoreceptors.

visual projection area [PHYSIO] The receptive center for visual images in the cortex of the brain, located in the walls and margins of the calcarine sulcus of the occipital lobe. Also known as Brodmann's area 17.

visual-righting reflex [PHYSIO] A reflex mechanism whereby righting of the head and body is caused by visual stimuli. Also known as optical-righting reflex.

visual yellow [BIOCHEM] An intermediary substance formed from rhodopsin in the retina after exposure to light; it is ultimately broken down to retinene and vitamin A.

Vitaceae [BOT] A family of dicotyledonous plants in the order Rhamnales; mostly tendril-bearing climbers with compound or lobed leaves, as in grapes (*Vitis*).

vital capacity [PHYSIO] The volume of air that can be forcibly expelled from the lungs after the deepest inspiration.

vitalism [BIOL] The theory that the activities of a living organism are under the guidance of an agency which has none of the attributes of matter or energy.

vitamin [BIOCHEM] An organic compound present in variable, minute quantities in natural foodstuffs and essential for the normal processes of growth and maintenance of the body; vitamins do not furnish energy, but are essential for energy transformation and regulation of metabolism.

vitamin A [BIOCHEM] $C_{20}H_{29}OH$ A pale-yellow alcohol that is soluble in fat and insoluble in water; found in liver oils and carotenoids, and produced synthetically; it is a component of visual pigments and is essential for normal growth and maintenance of epithelial tissue. Also known as antiinfective vitamin; antixerophthalmic vitamin; retinol.

vitamin B$_6$ [BIOCHEM] A vitamin which exists as three chemically related and water-soluble forms found in food: pyridoxine, pyridoxal, and pyridoxamine; dietary requirements and physiological activities are uncertain.

vitamin B$_{12}$ [BIOCHEM] A group of closely related polypyrrole compounds containing trivalent cobalt; the antipernicious anemia factor, essential for normal hemopoiesis. Also known as cobalamin; cyanocobalamin; extrinsic factor.

vitamin B complex [BIOCHEM] A group of water-soluble vitamins that include thiamine, riboflavin, nicotinic acid, pyridoxine, panthothenic acid, inositol, p-aminobenzoic acid, biotin, folic acid, and vitamin B$_{12}$.

vitamin D [BIOCHEM] Either of two fat-soluble, sterol-like compounds, calciferol or ergocalciferol (vitamin D$_2$) and cholecalciferol (vitamin D$_3$); occurs in fish liver oils and is essential for normal calcium and phosphorus deposition in bones and teeth. Also known as antirachitic vitamin.

vitamin E [BIOCHEM] $C_{29}H_{50}O_2$ Any of a series of eight related compounds called tocopherols, α-tocopherol having the highest biological activity; occurs in wheat germ and other oils and is believed to be needed in certain human physiological processes.

vitamin K [BIOCHEM] Any of three yellowish oils which are fat-soluble, nonsteroid, and nonsaponifiable; it is essential for formation of prothrombin. Also known as antihemorrhagic vitamin; prothrombin factor.

vitamin P [BIOCHEM] A substance, such as citrin or one or more of its components, believed to be concerned with maintenance of the normal state of the walls of small blood vessels.

vitellarium [INV ZOO] The part of the ovary in certain rotifers and flatworms that produces nutritive cells filled with yolk. Also known as yolk larva.

vitelline artery [EMBRYO] An artery passing from the yolk sac to the primitive aorta in young vertebrate embryos. Also known as omphalomesenteric artery.

vitelline duct [EMBRYO] The constricted part of the yolk sac opening into the midgut region of the future ileum. Also known as omphalomesenteric duct; umbilical duct.

vitelline membrane [CELL BIO] The cytoplasmic membrane on the surface of the mammalian ovum.

vitelline vein [EMBRYO] Any of the embryonic veins in vertebrates uniting the yolk sac and the sinus venosus; their proximal fused ends form the portal vein. Also known as omphalomesenteric vein.

vitellogenesis [PHYSIO] The process by which yolk is formed in the ooplasm of an oocyte.

Vitreoscilla [MICROBIO] A genus of bacteria in the family Beggiatoaceae; filaments are individual and contain cylindrical cells.

Vitreoscillaceae [MICROBIO] Formerly a family of bacteria in the order Beggiatoales; included organisms which have a filamentous habit and move by gliding, but never store sulfur, and rely on organic nutrients in their metabolism.

vitreous chamber [ANAT] A cavity of the eye posterior to the crystalline lens and anterior to the retina, which is filled with vitreous humor.

vitreous humor [PHYSIO] The transparent gel-like substance filling the greater part of the globe of the eye, the vitreous chamber. Also known as vitreous body.

vittate [BOT] 1. Having longitudinal stripes. 2. Bearing specialized oil tubes (vittae).

Viverridae [VERT ZOO] A family of carnivorous mammals in the superfamily Feloidea composed of the civets, genets, and mongooses.

Viviparidae [INV ZOO] A family of fresh-water gastropod mollusks in the order Pectinibranchia.

viviparous [PHYSIO] Bringing forth live young.

vocal fold [ANAT] Either of a pair of folds of tissue covered by mucous membrane in the larynx. Also known as vocal cord.

vocal sac [VERT ZOO] An expansible pocket of skin beneath the chin or behind the jaws of certain frogs; may be inflated to a great volume and serves as a resonator.

Vochysiaceae [BOT] A family of dicotyledonous plants in the order Polygalales characterized by mostly three carpels, usually stipulate leaves, one fertile stamen, and capsular fruit.

Voges-Proskauer test [MICROBIO] One of the four tests of the IMVIC test; a qualitative test for the formation of acetyl methylcarbinol from glucose, in which solutions of α-naphthol, potassium hydroxide, and creatinine are added to an incubated culture of test organisms in a glucose broth, and a pink to rose color indicates a positive reaction.

volar [ANAT] Pertaining to, or on the same side as, the palm of the hand or the sole of the foot.

vole [VERT ZOO] Any of about 79 species of rodent in the tribe Microtini of the family Cricetidae; individuals have a stout body with short legs, small ears, and a blunt nose.

voluntary muscle [PHYSIO] A muscle directly under the control of the will of the organism.

Volutidae [INV ZOO] A family of gastropod mollusks in the order Neogastropoda.

volutin [BIOCHEM] A basophilic substance, thought to be a nucleic acid, occurring as granules in the cytoplasm and vacuoles of algae and other microorganisms.

volva [MYCOL] A cuplike membrane surrounding the base of the stipe in certain gill fungi.

volvent nematocyst [INV ZOO] A nematocyst in the form of an unarmed, coiled tube that is closed at the end.

Volvocales [BOT] An order of one-celled or colonial green algae in the division Chlorophyta; individuals are motile with two, four, or rarely eight whiplike flagella.

Volvocida [INV ZOO] An order of the protozoan class Phytamastigophorea; individuals are grass-green or colorless, have one, two, four, or eight flagella, and thick cell walls of cellulose.

Vombatidae [VERT ZOO] A family of marsupial mammals in the order Diprotodonta in some classification systems.

vomer [ANAT] A skull bone below the ethmoid region constituting part of the nasal septum in most vertebrates.

vomeronasal cartilage [ANAT] A strip of hyaline cartilage extending from the anterior nasal spine upward and backward on either side of the septal cartilage of the nose and attached to the anterior margin of the vomer. Also known as Jacobson's cartilage.

vulture [VERT ZOO] The common name applied to any of various birds of prey in the families Cathartidae and Accipitridae of the order Falconiformes; the head of these birds is usually naked.

vulva [ANAT] The external genital organs of women.

vulval gland [ANAT] A scent gland in the vulval tissues of the human female.

W

wading bird [VERT ZOO] Any of the long-legged, long-necked birds composing the order Ciconiiformes, including storks, herons, egrets, and ibises.

Waldeyer's ring [ANAT] A circular arrangement of the lymphatic tissues formed by the palatine and pharyngeal tonsils and the lymphatic follicles at the base of the tongue and behind the posterior pillars of the fauces.

walking bird [VERT ZOO] Any bird of the order Columbiformes, including the pigeons, doves, and sandgrouse.

walnut [BOT] The common name for about a dozen species of deciduous trees in the genus *Juglans* characterized by pinnately compound, aromatic leaves and chambered or laminate pith; the edible nut of the tree is distinguished by a deeply furrowed or sculptured shell.

walrus [VERT ZOO] *Odobenus rosmarus*. The single species of the pinniped family Odobenidae distinguished by the upper canines in both sexes being prolonged as tusks.

wasp [INV ZOO] The common name for members of 67 families of the order Hymenoptera; all are important as parasites or predators of injurious pests.

water bug [INV ZOO] Any insect which lives in an aquatic habitat during all phases of its life history.

water conservation [ECOL] The protection, development, and efficient management of water resources for beneficial purposes.

watercress [BOT] *Nasturtium officinale*. A perennial cress generally grown in flooded soil beds and used for salads and food garnishing.

waterfowl [VERT ZOO] Aquatic birds which constitute the order Anseriformes, including the swans, ducks, geese, and screamers.

watermelon [BOT] *Citrullus vulgaris*. An annual trailing vine with light-yellow flowers and leaves having five to seven deep lobes; the edible, oblong or roundish fruit has a smooth, hard, green rind filled with sweet, tender, juicy, pink to red tissue containing many seeds.

water microbiology [MICROBIO] An aspect of microbiology that deals with the normal and adventitious microflora of natural and artificial water bodies.

water moccasin [VERT ZOO] *Agkistrodon piscivorus*. A semiaquatic venomous pit viper; skin is brownish or olive on the dorsal aspect, paler on the sides, and has indistinct black bars. Also known as cottonmouth.

water pollution [ECOL] Contamination of water by materials such as sewage effluent, chemicals, detergents, and fertilizer runoff.

water-vascular system [INV ZOO] An internal closed system of reservoirs and ducts containing a watery fluid, found only in echinoderms.

weasel [VERT ZOO] The common name for at least 12 species of small, slim carnivores which belong to the family Mustelidae and which have a reddish-brown coat with whitish underparts; species in the northern regions have white fur during the winter and are called ermine.

web [VERT ZOO] The membrane between digits in many birds and amphibians.

Weberian apparatus [VERT ZOO] A series of bony ossicles which form a chain connecting the swim bladder with the inner ear in fishes of the superorder Ostariophysi.

Weberian ossicle [VERT ZOO] One of a chain of three or four small bones that make up the Weberian apparatus.

Weber's law [PHYSIO] The law that the stimulus increment which can barely be detected (the just noticeable difference) is a constant fraction of the initial magnitude of the stimulus; this is only an approximate rule of thumb.

weed [BOT] A plant that is useless or of low economic value, especially one growing on cultivated land to the detriment of the crop.

weevil [INV ZOO] Any of various snout beetles whose larvae destroy crops by eating the interior of the fruit or grain, or bore through the bark into the pith of many trees.

Welwitschiales [BOT] An order of gymnosperms in the subdivision Geneticae represented by the single species *Welwitschia mirabilis* of southwestern Africa; distinguished by only two leaves and short, unbranched, cushion- or saucer-shaped woody main stem which tapers to a very long taproot.

wetwood [PL PATH] Wood having a water-soaked appearance because of a high water content; may be caused by bacteria or by physiological factors.

whale [VERT ZOO] A large marine mammal of the order Cetacea; the body is streamlined, the broad flat tail is used for propulsion, and the limbs are balancing structures.

wheat [BOT] A food grain crop of the genus *Triticum*; plants are self-pollinating; the inflorescence is a spike bearing sessile spikelets arranged alternately on a zigzag rachis.

wheat germ [BOT] The embryo of a wheat grain.

whelk [INV ZOO] A gastropod mollusk belonging to the order Neogastropoda; species are carnivorous but also scavenge.

whip grafting [BOT] A method of grafting by fitting a small tongue and notch cut in the base of the scion into corresponding cuts in the stock.

whitefish [VERT ZOO] Any of various food fishes in the family Salmonidae, especially of the genus *Coregonus*, characterized by an adipose dorsal fin and nearly toothless mouth.

whooping crane [VERT ZOO] *Grus americana*. A member of a rare North American migratory species of wading birds; the entire species forms a single population.

whorl [ANAT] A fingerprint pattern in which at least two deltas are present with a recurve in front of each. [BOT] An arrangement of several identical anatomical parts, such as petals, in a circle around the same point.

wild boar [VERT ZOO] *Sus scrofa*. A wild hog with coarse, grizzled hair and enlarged tusks or canines on both jaws. Also known as boar.

wildfire [PL PATH] A bacterial disease of tobacco caused by *Pseudomonas tabaci* and characterized by the appearance of brown spots surrounded by yellow rings, which turn dark, rot, and fall out.

Williamsoniaceae [PALEOBOT] A family of extinct plants in the order Cycadeoidales distinguished by profuse branching.

willow [BOT] A deciduous tree and shrub of the genus *Salix*, order Salicales; twigs are often yellow-green and bear alternate leaves which are characteristically long, narrow, and pointed, usually with fine teeth along the margins.

wilt [PL PATH] Any of various plant diseases characterized by drooping and shriveling, following loss of turgidity.

windburn [BOT] Injury to plant foliage, caused by strong, hot, dry winds.

wing [ZOO] Any of the paired appendages serving as organs of flight on many animals.

Winteraceae [BOT] A family of dicotyledonous plants in the order Magnoliales distinguished by hypogynous flowers, exstipulate leaves, air vessels absent, and stamens usually laminar.

Wirsung's duct [ANAT] The adult pancreatic duct in man, sheep, ganoid fish, teleost fish, and frog.

witches'-broom disease [PL PATH] An abnormal cluster of small branches or twigs that grow on a tree or shrub as a result of attack by fungi, viruses, dwarf mistletoes, or insect injury. Also known as hexenbesen; staghead.

withertip [PL PATH] A blighting of the terminal shoots or the tips of leaves associated with certain plant diseases, such as anthracnose of citrus plants.

Wolbachia [MICROBIO] A genus of the tribe Wolbachieae; coccoid, rod-shaped, and spherical cells; associated with, but not pathogenic for, arthropods.

Wolbachieae [MICROBIO] A tribe of the family Rickettsiaceae; rickettsialike organisms found principally in arthropods.

wolf [VERT ZOO] Any of several wild species of the genus *Canis* in the family Canidae which are fierce and rapacious, sometimes attacking humans; includes the red wolf, gray wolf, and coyote.

wolverine [VERT ZOO] *Gulo gulo*. A carnivorous mammal which is the largest and most vicious member of the family Mustelidae.

wood [BOT] The hard fibrous substance that makes up the trunks and large branches of trees beneath the bark. [ECOL] A dense growth of trees, more extensive than a grove and smaller than a forest.

woodpecker [VERT ZOO] A bird of the family Picidae characterized by stiff tail feathers and zygodactyl feet which enable them to cling to a tree trunk while drilling into the bark for insects.

wool [VERT ZOO] The soft undercoat of various animals such as sheep, angora, goat, camel, alpaca, llama, and vicuna.

worker [INV ZOO] One of the neuter, usually sterile individuals making up a caste of social insects, such as ants, termites, or bees, which labor for the colony.

worm [INV ZOO] 1. The common name for members of the Annelida. 2. Any of various elongated, naked, soft-bodied animals resembling an earthworm.

wren [VERT ZOO] Any of the various small brown singing birds in the family Troglodytidae; they are insectivorous and tend to inhabit dense, low vegetation.

wrist [ANAT] The part joining forearm and hand.

Wuchereria [INV ZOO] A genus of filarial worms parasitic in man in all worm regions of the world.

Wynyardiidae [PALEON] An extinct family of herbivorous marsupial mammals in the order Diprotodonta.

Xanthidae [INV ZOO] The mud crabs, a family of decapod crustaceans in the section Brachyura.

xanthine oxidase [BIOCHEM] A flavoprotein enzyme catalyzing the oxidation of certain purines.

xanthism [BIOL] A color variation in which an animal's normal coloring is largely replaced by yellow pigments. Also known as xanthochroism.

Xanthomonas [MICROBIO] A genus of bacteria in the family Pseudomonadaceae; straight rods that produce a yellow growth on agar media.

xanthomycin [MICROBIO] An antibiotic produced by a strain of *Streptomyces* and composed of two varieties, A and B; active in low concentrations against a number of gram-positive microorganisms.

xanthophore [CELL BIO] A yellow chromatophore.

Xanthophyceae [BOT] A class of yellow-green to green flagellate organisms of the division Chrysophyta; zoologists classify these organisms in the order Heterochlorida.

xanthophyll [BIOCHEM] $C_{40}H_{56}O_2$ Any of a group of yellow, alcohol-soluble carotenoid pigments that are oxygen derivatives of the carotenes, and are found in certain flowers, fruits, and leaves. Also known as lutein.

xanthurenic acid [BIOCHEM] $C_{10}H_7NO_4$ Sulfur yellow crystals with a melting point of 286°C; soluble in aqueous alkali hydroxides and carbonates; excreted by pyridoxine-deficient animals after ingestion of tryptophan.

Xantusiidae [VERT ZOO] The night lizards, a family of reptiles in the suborder Sauria.

X chromosome [GEN] The sex chromosome occurring in double dose in the homogametic sex and in single dose in the heterogametic sex.

Xenarthra [VERT ZOO] A suborder of mammals in the order Edentata including sloths, anteaters, and related forms; posterior vertebrae have extra articular facets and vertebrae in the hip, and shoulder regions tend to be fused.

xenogamy [BOT] Cross-fertilization between flowers on different plants.

Xenophyophorida [INV ZOO] An order of Protozoa in the subclass Granuloreticulosia; includes deep-sea forms that develop as discoid to fan-shaped branching forms which are multinucleate at maturity.

Xenopneusta [INV ZOO] A small order of wormlike animals belonging to the Echiurida.

Xenopterygii [VERT ZOO] The equivalent name for Gobiesociformes.

Xenosauridae [VERT ZOO] A family of four rare species of lizards in the suborder Sauria; composed of the Chinese lizard (*Shinisaurus crocodilurus*) and three Central American species of the genus *Xenosaurus*.

Xenungulata [PALEON] An order of large, digitigrade, extinct, tapirlike mammals with relatively short, slender limbs and five-toed feet with broad, flat phalanges; restricted to the Paleocene deposits of Brazil and Argentina.

xeric [ECOL] 1. Of or pertaining to a habitat having a low or inadequate supply of moisture. 2. Of or pertaining to an organism living in such an environment.

xerophyte [ECOL] A plant adapted to life in areas where the water supply is limited.

xerosere [ECOL] A temporary community in an ecological succession on dry, sterile ground such as rock, sand, or clay.

xiphidio cercaria [INV ZOO] A digenetic trematode larva having a stylet in the oral sucker.

Xiphiidae [VERT ZOO] The swordfishes, a family of perciform fishes in the suborder Scombroidei characterized by a tremendously produced bill.

xiphisternum [ANAT] The elongated posterior portion of the sternum.

Xiphodontidae [PALEON] A family of primitive tylopod ruminants in the superfamily Anaplotherioidea from the late Eocene to the middle Oligocene of Europe.

Xiphosura [INV ZOO] The equivalent name for Xiphosurida.

Xiphosurida [INV ZOO] A subclass of primitive arthropods in the class Merostomata characterized by cephalothoracic appendages, ocelli, book lungs, a somewhat trilobed body, and freely articulating styliform telson.

Xiphydriidae [INV ZOO] A family of the Hymenoptera in the superfamily Siricoidea.

X organ [INV ZOO] A cluster of neurosecretory cells of the medulla terminales, a portion of the brain lying in the eyestalk in stalk-eyed crustaceans.

Xyelidae [INV ZOO] A family of hymenopteran insects in the superfamily Megalodontoidea.

xylem [BOT] The principal water-conducting tissue and the chief supporting tissue of higher plants; composed of tracheids, vessel members, fibers, and parenchyma.

Xylocopidae [INV ZOO] A family of hairy tropical bees in the superfamily Apoidea.

Xylomyiidae [INV ZOO] A family of orthorrhaphous dipteran insects in the series Brachycera.

xylophagous [BIOL] Referring to an organism which feeds on wood.

xylose [BIOCHEM] $C_5H_{10}O_5$ A pentose sugar found in many woody materials; combustible, white crystals with a sweet taste; soluble in water and alcohol; melts about 148°C; used as a nonnutritive sweetener and in dyeing and tanning. Also known as wood sugar.

Xyridaceae [BOT] A family of terrestrial monocotyledonous plants in the order Commelinales characterized by an open leaf sheath, three stamens, and a simple racemose head for the inflorescence.

Y

yak [VERT ZOO] *Poephagus grunniens*. A heavily built, long-haired mammal of the order Artiodactyla, with a shoulder hump; related to the bison, and resembles it in having 14 pairs of ribs.

yam [BOT] 1. A plant of the genus *Dioscorea* grown for its edible fleshy root. 2. An erroneous name for the Puerto Rico variety of sweet potato; the edible, starchy tuberous root of the plant.

Y chromosome [GEN] The sex chromosome found only in the heterogametic sex.

yeast [MYCOL] A collective name for those fungi which possess, under normal conditions of growth, a vegetative body (thallus) consisting, at least in part, of simple, individual cells.

yellow dwarf [PL PATH] Any of several plant viral diseases characterized by yellowing of the foliage and stunting of the plant.

yellow fat cell [HISTOL] A large, generally spherical fat cell with a thin shell of protoplasm and a single enlarged fat droplet which appears yellowish.

yellow-green algae [BOT] The common name for members of the class Xanthophyceae.

yellow leaf blotch [PL PATH] A fungus disease of alfalfa caused by *Pyrenopeziza medicaginis* characterized by the appearance of yellow or orange blotches with small black dots on the foliage.

yellows [PL PATH] Any of various fungus diseases of plants characterized by yellowing of the leaves which later turn brown, become brittle, and die; affects cabbage, lettuce, cauliflower, peach, sugarbeet, and other plants.

Yersinia [MICROBIO] A genus of bacteria in the family Enterobacteriaceae; ovoid or rod-shaped cells that are nonmotile at 37°C (two species are motile at temperatures below 37°C); one species causes plague in humans and animals.

yew [BOT] A genus of evergreen trees and shrubs, *Taxus*, with the fruit, an aril, containing a single seed surrounded by a scarlet, fleshy, cuplike envelope; the leaves are flat and acicular.

yolk [BIOCHEM] 1. Nutritive material stored in an ovum. 2. The yellow spherical mass of food material that makes up the central portion of the egg of a bird or reptile.

yolk sac [EMBRYO] A distended extraembryonic extension, heavy-laden with yolk, through the umbilicus of the midgut of the vertebrate embryo.

Y organ [INV ZOO] Either of a pair of nonneural structures found in the anterior portion of the crustacean body; source of the molting hormone, ecdysone.

Young-Helmholtz theory [PHYSIO] A theory of color vision according to which there are three types of color receptors that respond to short, medium, and long waves respectively; primary colors are those that stimulate most successfully the three types of receptors. Also known as Helmholtz theory.

Younginiformes [PALEON] A suborder of extinct small lizardlike reptiles in the order Eosuchia, ranging from the Middle Permian to the Lower Triassic in South Africa.

Yponomeutidae [INV ZOO] A heterogeneous family of small, often brightly colored moths in the superfamily Tineoidea; the head is usually smooth with reduced or absent ocelli.

Ypsilothurlidae [INV ZOO] A family of echinoderms in the order Dactylochirotida having 8–10 tentacles, a permanent spire on the plates of the test, with the body being fusiform or U-shaped.

Zalambdalestidae [PALEON] A family of extinct insectivorous mammals belonging to the group Proteutherea; they occur in the Late Cretaceous of Mongolia.

Zanclidae [VERT ZOO] The Moorish idols, a family of Indo-Pacific perciform fishes in the suborder Acanthuroidei.

Zapodidae [VERT ZOO] The Northern Hemisphere jumping mice, a family of the order Rodentia with long legs and large feet adapted for jumping.

zebra [VERT ZOO] Any of three species of African mammals belonging to the family Equidae distinguished by a coat of black and white stripes.

zebu [VERT ZOO] A domestic breed of cattle, indigenous to India, belonging to the family Bovidae, distinguished by long drooping ears, a dorsal hump between the shoulders, and a dewlap under the neck; known as the Brahman in the United States.

Zeiformes [VERT ZOO] The dories, a small order of teleost fishes, distinguished by the absence of an orbitosphenoid bone, a spinous dorsal fin, and a pelvic fin with a spine and five to nine soft rays.

Zeoidea [VERT ZOO] An equivalent name for Zeiformes.

Zeomorphi [VERT ZOO] An equivalent name for Zeiformes.

zero population growth [ECOL] A theory which advocates that there be no increase in population, that each person replace only oneself, and that birth control be practiced in all nations.

Ziehl-Neelsen stain [MICROBIO] A procedure for acid-fast staining of tubercle bacilli with carbol fuchsin.

Zingiberaceae [BOT] A family of aromatic monocotyledonous plants in the order Zingiberales characterized by one functional stamen with two pollen sacs, distichously arranged leaves and bracts, and abundant oil cells.

Zingiberales [BOT] An order of monocotyledonous herbs or scarcely branched shrubs in the subclass Commelinidae characterized by pinnately veined leaves and irregular flowers that have well-differentiated sepals and petals, an inferior ovary, and either one or five functional stamens.

Z line [HISTOL] The line formed by attachment of the actin filaments between two sarcomeres.

Zoantharia [INV ZOO] A subclass of the class Anthozoa; individuals are monomorphic and most have retractile, simple, tubular tentacles.

Zoanthidea [INV ZOO] An order of anthozoans in the subclass Zoantharia; these are mostly colonial, sedentary, skeletonless, anemonelike animals that live in warm, shallow waters and coral reefs.

Zoarcidae [VERT ZOO] The eelpouts, a family of actinopterygian fishes in the order Gadiformes which inhabit cold northern and far southern seas.

zoea [INV ZOO] An early larval stage of decapod crustaceans distinguished by a relatively large cephalothorax, conspicuous eyes, and large, fringed antennae.

zonal centrifuge [BIOL] A centrifuge that uses a rotating chamber of large capacity in which to separate cell organelles by density-gradient centrifugation.

zona pellucida [HISTOL] The thick, solid, elastic envelope of the ovum. Also known as oolemma.

zonation [ECOL] Arrangement of organisms in biogeographic zones.

zonite [INV ZOO] A body segment in Diplopoda.

zoocecidium [PL PATH] A plant gall usually caused by an insect.

zoochlorellae [BIOL] Unicellular green algae which live as symbionts in the cytoplasm of certain protozoans, sponges, and other invertebrates.

zoochory [BOT] Dispersal of plant disseminules by animals.

zooecium [INV ZOO] The exoskeleton of a feeding zooid in bryozoans.

zoogeographic region [ECOL] A major unit of the earth's surface characterized by faunal homogeneity.

zoogeography [BIOL] The science that attempts to describe and explain the distribution of animals in space and time.

Zoogloea [MICROBIO] A genus of bacteria in the family Pseudomonadaceae; rod-shaped cells which are motile when young and later aggregate in flocs having dendritic outgrowths.

zoogloea [MICROBIO] A gelatinous or mucilaginous mass characteristic of certain bacteria grown in organic-rich fluid media.

zooid [INV ZOO] A more or less independent individual of colonial animals such as bryozoans and coral.

zoology [BIOL] The science that deals with knowledge of animal life.

Zoomastigina [INV ZOO] The equivalent name for Zoomastigophorea.

Zoomastigophorea [INV ZOO] A class of flagellate protozoans in the subphylum Sarcomastigophora; some are simple, some are specialized, and all are colorless.

zoonoses [BIOL] Diseases which are biologically adapted to and normally found in lower animals but which under some conditions also infect man.

zooplankton [ECOL] Microscopic animals which move passively in aquatic ecosystems.

zoosphere [ECOL] The world community of animals.

zoosporangium [BOT] A spore case bearing zoospores.

zoospore [BIOL] An independently motile spore.

zooxanthellae [BIOL] Microscopic yellow-green algae which live symbiotically in certain radiolarians and marine invertebrates.

Zoraptera [INV ZOO] An order of insects, related to termites and psocids, which live in decaying wood, sheltered from light; most individuals are wingless, pale in color, and blind.

Zoroasteridae [INV ZOO] A family of deep-water asteroid echinoderms in the order Forciculatida.

Zorotypidae [INV ZOO] The single family, containing one genus, *Zorotypus*, in the order Zoraptera.

Zosteraceae [BOT] A family of monocotyledonous plants in the order Najadales; the group is unique among flowering plants in that they grow submerged in shallow ocean waters near the shore.

Zosterophyllatae [PALEOBOT] *See* Zosterophyllopsida.

Zosterophyllopsida [PALEOBOT] A group of early land vascular plants ranging from the Lower to the Upper Devonian; individuals were leafless and rootless.

Zygaenidae [INV ZOO] A diverse family of small, often brightly colored African moths in the superfamily Zygaenoidea.

Zygaenoidea [INV ZOO] A superfamily of moths in the suborder Heteroneura characterized by complete venation, rudimentary palpi, and usually a rudimentary proboscis.

Zygnemataceae [BOT] A family of filamentous plants in the order Conjugales; they are differentiated into genera by chloroplast morphology, which may be spiral, bandlike, or cushionlike.

zygodactyl [VERT ZOO] Of birds, having a toe arrangement of two toes in front and two behind.

zygomatic bone [ANAT] A bone of the side of the face below the eye; forms part of the zygomatic arch and part of the orbit in mammals. Also known as malar bone.

zygomorphic [BIOL] Bilaterally symmetrical.

Zygomycetes [MYCOL] A class of fungi in the division Eumycetes.

zygopophysis [ANAT] One of the articular processes of the neural arch of a vertebra.

Zygoptera [INV ZOO] The damsel flies, a suborder of insects in the order Odonata; individuals are slender, dainty creatures, often with bright-blue or orange coloring and usually with clear or transparent wings.

zygote [EMBRYO] 1. An organism produced by the union of two gametes. 2. The fertilized ovum before cleavage.

zygotene [CELL BIO] The stage of meiotic prophase during which homologous chromosomes synapse; visible bodies in the nucleus are now bivalents. Also known as amphitene.

zygotic induction [VIROL] Phage induction following conjugation of a lysogenic bacterium with a nonlysogenic one.

zymase [BIOCHEM] A complex of enzymes that catalyze glycosis.

zymogen [BIOCHEM] The inactive precursor of an enzyme; liberates an active enzyme on reaction with an appropriate kinose. Also known as proenzyme.

zymogen granules [BIOCHEM] Granules of zymogen in gland cells, particularly those of the pancreatic acini and of the gastric chief cells.

zymogenic [MICROBIO] Obtaining energy by amylolitic processes.

Zymomonas [MICROBIO] A genus of gram-negative, anaerobic (but able to tolerate small amounts of oxygen), rod-shaped bacteria of uncertain affiliation; ferment glucose and fructose, with accumulation of ethanol and acetaldehyde in the medium.

zymophore [BIOCHEM] The active portion of an enzyme.

zymosterol [BIOCHEM] $C_{27}H_{43}OH$ An unsaturated sterol obtained from yeast fat; yields cholesterol on hydrogenation.

Zythiaceae [MYCOL] A family of fungi of the order Sphaeropsidales which contains many plant and insect pathogens.